Drug
Information
Handbook

for the
Criminal Justice
Professional

lexi-comp

Drug Information Handbook

— for the —
Criminal Justice Professional

Marcelline Burns, PhD
Research Psychologist
Southern California Research Institute
Los Angeles, CA

Thomas E. Page, MA
Sergeant
Los Angeles Police Department
Drug Recognition Expert Unit
Los Angeles, CA

Jerrold B. Leikin, MD
Associate Director, Emergency Services
Rush Presbyterian-St Luke's Medical Center
Professor of Medicine
Rush Medical College
Chicago, Illinois

LEXI-COMP INC
Hudson (Cleveland)

NOTICE

This handbook is intended to serve the user as a handy quick reference and not as a complete information resource. Material presented in this book is not intended for use out of context. It does not include information on every therapeutic or toxic agent available. The publication covers commonly used drugs, agents, and substances and is specifically designed to present certain important aspects of data in a more concise format than is generally found in the literature or product material supplied by manufacturers.

Drug information is constantly evolving because of ongoing research and clinical experience and is often subject to interpretation. While great care has been taken to ensure the accuracy of the information presented, the reader is advised that the authors, editors, reviewers, contributors, and publishers cannot be responsible for the continued currency of the information or for any errors, omissions, or the application of this information, or for any consequences arising therefrom. Therefore, the author(s) and/or the publisher shall have no liability to any person or entity with regard to claims, loss, or damage caused, or alleged to be caused, directly or indirectly, by the use of information contained herein. Because of the dynamic nature of drug information, readers are advised that decisions regarding drug therapy must be based on the independent judgment of the clinician, changing information about a drug (eg, as reflected in the literature and manufacturer's most current product information), and changing medical practices. The editors are not responsible for any inaccuracy of quotation or for any false or misleading implication that may arise due to the text or formulas as used or due to the quotation of revisions no longer official. Further, the *Drug Information Handbook for the Criminal Justice Professional* is not offered as a guide to dosing. The reader, herewith, is advised that information shown under the heading **Usual Dosage** is provided only as an indication of the amount of the drug typically given or taken during therapy. Actual dosing amount for any specific drug should be based on an in-depth evaluation of the individual patient's therapy requirement and strong consideration given to such issues as contraindications, warnings, precautions, adverse reactions, along with the interaction of other drugs. The manufacturers most current product information or other standard recognized references should always be consulted for such detailed information prior to drug use.

The editors and contributors have written this book in their private capacities. No official support or endorsement by any federal agency or pharmaceutical company is intended or inferred.

If you have any suggestions or questions regarding any information presented in this handbook, please contact our drug information pharmacist at

1-800-837-LEXI (5394)

This manual was produced using the FormuLex™ Program — a complete publishing service of Lexi-Comp Inc.

Lexi-Comp Inc
1100 Terex Road
Hudson, Ohio 44236
(330) 650-6506

ISBN 0-916589-60-9

TABLE OF CONTENTS

ABOUT THE AUTHORS

Marcelline Burns, PhD

Dr Burns, a Research Psychologist, is Director of the Southern California Research Institute (SCRI). Since the incorporation of SCRI in 1973, its staff has been continuously engaged in study of the effects of alcohol and other drugs on human performance. Driving simulators, tests of attention, information processing, memory, etc, are used in laboratory experiments to examine the effects of licit and illicit substances. Dr Burns' research is funded by public and private agencies and by pharmaceutical companies.

Beginning in 1975 under contract to NHTSA, Dr Burns and her colleagues, Dr Herbert Moskowitz and Dr Van K. Tharp, conducted a laboratory study to develop a battery of roadside tests. The Standardized Field Sobriety Tests (SFSTs) include Horizontal Gaze Nystagmus, Walk-and-Turn, and One-Leg Stand. To examine the accuracy of roadside decisions by officers who trained and experienced with the SFSTs, Dr Burns recently collaborated with law enforcement agencies and officers in field studies in Colorado and in Florida, and consulted on a San Diego study conducted by Dr Jack Stuster, Anacapa Sciences. She continues to testify and lecture concerning the scientific validity and reliability of the SFSTs.

Dr Burns worked closely with the officers who developed the LAPD drug recognition program. She has continued to support the program by consulting and lecturing about drug effects on performance and about DRE methodology. She was the site scientific investigator for the 173 Case Study in LAPD and has collaborated on additional NHTSA-sponsored study. She and Eugene Adler of the Arizona DPHS Crime Lab worked together on a 1995 validation study using records from the Phoenix DRE unit.

In 1993, Dr Burns was recognized by the U.S. Department of Transportation, NHTSA, with a Public Service Award. CANDID and the IACP honored her with an Award for Outstanding Research in the Area of Drug Impaired Driving in 1996.

Thomas E. Page, MA

Mr Page, a certified Drug Recognition Expert (DRE) and instructor, began a law enforcement career in 1977 as an officer with the Detroit Police Department. In 1981, Mr Page joined the Los Angeles Police Department (LAPD). He currently serves the LAPD as the Officer in Charge of the DRE Unit. Before undertaking a law enforcement career, Mr Page served the Wayne County, Michigan, Health Department for five years as a public health worker and supervisor, specializing in drug and alcohol abuse.

Mr Page was a coordinator for the 1985 Los Angeles Field Validation Test (173 case study) of the DRE Procedure. This study validated the effectiveness and reliability of a standardized and systematic approach to drug influence recognition. These procedures have been adopted nationwide by professionals in government, law enforcement, the military, private industry, and healthcare.

Mr Page has taught drug influence recognition, behavioral indicators of drug use, drug user identification for supervisors, instructional techniques, and other related topics to a wide range of audiences. These audiences include the American Bar Association, Northwestern University Traffic Institute, the California Department of Mental Health, the Swedish National Police Federation, the

Russian Procuracy Training Academy in Moscow, the Department of the Army, nurses, physicians, psychiatrists, toxicologists, and private industry.

Mr Page frequently provides testimony in court on drug influence signs and symptoms, horizontal gaze nystagmus, and the standardized field sobriety test. He has been accepted as an expert on these matters in courts in twelve states. He also serves as the law enforcement representative on a U.S. Department of Transportation (DOT) sponsored committee that developed curricula to train prosecutors to effectively prosecute the "drugged" driver.

Mr Page served as the first General Chairperson of the DRE Section of the International Association of Chiefs of Police (IACP), and has been a member of IACP's DRE Technical Advisory Panel. He is an advisory member of the Canadian Society of Forensic Science's Drugs and Driving Committee, and is a member of the National Safety Council's Committee on Alcohol and Other Drugs.

In 1996, Mr Page was presented the "First Annual Award for Outstanding Education in Drug Impaired Driving" by Citizens Against Drug Impaired Driving (CANDID) and the IACP.

Mr Page received his Bachelor of Arts degree in Industrial Psychology, and his Master of Arts degree in Urban Affairs from the University of Detroit.

Jerrold Blair Leikin, MD, FACP, FACEP, FACMT

Dr Leikin received his Medical Doctorate degree from the Chicago Medical School in 1980. Following a combined residency in Internal Medicine and Emergency Medicine at Evanston Hospital and Northwestern Memorial Hospital, he then completed a fellowship in Medical Toxicology at Cook County Hospital in Chicago.

Dr Leikin was physician-in-charge of medicine at the University of Illinois Hospital Emergency Department and Section Chief of Emergency Medicine within the Department of Medicine. Upon transfer to Rush-Presbyterian-St Luke's Medical Center, Dr Leikin became Associate Director of the Emergency Department while also serving as the Medical Director of the Illinois Poison Center. He was also Medical Director of the United States Drug Testing Laboratory from 1991-1996 and is currently Associate Director of the Toxicon Consortium, and holds an appointment as Professor of Medicine at Rush Medical College.

Dr Leikin has presented over 100 abstracts at national meetings while publishing over 100 articles in peer-reviewed medical journals. He has written several chapters on the subject of toxicology in critical care medicine, internal medicine, and observational medicine textbooks. He is an active member of the American Academy of Clinical Toxicology, American College of Medical Toxicology, the American College of Emergency Physicians, and the American Medical Association. He was elected a fellow of the American College of Medical Toxicology in September, 1997.

EDITORIAL ADVISORY PANEL

4

Larry D. Gray, PhD
Director of Microbiology
Bethesda North Hospital
Cincinnati, Ohio

Martin D. Higbee, PharmD
Associate Professor
Department of Pharmacy Practice
The University of Arizona
Tucson, Arizona

Jane Hurlburt Hodding, PharmD
Supervisor, Children's Pharmacy
Memorial Miller Children's Hospital
Long Beach, California

Rebecca T. Horvat, PhD
Assistant Professor of Pathology and Laboratory Medicine
University of Kansas Medical Center
Kansas City, Kansas

Naomi B. Ingrim, PharmD
Specialist in Poison Information
Central Texas Poison Center
Temple, TX

Carlos M. Isada, MD
Department of Infectious Disease
Cleveland Clinic Foundation
Cleveland, Ohio

David S. Jacobs, MD
President, Pathologists Chartered
Overland Park, Kansas

John E. Janosik, PharmD
Clinical Pharmacist
Lexi-Comp Inc
Hudson, Ohio

Bernard L. Kasten, Jr, MD, FCAP
Vice President/Medical Director
Corning Medical Laboratories
Teterboro, New Jersey

Donna M. Kraus, PharmD
Associate Professor of Pharmacy Practice
Departments of Pharmacy Practice and Pediatrics
Clinical Pharmacist
Pediatric Intensive Care Unit
University of Illinois at Chicago
Chicago, Illinois

Charles Lacy, RPh, PharmD
Drug Information Pharmacist
Cedars-Sinai Medical Center
Los Angeles, California

Leonard L. Lance, RPh, BSPharm
Pharmacist
Lexi-Comp Inc.
Hudson, Ohio

5

6

PREFACE

Public health and safety are placed in jeopardy by individuals who abuse or misuse alcohol and other drugs. Whenever so-called "recreational" use of licit and illicit substances, or the use of prescription and over-the-counter drugs for therapeutic purposes, impairs performance, behavior, and/or judgment, our roadways, public places, homes, and workplaces are more hazardous than they ought to be. This difficult problem is confronted daily by law enforcement, courts, and crime labs, and we are more (or less) safe in our environment largely due to the activities of police officers, prosecutors, and criminalists. They stand as a front line defense against harm as a consequence of the impairing effects of alcohol and other drugs.

The defense encompasses many tasks for criminal justice professionals. Briefly consider the difficulty of just one of those tasks.

A traffic officer observes a vehicle being driven unsafely, erratically, or in violation of a statute (possibly all-of-the-above). He stops the vehicle and approaches the driver. Within a few minutes, based on observations, interrogation, and brief roadside tests, he must decide whether the driver is impaired and whether he/she should be arrested or released.

If a decision is made to arrest, then additional questions arise. Is the individual impaired by alcohol or another drug? If it is a drug other than alcohol, what kind of drug is it?

Consider the odds of answering the questions correctly. Remember, the driver is a stranger. The circumstances provide no information about his/her usual behavior and appearance. There is a limited amount of time and few-to-no measurement instruments.

Fortunately, many criminal justice professionals have acquired skills through specialized training, which enable them to perform this and similar tasks with what is often an impressive level of accuracy. Nonetheless, the dimensions of the task means that police officers and other criminal justice professionals continue to require not only the best and most rigorous training, but also current, accurate, and comprehensive information about the hundreds and hundreds of potentially impairing substances.

This handbook is directed toward the latter need. Its compilation was driven by the intent to make accurate information about impairing substances immediately accessible to criminal justice professionals. Just as there is no precise measure of accidents which do not happen as a result of officers correct decisions, there will be no direct measure of the impact of the handbook... only the earnest hope of its editors and contributors that it will serve its purpose well.

ACKNOWLEDGMENTS

This handbook exists in its present form as the result of the concerted efforts of many individuals including the publisher and president of Lexi-Comp Inc, Robert D. Kerscher and Lynn D. Coppinger, managing editor.

Other members of the Lexi-Comp staff whose contributions deserve special mention include Barbara F. Kerscher, production manager; Diane Harbart, MT (ASCP), medical editor; Jeanne Wilson, Jennifer Rocky, Leslie Ruggles, and Julie Katzen, project managers; Alexandra Hart, composition specialist; Jackie Mizer, Ginger Conner, and Kate Schleicher, production assistants; Tracey J. Reinecke, graphics; Jerry M. Reeves, Marc L. Long, and Patrick Grubb, sales managers; Jay L. Katzen and Brian B. Vossler, product managers; Kenneth J. Hughes, manager of authoring systems; Kristin M. Thompson, Matthew C. Kerscher, Brad Bolinski, and Tina L. Collins, sales and marketing representatives; Edmund A. Harbart, vice-president, custom publishing division; Jack L. Stones, vice-president, reference publishing division; David C. Marcus and Sean Conrad, system analysts; Thury L. O'Connor, vice-president of technology; David J. Wasserbauer, vice-president, finance and administration; and Elizabeth M. Conlon and Rebecca A. Dryhurst, accounting.

Much of the material contained in this book was a result of pharmacy contributors throughout the United States and Canada. Lexi-Comp has assisted many medical institutions to develop hospital-specific formulary manuals that contain clinical drug information as well as dosing. Working with clinical pharmacists, hospital pharmacy and therapeutics committees, and hospital drug information centers, Lexi-Comp has developed an evolutionary drug database that reflects the practice of pharmacy in these major institutions.

In addition, the authors wish to thank their families, friends, and colleagues who supported them in their efforts to complete this handbook.

CONTRIBUTING AUTHOR

Cheryl A. Kapustka, PharmD

A special thanks to Cheryl A. Kapustka who contributed the section on "Chemical Submissive Agents" found in the Special Topics/Issues for the Criminal Justice Professional section of this handbook. Ms Kapustka received her bachelor's degree in psychology from the University of Illinois at Urbana-Champaign in 1993 and her doctorate in pharmacy from the University of Illinois at Chicago in 1997. She is a specialist in poison information at the Illinois Poison Center.

HOW TO USE THIS HANDBOOK

The *Drug Information Handbook for the Criminal Justice Professional* is divided into six sections.

The first section is a compilation of introductory text pertinent to the use of this book.

The drug and substance monograph section of the handbook, in which all drugs, agents, substances, industrial/household chemicals, envenomations, and biologicals are listed alphabetically, details information pertinent to each agent. Extensive cross-referencing is provided by brand names and synonyms.

The third section is comprised of several text chapters dealing with various subjects and issues pertinent to this title.

The fourth section is an invaluable appendix with various charts, tables, and conversion information.

The fifth section of this handbook is a glossary of terms that the user can refer to when using this text for definitions or further clarification. It is an excerpt of *Stedman's Medical Dictionary*, 26th ed, Baltimore, MD: Williams & Wilkins, 1995.

The last section of this handbook is comprised of a therapeutic category index, a unique classification system for drugs, and a Canadian Brand Names Index listing trade names used in Canada.

ALPHABETICAL LISTING OF DRUGS AND SUBSTANCES

Information is presented in a consistent format and provides the following:

Generic Name	U.S. adopted name
Pronunciation Guide	Phonetic pronunciation
Related Information	Cross-reference to other pertinent drug information found elsewhere in this handbook
Synonyms	Other names or accepted acronyms of the generic drug, agent, or substance
UN Number	United Nations/Department of Transportation number; usually found on a placard on the side of vehicle
Scientific Name	
Commonly Found In	Agent or substance having these properties
U.S. Brand Names	Trade names used in the United States
Canadian Brand Names	Trade names used in Canada
Therapeutic Category	Unique systematic classification of medications
Abuse Potential	Indicated only if there is potential
Impairment Potential	If there is a significant potential, it is indicated and sometimes further explained

HOW TO USE THIS HANDBOOK *(Continued)*

Use	Information pertaining to appropriate or inappropriate indications of the drug, agent, or substance. Includes both FDA approved and non-FDA approved indications.
Toxic Dose or Usual Dosage	Depending on the drug, agent, or substance - one of these dosage fields are present and will tell either the therapeutic dose or the toxic dose
Mechanism of Action or Mechanism of Toxic Action	How the drug works in the body to elicit a response
Pharmacodynamics/ Kinetics or Toxicodynamics/ Kinetics	The magnitude of a drug's effect depends on the drug concentration at the site of action. The pharmaco/ toxicodynamics are expressed in terms of onset of action and duration of action. Pharmaco/toxicokinetics are expressed in terms of absorption, distribution (including appearance in breast milk and crossing of the placenta), protein binding, metabolism, bioavailability, half-life, time to peak serum concentration, and elimination.
Signs/Symptoms of Acute Intoxication	Primarily clinical effects of acute exposure
Overdosage Treatment	Description of treatment modalities of adverse effects and overdose with emphasis on emergent decontamination
When to Transport to Hospital	Criteria when to seek emergency medical treatment. Doses listed are guidelines and, therefore, lesser amounts may still require transport. All suicide attempts should be transported.
Warnings/ Precautions	Cautions and hazardous conditions related to the drug, agent, or substance
Adverse Reactions	Side effects of drug, agent, or substance broken down by percentages (>1%), if known, and body system
Test Interactions	Information regarding effect or implications of laboratory tests while taking the medication
Reference Range	Therapeutic and toxic serum concentrations
Drug Interactions	Description of the interaction between the drug listed in the monograph and other drugs or drug classes
Dosage Forms	Information with regard to form, strength, and availability of the drug
Additional Information	
Specific References	Sources and literature used in the writing of the monograph

CLINICAL PHARMACOKINETICS AND TOXICOKINETICS

Pharmacokinetics is the study of the passage of drugs, toxins, or other substances through the body. Typically, this science focuses on the absorption, distribution, metabolism, and elimination of the substances by a human. From this work, mathematical representations of a specific substance and how it is handled by a specific individual can be constructed. A simple and common example of the application of pharmacokinetics in humans, clinical pharmacokinetics, is seen with alcohol or ethanol. Pharmacokinetic studies of ethanol have made it possible to reliably calculate the amount of ethanol an individual must drink in order to achieve specific blood concentrations at a specific body weight. Conversely, a known ethanol concentration and individual's weight can be used to "back-calculate" the amount of ethanol that had to be ingested to yield the observed concentration. These calculations can be further modified to account for the passage of time, how long an individual has been drinking alcohol, concentration, multiple and varying alcohol concentrations, and body weight. Clinical toxicokinetics refers to the application of pharmacokinetic principles, equations, and analyses to the evaluation and management of intoxicated or poisoned patients. Practical issues in data collection, analysis, and interpretation have not been well described and have usually been ignored in medical literature. This section provides an approach to the practice of clinical toxicokinetics focusing on optimizing the use of serum drug/toxin concentrations obtained from poisoned/intoxicated patients. It is a primer in the aspect of relating pertinent aspects of basic concepts to the clinical reality of evaluation and management of the poisoned or intoxicated patient in nonideal settings.

Key terms used in pharmacokinetics that must be defined and conceptually understood are peak serum concentration (C_{peak}), time to peak concentration (T_{max}), volume of distribution (V_d), clearance (Cl), elimination rate (k_e) and elimination half-life ($t^{1}/_2$).

C_{peak} is the highest concentration, in serum or blood typically, that a drug or toxin is measured in an individual. The absolute magnitude of this concentration is dependent on many variables such as dose ingested, patient weight, coingestants, underlying health status, diet, fluids, time since ingestion, dosage form (tablets, sustained-release tablets, liquids, etc), specific characteristics of the drug/toxin (ability to dissolve in gastric fluids etc), prior ingestions, etc. Many of these variable effects are known from studies in volunteers or patients where known doses were administered at known times after which a series of serum concentrations were obtained. These values are plotted on graphs and the resultant curve or line can be mathematically expressed. The most commonly used example would be the following formula:

$$Cp = (D/V_d) \, (e^{-ke \times t})$$

where Cp is a serum concentration (mg/L) at any time, D is the dose of the drug ingested (in mg), V_d is the volume of distribution for the drug (in L/kg), e is the natural logarithm, ke is the elimination rate of the drug (in hr^{-1}) and t is the time since ingestion (in hours). It should be noted that most concentrations are expressed in metric terms, specifically whenever possible mg/L. A notable exception is the alcohols, for instance ethanol is commonly discussed in dL (mg/100 mL) or values that will appear as 10 times greater than those reported by a laboratory.

CLINICAL PHARMACOKINETICS AND TOXICOKINETICS
(Continued)

Time to peak concentration is generally dependent only on the specific drug's solubility, dosage form, and the presence or absence of food, fluids, and other drugs. In most settings, it typically occurs within 1-2 hours of an oral ingestion. Enteric-coated and sustained-release tablets are notable exceptions. T_{max} with the latter dosage forms is typically 4-8 hours. The T_{max} has been noted to be markedly prolonged in overdose to as late as 24 hours with sustained-release products making the recognition of the presence of this product type critical in the proper monitoring and evaluation of these patients. Conversely, severe gastrointestinal trauma or concomitant ingestion with food products can markedly shorten the T_{max} reducing the time available to prevent serious consequences.

Volume of distribution (V_d) is an abstract mathematical concept to attempt to characterize how a drug spreads throughout the body. Imagine the body as a pitcher of water. Into that pitcher is placed a known quantity of drug. If the water is then sampled and analyzed, a concentration of the drug would result. If the amount of water was doubled for the same dose of drug, then the concentration would decrease by half. Similarly, if the amount of water was decreased by 50%, the concentration would increase twofold. The human body is not a pitcher of water, there is protein, bone, muscles, fat, etc, but frequently can be conceptualized as such. It is known that for any given drug, a specific dose given to normal individuals results in a specific C_{peak} at a specific T_{max}. Reproducible values for C_{peak} and C_{max} are known as population pharmacokinetic parameters. What should be quickly recognized is that if we know the dose and the concentration, the volume can be calculated and it is as follows:

$$C_p = (D/V_d)$$

When consistently documented, a population parameter V_d is accepted and used to predict necessary doses or resultant concentrations. Using ethanol as an example, the V_d for ethanol is 0.6 L/kg in adults. This means that in the mythical normal adult male of 70 kg (154 lb), the mg/L concentration of ethanol can be calculated by dividing the dose of ethanol (in mg) by the patient's weight (70 kg) times 0.6 or 42 liters. Note that ethanol, a water soluble chemical, is found in 0.6 L/kg of the body, this happens to be the accepted value for normal body water. Drugs (several common pain relievers) can have a very small V_d, as low as 4-5 liters, if that drug can only be found in the blood because it almost exclusively attaches to serum proteins or red blood cells. On the other hand, drugs can have a V_d of 300-500 liters, such as the benzodiazepines or antidepressants. Now, that average adult is not a pitcher of 300-500 liters of water. High V_d reflects a drug's ability to concentrate in specific areas, like the brain, which is much more fat than water. This means that a specific serum concentration for any drug does not represent the concentration of the drug in all other sites of the body. Rather, it frequently represents an equilibrium with varying concentrations in different body parts. Thus, the degree and rate of distribution (or spread) through the body need to be considered.

Consider two holes, one dug in common backyard soil and another at a beach in sand far from the shoreline. Into each, pour the same amount of water and wait 5 minutes. After the time, scoop out and measure water left in the hole. Which will have a greater value? Generally, the backyard hole will always have more water remaining because it seeps (distributes) much slower into soil than in sand. If we keep the backyard hole alone and repeat the experiment in dry heat or after heavy rain, new results will occur. The wet hole will hold new water longer because prior watering (or prior doses) have already filled (saturated) the ground. The last example is also a reliable metaphor for the difference between an acute ingestion, acute-on-chronic, and chronic ingestion. The wettest ground (sickest patient) typically occurs with an acute-on-chronic exposure (last heavy thunderstorm of spring always floods the basement) followed by chronic (daily spring rains) and finally acute exposure (thunderstorm). Exceptions can occur, a rainfall of 17 inches at once (massive oral overdose in suicide attempt with a potentially fatal drug) can be the worst also.

Returning to the issue of distribution, it is fortunate that close enough for medical purposes, most drugs can be characterized by a two-compartment model (a pitcher of water with a filter between two segments). The smaller compartment is the well perfused and readily filled area (the top part of the pitcher that water is poured into) which could be as simple as the blood supply alone from which a drug distributes to a larger area reflecting the drug's individual characteristics (filtering into the bottom compartment of the pitcher).

To mathematically characterize the two-compartment model described by studies in humans, natural logarithms were necessary to create graphs that had a straight line portion to the curve. This use has lead to labeling drugs capable of generating such results as being "linear" or "first order" kinetics (shortening of pharmacokinetics).

The pitcher of water metaphor is not complete as water does not spontaneously leave the pitcher without pouring, whereas the body spontaneously metabolizes and eliminates drugs and toxins through organs like the liver and kidneys. The summation of all these processes is referred to as an abstract mathematical concept called clearance (Cl), typically expressed as L/kg/hour. Typically, the total body clearance for any drug refers to the volume of blood per body weight from which all of the drug is removed in a given time period. When divided by the V_d, the units of measure L/kg conveniently cancel out leaving hr^{-1}. This is the unit of measure for a pharmacokinetic parameter called the elimination rate (k_e). When combined with the use of linear two-compartment models the elimination half-life can be converted to a parameter called the elimination half-life by the formula:

$$T_{1/2} = 0.693/k_e$$

This specifically represents the amount of time required for a drug concentration to fall by 50%. This provides the clinician with an ability to calculate and predict the probable length of time a patient may be intoxicated. The terminology and concept is identical to discussions of radioactivity and duration of fallout effects. It is a critical concept when it is considered that regardless of amount, for most drugs, the time to drop its concentration in half is constant and, with no new exposure, within 5 half-lives essentially no drug remains (<5%).

There are exceptions to the above. Several drugs at normal doses or some toxins, like ethanol, at low serum concentrations exceed (saturate) normal metabolic capacity. Once "saturation" occurs, then only a specific amount of drug is eliminated daily. Consider a tollway collection area. It can handle a wide number of autos daily up to the point that there are more cars than booths. At that saturation point, only a specific number of vehicles can be processed in a given unit of time.

A clear example is ethanol. Ethanol saturates the liver's ability to metabolize and eliminate it at fairly low concentrations. Commonly, ethanol is eliminated at a rate of 10-30 mg/dL/hour regardless of the starting concentration in a nonalcoholic individual. Thus, an individual with a concentration of 200 mg/dL will

CLINICAL PHARMACOKINETICS AND TOXICOKINETICS
(Continued)

require typically minimally 5-10 hours to pass before a concentration of 100 mg/dL will be reached. It becomes more difficult when one considers that the liver can adapt to ethanol and improve its ability to metabolize ethanol.

Evaluation of the intoxicated or poisoned patient, which includes serum drug concentrations, occurs prior to and is frequently a basis for selecting therapy and follow-up care. Typically, a patient presents with a history or suspicion of being poisoned. As intravenous access is initiated, common plasma laboratory determinations, including specific drug/toxin concentrations, are obtained. In known or highly suspected drug intoxications/overdoses, the patient's history is generally unreliable. For this reason, site evaluation and observer histories are very important. Serum "tox screens" (a panel that assays for multiple agents) are generally not useful, particularly as determined by management or patient disposition outcomes. The screens only consider a limited number of drug or drug classes. If such a screening is desired, notifying the laboratory facilities directly as to the primary suspicion(s) is critical to assure efficient use of the limited sampling amount (especially in children).

Individuals may be asked to return to the site of an incident to look for and retrieve relevant materials in circumstances where the history is ambiguous or unavailable. In these cases of delayed recognition or identification of an intoxication, it may still be of value to have any unused serum from the initial presentation blood sampling saved to be analyzed for a more complete interpretation of a case once a more accurate history is available.

These interpretations require an understanding of and ability to use pharmacokinetic formulas whose calculation's validity depends in part on the amount of information available regarding known variables affecting a specific drug/toxin.

SELECTED REFERENCES

Baselt RC and Cravey RH, *Disposition of Toxic Drugs and Chemicals in Man*, 4th ed, Foster City, CA: Chemical Toxicology Institute, 1995.

Bleecker ML and Hansen JA, *Occupational Neurology and Clinical Neurotoxicology*, Baltimore, MD: Williams and Wilkins, 1994.

Drug Interaction Facts, St Louis, MO: J.B. Lippincott Co (Facts and Comparisons Division), 1996.

Facts and Comparisons, St Louis, MO: J.B. Lippincott Co (Facts and Comparisons Division), 1996.

Handbook of Nonprescription Drugs, 9th ed, Washington, DC: American Pharmaceutical Association, 1990.

Isada CM, Kasten BL, Goldman MP, et al, *Infectious Disease Handbook*, Hudson, OH: Lexi-Comp Inc, 1997.

Jacobs DS, DeMott WR, Finley PR, et al, *Laboratory Test Handbook with Key Word Index*, Hudson, OH: Lexi-Comp Inc, 1996.

Lacy CF, Armstrong LL, Ingrim NB, and Lance LL, *Drug Information Handbook*, Hudson, OH: Lexi-Comp Inc, 1998.

Leikin JB and Paloucek FP, *Poisoning & Toxicology Compendium*, Hudson, OH: Lexi-Comp Inc, 1998.

McEvoy GK and Litvak K, *AHFS Drug Information*, Bethesda, MD: American Society of Hospital Pharmacists, 1996.

Semla TP, Beizer JL, and Higbee MD, *Geriatric Dosage Handbook*, Hudson, OH: Lexi-Comp Inc, 1998.

Stedman's Medical Dictionary, 26th ed, Baltimore, MD: Williams & Wilkins, 1995.

Taketomo CK, Hodding JH, and Kraus DM, *Pediatric Dosage Handbook*, Hudson, OH: Lexi-Comp Inc, 1998.

United States Pharmacopeia Dispensing Information (USP DI), Rockville, MD: United States Pharmacopeial Convention, Inc, 1997.

Wynn RL, Meiller TF, and Crossley HL, *Drug Information Handbook for Dentistry*, Hudson, OH: Lexi-Comp Inc, 1998.

ALPHABETICAL LISTING OF DRUGS
AND SUBSTANCES

Abicol® see Reserpine *on page 523*

Absinthium see Wormwood *on page 617*

Acalix® see Diltiazem *on page 201*

Acebutolol (a se BYOO toe lole)

U.S. Brand Names Sectral®

Canadian Brand Names Monitan®; Rhotral®

Therapeutic Category Antiarrhythmic Agent, Class II; Beta-Adrenergic Blocker

Impairment Potential Yes

Use Treatment of hypertension, ventricular arrhythmias, angina

Usual Dosage Oral:

Adults: 400-800 mg/day in 2 divided doses; maximum: 1200 mg/day

Elderly: Initial: 200-400 mg/day; dose reduction due to age related kidney disease will be necessary; do not exceed 800 mg/day

Mechanism of Action Competitively blocks beta$_1$-adrenergic receptors with little or no effect on beta$_2$-receptors except at high doses; exhibits membrane stabilizing and intrinsic sympathomimetic activity

Pharmacodynamics/kinetics

Absorption: Oral: Well absorbed (40%)

Half-life: 6-7 hours average

Time to peak: 2-4 hours

Signs and Symptoms of Acute Intoxication Cardiac disturbances, CNS toxicity, bronchospasm, hypoglycemia, and hyperkalemia. The most common cardiac symptoms include hypotension and bradycardia; atrioventricular block, intraventricular conduction disturbances, cardiogenic shock, and systole may occur with severe overdose, especially with membrane-depressant drugs (eg, propranolol); CNS effects include convulsions, coma, and respiratory arrest is commonly seen with propranolol and other membrane-depressant and lipid-soluble drugs

When to Transport to Hospital Transport any pediatric or adult ingestion over 1 g

Warnings/Precautions Abrupt withdrawal of beta-blockers may result in an exaggerated cardiac beta-adrenergic responsiveness. Symptomatology has included reports of tachycardia, hypertension, ischemia, angina, myocardial infarction, and sudden death. It is recommended that patients be tapered gradually off of beta-blockers over a 2-week period rather than via abrupt discontinuation.

Adverse Reactions

>10%: Fatigue

1% to 10%:

Cardiovascular: Chest pain, edema, bradycardia, hypotension

Central nervous system: Headache, dizziness, insomnia, depression, abnormal dreams

Dermatologic: Rash

Gastrointestinal: Constipation, diarrhea, dyspepsia, nausea, flatulence

Genitourinary: Polyuria

Neuromuscular & skeletal: Arthralgia, myalgia

Ocular: Abnormal vision

Respiratory: Dyspnea, rhinitis, cough

Drug Interactions

Decreased effect of beta-blockers with aluminum salts, barbiturates, calcium salts, cholestyramine, colestipol, NSAIDs, penicillins (ampicillin), rifampin, salicylates, and sulfinpyrazone due to decreased bioavailability and plasma levels; decreased effect of sulfonylureas with beta-blockers

Increased effect/toxicity of beta-blockers with calcium blockers (diltiazem, felodipine, nicardipine), oral contraceptives, flecainide, haloperidol (propranolol, hypotensive effects), H_2-antagonists (metoprolol, propranolol only by cimetidine, possibly ranitidine), hydralazine (metoprolol, propranolol), loop diuretics (propranolol, not atenolol), MAO inhibitors (metoprolol, nadolol, bradycardia), phenothiazines (propranolol), propafenone (metoprolol, propranolol), quinidine (in extensive metabolizers), ciprofloxacin, thyroid hormones (metoprolol, propranolol, when hypothyroid patient is converted to euthyroid state)

Beta-blockers may increase the effect/toxicity of flecainide, haloperidol (hypotensive effects), hydralazine, phenothiazines, acetaminophen, anticoagulants (propranolol, warfarin), benzodiazepines (not atenolol), clonidine (hypertensive crisis after or during withdrawal of either agent), epinephrine (initial hypertensive episode followed by bradycardia), nifedipine and verapamil lidocaine, ergots (peripheral ischemia), prazosin (postural hypotension)

Beta-blockers may affect the action or levels of ethanol, disopyramide, nondepolarizing muscle relaxants and theophylline although the effects are difficult to predict

Dosage Forms Capsule, as hydrochloride: 200 mg, 400 mg

Specific References

Kligman EW and Higbee MD, "Drug Therapy for Hypertension in the Elderly," *J Fam Pract*, 1989, 28(1):81-7.

Acephen® [OTC] *see* Acetaminophen *on next page*

Acepril® *see* Captopril *on page 101*

Aceta® [OTC] *see* Acetaminophen *on next page*

Acetaldehyde

Synonyms Acetic Aldehyde; Ethanal; Ethyl Aldehyde

UN Number 1089

Use Industrial agent; production of plastics, mirrors, aniline, disinfectants, explosives, varnishes, synthetics, acetic acid, acetic anhydride, food flavorings; also a combustion product of wood and fuels; found in tobacco smoke and car exhaust; found as a fermentation product in beer or wine; a metabolite of ethanol

Mechanism of Toxic Action Pulmonary/mucosal irritant ($\sim 1/10$ of an irritant as formaldehyde); can cause CNS depression; also may affect mitochondrial phosphorylation and inhibit myocardial protein synthesis

Toxicodynamics/kinetics Absorption: Oral/dermal/inhalation routes

Signs and Symptoms of Acute Intoxication Hypertension/tachycardia at low concentrations with hypotension/bradycardia at high concentrations; ocular irritation (at 50 ppm) with photophobia and lacrimation; bronchitis, cough, dyspnea, pulmonary edema, emesis (when ingested as a liquid), dermal burns, erythema

When to Transport to Hospital Transport any ingestion

Overdosage/Treatment Decontamination:

Dermal: Wash with soap and water

Inhalation: Administer 100% humidified oxygen

Additional Information A colorless liquid with a fruity taste; specific gravity: 0.78 as a liquid and 1.52 as a gas; in cigarette smoke, acetaldehyde content may approach 1 mg

TLA-TWA: 100 ppm

IDLH: 10,000 ppm

Odor threshold: 0.21 ppm

Specific References

Condouris GA and Havelin DM, "Acetaldehyde and Cardiac Arrhythmias," *Arch Int Pharmacodyn Ther*, 1987, 285(1):50-9.

Acetaminophen (a seet a MIN oh fen)

Related Information
Acetaminophen and Codeine *on next page*
Hydrocodone and Acetaminophen *on page 293*
Oxycodone and Acetaminophen *on page 453*

Synonyms APAP; N-Acetyl-P-Aminophenol; Paracetamol

U.S. Brand Names Acephen® [OTC]; Aceta® [OTC]; Apacet® [OTC]; Arthritis Foundation® Pain Reliever, Aspirin Free [OTC]; Aspirin Free Anacin® Maximum Strength [OTC]; Children's Silapap® [OTC]; Feverall™ [OTC]; Feverall™ Sprinkle Caps [OTC]; Genapap® [OTC]; Halenol® Childrens [OTC]; Infants Feverall™ [OTC]; Infants' Silapap® [OTC]; Junior Strength Panadol® [OTC]; Liquiprin® [OTC]; Mapap® [OTC]; Maranox® [OTC]; Neopap® [OTC]; Panadol® [OTC]; Redutemp® [OTC]; Ridenol® [OTC]; Tempra® [OTC]; Tylenol® [OTC]; Tylenol® Extended Relief [OTC]; Uni-Ace® [OTC]

Canadian Brand Names Abenol®; Atasol®; Pediatrix®; 222 AF®; Tantaphen®

Therapeutic Category Analgesic, Non-narcotic; Antipyretic

Use Treatment of mild to moderate pain and fever (analgesic)

Usual Dosage Oral, rectal (if fever not controlled with acetaminophen alone, administer with full doses of aspirin on an every 4- to 6-hour schedule, if aspirin is not otherwise contraindicated):

Children <12 years: 10-15 mg/kg/dose every 4-6 hours as needed; do **not** exceed 5 doses (2.6 g) in 24 hours; alternatively, the following doses may be used. See table.

Acetaminophen Dosing

Age	Dosage (mg)	Age	Dosage (mg)
0-3 mo	40	4-5 y	240
4-11 mo	80	6-8 y	320
1-2 y	120	9-10 y	400
2-3 y	160	11 y	480

Adults: 325-650 mg every 4-6 hours or 1000 mg 3-4 times/day; do **not** exceed 4 g/day

Toxic dosage for hepatitis: 200 mg/kg

Mechanism of Action Inhibits the synthesis of prostaglandins in the central nervous system and peripherally blocks pain impulse generation; produces antipyresis from inhibition of hypothalamic heat-regulating center

Pharmacodynamics/kinetics
Metabolism: Liver
Half-life:
Neonates: 2-5 hours
Adults: 1-3 hours
Time to peak serum concentration: Oral: 10-60 minutes after normal doses, may be delayed in acute overdoses

Signs and Symptoms of Acute Intoxication Hepatic necrosis, transient azotemia, renal tubular necrosis with acute toxicity, anemia, and GI disturbances with chronic toxicity.

When to Transport to Hospital Transport any ingestion over 200 mg/kg in children (<6 years of age) or over 150 mg/kg in adults

Overdosage/Treatment Acetylcysteine 140 mg/kg orally (loading) followed by 70 mg/kg every 4 hours for 17 doses is the antidote. Therapy should be initiated based upon laboratory analysis suggesting high probability of hepatotoxic potential. Activated charcoal is very effective at binding acetaminophen.

Warnings/Precautions May cause severe hepatic toxicity on overdose; use with caution in patients with alcoholic liver disease; chronic daily dosing in adults of 5-8 g of acetaminophen over several weeks or 3-4 g/day of acetaminophen for 1 year have resulted in liver damage

Adverse Reactions

<1%:

Renal: Nephrotoxicity with chronic overdose

Miscellaneous: Hypersensitivity reactions (rare)

Reference Range

Therapeutic concentration: 10-30 µg/mL

Toxic concentration: >200 µg/mL

Toxic concentration with probable hepatotoxicity: >200 µg/mL at 4 hours or 50 µg/mL at 12 hours

Drug Interactions

Decreased effect: Rifampin can interact to reduce the analgesic effectiveness of acetaminophen

Increased toxicity: Barbiturates, carbamazepine, hydantoins, sulfinpyrazone can increase the hepatotoxic potential of acetaminophen; chronic ethanol abuse increases risk for acetaminophen toxicity

Dosage Forms

Caplet: 160 mg, 325 mg, 500 mg

Caplet, extended: 650 mg

Capsule: 80 mg

Drops: 48 mg/mL (15 mL); 60 mg/0.6 mL (15 mL); 80 mg/0.8 mL (15 mL); 100 mg/mL (15 mL, 30 mL)

Elixir: 80 mg/5 mL, 120 mg/5 mL, 160 mg/5 mL, 167 mg/5 mL, 325 mg/5 mL

Liquid, oral: 160 mg/5 mL, 500 mg/15 mL

Solution: 100 mg/mL (15 mL); 120 mg/2.5 mL

Suppository, rectal: 80 mg, 120 mg, 125 mg, 300 mg, 325 mg, 650 mg

Suspension, oral: 160 mg/5 mL

Suspension, oral drops: 80 mg/0.8 mL

Tablet: 325 mg, 500 mg, 650 mg

Tablet, chewable: 80 mg, 160 mg

Additional Information Not sedating

Acetaminophen and Dextromethorphan

(a seet a MIN oh fen & dex troe meth OR fan)

U.S. Brand Names Bayer® Select® Chest Cold Caplets [OTC]; Drixoral® Cough & Sore Throat Liquid Caps [OTC]

Therapeutic Category Antitussive/Analgesic

Abuse Potential Yes

Impairment Potential Yes

Dosage Forms

Caplet: Acetaminophen 500 and dextromethorphan hydrobromide 15 mg

Capsule: Acetaminophen 325 and dextromethorphan hydrobromide 15 mg

Acetaminophen and Codeine (a seet a MIN oh fen & KOE deen)

Related Information

Acetaminophen *on previous page*

Codeine *on page 164*

Controlled Substances - Uses and Effects *on page 741*

Synonyms Codeine and Acetaminophen

U.S. Brand Names Capital® and Codeine; Phenaphen® With Codeine; Tylenol® With Codeine

(Continued)

Acetaminophen and Codeine *(Continued)*

Canadian Brand Names Atasol® 8, 15, 30 With Caffeine; Empracet® 30, 60; Emtec 30®; Lenoltec No 1, 2, 3, 4; Novo-Gesic-C8®; Novo-Gesic-C15®; Novo-Gesic-C30®

Therapeutic Category Analgesic, Narcotic

Dosage Forms

Capsule:

#2: Acetaminophen 325 mg and codeine phosphate 15 mg (C-III)

#3: Acetaminophen 325 mg and codeine phosphate 30 mg (C-III)

#4: Acetaminophen 325 mg and codeine phosphate 60 mg (C-III)

Elixir: Acetaminophen 120 mg and codeine phosphate 12 mg per 5 mL with alcohol 7% (C-V)

Suspension, oral, alcohol free: Acetaminophen 120 mg and codeine phosphate 12 mg per 5 mL (C-V)

Tablet: Acetaminophen 500 mg and codeine phosphate 30 mg (C-III); acetaminophen 650 mg and codeine phosphate 30 mg (C-III)

Tablet:

#1: Acetaminophen 300 mg and codeine phosphate 7.5 mg (C-III)

#2: Acetaminophen 300 mg and codeine phosphate 15 mg (C-III)

#3: Acetaminophen 300 mg and codeine phosphate 30 mg (C-III)

#4: Acetaminophen 300 mg and codeine phosphate 60 mg (C-III)

Acetaminophen and Diphenhydramine

(a seet a MIN oh fen & dye fen HYE dra meen)

U.S. Brand Names Arthritis Foundation® Nighttime [OTC]; Excedrin® P.M. [OTC]; Midol® PM [OTC]

Therapeutic Category Analgesic, Non-narcotic

Impairment Potential Yes; Impairment occurs at doses exceeding 50 mg

Gengo FM and Manning C, "A Review of the Effects of Antihistamines on Mental Processes Related to Automobile Driving," *J Allergy Clin Immunol*, 1990, 86(2): 1034-9.

Dosage Forms

Caplet:

Excedrin® P.M.: Acetaminophen 500 mg and diphenhydramine citrate 30 mg

Arthritis Foundation® Nighttime, Midol® PM: Acetaminophen 500 mg and diphenhydramine 25 mg

Liquid (wild berry flavor) (Excedrin® P.M.): Acetaminophen 1000 mg and diphenhydramine hydrochloride 50 mg per 30 mL (180 mL)

Acetaminophen and Hydrocodone see Hydrocodone and Acetaminophen *on page 293*

Acetaminophen and Oxycodone see Oxycodone and Acetaminophen *on page 453*

Acetaminophen and Phenyltoloxamine

(a seet a MIN oh fen & fen il to LOKS a meen)

U.S. Brand Names Percogesic® [OTC]

Therapeutic Category Analgesic, Non-narcotic

Dosage Forms Tablet: Acetaminophen 325 mg and phenyltoloxamine citrate 30 mg

Acetaminophen and Pseudoephedrine

(a seet a MIN oh fen & soo doe e FED rin)

U.S. Brand Names Allerest® No Drowsiness [OTC]; Bayer® Select Head Cold Caplets [OTC]; Coldrine® [OTC]; Dristan® Cold Caplets [OTC]; Dynafed®, Maximum Strength [OTC]; Ornex® No Drowsiness [OTC]; Sinarest®, No

Drowsiness [OTC]; Sine-Aid®, Maximum Strength [OTC]; Sine-Off® Maximum Strength No Drowsiness Formula [OTC]; Sinus Excedrin® Extra Strength [OTC]; Sinus-Relief® [OTC]; Sinutab® Without Drowsiness [OTC]; Tylenol® Sinus, Maximum Strength [OTC]

Therapeutic Category Decongestant/Analgesic

Abuse Potential Yes

Impairment Potential Yes

Dosage Forms Tablet:

Allerest® No Drowsiness; Coldrine®, Tylenol® Sinus, Maximum Strength; Ornex® No Drowsiness, Sinus-Relief®: Acetaminophen 325 mg and pseudoephedrine hydrochloride 30 mg

Bayer® Select Head Cold; Dristan® Cold; Dynafed®, Maximum Strength; Sinarest®, No Drowsiness; Sine-Aid®, Maximum Strength; Sine-Off® Maximum Strength No Drowsiness Formula; Sinus Excedrin® Extra Strength; Sinutab® Without Drowsiness; Tylenol® Sinus, Maximum Strength: Acetaminophen 500 mg and pseudoephedrine hydrochloride 30 mg

Acetaminophen, Aspirin, and Caffeine

(a seet a MIN oh fen, AS pir in, & KAF een)

U.S. Brand Names Excedrin®, Extra Strength [OTC]; Gelpirin® [OTC]; Goody's® Headache Powders

Therapeutic Category Analgesic, Non-narcotic

Dosage Forms

Geltab: Acetaminophen 250 mg, aspirin 250 mg, and caffeine 65 mg

Powder: Acetaminophen 250 mg, aspirin 520 mg, and caffeine 32.5 mg per dose

Tablet: Acetaminophen 125 mg, aspirin 240 mg, and caffeine 32 mg; acetaminophen 250 mg, aspirin 250 mg, and caffeine 65 mg

Acetaminophen, Chlorpheniramine, and Pseudoephedrine

(a seet a MIN oh fen, klor fen IR a meen, & soo doe e FED rin)

U.S. Brand Names Alka-Seltzer® Plus Cold Liqui-Gels Capsules [OTC]; Aspirin-Free Bayer® Select® Allergy Sinus Caplets [OTC]; Co-Hist® [OTC]; Sinutab® Tablets [OTC]

Therapeutic Category Antihistamine/Decongestant/Analgesic

Abuse Potential Yes

Impairment Potential Yes

Dosage Forms

Caplet: Acetaminophen 500 mg, chlorpheniramine maleate 2 mg, and pseudoephedrine hydrochloride 30 mg

Capsule: Acetaminophen 250 mg, chlorpheniramine maleate 2 mg, and pseudoephedrine hydrochloride 30 mg

Tablet: Acetaminophen 325 mg, chlorpheniramine maleate 2 mg, and pseudoephedrine hydrochloride 30 mg

Acetaminophen, Dextromethorphan, and Pseudoephedrine

(a seet a MIN oh fen, deks troe meth OR fan, & soo doe e FED rin)

U.S. Brand Names Alka-Seltzer® Plus Flu & Body Aches Non-Drowsy Liqui-Gels [OTC]; Comtrex® Maximum Strength Non-Drowsy [OTC]; Sudafed® Severe Cold [OTC]; Theraflu® Non-Drowsy Formula Maximum Strength [OTC]; Tylenol® Cold No Drowsiness [OTC]; Tylenol® Flu Maximum Strength [OTC]

Therapeutic Category Cold Preparation

Abuse Potential Yes

Impairment Potential Yes

(Continued)

23

Acetaminophen, Dextromethorphan, and Pseudoephedrine *(Continued)*

Dosage Forms Tablet:
Alka-Seltzer® Plus Flu & Body Aches Non-Drowsy: Acetaminophen 500 mg, dextromethorphan hydrobromide 10 mg, and pseudoephedrine hydrochloride 30 mg

Tylenol® Cold No Drowsiness: Acetaminophen 325 mg, dextromethorphan hydrobromide 15 mg, and pseudoephedrine hydrochloride 30 mg

Comtrex® Maximum Strength Non-Drowsy; Sudafed® Severe Cold; Theraflu® Non-Drowsy Formula Maximum Strength; Tylenol® Flu Maximum Strength: Acetaminophen 500 mg, dextromethorphan hydrobromide 15 mg, and pseudoephedrine hydrochloride 30 mg

Acetaminophen, Isometheptene, and Dichloralphenazone

(a seet a MIN oh fen, eye soe me THEP teen, & dye KLOR al FEN a zone)
U.S. Brand Names Isocom®; Isopap®; Midchlor®; Midrin®; Migratine®
Therapeutic Category Analgesic, Non-narcotic
Dosage Forms Capsule: Acetaminophen 326 mg, isometheptene mucate 65 mg, dichloralphenazone 100 mg

Aceten® *see* Captopril *on page 101*

Acetic Acid *see* Vinyl Acetate *on page 613*

Acetic Aldehyde *see* Acetaldehyde *on page 19*

Acetohexamide (a set oh HEKS a mide)

U.S. Brand Names Dymelor®
Therapeutic Category Antidiabetic Agent (Oral)
Use Adjunct to diet for the management of mild to moderately severe, stable, noninsulin-dependent (type II) diabetes mellitus
Usual Dosage Adults: Oral (elderly patients may be more sensitive and should be started at a lower dosage initially): 250 mg to 1.5 g/day in 1-2 divided doses; doses >1.5 g/day are not recommended; if dose is ≤1 g, administer as a single daily dose
Mechanism of Action Believed to cause hypoglycemia by stimulating insulin release from the pancreatic beta cells; reduces glucose output from the liver (decreases gluconeogenesis); insulin sensitivity is increased at peripheral target sites (alters receptor sensitivity/receptor density); potentiates effects of ADH; may produce mild diuresis and significant uricosuric activity
Pharmacodynamics/kinetics
Onset of effect: 1 hour
Peak hypoglycemic effects: 8-10 hours
Duration: 12-24 hours, prolonged with renal impairment
Metabolism: In the liver to potent active metabolite
Half-life:
Parent compound: 0.8-2.4 hours
Metabolite: 5-6 hours
Signs and Symptoms of Acute Intoxication Low blood sugar, tingling of lips and tongue, nausea, yawning, confusion, agitation, tachycardia, sweating, convulsions, stupor, and coma
When to Transport to Hospital Transport any pediatric ingestion, any symptomatic adult ingestion, or asymptomatic ingestion over 1.5 g
Overdosage/Treatment Hypoglycemia should be managed with 50 mL I.V. dextrose 50% followed immediately with a continuous infusion of 10% dextrose in water (administer at a rate sufficient enough to approach a serum glucose

level of 100 mg/dL). If the patient is awake and alert, oral sugar solutions (eg, orange juice) can be used as a temporizing manner.

Warnings/Precautions Advise patient to avoid alcohol or products containing alcohol; monitor for signs and symptoms of hypoglycemia (fatigue, excessive hunger, profuse sweating, or numbness of extremities)

Adverse Reactions

>10%:

Central nervous system: Headache, dizziness

Gastrointestinal: Constipation, diarrhea, heartburn, anorexia, epigastric fullness

1% to 10%: Dermatologic: Rash, urticaria, photosensitivity

Reference Range Target range: Adults:

Fasting blood glucose: <120 mg/dL

Adults: 80-140 mg/dL

Geriatrics: 100-150 mg/dL

Glycosylated hemoglobin: <7%

Drug Interactions

Monitor patient closely; large number of drugs interact with sulfonylureas

Decreased effect: Decreases hypoglycemic effect when coadministered with cholestyramine, diazoxide, hydantoins, rifampin, thiazides, loop or thiazide diuretics, and phenylbutazone

Increased effect: Increases hypoglycemia when coadministered with salicylates or beta-adrenergic blockers; MAO inhibitors; oral anticoagulants, NSAIDs, sulfonamides, phenylbutazone, insulin, clofibrate, fluconazole, gemfibrozil, H_2-antagonists, methyldopa, tricyclic antidepressants

Dosage Forms Tablet: 250 mg, 500 mg

Specific References

"Standards of Medical Care for Patients With Diabetes Mellitus. American Diabetes Association," *Diabetes Care*, 1994, 17(6):616-23.

Acetomorphine see Heroin on page 283

Acetone

Synonyms Dimethyl Formaldehyde; Dimethyl Ketone; 2-Propanone

UN Number 1090

Abuse Potential Yes

Impairment Potential Yes; Serum acetone level of 100 mg/dL is consistent with mild signs of intoxication and driving impairment

Jones AW, "Driving Under the Influence of Acetone," *J Toxicol Clin Toxicol*, 1997, 35(4):419-21.

Use Volatile solvent (ie, fingernail polish remover, glues, rubber cement); defatting agent in semiconductor industry

Mechanism of Toxic Action Sensitizes the heart to adrenaline thus causing faster heart rate

Toxicodynamics/kinetics

Absorption: Readily through the lungs (75% to 80%) and skin (more slowly) and gastrointestinal tract (74% to 83%)

Metabolism: Hepatic

Half-life, elimination: 17-25 hours

Elimination: Excreted through the lungs and urine

Signs and Symptoms of Acute Intoxication Sedation, vomiting, cough, ataxia, coma, seizures (in children), bronchial irritation, hyperglycemia, hypoglycemia, hypotension, narcosis, headache

When to Transport to Hospital Transport any symptomatic patient

Overdosage/Treatment

Decontamination: Ingestion: **Do not** induce vomiting; activated charcoal can adsorb 42% to 44% of acetone

(Continued)

Acetone *(Continued)*

Supportive therapy: Inhalation: Airway support and 100% humidified oxygen

Adverse Reactions

Cardiovascular: Tachycardia, sinus tachycardia

Central nervous system: Depression

Ocular: Eye irritation, lacrimation

Respiratory: Respiratory depression

Reference Range Toxic: Blood levels >330 mg/L; urinary acetone levels correlating to air acetone levels of 200 ppm and 750 ppm are 21.6 mg/L and 76.6 mg/L respectively; blood acetone levels associated with air acetone levels of 200 ppm and 750 ppm are 41.4 mg/L and 118 mg/L respectively; average amount of acetone in expired air of a healthy subject is ~1 µg/L

Additional Information Fruity odor, sweet taste; acetone is a metabolite of isopropyl alcohol; cigarette smoke contains <0.5 mg acetone per cigarette; no increased cancer risk; very water soluble; potentiates nervous system toxicity of ethanol

Odor threshold: 13-20 ppm

Ingestion: Toxic dose: 2-3 mL/kg

Inhalation:

TLV-TWA: 750 ppm

IDLH: 20,000 ppm

PEL-TWA: 1000 ppm

Acetonitrile

Related Information

Cyanide *on page 170*

Synonyms Cyanomethane; Methyl Cyanide

UN Number 1648

U.S. Brand Names Ardell Instant Glue Remover®; Artificial Nail Tip and Glue Remover®; Super Nail Glue Off®; Super Nail Off®

Use Highly polar solvent used in cosmetic nail remover

Mechanism of Toxic Action Converts to cyanide by the liver

Toxicodynamics/kinetics

Absorption: Dermal, oral, and inhalation

Metabolism: Hepatic hydrolysis to hydrogen cyanide

Half-life:

Acetonitrile: 32 hours

Cyanide: 15 hours

Signs and Symptoms of Acute Intoxication Myocardial depression, CNS stimulation followed by CNS depression, seizures, respiratory depression, congestive heart failure

When to Transport to Hospital Patients should be transported to hospital and treated for cyanide exposure following any ingestion

Overdosage/Treatment Decontamination:

Oral: Basic poison management; emesis is contraindicated due to rapid course of the neurologic symptoms; activated charcoal may be useful

Inhalation: Give 100% oxygen

Additional Information Decomposes to hydrogen cyanide gas at 120°C

Specific References

Geller RJ, Ekins BR, and Iknoian RC, "Cyanide Toxicity From Acetonitrile-Containing False Nail Remover," *Am J Emerg Med*, 1991, 9(3):268-70.

1-Acetoxy-Ethylene *see* Vinyl Acetate *on page 613*

Acetylene Tetrachloride *see* Tetrachloroethane *on page 566*

Acetylene Trichloride *see* Trichloroethylene *on page 594*

Acetylsalicylic Acid *see* Aspirin *on page 56*

Achromycin® *see* Tetracycline *on page 568*
Achromycin® V Oral *see* Tetracycline *on page 568*
Aciclovir *see* Acyclovir *on page 29*
Acidulated Phosphate Fluoride *see* Fluoride *on page 251*
Acidum Nicotinicum *see* Niacin *on page 428*

Acrivastine and Pseudoephedrine
(AK ri vas teen & soo doe e FED rin)
Synonyms Pseudoephedrine and Acrivastine
U.S. Brand Names Semprex-D®
Therapeutic Category Antihistamine/Decongestant Combination
Abuse Potential Yes
Impairment Potential Yes
Dosage Forms Capsule: Acrivastine 8 mg and pseudoephedrine hydrochloride 60 mg

Acrolein
Synonyms Propylene Aldehyde; Pyran Aldehyde
UN Number 2607; 1092
U.S. Brand Names Aqualin®; Magnacide H®
Use Manufacture of pharmaceuticals, herbicides, textiles, and as a tear gas; found as an irritant gas generated by fire; production of acrylic acid; as a tissue fixative, biocide, and slimicide in paper industry
Mechanism of Toxic Action Irritation of mucous membranes; suppresses glycolysis and reacts with sulfhydryl groups of proteins; release of catecholamines is noted; high water stability can lead to primary upper airway damage
Toxicodynamics/kinetics
Absorption: Through ingestion and inhalation
Metabolism: Hepatic to S-carboxy ethyl mercapturic acid methyl ester
Signs and Symptoms of Acute Intoxication Lacrimation, erythema, bronchial constriction, dyspnea, hypertension, coma, tachycardia, cough, tachypnea at atmosphere levels over 0.6 ppm
When to Transport to Hospital Symptomatic patients require immediate hospital transport
Overdosage/Treatment Decontamination: Inhalation: Humidified oxygen
Adverse Reactions
Cardiovascular: Sinus tachycardia
Respiratory: Pulmonary edema
Additional Information One of the major irritants in smog; yellow liquid with pungent odor (acrid)
Odor threshold
Water: 0.11 ppm
Air: 0.16 ppm
Toxic dose for irritation: 10 ppm
TLV-TWA: 0.1 ppm
IDLH: 5 ppm
PEL-TWA: 0.1 ppm
Specific References
U.S. Department of Health and Human Services, "Toxicological Profile for Acrolein TP-90/01," Agency for Toxic Substances and Diseases Registry, December 1990.

Acrylonitrile
Synonyms Cyanoethylene; 2-Propenenitrile; Vinyl Cyanide
UN Number 1093
(Continued)

27

Acrylonitrile *(Continued)*

Use Raw material in acrylic/modacrylic fibers; also used in the manufacture of plastics, rubber, acrylics, and adhesives; used as a fumigant and pesticide

Mechanism of Toxic Action Liver conversion to cyanide can produce signs and symptoms of cyanide

Toxicodynamics/kinetics

Absorption:

Inhalation: 52%

Dermal: 0.6 mg/cm²/hour

Metabolism: To 2-cyanoethylene oxide then converted to cyanide in the liver

Half-life: 7-8 hours

Elimination: Renal (68%)

When to Transport to Hospital Patients should be transported to the hospital and treated for cyanide poisoning following any ingestion

Overdosage/Treatment Decontamination: Basic poison management (lavage within 1 hour/activated charcoal); emesis is contraindicated due to rapid course of the neurologic symptoms; give 100% oxygen

Adverse Reactions

Cardiovascular: Tachycardia

Central nervous system: Dizziness, headache, seizures

Dermatologic: Dermal irritation, desquamation, toxic epidermal necrosis may develop in 3 weeks

Endocrine & metabolic: Lactic acidosis

Gastrointestinal: Nausea, diarrhea, vomiting

Hematologic: Anemia

Hepatic: Jaundice, hepatic injury

Neuromuscular & skeletal: Limb weakness

Ocular: Conjunctivitis

Respiratory: Irregular breathing, dyspnea

Reference Range Plasma thiocyanate levels >20 mg/L in nonsmokers or 30 mg/L in smokers is consistent with exposure to acrylonitrile; exposure to an average air level of 4.2 ppm of acrylonitrile over an 8-hour day produces a urinary acrylonitrile level of 360 µg/L and a urinary thiocyanate level of 11.4 mg/L

Additional Information Levels of 16-100 ppm for 20-45 minutes can produce symptoms; odor is pungent (onion/garlic-like); children are more susceptible than adults; will be absorbed through leather products; associated with increase in prostate, colon, lung, and stomach cancer; full recovery will usually occur if patient survives for 4 hours

TLV-TWA: 2 ppm

IDLH: 4000 ppm

Odor threshold in water: 19 ppm

Specific References

U.S. Department of Health and Human Services, *Public Health Service Toxicological Profile for Acrylonitrile TP-90/02*, Agency for Toxic Substances and Diseases Registry, December, 1990.

ACT® [OTC] *see* Fluoride *on page 251*

Actacode *see* Codeine *on page 164*

Actagen-C® *see* Triprolidine, Pseudoephedrine, and Codeine *on page 602*

Acticort™ *see* Hydrocortisone *on page 297*

Actifed® Allergy Tablet (Night) [OTC] *see* Diphenhydramine and Pseudoephedrine *on page 207*

Actifed® With Codeine *see* Triprolidine, Pseudoephedrine, and Codeine *on page 602*

Actrafan® HM *see* Insulin Preparations *on page 314*

Actrap® MC *see* Insulin Preparations *on page 314*

Actron® *see* Ketoprofen *on page 328*

Acutrim® [OTC] *see* Phenylpropanolamine *on page 481*

ACV *see* Acyclovir *on this page*

Acycloguanosine *see* Acyclovir *on this page*

Acyclovir (ay SYE kloe veer)

Related Information

Valacyclovir *on page 605*

Synonyms Aciclovir; ACV; Acycloguanosine

U.S. Brand Names Zovirax®

Canadian Brand Names Avirax®

Therapeutic Category Antiviral Agent

Use Treatment of initial and prophylaxis of recurrent mucosal and cutaneous herpes simplex (HSV-1 and HSV-2) infections; herpes simplex encephalitis; herpes zoster; genital herpes infection; varicella-zoster infections in healthy, nonpregnant persons >13 years of age, children >12 months of age who have a chronic skin or lung disorder or are receiving long-term aspirin therapy, and immunocompromised patients; for herpes zoster, acyclovir should be started within 72 hours of the appearance of the rash to be effective; acyclovir will not prevent postherpetic neuralgias

Usual Dosage

Dosing weight should be based on the smaller of lean body weight or total body weight

Adult determination of lean body weight (LBW) in kg:

LBW males: 50 kg + (2.3 kg x inches >5 feet)

LBW females: 45 kg + (2.3 kg x inches >5 feet)

Treatment of herpes simplex virus infections: Children and Adults: I.V.:

Mucocutaneous HSV infection: 750 mg/m²/day divided every 8 hours or 5 mg/kg/dose every 8 hours for 5-10 days

HSV encephalitis: 1500 mg/m²/day divided every 8 hours for 5-10 days

Treatment of herpes simplex virus infections: Adults:

Oral: Treatment: 200 mg every 4 hours while awake (5 times/day)

Topical: ½" ribbon of ointment for a 4" square surface area every 3 hours (6 times/day)

Treatment of varicella-zoster virus (chickenpox) infections:

Oral:

Children: 10-20 mg/kg/dose (up to 800 mg) 4 times/day for 5 days; begin treatment within the first 24 hours of rash onset

Adults: 600-800 mg/dose every 4 hours while awake (5 times/day) for 7-10 days or 1000 mg every 6 hours for 5 days

I.V.: Children and Adults: 1500 mg/m²/day divided every 8 hours or 10 mg/kg/dose every 8 hours for 7 days

Treatment of herpes zoster infections:

Oral:

Children (immunocompromised): 250-600 mg/m²/dose 4-5 times/day for 7-10 days

Adults (immunocompromised): 800 mg every 4 hours (5 times/day) for 7-10 days

I.V.:

Children and Adults (immunocompromised): 10-12 mg/kg/dose every 8 hours

Older Adults (immunocompromised): 7.5 mg/kg/dose every 8 hours

If nephrotoxicity occurs: 5 mg/kg/dose every 8 hours

(Continued)

Acyclovir *(Continued)*

Prophylaxis in immunocompromised patients:

Varicella zoster or herpes zoster in HIV-positive patients: Adults: Oral: 400 mg every 4 hours (5 times/day) for 7-10 days

Bone marrow transplant recipients: Children and Adults: I.V.:

Autologous patients who are HSV seropositive: 150 mg/m²/dose (5 mg/kg) every 12 hours; with clinical symptoms of herpes simplex: 150 mg/m²/dose every 8 hours

Autologous patients who are CMV seropositive: 500 mg/m²/dose (10 mg/kg) every 8 hours; for clinically symptomatic CMV infection, consider replacing acyclovir with ganciclovir

Prophylaxis of herpes simplex virus infections: Adults: 200 mg 3-4 times/day or 400 mg twice daily

Mechanism of Action Inhibits DNA synthesis and viral replication by competing with deoxyguanosine triphosphate for viral DNA polymerase and being incorporated into viral DNA

Pharmacodynamics/kinetics

Absorption: Oral: 15% to 30%; food does not appear to affect absorption

Distribution: Widely distributed throughout the body including brain, kidney, lungs, liver, spleen, muscle, uterus, vagina, and CSF

Metabolism: Small amount of liver metabolism

Half-life, terminal phase:

Neonates: 4 hours

Children 1-12 years: 2-3 hours

Adults: 3 hours

Time to peak serum concentration:

Oral: Within 1.5-2 hours

I.V.: Within 1 hour

Signs and Symptoms of Acute Intoxication Elevated serum creatinine, renal failure, decreased mental status, visual hallucinations can occur

When to Transport to Hospital Transport any patient with altered mental status

Warnings/Precautions Use with caution in patients with pre-existing renal disease or in those receiving other nephrotoxic drugs concurrently; maintain adequate urine output during the first 2 hours after I.V. infusion; use with caution in patients with underlying neurologic abnormalities, serious hepatic or electrolyte abnormalities, or substantial hypoxia

Adverse Reactions

>10%:

Central nervous system: Headache

Local: Inflammation at injection site

1% to 10%:

Central nervous system: Lethargy, dizziness, seizures, confusion, agitation, coma

Dermatologic: Rash

Gastrointestinal: Nausea, vomiting

Neuromuscular & skeletal: Tremor

Renal: Impaired renal function

Drug Interactions Increased CNS side effects with zidovudine and probenecid

Dosage Forms

Capsule: 200 mg

Powder for Injection: 500 mg (10 mL); 1000 mg (20 mL)

Ointment, topical: 5% [50 mg/g] (3 g, 15 g)

Suspension, oral (banana flavor): 200 mg/5 mL

Tablet: 400 mg, 800 mg

Specific References
Whitley RJ and Gnann JW Jr, "Acyclovir: A Decade Later," *N Engl J Med*, 1992, 327(11):782-3.

Adalat® *see* Nifedipine *on page 433*

Adamantanamine Hydrochloride *see* Amantadine *on page 37*

Adapin® *see* Doxepin *on page 211*

Adderall® *see* Dextroamphetamine and Amphetamine *on page 187*

Adifax® *see* Dexfenfluramine *on page 185*

Adipex-P® *see* Phentermine *on page 478*

Adumbran® *see* Oxazepam *on page 450*

Advil® [OTC] *see* Ibuprofen *on page 308*

Advil® Cold & Sinus Caplets [OTC] *see* Pseudoephedrine and Ibuprofen *on page 517*

Aerolate® *see* Theophylline Salts *on page 571*

Aerolate III® *see* Theophylline Salts *on page 571*

Aerolate JR® *see* Theophylline Salts *on page 571*

Aerolate SR® Aminophyllin™ *see* Theophylline Salts *on page 571*

Aeroseb-Dex® *see* Dexamethasone *on page 182*

Aeroseb-HC® *see* Hydrocortisone *on page 297*

Afrinol® [OTC] *see* Pseudoephedrine *on page 516*

Afrodex® *see* Yohimbine *on page 618*

AHD 2000® *see* Ethyl Alcohol *on page 233*

A-HydroCort® *see* Hydrocortisone *on page 297*

Airet® *see* Albuterol *on this page*

AK-Con® *see* Naphazoline *on page 422*

AK-Dex® Ophthalmic *see* Dexamethasone *on page 182*

AK-Dilate® Ophthalmic Solution *see* Phenylephrine *on page 479*

AK-Homatropine® *see* Homatropine *on page 288*

Akineton® *see* Biperiden *on page 77*

AK-Nefrin® Ophthalmic Solution *see* Phenylephrine *on page 479*

AK-Pred® *see* Prednisolone *on page 495*

Ala-Cort® *see* Hydrocortisone *on page 297*

Ala-Scalp™ *see* Hydrocortisone *on page 297*

Ala-Tet® Oral *see* Tetracycline *on page 568*

Albalon® Liquifilm® *see* Naphazoline *on page 422*

Albuterol (al BYOO ter ole)

Synonyms Salbutamol
U.S. Brand Names Airet®; Proventil®; Proventil® HFA; Ventolin®; Ventolin® Rotocaps®; Volmax®
Canadian Brand Names Apo-Salvent®; Novo-Salmol®; Sabulin®
Therapeutic Category Adrenergic Agonist Agent
Use Bronchodilator in reversible airway obstruction due to asthma or COPD
Usual Dosage
Oral:
Children:
2-6 years: 0.1-0.2 mg/kg/dose 3 times/day; maximum dose not to exceed 12 mg/day (divided doses)
6-12 years: 2 mg/dose 3-4 times/day; maximum dose not to exceed 24 mg/day (divided doses)
Children >12 years and Adults: 2-4 mg/dose 3-4 times/day; maximum dose not to exceed 32 mg/day (divided doses)
Elderly: 2 mg 3-4 times/day; maximum: 8 mg 4 times/day
(Continued)

Albuterol *(Continued)*

Inhalation MDI: 90 mcg/spray:

Children <12 years: 1-2 inhalations 4 times/day using a tube spacer

Children ≥12 years and Adults: 1-2 inhalations every 4-6 hours; maximum: 12 inhalations/day

Exercise-induced bronchospasm: 2 inhalations 15 minutes before exercising

Inhalation: Nebulization: 2.5 mg = 0.5 mL of the 0.5% inhalation solution to be diluted in 1-2.5 mL of NS **or** 0.01-0.05 mL/kg of 0.5% solution every 4-6 hours; intensive care patients may require more frequent administration; minimum dose: 0.1 mL; maximum dose: 1 mL diluted in 1-2 mL normal saline

<5 years: 1.25-2.5 mg every 4-6 hours as needed

>5 years: 2.5-5 mg every 4-6 hours as needed

Mechanism of Action Relaxes bronchial smooth muscle by action on beta$_2$-receptors in the lung with little effect on heart rate

Pharmacodynamics/kinetics

Peak effect:

Oral: 2-3 hours

Nebulization/oral inhalation: Within 0.5-2 hours

Duration of action:

Oral: 4-6 hours

Nebulization/oral inhalation: 3-4 hours

Metabolism: By the liver to inactive sulfate metabolites

Half-life:

Inhalation: 3.8 hours

Oral: 3.7-5 hours

Elimination: 30% appears in urine as unchanged drug

Signs and Symptoms of Acute Intoxication Hypertension, tachycardia, angina, low potassium in the bloodstream, tremor, palpitations

When to Transport to Hospital Transport any pediatric (<6 years of age) ingestion over 1 mg/kg or any symptomatic patient

Warnings/Precautions Use with caution in patients with hyperthyroidism, diabetes mellitus, or sensitivity to sympathomimetic amines; cardiovascular disorders including coronary insufficiency or hypertension; excessive use may result in tolerance

Some adverse reactions may occur more frequently in children 2-5 years of age than in adults and older children

Because of its minimal effect on beta$_1$-receptors and its relatively long duration of action, albuterol is a rational choice in the elderly when a beta agonist is indicated. All patients should utilize a spacer device when using a metered dose inhaler. Oral use should be avoided in the elderly due to adverse effects.

Adverse Reactions

>10%:

Cardiovascular: Tachycardia, palpitations, pounding heartbeat

Gastrointestinal: GI upset, nausea

1% to 10%:

Cardiovascular: Flushing of face, hypertension or hypotension

Central nervous system: Nervousness, CNS stimulation, hyperactivity, insomnia, dizziness, lightheadedness, drowsiness, headache

Gastrointestinal: Xerostomia, heartburn, vomiting, unusual taste

Genitourinary: Dysuria

Neuromuscular & skeletal: Muscle cramping, tremor, weakness

Respiratory: Coughing

Miscellaneous: Diaphoresis (increased)

Test Interactions ↑ renin (S), ↑ aldosterone (S)

Drug Interactions
Decreased effect: Beta-adrenergic blockers (eg, propranolol)
Increased therapeutic effect: Inhaled ipratropium may increase duration of bronchodilation, nifedipine may increase FEV-1
Increased toxicity: Cardiovascular effects are potentiated in patients also receiving MAO inhibitors, tricyclic antidepressants, sympathomimetic agents (eg, amphetamine, dopamine, dobutamine), inhaled anesthetics (eg, enflurane)

Dosage Forms
Aerosol (Proventil®, Ventolin®): 90 mcg/dose (17 g) [200 doses]
Aerosol, chlorofluorocarbon free (Proventil® HFA): 90 mcg/dose (17 g)
Capsule for oral inhalation (Ventolin® Rotacaps®): 200 mcg [to be used with Rotahaler® inhalation device]
Solution, inhalation: 0.083% (3 mL); 0.5% (20 mL)
Airet®: 0.083%
Proventil®: 0.083% (3 mL); 0.5% (20 mL)
Ventolin®: 0.5% (20 mL)
Syrup, as sulfate: 2 mg/5 mL (480 mL)
Proventil®, Ventolin®: 2 mg/5 mL (480 mL)
Tablet, as sulfate: 2 mg, 4 mg
Proventil®, Ventolin®: 2 mg, 4 mg
Tablet, extended release:
Proventil® Repetabs®: 4 mg
Volmax®: 4 mg, 8 mg

Specific References
Leikin JB, Linowiecki KA, Soglin DF, et al, "Hypokalemia After Pediatric Albuterol Overdose: A Case Series," *Am J Emerg Med*, 1994, 12(1):64-6.

Alcohol, Semiquantitative, Urine

Synonyms Ethyl Alcohol, Urine; Urine Alcohol Level; Urine Ethanol
Reference Range Negative
Additional Information Ethanol is absorbed rapidly from the GI tract. Peak blood levels usually occur within 30-60 minutes on an empty stomach. Food in the stomach can delay the absorption of alcohol. Ethanol is metabolized by the liver to acetaldehyde. Once peak blood ethanol levels are reached, disappearance is semilinear; a 70 kg man metabolizes 7-10 g alcohol/hour (20±10 mg/dL/hour). The average urine/blood ratio is 1.35 in the postabsorptive state. Signs and symptoms of intoxication in the presence of low alcohol levels could indicate a serious acute medical problem requiring immediate attention or other substances. The half-lives and effectiveness of certain drugs (eg, barbiturates, etc) are increased in the presence of ethanol.

Alcohol, Serum

Synonyms Ethanol, Blood; Ethyl Alcohol, Blood; EtOH
Use Quantitation of alcohol level for medical or legal purposes; screen unconscious patients; used to diagnose alcohol intoxication and determine appropriate therapy; screen for alcoholism and monitor ethanol treatment for methanol intoxication. Must be tested as possible cause of coma of unknown etiology since alcohol intoxication may mimic diabetic coma, cerebral trauma, and drug overdose.
Reference Range Blood: negative

Alcojel see Isopropyl Alcohol *on page 323*
Alconefrin® Nasal Solution [OTC] see Phenylephrine *on page 479*
Aldace see Spironolactone *on page 544*
Aldactone® see Spironolactone *on page 544*
Aldoclor® see Chlorothiazide and Methyldopa *on page 132*

Aldomet® *see* Methyldopa *on page 393*

Aldopur® *see* Spironolactone *on page 544*

Aldoril® *see* Methyldopa and Hydrochlorothiazide *on page 395*

Alergist® *see* Terfenadine *on page 563*

Alersule Forte® *see* Chlorpheniramine, Phenylephrine, and Methscopolamine *on page 136*

Aleve® [OTC] *see* Naproxen *on page 423*

Alfa-Tox® *see* Diazinon *on page 192*

Alfenta® *see* Alfentanil *on this page*

Alfentanil (al FEN ta nil)

Related Information
Controlled Substances - Uses and Effects *on page 741*

U.S. Brand Names Alfenta®

Therapeutic Category Analgesic, Narcotic; General Anesthetic

Abuse Potential Yes

Impairment Potential Yes

Use Analgesic adjunct given by continuous infusion or in incremental doses in maintenance of anesthesia with barbiturate or N_2O or a primary anesthetic agent for the induction of anesthesia in patients undergoing general surgery in which endotracheal intubation and mechanical ventilation are required

Usual Dosage Doses should be titrated to appropriate effects; wide range of doses is dependent upon desired degree of analgesia/anesthesia

Children <12 years: Dose not established

Adults: Dose should be based on ideal body weight; see table.

Alfentanil

Indication	Approx Duration of Anesthesia (min)	Induction Period (Initial Dose) (mcg/kg)	Maintenance Period (Increments/ Infusion)	Total Dose (mcg/kg)	Effects
Incremental injection	≤30	8-20	3-5 mcg/kg or 0.5-1 mcg/kg/ min	8-40	Spontaneously breathing or assisted ventilation when required.
	30-60	20-50	5-15 mcg/kg	Up to 75	Assisted or controlled ventilation required. Attenuation of response to laryngoscopy and intubation.
Continuous infusion	>45	50-75	0.5-3 mcg/kg/ min average infusion rate 1-1.5 mcg/kg/ min	Dependent on duration of procedure	Assisted or controlled ventilation required. Some attenuation of response to intubation and incision, with intraoperative stability.
Anesthetic induction	>45	130-245	0.5-1.5 mcg/ kg/min or general anesthetic	Dependent on duration of procedure	Assisted or controlled ventilation required. Administer slowly (over 3 minutes). Concentration of inhalation agents reduced by 30% to 50% for initial hour.

Mechanism of Action Binds with stereospecific receptors at many sites within the CNS, increases pain threshold, alters pain perception, inhibits ascending pain pathways; is an ultra short-acting narcotic

Pharmacodynamics/kinetics

Half-life, elimination:

Newborns, premature: 5.33-8.75 hours

Children: 40-60 minutes

Adults: 83-97 minutes

Signs and Symptoms of Acute Intoxication Miosis, respiratory depression, seizures, CNS depression

When to Transport to Hospital Transport any pediatric patient or any adult symptomatic patient

Warnings/Precautions Drug dependence, head injury, acute asthma and respiratory conditions; hypotension has occurred in neonates with respiratory distress syndrome; use caution when administering to patients with bradyarrhythmias; rapid I.V. infusion may result in skeletal muscle and chest wall rigidity → impaired ventilation → respiratory distress/arrest; inject slowly over 3-5 minutes; nondepolarizing skeletal muscle relaxant may be required. Alfentanil may produce more hypotension compared to fentanyl, therefore, be sure to administer slowly and ensure patient has adequate hydration.

Adverse Reactions

>10%:

Cardiovascular: Bradycardia, peripheral vasodilation

Central nervous system: Drowsiness, sedation, increased intracranial pressure

Gastrointestinal: Nausea, vomiting, constipation

Endocrine & metabolic: Antidiuretic hormone release

Ocular: Miosis

1% to 10%:

Cardiovascular: Cardiac arrhythmias, orthostatic hypotension

Central nervous system: Confusion, CNS depression

Ocular: Blurred vision

Reference Range 100-340 ng/mL (depending upon procedure)

Drug Interactions Cytochrome P-450 3A enzyme substrate

Decreased effect: Phenothiazines may antagonize the analgesic effect of opiate agonists

Increased effect: Dextroamphetamine may enhance the analgesic effect of morphine and other opiate agonists

Increased toxicity: CNS depressants (eg, benzodiazepines, barbiturates, phenothiazines, tricyclic antidepressants), erythromycin, reserpine, beta-blockers

Dosage Forms Injection, preservative free, as hydrochloride: 500 mcg/mL (2 mL, 5 mL, 10 mL, 20 mL)

Specific References

Meistelman C, Saint-Maurice C, Lepaul M, et al, "A Comparison of Alfentanil Pharmacokinetics in Children and Adults," *Anesthesiology*, 1987, 66(1):13-6.

Algocor® *see* Gallopamil *on page 262*

Algopent® *see* Pentazocine *on page 463*

Alimemazine Tartrate *see* Trimeprazine *on page 598*

Alinam® *see* Chlormezanone *on page 126*

Aliseum® *see* Diazepam *on page 189*

Alka-Seltzer® Plus Cold Liqui-Gels Capsules [OTC] *see* Acetaminophen, Chlorpheniramine, and Pseudoephedrine *on page 23*

Alka-Seltzer® Plus Flu & Body Aches Non-Drowsy Liqui-Gels [OTC] *see* Acetaminophen, Dextromethorphan, and Pseudoephedrine *on page 23*

Allegron® *see* Nortriptyline *on page 440*

Aller-Chlor® [OTC] *see* Chlorpheniramine *on page 132*

Allerest® 12 Hour Capsule [OTC] *see* Chlorpheniramine and Phenylpropanolamine *on page 134*

Allerest® Eye Drops [OTC] *see* Naphazoline *on page 422*

Allerest® Maximum Strength [OTC] *see* Chlorpheniramine and Pseudoephedrine *on page 134*

Allerest® No Drowsiness [OTC] *see* Acetaminophen and Pseudoephedrine *on page 22*

Aller-eze® *see* Clemastine *on page 149*

Allerfrin® w/Codeine *see* Triprolidine, Pseudoephedrine, and Codeine *on page 602*

Allergefon® *see* Carbinoxamine *on page 106*

AllerMax® Oral [OTC] *see* Diphenhydramine *on page 205*

Allerplus® *see* Terfenadine *on page 563*

Allocar® *see* Digoxin *on page 199*

Alodorm® *see* Nitrazepam *on page 435*

Alor® 5/500 *see* Hydrocodone and Aspirin *on page 294*

Alpha Alpha-Dimethyl Phenethylamine *see* Phentermine *on page 478*

Alphamul® [OTC] *see* Castor Oil *on page 118*

Alprazolam (al PRAY zoe lam)

Related Information
Controlled Substances - Uses and Effects *on page 741*

U.S. Brand Names Xanax®

Canadian Brand Names Apo-Alpraz®; Novo-Aloprazol®; Nu-Alprax®

Therapeutic Category Benzodiazepine

Abuse Potential Yes

Impairment Potential Yes; Cognitive and psychomotor deficits occur in the elderly at doses of 0.25 and 0.5 mg. At the lower dose, the effect appear to last for 2.5 hours.

Pomara N, Tun H, DaSilva D, et al, "Benzodiazepine Use and Crash Risk in Older Patients," *JAMA*, 1998, 279(2):113-4.

Use Treatment of anxiety; adjunct in the treatment of depression; management of panic attacks

Usual Dosage Oral:
Children <18 years: Safety and dose have not been established
Adults:
Anxiety: Effective doses are 0.5-4 mg/day in divided doses; the manufacturer recommends starting at 0.25-0.5 mg 3 times/day; titrate dose upward; maximum: 4 mg/day
Depression: Average dose required: 2.5-3 mg/day in divided doses
Alcohol withdrawal: Usual dose: 2-2.5 mg/day in divided doses
Panic disorder: Many patients obtain relief at 2 mg/day, as much as 6 mg/day may be required

Note: Treatment >4 months should be re-evaluated to determine the patient's need for the drug

Mechanism of Action Binds at stereospecific receptors at several sites within the central nervous system, including the limbic system, reticular formation

Pharmacodynamics/kinetics
Metabolism: Extensive in the liver; major metabolite is inactive
Half-life: 12-15 hours
Time to peak serum concentration: Within 1-2 hours

Signs and Symptoms of Acute Intoxication Somnolence, confusion, coma, gaze nystagmus, diminished reflexes

When to Transport to Hospital Transport any pediatric exposure, any patient with change in mental status, or any adult ingestion over 8 mg

Overdosage/Treatment Treatment for benzodiazepine overdose is supportive. Rarely is mechanical ventilation required; flumazenil has been shown to selectively block the binding of benzodiazepines to CNS receptors, resulting in a reversal of benzodiazepine-induced sedation; however, its use may not alter the course of overdose.

Warnings/Precautions Withdrawal symptoms including seizures have occurred 18 hours to 3 days after abrupt discontinuation; when discontinuing therapy, decrease daily dose by no more than 0.5 mg every 3 days; reduce dose in patients with significant hepatic disease. Not intended for management of anxieties and minor distresses associated with everyday life.

Adverse Reactions

>10%:

Cardiovascular: Tachycardia, chest pain

Central nervous system: Drowsiness, fatigue, ataxia, lightheadedness, memory impairment, insomnia, anxiety, depression, headache

Dermatologic: Rash

Endocrine & metabolic: Decreased libido

Gastrointestinal: Xerostomia, constipation, decreased salivation, nausea, vomiting, diarrhea, increased or decreased appetite

Neuromuscular & skeletal: Dysarthria

Ocular: Blurred vision

Miscellaneous: Diaphoresis

1% to 10%:

Cardiovascular: Syncope, hypotension

Central nervous system: Confusion, nervousness, dizziness, akathisia

Dermatologic: Dermatitis

Gastrointestinal: Weight gain or loss, increased salivation

Neuromuscular & skeletal: Rigidity, tremor, muscle cramps

Otic: Tinnitus

Respiratory: Nasal congestion, hyperventilation

Drug Interactions

Decreased therapeutic effect: Carbamazepine, disulfiram

Increased toxicity: Oral contraceptives, CNS depressants, cimetidine, lithium

Dosage Forms Tablet: 0.25 mg, 0.5 mg, 1 mg, 2 mg

Specific References

McCormick SR, Nielsen J, and Jatlow PI, "Alprazolam Overdose, Clinical Findings and Serum Concentrations in Two Cases," *J Clin Psychiatry*, 1985, 46(6):247-8.

AL-R® [OTC] *see* Chlorpheniramine *on page 132*

Alupent® *see* Metaproterenol *on page 376*

Alupram® *see* Diazepam *on page 189*

Amantadine (a MAN ta deen)

Synonyms Adamantanamine Hydrochloride

U.S. Brand Names Symmetrel®

Canadian Brand Names Endantadine®; PMS-Amantadine®

Therapeutic Category Anti-Parkinson's Agent; Antiviral Agent

Use Symptomatic and adjunct treatment of parkinsonism; prophylaxis and treatment of influenza A viral infection; treatment of drug-induced extrapyramidal symptoms

Usual Dosage

Children:

1-9 years: (<45 kg): 5-9 mg/kg/day in 1-2 divided doses to a maximum of 150 mg/day

(Continued)

Amantadine *(Continued)*

    10-12 years: 100-200 mg/day in 1-2 divided doses
    Prophylaxis: Administer for 10-21 days following exposure if the vaccine is concurrently given or for 90 days following exposure if the vaccine is unavailable or contraindicated and re-exposure is possible
    Adults:
      Parkinson's disease: 100 mg twice daily
      Influenza A viral infection: 200 mg/day in 1-2 divided doses
      Prophylaxis: Minimum 10-day course of therapy following exposure if the vaccine is concurrently given or for 90 days following exposure if the vaccine is unavailable or contraindicated and re-exposure is possible
    Elderly patients should take the drug in 2 daily doses rather than a single dose to avoid adverse neurologic reactions

Mechanism of Action As an antiviral, blocks the uncoating of influenza A virus preventing penetration of virus into host; antiparkinsonian activity may be due to its blocking the reuptake of dopamine into presynaptic neurons and causing direct stimulation of postsynaptic receptors

Pharmacodynamics/kinetics
    Onset of antidyskinetic action: Within 48 hours
    Absorption: Well absorbed from GI tract
    Protein binding:
      Normal renal function: ~67%
      Hemodialysis patients: ~59%
    Metabolism: Not appreciable, small amounts of an acetyl metabolite identified
    Half-life:
      Normal renal function: 2-7 hours
      End stage renal disease: 7-10 days
    Time to peak: 1-4 hours

Signs and Symptoms of Acute Intoxication Nausea, vomiting, slurred speech, blurred vision, lethargy, hallucinations, seizures, myoclonic jerking

When to Transport to Hospital Transport any symptomatic patient

Warnings/Precautions Use with caution in patients with liver disease, a history of recurrent and eczematoid dermatitis, uncontrolled psychosis or severe psychoneurosis, seizures and in those receiving CNS stimulant drugs; when treating Parkinson's disease, do not discontinue abruptly. In many patients, the therapeutic benefits of amantadine are limited to a few months. Elderly patients may be more susceptible to the CNS effects (using 2 divided daily doses may minimize this effect).

Adverse Reactions 1% to 10%:
    Cardiovascular: Orthostatic hypotension, peripheral edema
    Central nervous system: Insomnia, depression, anxiety, irritability, dizziness, hallucinations, ataxia, headache, somnolence, nervousness, dream abnormality, agitation, fatigue
    Dermatologic: Livedo reticularis
    Gastrointestinal: Nausea, anorexia, constipation, diarrhea, xerostomia
    Respiratory: Dry nose

Drug Interactions
    Increased effect: Drugs with anticholinergic or CNS stimulant activity
    Increased toxicity/levels: Hydrochlorothiazide plus triamterene, amiloride

Dosage Forms
    Amantadine hydrochloride:
      Capsule: 100 mg
      Syrup: 50 mg/5 mL (480 mL)

Specific References
Farrell S, Lee DC, and McNamara B, "Amantadine Overdose: Considerations for the Treatment of Cardiac Toxicity," *Clin Toxicol*, 1995, 33(5):516-7.

Amaphen® *see* Butalbital Compound *on page 93*

Amaxin® *see* Chlorthalidone *on page 144*

Amazin® *see* Chlorpromazine *on page 138*

Ambenyl® Cough Syrup *see* Bromodiphenhydramine and Codeine *on page 84*

Ambien™ *see* Zolpidem *on page 621*

Americaine® [OTC] *see* Benzocaine *on page 70*

Amesec® [OTC] *see* Aminophylline, Amobarbital, and Ephedrine *on this page*

Amfebutamone *see* Bupropion *on page 90*

Amfepramone *see* Diethylpropion *on page 196*

Amgenal® Cough Syrup *see* Bromodiphenhydramine and Codeine *on page 84*

Aminobenzylpenicillin *see* Ampicillin *on page 48*

Aminophylline *see* Theophylline Salts *on page 571*

Aminophylline, Amobarbital, and Ephedrine
(am in OFF i lin, am oh BAR bi tal, & e FED rin)
U.S. Brand Names Amesec® [OTC]
Therapeutic Category Theophylline Derivative
Abuse Potential Yes
Impairment Potential Yes
Dosage Forms Capsule: Aminophylline 130 mg, amobarbital 24 mg, and ephedrine sulfate 24 mg

Ami-Tex LA® *see* Guaifenesin and Phenylpropanolamine *on page 272*

Amitraz
Related Information
Xylene *on page 617*
Synonyms Azadiene; Azaform; Triazid; U-36059
U.S. Brand Names BAAM®; Ectodex®; Mitac®; Taktic®; Triatox®
Use A topical veterinary ectoparasiticide effective against lice, mice and ticks; also used for mite controls on fruit and control of pear psylla on pears
Mechanism of Toxic Action A formamidine compound that is an alpha$_2$ adrenoceptor agonist along with a sedative effect
Toxicodynamics/kinetics Metabolism: Hepatic to an aromatic amine (2,4-dimethyl aniline)
Signs and Symptoms of Acute Intoxication Bradycardia, miosis, hyperglycemia, hypokalemia, drowsiness, emesis, hypotension, central nervous system depression, headache, coma, flushing
When to Transport to Hospital Transport any symptomatic patient
Overdosage/Treatment Decontamination:
Dermal: Wash with soap and water
Ocular: Irrigate copiously with saline
Reference Range Blood amitraz concentration of 3.7 mg/L associated with deep coma following an ingestion of up to 12.5 g of amitraz
Additional Information Usually associated with a xylene vehicle; found in concentrations of 1 g of amitraz/5 mL of solution; when heated can decompose to nitrogen oxide fumes; LD-50 in dogs: 100 mg/kg
How supplied:
Emulsifiable concentrate: 50-200 g/L
Powder:
Wettable: 500 g/L
Dog shampoo (dispersal powder): 250 or 500 g/L
(Continued)

Amitraz *(Continued)*

Specific References

Kennel O, Prince C, and Garnier R, "Four Cases of Amitraz Poisoning in Humans," *Vet Hum Toxicol*, 1996, 38(1):28-30.

Amitriptyline (a mee TRIP ti leen)

U.S. Brand Names Elavil®

Canadian Brand Names Apo-Amitriptyline®; Levate®; Novo-Tryptin®

Therapeutic Category Antidepressant

Impairment Potential Yes: Doses of 50 mg can cause impairment; over a five-time increased risk of injurious auto crash involvement following ingestion ≥125 mg amitriptyline in elderly drivers.

Use Treatment of various forms of depression, often in conjunction with psychotherapy; analgesic for certain chronic and neuropathic pain, prophylaxis against migraine headaches

Usual Dosage Oral:

Children: Pain management: Initial: 0.1 mg/kg at bedtime, may advance as tolerated over 2-3 weeks to 0.5-2 mg/day at bedtime

Adolescents: Initial: 25-50 mg/day; may administer in divided doses; increase gradually to 100 mg/day in divided doses

Adults: 30-100 mg/day single dose at bedtime or in divided doses; dose may be gradually increased up to 300 mg/day; once symptoms are controlled, decrease gradually to lowest effective dose

Mechanism of Action Increases the synaptic concentration of serotonin and/or norepinephrine in the central nervous system by inhibition of their reuptake by the presynaptic neuronal membrane

Pharmacodynamics/kinetics

Onset of therapeutic effect: 7-21 days

Desired therapeutic effect (for depression) may take as long as 3-4 weeks, at that point dosage should be reduced to lowest effective level

When used for migraine headache prophylaxis, therapeutic effect may take as long as 6 weeks; a higher dosage may be required in a heavy smoker, because of increased metabolism

Distribution: Crosses placenta; enters breast milk

Metabolism: In the liver to nortriptyline (active), hydroxy derivatives, and conjugated derivatives; metabolism may be impaired in the elderly

Half-life: Adults: 9-25 hours (15-hour average)

Time to peak serum concentration: Within 4 hours

Signs and Symptoms of Acute Intoxication Agitation, confusion, hallucinations, urinary retention, hypothermia, hypotension, ventricular tachycardia, seizures

When to Transport to Hospital Transport any symptomatic patient or any patient taking more than the recommended doses

Warnings/Precautions

Amitriptyline should not be abruptly discontinued in patients receiving high doses for prolonged periods

Use with caution in patients with cardiac conduction disturbances; an EKG prior to initiation of therapy is advised; use with caution in patients with a history of hyperthyroidism, renal or hepatic impairment

The most anticholinergic and sedating of the antidepressants; pronounced effects on the cardiovascular system (hypotension), hence, many psychiatrists agree it is best to avoid in the elderly

Adverse Reactions Anticholinergic effects may be pronounced; moderate to marked sedation can occur (tolerance to these effects usually occurs)

>10%:
  Central nervous system: Dizziness, drowsiness, headache
  Gastrointestinal: Xerostomia, constipation, increased appetite, nausea, unpleasant taste, weight gain
  Neuromuscular & skeletal: Weakness

1% to 10%:
  Cardiovascular: Hypotension, postural hypotension, arrhythmias, tachycardia, sudden death
  Central nervous system: Nervousness, restlessness, parkinsonian syndrome, insomnia, sedation, fatigue, anxiety, impaired cognitive function, seizures have occurred occasionally, extrapyramidal symptoms are possible
  Gastrointestinal: Diarrhea, heartburn
  Genitourinary: Sexual dysfunction, urinary retention
  Neuromuscular & skeletal: Tremor
  Ocular: Eye pain, blurred vision
  Miscellaneous: Diaphoresis (excessive)

Reference Range Therapeutic: Amitriptyline and nortriptyline 100-250 ng/mL (SI: 360-900 nmol/L); nortriptyline 50-150 ng/mL (SI: 190-570 nmol/L); Toxic: >0.5 µg/mL; plasma levels do not always correlate with clinical effectiveness

Drug Interactions
Decreased effect: Phenobarbital may increase the metabolism of amitriptyline; amitriptyline blocks the uptake of guanethidine and thus prevents the hypotensive effect of guanethidine
Increased toxicity: Clonidine → hypertensive crisis; amitriptyline may be additive with or may potentiate the action of other CNS depressants such as sedatives or hypnotics; with MAO inhibitors, hyperpyrexia, hypertension, tachycardia, confusion, seizures, and **deaths have been reported**; amitriptyline may increase the prothrombin time in patients stabilized on warfarin; amitriptyline potentiates the pressor and cardiac effects of sympathomimetic agents such as isoproterenol, epinephrine, etc; cimetidine and methylphenidate may decrease the metabolism of amitriptyline; additive anticholinergic effects seen with other anticholinergic agents

Dosage Forms
Amitriptyline hydrochloride:
  Injection: 10 mg/mL (10 mL)
  Tablet: 10 mg, 25 mg, 50 mg, 75 mg, 100 mg, 150 mg

Specific References
Clark CH and Nicholson AN, "Performance Studies With Antihistamines," *Br J Clin Pharmacol*, 1978, 6(1):31-5.
Moskowitz H and Burns MM, "Cognitive Performance in Geriatric Subjects After Acute Treatment With Antidepressants," *Neuropsychobiology*, 1986, 15(Suppl 1):38-43.
Starmer G, "Antihistamines and Highway Safety," *Accid Anal Prev*, 1985, 17(4):311-7.
Warrington SJ, Anker SI, and Turner P, "An Evaluation of Possible Interactions Between Ethanol and Trazodone or Amitriptyline," *Br J Clin Pharmacol*, 1984, 18(4):549-57.

Amitriptyline and Chlordiazepoxide
(a mee TRIP ti leen & klor dye az e POKS ide)
Synonyms Chlordiazepoxide and Amitriptyline
U.S. Brand Names Limbitrol® DS 10-25
Therapeutic Category Antidepressant
Abuse Potential Yes
Impairment Potential Yes
(Continued)

Amitriptyline and Chlordiazepoxide *(Continued)*

Chlordiazepoxide: Brief or extended period (up to 1 year) of use is consistent with driving impairment in the elderly. The impairment is greatest in the first 7 days of use.

Amitriptyline: Doses of 50 mg can cause impairment; over a five-time increased risk of injurious auto crash involvement following ingestion ≥125 mg amitriptyline in elderly drivers.

Dosage Forms Tablet:

5-12.5: Amitriptyline hydrochloride 12.5 mg and chlordiazepoxide 5 mg
10-25: Amitriptyline hydrochloride 25 mg and chlordiazepoxide 10 mg

Amitriptyline and Perphenazine

(a mee TRIP ti leen & per FEN a zeen)

Synonyms Perphenazine and Amitriptyline

U.S. Brand Names Etrafon®; Triavil®

Canadian Brand Names Elavil Plus®; Apo®-Peram; PMS-Levazine; Proavil

Therapeutic Category Antidepressant

Impairment Potential Yes: Doses of 50 mg (amitriptyline) can cause impairment; over a five-time increased risk of injurious auto crash involvement following ingestion ≥125 mg amitriptyline in elderly drivers.

Reference Range Metabolism may be impaired in the elderly; Toxic: >0.5 µg/mL

Dosage Forms Tablet:

2-10: Amitriptyline hydrochloride 10 mg and perphenazine 2 mg
4-10: Amitriptyline hydrochloride 10 mg and perphenazine 4 mg
2-25: Amitriptyline hydrochloride 25 mg and perphenazine 2 mg
4-25: Amitriptyline hydrochloride 25 mg and perphenazine 4 mg
4-50: Amitriptyline hydrochloride 50 mg and perphenazine 4 mg

Amlodipine and Benazepril (am LOE di peen & ben AY ze pril)

U.S. Brand Names Lotrel™

Therapeutic Category Antihypertensive, Combination

Dosage Forms Capsule:

Amlodipine 2.5 mg and benazepril hydrochloride 10 mg
Amlodipine 5 mg and benazepril hydrochloride 10 mg
Amlodipine 5 mg and benazepril hydrochloride 20 mg

Ammonia

Synonyms Spirit of Hartshorn

UN Number 2073; 2672; 1005

Commonly Found In Household cleaners (5% to 10%) and bleach

Use Household cleaner; primarily in fertilizers; manufacture of nitrous oxide; petroleum refining

Mechanism of Toxic Action Tissue injury of moist mucosal membranes caused by reaction with water to form ammonia hydroxide; can cause burns by liquefaction necrosis

Toxicodynamics/kinetics

Absorption: Not well absorbed
Metabolism: Hepatic to urea and glutamine

Signs and Symptoms of Acute Intoxication Conjunctivitis, corneal defects, chest pain, upper airway irritation, burns, dyspnea, pulmonary edema, urticaria, gastrointestinal irritant, coma, headache, salivation, lacrimation, swelling, cough, wheezing, nausea, vomiting. Long-term sequelae include bronchiolitis obliterans, peribronchial fibrosis (lung toxicity).

When to Transport to Hospital Transport any symptomatic patient

Overdosage/Treatment Decontamination: **Do not** induce emesis or perform gastric lavage

Adverse Reactions

Cardiovascular: Chest pain

Dermatologic: Immunologic contact urticaria

Gastrointestinal: Salivation

Respiratory: Reactive airways disease syndrome, hyposmia

Miscellaneous: Mucosal irritation

Additional Information Colorless liquid; penetrating pungent odor; stable, colorless gas; highly water soluble; alkali (pH 11.6); irritation can occur at 400 ppm; stomatitis can occur at ammonia concentrations of 50 ppm; the mixture of ammonia with hypochlorite bleach can result in chloramine which can produce pulmonary edema

Odor threshold: 25-48 ppm (air); 1.5 ppm (water)

Atmospheric half-life: 2-3 days

TLV-TWA: 25 ppm

IDLH: 500 ppm

Specific References

Arwood R, Hammond J, and Ward GG, "Ammonia Inhalation," *J Trauma*, 1985, 25(5):444-7.

Ammonium Sulfite *see* Sulfite Food Poisoning *on page 553*

Amoban® *see* Zopiclone *on page 621*

Amobarbital and Secobarbital

(am oh BAR bi tal & see koe BAR bi tal)

Related Information

Controlled Substances - Uses and Effects *on page 741*

Secobarbital *on page 534*

Synonyms Secobarbital and Amobarbital

U.S. Brand Names Tuinal®

Therapeutic Category Barbiturate

Abuse Potential Yes

Impairment Potential Yes

Use Short-term treatment of insomnia

Usual Dosage Adults: Oral: 1-2 capsules at bedtime

Signs and Symptoms of Acute Intoxication Unsteady gait, slurred speech, myasthenia gravis (exacerbation or precipitation of), ptosis, vision color changes (green tinge); confusion, jaundice, hypothermia, gaze nystagmus, fever, hypotension, CNS depression; can cause bezoars

Warnings/Precautions Safety has not been established in children <6 years of age; potential for drug dependency exists; avoid alcoholic beverages; use with caution in patients with CHF, hepatic or renal impairment, hypovolemic shock

Adverse Reactions

>10%:

Central nervous system: Dizziness, lightheadedness, drowsiness, "hang-over" effect

Local: Pain at injection site

1% to 10%:

Central nervous system: Confusion, mental depression, unusual excitement, nervousness, faint feeling, headache, insomnia, nightmares

Gastrointestinal: Constipation, nausea, vomiting

Drug Interactions CNS depressants, antidepressants, doxycycline, cimetidine, anticoagulants, oral contraceptives

(Continued)

Amobarbital and Secobarbital *(Continued)*
Dosage Forms
Capsule:
100: Amobarbital 50 mg and secobarbital 50 mg
200: Amobarbital 100 mg and secobarbital 100 mg

Amoxapine (a MOKS a peen)
U.S. Brand Names Asendin®
Therapeutic Category Antidepressant
Use Treatment of neurotic and endogenous depression and mixed symptoms of anxiety and depression
Usual Dosage Once symptoms are controlled, decrease gradually to lowest effective dose. Maintenance dose is usually given at bedtime to reduce daytime sedation. Oral:

Children: Not established in children <16 years of age
Adolescents: Initial: 25-50 mg/day; increase gradually to 100 mg/day; may administer as divided doses or as a single dose at bedtime
Adults: Initial: 25 mg 2-3 times/day, if tolerated, dosage may be increased to 100 mg 2-3 times/day; may be given in a single bedtime dose when dosage <300 mg/day
Elderly: Initial: 25 mg at bedtime increased by 25 mg weekly for outpatients and every 3 days for inpatients if tolerated; usual dose: 50-150 mg/day, but doses up to 300 mg may be necessary

Maximum daily dose:
Inpatient: 600 mg
Outpatient: 400 mg
Mechanism of Action Reduces the reuptake of serotonin and norepinephrine and blocks the response of dopamine receptors to dopamine
Pharmacodynamics/kinetics
Onset of antidepressant effect: Usually occurs after 1-2 weeks
Absorption: Oral: Rapidly and well absorbed
Metabolism: Extensive in the liver
Half-life:
Parent drug: 11-16 hours
Active metabolite (8-hydroxy): Adults: 30 hours
Time to peak serum concentration: Within 1-2 hours
Signs and Symptoms of Acute Intoxication Grand mal convulsions, acidosis, coma, renal failure
When to Transport to Hospital Transport any pediatric exposure or any adult patient ingesting more than 8 mg/kg or exhibiting a change in mental status
Warnings/Precautions Use with caution in patients with seizures, cardiac conduction disturbances, cardiovascular diseases, urinary retention, hyperthyroidism, or those receiving thyroid replacement; do not discontinue abruptly in patients receiving high doses chronically; tolerance develops in 1-3 months in some patients, close medical follow-up is essential
Adverse Reactions
>10%:
Central nervous system: Drowsiness
Gastrointestinal: Xerostomia, constipation, nausea, unpleasant taste, weight gain
1% to 10%:
Central nervous system: Dizziness, headache, confusion, nervousness, restlessness, insomnia, ataxia, excitement
Dermatologic: Edema, skin rash
Endocrine: Elevated prolactin levels

Gastrointestinal: Increased appetite
Neuromuscular & skeletal: Tremor, weakness
Ocular: Blurred vision
Miscellaneous: Diaphoresis

Reference Range Therapeutic: Amoxapine: 20-100 ng/mL (SI: 64-319 nmol/L); 8-OH amoxapine: 150-400 ng/mL (SI: 478-1275 nmol/L); both: 200-500 ng/mL (SI: 637-1594 nmol/L)

Drug Interactions
Decreased effect of clonidine, guanethidine
Increased effect of CNS depressants, adrenergic agents, anticholinergic agents
Increased toxicity of MAO inhibitors (hyperpyrexia, tachycardia, hypertension, seizures and death may occur); similar interactions as with other tricyclics may occur

Dosage Forms Tablet: 25 mg, 50 mg, 100 mg, 150 mg

Specific References
Tasset JJ and Pesce AJ, "Amoxapine in Human Overdose," *J Anal Toxicol*, 1984, 8(3):124-8.

Amoxicillin (a moks i SIL in)

Synonyms Amoxycillin; *p*-Hydroxyampicillin

U.S. Brand Names Amoxil®; Biomox®; Polymox®; Trimox®; Wymox®

Canadian Brand Names Apo-Amoxi®; Novamoxin®; Nu-Amoxi®; Pro-Amox®

Therapeutic Category Penicillin

Use Treatment of otitis media, sinusitis, and infections caused by susceptible organisms involving the respiratory tract, skin, and urinary tract; prophylaxis of bacterial endocarditis

Usual Dosage Oral:
Children: 25-100 mg/kg/day in divided doses every 8 hours
Uncomplicated gonorrhea: ≥2 years: 50 mg/kg plus probenecid 25 mg/kg in a single dose; do not use this regimen in children <2 years of age, probenecid is contraindicated in this age group
Subacute bacterial endocarditis prophylaxis: 50 mg/kg 1 hour before procedure and 25 mg/kg 6 hours later

Adults: 250-500 mg every 8 hours; maximum dose: 2-3 g/day
Uncomplicated gonorrhea: 3 g plus probenecid 1 g in a single dose
Endocarditis prophylaxis: 3 g 1 hour before procedure and 1.5 g 6 hours later
Erythema migrans: 500 mg 3 times/day for 20 days

Mechanism of Action Interferes with bacterial cell wall synthesis during active multiplication, causing cell wall death and resultant bactericidal activity against susceptible bacteria

Pharmacodynamics/kinetics
Absorption: Oral: Rapid and nearly complete (89%); food does not interfere clinically
Metabolism: Partial to penicilloic acid in the liver
Half-life:
Neonates, full-term: 3.7 hours
Infants and Children: 1-2 hours
Patients with renal impairment: 7-21 hours
Time to peak serum concentration:
Capsule: Within 2 hours
Suspension: 1 hour

Signs and Symptoms of Acute Intoxication Neuromuscular sensitivity, pemphigus, acute renal failure, hematuria; many beta-lactam containing antibiotics have the potential to cause neuromuscular hyperirritability or convulsive seizures
(Continued)

Amoxicillin *(Continued)*

When to Transport to Hospital Transport any symptomatic patient

Warnings/Precautions In patients with renal impairment, doses and/or frequency of administration should be modified in response to the degree of renal impairment; high percentage of patients with infectious mononucleosis have developed rash during therapy with amoxicillin

Adverse Reactions 1% to 10%:
Central nervous system: Fever
Dermatologic: Urticaria
Miscellaneous: Allergic reactions

Reference Range After a 250 mg oral dose, peak plasma level of 5 µg/mL and urine level >300 µg/mL have been noted

Drug Interactions
Decreased effect of oral contraceptives; tetracyclines may decrease efficacy of penicillins; amiloride reduces intestinal absorption of amoxicillin
Increased levels with probenecid; allopurinol theoretically has an additive potential for amoxicillin rash; oral bioavailability increased by 16% when given with cimetidine

Dosage Forms
Capsule: 250 mg, 500 mg
Powder for oral suspension: 125 mg/5 mL (5 mL, 80 mL, 100 mL, 150 mL, 200 mL); 250 mg/5 mL (5 mL, 80 mL, 100 mL, 150 mL, 200 mL)
Powder for oral suspension, drops: 50 mg/mL (15 mL, 30 mL)
Tablet, chewable: 125 mg, 250 mg

Additional Information Food does not interfere with absorption; rash that appears after a few days of therapy may indicate hypersensitivity

Specific References
Stell IM and Ojo OA, "Amoxycillin-Induced Hallucinations - A Variant of Hoigne's Syndrome?" *Br J Clin Pract*, 1996, 50:279.

Amoxicillin and Clavulanate Potassium

(a moks i SIL in & klav yoo LAN ate poe TASS ee um)

Synonyms Amoxicillin and Clavulanic Acid

U.S. Brand Names Augmentin®

Canadian Brand Names Clavulin®

Therapeutic Category Penicillin

Dosage Forms
Suspension, oral:
125 (banana flavor): Amoxicillin trihydrate 125 mg and clavulanate potassium 31.25 mg per 5 mL (75 mL, 150 mL)
200: Amoxicillin 200 mg and clavulanate potassium 28.5 mg per 5 mL (50 mL, 75 mL, 100 mL)
250 (orange flavor): Amoxicillin trihydrate 250 mg and clavulanate potassium 62.5 mg per 5 mL (75 mL, 150 mL)
400: Amoxicillin 400 mg and clavulanate potassium 57 mg per 5 mL (50 mL, 75 mL, 100 mL)
Tablet:
250: Amoxicillin trihydrate 250 mg and clavulanate potassium 125 mg
500: Amoxicillin trihydrate 500 mg and clavulanate potassium 125 mg
875: Amoxicillin trihydrate 875 mg and clavulanate potassium 125 mg
Tablet, chewable:
125: Amoxicillin trihydrate 125 mg and clavulanate potassium 31.25 mg
200: Amoxicillin trihydrate 200 mg and clavulanate potassium 28.5 mg
250: Amoxicillin trihydrate 250 mg and clavulanate potassium 62.5 mg
400: Amoxicillin trihydrate 400 mg and clavulanate potassium 57 mg

Amoxicillin and Clavulanic Acid *see* Amoxicillin and Clavulanate Potassium *on previous page*

Amoxil® *see* Amoxicillin *on page 45*

Amoxycillin *see* Amoxicillin *on page 45*

Amphetamine (am FET a meen)
Related Information
Controlled Substances - Uses and Effects *on page 741*
Synonyms Racemic Amphetamine Sulfate
Therapeutic Category Amphetamine
Abuse Potential Yes
Impairment Potential Yes
Use
Treatment of narcolepsy; exogenous obesity; abnormal behavioral syndrome in children (minimal brain dysfunction); attention deficit hyperactive disorder (ADHD)
Usual Dosage Oral:
Narcolepsy:

Children:

6-12 years: 5 mg/day, increase by 5 mg at weekly intervals

>12 years: 10 mg/day, increase by 10 mg at weekly intervals

Adults: 5-60 mg/day in 2-3 divided doses

Attention deficit disorder: Children:

3-5 years: 2.5 mg/day, increase by 2.5 mg at weekly intervals

>6 years: 5 mg/day, increase by 5 mg at weekly intervals not to exceed 40 mg/day

Short-term adjunct to exogenous obesity: Children >12 years and Adults: 10 mg or 15 mg long-acting capsule daily, up to 30 mg/day; or 5-30 mg/day in divided doses (immediate release tablets only)

Mechanism of Action
The amphetamines are noncatechol sympathomimetic amines with pharmacologic actions similar to ephedrine. They require breakdown by monoamine oxidase for inactivation; produce central nervous system and respiratory stimulation, a pressor response, mydriasis, bronchodilation, and contraction of the urinary sphincter; thought to have a direct effect on both alpha- and beta-receptor sites in the peripheral system, as well as release stores of norepinephrine in adrenergic nerve terminals. The central nervous system action is thought to occur in the cerebral cortex and reticular-activating system. The anorexigenic effect is probably secondary to the CNS-stimulating effect; the site of action is probably the hypothalamic feeding center.

Signs and Symptoms of Acute Intoxication
Tachycardia, bradycardia, mydriasis, hypertension, hypotension, chills, diaphoresis, nausea, vomiting, weight loss, psychomotor agitation or retardation, muscular weakness, respiratory depression, chest pain, cardiac arrhythmias, confusion, seizures, dyskinesia, dystonia, coma

When to Transport to Hospital
Transport any pediatric exposure (<3 years of age), any patient exhibiting cardiac symptoms, or any agitated or lethargic patient

Warnings/Precautions
Cardiovascular disease, nephritis, angina pectoris, hypertension, glaucoma, patients with a history of drug abuse, known hypersensitivity to amphetamine

Adverse Reactions
>10%:

Cardiovascular: Arrhythmia

Central nervous system: False feeling of well being, nervousness, restlessness, insomnia

1% to 10%:

Cardiovascular: Hypertension

(Continued)

Amphetamine *(Continued)*

Central nervous system: Mood or mental changes, dizziness, lightheadedness, headache

Endocrine & metabolic: Changes in libido

Gastrointestinal: Diarrhea, nausea, vomiting, stomach cramps, constipation, anorexia, weight loss, xerostomia

Ocular: Blurred vision

Miscellaneous: Diaphoresis (increased)

Reference Range Therapeutic: 20-30 ng/mL; Toxic: >200 ng/mL

Can be detected in urine 3 hours after use; usually detectable 24-48 hours after use

Drug Interactions Increased toxicity of MAO inhibitors (hyperpyrexia, hypertension, arrhythmias, seizures, cerebral hemorrhage, and death has occurred)

Dosage Forms Tablet, as sulfate: 5 mg, 10 mg

Additional Information Amphetamines increase the heart and breathing rate and blood pressure, dilate pupils, and decrease appetite. The user can experience a dry mouth, sweating, headache, blurred vision, dizziness, sleeplessness, and anxiety. Extremely high doses can cause people to flush or become pale; they can cause a rapid or irregular heartbeat, tremors, loss of coordination, and even physical collapse. People who use a large dose over a long period of time may develop an amphetamine psychosis: seeing, hearing, and feeling things that do not exist, having irrational thoughts or beliefs and feeling that people are out to get them. People in this extremely suspicious state frequently exhibit bizarre and sometimes violent behavior. Tolerance to the drug is developed after repeated use. Life-threatening overdoses are rare. Alum (25 g/L) can elicit a false-negative urinary assay for methamphetamine; urine will be acidic in these cases.

Specific References

Ellinwood EH Jr and Nikaido AM, "Stimulant-Induced Impairment: A Perspective Across Dose and Duration of Use," *Alcohol, Drugs, and Driving*, 1987, 3(1).

Hurst PM, "Amphetamines and Driving," *Alcohol, Drugs, and Driving*, 1987, 3(1):9-11.

Ampicillin *(am pi SIL in)*

Synonyms Aminobenzylpenicillin

U.S. Brand Names Marcillin®; Omnipen®; Omnipen®-N; Polycillin®; Polycillin-N®; Principen®; Totacillin®; Totacillin®-N

Canadian Brand Names Ampicin® Sodium; Apo-Ampi® Trihydrate; Jaa Amp® Trihydrate; Nu-Ampi® Trihydrate; Pro-Ampi® Trihydrate; Taro-Ampicillin® Trihydrate

Therapeutic Category Penicillin

Use Treatment of susceptible bacterial infections; use for bacterial infections due to alkali burns

Usual Dosage

Infants and Children: I.M., I.V.: 100-200 mg/kg/day in 4-6 divided doses; meningitis: 200 mg/kg/day in 4-6 divided doses; maximum dose: 12 g/day

Children: Oral: 50-100 mg/kg/day divided every 6 hours; maximum dose: 2-3 g/day

Adults:

Oral: 250-500 mg every 6 hours

I.M.: 500 mg to 1.5 g every 4-6 hours

I.V.: 500 mg to 3 g every 4-6 hours; maximum dose: 12 g/day

Sepsis/meningitis: 150-250 mg/kg/24 hours divided every 3-4 hours

Mechanism of Action Interferes with bacterial cell wall synthesis during active multiplication, causing cell wall death and resultant bactericidal activity against susceptible bacteria

Pharmacodynamics/kinetics

Absorption: Oral: 50%

Half-life:

Neonates:

2-7 days: 4 hours

8-14 days: 2.8 hours

15-30 days: 1.7 hours

Children and Adults: 1-1.8 hours

Anuric patients: 8-20 hours

Time to peak serum concentration: Oral: Within 1-2 hours

Signs and Symptoms of Acute Intoxication Cholestatic jaundice, erythema multiforme, toxic epidermal necrolysis, deafness, myocarditis, myalgia, hypoprothrombinemia, colitis, hypokalemia

When to Transport to Hospital Transport any pediatric (<6 years of age) ingestion over 250 mg/kg or any patient with change in mental status

Warnings/Precautions Dosage adjustment may be necessary in patients with renal impairment; high percentage of patients with infectious mononucleosis have developed rash during therapy with ampicillin; use with caution in patients allergic to cephalosporins

Adverse Reactions

>10%:

Central nervous system: Pain

Dermatologic: Rash (appearance of a rash should be carefully evaluated to differentiate a nonallergic ampicillin rash from a hypersensitivity reaction; incidence is higher in patients with viral infections, *Salmonella* infections, lymphocytic leukemia, or patients that have hyperuricemia)

Gastrointestinal: Diarrhea, vomiting, oral candidiasis

1% to 10%: Gastrointestinal: Severe abdominal or stomach cramps

Drug Interactions

Decreased effect of oral contraceptives

Increased levels with probenecid; allopurinol theoretically has an additive potential for amoxicillin rash

Dosage Forms

Capsule, as anhydrous: 250 mg, 500 mg

Powder for injection, as sodium: 125 mg, 250 mg, 500 mg, 1 g, 2 g, 10 g

Ampicillin trihydrate:

Capsule: 250 mg, 500 mg

Powder for oral suspension: 125 mg/5 mL (5 mL unit dose, 80 mL, 100 mL, 150 mL, 200 mL); 250 mg/5 mL (5 mL unit dose, 80 mL, 100 mL, 150 mL, 200 mL); 500 mg/5 mL (5 mL unit dose, 100 mL)

Powder for oral suspension, drops: 100 mg/mL (20 mL)

Additional Information

Sodium content of 5 mL suspension (250 mg/5 mL): 10 mg (0.4 mEq)

Sodium content of 1 g: 66.7 mg (3 mEq)

Specific References

Lim JT and Ng SK, "An Unusual Drug Eruption to Ampicillin," *Cutis*, 1995, 56(3):163-4.

Amyl Nitrite (AM il NYE trite)

Synonyms Isoamyl Nitrite

Therapeutic Category Vasodilator

Abuse Potential Yes

Impairment Potential Yes

(Continued)

49

Amyl Nitrite *(Continued)*

Use Coronary vasodilator in angina pectoris; adjunct in treatment of cyanide poisoning; used to produce changes in the intensity of heart murmurs

Usual Dosage Adults: 1-6 inhalations from one capsule are usually sufficient to produce the desired effect

Pharmacodynamics/kinetics
Onset of action: Angina relieved within 30 seconds
Duration: 3-15 minutes

When to Transport to Hospital Transport any pediatic exposure or any patient with change in mental status or cardiac symptoms

Overdosage/Treatment Treatment includes general supportive measures for transient hypotension; I.V. fluids; Trendelenburg position, vasopressors

Warnings/Precautions Use with caution in patients with increased intracranial pressure, low systolic blood pressure, and coronary artery disease

Adverse Reactions 1% to 10%:
Cardiovascular: Postural hypotension, cutaneous flushing of head, neck, and clavicular area
Central nervous system: Headache
Hematologic: Hemolytic anemia

Drug Interactions Increased toxicity: Alcohol

Dosage Forms Inhalant, crushable glass perles: 0.18 mL, 0.3 mL

Specific References
Schwartz RH, "When to Suspect Inhalant Abuse," *Patient Care*, 1989, 23:39-64.

Anabolin® Injection *see* Nandrolone *on page 421*

Anacin® [OTC] *see* Aspirin *on page 56*

Anadrol® *see* Oxymetholone *on page 454*

Anafranil® *see* Clomipramine *on page 151*

Anamine® Syrup [OTC] *see* Chlorpheniramine and Pseudoephedrine *on page 134*

Anaplex® Liquid [OTC] *see* Chlorpheniramine and Pseudoephedrine *on page 134*

Anaprox® *see* Naproxen *on page 423*

Anaspaz® *see* Hyoscyamine *on page 305*

Anatuss® [OTC] *see* Guaifenesin, Phenylpropanolamine, and Dextromethorphan *on page 274*

Anatuss® DM [OTC] *see* Guaifenesin, Pseudoephedrine, and Dextromethorphan *on page 275*

Anbesol® [OTC] *see* Benzocaine *on page 70*

Anbesol® Maximum Strength [OTC] *see* Benzocaine *on page 70*

Andec® *see* Carbinoxamine *on page 106*

Andriol® *see* Testosterone *on page 564*

Andro-Cyp® Injection *see* Testosterone *on page 564*

Andro/Fem® Injection *see* Estradiol and Testosterone *on page 229*

Android® *see* Methyltestosterone *on page 398*

Andro® Injection *see* Testosterone *on page 564*

Andro-L.A.® Injection *see* Testosterone *on page 564*

Androlone®-D Injection *see* Nandrolone *on page 421*

Androlone® Injection *see* Nandrolone *on page 421*

Andronate® Injection *see* Testosterone *on page 564*

Andropository® Injection *see* Testosterone *on page 564*

Anemone Camphor *see* Camphor *on page 99*

Anergan® *see* Promethazine *on page 505*

Anestacon® *see* Lidocaine *on page 345*

Anexsia® *see* Hydrocodone and Acetaminophen *on page 293*

Angilol® *see* Propranolol *on page 510*

(6)-Annulene *see* Benzene *on page 69*

Anodynos-DHC® *see* Hydrocodone and Acetaminophen *on page 293*

Anoquan® *see* Butalbital Compound *on page 93*

Anorex® *see* Diethylpropion *on page 196*

Antabuse® *see* Disulfiram *on page 208*

Antaxone® *see* Naltrexone *on page 420*

Antihist-1® [OTC] *see* Clemastine *on page 149*

Antihist-D® *see* Clemastine and Phenylpropanolamine *on page 150*

Antil® *see* Cimetidine *on page 147*

Antisacer® *see* Phenytoin *on page 483*

Antispas® *see* Dicyclomine *on page 194*

Anti-Tuss® Expectorant [OTC] *see* Guaifenesin *on page 269*

Antituxil-Z® *see* Zipeprol *on page 620*

Antivert® *see* Meclizine *on page 361*

Antrizine® *see* Meclizine *on page 361*

Anucort-HC® *see* Hydrocortisone *on page 297*

Anumed HC™ *see* Hydrocortisone *on page 297*

Anusol-HC® [OTC] *see* Hydrocortisone *on page 297*

Anxanil® *see* Hydroxyzine *on page 303*

Apacet® [OTC] *see* Acetaminophen *on page 20*

APAP *see* Acetaminophen *on page 20*

Aphilan R® *see* Buclizine *on page 88*

Aphrodine Hydrochloride *see* Yohimbine *on page 618*

Aphrodyne™ *see* Yohimbine *on page 618*

Apodorm® *see* Nitrazepam *on page 435*

Apo-Nadol® *see* Nadolol *on page 417*

A-Poxide® *see* Chlordiazepoxide *on page 124*

Appalachian Tea *see* Holly *on page 287*

Apresazide® *see* Hydralazine and Hydrochlorothiazide *on page 291*

Apresoline® *see* Hydralazine *on page 289*

Aprobarbital *see* Barbiturates, Quantitative, Blood *on page 64*

Aprodine® w/C *see* Triprolidine, Pseudoephedrine, and Codeine *on page 602*

Apsolol® *see* Propranolol *on page 510*

Aquachloral® Supprettes® *see* Chloral Hydrate *on page 122*

Aqualin® *see* Acrolein *on page 27*

Aquaphyllin® *see* Theophylline Salts *on page 571*

Aquazide-H® *see* Hydrochlorothiazide *on page 291*

Aqueous Testosterone *see* Testosterone *on page 564*

Ardell Instant Glue Remover® *see* Acetonitrile *on page 26*

Ardeytropin® *see* Tryptophan *on page 602*

Arem® *see* Nitrazepam *on page 435*

Arm-a-Med® Metaproterenol *see* Metaproterenol *on page 376*

A.R.M.® Caplet [OTC] *see* Chlorpheniramine and Phenylpropanolamine *on page 134*

Arrestin® *see* Trimethobenzamide *on page 599*

Arret® *see* Loperamide *on page 349*

Arsenate *see* Arsenic *on next page*

Arsenic

Synonyms Arsenate; Arsenite

UN Number 1554; 1558; 1573

Commonly Found In Pesticides, rodenticides, ant poisons, wood preservative, microchips, well water, seafood

Mechanism of Toxic Action Multisystem disease secondary to inhibition of cellular respiration

Toxicodynamics/kinetics

Absorption: Orally, inhalation, and dermally

Half-life: 42-48 hours

Signs and Symptoms of Acute Intoxication Torsade de pointes, neuritis, lacrimation, pancytopenia, encephalopathy, stocking glove sensory neuropathy, Mees' lines (on nail beds forms at 4-6 weeks postexposure), hematuria, leukopenia, garlic-like breath, blindness, fasciculations, agranulocytosis, hypotension, tachycardia, seizures, fever, paresthesia, radiopaque, tremor, myoglobinuria, alopecia, sweating, cough, hemolytic anemia

When to Transport to Hospital Transport any suspected exposure

Overdosage/Treatment

Decontamination:

Dermal: Remove contaminated clothing, wash with soap and water

Ocular: Copious irrigation with saline

Adverse Reactions

Cardiovascular: Cardiotoxicity, tachycardia, acrocyanosis, Raynaud's phenomenon, congestive heart failure, myocardial depression, myocarditis, pericardial effusion/pericarditis, sinus tachycardia, tachycardia (supraventricular), vasodilation

Central nervous system: Neurotoxicity, axonopathy (peripheral), fever, hyperthermia, memory disturbance, Jarisch-Herxheimer reaction, delirium, psychosis

Dermatologic: Desquamation (scaling), hyperpigmentation, alopecia

Gastrointestinal: Gastrointestinal pathology, nausea, vomiting, metallic taste, salivation, feces discoloration (black), bloody diarrhea, abdominal pain, garlic odor

Hematologic: Bone marrow suppression, neutropenia, pancytopenia (leukopenia, thrombocytopenia, aplastic anemia)

Renal: Tubular necrosis (acute), hematuria

Miscellaneous: Basal cell carcinoma

Reference Range Urine concentrations in nonexposed individuals ≤50 µg/L; hair concentrations detectable 30 hours postingestion; urine ≥100 µg/L is suggestive for chronic exposure; blood not usually helpful, although blood arsenic levels >1000 µg/L usually associated with fatality; background blood arsenic level is usually <1 µg/L

Blood: <5 µg/dL (SI: <93.5 nmol/g); heparinized whole blood and serum have been used for arsenic determination. Blood levels of arsenic have a short half-life and are useful only within a few days of exposure. Urine arsenic concentration is a better measure of arsenic poisoning. In addition to pesticides, rodenticides, weed killers, paint, and wood preservatives contain arsenic.

Hair: Up to 65 µg/100 g (SI: 8.7 nmol/g); nail: 90-180 µg/100 g (SI: 12-24 nmol/g); arsenic accumulates in bones, hair, and nails and is used to detect chronic exposure, since arsenic is laid down in keratin soon after ingestion. Arsenic binds to protein sulfhydryl groups. Variations in arsenic hair levels may be due to geographic location and exposure to industrial waste and drinking water.

Ranges for urine arsenic levels can be variable among different laboratories. A general guideline is given: normal: 0-50 µg/L (SI: 0-0.65 µmol/L); chronic industrial exposure: >100 µg/L (SI: >1.3 µmol/L). The 24-hour urinary excretion rate should be <50 µg/24 hours. 25 mL acidified gastric washing is acceptable for arsenic analysis; gastric content normally contains no arsenic. Random urine samples are acceptable. Refrain from eating seafood for 1 week prior to 24-hour urine collection.

Additional Information Causes garlic odor; present in seafood; seafood contains arsenobetaine and arsenocholine; dietary history is important; found in some homeopathic medications; radiopaque compound but rapid absorption makes observation unlikely; arsine gas most toxic, then trivalent arsenite, then pentavalent arsenate; acute exposure can cause chronic symptoms; bone marrow, skin, and peripheral nerve system usual targets of chronic exposure; found in earth's crust at an arsenic level of 2 ppm; Chinese herbal balls may contain from 7.8-621.3 mg of mercury and from 0.1-36.6 mg of arsenic

TLV-TWA: 0.2 mg/m^3
Toxic dose: 120-200 mg
Urban arsenic levels of ambient air: 20-30 ng/m^3
Arsenic levels in ground water: 1-2 ppb
Arsenic levels in selected media:
  Grains: 0.22 ppm
  Meat: 0.14 ppm
  Seafood: 4-5 ppm
  Cigarette: 1.5 ppm
Estimated daily intake of arsenic (adult):
  Nonsmoker: 51.5 mcg
  Smoker (2 packs/day): 63.5 mcg
  Drinking water: 10 mcg
  Food: 45 mcg

Specific References
Gorby MS, "Arsenic Poisoning," *West J Med*, 1988, 149(3):308-15.

Arsenite *see* Arsenic *on previous page*

Arteolol® *see* Carteolol *on page 115*

Arthritis Foundation® Nighttime [OTC] *see* Acetaminophen and Diphenhydramine *on page 22*

Arthritis Foundation® Pain Reliever [OTC] *see* Aspirin *on page 56*

Arthritis Foundation® Pain Reliever, Aspirin Free [OTC] *see* Acetaminophen *on page 20*

Artic® *see* Chloromethane *on page 130*

Articulose-50® *see* Prednisolone *on page 495*

Artificial Nail Tip and Glue Remover® *see* Acetonitrile *on page 26*

A.S.A. [OTC] *see* Aspirin *on page 56*

ASA *see* Aspirin *on page 56*

Asaurex® *see* Cimetidine *on page 147*

Ascorbic Acid (a SKOR bik AS id)

Synonyms Vitamin C

U.S. Brand Names Ascorbicap® [OTC]; C-Crystals® [OTC]; Cebid® Timecelles® [OTC]; Cecon® [OTC]; Cevalin® [OTC]; Cevi-Bid® [OTC]; Ce-Vi-Sol® [OTC]; Dull-C® [OTC]; Flavorcee® [OTC]; N'ice® Vitamin C Drops [OTC]; Vita-C® [OTC]

Canadian Brand Names Apo-C®; Ascorbic 500; Redoxon®; Revitalose® C-1000®

Therapeutic Category Vitamin, Water Soluble

Use Prevention and treatment of scurvy and to acidify the urine
(Continued)

Ascorbic Acid *(Continued)*

Investigational: In large doses to decrease the severity of "colds"; dietary supplementation; a 20-year study was recently completed involving 730 individuals which indicates a possible decreased risk of death by stroke when ascorbic acid at doses of ≥45 mg/day was administered

Usual Dosage Oral, I.M., I.V., S.C.:

Recommended daily allowance (RDA):

<6 months: 30 mg
6 months to 1 year: 35 mg
1-3 years: 40 mg
4-10 years: 45 mg
11-14 years: 50 mg
>14 years and Adults: 60 mg

Children:
Scurvy: 100-300 mg/day in divided doses for at least 2 weeks
Urinary acidification: 500 mg every 6-8 hours
Dietary supplement: 35-100 mg/day

Adults:
Scurvy: 100-250 mg 1-2 times/day for at least 2 weeks
Urinary acidification: 4-12 g/day in 3-4 divided doses
Prevention and treatment of colds: 1-3 g/day
Dietary supplement: 50-200 mg/day

Mechanism of Action Not fully understood; necessary for collagen formation and tissue repair; involved in some oxidation-reduction reactions as well as other metabolic pathways, such as synthesis of carnitine, steroids, and catecholamines and conversion of folic acid to folinic acid

Pharmacodynamics/kinetics

Absorption: Oral: Readily absorbed; an active process and is thought to be dose-dependent

Metabolism: In the liver by oxidation and sulfation

Signs and Symptoms of Acute Intoxication Renal calculi, nausea, gastritis, diarrhea

When to Transport to Hospital Transport any symptomatic patient or any ingestion over 1 g

Warnings/Precautions Diabetics and patients prone to recurrent renal calculi (eg, dialysis patients) should not take excessive doses for extended periods of time

Adverse Reactions 1% to 10%: Renal: Hyperoxaluria

Test Interactions False-positive urinary glucose with cupric sulfate reagent, false-negative urinary glucose with glucose oxidase method; false-negative stool occult blood 48-72 hours after ascorbic acid ingestion

Drug Interactions

Decreased effect:
Ascorbic acid decreases propranolol peak (maximum) serum concentration and AUC and increases the T_{max} significantly, resulting in increased bradycardia, possibly due to decreased absorption and first-pass metabolism (n=5)
Aspirin decreases ascorbate levels, increases aspirin
Fluphenazine decreases fluphenazine levels
Warfarin decreases effect
Increased effect: Iron enhances absorption; oral contraceptives increase contraceptive effect

Dosage Forms

Capsule, timed release: 500 mg
Crystals: 4 g/teaspoonful (100 g, 500 g); 5 g/teaspoonful (180 g)
Injection: 250 mg/mL (2 mL, 30 mL); 500 mg/mL (2 mL, 50 mL)

Liquid, oral: 35 mg/0.6 mL (50 mL)
Lozenges: 60 mg
Powder: 4 g/teaspoonful (100 g, 500 g)
Solution, oral: 100 mg/mL (50 mL)
Syrup: 500 mg/5 mL (5 mL, 10 mL, 120 mL, 480 mL)
Tablet: 25 mg, 50 mg, 100 mg, 250 mg, 500 mg, 1000 mg
Tablet:
Chewable: 100 mg, 250 mg, 500 mg
Timed release: 500 mg, 1000 mg, 1500 mg
Additional Information Sodium content of 1 g: ~5 mEq
Specific References
Lawton JM, Conway LT, Crosson JT, et al, "Acute Oxalate Nephropathy After Massive Ascorbic Acid Administration," *Arch Intern Med*, 1985, 145(5):950-1.

Ascorbicap® [OTC] *see* Ascorbic Acid *on page 53*

Ascriptin® [OTC] *see* Aspirin *on next page*

Asendin® *see* Amoxapine *on page 44*

Asmalix® *see* Theophylline Salts *on page 571*

Aspergum® [OTC] *see* Aspirin *on next page*

Asphalt

Related Information
Carbon Monoxide *on page 109*

Synonyms Road Tar

UN Number 1999

Use Road surfacing or roof sealant agent; also used in paints, electrical adhesive, radioactive waste disposal

Mechanism of Toxic Action Can cause thermal injury; generally exhibits high viscosity, low volatility and high surface tension

When to Transport to Hospital Transport any exposure

Overdosage/Treatment Decontamination:

Dermal: Initially immerse affected area in cool water; emulsifying agents can assist in debridement. Bacitracin can be used as a topical antibiotic. Liquid Tween® 80 (polysorbate 80), can be applied to affected area; cover with wet dressings for 6 hours and then irrigate with saline. This procedure may be repeated until tar is removed. Alternatively a neosporin-based cream (Neosporin®-G-Cream) can be used in above manner while covering affected area with sterile wet dressing for 24 hours, then irrigate with saline (complete removal may take 3 days). Other, less effective agents include Neosporin® ointment, mineral oil, petrolatum, or lanolin. Additionally, butter or mayonnaise has been used as an emulsifier with some success. Medi-Sol (De-Solv-it; Orange-Sol) or Unibase® with triple-antibiotic ointments can also be used. Thermal burns should be treated in traditional manner after removal. Do **not** debride tar mechanically without using an emulsifying agent; **do not** use gasoline, kerosene, or acetone to irrigate.

Inhalations: Administer 100% humidified oxygen

Ocular: Initially irrigate with saline copiously; irrigation can also include sterile surface active solvents (ie, Shur-Clens®) with saline to facilitate tar removal; additionally, a polysorbate with neomycin sulfate can be used to remove tar from conjunctiva

Adverse Reactions

Central nervous system: Headache, hyperthermia

Dermatologic: Thermal burns, oil acne, hyperpigmentation, fingernail discoloration (black)

Gastrointestinal: Upon ingestion, concretions and bezoars can develop

Ocular: Eye irritation

Respiratory: Cough

(Continued)

Asphalt *(Continued)*

Additional Information TLV-TWA (Fume): 5 mg/m³; fumes from asphalt may contain carbon monoxide, hydrocarbons or hydrogen sulfide; specific gravity: 0.95-1.1

Specific References

Tsou TJ, Hutson HR, Bear M, et al, "De-Solv-It for Hot Paving Asphalt Burn: Case Report," *Acad Emerg Med*, 1996, 3(1):88-9.

Aspirin (AS pir in)

Related Information

Aspirin and Codeine *on page 58*
Hydrocodone and Aspirin *on page 294*
Oxycodone and Aspirin *on page 454*

Synonyms Acetylsalicylic Acid; ASA

U.S. Brand Names Anacin® [OTC]; Arthritis Foundation® Pain Reliever [OTC]; A.S.A. [OTC]; Ascriptin® [OTC]; Aspergum® [OTC]; Asprimox® [OTC]; Bayer® Aspirin [OTC]; Bayer® Buffered Aspirin [OTC]; Bayer® Low Adult Strength [OTC]; Bufferin® [OTC]; Buffex® [OTC]; Cama® Arthritis Pain Reliever [OTC]; Easprin®; Ecotrin® [OTC]; Ecotrin® Low Adult Strength [OTC]; Empirin® [OTC]; Extra Strength Adprin-B® [OTC]; Extra Strength Bayer® Enteric 500 Aspirin [OTC]; Extra Strength Bayer® Plus [OTC]; Halfprin® 81® [OTC]; Regular Strength Bayer® Enteric 500 Aspirin [OTC]; St Joseph® Adult Chewable Aspirin [OTC]; ZORprin®

Canadian Brand Names ASA®; Apo-ASA®; Asaphen®; Entrophen®; Novasen®; MSD® Enteric Coated ASA

Therapeutic Category Analgesic, Non-narcotic; Antiplatelet Agent; Antipyretic; Nonsteroidal Anti-Inflammatory Agent (NSAID)

Use Treatment of mild to moderate pain, inflammation, and fever; may be used as a prophylaxis of myocardial infarction and transient ischemic episodes; management of rheumatoid arthritis, rheumatic fever, osteoarthritis, and gout (high dose)

Usual Dosage

Children:

Analgesic and antipyretic: Oral, rectal: 10-15 mg/kg/dose every 4-6 hours, up to a total of 60-80 mg/kg/24 hours

Anti-inflammatory: Oral: Initial: 60-90 mg/kg/day in divided doses; usual maintenance: 80-100 mg/kg/day divided every 6-8 hours, maximum dose: 3.6 g/day; monitor serum concentrations

Kawasaki disease: Oral: 80-100 mg/kg/day divided every 6 hours; after fever resolves: 8-10 mg/kg/day once daily; monitor serum concentrations

Antirheumatic: Oral: 60-100 mg/kg/day in divided doses every 4 hours

Adults:

Analgesic and antipyretic: Oral, rectal: 325-650 mg every 4-6 hours up to 4 g/day

Anti-inflammatory: Oral: Initial: 2.4-3.6 g/day in divided doses; usual maintenance: 3.6-5.4 g/day; monitor serum concentrations

TIA: Oral: 1.3 g/day in 2-4 divided doses

Myocardial infarction prophylaxis: 160-325 mg/day

Mechanism of Action Inhibits prostaglandin synthesis, acts on the hypothalamus heat-regulating center to reduce fever, blocks prostaglandin synthetase action which prevents formation of the platelet-aggregating substance thromboxane A_2

Pharmacodynamics/kinetics

Absorption: From stomach and small intestine

Distribution: Readily distributes into most body fluids and tissues

Metabolism: Hydrolyzed to salicylate (active) by esterases in the GI mucosa, red blood cells, synovial fluid and blood; metabolism of salicylate occurs primarily by hepatic microsomal enzymes; metabolic pathways are saturable

Half-life:

Parent drug: 15-20 minutes

Salicylates (dose-dependent): From 3 hours at lower doses (300-600 mg), to 5-6 hours (after 1 g) to 10 hours with higher doses

Time to peak serum concentration: ~1-2 hours

Signs and Symptoms of Acute Intoxication Tinnitus, headache, dizziness, confusion, metabolic acidosis, hyperpyrexia, hypoglycemia, coma, tachypnea

When to Transport to Hospital Transport any ingestion over 200 mg/kg in pediatric patients (<6 years of age) or any symptomatic patient

Warnings/Precautions Use with caution in patients with platelet and bleeding disorders, renal dysfunction, erosive gastritis, or peptic ulcer disease, previous nonreaction does not guarantee future safe taking of medication; do not use aspirin in children <16 years of age for chickenpox or flu symptoms due to the association with Reye's syndrome

Otic: Discontinue use if dizziness, tinnitus, or impaired hearing occurs; surgical patients: avoid ASA if possible, for 1 week prior to surgery because of the possibility of postoperative bleeding; use with caution in impaired hepatic function

Elderly are a high-risk population for adverse effects from nonsteroidal anti-inflammatory agents. As much as 60% of elderly with GI complications to NSAIDs can develop peptic ulceration and/or hemorrhage asymptomatically. Also, concomitant disease and drug use contribute to the risk for GI adverse effects. Use lowest effective dose for shortest period possible. Consider renal function decline with age. Use of NSAIDs can compromise existing renal function. Tinnitus may be a difficult and unreliable indication of toxicity due to age-related hearing loss or eighth cranial nerve damage. CNS adverse effects such as confusion, agitation, and hallucination are generally seen in overdose or high-dose situations, but elderly may demonstrate these adverse effects at lower doses than younger adults.

Adverse Reactions

>10%: Gastrointestinal: Nausea, vomiting, dyspepsia, epigastric discomfort, heartburn, stomach pains

Serum Salicylate: Clinical Correlations

Serum Salicylate Concentration (mcg/mL)	Desired Effects	Adverse Effects/Intoxication
~100	Antiplatelet Antipyresis Analgesia	GI intolerance and bleeding, hypersensitivity, hemostatic defects
150-300	Anti-inflammatory	Mild salicylism
250-400	Treatment of rheumatic fever	Nausea/vomiting, hyperventilation, salicylism, flushing, sweating, thirst, headache, diarrhea, and tachycardia
>400-500		Respiratory alkalosis, hemorrhage, excitement, confusion, asterixis, pulmonary edema, convulsions, tetany, metabolic acidosis, fever, coma, cardiovascular collapse, renal and respiratory failure

(Continued)

Aspirin *(Continued)*

1% to 10%:
Central nervous system: Fatigue
Dermatologic: Rash, urticaria
Gastrointestinal: Gastrointestinal ulceration
Hematologic: Hemolytic anemia
Neuromuscular & skeletal: Weakness
Respiratory: Dyspnea
Miscellaneous: Anaphylactic shock

Reference Range Timing of serum samples: Peak levels usually occur 2 hours after ingestion. Salicylate serum concentrations correlate with the pharmacological actions and adverse effects observed. See table.

Drug Interactions
Decreased effect: Possible decreased serum concentration of NSAIDs; aspirin may antagonize effects of probenecid
Increased toxicity: Aspirin may increase methotrexate serum levels and may displace valproic acid from binding sites which can result in toxicity; warfarin and aspirin may increase bleeding; NSAIDs and aspirin may increase GI adverse effects

Dosage Forms
Capsule: 356.4 mg and caffeine 30 mg
Suppository, rectal: 60 mg, 120 mg, 125 mg, 130 mg, 195 mg, 200 mg, 300 mg, 325 mg, 600 mg, 650 mg, 1.2 g
Tablet: 65 mg, 75 mg, 81 mg, 325 mg, 500 mg
Tablet: 400 mg and caffeine 32 mg
Tablet:
Buffered: 325 mg and magnesium-aluminum hydroxide 150 mg; 325 mg, magnesium hydroxide 75 mg, aluminum hydroxide 75 mg, buffered with calcium carbonate; 325 mg and magnesium-aluminum hydroxide 75 mg
Chewable: 81 mg
Controlled release: 800 mg
Delayed release: 81 mg
Enteric coated: 81 mg, 325 mg, 500 mg, 650 mg, 975 mg
Gum: 227.5 mg
Timed release: 650 mg

Specific References
Weissmann G, "Aspirin," *Sci Am*, 1991, 264(1):84-90.

Aspirin and Codeine (AS pir in & KOE deen)

Related Information
Aspirin *on page 56*
Codeine *on page 164*
Controlled Substances - Uses and Effects *on page 741*

Synonyms Codeine and Aspirin

U.S. Brand Names Empirin® With Codeine

Canadian Brand Names Coryphen® Codeine; 222® Tablets; 282® Tablets; 292® Tablets

Therapeutic Category Analgesic, Narcotic

Dosage Forms Tablet:
#2: Aspirin 325 mg and codeine phosphate 15 mg
#3: Aspirin 325 mg and codeine phosphate 30 mg
#4: Aspirin 325 mg and codeine phosphate 60 mg

Aspirin and Meprobamate (AS pir in & me proe BA mate)

Synonyms Meprobamate and Aspirin

U.S. Brand Names Equagesic®

Therapeutic Category Skeletal Muscle Relaxant
Abuse Potential Yes
Impairment Potential Yes; Serum meprobamate levels >60 mg/L associated with impairment

Baselt RC and Cravey RH, *Disposition of Toxic Drugs and Chemicals in Man*, 4th ed, Foster City, CA: Chemical Toxicology Institute, 1995, 460.
Dosage Forms Tablet: Aspirin 325 mg and meprobamate 200 mg

Aspirin Free Anacin® Maximum Strength [OTC] *see* Acetaminophen *on page 20*

Aspirin-Free Bayer® Select® Allergy Sinus Caplets [OTC] *see* Acetaminophen, Chlorpheniramine, and Pseudoephedrine *on page 23*

Asprimox® [OTC] *see* Aspirin *on page 56*

Assenzio *see* Wormwood *on page 617*

Astemizole (a STEM mi zole)
U.S. Brand Names Hismanal®
Therapeutic Category Antihistamine
Use Perennial and seasonal allergic rhinitis and other allergic symptoms including urticaria
Usual Dosage Oral:
Children:
<6 years: 0.2 mg/kg/day
6-12 years: 5 mg/day
Children >12 years and Adults: 10-30 mg/day; administer 30 mg on first day, 20 mg on second day, then 10 mg/day in a single dose
Mechanism of Action Competes with histamine for H_1-receptor sites on effector cells in the gastrointestinal tract, blood vessels, and respiratory tract; binds to lung receptors significantly greater than it binds to cerebellar receptors, resulting in a reduced sedative potential. Nonsedating action reportedly due to the drug's low lipid solubility and poor penetration through the blood-brain barrier.
Pharmacodynamics/kinetics Long-acting, with steady-state plasma levels seen within 4-8 weeks following initiation of chronic therapy
Protein binding: 97%
Metabolism: Undergoes extensive liver metabolism to active and inactive metabolites
Half-life: 20 hours
Time to peak serum concentration: Oral: Long-acting, with steady-state plasma levels of parent compound and metabolites seen within 4-8 weeks following initiation of chronic therapy; peak plasma levels appear in 1-4 hours following administration
Signs and Symptoms of Acute Intoxication Sedation, apnea, diminished mental alertness, ventricular tachycardia, torsade de pointes
When to Transport to Hospital Transport any symptomatic patient or any asymptomatic ingestion over 1 mg/kg
Warnings/Precautions Use with caution in patients receiving drugs which prolong QRS or Q-T interval; rare cases of severe cardiovascular events (cardiac arrest, arrhythmias) have been reported in the following situations: overdose (even as low as 20-30 mg/day), significant hepatic dysfunction, when used in combination with quinine, erythromycin, ketoconazole, or itraconazole; safety and efficacy in children <12 years of age have not been established; discontinue therapy immediately with signs of cardiotoxicity including syncope
Adverse Reactions 1% to 10%:
Central nervous system: Drowsiness, headache, fatigue, nervousness, dizziness
(Continued)

Astemizole *(Continued)*

Gastrointestinal: Appetite increase, weight gain, nausea, diarrhea, abdominal pain, xerostomia
Neuromuscular & skeletal: Arthralgia
Respiratory: Pharyngitis
Drug Interactions Increased toxicity: CNS depressants (sedation), triazole antifungals, macrolide antibiotics and quinine may inhibit the metabolism of astemizole resulting in potentially life-threatening arrhythmias (torsade de pointes, etc.)
Dosage Forms Tablet: 10 mg
Specific References
Nicholson AN and Stone BM, "Performance Studies With the H1-Histamine Receptor Antagonists, Astemizole and Terfenadine," *Br J Clin Pharmacol*, 1982, 13(2):199-202.

Asthma Weed *see* Indian Tobacco *on page 312*
Astramorph™ PF *see* Morphine Sulfate *on page 410*
Atarax® *see* Hydroxyzine *on page 303*
Atazina® *see* Hydroxyzine *on page 303*

Atenolol *(a TEN oh lole)*
U.S. Brand Names Tenormin®
Canadian Brand Names Apo-Atenol®; Novo-Atenol®; Nu-Atenol®; Taro-Atenol®
Therapeutic Category Beta-Adrenergic Blocker
Use Treatment of hypertension, alone or in combination with other agents; management of angina pectoris, postmyocardial infarction patients

Unlabeled use: Acute alcohol withdrawal, supraventricular and ventricular arrhythmias, and migraine headache prophylaxis
Usual Dosage
Oral:
Children: 1-2 mg/kg/dose given daily
Adults:
Hypertension: 50 mg once daily, may increase to 100 mg/day; doses >100 mg are unlikely to produce any further benefit
Angina pectoris: 50 mg once daily, may increase to 100 mg/day; some patients may require 200 mg/day
Postmyocardial infarction: Follow I.V. dose with 100 mg/day or 50 mg twice daily for 6-9 days postmyocardial infarction
I.V.: Postmyocardial infarction: Early treatment: 5 mg slow I.V. over 5 minutes; may repeat in 10 minutes; if both doses are tolerated, may start oral atenolol 50 mg every 12 hours or 100 mg/day for 6-9 days postmyocardial infarction
Mechanism of Action Competitively blocks response to beta-adrenergic stimulation, selectively blocks beta$_1$-receptors with little or no effect on beta$_2$-receptors except at high doses
Pharmacodynamics/kinetics
Absorption: Incomplete from GI tract
Distribution: Low lipophilicity; does **not** cross the blood-brain barrier
Protein binding: Low at 3% to 15%
Metabolism: Partial hepatic
Half-life, beta:
Neonates: Mean: 16 hours, up to 35 hours
Children: 4.6 hours; children >10 years of age may have longer half-life (>5 hours) compared to children 5-10 years of age (<5 hours)
Adults:
Normal renal function: 6-9 hours, longer in those with renal impairment

End stage renal disease: 15-35 hours
Time to peak: Oral: Within 2-4 hours

Signs and Symptoms of Acute Intoxication Cardiac disturbances, CNS toxicity, bronchospasm, dyspnea, hypoglycemia and hyperkalemia. The most common cardiac symptoms include hypotension and bradycardia; atrioventricular block, intraventricular conduction disturbances, cardiogenic shock, and systole may occur with severe overdose, especially with membrane-depressant drugs (eg, propranolol); CNS effects include convulsions, coma, and respiratory arrest (commonly seen with propranolol and other membrane-depressant and lipid-soluble drugs).

When to Transport to Hospital Transport any symptomatic patient or any ingestion over 3 mg/kg

Warnings/Precautions Safety and efficacy in children have not been established; administer with caution to patients (especially the elderly) with bronchospastic disease, CHF, renal dysfunction, severe peripheral vascular disease, myasthenia gravis, diabetes mellitus, hyperthyroidism. **Abrupt withdrawal of the drug should be avoided,** drug should be discontinued over 1-2 weeks; may potentiate hypoglycemia in a diabetic patient and mask signs and symptoms; modify dosage in patients with renal impairment.

Adverse Reactions 1% to 10%:
Cardiovascular: Persistent bradycardia, hypotension, chest pain, edema, heart failure, second or third degree A-V block, Raynaud's phenomenon
Central nervous system: Dizziness, fatigue, insomnia, lethargy, confusion, mental impairment, depression, headache, nightmares
Gastrointestinal: Constipation, diarrhea, nausea
Genitourinary: Impotence

Drug Interactions
Decreased effect of beta-blockers with aluminum salts, barbiturates, calcium salts, cholestyramine, colestipol, NSAIDs, penicillins (ampicillin), rifampin, salicylates, and sulfinpyrazone due to decreased bioavailability and plasma levels
Beta-blockers may decrease the effect of sulfonylureas
Increased effect/toxicity of beta-blockers with calcium blockers (diltiazem, felodipine, nicardipine), contraceptives, flecainide, haloperidol (propranolol, hypotensive effects), H_2-antagonists (metoprolol, propranolol only by cimetidine, possibly ranitidine), hydralazine (metoprolol, propranolol), MAO inhibitors (metoprolol, nadolol, bradycardia), phenothiazines (propranolol), propafenone (metoprolol, propranolol), quinidine (in extensive metabolizers), ciprofloxacin, thyroid hormones (metoprolol, propranolol, when hypothyroid patient is converted to euthyroid state)
Beta-blockers may increase the effect/toxicity of flecainide, haloperidol (hypotensive effects), hydralazine, phenothiazines, acetaminophen, anticoagulants (propranolol, warfarin), benzodiazepines (not atenolol), clonidine (hypertensive crisis after or during withdrawal of either agent), epinephrine (initial hypertensive episode followed by bradycardia), nifedipine and verapamil lidocaine, ergots (peripheral ischemia), prazosin (postural hypotension)
Beta-blockers may affect the action or levels of ethanol, disopyramide, nondepolarizing muscle relaxants and theophylline although the effects are difficult to predict

Dosage Forms
Injection: 0.5 mg/mL (10 mL)
Tablet: 25 mg, 50 mg, 100 mg

Specific References
Shanahan FL and Counihan TB, "Atenolol Self-Poisoning," *Br Med J*, 1978, 2(6139):773.

Atensine® *see* Diazepam *on page 189*

Ativan® *see* Lorazepam *on page 351*

Atozine® *see* Hydroxyzine *on page 303*

Atrimon® *see* Tryptophan *on page 602*

Atrohist® Plus *see* Chlorpheniramine, Phenylephrine, Phenylpropanolamine, and Belladonna Alkaloids *on page 136*

Atropa belladonna see Deadly Nightshade *on page 178*

Atropine and Diphenoxylate *see* Diphenoxylate and Atropine *on page 207*

Augmentin® *see* Amoxicillin and Clavulanate Potassium *on page 46*

Aurorix® *see* Moclobemide *on page 406*

Aventyl® Hydrochloride *see* Nortriptyline *on page 440*

Axotal® *see* Butalbital Compound *on page 93*

Azabenzine *see* Pyridine *on page 518*

Azadiene *see* Amitraz *on page 39*

Azaform *see* Amitraz *on page 39*

6-Azamianserin *see* Mirtazapine *on page 405*

Azatadine (a ZA ta deen)

U.S. Brand Names Optimine®

Therapeutic Category Antihistamine

Use Treatment of perennial and seasonal allergic rhinitis and chronic urticaria

Usual Dosage Children >12 years and Adults: Oral: 1-2 mg twice daily

Mechanism of Action Azatadine is a piperidine-derivative antihistamine; has both anticholinergic and antiserotonin activity; has been demonstrated to inhibit mediator release from human mast cells *in vitro*; mechanism of this action is suggested to prevent calcium entry into the mast cell through voltage-dependent calcium channels

Pharmacodynamics/kinetics

Absorption: Oral: Rapid and extensive

Half-life, elimination: ~8.7 hours

Signs and Symptoms of Acute Intoxication CNS depression or stimulation, dry mouth, flushed skin, fixed and dilated pupils, apnea

When to Transport to Hospital Transport any pediatric exposure, any symptomatic patient, or any patient exhibiting cardiac symptoms

Warnings/Precautions Sedation and somnolence are the most commonly reported adverse effects

Adverse Reactions

>10%:

Central nervous system: Slight to moderate drowsiness

Respiratory: Thickening of bronchial secretions

1% to 10%:

Central nervous system: Headache, fatigue, nervousness, dizziness

Gastrointestinal: Appetite increase, weight gain, nausea, diarrhea, abdominal pain, xerostomia

Neuromuscular & skeletal: Arthralgia

Respiratory: Pharyngitis

Drug Interactions Increased effect/toxicity: Procarbazine, CNS depressants, tricyclic antidepressants, alcohol

Dosage Forms Tablet, as maleate: 1 mg

Specific References

Joske DJ, "Dystonic Reaction to Azatadine," *Med J Aust*, 1984, 141(7):449.

Azdone® *see* Hydrocodone and Aspirin *on page 294*

Azine *see* Pyridine *on page 518*

Azium *see* Sodium Azide *on page 541*

Azomide *see* Sodium Azide *on page 541*

AZT + 3TC *see Zidovudine and Lamivudine on page 619*

Azupamil® *see Verapamil on page 609*

BAAM® *see Amitraz on page 39*

Babee Teething® [OTC] *see Benzocaine on page 70*

B-A-C® *see Butalbital Compound on page 93*

Baclofen (BAK loe fen)

U.S. Brand Names Lioresal®
Canadian Brand Names Alpha-Baclofen®; PMS-Baclofen®
Therapeutic Category Skeletal Muscle Relaxant
Abuse Potential Yes
Impairment Potential Yes
Use Treatment of reversible spasticity associated with multiple sclerosis or spinal cord lesions

There are a number of unlabeled uses for baclofen including, intractable hiccups, intractable pain relief, and bladder spasticity

Usual Dosage Oral:

Children:

2-7 years: Initial: 10-15 mg/24 hours divided every 8 hours; titrate dose every 3 days in increments of 5-15 mg/day to a maximum of 40 mg/day

≥8 years: Maximum: 60 mg/day in 3 divided doses

Adults: 5 mg 3 times/day, may increase 5 mg/dose every 3 days to a maximum of 80 mg/day

Hiccups: Usual effective dose: 10-20 mg 2-3 times/day

Mechanism of Action Inhibits the transmission of both monosynaptic and polysynaptic reflexes at the spinal cord level, possibly by hyperpolarization of primary afferent fiber terminals, with resultant relief of muscle spasticity

Pharmacodynamics/kinetics

Onset of action: Muscle relaxation effect requires 3-4 days

Peak effect: Maximal clinical effect is not seen for 5-10 days

Absorption: Oral: Rapid; absorption from GI tract is thought to be dose dependent

Protein binding: 30%

Metabolism: Minimally in the liver

Half-life: 3.5 hours

Time to peak serum concentration: Oral: Within 2-3 hours

Elimination: 85% of oral dose excreted in urine and feces as unchanged drug

Signs and Symptoms of Acute Intoxication Vomiting, muscle hypotonia, salivation, drowsiness, coma, seizures, respiratory depression

When to Transport to Hospital Transport any pediatric ingestion (<6 years of age) over 5 mg/kg or any symptomatic patient

Warnings/Precautions Use with caution in patients with seizure disorder, impaired renal function; avoid abrupt withdrawal of the drug; elderly are more sensitive to the effects of baclofen and are more likely to experience adverse CNS effects at higher doses.

Adverse Reactions

>10%:

Central nervous system: Drowsiness, vertigo, dizziness, psychiatric disturbances, insomnia, slurred speech, ataxia, hypotonia

Neuromuscular & skeletal: Weakness

1% to 10%:

Cardiovascular: Hypotension

Central nervous system: Fatigue, confusion, headache, insomnia

Dermatologic: Rash

Gastrointestinal: Nausea, constipation

Genitourinary: Polyuria

(Continued)

63

Baclofen (Continued)

Drug Interactions
Increased effect: Narcotic analgesics, benzodiazepines, hypertensive agents
Increased toxicity: CNS depressants and alcohol (sedation), tricyclic antidepressants (short-term memory loss), clindamycin (neuromuscular blockade),
guanabenz (sedation), MAO inhibitors (decrease blood pressure, CNS, and
respiratory effects)

Dosage Forms
Injection, intrathecal, preservative free: 500 mcg/mL (20 mL); 2000 mcg/mL (5
mL)
Tablet: 10 mg, 20 mg

Specific References
Cooke DE and Glasstone MA, "Baclofen Poisoning in Children," *Vet Hum
Toxicol*, 1994, 36(5):448-50.

Bactrim™ *see* Co-Trimoxazole *on page 168*

Bactrim™ DS *see* Co-Trimoxazole *on page 168*

Baker's P&S [OTC] *see* Phenol *on page 476*

Baldex® *see* Dexamethasone *on page 182*

Bancap® *see* Butalbital Compound *on page 93*

Bancap HC® *see* Hydrocodone and Acetaminophen *on page 293*

Banophen® Decongestant Capsule [OTC] *see* Diphenhydramine and Pseudoephedrine *on page 207*

Banophen® Oral [OTC] *see* Diphenhydramine *on page 205*

Barbidonna® *see* Hyoscyamine, Atropine, Scopolamine, and Phenobarbital *on
page 306*

Barbita® *see* Phenobarbital *on page 474*

Barbiturates, Qualitative, Urine

Use Urine drugs of abuse testing, pre-employment screens, random drug testing

Reference Range Less than cutoff

Additional Information Barbiturates are nonselective CNS depressants that
may be used as sedative-hypnotics or anticonvulsants. They are capable of
producing all levels of CNS mood effects from sedation to hypnosis to deep
coma and anesthesia. Sensory cortex functions, cerebellar functions, and
motor activity are decreased. Secobarbital and pentobarbital are short-term
hypnotics and lose effectiveness after about 2 weeks of continued usage.
Withdrawal symptoms from any barbiturate may be severe and may include
convulsions and delirium. The presence of barbiturates in urine is presumptively positive at a level >300 ng/mL using secobarbital as a standard and can
indicate prescribed or abused intake of this class of drugs. The presence of
these drugs should be confirmed.

Specific References
Maurer HH, "Identification and Differentiation of Barbiturates and Their Metabo-
lites in Urine," *J Chromatogr*, 1990, 530:307-26.
Pesce AJ, "Barbiturates," *Clinical Chemistry - Theory, Analysis, and Correla-
tion*, 2nd ed, Kaplan LA and Pesce AJ, eds, St Louis, MO: Mosby-Year Book
Inc, 1989, 1081-7.

Barbiturates, Quantitative, Blood

Applies to Aprobarbital; Butalbital; Talbutal

Use Evaluate barbiturate toxicity, drug abuse, therapeutic levels; if barbiturates
are suspected in a drug overdose, determination of long-, medium-, or short-
acting may influence treatment.

Reference Range Negative. Therapeutic: short-acting (secobarbital): 1-5 µg/
mL (SI: 4.2-21.0 µmol/L); intermediate-acting (amobarbital): 5-15 µg/mL (SI:

22-66 µmol/L); long-acting (phenobarbital): 15-40 µg/mL (SI: 65-172 µmol/L); for seizure control, phenobarbital therapeutic levels: 10-30 µg/mL (SI: 43-129 µmol/L)

Additional Information To monitor therapeutic phenobarbital level see listing for Phenobarbital, Blood. Barbiturates are sedative hypnotics and frequent drugs of abuse, alone and in combination with alcohol and/or amphetamines. If overdosage occurs, coma and death may result. The implication of any concentration is more serious for short-acting barbiturates than for phenobarbital. The toxic or lethal blood level varies with many factors and cannot be stated with certainty. Lethal blood levels determined at autopsy may be as low as 60 µg/mL (SI: 258 µmol/L) for long-acting (barbital and phenobarbital) and 10 µg/mL (SI: 43 µmol/L) for intermediate- and short-acting barbiturates (amobarbital, butabarbital, butalbital, pentobarbital, secobarbital). In presence of alcohol or other depressant drugs, the lethal concentrations may be lower. Addicts, however, may tolerate with no ill effect levels which would be acutely toxic to a nonaddicted individual. The long-acting drugs are metabolized slowly and depend primarily on the kidney for elimination, the short- and intermediate-acting drugs are metabolized primarily by the liver and are much less dependent on the kidney for excretion. Except for barbital, all barbiturates are primarily transformed by the liver. Only barbital is dependent mainly on renal excretion for termination of its pharmacological action. Individual barbiturates can be identified and separated from each other by HPLC.

Barbiturates can be assayed in **urine** or **gastric contents**. The presence of barbiturates in urine is presumptively positive at a level ≥300 ng/mL using secobarbital as a standard and can indicate prescribed or abused intake of this class of drugs. The presence of these drugs should be confirmed. The most commonly abused barbiturates are secobarbital (red devils), pentobarbital (yellow jackets), and amobarbital (blue angels). Short- and intermediate-acting barbiturates can be detected in urine 24-72 hours following ingestion, longer-acting drugs up to 7 days.

Barblac® see Pindolol on page 488

Battery Acid see Sulfuric Acid on page 554

Bay Clor® see Chlorpromazine on page 138

Bayer® Aspirin [OTC] see Aspirin on page 56

Bayer® Buffered Aspirin [OTC] see Aspirin on page 56

Bayer® Low Adult Strength [OTC] see Aspirin on page 56

Bayer® Select® Chest Cold Caplets [OTC] see Acetaminophen and Dextromethorphan on page 21

Bayer® Select Head Cold Caplets [OTC] see Acetaminophen and Pseudoephedrine on page 22

Baylocaine® see Lidocaine on page 345

Bazinon® see Diazinon on page 192

Beaden® see Propranolol on page 510

Beamat® see Cimetidine on page 147

Bechizolo® see Zipeprol on page 620

Bedranol® see Propranolol on page 510

Beef NPH Iletin® II see Insulin Preparations on page 314

Beef Regular Iletin® II see Insulin Preparations on page 314

Beer see Ethyl Alcohol on page 233

Belix® Oral [OTC] see Diphenhydramine on page 205

Belladonna (bel a DON a)

Therapeutic Category Anticholinergic Agent

Use Decrease gastrointestinal activity in functional bowel disorders and to delay gastric emptying as well as decrease gastric secretion

Usual Dosage Tincture: Oral:

Children: 0.03 mL/kg 3 times/day

Adults: 0.6-1 mL 3-4 times/day

Mechanism of Action Belladonna is a mixture of the anticholinergic alkaloids atropine, hyoscyamine, and scopolamine (hyoscine). The belladonna alkaloids act primarily by competitive inhibition of the muscarinic actions of acetylcholine on structures innervated by postganglionic cholinergic neurons and on smooth muscle. The resulting effects include antisecretory activity on exocrine glands and intestinal mucosa and smooth muscle relaxation. The anticholinergic properties of scopolamine and atropine differ in that scopolamine has a more potent activity on the iris, ciliary body, and certain secretory glands; has more potent activity on the heart, intestine, and bronchial muscle, and a more prolonged duration of action; in contrast, hyoscyamine has actions similar to those of atropine, but is more potent in both its central and peripheral effects

Signs and Symptoms of Acute Intoxication Anticholinergic toxicity may be caused by strong binding of a belladonna alkaloid to cholinergic receptors; anticholinesterase inhibitors reduce acetylcholinesterase, the enzyme that breaks down acetylcholine and thereby allows acetylcholine to accumulate and compete for receptor binding with the offending anticholinergic

When to Transport to Hospital Transport any patient with cardiac and central nervous symptoms or any pediatric ingestion over 0.1 mL/kg

Adverse Reactions

>10%:

Dermatologic: Dry skin

Gastrointestinal: Constipation, dry throat, xerostomia

Respiratory: Dry nose

Miscellaneous: Decreased diaphoresis

1% to 10%:

Dermatologic: Increased sensitivity to light

Endocrine & metabolic: Decreased flow of breast milk, dysphagia

Drug Interactions Phenothiazines, amantadine, antiparkinsonian drugs, glutethimide, meperidine, tricyclic antidepressants, antiarrhythmic agents, some antihistamines

Dosage Forms Tincture: Belladonna alkaloids (principally hyoscyamine and atropine) 0.3 mg/mL with alcohol 65% to 70% (120 mL, 480 mL, 3780 mL)

Belladonna and Opium (bel a DON a & OH pee um)

Synonyms Opium and Belladonna

U.S. Brand Names B&O Supprettes®

Canadian Brand Names PMS-Opium & Beladonna

Therapeutic Category Analgesic, Narcotic

Abuse Potential Yes

Impairment Potential Yes

Dosage Forms Suppository:

#15 A: Belladonna extract 15 mg and opium 30 mg

#16 A: Belladonna extract 15 mg and opium 60 mg

Belladonna, Phenobarbital, and Ergotamine Tartrate

(bel a DON a, fee noe BAR bi tal, & er GOT a meen TAR trate)

U.S. Brand Names Bellergal-S®; Bel-Phen-Ergot S®; Phenerbel-S®

Canadian Brand Names Belergal®; Bellergal® Spacetabs®

Therapeutic Category Ergot Alkaloid

Abuse Potential Yes

Impairment Potential Yes

Dosage Forms Tablet, sustained release: l-alkaloids of belladonna 0.2 mg, phenobarbital 40 mg, and ergotamine tartrate 0.6 mg

Bellergal-S® *see* Belladonna, Phenobarbital, and Ergotamine Tartrate *on previous page*

Beloc® *see* Metoprolol *on page 400*

Bel-Phen-Ergot S® *see* Belladonna, Phenobarbital, and Ergotamine Tartrate *on previous page*

Bemote® *see* Dicyclomine *on page 194*

Benadryl® Decongestant Allergy Tablet [OTC] *see* Diphenhydramine and Pseudoephedrine *on page 207*

Benadryl® Injection *see* Diphenhydramine *on page 205*

Benadryl® Oral [OTC] *see* Diphenhydramine *on page 205*

Benadryl® Topical *see* Diphenhydramine *on page 205*

Ben-Allergin-50® Injection *see* Diphenhydramine *on page 205*

Benazepril (ben AY ze pril)

U.S. Brand Names Lotensin®

Therapeutic Category Angiotensin-Converting Enzyme (ACE) Inhibitors

Use Treatment of hypertension, either alone or in combination with other antihypertensive agents

Usual Dosage Adults: Oral: 20-40 mg/day as a single dose or 2 divided doses; maximum daily dose: 80 mg

Mechanism of Action Competitive inhibition of angiotensin I being converted to angiotensin II, a potent vasoconstrictor, through the angiotensin I-converting enzyme (ACE) activity, with resultant lower levels of angiotensin II which causes an increase in plasma renin activity and a reduction in aldosterone secretion

Pharmacodynamics/kinetics

Reduction in plasma angiotensin-converting enzyme activity: Oral:
   Peak effect: 1-2 hours after administration of 2-20 mg dose
   Duration of action: >90% inhibition for 24 hours has been observed after 5-20 mg dose
Reduction in blood pressure:
   Peak effect after single oral dose: 2-6 hours
   Maximum response With continuous therapy: 2 weeks
Absorption: Rapid (37% of each oral dose); food does not alter significantly; metabolite (benazeprilat) itself unsuitable for oral administration due to poor absorption
Metabolism: Rapid and extensive in the liver to its active metabolite, benazeprilat, via enzymatic hydrolysis
Half-life:
   Parent drug: 0.6 hour
   Metabolite elimination: 22 hours (from 24 hours after dosing onward)
   Metabolite: 1.5-2 hours after fasting or 2-4 hours after a meal
Time to peak: 1-1.5 hours (unchanged parent drug)

Signs and Symptoms of Acute Intoxication Mild hypotension has been the only toxic effect seen with acute overdose. Bradycardia may also occur; hyperkalemia occurs even with therapeutic doses, especially in patients with renal insufficiency and those taking NSAIDs.

When to Transport to Hospital Transport any pediatric exposure, any symptomatic patient, or any ingestion exceeding 100 mg

(Continued)

Benazepril *(Continued)*

Overdosage/Treatment Following initiation of essential overdose management, toxic symptom treatment and supportive treatment should be initiated. Hypotension usually responds to I.V. fluids or Trendelenburg positioning.

Warnings/Precautions Use with caution in patients with collagen vascular disease, hypovolemia, valvular stenosis, hyperkalemia, recent anesthesia; modify dosage in patients with renal impairment (especially renal artery stenosis), severe congestive heart failure, or with coadministered diuretic therapy; experience in children is limited; severe hypotension may occur in patients who are sodium and/or volume depleted; initiate lower doses and monitor closely when starting therapy in these patients

Adverse Reactions 1% to 10%:

Central nervous system: Headache, dizziness, fatigue, somnolence, postural dizziness

Gastrointestinal: Nausea

Respiratory: Transient cough

Drug Interactions See table.

Drug-Drug Interactions With ACEIs

Precipitant Drug	Drug (Category) and Effect	Description
Antacids	ACE Inhibitors: decreased	Decreased bioavailability of ACEIs. May be more likely with captopril. Separate administration times by 1-2 hours.
NSAIDs (indomethacin)	ACEIs: decreased	Reduced hypotensive effects of ACEIs. More prominent in low renin or volume dependent hypertensive patients.
Phenothiazines	ACEIs: increased	Pharmacologic effects of ACEIs may be increased.
ACEIs	Allopurinol: increased	Higher risk of hypersensitivity reaction possible when given concurrently. Three case reports of Stevens-Johnson syndrome with captopril.
ACEIs	Digoxin: increased	Increased plasma digoxin levels.
ACEIs	Lithium: increased	Increased serum lithium levels and symptoms of toxicity may occur.
ACEIs	Potassium preps/potassium sparing diuretics increased	Coadministration may result in elevated potassium levels.

Dosage Forms Tablet, as hydrochloride: 5 mg, 10 mg, 20 mg, 40 mg

Specific References

Waeber G, Fasanella d'Amore TF, Nussberger J, et al, "Effect on Blood Pressure and the Renin-Angiotensin System of Repeated Doses of the Converting Enzyme Inhibitor CGS 14824 A," *Eur J Clin Pharmacol*, 1987, 31(6):643-6.

Benazepril and Hydrochlorothiazide

(ben AY ze pril & hye droe klor oh THYE a zide)

U.S. Brand Names Lotensin HCT®

Therapeutic Category Antihypertensive, Combination

Dosage Forms Tablet: Benazepril 5 mg and hydrochlorothiazide 6.25 mg; benazepril 10 mg and hydrochlorothiazide 12.5 mg; benazepril 20 mg and hydrochlorothiazide 12.5 mg; benazepril 20 mg and hydrochlorothiazide 25 mg

Benozil® *see* Flurazepam *on page 256*

Bentyl® Hydrochloride *see* Dicyclomine *on page 194*

Bentylol® *see* Dicyclomine *on page 194*

Benylin® Cough Syrup [OTC] *see* Diphenhydramine *on page 205*

Benylin DM® [OTC] *see* Dextromethorphan *on page 187*

Benylin® Expectorant [OTC] *see* Guaifenesin and Dextromethorphan *on page 271*

Benylin® Pediatric [OTC] *see* Dextromethorphan *on page 187*

Benzamide *see* Diethyltoluamide *on page 197*

Benzedrex® [OTC] *see* Propylhexedrine *on page 513*

Benzene

Related Information

Gasoline *on page 264*

Synonyms (6)-Annulene; Carbon Oil; Mineral Naphtha; Phene; Phenyl Hydride

UN Number 1114

Commonly Found In Industrial solvent, gasoline (0.81% to 1.35%, higher percentage in Europe)

U.S. Brand Names Polystream®

Abuse Potential Yes

Impairment Potential Yes

Use In lacquers, manufacture of dyes, oil cloths, varnishes

Mechanism of Toxic Action Hematotoxicity, CNS depression, leukemogenic

Toxicodynamics/kinetics

Absorption:

Inhalation: Rapid (70% to 80% within first 5 minutes)

Oral: 90% to 97% of dose in rodent models

Dermal: <1%; absorption rate: 0.4 mg/cm^2/hour

Metabolism: Hepatic via cytochrome P-450-dependent mixed function oxidase through two detoxification pathways: 1) via glutathione to mercapturic acid, and 2) through sulfate/glucuronide conjugation. Hematotoxic metabolites include hydroquinone, phenol, muconic dialdehyde, and catechol.

Half-life: 8 hours

Elimination: Renal (<1%) and by inhalation (16% to 42%); through dermal absorption as much as 30% can be excreted through the kidneys as phenol. Oral ingestion (rabbit model), 43% was eliminated through the lungs (1.5% as carbon dioxide), with urinary excretion accounting for 33%.

Signs and Symptoms of Acute Intoxication Cough, hoarseness, aspiration, dementia, blistering, headache, coma, seizures, dizziness, hematuria, ataxia, mydriasis, leukopenia, paresthesia, ototoxicity, tinnitus

When to Transport to Hospital Transport any ingestion or significant inhalation exposure

Overdosage/Treatment Supportive therapy: Move patient to fresh air; give 100% humidified oxygen; avoid epinephrine; ingestion - basic poison management; diazepam and/or phenytoin may be helpful in controlling seizures; indomethacin has been demonstrated to decrease myelotoxicity in rodent models but human data is lacking

Adverse Reactions

Cardiovascular: Cardiac toxicity

Central nervous system: CNS depression, euphoria

Gastrointestinal: Feces discoloration (black), burning sensation of mucous membranes

Hematologic: Leukemia usually after chronic exposure, aplastic anemia, neutropenia, megaloblastic anemia, agranulocytosis, malignant lymphoma

Hepatic: Hepatotoxicity

Respiratory: Bronchial irritation, pulmonary edema

(Continued)

Benzene *(Continued)*

Reference Range Urine phenol level >10 mg/L, blood benzene level of 0.2 mg/L is consistent with exposure of 25 ppm

Drug Interactions Ethyl alcohol can potentiate the severity of benzene-induced hematological abnormalities

Additional Information Atmospheric half-life of benzene is ~5.6 days. In water, it is ~17 days, although the half-life of its hydroxyl radicals in water may be 8-9 months.

Benzene has been substantially reduced in automotive gasoline after 1995 (see Gasoline monograph). It has been estimated that benzene exposure to pumping gasoline at service stations is ~1 ppm; ambient median benzene levels in urban areas is ~12.6 ppb while California's median benzene level is much lower (3.3 ppb) due to stricter gasoline requirements. Biomarkers indicative for significant benzene (below 4000/mm^3), low erythrocyte counts (below 4,000,000/m^3), or elevated leukocyte alkaline phosphatase levels.

Lethal dose: 100 mL
TLV-TWA: 1 ppm
IDLH: 2000 ppm
PEL-TWA: 1-10 ppm

Specific References
U.S. Department of Health and Human Services, *Toxicological Profile for Benzene TP-92/03*, Agency for Toxic Substances and Diseases Registry, April, 1993.

Benzene Chloride *see* Chlorobenzene *on page 128*
Benzin *see* Petroleum Distillates - Naphtha *on page 469*
Benzinoform® *see* Carbon Tetrachloride *on page 113*

Benzocaine (BEN zoe kane)

Synonyms Ethyl Aminobenzoate

U.S. Brand Names Americaine® [OTC]; Anbesol® [OTC]; Anbesol® Maximum Strength [OTC]; Babee Teething® [OTC]; Benzocol® [OTC]; Benzodent® [OTC]; Chigger-Tox® [OTC]; Cylex® [OTC]; Dermoplast® [OTC]; Foille Medicated First Aid® [OTC]; Foille® [OTC]; Hurricaine®; Lanacane® [OTC]; Maximum Strength Anbesol® [OTC]; Maximum Strength Orajel® [OTC]; Mycinettes® [OTC]; Numzitdent® [OTC]; Numzit Teething® [OTC]; Orabase®-B [OTC]; Orabase®-O [OTC]; Orajel® Brace-Aid Oral Anesthetic [OTC]; Orajel® Mouth-Aid [OTC]; Orajel® Maximum Strength [OTC]; Orasept® [OTC]; Orasol® [OTC]; Oratect® [OTC]; Rhulicaine® [OTC]; Rid-A-Pain® [OTC]; Slim-Mint® [OTC]; Solarcaine® [OTC]; Spec-T® [OTC]; Tanac® [OTC]; Unguentine® [OTC]; Vicks Children's Chloraseptic® [OTC]; Vicks Chloraseptic® Sore Throat [OTC]; ZilaDent® [OTC]

Therapeutic Category Local Anesthetic

Use Temporary relief of pain associated with local anesthetic for pruritic dermatosis, pruritus, minor burns, acute congestive and serious otitis media, swimmer's ear, otitis externa, toothache, minor sore throat pain, canker sores, hemorrhoids, rectal fissures, anesthetic lubricant for passage of catheters and endoscopic tubes; nonprescription diet aide

Usual Dosage
Children and Adults:
Mucous membranes: Dosage varies depending on area to be anesthetized and vascularity of tissues
Oral mouth/throat preparations: Do not administer for >2 days or in children <2 years of age, unless directed by a physician; refer to specific package labeling
Topical: Apply to affected area as needed

Adults: Nonprescription diet aid: 6-15 mg just prior to food consumption, not to exceed 45 mg/day

Mechanism of Action Ester local anesthetic blocks both the initiation and conduction of nerve impulses by decreasing the neuronal membrane's permeability to sodium ions, which results in inhibition of depolarization with resultant blockade of conduction

Pharmacodynamics/kinetics

Absorption: Topical: Poorly absorbed after administration to intact skin, but well absorbed from mucous membranes and traumatized skin

Metabolism: Hydrolyzed in the plasma and, to a lesser extent, the liver by cholinesterase

Signs and Symptoms of Acute Intoxication Methemoglobinemia has been reported with benzocaine in oral overdose

When to Transport to Hospital Transport any pediatric (<6 years of age) ingestion over 100 mg/kg or any patient with facial swelling or cardiopulmonary symptoms

Warnings/Precautions Not intended for use when infections are present

Adverse Reactions Dose-related and may result in high plasma levels

1% to 10%:

Dermatologic: Angioedema, contact dermatitis

Local: Burning, stinging

Dosage Forms

Topical for mucous membranes:

Gel: 6% (7.5 g); 20% (2.5 g, 3.75 g, 7.5 g, 30 g)

Liquid: 20% (3.75 mL, 9 mL, 13.3 mL, 30 mL)

Topical for skin disorders:

Aerosol, external use: 5% (92 mL, 105 g); 20% (82.5 mL, 90 mL, 92 mL, 150 mL)

Cream: (30 g, 60 g); 5% (30 g, 1 lb); 6% (28.4 g)

Lotion: (120 mL); 8% (90 mL)

Ointment: 5% (3.5 g, 28 g)

Spray: 5% (97.5 mL); 20% (20 g, 60 g, 120 g, 13.3 mL, 120 mL)

Mouth/throat preparations:

Cream: 5% (10 g)

Gel: 6.3% (7.5 g); 7.5% (7.2 g, 9.45 g, 14.1 g); 10% (6 g, 9.45 g, 10 g, 15 g); 15% (10.5 g); 20% (9.45 g, 14.1 g)

Liquid: (3.7 mL); 5% (8.8 mL); 6.3% (9 mL, 22 mL, 14.79 mL); 10% (13 mL); 20% (13.3 mL)

Lotion: 0.2% (15 mL); 2.5% (15 mL)

Lozenges: 5 mg, 6 mg, 10 mg, 15 mg

Ointment: 20% (30 g)

Paste: 20% (5 g, 15 g)

Nonprescription diet aid:

Candy: 6 mg

Gum: 6 mg

Specific References

Bachmann P, Berthier JC, Storme B, et al, "Methemoglobinemia From Ingestion of Benzocaine. A Case of Pediatric Intoxication," *J Toxicol Clin Exp*, 1986, 6(2):123-8.

Benzocol® [OTC] *see* Benzocaine *on previous page*
Benzodent® [OTC] *see* Benzocaine *on previous page*

Benzodiazepines, Qualitative, Urine

Synonyms Tranquilizers (Valium®, Librium®, etc)

Use Drug abuse evaluation; toxicity assessment

(Continued)

Benzodiazepines, Qualitative, Urine *(Continued)*

Reference Range None present unless prescribed. When used as drug-of-abuse screen, negative (less than cutoff).

Additional Information The benzodiazepines are a class of chemically-related central nervous system depressants used as sedative-hypnotics to treat sleep disorders, anxiety, alcohol withdrawal, and seizure disorders. The drug class in low doses can cause sedation, drowsiness, blurred vision, fatigue, mental depression, and loss of coordination. In higher doses or used chronically, they can cause confusion, slurred speech, hypotension, and diminished reflexes. Chronic use may produce a physical dependence and a withdrawal syndrome which can last for weeks. Urine should be screened for benzodiazepines in suspected overdose cases, or as part of an abused drug program. Immunoassay screens detect a broad range of drugs and their metabolites in this class using either oxazepam or nordiazepam as positive controls. Using the latter, the test is more specific and more sensitive for detecting flurazepam. Positive screen results (usually >300 ng/mL of urine metabolites) should be confirmed by an alternate technique. High concentrations of fenoprofen, flurbiprofen, indomethacin, ketoprofen, and tolmetin may give a false-positive result by a TDx assay. Oxaprozine may cause false-positive urine benzodiazepine result by immunoassay. Flunitrazepam is detected in urine by GC/MS but not by EMIT assay techniques. Sertraline may cause a false-positive urinary benzodiazepine assay using the original cloned enzyme donor immunoassay system.

Specific References

Boussairi A, Dupeyron JP, Hernandez B, et al, "Urine Benzodiazepines Screening of Involuntarily Drugged and Robbed or Raped Patients," *J Toxicol Clin Toxicol*, 1996, 34(6):721-4.

Benzphetamine (benz FET a meen)

Related Information

Controlled Substances - Uses and Effects *on page 741*

U.S. Brand Names Didrex®

Therapeutic Category Anorexiant

Abuse Potential Yes

Impairment Potential Yes

Use Short-term adjunct in exogenous obesity

Usual Dosage Adults: Oral: 25-50 mg 2-3 times/day, preferably twice daily, midmorning and midafternoon; maximum dose: 50 mg 3 times/day

Mechanism of Action Noncatechol sympathomimetic amines with pharmacologic actions similar to ephedrine; require breakdown by monoamine oxidase for inactivation; produce central nervous system and respiratory stimulation, a pressor response, mydriasis, bronchodilation, and contraction of the urinary sphincter; thought to have a direct effect on both alpha- and beta-receptor sites in the peripheral system, as well as release stores of norepinephrine in adrenergic nerve terminals; central nervous system action is thought to occur in the cerebral cortex and reticular-activating system; anorexigenic effect is probably secondary to the CNS-stimulating effect; the site of action is probably the hypothalamic feeding center

When to Transport to Hospital Transport any pediatric exposure, any patient with cardiopulmonary or central nervous system symptoms, or any patient with a fever

Warnings/Precautions Cardiovascular disease, nephritis, angina pectoris, hypertension, glaucoma, patients with a history of drug abuse

Adverse Reactions

>10%:

Cardiovascular: Arrhythmia

Central nervous system: False feeling of well being, nervousness, restlessness, insomnia

1% to 10%:

Cardiovascular: Hypertension,

Central nervous system: Mood or mental changes, dizziness, lightheadedness, headache, xerostomia

Endocrine & metabolic: changes in libido

Gastrointestinal: diarrhea, nausea, vomiting, stomach cramps, constipation, anorexia, weight loss

Ocular: Blurred vision

Miscellaneous: Increased diaphoresis

Dosage Forms Tablet, as hydrochloride: 25 mg, 50 mg

Benztropine (BENZ troe peen)

U.S. Brand Names Cogentin®

Canadian Brand Names PMS-Benztropine®

Therapeutic Category Anticholinergic Agent; Anti-Parkinson's Agent

Use Adjunctive treatment of Parkinson's disease; also used in treatment of drug-induced extrapyramidal effects (except tardive dyskinesia) and acute dystonic reactions

Usual Dosage Use in children <3 years of age should be reserved for life-threatening emergencies

Drug-induced extrapyramidal reaction: Oral, I.M., I.V.:

Children >3 years: 0.02-0.05 mg/kg/dose 1-2 times/day

Adults: 1-4 mg/dose 1-2 times/day

Acute dystonia: Adults: I.M., I.V.: 1-2 mg

Parkinsonism: Oral:

Adults: 0.5-6 mg/day in 1-2 divided doses; if one dose is greater, administer at bedtime; titrate dose in 0.5 mg increments at 5- to 6-day intervals

Elderly: Initial: 0.5 mg once or twice daily; increase by 0.5 mg as needed at 5-6 days; maximum: 6 mg/day

Mechanism of Action Thought to partially block striatal cholinergic receptors to help balance cholinergic and dopaminergic activity

Pharmacodynamics/kinetics

Onset of action:

Oral: Within 1 hour

Parenteral: Within 15 minutes

Duration of action: 6-48 hours (wide range)

Signs and Symptoms of Acute Intoxication CNS depression, confusion, nervousness, hallucinations, dizziness, blurred vision, nausea, vomiting, hyperthermia

When to Transport to Hospital Transport any pediatric ingestion over 0.1 mg/kg or any adult symptomatic patient

Warnings/Precautions Use with caution in hot weather or during exercise. Elderly patients frequently develop increased sensitivity and require strict dosage regulation - side effects may be more severe in elderly patients with atherosclerotic changes. Use with caution in patients with tachycardia, cardiac arrhythmias, hypertension, hypotension, prostatic hypertrophy (especially in the elderly) or any tendency toward urinary retention, liver or kidney disorders and obstructive disease of the GI or GU tract. When given in large doses or to susceptible patients, may cause weakness and inability to move particular muscle groups.

Adverse Reactions

>10%:

Dermatologic: Dry skin

Gastrointestinal: Constipation, dry throat, xerostomia

(Continued)

Benztropine *(Continued)*

Respiratory: Dry nose
Miscellaneous: Diaphoresis (decreased)
1% to 10%:
Dermatologic: Increased sensitivity to light
Endocrine & metabolic: Decreased flow of breast milk
Gastrointestinal: Dysphagia

Drug Interactions
Decreased effect: May increase gastric degradation of levodopa and decrease
the amount of levodopa absorbed by delaying gastric emptying - the opposite
may be true for digoxin
Increased toxicity: Central anticholinergic syndrome can occur when administered with narcotic analgesics, phenothiazines and other antipsychotics,
tricyclic antidepressants, quinidine and some other antiarrhythmics, and antihistamines

Dosage Forms
Benztropine mesylate:
Injection: 1 mg/mL (2 mL)
Tablet: 0.5 mg, 1 mg, 2 mg

Specific References
Rosano TG, Meola JM, Wolf BC, et al, "Benztropine Identification and Quantitation in a Suicidal Overdose," *J Anal Toxicol*, 1994, 18(6):348-53.

Bepridil *(BE pri dil)*

U.S. Brand Names Vascor®
Canadian Brand Names Bapadin®
Therapeutic Category Calcium Channel Blocker
Use Treatment of chronic stable angina; due to side effect profile, reserve for
patients who have been intolerant of other antianginal therapy; bepridil may be
used alone or in combination with nitrates or beta-blockers
Usual Dosage Adults: Oral: Initial: 200 mg/day, then adjust dose at 10-day
intervals until optimal response is achieved; maximum daily dose: 400 mg
Mechanism of Action Bepridil, a type 4 calcium antagonist, possesses characteristics of the traditional calcium antagonists, inhibiting calcium ion from
entering the "slow channels" or select voltage-sensitive areas of vascular
smooth muscle and myocardium during depolarization and producing a relaxation of coronary vascular smooth muscle and coronary vasodilation. However,
bepridil may also inhibit fast sodium channels (inward), which may account for
some of its side effects (eg, arrhythmias); a direct bradycardia effect of bepridil
has been postulated via direct action on the S-A node.

Pharmacodynamics/kinetics
Onset of action: 1 hour
Absorption: Oral: 100%
Metabolism: Hepatic
Bioavailability: 60%
Half-life: 24 hours
Time to peak: 2-3 hours

Signs and Symptoms of Acute Intoxication The primary cardiac symptoms
of calcium blocker overdose includes hypotension and bradycardia. The hypotension is caused by peripheral vasodilation, myocardial depression, and bradycardia. Bradycardia results from sinus bradycardia, second- or third-degree
atrioventricular block, or sinus arrest with junctional rhythm. Intraventricular
conduction is usually not affected

The noncardiac symptoms include confusion, stupor, nausea, vomiting, metabolic acidosis and hyperglycemia

When to Transport to Hospital Transport any symptomatic patient

Warnings/Precautions Use with great caution in patients with history of serious ventricular arrhythmias, IHSS, congenital Q-T interval prolongation, or other drugs that prolong Q-T interval; reserve for patients in whom other antianginals have failed. Carefully titrate dosages for patients with impaired renal or hepatic function; use caution when treating patients with congestive heart failure, sick-sinus syndrome, severe left ventricular dysfunction, hypertrophic cardiomyopathy (especially obstructive), concomitant therapy with beta-blockers or digoxin, edema, or increased intracranial pressure with cranial tumors; do not abruptly withdraw (may cause chest pain); elderly may experience hypotension and constipation more readily.

Adverse Reactions

>10%:

Central nervous system: Dizziness, headache

Gastrointestinal: Nausea, dyspepsia, abdominal pain, GI distress

Neuromuscular & skeletal: Weakness

1% to 10%:

Cardiovascular: Bradycardia, palpitations

Central nervous system: Nervousness

Gastrointestinal: Diarrhea, anorexia, xerostomia

Miscellaneous: Flu syndrome

Reference Range 1-2 ng/mL

Drug Interactions Increased toxicity/effect/levels:

Bepridil and cyclosporine may increase cyclosporine levels (other calcium channel blockers have been shown to interact)

Bepridil and digitalis glycoside may increase digitalis glycoside levels

Dosage Forms Tablet, as hydrochloride: 200 mg, 300 mg, 400 mg

Additional Information Although there is some initial data which may show increased risk of myocardial infarction following treatment of hypertension with calcium antagonists, controlled trials (eg, ALL-HAT) are ongoing to examine the long-term effects of not only calcium antagonists but other antihypertensives in preventing heart disease. Until these studies are completed, patients taking calcium antagonists should be encouraged to continue with prescribed antihypertensive regimens, although a switch from high-dose, short-acting agents to sustained release products may be warranted. It is also generally agreed that calcium antagonists should be avoided as the primary treatment for hypertension unless diuretics or beta-blockers are contraindicated and for the primary treatment of angina following acute myocardial infarction.

Specific References

Viallon A, Page Y, Lafond P, et al, "Bepridil and Torsade de Pointes: Are the Precautions of Use Respected?" *Therapie*, 1994, 49(5):431-4.

Beprolo® *see* Metoprolol *on page 400*

Bercema *see* Methyl Bromide *on page 393*

Berkolol® *see* Propranolol *on page 510*

Berkomine® *see* Imipramine *on page 309*

Bertholite *see* Chlorine *on page 125*

Bespar® *see* Buspirone *on page 91*

Betadren® *see* Pindolol *on page 488*

Betaloc® *see* Metoprolol *on page 400*

Betapace® *see* Sotalol *on page 543*

Beta-Subunit Human Chorionic Gonadotropin, Urine or Serum *see* Pregnancy Test *on page 499*

Betaxolol (be TAKS oh lol)

U.S. Brand Names Betoptic®; Betoptic® S; Kerlone®

Therapeutic Category Beta-Adrenergic Blocker

Use Treatment of chronic open-angle glaucoma, ocular hypertension; management of hypertension

Usual Dosage Adults:

Ophthalmic: Instill 1 drop twice daily

Oral: 10 mg/day; may increase dose to 20 mg/day after 7-14 days if desired response is not achieved; initial dose in elderly patients: 5 mg/day

Mechanism of Action Competitively blocks beta$_1$-receptors, with little or no effect on beta$_2$-receptors; lipophilic; no membrane stabilizing effect

Pharmacodynamics/kinetics

Onset of action:

Ophthalmic: Within 30-60 minutes with maximal effects occurring within 2 hours

Oral: Blood pressure significantly decreases within 3 hours

Duration: Oral: 25 hours

Metabolism: To multiple metabolites in the liver

Bioavailability: 75%

Half-life: 12-22 hours

Time to peak serum concentration: Ophthalmic solution or suspension: 2 hours

Signs and Symptoms of Acute Intoxication Bradycardia, photophobia, abdominal pain, depression, ataxia, night terrors, hypotension

When to Transport to Hospital Transport any pediatric exposure or any symptomatic patient

Warnings/Precautions Use with caution in patients with diabetes mellitus, asthma, cardiac failure

Adverse Reactions 1% to 10%:

Cardiovascular: Bradycardia, palpitations, edema, congestive heart failure

Central nervous system: Dizziness, fatigue, lethargy, headache

Dermatologic: Erythema, itching

Ocular: Mild ocular stinging and discomfort, tearing, photophobia, decreased corneal sensitivity, keratitis

Miscellaneous: Cold extremities

Reference Range Oral dose of 20 mg produces a level of 42.6 ng/mL 4-6 hours after ingestion; postmortem blood level of 36,000 mcg/mL reported in a betaxolol-poisoned fatality

Drug Interactions

Ophthalmic: Topical miotics, topical dipivefrin, topical epinephrine, systemic chronic anhydrous inhibitors, systemic beta-blockers, reserpine

Systemic: Other hypotensive agents, sympathomimetics, lidocaine, verapamil

Dosage Forms

Betaxolol hydrochloride:

Solution, ophthalmic (Betoptic®): 0.5% (2.5 mL, 5 mL, 10 mL)

Suspension, ophthalmic (Betoptic® S): 0.25% (2.5 mL, 10 mL, 15 mL)

Tablet (Kerlone®): 10 mg, 20 mg

Additional Information Because of betaxolol's low lipid solubility, it is less likely to enter the CNS, decreasing the likelihood of CNS side effects

Specific References

Berthault F, Kintz P, Tracqui A, et al, "A Fatal Case of Betaxolol Poisoning," *J Anal Toxicol*, 1997, 21:228-31.

Betimol® Ophthalmic *see* Timolol *on page 583*

Betoptic® *see* Betaxolol *on this page*

Betoptic® S *see* Betaxolol *on this page*

Bexophene® *see* Propoxyphene and Aspirin *on page 510*

Bikalm® *see* Zolpidem *on page 621*

Biohist®-LA *see* Carbinoxamine and Pseudoephedrine *on page 107*

Biomioran® *see* Chlorzoxazone *on page 145*

Biomox® *see* Amoxicillin *on page 45*

Bionic *see* Niacin *on page 428*

Biotonin® *see* Tryptophan *on page 602*

Biperiden (bye PER i den)

U.S. Brand Names Akineton®; Retard®

Therapeutic Category Anticholinergic Agent; Anti-Parkinson's Agent

Use Treatment of all forms of parkinsonism including drug-induced type (extrapyramidal symptoms)

Usual Dosage Adults: Oral:
Parkinsonism: 2 mg 3-4 times/day
Extrapyramidal: 2 mg 1-3 times/day

Mechanism of Action Biperiden is a weak anticholinergic agent. The beneficial effects in Parkinson's disease and neuroleptic-induced extrapyramidal reactions are believed to be due to the inhibition of striatal cholinergic receptors.

Pharmacodynamics/kinetics
Distribution: V_d: 24 L/kg
Bioavailability: 29%
Half-life: 18.4-24.3 hours
Time to peak serum concentration: 1-1.5 hours

Signs and Symptoms of Acute Intoxication Mydriasis, tachycardia, hyperthermia, ileus, dry mouth, hypertension, urinary retention

When to Transport to Hospital Transport any symptomatic patient or any ingestion over 0.1 mg/kg

Warnings/Precautions Use with caution in patients with angle-closure glaucoma, peptic ulcer, urinary tract obstruction, tardive dyskinesia, myasthenia gravis, cardiac arrhythmias, hyperthyroidism; some preparations contain sodium bisulfite; syrup contains alcohol

Adverse Reactions
>10%:
Dermatologic: Dry skin
Gastrointestinal: Constipation, xerostomia, dry throat
Respiratory: Dry nose
Miscellaneous: Diaphoresis (decreased)
<10%:
Cardiovascular: Hypotension (orthostatic), fibrillation (ventricular), tachycardia, palpitations
Central nervous system: Confusion, drowsiness, headache, loss of memory, ataxia, tiredness, euphoria, agitation, paranoia, delusions, visual hallucinations, cognitive dysfunction, hypothermia
Dermatologic: Skin rash
Endocrine & metabolic: Breast milk (decreased flow)
Gastrointestinal: Dysphagia, bloated feeling, nausea, vomiting
Genitourinary: Dysuria
Neuromuscular & skeletal: Weakness
Ocular: Intraocular pain (increased), blurred vision, sensitivity to light (increased)

Reference Range After a 4 mg oral dose, peak plasma levels range from 3.9-6.3 ng/mL

Drug Interactions
Decreased effect of levodopa (↓ absorption); can lower serum bromocriptine levels by ~30%
(Continued)

Biperiden *(Continued)*

Increased toxicity (central anticholinergic syndrome): Narcotic analgesics, phenothiazines, and other antipsychotics, tricyclic antidepressants, some antihistamines, quinidine, disopyramide

Dosage Forms

Injection, as lactate: 5 mg/mL (1 mL)

Tablet, as hydrochloride: 2 mg

Specific References

Pullen GP, Best NR, and Maguire J, "Anticholinergic Drug Abuse: A Common Problem?" *Br Med J (Clin Res Ed)*, 1984, 289(6445):612-3.

Bis(2-Chloroethyl) Sulfide *see* Mustard Gas *on page 414*

Bisobloc® *see* Bisoprolol *on this page*

Bisoprolol *(bis OH proe lol)*

U.S. Brand Names Bisobloc®; Concor®; Detensiel®; Emconcor®; Emcor®; Euradal®; Monocor®; Soprol®; Zebeta®

Therapeutic Category Beta-Adrenergic Blocker

Use Treatment of hypertension, alone or in combination with other agents

Usual Dosage Adults: Oral: 5 mg once daily, may be increased to 10 mg, and then up to 20 mg once daily, if necessary; may be given without regard to meals

Mechanism of Action Selective inhibitor of beta$_1$-adrenergic receptors; competitively blocks beta$_1$-receptors, with little or no effect on beta$_2$-receptors at doses <10 mg

Pharmacodynamics/kinetics

Absorption: Rapid and almost complete from gastrointestinal tract (90%)

Metabolism: Extensively (50%) metabolized in the liver

Half-life: 9-13 hours; 21 hours in patients with liver disease

Time to peak serum concentration: 1.7-3 hours

Signs and Symptoms of Acute Intoxication Bradycardia, hypotension, wheezing, ataxia, night terrors, cough, insomnia, impotence, hypoglycemia, cold extremities

When to Transport to Hospital Transport any pediatric ingestion or any symptomatic patient

Warnings/Precautions Use with caution in patients with inadequate myocardial function; acute withdrawal may exacerbate symptoms; use with caution in patients undergoing anesthesia and in those with bronchospastic disease, hyperthyroidism, and impaired hepatic function

Adverse Reactions

>10%: Central nervous system: Fatigue, lethargy

1% to 10%:

Central nervous system: Headache, dizziness, insomnia, confusion, depression, abnormal dreams

Cardiovascular: Hypotension, chest pain, heart failure, Raynaud's phenomenon, heart block, edema, bradycardia

Dermatologic: Rash

Gastrointestinal: Constipation, diarrhea, dyspepsia, nausea, flatulence, anorexia

Genitourinary: Polyuria, impotence, urinary retention

Neuromuscular & skeletal: Arthralgia, myalgia

Ocular: Abnormal vision

Respiratory: Dyspnea, rhinitis, cough

Drug Interactions

Decreased effect/levels with barbiturates, rifampin, sulfinpyrazone

Increased effect/toxicity/levels of and with flecainide; increased effect of ritodrine; bradycardia with amiodarone

Dosage Forms Tablet, as fumarate: 5 mg, 10 mg

Specific References

Harry P, Lannehoa Y, Turcant A, et al, "Massive Poisoning With The β-Blocker Bisoprolol and Hypoglycemia," *Vet Hum Toxicol*, 1996, 38(6):463.

Bittersweet Nightshade *see* Deadly Nightshade *on page 178*

Bitter Wormwood *see* Wormwood *on page 617*

Black Widow Spider

Scientific Name *Latrodectus mactans*

Mechanism of Toxic Action Envenomation (neurotoxin and alpha-latrotoxin)

Signs and Symptoms of Acute Intoxication Initial bite may be sharply painful or unrecognized; possible papule or punctum on exam with surrounding skin slightly erythematous and indurated; within 30-60 minutes of the bite, however, involuntary spasm and rigidity affect the large muscle groups of the abdomen and limbs; fever (10% to 15%), tachypnea, tachycardia, ptosis, dyspnea, hyperreflexia, headaches (5% to 25%), nausea, vomiting, abdominal pain (15% to 50%), hypersalivation

When to Transport to Hospital Transport any symptomatic patient or any suspected exposure

Overdosage/Treatment

Decontamination: Wound care including tetanus prophylaxis; pain and muscle spasm may be managed initially with calcium gluconate 10% solution at 10 mL/dose; may start calcium infusion

Antivenin is available and should be reserved for cases involving respiratory arrest, seizures, uncontrolled hypertension, or pregnancy; usual therapeutic dose: I.V. infusion: 1-2 vials

Supportive therapy: Alternative muscle relaxants including methocarbamol or benzodiazepines

Adverse Reactions

Cardiovascular: Hypertension

Dermatologic: Target lesions, erythema, edema, toxic epidermal necrolysis, urticarial rash

Genitourinary: Priapism, urinary retention

Hematologic: Leukocytosis

Neuromuscular & skeletal: Fasciculations, muscle weakness

Ocular: Ptosis

Renal: Pyuria, proteinuria, microscopic hematuria

Respiratory: Respiratory arrest

Miscellaneous: Lymphadenopathy, diaphoresis

Additional Information Female responsible for all envenomations

Range: Found throughout the U.S.; web found in corners of buildings, gardens, and fields

Specific References

Woestman R, Perkin R, and Van Stralen D, "The Black Widow: Is She Deadly to Children?" *Pediatr Emerg Care*, 1996, 12(5):360-4.

Bladder Pod *see* Indian Tobacco *on page 312*

Blocadren® Oral *see* Timolol *on page 583*

Blox® *see* Loperamide *on page 349*

Blue Blindweed *see* Deadly Nightshade *on page 178*

Blue Nightshade *see* Deadly Nightshade *on page 178*

Blue Star *see* Morning Glory *on page 409*

Body Louse *see* Lice *on page 343*

Bonine® [OTC] *see* Meclizine *on page 361*

Bonoform® see Tetrachloroethane *on page 566*
Boracic Acid see Boric Acid *on this page*

Borates

Synonyms Boric Anhydride; Boron Oxide; Boron Sesquioxide; Boron Trioxide; Magnesium Perborate; Sodium Biborate; Sodium Borate; Sodium Metaborate; Sodium Perborate; Sodium Pyroborate; Sodium Tetraborate

UN Number 1458; 2692; 1008

U.S. Brand Names Borax®; Dobill's Solution®

Use Various; used in herbicides; common ingredient of medicated powders, skin lotions, mouthwashes, toothpastes, powders, water softeners, topical astringents and antiseptics; also used in making glass fibers, enamels, glazes, fire-resistant materials, pigments, paints, catalysts, photographic agents, and insecticides; found in rodent and ant poisons

Toxicodynamics/kinetics
Absorption: Through gastrointestinal tract, mucous membranes, and abraded and denuded skin
Half-life: 5-27 hours
Peak CNS concentration: In 3 hours

Signs and Symptoms of Acute Intoxication Toxicity may be delayed for hours; gastrointestinal upset and vomiting (emesis has been described as blue-green), and retching, CNS depression, restlessness, irritability, and seizures occur from chronic exposure; death results from dehydration, shock, circulatory collapse and renal failure. Renal failure, oliguria, anuria occur several days after exposure; metabolic acidosis may occur; erythematous rash, usually on buttocks and scrotum, with desquamation occurring where rash is persistent and mucous membranes, perianal and anal surfaces. Alopecia totalis can occur with acute or chronic poisoning.

When to Transport to Hospital Transport any pediatric exposure (<6 years of age) over 200 mg/kg or any symptomatic patient

Overdosage/Treatment Decontamination:
Dermal: Wash skin with soap and water
Ocular: Irrigate with saline

Warnings/Precautions High affinity for brain, liver, and kidney; damage to tissues, especially renal tubular epithelium may be irreversible

Adverse Reactions
Central nervous system: Fever, hyperthermia
Miscellaneous: Toxic shock-like syndrome

Reference Range Normal: 0.0-0.72 mg/dL in children; 0.0-0.2 mg/dL in adults; levels do not seem to correlate well with severity of symptoms; levels >40 mg/dL associated with fatality in infants

Additional Information How supplied:
Boric acid: White powder or crystalline solid
Sodium tetraborate anhydrous: Light gray and odorless
Sodium tetraborate decahydrate and pentahydrate: White, odorless, crystalline solids

Specific References
Siegel E and Wason S, "Boric Acid Toxicity," *Pediatr Clin North Am*, 1986, 33(2):363-7.

Borax® see Borates *on this page*

Boric Acid (BOR ik AS id)

Synonyms Boracic Acid; Orthoboric Acid
U.S. Brand Names Borofax® [OTC]; Boroformol®; Borsyre®; Dri-Ear® [OTC]; Komex®; Sassolite®; Swim-Ear® [OTC]; Viskos®
Therapeutic Category Pharmaceutical Aid

Use Food preservatives, emulsifiers, neutralizers, antifungal water softeners, contact lens cleaner, antiseptics, pesticides (for cockroaches)

Ophthalmic: Mild antiseptic used for inflamed eyelids

Topical ointment: Temporary relief of chapped, chafed, or dry skin, diaper rash, abrasions, minor burns, sunburn, insect bites, and other skin irritations

Usual Dosage Apply to lower eyelid 1-2 times/day

Mechanism of Action Disinfectant, astringent

Pharmacodynamics/kinetics

Absorption: Not well absorbed through intact skin; absorbed well through inflamed skin

Half-life: 12 hours

Elimination: Renal, within 96 hours of ingestion

Signs and Symptoms of Acute Intoxication Elevated liver function tests, dry skin, dermatitis, desquamation, circulatory collapse, hyperthermia, toxic epidermal necrolysis, seizures, urine discoloration (blue-green), diarrhea, cardiovascular collapse, confusion

When to Transport to Hospital Transport any ingestion over 200 mg/kg or 12 g total or any symptomatic patient

Adverse Reactions

Central nervous system: CNS stimulation followed by CNS depression, fever

Dermatologic: Erythematous skin eruptions, pruritus, alopecia, erythrodermic desquamation (2-3 days after exposure) (boiled lobster appearance)

Gastrointestinal: Gastrointestinal disturbance, vomiting, nausea, diarrhea, feces discoloration (black), feces discoloration (blue), feces discoloration (blue-green)

Hepatic: Liver function tests (elevated)

Renal: Acute tubular necrosis

Reference Range Normal boric acid levels: Children: 0.0-0.7 mg/dL; Adults: 0.0-0.2 mg/dL; levels of 2.0-15.0 mg/dL are associated with survival; levels >40.0 mg/dL are associated with lethality

Dosage Forms

Ointment:

Ophthalmic: 5% (3.5 g); 10% (3.5 g)

Topical: 5% (52.5 g); 10% (28 g)

Topical (Borofax®): 5% boric acid and lanolin (1¾ oz)

Solution, otic: 2.75% with isopropyl alcohol (30 mL)

Additional Information Not a corrosive substance

Specific References

Litovitz TL, Klein-Schwartz W, Oderda GM, et al, "Clinical Manifestations of Toxicity in a Series of 784 Boric Acid Ingestions," *Am J Emerg Med*, 1992, 10:545-7.

Boric Anhydride *see* Borates *on previous page*

Borofax® [OTC] *see* Boric Acid *on previous page*

Boroformol® *see* Boric Acid *on previous page*

Boron Oxide *see* Borates *on previous page*

Boron Sesquioxide *see* Borates *on previous page*

Boron Trioxide *see* Borates *on previous page*

Borsyre® *see* Boric Acid *on previous page*

Bosisto's® Eucalyptus Spray *see* Eucalyptus Oil *on page 241*

B&O Supprettes® *see* Belladonna and Opium *on page 66*

BQ® Tablet [OTC] *see* Chlorpheniramine, Phenylpropanolamine, and Acetaminophen *on page 137*

Brek® *see* Loperamide *on page 349*

Breonesin® [OTC] *see* Guaifenesin *on page 269*

Brethaire® *see* Terbutaline *on page 561*

Brethine® see Terbutaline on page 561

Brevital® Sodium see Methohexital on page 391

Bricanyl® see Terbutaline on page 561

Britiazim® see Diltiazem on page 201

Brofed® Elixir [OTC] see Brompheniramine and Pseudoephedrine on page 86

Bromaline® Elixir [OTC] see Brompheniramine and Phenylpropanolamine on page 85

Bromanate® DC see Brompheniramine, Phenylpropanolamine, and Codeine on page 86

Bromanate® Elixir [OTC] see Brompheniramine and Phenylpropanolamine on page 85

Bromanyl® Cough Syrup see Bromodiphenhydramine and Codeine on page 84

Bromarest® [OTC] see Brompheniramine on page 84

Bromatapp® [OTC] see Brompheniramine and Phenylpropanolamine on page 85

Brombay® [OTC] see Brompheniramine on page 84

Bromfed® Syrup [OTC] see Brompheniramine and Pseudoephedrine on page 86

Bromfed® Tablet [OTC] see Brompheniramine and Pseudoephedrine on page 86

Bromfenex® see Brompheniramine and Pseudoephedrine on page 86

Bromfenex® PD see Brompheniramine and Pseudoephedrine on page 86

Bromides (BROE mydez)

Commonly Found In Sodium, potassium, and ammonium bromide; also in multiple medications as salt form of drug; dextromethorphan hydrobromide, homatropine hydrobromide, neostigmine, potassium, propantheline, pyridostigmine, quinine hydrobromide, scopolamine hydrobromide; although this source of bromism has been rare in the U.S. since 1974.

Therapeutic Category Analgesic, Narcotic

Abuse Potential Yes

Impairment Potential Yes

Mechanism of Action Central nervous system depressant

Pharmacodynamics/kinetics

Absorption: ≥90%, can form bezoar in the GI tract

Half-life: 9-15 days

Signs and Symptoms of Acute Intoxication Vomiting, ataxia, pseudotumor cerebri, nausea, hypothyroidism, dementia, sedation, photophobia, hallucinations, gaze nystagmus, slurred speech, tremors, amnesia, mydriasis, erythema multiforme, decreased anion gap; chronic toxicity often causes acne-like rash, papilledema, gastric bezoar

When to Transport to Hospital Transport any symptomatic patient

Adverse Reactions

Central nervous system: Headache, slurred speech, hallucinations, retrograde amnesia, memory disturbance, hyperesthesia, CNS depression, depression

Dermatologic: Papules, erythematous pustular usually on legs, acneiform eruptions

Endocrine & metabolic: Hypochloremia, hypothyroidism

Gastrointestinal: Nausea, vomiting, anorexia, feces discoloration (black)

Neuromuscular & skeletal: Hypo- or areflexia, tremors, clonus

Test Interactions Causes negative anion gap: Bromide can interfere with chloride determinations on virtually all standard laboratory tests (including sequential multiple analyzers). It can also interfere with bicarbonate determinations in some analyzers.

Reference Range Therapeutic serum bromine levels: 5-50 µg/mL; symptoms of toxicity from bromides usually occur at serum bromine levels >1500 µg/mL; coma >2000 µg/mL; fatal levels >3000 µg/mL

Specific References
James LP, Farrar HC, Griebel ML, et al, "Bromism: Intoxication From a Rare Anticonvulsant Therapy," *Pediatr Emerg Care*, 1997, 13(4):268-70.

Bromocriptine (broe moe KRIP teen)

U.S. Brand Names Parlodel®

Canadian Brand Names Apo® Bromocriptine

Therapeutic Category Anti-Parkinson's Agent; Ergot Alkaloid

Use
Usually used with levodopa or levodopa/carbidopa to treat Parkinson's disease - treatment of parkinsonism in patients unresponsive or allergic to levodopa

Prolactin-secreting pituitary adenomas

Acromegaly

Amenorrhea/galactorrhea secondary to hyperprolactinemia in the absence of primary tumor

The indication for prevention of postpartum lactation has been withdrawn voluntarily by Sandoz Pharmaceuticals Corporation

Usual Dosage Adults: Oral:
Parkinsonism: 1.25 mg 2 times/day, increased by 2.5 mg/day in 2- to 4-week intervals (usual dose range is 30-90 mg/day in 3 divided doses), though elderly patients can usually be managed on lower doses

Hyperprolactinemia: 2.5 mg 2-3 times/day

Acromegaly: Initial: 1.25-2.5 mg increasing as necessary every 3-7 days; usual dose: 20-30 mg/day

Mechanism of Action Semisynthetic ergot alkaloid derivative with dopaminergic properties; inhibits prolactin secretion and can improve symptoms of Parkinson's disease by directly stimulating dopamine receptors in the corpus stratum

Pharmacodynamics/kinetics
Metabolism: Majority of drug metabolized in the liver
Half-life (biphasic):
Initial: 6-8 hours
Terminal: 50 hours
Time to peak serum concentration: Oral: Within 1-2 hours

Signs and Symptoms of Acute Intoxication Nausea, vomiting, hypotension

When to Transport to Hospital Transport any pediatric exposure, any symptomatic patient, or any patient with mental status changes

Overdosage/Treatment Hypotension, when unresponsive to I.V. fluids or Trendelenburg positioning, often responds to norepinephrine infusions started at 0.1-0.2 mcg/kg/minute followed by a titrated infusion

Warnings/Precautions Use with caution in patients with impaired renal or hepatic function

Adverse Reactions Incidence of adverse effects is high, especially at beginning of treatment and with dosages >20 mg/day

1% to 10%:
Cardiovascular: Hypotension, Raynaud's phenomenon
Central nervous system: Mental depression, confusion, hallucinations
Gastrointestinal: Nausea, constipation, anorexia
Neuromuscular & skeletal: Leg cramps
Respiratory: Nasal congestion

Drug Interactions
Decreased effect: Amitriptyline, butyrophenones, imipramine, methyldopa, phenothiazines, reserpine, → ↓ bromocriptine's efficacy at reducing prolactin
(Continued)

Bromocriptine (Continued)

Increased toxicity: Ergot alkaloids (↑ cardiovascular toxicity)

Dosage Forms
Bromocriptine mesylate:
Capsule: 5 mg
Tablet: 2.5 mg

Specific References
Dackis CA and Gold MS, "Bromocriptine as Treatment of Cocaine Abuse," *Lancet*, 1985, 1(8438):1151-2.

Bromodiphenhydramine and Codeine

(brome oh dye fen HYE dra meen & KOE deen)

Synonyms Codeine and Bromodiphenhydramine

U.S. Brand Names Ambenyl® Cough Syrup; Amgenal® Cough Syrup; Bromanyl® Cough Syrup; Bromotuss® w/Codeine Cough Syrup

Therapeutic Category Antihistamine/Antitussive

Abuse Potential Yes

Impairment Potential Yes

Dosage Forms Liquid: Bromodiphenhydramine hydrochloride 12.5 mg and codeine phosphate 10 mg per 5 mL

Bromomethane *see* Methyl Bromide *on page 393*

Bromotuss® w/Codeine Cough Syrup *see* Bromodiphenhydramine and Codeine *on this page*

Bromphen® [OTC] *see* Brompheniramine *on this page*

Bromphen DC® w/Codeine *see* Brompheniramine, Phenylpropanolamine, and Codeine *on page 86*

Brompheniramine (brome fen IR a meen)

Synonyms Parabromdylamine

U.S. Brand Names Bromarest® [OTC]; Brombay® [OTC]; Bromphen® [OTC]; Brotane® [OTC]; Chlorphed® [OTC]; Codimal-A®; Cophene-B®; Dehist®; Diamine T.D.® [OTC]; Dimetane® [OTC]; Dimetapp®; Histaject®; Nasahist B®; ND-Stat®; Oraminic® II; Sinusol-B®; Veltane®

Therapeutic Category Antihistamine

Use Perennial and seasonal allergic rhinitis and other allergic symptoms including rash

Usual Dosage Oral:
Children:
<6 years: 0.125 mg/kg/dose given every 6 hours; maximum: 6-8 mg/day
6-12 years: 2-4 mg every 6-8 hours; maximum: 12-16 mg/day
Adults: 4 mg every 4-6 hours or 8 mg of sustained release form every 8-12 hours or 12 mg of sustained release every 12 hours; maximum: 24 mg/day

Mechanism of Action Competes with histamine for H_1-receptor sites on effector cells in the gastrointestinal tract, blood vessels, and respiratory tract

Pharmacodynamics/kinetics
Onset of action: Begins within 15-30 minutes; maximal clinical effects seen within 3-9 hours
Duration: Varies with formulation, up to 48 hours
Absorption: Well absorbed from gastrointestinal tract after administration
Distribution: Wide throughout body
Metabolism: Extensive by the liver
Half-life: 12-34 hours
Time to peak serum concentration: Within 2-5 hours
Elimination: In urine as inactive metabolites; 2% fecal elimination

Signs and Symptoms of Acute Intoxication Dry mouth, mydriasis, agranulocytosis, neutropenia, CNS depression, flushing

When to Transport to Hospital Transport any symptomatic patient or any ingestion over 0.5 mg/kg

Overdosage/Treatment There is no specific treatment for an antihistamine overdose, however, most of its clinical toxicity is due to anticholinergic effects. Anticholinesterase inhibitors may be useful by reducing acetylcholinesterase. Anticholinesterase inhibitors include physostigmine, neostigmine, pyridostigmine and edrophonium. For anticholinergic overdose with severe life-threatening symptoms, physostigmine 1-2 mg (0.5 or 0.02 mg/kg for children) I.V., slowly may be given to reverse these effects.

Warnings/Precautions Use with caution in patients with heart disease, hypertension, thyroid disease, and asthma

Adverse Reactions
>10%:
  Central nervous system: Slight to moderate drowsiness (compared with other first generation antihistamines, brompheniramine is relatively nonsedating)
  Respiratory: Thickening of bronchial secretions
1% to 10%:
  Central nervous system: Headache, fatigue, nervousness, dizziness
  Gastrointestinal: Appetite increase, weight gain, nausea, diarrhea, abdominal pain, xerostomia
  Neuromuscular & skeletal: Arthralgia
  Respiratory: Pharyngitis

Reference Range Average steady-state concentrations: 18-22 ng/mL

Drug Interactions CNS depressants, MAO inhibitors

Dosage Forms
Brompheniramine maleate:
  Elixir: 2 mg/5 mL with 3% alcohol (120 mL, 480 mL, 4000 mL)
  Injection: 10 mg/mL (10 mL)
  Tablet: 4 mg, 8 mg, 12 mg
  Tablet, sustained release: 8 mg, 12 mg

Additional Information Causes less drowsiness than some antihistamines

Specific References
Lin CC, Kim HK, Lim J, et al, "Steady-State Bioavailability of Dexbrompheniramine and Pseudoephedrine From a Repeat-Action Combination Tablet," *J Pharm Sci*, 1985, 74(1):25-8.

Brompheniramine and Phenylephrine
(brome fen IR a meen & fen il EF rin)
U.S. Brand Names Dimetane® Decongestant Elixir [OTC]
Therapeutic Category Antihistamine/Decongestant Combination
Dosage Forms Elixir: Brompheniramine maleate 4 mg and phenylephrine hydrochloride 5 mg per 5 mL

Brompheniramine and Phenylpropanolamine
(brome fen IR a meen & fen il proe pa NOLE a meen)
Synonyms Phenylpropanolamine and Brompheniramine
U.S. Brand Names Bromaline® Elixir [OTC]; Bromanate® Elixir [OTC]; Bromatapp® [OTC]; Bromphen® Tablet [OTC]; Cold & Allergy® Elixir [OTC]; Dimaphen® Elixir [OTC]; Dimaphen® Tablets [OTC]; Dimetapp® 4-Hour Liqui-Gel Capsule [OTC]; Dimetapp® Elixir [OTC]; Dimetapp® Extentabs® [OTC]; Dimetapp® Tablet [OTC]; Genatap® Elixir [OTC]; Tamine® [OTC]; Vicks® DayQuil® Allergy Relief 4 Hour Tablet [OTC]
Therapeutic Category Antihistamine/Decongestant Combination
Abuse Potential Yes
(Continued)

Brompheniramine and Phenylpropanolamine
(Continued)
Impairment Potential Yes
Dosage Forms
    Capsule (Dimetapp® 4-Hour Liqui-Gel): Brompheniramine maleate 4 mg and phenylpropanolamine hydrochloride 25 mg
    Liquid (Bromaline®, Bromanate®, Cold & Allergy®, Dimaphen®, Dimetapp®, Genatap®): Brompheniramine maleate 2 mg and phenylpropanolamine hydrochloride 12.5 mg per 5 mL
    Tablet (Dimaphen®, Dimetapp®, Vicks® DayQuil® Allergy Relief 4 Hour): Brompheniramine maleate 4 mg and phenylpropanolamine hydrochloride 25 mg
    Tablet, sustained release: Brompheniramine maleate 12 mg and phenylpropanolamine hydrochloride 75 mg

Brompheniramine and Pseudoephedrine
(brome fen IR a meen & soo doe e FED rin)
U.S. Brand Names Brofed® Elixir [OTC]; Bromfed® Syrup [OTC]; Bromfed® Tablet [OTC]; Bromfenex®; Bromfenex® PD; Drixoral® Syrup [OTC]; Iofed®; Iofed® PD
Therapeutic Category Antihistamine/Decongestant Combination
Abuse Potential Yes
Impairment Potential Yes
Dosage Forms
    Capsule, extended release:
      Bromfenex® PD, Iofed® PD: Brompheniramine maleate 6 mg and pseudoephedrine hydrochloride 60 mg
      Bromfenex®, Iofed®: Brompheniramine maleate 12 mg and pseudoephedrine hydrochloride 120 mg
    Elixir:
      Brofed®: Brompheniramine maleate 4 mg and pseudoephedrine hydrochloride 30 mg per 5 mL
      Bromfed®: Brompheniramine maleate 2 mg and pseudoephedrine hydrochloride 30 mg per 5 mL
      Drixoral®: Brompheniramine maleate 2 mg and pseudoephedrine sulfate 30 mg per 5 mL
    Tablet (Bromfed®): Brompheniramine maleate 4 mg and pseudoephedrine hydrochloride 60 mg

Brompheniramine, Phenylpropanolamine, and Codeine
(brome fen IR a meen, fen il proe pa NOLE a meen, & KOE deen)
U.S. Brand Names Bromanate® DC; Bromphen DC® w/Codeine; Dimetane®-DC; Myphetane® DC; Poly-Histine® CS
Therapeutic Category Antihistamine/Decongestant/Antitussive
Abuse Potential Yes
Impairment Potential Yes
Dosage Forms Liquid: Brompheniramine maleate 2 mg, phenylpropanolamine hydrochloride 12.5 mg, and codeine phosphate 10 mg per 5 mL with alcohol 0.95% (480 mL)

Bromphen® Tablet [OTC] *see* Brompheniramine and Phenylpropanolamine *on previous page*

Bronchial® *see* Theophylline and Guaifenesin *on page 571*

Bronco® *see* Glyphosate *on page 269*

Bronkodyl® *see* Theophylline Salts *on page 571*

Bronocozina® *see* Zipeprol *on page 620*

Brontex® Liquid *see* Guaifenesin and Codeine *on page 271*

Brontex® Tablet *see* Guaifenesin and Codeine *on page 271*

Bronx® *see* Zipeprol *on page 620*

Brotane® [OTC] *see* Brompheniramine *on page 84*

Brown Recluse Spider

Synonyms "Fiddle Back" Spider; Violin Brown Recluse Spider

Scientific Name *Loxosceles reclusa*

Mechanism of Toxic Action Toxin has sphingomyelinase activity which has lytic action on red blood cells

Signs and Symptoms of Acute Intoxication Mild erythema and pruritus can progress to severe skin ulceration; systemic findings occur at 1-3 days and can include hypotension, severe vomiting, myalgias, myopathy, hemolysis, anemia, hemolytic anemia, dark urine, fever, nausea, thrombocytopenia; bite site may have a "halo" appearance with a small pustule surrounded by pallor; wound can become necrotic in 3 days; death may be related to disseminated intravascular coagulation or renal failure

When to Transport to Hospital Transport any suspected exposure

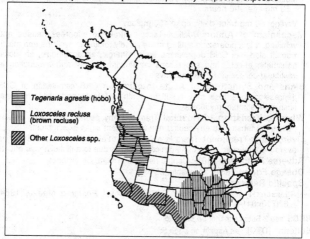

Tegenaria agrestis (hobo)

Loxosceles reclusa (brown recluse)

Other *Loxosceles* spp.

From "Necrotic Arachnidism," *MMWR Morb Mortal Wkly Rep*, 1996, 45(21):435.

Overdosage/Treatment Supportive therapy: Elevate affected limb; antihistamine may be given for pruritus; dexamethasone (4 mg I.M. 4 times/day) can be helpful if given early in the course; dapsone (50-200 mg orally divided into twice daily dosing) or colchicine (1.2 mg orally, then 0.6 mg every 2 hours for 2 days, then 0.6 mg every 4 hours for 2 days) may be helpful to avoid cutaneous necrosis; ice packs may relieve pain/heat may exacerbate pain; hyperbaric oxygen has been used (2-6 days postbite) in order to improve necrotic lesions. Hyperbaric oxygen if used within 48 hours may reduce skin necrosis. A recent rabbit study did not reveal any benefit of hyperbaric oxygen, dapsone, or cyproheptadine in the treatment of brown recluse spider envenomation. Nitropatches applied over the bite site for 12 hours may be helpful in reducing pain (Continued)

Brown Recluse Spider *(Continued)*

and skin necrosis, although it must be noted that this method is unproven and has not been formally studied.

Additional Information Bites usually occur at night; dorsal cephalothorax has characteristic fiddle-shaped marking

Range: South/Southwestern U.S., Illinois, Iowa, Ohio, not found in Pacific northwest; necrotic arachnidism is likely due to *Tegenaria agrestis* bites

Specific References

Erickson T, Hryhorczuk DO, Lipscomb JW, et al, "Brown Recluse Spider Bites in an Urban Wilderness," *J Wilderness Medicine*, 1990, 1:258-64.

Bucladin®-S Softab® *see* Buclizine *on this page*

Buclizine *(BYOO kli zeen)*

U.S. Brand Names Aphilan R®; Bucladin®-S Softab®

Therapeutic Category Antihistamine

Use Prevention and treatment of motion sickness; symptomatic treatment of vertigo; adjunctive therapy for migraine headache

Usual Dosage Adults: Oral:

Motion sickness (prophylaxis): 50 mg 30 minutes prior to traveling; may repeat 50 mg after 4-6 hours

Vertigo: 50 mg twice daily, up to 150 mg/day

Mechanism of Action Buclizine acts centrally to suppress nausea and vomiting. It is a piperazine antihistamine closely related to cyclizine and meclizine. It also has CNS depressant, anticholinergic, antispasmodic, and local anesthetic effects, and suppresses labyrinthine activity and conduction in vestibular-cerebellar nerve pathways.

Signs and Symptoms of Acute Intoxication CNS stimulation or CNS depression; overdose may result in death in infants and children; facial flushing, insomnia, mydriasis

When to Transport to Hospital Transport any pediatric exposure or any patient demonstrating any central nervous system signs or symptoms

Overdosage/Treatment There is no specific treatment for an antihistamine overdose, however, most of its clinical toxicity is due to anticholinergic effects

Adverse Reactions >10%: Central nervous system: Drowsiness

Dosage Forms Tablet, chewable: 50 mg

Specific References

Atkinson R and Appenzeller O, "Headache," *Postgrad Med J*, 1984, 60(710):841-6.

BUCS *see* 2-Butoxyethanol *on page 96*

Bufferin® [OTC] *see* Aspirin *on page 56*

Buffex® [OTC] *see* Aspirin *on page 56*

Bufotenine

Related Information

Controlled Substances - Uses and Effects *on page 741*

Synonyms Bufox® (France); Ch'an Su; Hallucinogenic Snuff

Commonly Found In Skin glands (parotid glands) of toads (*Bufo alvarius*, Colorado river toad) and *Bufo marinus* (cane toad); in the seeds and leaves of *Piptadenia peregrina* and *Piptadenia macrocarpa*; found in the Chinese preparation Yixin Wan, Kyushin, and Lu-Shen Wan; also found in the mushrooms *Amanita citrina*, *Amanita porphyria*, and *Amanita tomentella*

Abuse Potential Yes

Impairment Potential Yes

Mechanism of Toxic Action Indole alkaloid with serotonergic activity; also inhibits sodium, potassium, and muscle ATP, ACE activity in muscle similar to digoxin

Signs and Symptoms of Acute Intoxication Salivation, seizures, cardiac arrhythmias similar to digitalis toxicity, hypokalemia, dyspnea, hallucinations, mental status changes

When to Transport to Hospital Transport any symptomatic patient

Test Interactions Cross reacts to give a positive digoxin reading in immunoreactive assays; cardioactive steroids of the bufadienolide class may cross react with polyclonal digoxin immunoassays

Reference Range Serum digoxin levels as high as 3.9 ng/mL have been described

Additional Information Usual mechanism of abuse is through licking the skin of the toad, although "toad smoking" and ingestions have occurred; the Colorado river toad is found in the Sonoran desert of Northern Mexico along with Southern California and Arizona; while the toads primarily live underground, they do emerge during the rainy season in midsummer; not centrally active at oral doses of 50 mg or I.V. doses of 20 mg or I.M. doses of 40 mg; 100 kg of *Amanita citrina* contains only 7 g of bufotenine. Adverse reactions to bufotenin should be reported to FDA's Med Watch Program: (800)332-1088 or (301)738-7553.

Specific References

CDC, "Deaths Associated With a Purported Aphrodisiac - New York City, February 1993-May 1995," *MMWR Morb Mortal Wkly Rep*, 1995, 44(46):853-5, 861.

Bufox® (France) *see* Bufotenine *on previous page*

Bupap® *see* Butalbital Compound *on page 93*

Buprenex® *see* Buprenorphine *on this page*

Buprenorphine (byoo pre NOR feen)

Related Information

Controlled Substances - Uses and Effects *on page 741*

U.S. Brand Names Buprenex®

Therapeutic Category Analgesic, Narcotic

Abuse Potential Yes

Impairment Potential Yes

Use Management of moderate to severe pain

Usual Dosage I.M., slow I.V.:

Children ≥13 years and Adults: 0.3-0.6 mg every 6 hours as needed

Elderly: 0.15 mg every 6 hours; elderly patients are more likely to suffer from confusion and drowsiness compared to younger patients

Long-term use is not recommended

Maximum survivable dose: 16 mg

Mechanism of Action Opiate agonist/antagonist that produces analgesia by binding to kappa and mu opiate receptors in the CNS

Pharmacodynamics/kinetics

Onset of analgesia: I.M.: Within 10-30 minutes

Duration: Dose related; from 7 hours (1 mg total dose) to 24 hours (7 mg total dose)

Absorption:

I.M., S.C.: 90% to 100%

Sublingual: 31%

Metabolism: Mainly in the liver; undergoes extensive metabolism to norbuprenorphine

Half-life: 2.2-3 hours

(Continued)

Buprenorphine *(Continued)*

Signs and Symptoms of Acute Intoxication CNS depression, dysphoria, depression, pinpoint pupils, hypotension, bradycardia

When to Transport to Hospital Transport any symptomatic patient

Overdosage/Treatment Supportive therapy: Naloxone in large doses (5-10 mg) and/or a continuous infusion may be necessary to reverse respiratory depression

Warnings/Precautions If used in narcotic dependent patients, may cause withdrawal effects; may increase cerebrospinal fluid pressure, use with caution in head injuries; can produce change in consciousness which hampers patient evaluation; naloxone may not be effective in reversing apnea; use with caution in the elderly, debilitated hypothyroidism, Addison's disease, prostatic hypertrophy; can increase intracholedochal pressure

Adverse Reactions
>10%: Central nervous system: Drowsiness
1% to 10%:
    Cardiovascular: Hypotension
    Central nervous system: Respiratory depression, dizziness, headache
    Gastrointestinal: Vomiting, nausea

Reference Range I.V. dose of 0.3 mg results in a plasma buprenorphine level of 0.5 µg/L

Drug Interactions Increased toxicity: Barbiturates, opiates, guanabenz, MAO inhibitors, biperiden, benzodiazepines (increased CNS and respiratory depression); use with ketorolac (I.M.) with epidural buprenorphine can cause respiratory depression

Dosage Forms Injection, as hydrochloride: 0.3 mg/mL (1 mL)

Additional Information Buprenorphine 0.3 mg = morphine 10 mg = meperidine 75 mg; has longer duration of action than either agent

Specific References
Barkin RL and Richtsmeier AJ, "Alternative Agents in Pharmacological Management of Sickle Cell Pain Crisis Complicated by Acute Pancreatitis," *Am J Therapeut*, 1995, 2:819-23.

Bupropion *(byoo PROE pee on)*

Synonyms Amfebutamone

U.S. Brand Names Wellbutrin®; Wellbutrin® SR; Zyban®

Therapeutic Category Antidepressant

Use Treatment of depression

Usual Dosage Adults: Oral: 100 mg 3 times/day; begin at 100 mg twice daily; may increase to a maximum dose of 450 mg/day

Mechanism of Action Bupropion is an antidepressant structurally different from all other previously marketed antidepressants; like other antidepressants the mechanism of bupropion's activity is not fully understood; the drug is a weak blocker of serotonin and norepinephrine re-uptake, inhibits neuronal dopamine re-uptake and is not a monoamine oxidase A or B inhibitor

Pharmacodynamics/kinetics
Onset of action: 1-3 weeks
Absorption: Rapid from the gastrointestinal tract
Distribution: V_d: 27-63 L/kg; readily crosses blood-brain barrier
Protein binding: 75% to 88%
Metabolism: Extensive in the liver to multiple metabolites of which M-chlorohippuric acid is the major metabolite
Half-life: 14 hours (prolonged in cirrhotic patients)
Time to peak serum concentration: Oral: Within 3 hours

Elimination:

Renal: <1% excreted in urine unchanged; >60% excreted as metabolites within 24 hours; >80% within 96 hours

Hepatic: <10% (bupropion and metabolites) in feces

Signs and Symptoms of Acute Intoxication Labored breathing, Parkinson's-like symptoms, delirium, insomnia, impotence, salivation, leukopenia, mania, arched back, ataxia, seizures (dose related - 21% incidence), muscle rigidity, hypokalemia, confusion, vomiting, sinus tachycardia, slurred speech, fever, hypophosphatemia

When to Transport to Hospital Transport any pediatric exposure, any symptomatic patient, or any ingestion over 300 mg

Overdosage/Treatment

Decontamination: Lavage (within 12 hours)/activated charcoal

Supportive therapy: I.V. diazepam or lorazepam is useful in treating seizures

Enhancement of elimination: Multiple dose of activated charcoal may be useful

Warnings/Precautions Estimated seizure potential is increased many fold in doses in the 450-600 mg/day dosage; giving a single dose of 150 mg or less will lessen the seizure potential; use in patients with renal or hepatic impairment increases the possibilities of possible toxic effects

Adverse Reactions

>10%:

Central nervous system: Agitation, insomnia, fever, headache, psychosis, confusion, anxiety, restlessness, dizziness, seizures, chills, akathisia

Gastrointestinal: Nausea, vomiting, xerostomia, constipation, weight loss

Genitourinary: Impotence

Neuromuscular & skeletal: Tremor

1% to 10%:

Central nervous system: Hallucinations, fatigue

Dermatologic: Rash

Ocular: Blurred vision

Test Interactions Fluoxetine can interfere with bupropion quantitation by HPLC analysis in plasma or serum

Reference Range Blood levels >170 ng/mL associated with seizures and therapeutic level is 50-100 ng/mL; level of 446 ng/mL associated with a fatality

Drug Interactions Carbamazepine, phenytoin, cimetidine, phenobarbital, levodopa, MAO inhibitors

Dosage Forms

Tablet (Wellbutrin®): 75 mg, 100 mg

Tablet, sustained release (Wellbutrin® SR, Zyban®): 100 mg, 150 mg

Additional Information Does not have adverse anticholinergic effects; voluntarily withdrawn in 1986; reintroduced in 1989

Specific References

Harris CR, Gualtieri J, and Stark G, "Fatal Bupropion Overdose," *J Toxicol Clin Toxicol*, 1997, 35(3):321-4.

Buscapina® see Scopolamine *on page 532*

BuSpar® see Buspirone *on this page*

Buspirone (byoo SPYE rone)

U.S. Brand Names Bespar®; BuSpar®

Therapeutic Category Antianxiety Agent

Use Management of anxiety; to treat bruxism induced by serotonin reuptake inhibitors

Usual Dosage Adults:

Oral: 15 mg/day (5 mg 3 times/day); may increase in increments of 5 mg/day every 2-4 days to a maximum of 60 mg/day

Bruxism: 5 mg every night at bedtime

(Continued)

Buspirone *(Continued)*

Mechanism of Action Selectively antagonizes CNS serotonin 5-HT$_1$A receptors without affecting benzodiazepine-GABA receptors; an azaspirodecanedione derivative with lower potential for addition or sedation than other anxiolytics

Pharmacodynamics/kinetics
  Onset of action: May require 1-2 weeks; because buspirone does not cause muscle relaxation or significant sedation, patient may not immediately notice effects of medication
  Absorption: Rapid and complete from gastrointestinal tract
  Metabolism: In the liver by oxidation and undergoes extensive metabolism
  Bioavailability: Extensive first-pass metabolism limits it
  Half-life: 2-3 hours
  Time to peak serum concentration: Within 40-60 minutes
  Elimination:
    Renal: 29% to 63% excreted in urine within 24 hours primarily as metabolites; clearance: 2.2 L/minute
    Fecal: 18% to 38% excreted
  Studies in the elderly found no significant changes in pharmacokinetic parameters

Signs and Symptoms of Acute Intoxication Dizziness, drowsiness, depression, dysphoria, hyperprolactinemia, dry mouth, pinpoint pupils, memory loss, lightheadedness, extrapyramidal reaction, nausea, vomiting, bradycardia, seizures, leukopenia, neutropenia, agranulocytosis, granulocytopenia

When to Transport to Hospital Transport any pediatric exposure, any lethargic patient, or any symptomatic patient

Warnings/Precautions Safety and efficacy not established in children <18 years of age; avoid alcoholic beverages; causes less sedation than other anxiolytics, but patients should be cautioned about driving until they are certain buspirone does not affect them adversely; use in hepatic or renal impairment is not recommended

Adverse Reactions
  >10%:
    Central nervous system: Dizziness, lightheadedness, headache, restlessness
    Gastrointestinal: Nausea
  1% to 10%: Central nervous system: Drowsiness

Reference Range Peak plasma levels ≤6 ng/mL noted up to 90 minutes after a 20 mg dose

Drug Interactions MAO inhibitors, cimetidine, alcohol, highly protein bound drugs, haloperidol; metabolism is slowed with fluoxetine

Dosage Forms Tablet, as hydrochloride: 5 mg, 10 mg

Additional Information Has shown little potential for abuse; related to ipsapirone; avoid when breast-feeding; unpleasant taste; buspirone (15-60 mg/day) may be useful in treatment of sexual dysfunction during treatment with a selective serotonin reuptake inhibitor

Specific References
  Lader M, "Assessing the Potential for Buspirone Dependence or Abuse and Effects of Its Withdrawal," *Am J Med*, 1987, 82(Suppl 5A):20-6.
  Moskowitz H and Smiley A, "Effects of Chronically Administered Buspirone and Diazepam on Driving Related Skills Performance," *J Clin Psychiatry*, 1982, 43(12):45-55.

Butabarbital Sodium *(byoo ta BAR bi tal SOW dee um)*

U.S. Brand Names Butalan®; Buticaps®; Butisol Sodium®

Therapeutic Category Barbiturate

Abuse Potential Yes

Impairment Potential Yes

Use Sedative, hypnotic

Usual Dosage Oral:

Children: Preop: 2-6 mg/kg/dose; maximum: 100 mg

Adults:

Sedative: 15-30 mg 3-4 times/day

Hypnotic: 50-100 mg

Preop: 50-100 mg 1-1½ hours before surgery

Mechanism of Action Interferes with transmission of impulses from the thalamus to the cortex of the brain resulting in an imbalance in central inhibitory and facilitatory mechanisms

Pharmacodynamics/kinetics

Metabolism: In the liver

Half-life: 40-140 hours

Time to peak serum concentration: Oral: Within 40-60 minutes

Signs and Symptoms of Acute Intoxication Slurred speech, confusion, gaze nystagmus, tachycardia, hypotension

When to Transport to Hospital Transport any patient exhibiting any signs or symptoms of acute overdose or ingestions over 2 mg/kg

Adverse Reactions

>10%: Central nervous system: Dizziness, lightheadedness, drowsiness, "hangover" effect

1% to 10%:

Central nervous system: Confusion, mental depression, unusual excitement, nervousness, faint feeling, headache, insomnia, nightmares

Gastrointestinal: Constipation, nausea, vomiting

Reference Range Therapeutic: Mildly sedated: 3-25 μg/mL; Toxic: 28-73 μg/mL

Drug Interactions

Decreased effect: Phenothiazines, haloperidol, quinidine, cyclosporine, TCAs, corticosteroids, theophylline, ethosuximide, warfarin, oral contraceptives, chloramphenicol, griseofulvin, doxycycline, beta-blockers

Increased effect/toxicity: Propoxyphene, benzodiazepines, CNS depressants, valproic acid, methylphenidate, chloramphenicol

Dosage Forms

Capsule: 15 mg, 30 mg

Elixir, with alcohol 7%: 30 mg/5 mL (480 mL, 3780 mL); 33.3 mg/5 mL (480 mL, 3780 mL)

Tablet: 15 mg, 30 mg, 50 mg, 100 mg

Butace® *see* Butalbital Compound *on this page*

Butalan® *see* Butabarbital Sodium *on previous page*

Butalbital *see* Barbiturates, Quantitative, Blood *on page 64*

Butalbital Compound (byoo TAL bi tal KOM pound)

Related Information

Controlled Substances - Uses and Effects *on page 741*

U.S. Brand Names Amaphen®; Anoquan®; Axotal®; B-A-C®; Bancap®; Bupap®; Butace®; Endolor®; Esgic®; Esgic-Plus®; Femcet®; Fiorgen PF®; Fioricet®; Fiorinal®; G-1®; Isollyl Improved®; Lanorinal®; Marnal®; Medigesic®; Phrenilin®; Phrenilin® Forte; Repan®; Sedapap-10®; Triapin®; Two-Dyne®

Canadian Brand Names Tecnal®

Therapeutic Category Barbiturate

Abuse Potential Yes

Impairment Potential Yes

Use Relief of symptomatic complex of tension or muscle contraction headache

(Continued)

Butalbital Compound *(Continued)*

Usual Dosage Adults: Oral: 1-2 tablets or capsules every 4 hours; not to exceed 6/day

Mechanism of Action Butalbital, like other barbiturates, has a generalized depressant effect on the central nervous system (CNS). Barbiturates have little effect on peripheral nerves or muscle at usual therapeutic doses. However, at toxic doses serious effects on the cardiovascular system and other peripheral systems may be observed. These effects may result in hypotension or skeletal muscle weakness. While all areas of the central nervous system are acted on by barbiturates, the mesencephalic reticular activating system is extremely sensitive to their effects. Barbiturates act at synapses where gamma-amino-benzoic acid is a neurotransmitter, but they may act in other areas as well.

Signs and Symptoms of Acute Intoxication Slurred speech, confusion, gaze nystagmus, tachycardia, hypotension, tinnitus, headache, dizziness, confusion, metabolic acidosis, hyperpyrexia, hypoglycemia, coma, hepatic necrosis, blood dyscrasias, respiratory depression

When to Transport to Hospital Transport any pediatric exposure, any symptomatic patient, or any ingestion over 5 tablets

Warnings/Precautions Children and teenagers should not use for chickenpox or flu symptoms before a physician is consulted about Reye's syndrome (Fiorinal®)

Adverse Reactions

>10%:

Central nervous system: Dizziness, lightheadedness, drowsiness, "hangover" effect

Gastrointestinal: Nausea, heartburn, stomach pains, dyspepsia, epigastric discomfort

1% to 10%:

Central nervous system: Confusion, mental depression, unusual excitement, nervousness, faint feeling, headache, insomnia, nightmares, fatigue

Dermatologic: Rash

Gastrointestinal: Constipation, vomiting, gastrointestinal ulceration

Hematologic: Hemolytic anemia

Neuromuscular & skeletal: Weakness

Respiratory: Dyspnea

Miscellaneous: Anaphylactic shock

<1%:

Cardiovascular: Hypotension

Central nervous system: Hallucinations, jitters

Dermatologic: Exfoliative dermatitis, Stevens-Johnson syndrome

Hematologic: Agranulocytosis, megaloblastic anemia, occult bleeding, prolongation of bleeding time, leukopenia, thrombocytopenia, iron deficiency anemia

Hepatic: Hepatotoxicity

Local: Thrombophlebitis

Renal: Impaired renal function

Respiratory: Respiratory depression, bronchospasm

Drug Interactions

Decreased effect: Phenothiazines, haloperidol, quinidine, cyclosporine, TCAs, corticosteroids, theophylline, ethosuximide, warfarin, oral contraceptives, chloramphenicol, griseofulvin, doxycycline, beta-blockers

Increased effect/toxicity: Propoxyphene, benzodiazepines, CNS depressants, valproic acid, methylphenidate, chloramphenicol

Dosage Forms
Capsule, with acetaminophen:
Amaphen®, Anoquan®, Butace®, Endolor®, Esgic®, Femcet®, G-1®, Medigesic®, Repan®, Two-Dyne®: Butalbital 50 mg, caffeine 40 mg, and acetaminophen 325 mg
Bancap®, Triapin®: Butalbital 50 mg and acetaminophen 325 mg
Phrenilin® Forte: Butalbital 50 mg and acetaminophen 650 mg
Capsule, with aspirin: (Fiorgen PF®, Fiorinal®, Isollyl Improved®, Lanorinal®, Marnal®): Butalbital 50 mg, caffeine 40 mg, and aspirin 325 mg
Tablet, with acetaminophen:
Esgic®, Fioricet®, Repan®: Butalbital 50 mg, caffeine 40 mg, and acetaminophen 325 mg
Phrenilin®: Butalbital 50 mg and acetaminophen 325 mg
Sedapap-10®: Butalbital 50 mg and acetaminophen 650 mg
Tablet, with aspirin:
Axotal®: Butalbital 50 mg and aspirin 650 mg
B-A-C®: Butalbital 50 mg, caffeine 40 mg, and aspirin 650 mg
Fiorinal®, Isollyl Improved®, Lanorinal®, Marnal®: Butalbital 50 mg, caffeine 40 mg, and aspirin 325 mg

Butalbital Compound and Codeine
(byoo TAL bi tal KOM pound & KOE deen)
Related Information
Codeine *on page 164*
Controlled Substances - Uses and Effects *on page 741*
Synonyms Codeine and Butalbital Compound
U.S. Brand Names Fiorinal® With Codeine
Canadian Brand Names Fiorinal®-C ¼, ½; Tecnal C¼, C½
Therapeutic Category Analgesic, Narcotic; Barbiturate
Dosage Forms Capsule: Butalbital 50 mg, caffeine 40 mg, aspirin 325 mg and codeine phosphate 30 mg

Butan-l-ol *see* Butyl Alcohol *on page 97*
Butanol *see* Butyl Alcohol *on page 97*
2-Butanone *see* Methyl Ethyl Ketone *on page 396*
Buticaps® *see* Butabarbital Sodium *on page 92*
Butisol Sodium® *see* Butabarbital Sodium *on page 92*

Butorphanol (byoo TOR fa nole)
U.S. Brand Names Stadol®; Stadol® NS
Therapeutic Category Analgesic, Narcotic
Abuse Potential Yes
Impairment Potential Yes
Use Management of moderate to severe pain
Usual Dosage Adults: Nasal spray: Headache: 1 spray in 1 nostril; if adequate pain relief is not achieved within 60-90 minutes, an additional 1 spray in 1 nostril may be given (each spray gives ~1 mg of butorphanol)
Mechanism of Action Mixed narcotic agonist-antagonist with central analgesic actions; binds to opiate receptors in the CNS, causing inhibition of ascending pain pathways, altering the perception of and response to pain; produces generalized CNS depression
Pharmacodynamics/kinetics
Peak effect:
I.M.: Within 0.5-1 hour
I.V.: Within 4-5 minutes
Absorption: Rapidly and well absorbed
Metabolism: In the liver
(Continued)

Butorphanol (Continued)

Half-life: 2.5-4 hours
Elimination: Primarily in urine

Signs and Symptoms of Acute Intoxication Symptoms of overdose include respiratory depression, cardiac and CNS depression

When to Transport to Hospital Transport any pediatric exposure or any symptomatic patient

Overdosage/Treatment Treatment includes support of the patient's airway, establishment of an I.V. line and administration of naloxone 2 mg I.V. (0.01 mg/kg for children) with repeat administration as necessary up to a total of 10 mg

Warnings/Precautions Use with caution in patients with hepatic/renal dysfunction, may elevate CSF pressure, may increase cardiac workload

Adverse Reactions
>10%: Central nervous system: Drowsiness
1% to 10%:
Cardiovascular: Flushing of the face, hypotension
Central nervous system: Dizziness, lightheadedness, headache
Gastrointestinal: Anorexia, nausea, vomiting
Genitourinary: Decreased urination
Miscellaneous: Diaphoresis (increased)

Reference Range 0.7-1.5 ng/mL

Drug Interactions Increased toxicity: CNS depressants, phenothiazines, barbiturates, skeletal muscle relaxants, alfentanil, guanabenz, MAO inhibitors

Dosage Forms
Butorphanol tartrate:
Injection: 1 mg/mL (1 mL); 2 mg/mL (1 mL, 2 mL, 10 mL)
Spray, nasal: 10 mg/mL [14-15 doses] (2.5 mL)

Specific References
Pachter IJ and Evens RP, "Butorphanol," Drug Alcohol Depend, 1985, 14(3-4):325-38.

2-Butoxy-1-Ethanol see 2-Butoxyethanol on this page

2-Butoxyethanol

Synonyms BUCS; 2-Butoxy-1-Ethanol; Ethylene Glycol Monobutyl Ether
UN Number 2369
U.S. Brand Names Butyl Cellulosolve

Use Solvent/cleaning agent; dry cleaning, textile (dyeing), in inks, paint thinners, and protective coatings; often found in window/glass cleaners (usually <10% concentrations)

Mechanism of Toxic Action Both 2-butoxyethanol and its metabolite 2-butoxyacetic acid cause elevated osmotic fragility of red blood cells resulting in hemolysis

Toxicodynamics/kinetics
Absorption: Inhalation (57%), oral and dermal
Metabolism: Hepatic oxidation via alcohol dehydrogenase to butoxyacetaldehyde with further oxidation to 2-butoxyacetic acid
Half-life:
Oral: 210 minutes
Dermal: 34 minutes

When to Transport to Hospital Transport any ingestion or significant inhalation

Adverse Reactions
Cardiovascular: Tachycardia, hypotension
Central nervous system: Headache, coma
Endocrine & metabolic: Metabolic acidosis (lactic), hypokalemia

Gastrointestinal: Eructation
Hematologic: Hemolytic anemia
Ocular: Eye irritation, mydriasis (reacts to light)
Renal: Hematuria, albuminuria, oxaluria
Respiratory: Nasal/pharyngeal irritation

Additional Information
Atmospheric half-life: <1 day
Water half-life: ~5 days
Soil half-life: 1 week to 1 month
TWA-TLV: 25 ppm
A colorless liquid with a faint odor
Odor threshold: 0.1-0.4 ppm

Specific References
Dean BS and Krenzelok EP, "Clinical Evaluation of Pediatric Ethylene Glycol Monobutyl Ether Poisonings," *J Toxicol Clin Toxicol*, 1992, 30(4):557-63.

Butyl Alcohol

Synonyms Butan-l-ol; Butanol; Butyl Hydroxide; Propylcarbinol; Propylmethanol

UN Number 1120

Use In solvents in paints, lacquers, and resins; also used as extractants in the manufacture of pharmaceuticals; has been used as a sedative

Mechanism of Toxic Action Central nervous system depression

Toxicodynamics/kinetics
Absorption: Rapid from the gastrointestinal tract and dermally
Elimination: By the kidneys faster than ethanol

Signs and Symptoms of Acute Intoxication Eye irritation (at 50 ppm), porphyria, cornea abnormalities, respiratory depression, feces discoloration (black), dizziness, drowsiness, fatigue, dermal erythema, slight headache, keratitis, cough, ataxia, confusion, coma, vomiting, diarrhea

When to Transport to Hospital Transport any symptomatic patient or any suspected ingestion

Adverse Reactions
Central nervous system: Depression
Gastrointestinal: Irritant to mucous membranes

Additional Information Fuel oil odor is irritating; in pregnancy, tert-butyl alcohol may be fetotoxic
Odor threshold: 50 ppm
TLV-TWA: 100 ppm
Minimum toxic dose: 3-7 oz

Specific References
Kristiansen U, Vinggaard AM, and Nielsen GD, "The Effects of n-Butanol Vapour on Respiratory Rate and Tidal Volume," *Arch Toxicol*, 1988, 61(3):229-36.

Butyl Cellulosolve *see* 2-Butoxyethanol *on previous page*

Butyl Hydroxide *see* Butyl Alcohol *on this page*

BW-430-C *see* Lamotrigine *on page 334*

Byclomine® *see* Dicyclomine *on page 194*

Bydramine® Cough Syrup [OTC] *see* Diphenhydramine *on page 205*

CAF *see* Chloroacetophenone *on page 127*

Cafatine® *see* Ergotamine *on page 224*

Cafatine-PB® *see* Ergotamine *on page 224*

Cafergot® *see* Ergotamine *on page 224*

Cafetrate® *see* Ergotamine *on page 224*

Caffeine (KAF een)

Related Information

Maté *on page 360*

Therapeutic Category Respiratory Stimulant

Use Central nervous system stimulant; used in the treatment of idiopathic apnea of prematurity. Has several advantages over theophylline in the treatment of neonatal apnea, its half-life is about 3 times as long, allowing once daily dosing, drug levels do not need to be drawn at peak and trough; has a wider therapeutic window, allowing more room between an effective concentration and toxicity.

Usual Dosage Apnea of prematurity: Oral:

Loading dose: 10-20 mg/kg as caffeine citrate (5-10 mg/kg as caffeine base). If theophylline has been administered to the patient within the previous 5 days, a full or modified loading dose (50% to 75% of a loading dose) may be given at the discretion of the physician.

Maintenance dose: 5-10 mg/kg/day as caffeine citrate (2.5-5 mg/kg/day as caffeine base) once daily starting 24 hours after the loading dose. Maintenance dose is adjusted based on patient's response, (efficacy and adverse effects), and serum caffeine concentrations.

Mechanism of Action Increases levels of 3-5-AMP by inhibiting phosphodiesterase; methyl xanthine, CNS stimulant which increases medullary respiratory center sensitivity to carbon dioxide, stimulates central inspiratory drive, and improves skeletal muscle contraction (diaphragmatic contractility)

Pharmacodynamics/kinetics

Half-life:

Neonates: 60-100 hours

Adults: 3-6 hours

Time to peak serum concentration: Oral: Within 1-1.5 hours

Signs and Symptoms of Acute Intoxication GI pain, mild delirium, insomnia, diuresis, dehydration, fever, cardiac arrhythmias, tonic-clonic seizures

When to Transport to Hospital Transport any pediatric patient (<6 years of age) ingesting over 15 mg/kg or any symptomatic patient

Warnings/Precautions Use with caution in patients with a history of peptic ulcer; avoid in patients with symptomatic cardiac arrhythmias; parenteral caffeine is only available in the United States as a sodium benzoate salt. Due to reports of sodium benzoate inducing kernicterus by displacement of bilirubin and causing the gasping syndrome in newborns, use should be avoided in neonates.

Adverse Reactions

>10%:

Cardiovascular: Cardiac arrhythmias, tachycardia, extrasystoles

Central nervous system: Insomnia, restlessness, agitation, irritability,

Gastrointestinal: Nausea, vomiting, gastric irritation

Test Interactions ↑ uric acid (S), slight increase in urine levels of VMA, catecholamines

Reference Range

Therapeutic: 3-15 µg/mL

Toxic: >50 µg/mL

Drug Interactions

Caffeine may antagonize the cardiovascular effects of adenosine

Increased effects/levels of caffeine: Cimetidine, oral contraceptives, disulfiram, phenylpropanolamine, quinolones

Increased effects/levels of theophylline, beta-agonists (increased positive inotropic and chronotropic effects)

Dosage Forms

Solution, oral: 20 mg/mL [anhydrous caffeine 10 mg/mL], (can be extemporaneously prepared by pharmacy)

Tablet: 65 mg [anhydrous caffeine 32.5 mg]

Additional Information Has several advantages over theophylline in the treatment of neonatal apnea, its half-life is about 3 times as long, allowing once daily dosing, drug levels do not need to be drawn at peak and trough; has a wider therapeutic window, allowing more room between an effective concentration and toxicity; 2 mg caffeine citrate = 1 mg caffeine base

Calabren® see Glyburide on page 267

Calan® see Verapamil on page 609

Calcium Sulfite see Sulfite Food Poisoning on page 553

Caldecort® [OTC] see Hydrocortisone on page 297

Caldecort® Anti-Itch Spray [OTC] see Hydrocortisone on page 297

Calmazine® see Trifluoperazine on page 596

Calmotal® see Promazine on page 504

Calm-X® [OTC] see Dimenhydrinate on page 203

Cama® Arthritis Pain Reliever [OTC] see Aspirin on page 56

2-Camphanone see Camphor on this page

Camphor (KAM for)

Synonyms Anemone Camphor; 2-Camphanone; Formosa Camphor; Gum Camphor; Huile de Camphre; Kampfer; Laurel Camphor; Matricaria Camphor

UN Number 2717

U.S. Brand Names Mentholatum® Vapor Rub; Vicks® Vaporub®; Vicks® Vaposteam®

Therapeutic Category Pharmaceutical Aid

Use Plasticizer, moth repellent, preservative in pharmaceuticals and cosmetics, in lacquers and varnishes, explosives, and pyrotechnics; used as an antipruritic, topical rubefacient, aphrodisiac, abortifacient, contraceptive, cold remedy, suppressor of lactation, and antiseptic; camphorated liniment or oil usually contains 20% camphor; camphor spirits usually 10%

Usual Dosage Minimum lethal dose: 1 g (50 mg/kg)

Mechanism of Action Stimulant of cerebral cortex

Pharmacodynamics/kinetics

Absorption: Readily through skin and mucous membranes

Metabolism: Rapidly oxidized and conjugated in liver; metabolites may accumulate in fat stores

Half-life: 93-167 minutes

Peak effect: 90 minutes

Elimination: Odor of camphor may appear in urine; excreted primarily in urine; can also be excreted through the lungs

Signs and Symptoms of Acute Intoxication Convulsions may occur suddenly without warning or may be preceded by fasciculations, dementia, hyperventilation, mental confusion, irritability, tremors, neuromuscular hyperactivity, and jerky movements of extremities; seizures may be followed by coma and apnea. Vomiting may occur shortly after ingestion (a gastrointestinal irritant); hepatic transaminase may be mildly and briefly elevated; chronic ingestion may cause granulomatous hepatitis; distinctive oral odor may be apparent; tachycardia, CNS depression, renal failure.

When to Transport to Hospital Transport any pediatric (<6 years of age) patient ingesting over 10 mg/kg or any symptomatic patient

Adverse Reactions

Cardiovascular: Tachycardia, Reye's syndrome, sinus tachycardia

Central nervous system: Headache, dizziness, delirium, seizures, coma

(Continued)

Camphor *(Continued)*

Dermatologic: Nonimmunologic contact urticaria
Gastrointestinal: Nausea, vomiting
Hepatic: Liver function tests (elevated)
Neuromuscular & skeletal: Myoclonus, fasciculations
Ocular: Mydriasis, strabismus
Renal: Albuminuria
Respiratory: Tachypnea

Reference Range Levels >14.5 mg/L associated with seizures

Dosage Forms Translucent crystalline mass, blocks, or powder

Additional Information Odor is aromatic and pungent; aromatic taste produces sensation of cold

TLV-TWA: 5 ppm

IDLH: 200 mg/m³ (by inhalation)

Specific References

Siegel E and Wason S, "Camphor Toxicity," *Pediatr Clin North Am*, 1986, 33(2):375-9.

Camphorated Tincture of Opium see Paregoric on page 459

Cannabinoids, Qualitative

Synonyms Cannabis; Carboxy THC; Grass; Hashish; Hemp; Herb and Al; Marijuana; 11-Nor-9-Carboxy-Delta-9-Tetrahydrocannabinol; Pot; THC (Delta-9-Tetrahydrocannabinol); Weed

Use Drug abuse evaluation; toxicity assessment

Reference Range Negative (less than cutoff); levels >10 ng/mL reported as confirmed positive

Additional Information A marijuana cigarette is made form the dried particles of the plant, *Cannabis sativa*. The immediate effects of smoking marijuana include a faster heartbeat and pulse rate, bloodshot eyes, and a dry mouth and throat. The drug can impair or reduce short-term memory, alter sense of time, and reduce the ability to do things which require concentration, swift reactions and coordination, such as driving and operating machinery.

While positive urine FPIA screen virtually will not occur due to passive inhalation at a cutoff of 100 ng/mL, there may be positive EMIT screen in children at threshold of 10 ng/mL.

Driving experiments show that marijuana affects a wide range of skills needed for safe driving. Thinking and reflexes are slowed, making it hard for drivers to respond to sudden unexpected events. Furthermore, a driver's ability to "track" through curves, brake quickly, and maintain speed and proper distance between vehicles is affected. Research shows that these skills are impaired for at least 4-6 hours after smoking a single marijuana cigarette. If a driver drinks alcohol along with using marijuana, the risks of a vehicular collision greatly increase.

Specific References

Huestis MA, Mitchell JM, and Cone EJ, "Detection Times of Marijuana Metabolites in Urine by Immunoassay and GC-MS," *J Anal Toxicol*, 1995, 19(6):443-9.

Cannabis see Cannabinoids, Qualitative on this page

Capital® and Codeine see Acetaminophen and Codeine on page 21

Capoten® see Captopril on next page

Capozide® see Captopril and Hydrochlorothiazide on page 102

Captopril (KAP toe pril)

U.S. Brand Names Acepril®; Aceten®; Capoten®; Cor Tensobon®; Garranil®; Katopil®; Zorkaptil®

Canadian Brand Names Apo-Capto®; Novo-Captopril®; Nu-Capto®; Syn-Captopril®

Therapeutic Category Angiotensin-Converting Enzyme (ACE) Inhibitors

Use Management of hypertension and treatment of congestive heart failure; increase circulation in Raynaud's phenomenon; idiopathic edema
Investigational: Acute pulmonary edema

Usual Dosage Note: Dosage must be titrated according to patient's response; use lowest effective dose. Oral:

Infants: Initial: 0.15-0.3 mg/kg/dose; titrate dose upward to maximum of 6 mg/kg/day in 1-4 divided doses; usual required dose: 2.5-6 mg/kg/day

Children: Initial: 0.5 mg/kg/dose; titrate upward to maximum of 6 mg/kg/day in 2-4 divided doses

Older Children: Initial: 6.25-12.5 mg/dose every 12-24 hours; titrate upward to maximum of 6 mg/kg/day

Adolescents and Adults: Initial: 12.5-25 mg/dose given every 8-12 hours; increase by 25 mg/dose to maximum of 450 mg/day

Acute pulmonary edema: Sublingual:
Blood pressure >110 mm Hg: 25 mg
Blood pressure 90-110 mm Hg: 12.5 mg

Note: Smaller dosages given every 8-12 hours are indicated in patients with renal dysfunction. Renal function and leukocyte count should be carefully monitored during therapy.

Mechanism of Action Competitive inhibitor of angiotensin-converting enzyme (ACE); prevents conversion of angiotensin I to angiotensin II, a potent vasoconstrictor; results in lower levels of angiotensin II which causes an increase in plasma renin activity and a reduction in aldosterone secretion

Pharmacodynamics/kinetics

Onset of action: Single dose: 15-60 minutes

Duration of hypotensive action: 5-10 hours

Absorption: Oral: 60% to 75% absorbed from gastrointestinal tract; reduced 30% to 40% in presence of food

Metabolism: Hepatic, 50%

Half-life:
Normal adult: Dependent upon renal and cardiac function: 1.9 hours
Congestive heart failure: 2.06 hours
Anuria: 20-40 hours

Time to peak serum concentration: Within 1-2 hours

Signs and Symptoms of Acute Intoxication Severe hypotension, sweating, eosinophilia, pemphigus, dysosmia, bone marrow depression, hypoglycemia, diarrhea, coagulopathy, oliguria, lichenoid eruptions, hyperthermia, photosensitivity, cholestatic jaundice, night terrors, tubular necrosis, nephrotic syndrome, bullous skin disease/pemphigoid, pericarditis, hematuria, Parkinson's-like symptoms, hyperkalemia, hyponatremia, renal insufficiency, drowsiness, atrial ectopy, alopecia, fever, seizures, ototoxicity; tinnitus, wheezing

When to Transport to Hospital Transport any pediatric (<6 years of age) ingestion over 4 mg/kg, any symptomatic patient, or any patient with facial swelling

Warnings/Precautions Use with caution and modify dosage in patients with renal impairment; monitor BUN, serum creatinine, and renal function; use with caution in patients with collagen vascular disease

Adverse Reactions 1% to 10%:
Cardiovascular: Tachycardia, chest pain, palpitations
(Continued)

Captopril *(Continued)*

Central nervous system: Insomnia, headache, dizziness, fatigue, malaise
Dermatologic: Rash, pruritus, alopecia
Gastrointestinal: Abdominal pain, vomiting, nausea, diarrhea, anorexia, constipation, abnormal taste
Neuromuscular & skeletal: Paresthesias
Renal: Oliguria
Respiratory: Transient cough

Reference Range Plasma level of 6 µg/mL associated with hypotension while a level of 60 µg/mL associated with fatality

Drug Interactions Captopril + potassium-sparing diuretics cause an additive hyperkalemic effect; captopril + indomethacin or nonsteroidal anti-inflammatory agents cause a reduced antihypertensive response to captopril; leukopenia associated when given with azathioprine, can increase serum digoxin levels; use with cimetidine can cause paresthesia; allergic reactions including Stevens-Johnson syndrome associated with use of allopurinol; see table.

Drug-Drug Interactions With ACEIs

Precipitant Drug	Drug (Category) and Effect	Description
Antacids	ACE Inhibitors: decreased	Decreased bioavailability of ACEIs. May be more likely with captopril. Separate administration times by 1-2 hours.
NSAIDs (indomethacin)	ACEIs: decreased	Reduced hypotensive effects of ACEIs. More prominent in low renin or volume dependent hypertensive patients.
Phenothiazines	ACEIs: increased	Pharmacologic effects of ACEIs may be increased.
ACEIs	Allopurinol: increased	Higher risk of hypersensitivity reaction possible when given concurrently. Three case reports of Stevens-Johnson syndrome with captopril.
ACEIs	Digoxin: increased	Increased plasma digoxin levels.
ACEIs	Lithium: increased	Increased serum lithium levels and symptoms of toxicity may occur.
ACEIs	Potassium preps/potassium sparing diuretics increased	Coadministration may result in elevated potassium levels.

Dosage Forms Tablet: 12.5 mg, 25 mg, 50 mg, 100 mg
Additional Information Most effective for treating hypertension in young, white patients; conversion factor from captopril to lisinopril is 5:1
Specific References
Augenstein WL, Kulig KW, and Rumack BH, "Captopril Overdose Resulting in Hypotension," *JAMA*, 1988, 259(22):3302-5.

Captopril and Hydrochlorothiazide

(KAP toe pril & hye droe klor oh THYE a zide)
U.S. Brand Names Capozide®
Therapeutic Category Antihypertensive, Combination
Dosage Forms Tablet:
25/15: Captopril 25 mg and hydrochlorothiazide 15 mg
25/25: Captopril 25 mg and hydrochlorothiazide 25 mg
50/15: Captopril 50 mg and hydrochlorothiazide 15 mg

50/25: Captopril 50 mg and hydrochlorothiazide 25 mg

Caramiphen and Phenylpropanolamine
(kar AM i fen & fen il proe pa NOLE a meen)

Synonyms Phenylpropanolamine and Caramiphen

U.S. Brand Names Ordrine AT® Extended Release Capsule; Rescaps-D® S.R. Capsule; Tuss-Allergine® Modified T.D. Capsule; Tussogest® Extended Release Capsule

Therapeutic Category Antihistamine/Decongestant Combination

Abuse Potential Yes

Impairment Potential Yes

Dosage Forms

Capsule, timed release: Caramiphen edisylate 40 mg and phenylpropanolamine hydrochloride 75 mg

Liquid: Caramiphen edisylate 6.7 mg and phenylpropanolamine hydrochloride 12.5 mg per 5 mL

Carbamazepine (kar ba MAZ e peen)

Synonyms Carbamazepinum

U.S. Brand Names Carbategretal®; Carbazep®; Epitrol®; Tegretol®

Canadian Brand Names Apo-Carbamazepine®; Mazepine®; Novo-Carbamaz®; Nu-Carbamazepine®; PMS-Carbamazepine®

Therapeutic Category Anticonvulsant

Use Prophylaxis of generalized tonic-clonic, partial (especially complex partial), and mixed partial or generalized seizure disorder; may be used to relieve pain in trigeminal neuralgia or diabetic neuropathy; has been used to treat bipolar disorders

Usual Dosage Oral (dosage must be adjusted according to patient's response and serum concentrations):

Children:

<6 years: Initial: 5 mg/kg/day; dosage may be increased every 5-7 days to 10 mg/kg/day; then up to 20 mg/kg/day if necessary; administer in 2-4 divided doses/day

6-12 years: Initial: 100 mg twice daily or 10 mg/kg/day in 2 divided doses; increase by 100 mg/day at weekly intervals depending upon response; usual maintenance: 20-30 mg/kg/day in 2-4 divided doses/day; maximum dose: 1000 mg/day

Children >12 years and Adults: 200 mg twice daily to start, increase by 200 mg/day at weekly intervals until therapeutic levels achieved; usual dose: 800-1200 mg/day in 3-4 divided doses; some patients have required up to 1.6-2.4 g/day

Mechanism of Action May depress activity in the nucleus ventralis of the thalamus or decrease synaptic transmission or to decrease summation of temporal stimulation leading to neural discharge by limiting influx of sodium ions across cell membrane or other unknown mechanisms; stimulates the release of ADH and potentiates its action in promoting reabsorption of water; chemically related to tricyclic antidepressants; in addition to anticonvulsant effects, carbamazepine has anticholinergic, antineuralgic, antidiuretic, muscle relaxant, and antiarrhythmic properties. May also decrease the turnover of γ-aminobutyric acid (GABA).

Pharmacodynamics/kinetics

Onset of action: Anticonvulsant effect varies from hours to days, depending on individual patient; a stable therapeutic concentration may require a month to achieve due to to autoinduction of metabolism; relief of pain of trigeminal neuralgia occurs 8-72 hours; antimanic response, usually 7-10 days

Absorption: Slow from gastrointestinal tract

(Continued)

103

Carbamazepine *(Continued)*

Metabolism: In the liver to active epoxide; induces liver enzymes to metabolite increase metabolism and shorten half-life over time

Bioavailability: Oral: 85% to 90%

Half-life:

Initial: 18-55 hours

Multiple dosing:

Children: 8-14 hours

Adults: 12-17 hours

Overdose: 24-26 hours

Time to peak serum concentration: Within 4-8 hours

Signs and Symptoms of Acute Intoxication Dizziness, exfoliative dermatitis, hypothyroidism, hyponatremia, mania, chorea (extrapyramidal), toxic epidermal necrolysis, hyperreflexia, lichenoid eruptions, hyperthermia, dysosmia, extrapyramidal reaction, cognitive dysfunction, lymphoma, gingival hyperplasia, ileus, photosensitivity, bone marrow depression, leukemoid reaction, cholestatic jaundice, encephalopathy, jaundice, ataxia, A-V block, neuroleptic malignant syndrome, myoclonus, nausea, delirium, cough, vomiting, tremors, agitation, urinary retention, arrhythmias, coma, apnea, seizures, mydriasis, erythema multiforme, hypotension, drowsiness, hypothermia, leukocytosis, decreased gastrointestinal motility, oliguria, P-R prolongation, QRS prolongation, Q-T prolongation, alopecia, bradycardia, flushing, fever, leukopenia, neutropenia, agranulocytosis, granulocytopenia

When to Transport to Hospital Transport any pediatric (<6 years of age) ingestion over 20 mg/kg or any symptomatic patient

Warnings/Precautions Potentially fatal blood cell abnormalities have been reported following treatment; early detection of hematologic change is important; advise patients of early signs and symptoms which are fever, sore throat, stomatitis, infections, easy bruising, petechial or purpuric hemorrhage; MAO inhibitors should be discontinued for a minimum of 14 days before carbamazepine is begun; administer with caution to patients with history of cardiac damage or hepatic disease

Adverse Reactions

Dermatologic: Rash; but does not necessarily mean the drug should not be stopped

>10%:

Central nervous system: Sedation, dizziness, fatigue, ataxia, confusion

Gastrointestinal: Nausea, vomiting

Ocular: Blurred vision

1% to 10%:

Dermatologic: Stevens-Johnson syndrome, toxic epidermal necrolysis

Endocrine & metabolic: Hyponatremia, SIADH

Gastrointestinal: Diarrhea

Miscellaneous: Diaphoresis

Test Interactions May cause a false-positive for urine immunoassay for tricyclic antidepressants

Reference Range Therapeutic: 4-12 μg/mL (SI: 17-51 μmol/L). Patients who require higher levels (8-12 μg/mL) (SI: 34-51 μmol/L) should be watched closely. Side effects including CNS effects occur commonly at higher dosage levels. If other anticonvulsants are given, therapeutic range is 4-8 μg/mL (SI: 17-34 μmol/L)

Drug Interactions Erythromycin, isoniazid, propoxyphene, verapamil, diltiazem, and cimetidine may inhibit hepatic metabolism of carbamazepine with resultant increase of carbamazepine serum concentrations and toxicity;

carbamazepine may induce the metabolism of imipramine, warfarin, haloperidol, doxycycline, oral contraceptives, phenytoin, theophylline, benzodiazepines, ethosuximide, valproic acid, corticosteroids and thyroid hormones; synergistic anticonvulsant effect with propranolol; metronidazole can increase carbamazepine plasma level; CNS disorders with concomitant erythromycin and clarithromycin; carbamazepine and phenytoin may increase hepatic metabolism of midazolam; neurotoxicity (tremors, ataxia) may develop within 2 weeks with concomitant administration of lithium and carbamazepine; use with nefazodone can result in increased carbamazepine serum levels

Dosage Forms

Suspension, oral (citrus-vanilla flavor): 100 mg/5 mL (450 mL)

Tablet: 200 mg

Tablet, chewable: 100 mg

Tablet, extended release: 100 mg, 200 mg, 400 mg

Additional Information Suspension dosage form must be given on a 3-4 times/day schedule versus tablets which can be given 2-4 times/day; EKG changes do **not** correlate with serum carbamazepine levels; it is hypothesized that hematological toxicity and immune system toxicity is due to 9-acridine carboxaldehyde metabolite. Carbamazepine (400-800 mg/day) has been used to treat cocaine dependence.

Specific References

Apfelbaum JD, Caravati EM, Kerns WP 2nd, et al, "Cardiovascular Effects of Carbamazepine Toxicity," *Ann Emerg Med*, 1995, 25(5):631-5.

Carbamazepinum see Carbamazepine on page 103

Carbategretal® see Carbamazepine on page 103

Carbazep® see Carbamazepine on page 103

Carbidopa (kar bi DOE pa)

U.S. Brand Names Lodosyn®

Therapeutic Category Anti-Parkinson's Agent; Dopaminergic Agent (Antiparkinson's)

Use Given with levodopa in the treatment of parkinsonism to enable a lower dosage of levodopa to be used and a more rapid response to be obtained and to decrease side-effects; for details of administration and dosage, see Levodopa

Has no effect without levodopa

Usual Dosage Adults: Oral: 70-100 mg/day; maximum daily dose: 200 mg

Mechanism of Action Carbidopa is a peripheral decarboxylase inhibitor with little or no pharmacological activity when given alone in usual doses. It inhibits the peripheral decarboxylation of levodopa to dopamine; and as it does not cross the blood-brain barrier, unlike levodopa, effective brain concentrations of dopamine are produced with lower doses of levodopa. At the same time, reduced peripheral formation of dopamine reduces peripheral side-effects, notably nausea and vomiting, and cardiac arrhythmias, although the dyskinesias and adverse mental effects associated with levodopa therapy tend to develop earlier.

Pharmacodynamics/kinetics

Absorption: Rapid but incomplete from GI tract

Distribution: Does not cross the blood-brain barrier; in rats, it has been reported to cross the placenta and to be excreted in milk

Elimination: Rapidly excreted in urine both unchanged and in the form of metabolites

When to Transport to Hospital Transport any pediatric ingestion, any symptomatic patient, or any ingestion over 300 mg

Adverse Reactions Adverse reactions are associated with concomitant administration with levodopa

(Continued)

Carbidopa *(Continued)*

>10%: Central nervous system: Anxiety, confusion, nervousness, mental depression

1% to 10%:

Cardiovascular: Orthostatic hypotension, palpitations, cardiac arrhythmias

Central nervous system: Memory loss, nervousness, insomnia, fatigue, hallucinations, ataxia, dystonic movements

Gastrointestinal: Nausea, vomiting, GI bleeding

Ocular: Blurred vision

Drug Interactions Increased toxicity: Tricyclic antidepressant → hypertensive reactions and dyskinesia

Dosage Forms Tablet: 25 mg

Carbidopa and Levodopa *see* Levodopa and Carbidopa *on page 339*

Carbinol *see* Methanol *on page 386*

Carbinoxamine (kar bi NOKS a meen)

U.S. Brand Names Allergefon®; Andec®; Carbodec®; Chemdec®; Clistin®; Humex®; Lergefin®; Naldecol®; Polistine®; Rondec®; Toscal®; Tussafed®; Tylex®; Ziriton®

Therapeutic Category Antihistamine

Use Allergic rhinitis

Usual Dosage

Children: 0.2-0.4 mg/kg/day

Adults: 4-8 mg given 3 or 4 times/day

Mechanism of Action An ethanolamine antihistamine which blocks acetylcholine at muscarinic receptors; also has serotonin antagonist effects

Pharmacodynamics/kinetics

Duration of action: 3-6 hours

Half-life: 10-24 hours

Signs and Symptoms of Acute Intoxication Diplopia, dry mouth, tachycardia, visual hallucinations, ataxia, tremor, seizures, fever, mydriasis, coma; usually occur within 2 hours of ingestion

When to Transport to Hospital Transport any symptomatic patient or any ingestion over 1 mg/kg

Adverse Reactions

Central nervous system: Drowsiness, dizziness

Dermatologic: Contact dermatitis

Gastrointestinal: Anorexia, diarrhea, nausea, xerostomia, vomiting

Genitourinary: Dysuria

Renal: Polyuria

Respiratory: Thickening of bronchial secretions

Drug Interactions May enhance CNS depression caused by ethanol, tricyclic antidepressants and barbiturates; MAO inhibitors may prolong the anticholinergic actions of this antihistamine

Dosage Forms

Carbinoxamine maleate:

Syrup: 2 mg/5 mL

Tablet: 4 mg, 8 mg, 12 mg

Specific References

Cockrell JL, "Acute Hallucinogenic Reaction to Carbinoxamine Maleate," *J Toxicol Clin Toxicol*, 1987, 25(1-2):161-7.

Carbinoxamine and Pseudoephedrine

(kar bi NOKS a meen & soo doe e FED rin)

U.S. Brand Names Biohist®-LA; Carbiset® Tablet; Carbiset-TR® Tablet; Carbodec® Syrup; Carbodec® Tablet; Carbodec TR® Tablet; Cardec-S® Syrup; Rondec® Drops; Rondec® Filmtab®; Rondec® Syrup; Rondec-TR®

Therapeutic Category Antihistamine/Decongestant Combination

Abuse Potential Yes

Impairment Potential Yes

Dosage Forms

Drops: Carbinoxamine maleate 2 mg and pseudoephedrine hydrochloride 25 mg per mL (30 mL with dropper)

Syrup: Carbinoxamine maleate 4 mg and pseudoephedrine hydrochloride 60 mg per 5 mL (120 mL, 480 mL)

Tablet:

Film-coated: Carbinoxamine maleate 4 mg and pseudoephedrine hydrochloride 60 mg

Sustained release: Carbinoxamine maleate 8 mg and pseudoephedrine hydrochloride 120 mg

Carbinoxamine, Pseudoephedrine, and Dextromethorphan

(kar bi NOKS a meen, soo doe e FED rin, & deks troe meth OR fan)

U.S. Brand Names Carbodec DM®; Cardec DM®; Pseudo-Car® DM; Rondamine-DM® Drops; Rondec®-DM; Tussafed® Drops

Therapeutic Category Antihistamine/Decongestant/Antitussive

Abuse Potential Yes

Impairment Potential Yes

Dosage Forms

Drops: Carbinoxamine maleate 2 mg, pseudoephedrine hydrochloride 25 mg, and dextromethorphan hydrobromide 4 mg per mL (30 mL)

Syrup: Carbinoxamine maleate 4 mg, pseudoephedrine hydrochloride 60 mg, and dextromethorphan hydrobromide 15 mg per 5 mL (120 mL, 480 mL, 4000 mL)

Carbiset® Tablet see Carbinoxamine and Pseudoephedrine on this page

Carbiset-TR® Tablet see Carbinoxamine and Pseudoephedrine on this page

Carbodec® see Carbinoxamine on previous page

Carbodec DM® see Carbinoxamine, Pseudoephedrine, and Dextromethorphan on this page

Carbodec® Syrup see Carbinoxamine and Pseudoephedrine on this page

Carbodec® Tablet see Carbinoxamine and Pseudoephedrine on this page

Carbodec TR® Tablet see Carbinoxamine and Pseudoephedrine on this page

Carbolic Acid see Phenol on page 476

Carbon Bisulfide see Carbon Disulfide on next page

Carbon Chloride see Carbon Tetrachloride on page 113

Carbon Dioxide

Synonyms Carbonic Acid Gas; Carbonic Anhydride; CO_2; Dry Ice

UN Number 1013; 1845 (dry ice)

Use In urea synthesis; manufacture of soft drinks; used in fire extinguishers; dry ice; exposure can also occur from brewing, mining, and foundry work; dry ice has been used for cryotherapy (to treat warts/nevi)

Mechanism of Toxic Action

Inhalation: Simple asphyxiant (a colorless, odorless gas)

Solid form (as dry ice): Can cause freeze injury

(Continued)

Carbon Dioxide (Continued)

When to Transport to Hospital Transport any symptomatic patient

Overdosage/Treatment

Inhalation: Administer 100% humidified oxygen

Supportive: Freeze injury due to dermal exposure to dry ice should be managed with rapid rewarming (water bath 40°C to 42°C for 1/2 hour) with digit or extremity elevation; management is otherwise similar to that of a thermal burn

Adverse Reactions

Cardiovascular: Tachycardia, hypotension, cyanosis, edema, chest pain, angina

Central nervous system: Insomnia, headache, dizziness, confusion, lightheadedness, memory loss, ataxia, coma, seizures, delirium, panic attacks, psychosis

Endocrine & metabolic: Metabolic acidosis (dry ice)

Gastrointestinal: Nausea, throat irritation

Ocular: Vision (decreased), photophobia, eye irritation, color vision abnormalities, diplopia, ptosis

Respiratory: Cough, respiratory acidosis, apnea, tachypnea, hyposmia

Additional Information Signs of asphyxia can occur at oxygen concentrations below 16%; oxygen levels below 10% may be lethal; ambient carbon dioxide concentrations over 35% can cause circulatory and respiratory depression; symptoms can occur at 1% concentration; TLV: 5000 ppm; IDLH: 50,000 ppm lethal carbon dioxide concentration in one minute inhalation: 100,000 ppm; specific gravity: 1.101

Carbon dioxide build-up due to inadequate ventilation is one of the major causes of "sick building syndrome." (about 52% of cases of sick building syndrome) Recommend indoor ventilation rate for general office environment is 20 cfm (0.56 m³/min), which allows for indoor carbon dioxide to rise about 0.05 volume % above outdoor carbon dioxide levels

For seven occupants per 1000 square feet (93 m²) with 10 feet (3 m) of office ceiling, there should be 0.84 air changes per hour (8400 cubic foot/hour of outdoor air)

Dry ice is solid carbon dioxide maintained at -80°F (-26°C); can cause freeze injury if directly applied to skin and can cause asphyxiation if gas sublimes in an enclosed room; can combine with moisture to condense in thick, low lying fog

60% of carbon dioxide production remains in atmosphere (where upon it is used for plant photosynthesis). The green house effect occurs from increases in carbon dioxide (about 1 ppm yearly) due to increased formation (combustion) and reduced decomposition (deforestation). Carbon dioxide does not support combustion soluble in water (1:1 ratio); with no caustic effect

Inhalation of carbon dioxide (10% concentration) can raise intraocular pressure

Specific References

Takaoka M, Morinaga K, Karakowa K, et al, "A Case Report of Acute Carbon Dioxide Intoxication by Dry Ice," *Jpn J Toxicol*, 1988, 1:87.

Carbon Disulfide

Synonyms Carbon Bisulfide; Carbon Sulfide; Dithiocarbonic Anhydride

UN Number 1131

U.S. Brand Names Caswell No 162; Weeviltox®

Use Organic solvent used in gums and resins; used in manufacture of matches, instant color photography, corrosion inhibitors, gold and nickel plating, and rayon

Mechanism of Toxic Action Reacts with amino and thiols to inhibit cellular functions; damages the hepatic enzyme systems

Toxicodynamics/kinetics

Absorption: Dermal absorption does occur; lipid soluble

Metabolism: Hepatic cytochrome P-450 to carbonyl sulfide; also detoxified by glutathione pathway in the liver

Half-life: <1 hour

Elimination: Excreted by the lungs

Signs and Symptoms of Acute Intoxication Headache, tremor, neuritis, nausea, vomiting, burning of upper airway, cranial nerve palsies, hypertension, rotten egg breath, dyspnea, dizziness, diplopia, seizures, psychosis, possibly diabetogenic; death can occur from respiratory paralysis

When to Transport to Hospital Transport any exposed patient

Overdosage/Treatment

Decontamination: Inhalation: Administer 100% humidified oxygen

Supportive therapy: Avoid catecholamines due to probable monoamine oxidase inhibition; diazepam/lorazepam can be used for seizures; pyridoxine use for neurologic toxicity is unproven; although its use is unproven, there is a theoretical basis in which to use acetylcysteine to help detoxify carbon disulfide

Adverse Reactions

Cardiovascular: May be atherosclerogenic, angina, chest pain

Central nervous system: CNS depression, polyneuropathy, parkinsonism, hypothermia, seizures, memory disturbance, depression, mania

Dermatologic: Burns on dermal contact

Hepatic: Fatty degeneration of liver

Neuromuscular & skeletal: Paresthesia

Ocular: Color vision abnormalities

Respiratory: Dyspnea, hyposmia

Reference Range Monitor urine level of 2-thiothiazolidine-4-carboxylic acid; blood carbon disulfide levels ranging from 0.1-0.78 mg/L associated with air levels of ~80 ppm

Additional Information Colorless liquid; may have aromatic, sweet odor; similar effect of disulfiram; parkinsonism has been described

Fatal oral dose: 15 mL

TLV-TWA: 10 ppm

IDLH: 500 ppm

PEL-TWA: 4 ppm

Odor threshold: 0.1 ppm

Atmospheric half-life: 12 days

Water half-life: ~1 year

Specific References

U.S. Department of Health and Human Services, "Toxicological Profile for Carbon Disulfide," Agency for Toxic Substances and Diseases Registry, July, 1994.

Carbonic Acid Gas see Carbon Dioxide on page 107
Carbonic Anhydride see Carbon Dioxide on page 107
Carbonic Oxide see Carbon Monoxide on this page

Carbon Monoxide

Synonyms Carbonic Oxide; Carbon Oxide; CO; Exhaust Gas; Flue Gas

UN Number 1016

Commonly Found In Auto exhaust, byproduct of methylene chloride; produced in a closed space fire due to incomplete combustion of materials

Impairment Potential Yes; Carboxyhemoglobin levels >15% are likely to result in impairment

(Continued)

Carbon Monoxide *(Continued)*

Leikin JB and Paloucek FP, *Poisoning and Toxicology Compendium*, Hudson, OH: Lexi-Comp, Inc, 1998.

Mechanism of Toxic Action Causes tissue hypoxia and inhibition of cellular respiration

Toxicodynamics/kinetics

Absorption: Readily through the lungs; does not accumulate over time

Half-life: 5-6 hours in room air; 30-90 minutes in 100% oxygen; 30 minutes in hyperbaric oxygen

Elimination: Through the lungs; see figure.

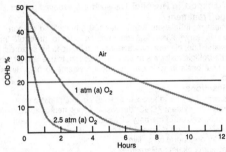

Carbon monoxide elimination. Used with permission and adapted from Winter PM and Miller JN, "Carbon Monoxide Poisoning," *JAMA*, 1976, 236:1502-4.

Signs and Symptoms of Acute Intoxication Frontal headache, ataxia, tremor, nausea, vomiting, blurred vision, aspiration, dementia, A-V block, arrhythmias, angina, visual changes, dyspnea with hyperventilation, gaze nystagmus, dizziness, encephalopathy, seizures, disorientation, hypothermia, drowsiness, hyperglycemia, hypotension, mydriasis, tachycardia, ototoxicity, tinnitus, bradycardia, myoglobinuria

When to Transport to Hospital Transport any symptomatic exposure

Overdosage/Treatment

Decontamination: 100% humidified oxygen; hyperbaric oxygen for patients with acute neurotoxicity, patients with angina, maternal carboxyhemoglobin of 20% in pregnant patients, or asymptomatic carboxyhemoglobin of 30%. **Do not** consider hypothermia or exchange transfusion.

Adverse Reactions

Cardiovascular: Cardiac abnormalities most pronounced, syncope, sinus bradycardia, cardiomyopathy, cardiomegaly, chest pain, palpitations, sinus tachycardia

Central nervous system: CNS effects, acute neurological abnormalities including dementia, drowsiness, coma, seizures, headache, confabulation, Parkinson-like syndrome, memory disturbance, depression, psychosis

Delayed neurological sequelae observed within 40 days of significant carbon monoxide poisoning (12% to 43% incidence) including disorientation, bradykinesia, chorea (extrapyramidal), equilibrium disturbances, apathy, cogwheel rigidity, aphasia, incontinence, personality changes, short-term memory deficit, seizure disorders, and chronic headaches

Dermatologic: Bullous lesions

Neuromuscular & skeletal: Chorea, apraxia, neuropathy (peripheral), rhabdomyolysis

Ocular: Cortical blindness

Otic: Deafness

Reference Range Carboxyhemoglobin level by CO-Oximeter™: Endogenous level: ≤0.65; smokers may have from 3% to 8%

Severe symptoms may start at 10%; >35% is associated with fatalities from acute exposure; BEI is <8%; venous and arterial samples are equivalent

Additional Information Colorless, odorless gas; delayed neurotoxicity consisting of short-term memory deficit, ataxia, cognitive impairment may occur 2-3 weeks after an acute exposure; Parkinson syndrome may occur; carbon monoxide detectors are usually set to alarm at indoor carbon monoxide air concentrations of 100 ppm (within 90 minutes), 200 ppm (within 35 minutes), or 400 ppm (within 15 minutes); essentially it is at these concentrations with corresponding time exposure duration that will result in a carboxyhemoglobin level of 10% during periods of heavy exertion. A carbon monoxide detector shall operate at or below the plotted limits for the 10% COHb curve as shown in the table. If the detector employs a variable sensitivity setting, test measurements are to be made at maximum and minimum settings. For this test, three carbon monoxide concentrations (100, 200, 400 ppm) are to be used as specified in the table.

Carbon Monoxide Concentration (ppm Co)
vs.
Time (minutes)

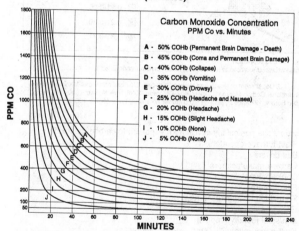

According to estimates from the Bureau of Labor statistics, carbon monoxide accounted for 867 nonfatal work-related carbon monoxide exposures in private industry and 32 work-related deaths in 1992

TLV-TWA: 50 ppm

IDLH: 1500 ppm

PEL-TWA: 35 ppm

May also result from methylene chloride exposure

Half-life for carboxyhemoglobin elimination is ~27.5 minutes with use of an inflatable portable hyperbaric chamber (modified Ganow bag) at 1.58 ATA

Automobile exhaust may contain as high as 7% carbon monoxide

(Continued)

Carbon Monoxide *(Continued)*

Rate* of Deaths From Unintentional Motor-Vehicle-Related Carbon Monoxide Poisoning†, By State—United States, 1979-1992

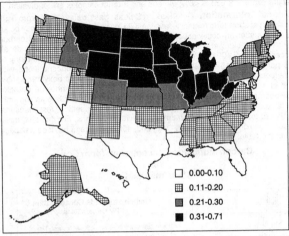

* Per 100,000 population
† *International Classification of Diseases, Ninth Revision*, code E868.2.

From U.S. Department of Health and Human Services, "Deaths From Motor-Vehicle-Related Unintentional Carbon Monoxide Poisoning—Colorado, 1996, New Mexico, 1980-1995, and United States, 1979-1992", *MMWR Morb Mortal Wkly Rep*, 1996, 45(47): 1031.

Occupations particularly at risk from exposure to carbon monoxide:
    Blast furnace operators
    Bus drivers
    Carbide manufacturers
    Cooks/bakers
    Fire fighters
    Formaldehyde manufacturers
    Garage mechanics
    Iron/steel foundry (cupola)
    Kraft paper pulp mills (Kraft recovery furnaces)
    Lead molders
    Miners
    Operators of snow melting machines
    Petroleum-refining plants (catalytic cracking units)
    Pulmonary function test practitioners
    Skating rinks (from Zamboni ice cleaners)
    Tollway booth collectors
    Traffic policeman
    Warehouse storage and loading facilities (forklift operators)
    Welders

Celebrities in whom carbon monoxide was involved in their death:
Ron Luciano (baseball umpire) 1995
Kevin Carter (photojournalist) 1994
Vitas Gerulaitis (tennis player) 1994
Jug McSpadden (golfer)
Emile Zola (novelist)

Specific References

Balzan MV, Agius G, and Debona AG, "Carbon Monoxide Poisoning: Easy to Treat But Difficult to Recognize," *Postgrad Med J*, 1996, 72(850):470-3.

Carbon Nitride Ion *see* Cyanide *on page 170*

Carbon Oil *see* Benzene *on page 69*

Carbon Oxide *see* Carbon Monoxide *on page 109*

Carbon Sulfide *see* Carbon Disulfide *on page 108*

Carbon Tetrachloride

Synonyms Carbon Chloride; Perchlormethane; Tetrachloromethane; Tetrasol

UN Number 1846

U.S. Brand Names Benzinoform®; Fasciolin®; Flukoids®; Freon 10®; Halon 104®; Tetraform®

Use In the production of fluorocarbons, fumigation of grain, and as an insecticide

Mechanism of Toxic Action Antihelmintic; cirrhosis of liver, renal insufficiency; free radicals bind to hepatocytes which lead to lipid peroxidation and cell death

Toxicodynamics/kinetics

Absorption: Readily from the skin, lungs, and gastrointestinal tract (85%; rapid, within 10 minutes); can produce renal or hepatic toxicity from any of these sites

Metabolism: In the liver, metabolites include hexachloroethane, carbon dioxide, and phosgene

Half-life:
Oral: 40-85 hours
Inhalation: 1-40 hours

Elimination: Excreted through the lungs (50% to 80%) as carbon dioxide

Signs and Symptoms of Acute Intoxication Confusion, delirium, coma, dementia, ataxia, tremor (intention), vomiting, nausea, jaundice, anuria, aplastic anemia, hematuria, erythema of skin, seizures

When to Transport to Hospital Transport any exposed patient

Overdosage/Treatment

Decontamination: Administer 100% humidified oxygen; for ingestion - basic poison management; avoid ipecac; **do not** use catecholamines due to enhancement of ventricular arrhythmia; avoid enzyme-inducing agents such as phenobarbital

Supportive therapy: Hyperbaric oxygen may be of benefit to prevent hepatitis

Adverse Reactions

Cardiovascular: Tachycardia, sinus tachycardia
Central nervous system: Memory disturbance
Gastrointestinal: Feces discoloration (clay/putty)
Hepatic: Hepatotoxicity, centrilobular hepatic necrosis
Ocular: Eye irritation
Miscellaneous: Suspected human carcinogen (liver cancer and leukemia)

Reference Range Toxic: 2.0-5.0 mg/dL

Additional Information Colorless liquid with odor of chloroform; N-acetylcysteine may be of benefit (research studies); radiopaque

Lethal dose: 43 mg/kg
TLV-TWA: 5 ppm
IDLH: 300 ppm

(Continued)

113

Carbon Tetrachloride *(Continued)*

PEL-TWA: 2 ppm
Atmospheric half-life: Over 30 years
Water half-life: ~6-12 months
Soil half-life: 6-12 months
Average urban ambient carbon tetrachloride levels: 0.1-0.3 ppb; average indoor carbon tetrachloride level: 0.2-0.4 ppb; median drinking water carbon tetrachloride level: 0.3-0.7 mcg/L; average daily exposure of carbon tetrachloride: ~0.11 mcg/kg

Specific References
U.S. Department of Health and Human Services, *Toxicological Profile for Carbon Tetrachloride TP-93/02*, Agency for Toxic Substances and Diseases Registry, May, 1994.

Carboxy THC *see* Cannabinoids, Qualitative *on page 100*
Cardec DM® *see* Carbinoxamine, Pseudoephedrine, and Dextromethorphan *on page 107*
Cardec-S® Syrup *see* Carbinoxamine and Pseudoephedrine *on page 107*
Cardene® *see* Nicardipine *on page 429*
Cardene® SR *see* Nicardipine *on page 429*
Cardioreg® *see* Digoxin *on page 199*
Cardizem® *see* Diltiazem *on page 201*
Cardizem® CD *see* Diltiazem *on page 201*
Cardizem® SR *see* Diltiazem *on page 201*
Cardura® *see* Doxazosin *on page 210*
Carisoma® *see* Carisoprodol *on this page*
Carisoprodate *see* Carisoprodol *on this page*

Carisoprodol *(kar i soe PROE dole)*

Related Information
Meprobamate *on page 371*

Synonyms Carisoprodate; Isobamate; Isopropylmeprobamate
U.S. Brand Names Carisoma®; Flexartal®; Rela®; Sanoma®; Sodol®; Soma®; Somadril®; Soprodol®; Soridol®
Therapeutic Category Skeletal Muscle Relaxant
Abuse Potential Yes
Impairment Potential Yes
Use Skeletal muscle relaxant
Usual Dosage Adults: Oral: 350 mg 3-4 times/day; take last dose at bedtime; compound: 1-2 tablets 4 times/day
Minimal lethal dose: 3.5 g (pediatrics)
Mechanism of Action Precise mechanism is not yet clear, but many effects have been ascribed to its central depressant actions
Pharmacodynamics/kinetics
Onset of action: Within 30 minutes
Duration: 4-6 hours
Metabolism: By the liver to meprobamate and hydroxymeprobamate
Half-life: 8 hours
Signs and Symptoms of Acute Intoxication CNS depression, lightheadedness, insomnia, depression, erythema multiforme, stupor, coma, shock, respiratory depression, gaze nystagmus, dizziness
When to Transport to Hospital Transport any pediatric exposure, any symptomatic patient, or any ingestion over 1 g
Warnings/Precautions Use with caution in renal and hepatic dysfunction

Adverse Reactions
>10%: Central nervous system: Drowsiness
1% to 10%:
Cardiovascular: Tachycardia, tightness in chest, flushing of face, syncope
Central nervous system: Mental depression, allergic fever, dizziness, light-headedness, headache, paradoxical CNS stimulation
Dermatologic: Angioedema
Gastrointestinal: Nausea, vomiting, stomach cramps
Neuromuscular & skeletal: Trembling
Ocular: Burning eyes
Respiratory: Shortness of breath
Miscellaneous: Hiccups

Reference Range 600 mg oral dose can produce peak carisoprodol plasma level between 9-20 mg/L; plasma levels >30 mg/L associated with stupor, coma, or death; serum meprobamate levels >60 μg/mL associated with toxicity; meprobamate levels >142 μg/mL associated with fatality

Drug Interactions Potentiated with alcohol, guanabenz, meprobamate or other CNS depressants; enhance neuromuscular blockade when given with clindamycin; use with MAO inhibitors may cause hypotension and respiratory depression

Dosage Forms
Tablet:
Rela®, Sodol®, Soma®, Soprodol®, Soridol®: 350 mg
Soma® Compound: Carisoprodol 200 mg and aspirin 325 mg

Specific References
Backer RC, Zumwalt R, McFeeley P, et al, "Carisoprodol Concentrations From Different Anatomical Sites: Three Overdose Cases," *J Anal Toxicol*, 1990, 14(5):332-4.

Carisoprodol and Aspirin (kar i soe PROE dole & AS pir in)
U.S. Brand Names Soma® Compound
Therapeutic Category Skeletal Muscle Relaxant
Abuse Potential Yes
Impairment Potential Yes
Dosage Forms Tablet: Carisoprodol 200 mg and aspirin 325 mg

Carisoprodol, Aspirin, and Codeine
(kar i soe PROE dole, AS pir in, and KOE deen)
U.S. Brand Names Soma® Compound w/Codeine
Therapeutic Category Skeletal Muscle Relaxant
Abuse Potential Yes
Impairment Potential Yes
Dosage Forms Tablet: Carisoprodol 200 mg, aspirin 325 mg, and codeine phosphate 16 mg

Carteolol (KAR tee oh lole)
U.S. Brand Names Arteolol®; Cartrol®; Endak®; Mikelan®; Ocupress®; Teoptic®
Therapeutic Category Beta-Adrenergic Blocker
Use Management of hypertension; eye drops: open-angle glaucoma or intraocular hypertension
Usual Dosage Adults:
Oral: 2.5 mg as a single daily dose, with a maintenance dose normally 2.5-5 mg once daily
Ophthalmic: Instill 1 drop in eye(s) twice daily
(Continued)

Carteolol (Continued)

Mechanism of Action Blocks both beta$_1$- and beta$_2$-receptors and has mild intrinsic sympathomimetic activity; has negative inotropic and chronotropic effects and can significantly slow A-V nodal conduction

Pharmacodynamics/kinetics

Protein binding: 23% to 30%

Metabolism: Hepatic (30% to 50%) to an active metabolite 8-hydroxycarteolol

Bioavailability: 85%

Half-life:

Parent compound: 6 hours

Metabolite: 8-12 hours

Time to peak plasma concentration: 1-3 hours

Elimination: Renal; clearance: 6.5 mL/minute/kg

Signs and Symptoms of Acute Intoxication Severe hypotension, cough, ataxia, purpura, night terrors, insomnia, impotence, congestive heart failure, arrhythmias, colitis, sinus bradycardia, heart/respiratory failure and wheezing; pulmonary edema, mesenteric ischemia, cardiovascular collapse

When to Transport to Hospital Transport any pediatric exposure, any patient with cardiopulmonary or central nervous system complaints, or any ingestion over 10 mg

Adverse Reactions

1% to 10%:

Cardiovascular: Congestive heart failure, arrhythmia

Central nervous system: Mental depression, headache, dizziness

Neuromuscular & skeletal: Back pain, arthralgia

Dosage Forms

Carteolol hydrochloride:

Solution, ophthalmic (Ocupress®): 1% (5 mL, 10 mL)

Tablet (Cartrol®): 2.5 mg, 5 mg

Additional Information Under investigation in phase II trials in the USA

Specific References

Ishizaki T, Ohnishi A, Sasaki T, et al, "Concentration-Effect and Time-Effect Relationships on Carteolol," *Eur J Clin Pharmacol*, 1983, 25(6):749-57.

Cartrol® see Carteolol *on previous page*

Carvedilol (KAR ve dil ole)

U.S. Brand Names Coreg®; Kredex®

Therapeutic Category Beta-Adrenergic Blocker

Use Investigational: Angina, hypertension, congestive heart failure

Usual Dosage

Congestive heart failure (ejection fraction >35%): 6.25 mg 2 times/day for 2 weeks; maximum dose: 50 mg 2 times/day

Hypertension: 25-50 mg 2 times/day; starting dose is 6.25 mg 2 times/day; can be increased in 1-2 weeks to 12.5 mg 2 times/day; can again be increased in 1-2 weeks to 25 mg 2 times/day; maximum daily dose: 50 mg

Mechanism of Action Noncardioselective beta-blocking agent with calcium channel blocking activity at higher dose (about 30 times the normal dose); similar to labetalol in that there is some alpha$_1$-adrenergic antagonist effect, thus acting as a vasodilator; less alpha$_1$ effect than labetalol or prazosin

Pharmacodynamics/kinetics

Onset of action: 1 hour

Absorption: 22% to 24% (oral); not affected by food

Metabolism: Hepatic

Half-life: 4-8 hours

When to Transport to Hospital Transport any pediatric exposure, any symptomatic patient, or any ingestion over 100 mg

Warnings/Precautions Use with caution in patients with bronchospasm, hepatic disease, intermittent claudication, elderly patients

Adverse Reactions 1% to 10%:
Cardiovascular: Bradycardia, postural hypotension, edema
Central nervous system: Dizziness, somnolence, insomnia, fatigue
Gastrointestinal: Diarrhea, abdominal pain
Neuromuscular & skeletal: Back pain
Respiratory: Rhinitis, pharyngitis, dyspnea

Reference Range Peak serum levels of ~122 µg/L achieved after oral 50 mg dose

Drug Interactions Increases absorption of digoxin

Additional Information High concentrations of carvedilol (>1 µmol/L) can cause calcium channel blocking effect; not useful for pheochromocytoma; should be taken with food

Specific References
Chen CP and Chow MS, "Focus on Carvedilol: A Novel β-Adrenergic Blocking Agent for the Treatment of Congestive Heart Failure," *Formulary*, 1997, 32:795-805.

Caryoph see Clove on page 158
Cassena see Holly on page 287

Castor Bean

Synonyms Castor-Oil Plant; Mole Bean

Scientific Name *Ricinus communis*

Mechanism of Action Contains ricin: A toxalbumin which inhibits protein metabolism and DNA synthesis; can cause agglutination of defibrinated blood *in vitro*

Pharmacodynamics/kinetics
Absorption: Poorly absorbed orally; can be absorbed by inhalation
Half-life: 48 hours
Elimination: Renal

Signs and Symptoms of Acute Intoxication Contact dermatitis, gastrointestinal irritation, oropharyngeal burning, abdominal burning, nausea, vomiting, gastrointestinal hemorrhage, diarrhea, thirst, seizures, anaphylaxis, fever, hypotension, tachycardia, bronchospasm, elevation of hepatic enzymes and serum creatinine can occur; hematuria, shivering, general weakness can also be seen; miosis and urticaria can also be noted; latent period to symptoms may be as long as 8 hours

When to Transport to Hospital Transport any symptomatic patient or ingestions over 1 castor bean per kg body weight

Overdosage/Treatment Decontamination:
Dermal: Wash with soap and water
Inhalation: Give 100% humidified oxygen
Ocular: Copious irrigation with saline for at least 20 minutes

Reference Range Following adult ingestion of 30 beans, a plasma and urine ricin level was 1.5 µg/L and 0.3 µg/L respectively

Additional Information Ricin is not dialyzable but water soluble and heat labile. The seeds and foliage are toxic parts of the plant. By injection, ricin can be quite toxic with the lethal dose estimated at 0.0001 mg/kg of animal's weight or 1 mg/kg in humans; lethal dose by oral ingestion is about 5-8 seeds. Chewing seeds increases the toxic potential with lethality occurring after 1 or 2 seed ingestion. Due to ricin's insolubility in oil, castor oil is not toxic and can be used as a laxative or a lubricant in industry. The plant is found in southern United States, Guam, and Hawaii. The bean has a hard coat which
(Continued)

117

Castor Bean (Continued)

needs to be ruptured for toxicity to occur. Hepatic/adrenal/renal toxicity may occur after 2-5 days postexposure. As of 1996, 15 deaths in 839 case reports have been documented (most occurring before 1945).

Specific References

Challoner KR and McCarron MM, "Castor Bean Intoxication," *Ann Emerg Med*, 1990, 19(10):1177-83.

Castor Oil (KAS tor oyl)

Synonyms Oleum Ricini; Ricinus Oil

U.S. Brand Names Alphamul® [OTC]; Emulsoil® [OTC]; Fleet® Flavored Castor Oil [OTC]; Laxopol®; Neoloid® [OTC]; Palmil®; Purge® [OTC]; Ricifruit®; Unisol®

Therapeutic Category Laxative

Use Preparation for rectal or bowel examination or surgery; rarely used to relieve constipation; also applied to skin as emollient and protectant

Usual Dosage Oral:

Liquid:

Infants <2 years: 1-5 mL or 15 mL/m^2/dose as a single dose

Children 2-11 years: 5-15 mL as a single dose

Children ≥12 years and Adults: 15-60 mL as a single dose

Emulsified:

36.4%:

Infants: 2.5-7.5 mL/dose

Children <2 years: 5-15 mL/dose

Children 2-11 years: 7.5-30 mL/dose

Children ≥12 years and Adults: 30-60 mL/dose

60% to 67%:

Children <2 years: 1.25-5 mL

Children 2-12 years: 5-15 mL

Adults: 15-45 mL

95%, mix with ½ to 1 full glass liquid:

Children: 5-10 mL

Adults: 15-60 mL

Mechanism of Action Acts primarily in the small intestine; hydrolyzed to ricinoleic acid which reduces net absorption of fluid and electrolytes and stimulates peristalsis; oil is expressed from the seeds of *Ricinus communis*

Pharmacodynamics/kinetics

Onset of action: Oral: 2-6 hours

Absorption: Orally

Metabolism: By pancreatic lipases to glycerol and ricinoleic acid

When to Transport to Hospital Transport any symptomatic patient or ingestion over 100 mL

Overdosage/Treatment

Decontamination: Lavage (within 1 hour)/activated charcoal without a cathartic

Supportive therapy: Intravenous fluid and electrolyte replacement; restrict solid food

Warnings/Precautions Use only when a prompt and thorough catharsis is desired; use with caution during menstruation

Adverse Reactions 1% to 10%:

Central nervous system: Dizziness

Endocrine & metabolic: Electrolyte disturbance

Gastrointestinal: Abdominal cramps, nausea, diarrhea

Drug Interactions May decrease the effects of oral anticoagulants by decreasing absorption

118

Dosage Forms
Emulsion, oral:
Alphamul®: 60% (90 mL, 3780 mL)
Emulsoil®: 95% (63 mL)
Fleet® Flavored Castor Oil: 67% (45 mL, 90 mL)
Neoloid®: 36.4% (118 mL)
Liquid, oral:
100% (60 mL, 120 mL, 480 mL)
Purge®: 95% (30 mL, 60 mL)
Additional Information Yellow liquid
Specific References
Brandle I, Bovjnah-Khovadja A, and Foussereau J, "Allergy to Castor Oil," *Contact Dermatitis*, 1983, 9:424-5.

Castor-Oil Plant *see Castor Bean on page 117*
Caswell No 162 *see Carbon Disulfide on page 108*
Caswell No 183A *see Chlorobenzene on page 128*
Catapres® *see Clonidine on page 154*
Catapressan® *see Clonidine on page 154*
Catapres-TTS® *see Clonidine on page 154*

Cathinone

Related Information
Methcathinone *on page 389*
Synonyms Khat
Abuse Potential Yes
Impairment Potential Yes
Usual Dosage
Khat (0.1% to 0.3% cathinone): 100-200 g
Anorexiant: 15-60 mg
Mechanism of Action Derived from the leaves of the *Catha edulis* (Khat) plant (an evergreen bush which grows up to 5 meters in Eastern Africa at high altitudes); this stimulant possesses local anesthetic, anorectic, and neuromuscular junction blocking activities; may have some monoamine oxidase inhibition properties; similar in action to cocaine or amphetamines
Pharmacodynamics/kinetics
Onset of action: 20 minutes
Duration of action: 2 hours
Metabolism: To norephedrine and norpseudoephedrine
Elimination: Renal
When to Transport to Hospital Transport any agitated patient or any patient with change in mental status or cardiopulmonary complaint
Adverse Reactions
Cardiovascular: Tachycardia, hypertension, palpitations, flushing
Central nervous system: Fever, insomnia, headache, mania, visual/auditory hallucinations, euphoria, psychosis, paranoia, hyperthermia
Gastrointestinal: Xerostomia, anorexia, constipation
Genitourinary: Urinary retention, impotence
Neuromuscular & skeletal: Tremors, rhabdomyolysis
Ocular: Mydriasis
Respiratory: Tachypnea, dyspnea
Miscellaneous: Diaphoresis
Test Interactions May give false-positive urinary amphetamine or phenylpropanolamine radioimmunoassay test
Additional Information Khat is usually utilized by chewing the leaves and swallowing its juice; red khat has a higher cathinone content than white khat; (Continued)

Cathinone *(Continued)*

khat addiction can be treated with bromocriptine mesylate (1.25 mg every 6 hours as an initial dose); for medicinal purposes (as an anorexiant): 15-60 mg

Specific References

Yousef G, Huq Z, and Lambert T, "Khat Chewing as a Cause of Psychosis," *Br J Hosp Med*, 1995, 54(7):322-6.

CBZ *see Cyclobenzaprine on page 173*

C-Crystals® [OTC] *see Ascorbic Acid on page 53*

Cebid® Timecelles® [OTC] *see Ascorbic Acid on page 53*

Cecon® [OTC] *see Ascorbic Acid on page 53*

Celance® *see Pergolide on page 466*

Cellon® *see Tetrachloroethane on page 566*

Celontin® *see Methsuximide on page 392*

Celupan® *see Naltrexone on page 420*

Cenafed® [OTC] *see Pseudoephedrine on page 516*

Centralgine® *see Meperidine on page 367*

Centrax® *see Prazepam on page 493*

Cepastat® [OTC] *see Phenol on page 476*

Cerose-DM® [OTC] *see Chlorpheniramine, Phenylephrine, and Dextromethorphan on page 136*

Certox® *see Strychnine on page 549*

Cesamet® *see Nabilone on page 415*

Cetacort® *see Hydrocortisone on page 297*

Cetirizine *(se Tl´ ra zeen)*

Synonyms P-071; UCB-P071

U.S. Brand Names Formistin®: Reactine®: Virlix®: Zyrlex®; Zyrtec®

Therapeutic Category Antihistamine

Impairment Potential Yes: Minimal mental performance changes may occur at doses of 20 mg (none at lower doses)

Use Allergic rhinitis, atopic dermatitis, chronic urticaria, asthma (allergen-induced; FDA approved for allergic rhinitis and chronic urticaria)

Usual Dosage

Allergen-induced asthma: 5-10 mg 2 times/day

Allergic rhinitis: ~10 mg/day

Urticaria: 10 mg 1-2 times/day

Reduce dosage in elderly, renal or liver dysfunction patients

Mechanism of Action Potent antihistamine (H_1 receptor antagonist) with little antimuscarinic effects. It is a carboxylated metabolite of hydroxyzine. Also inhibits inflammatory cell migration, and exhibits a mild bronchodilatory effect

Pharmacodynamics/kinetics

Absorption: 1 hour

Metabolism: Hepatic

Half-life:

Infants: 3.1 hours

Children: 6-7 hours

Adults: 7-11 hours

Renal failure: 18-21 hours

When to Transport to Hospital Transport lethargic patients, patients with cardiopulmonary complaints, or ingestions over 30 mg

Adverse Reactions

>10%: Central nervous system: Headache has been reported to occur in 10% to 12% of patients, drowsiness has been reported in as much as 26% of patients on high doses

1% to 10%:

Central nervous system: Somnolence, fatigue, dizziness

Gastrointestinal: Xerostomia

Reference Range Peak levels after a 10 mg oral dose: ~341 ng/mL and 978 ng/mL in adults and pediatric patients, respectively

Drug Interactions Increased anticoagulant activity when used with acenocoumarol

Dosage Forms

Cetirizine hydrochloride:

Syrup: 5 mg/5 mL (120 mL)

Tablet: 5 mg, 10 mg

Specific References

Ridout SM and Tariq SM, "Cetirizine Overdose in a Young Child," *J Allergy Clin Immunol*, 1997, 99:860-1.

Cevalin® [OTC] *see* Ascorbic Acid *on page 53*

Cevi-Bid® [OTC] *see* Ascorbic Acid *on page 53*

Ce-Vi-Sol® [OTC] *see* Ascorbic Acid *on page 53*

CF 2 *see* Trichloroethane *on page 594*

Chain-of-Custody Protocol

Synonyms Specimen Chain-of-Custody Protocol

Applies to Medical Legal Specimens

Use Chain-of-custody is a legal term that describes a method to maintain sample integrity in the collection, handling, and storage of urine samples.

Reference Range Normal: all seals intact and Chain-of-Custody form completed.

Additional Information The chain-of-custody protocol is a clerical and custodial service offered by the laboratory to document specimen transfer and provide for extended specimen storage. A written record of specimen transfer from patient, to analyst, to storage and disposal is maintained on all specimens covered by chain-of-custody. All drug screens, blood alcohols, or any other tests that have medicolegal significance should be accompanied by Chain-of-Custody form and a written release form. (Department of Transportation collections or any collection involving Medical Review officers.)

Specific References

Smith ML, Bronner WE, Shimomura ET, et al, "Quality Assurance in Drug Testing Laboratories," *Clin Lab Med*, 1990, 10(3):503-16.

Chameleon Mineral *see* Potassium Permanganate *on page 491*

Ch'an Su *see* Bufotenine *on page 88*

Chemdec® *see* Carbinoxamine *on page 106*

Cheracol® *see* Guaifenesin and Codeine *on page 271*

Cheracol® D [OTC] *see* Guaifenesin and Dextromethorphan *on page 271*

Chigger-Tox® [OTC] *see* Benzocaine *on page 70*

Children's Hold® [OTC] *see* Dextromethorphan *on page 187*

Children's Silapap® [OTC] *see* Acetaminophen *on page 20*

Chinese Restaurant Syndrome *see* Monosodium Glutamate Food Poisoning *on page 409*

Chinese Seasoning *see* Monosodium Glutamate Food Poisoning *on page 409*

Chlo-Amine® [OTC] *see* Chlorpheniramine *on page 132*

Chlorafed® Liquid [OTC] *see* Chlorpheniramine and Pseudoephedrine *on page 134*

Chloral Hydrate (KLOR al HYE drate)

Related Information

Controlled Substances - Uses and Effects *on page 741*

Synonyms Kloral Hydrat; Trichloroacetaldehyde Monohydrate

U.S. Brand Names Aquachloral® Supprettes®; Chloralix®; Kloral®; Noctec®; Rectules®; SK-Choral® Hydrate

Canadian Brand Names Novo-Chlorhydrate®; PMS®-Chloral Hydrate

Therapeutic Category Hypnotic, Nonbarbiturate

Abuse Potential Yes

Impairment Potential Yes

Use Short-term sedative and hypnotic (<2 weeks), sedative/hypnotic for dental and diagnostic procedures; sedative prior to EEG evaluations

Usual Dosage

Children:

Sedation, anxiety: Oral, rectal: 5-15 mg/kg/dose every 8 hours, maximum: 500 mg/dose

Prior to EEG: Oral, rectal: 20-25 mg/kg/dose, 30-60 minutes prior to EEG; may repeat in 30 minutes to maximum of 100 mg/kg or 2 g total

Hypnotic: Oral, rectal: 20-40 mg/kg/dose up to a maximum of 50 mg/kg/24 hours or 1 g/dose or 2 g/24 hours

Sedation, nonpainful procedure: Oral: 50-75 mg/kg/dose 30-60 minutes prior to procedure; may repeat 30 minutes after initial dose if needed, to a total maximum dose of 120 mg/kg or 1 g total

Adults: Oral, rectal:

Sedation, anxiety: 250 mg 3 times/day

Hypnotic: 500-1000 mg at bedtime or 30 minutes prior to procedure, not to exceed 2 g/24 hours

Mechanism of Action Central nervous system depressant effects are due to its active metabolite trichloroethanol, mechanism unknown; highly lipid soluble

Pharmacodynamics/kinetics

Onset of action: Within 30-60 minutes

Duration: ~4-8 hours

Absorption: Oral, rectal: Well absorbed

Metabolism: Rapid to trichloroethanol; variable amounts metabolized in liver and kidney to trichloroacetic acid (inactive)

Half-life: As long as 35 hours in an overdose setting

Trichloroethanol: 8-11 hours

Neonates: 3-5 hours

Signs and Symptoms of Acute Intoxication Hypotension, acne, tachycardia (ventricular), respiratory depression, hyporeflexia, laryngospasm, acetone breath, ileus, myoglobinuria, gaze nystagmus, thirst, ptosis, jaundice, coma, hypothermia, cardiac arrhythmias, torsade de pointes, eczema, myocardial depression, ventricular ectopy, alopecia, cough, leukopenia, neutropenia, agranulocytosis, granulocytopenia, rhabdomyolysis

When to Transport to Hospital Transport any pediatric ingestion (<6 years of age) over 50 mg/kg or any symptomatic patient

Warnings/Precautions Trichloroethanol (TCE), a metabolite of chloral hydrate, is a carcinogen in mice; there is no data in humans; use with caution in patients with porphyria; use with caution in neonates, drug may accumulate with repeated use, prolonged use in neonates associated with hyperbilirubinemia

Adverse Reactions

>10%: Gastrointestinal: Gastric irritation, nausea, vomiting, diarrhea

1% to 10%:

Central nervous system: Ataxia, hallucinations, drowsiness, "hangover" effect

Dermatologic: Rash, urticaria

Reference Range Therapeutic: 2-12 µg/mL of trichloroethanol; 25 µg/mL of trichloroethanol correlated with fatalities

Drug Interactions May potentiate effects of warfarin, central nervous system depressants, alcohol; vasodilation reaction (flushing, tachycardia, etc) may occur with concurrent use of alcohol; concomitant use of furosemide (I.V.) may result in flushing, sweating, and blood pressure changes

Dosage Forms

Capsule: 250 mg, 500 mg

Suppository, rectal: 324 mg, 500 mg, 648 mg

Syrup: 250 mg/5 mL (10 mL); 500 mg/5 mL (5 mL, 10 mL, 480 mL)

Additional Information Tolerance to hypnotic effect develops, therefore, not recommended for use >2 weeks; taper dosage to avoid withdrawal with prolonged use; radiopaque; genotoxic; question of carcinogenesis is unanswered

Specific References

Sing K, Erickson T, Amitai Y, et al, "Chloral Hydrate Toxicity From Oral and Intravenous Administration," *J Toxicol Clin Toxicol*, 1996, 34(1):101-6.

Chloralix® see Chloral Hydrate *on previous page*

Chloraseptic® [OTC] see Phenol *on page 476*

Chlorate® [OTC] see Chlorpheniramine *on page 132*

Chlordecone

Synonyms Decachloroketone

U.S. Brand Names Compound 1189®; Kepone®; Merex®

Use Insecticide (fire ant, slugs, grass mole cricket, tobacco fireworm) on tobacco, shrubs, and banana plants

Mechanism of Toxic Action Increases permeability of neuronal membrane; has estrogenic properties

Toxicodynamics/kinetics

Absorption: Inhalation, oral (90%), and dermal

Metabolism: Hepatic reduction to chlordecone alcohol

Half-life: 63-148 days

Elimination: Primarily fecal (biliary)

When to Transport to Hospital Tranport any exposure

Overdosage/Treatment Decontamination:

Dermal: Wash with soap and water

Ocular: Copious irrigation with saline

Adverse Reactions

Cardiovascular: Pleuritic chest pain, edema, angina

Central nervous system: Auditory and visual hallucinations, headache, slurred speech, ataxia, intracranial pressure (increased)

Dermatologic: Rash, maculopapular rash

Gastrointestinal: Nausea

Genitourinary: Oligospermia

Hepatic: Alkaline phosphatase (elevated)

Neuromuscular & skeletal: Tremors, arthralgia, neuropathy (peripheral)

Ocular: Cataracts, papilledema

Reference Range Blood chlordecone levels >1 ppm associated with neurotoxicity; blood levels >2000 ng/mL associated with tremor

Additional Information FDA action level for oysters, clams, mussels, and fin fish: 0.03 ppm; crabs: 0.4 ppm; high bioaccumulation potential in fish

(Continued)

Chlordecone *(Continued)*

Specific References

Taylor JR, "Neurological Manifestations in Humans Exposed to Chlordecone: Follow-up Results," *Neurotoxicology*, 1985, 6(1):231-6.

Chlordiazepoxide (klor dye az e POKS ide)

Related Information

Controlled Substances - Uses and Effects *on page 741*

Synonyms Methaminodiazepoxide Hydrochloride

U.S. Brand Names A-Poxide®; Equibral®; Libritabs®; Librium®; Mitran®; Resposan-10®; SK-Lygen®; Smail®; Solium®; Tropium®

Canadian Brand Names Apo-Chlordiazepoxide®; Corax®; Medilium®; Novo-Poxide®; Solium®

Therapeutic Category Benzodiazepine

Abuse Potential Yes

Impairment Potential Yes; Brief or extended period (up to 1 year) of use is consistent with driving impairment in the elderly. The impairment is greatest in the first 7 days of use.

Use Management of anxiety and as a preoperative sedative, symptoms of alcohol withdrawal

Usual Dosage I.M. route is not recommended

Children:

<6 years: Not recommended

>6 years: Anxiety: Oral, I.M.: 0.5 mg/kg/24 hours divided every 6-8 hours

Adults:

Anxiety:

Oral: 15-100 mg divided 3-4 times/day

I.M., I.V.: Initial: 50-100 mg followed by 25-50 mg 3-4 times/day as needed

Preoperative anxiety: I.M.: 50-100 mg prior to surgery

Alcohol withdrawal symptoms: Oral, I.V.: 50-100 mg to start, dose may be repeated in 2-4 hours as necessary to a maximum of 300 mg/24 hours

Mechanism of Action Benzodiazepine anxiolytic sedative that produces CNS depression at the subcortical level, except at high doses, whereby it works at the cortical level

Pharmacodynamics/kinetics

Onset of action: 30-45 minutes; depends largely on absorption rate

Absorption: Well absorbed from gastrointestinal tract; may be slow and erratic depending upon the site of administration

Metabolism: Extensive in the liver to demoxepam (active), demethylchlordiazepoxide (active), and oxazepam (active)

Half-life:

Parent compound: 5-25 hours

Demoxepam: 24-96 hours

Time to peak serum concentration: Oral: 1-4 hours

Elimination: Very little excretion in urine as unchanged drug; clearance: 0.4-0.5 mL/minute/kg

Signs and Symptoms of Acute Intoxication Hypotension, respiratory depression, coma, galactorrhea, myoglobinuria, hypothermia, lactation, ejaculatory disturbances, photosensitivity, cardiac arrhythmias, jaundice, hiccups, leukopenia, neutropenia, agranulocytosis, granulocytopenia, hyperglycemia, rhabdomyolysis, gaze nystagmus

When to Transport to Hospital Transport any pediatric (<6 years of age) exposure or any patient with central nervous system depression

Warnings/Precautions Mental impairment, reflex slowing, drug dependence; not considered a drug of choice in the elderly

Adverse Reactions

>10%:

Cardiovascular: Chest pain

Central nervous system: Drowsiness, fatigue, ataxia, lightheadedness, memory impairment, insomnia, anxiety, depression, headache

Dermatologic: Skin eruptions, rash

Endocrine & metabolic: Decreased libido

Gastrointestinal: Nausea, constipation, vomiting, diarrhea, xerostomia, increased or decreased appetite, decreased salivation

Neuromuscular & skeletal: Dysarthria

Ocular: Blurred vision

Miscellaneous: Diaphoresis

1% to 10%:

Cardiovascular: Hypotension, tachycardia, edema, syncope

Central nervous system: Ataxia, confusion, mental impairment, nervousness, dizziness, akathisia

Dermatologic: Dermatitis

Gastrointestinal: Weight gain or loss, increased salivation

Neuromuscular & skeletal: Rigidity, tremor, muscle cramps

Ocular: Blurred vision

Otic: Tinnitus

Respiratory: Nasal congestion, hyperventilation

Reference Range

Therapeutic: 0.1-3 µg/mL (SI: 0-10 µmol/L)

Toxic: >23 µg/mL (SI: >77 µmol/L); toxicity may be related to demoxepam levels >10 µg/mL

Urine drug screens can remain positive for 30 days

Drug Interactions Oral anticoagulants, alcohol, ketoconazole, tricyclic antidepressants, sedatives, hypnotics, and MAO inhibitors all increase CNS depression; oral contraceptives, cimetidine, and disulfiram inhibit chlordiazepoxide metabolism; larger doses may be required in smokers to achieve similar sedative effects as in nonsmokers

Dosage Forms

Capsule, as hydrochloride: 5 mg, 10 mg, 25 mg

Powder for injection, as hydrochloride: 100 mg

Tablet: 5 mg, 10 mg, 25 mg

Additional Information Often formulated with amitriptyline hydrochloride

Specific References

Minder EI, "Toxicity in a Case of Acute and Massive Overdose of Chlordiazepoxide and Its Correlation to Blood Concentration," *J Toxicol Clin Toxicol*, 1989, 27(1-2):117-27.

Murray JB, "Effects of Valium and Librium on Human Psychomotor and Cognitive Functions," *Genet Psychol Monogr*, 1984, 109:167-97.

Chlordiazepoxide and Amitriptyline see Amitriptyline and Chlordiazepoxide on page 41

Chlordiazepoxide and Clidinium see Clidinium and Chlordiazepoxide on page 150

Chlorine

Synonyms Bertholite

UN Number 1017

Commonly Found In War gas used in World War I; can be produced by mixing bleach with acid

Use In paper pulp mills and for swimming pools; also used in bleaching; used as a water disinfectant

(Continued)

Chlorine *(Continued)*

Mechanism of Toxic Action Converted to hydrogen chloride in lung parenchyma, strong irritant; free radical generation may be present

Toxicodynamics/kinetics Absorption: Not well absorbed, low solubility

Signs and Symptoms of Acute Intoxication Eye irritation, airway irritation, hypotension, dyspnea, headache, vomiting, dermal burns, hypertension, cough, stomatitis, wheezing, chest pain, hyperchloremic metabolic acidosis

When to Transport to Hospital Transport any symptomatic patient

Overdosage/Treatment Supportive therapy: Administer 100% humidified oxygen; a 3.75% to 5% sodium bicarbonate solution by nebulization may be helpful for acute respiratory symptoms; wheezing can be treated with beta-adrenergic agonists; steroids of no proven benefit

Adverse Reactions

Cardiovascular: Cardiovascular collapse, chest pain, angina

Ocular: Lacrimation

Respiratory: Pulmonary edema, bronchoconstriction, reactive airways disease syndrome

Miscellaneous: Risk for lymphoma (increased)

Reference Range Not measurable

Additional Information Green-yellow gas; mixing hypochlorite (bleach) with an acid can release chlorine gas; mixing hypochlorite (bleach) with ammonia can release chloramine gas; as a water disinfectant, chlorine is bactericidal at levels of 0.2 mg/L and cysticidal at 1.5-2 residual free chlorine (pH 7)

Taste threshold: 5 ppm

Odor threshold: 3.5 ppm

TLV-TWA: 0.5 ppm

IDLH: 30 ppm

PEL-TWA: 0.5 ppm

Specific References

Krenzelok E and Mrvos R, "Chlorine/Chloramine," *J Toxicol Clin Toxicol*, 1995, 33(4):355-7.

Chlormezanone *(klor me ZA none)*

U.S. Brand Names Alinam®; Muskel Trancopal®; Trancopal®

Therapeutic Category Antianxiety Agent

Use Anxiety; insomnia; muscle spasm

Usual Dosage Oral:

Children >5 years: 50-100 mg 3-4 times/day

Adults:

Anxiety: 100-200 mg 3-4 times/day

Insomnia: 400 mg at bedtime (200 mg in elderly patients)

Muscle spasm: 200-400 mg 3-4 times/day

Mechanism of Action Precise mechanism is not yet clear, but many effects have been ascribed to its central depressant actions

Pharmacodynamics/kinetics

Peak plasma level: 2 hours

Duration of action: >6 hours

Metabolism: Hydrolysis in the stomach and then metabolized in the liver (4-chlorohippuric acid is the major metabolite)

Half-life: 19-53 hours

Signs and Symptoms of Acute Intoxication Hypotension, tachycardia, ataxia, coma, hyporeflexia, hot dry skin, mydriasis

When to Transport to Hospital Transport any pediatric (<5 years of age) exposure, any symptomatic patient, or any ingestion over 500 mg

Overdosage/Treatment

Decontamination: Lavage (within 2 hours of ingestion)/activated charcoal

Supportive therapy: Benzodiazepines for seizure control

Enhancement of elimination: Forced diuresis is not helpful; multiple dosing of activated charcoal may be helpful. Following attempts to enhance drug elimination, hypotension should be treated with I.V. fluids and/or Trendelenburg positioning.

Adverse Reactions

Cardiovascular: Flushing, toxic epidermal necrosis

Central nervous system: Drowsiness, confusion, headache

Gastrointestinal: Nausea, xerostomia

Hematologic: Porphyrinogenic

Hepatic: Reversible jaundice, hepatitis

Neuromuscular & skeletal: Tremor, muscle weakness

Respiratory: Hyposmia

Reference Range Therapeutic range (in a steady state of 600 mg/day for 5 days): ~ 10-14 µg/mL. Levels over 18 µg/mL are associated with mild toxicity (weakness, ataxia, tachycardia) while a postmortem blood and urine chlormezanone level in a fatality was 53 µg/mL and 31 µg/mL respectively.

Drug Interactions Use of alcohol or other central nervous system depressants can have an additive effect

Dosage Forms Caplet: 100 mg, 200 mg

Specific References

Kirkham BW and Edelman JB, "Overdose of Chlormezanone: A New Clinical Picture," *Br Med J*, 1986, 292:732.

Chloroacetophenone

Synonyms CAF; CN; MACE; Phenacyl Chloride

UN Number 1697

Use Active ingredient in tear gas

Mechanism of Toxic Action Lacrimator - irritation due to the active halogen group reacting with sulfhydryl groups

Toxicodynamics/kinetics

Onset of effect: Rapid

Duration: Usually resolves in 30 minutes, skin effects may last for 2-3 hours

Absorption: Not absorbed

Signs and Symptoms of Acute Intoxication Rhinorrhea, sneezing, erythema, lacrimation, pharyngitis, agitation, tearing, eye pain, skin irritation, broncho- and laryngospasm, nausea, vomiting, coughing

When to Transport to Hospital Transport any patient with cardiopulmonary complaint

Overdosage/Treatment Decontamination: Move patient to fresh air and monitor for wheezing; personnel should avoid contaminating themselves; wash skin with soap and water; avoid rubbing of eyes as it may prolong effect; copious irrigation needed

Adverse Reactions

Ocular: Ocular burning, blepharospasms, cataract

Respiratory: Bronchospasm (may be delayed for 36 hours), pulmonary edema (may be delayed for 24 hours)

Additional Information Fragrant odor of apple blossom; can be detected using gas chromatography/mass spectrophotometry (GC/MS)

TLV-TWA: 0.05 ppm

IDLH: 100 mg/m^3

PEL-TWA: 0.05 ppm

(Continued)

127

Chloroacetophenone *(Continued)*
Specific References
Hu H, Fine J, Epstein P, et al, "Tear Gas - Harrassing Agent or Toxic Chemical Weapon?" *JAMA*, 1989, 262(5):660-3.

Chlorobenzene
Synonyms Benzene Chloride; MCB; Monochlorobenzene
UN Number 1134
U.S. Brand Names Caswell No 183A
Use Solvent used in production of DDT, phenol compounds (replaced primarily by cumene), diisocyanate, nitrochlorobenzene, and degreasing car parts
Toxicodynamics/kinetics
Absorption:
Inhalation: 38% to 45%
Gastrointestinal: 31%
Metabolism: Hepatic transition to 4-chlorophenol and through glutathione conjugation to parachlorophenyl mercapturic acid
When to Transport to Hospital Transport any exposed patient
Overdosage/Treatment
Decontamination:
Ocular: Irrigate with normal saline
Dermal: Wash with soap and water
Inhalation: Respiratory support with administration of 100% humidified oxygen
Adverse Reactions
Cardiovascular: Cyanosis
Central nervous system: CNS depression, seizures, coma, hyperesthesia
Hematologic: Methemoglobinemia
Neuromuscular & skeletal: Muscle spasms, neuritis, myoclonus
Miscellaneous: Mucosal irritant (at levels >200 ppm)
Reference Range Levels of residents living near a former toxic chemical dump ranged from 25-120 µg/L of chlorobenzene in the urine and 0.05-17 ng/L of chlorobenzene in blood
Additional Information This compound can decompose through heating to chlorine gas
Odor threshold: 0.21 ppm
IDLH: 2400 ppm
PEL-TWA: 75 ppm
Specific References
U.S. Department of Health and Human Services, *Toxicological Profile for Chlorobenzene TP-90-06*, Agency for Toxic Substances and Diseases Registry, December, 1990.

Chlorobenzoxazoline *see* Chlorzoxazone *on page 145*

Chlorobenzylidene Malonitrile
Related Information
Chloroacetophenone *on previous page*
Synonyms CS; Ortho-Chlorobenzylidene Malonitrile
U.S. Brand Names Deep Freeze; Paralyzer
Use Active ingredient in tear gas
Mechanism of Toxic Action Lacrimator: May be metabolized to thiocyanate in peripheral tissues
Toxicodynamics/kinetics
Onset of action: Immediate

Metabolism: Hepatic hydrolysis to O-chlorobenzaldehyde and malononitrile; peripheral metabolism may produce thiocyanate

Signs and Symptoms of Acute Intoxication Rhinorrhea, sneezing, erythema, lacrimation, pharyngitis, agitation, tearing, eye pain, skin irritation, broncho- and laryngospasm, nausea, vomiting, coughing, reactive airways disease syndrome

When to Transport to Hospital Transport any patient exhibiting cardipulmonary complaints

Overdosage/Treatment

Decontamination: Move patient to fresh air and monitor for wheezing; personnel should avoid contaminating themselves; wash skin with soap and water; avoid rubbing of eyes as it may prolong effect; copious irrigation needed; recovery usually will occur within 10-20 minutes

Dermal: Skin can be washed with a mild alkaline solution (6% sodium bicarbonate, 3% sodium carbonate and 1% benzalkonium chloride) to hasten elimination

Monitor for cyanide in cases of ingestion or extremely high exposure

Adverse Reactions

Dermatologic: Dermal burns

Ocular: Ocular burning, blepharospasms, cataract

Respiratory: Bronchospasm (may be delayed for 36 hours), pulmonary edema (may be delayed for 24 hours)

Additional Information LD-50 (respiratory concentration) is estimated to be 25,000-150,000 mg/m^3/minute; soft contact lenses may minimize exposure; a white crystalline solid (density: 1.3) with a pepper odor

IDLH: 2 mg/m^3

PEL-TWA: 0.05 ppm

Specific References

Anderson PJ, Lau GS, Taylor WR, et al, "Acute Effects of the Potent Lacrimator O-Chlorobenzylidene Malononitrile (CS) Tear Gas," *Hum Exp Toxicol*, 1996, 15(6):461-5.

Chloroethylene *see* Vinyl Chloride *on page 613*

Chloroform

Synonyms Formyl Trichloride; Freon 20; Methane Trichloride; TCM; Trichloroform; Trichloromethane

UN Number 1888

Abuse Potential Yes

Impairment Potential Yes

Use Solvent, grain fumigant, found in emulsions, spirits, tinctures; has been used as an anesthetic agent, refrigerant, and aerosol propellant

Mechanism of Toxic Action A direct depressant on the respiratory center in the brainstem; interferes with gangliosides in neuronal membranes and phospholipids on surfactant layer in lungs; can cause lipid peroxidation

Toxicodynamics/kinetics

Absorption: Well through inhalation, oral, and dermal exposure

Metabolism: To chlormethanol, hydrochloric acid, phosgene, chloride, and CO$_2$

Half-life: Inhalation: 8 hours

Elimination: Primarily from lungs in the form of chloroform and carbon dioxide; <1% excreted in urine

Signs and Symptoms of Acute Intoxication Burning, corneal injury, urticaria, conjunctivitis may occur with eye exposure; cardiac arrhythmias, mydriasis, gaze nystagmus, acetone breath, cardiac arrest have been reported; respiratory depression, chemical pneumonitis, and pulmonary edema may occur; CNS depression occurs; chronic use may produce degenerative brain changes and psychotic behavior; nausea, hemolysis, hepatitis, hepatomegaly, (Continued)

129

Chloroform *(Continued)*

vomiting, headache, drowsiness, dizziness, hypotension, dry mouth, fibrillation, bradycardia, tachycardia (ventricular)

When to Transport to Hospital Transport any exposed patient

Overdosage/Treatment

Decontamination: Remove from area of exposure and remove clothing; wash thoroughly; administer 100% humidified oxygen

Supportive therapy: Treatment of cardiac and respiratory status; lidocaine, propranolol, bretylium, phenytoin, disopyramide, or overdrive pacing has been used in treatment of PVCs; atropine may be used if severe bradycardia is present. If oral ingestion, radiograph may show radiopacity; monitor blood glucose, urinalysis, LFTs and renal function; administration of N-acetylcysteine for treatment of hepatitis is still theoretical.

Adverse Reactions

Cardiovascular: Sinus bradycardia, sinus tachycardia, arrhythmias (ventricular), vasodilation

Central nervous system: Psychosis

Dermatologic: Nonimmunologic contact urticaria

Gastrointestinal: Nausea and vomiting can occur at doses of 22-237 ppm

Hepatic: Centrilobular hepatic necrosis

Reference Range Blood chloroform levels with anesthesia: 0.07-0.165 mg/mL

Drug Interactions Thiopentone can increase incidence of hypotension

Additional Information Listed as a suspected carcinogen/radiopaque

TLV-TWA: 10 ppm

Anesthetic dose: 8000-10,000 ppm

Fatal dose: 40,000 ppm

Odor threshold:

Air: 85 ppm

Water: 2.4 ppm

Atmospheric half-life: 80 days

Water (pH 9) half-life: 25-37 years

Specific References

Deveaux M, Semoud A, Hedouin V, et al, "An Unusual Fatal Case of Chloroform Poisoning," *J Anal Toxicol*, 1997, 21:78.

Chloromethane

Synonyms Methyl Chloride; Monochloromethane

UN Number 1063

U.S. Brand Names Artic®; Freon 40; R40

Use Chlorinated hydrocarbon used in the production of silicones, butyl rubber, methyl cellulose; was also used as a refrigerant (although this use has declined over the past 30 years), as a propellant, and as a herbicide; also used in molding polystyrene and polyurethane foams and as an oil extractant

Toxicodynamics/kinetics

Absorption: Not absorbed through intact skin

Metabolism: Hepatic to formaldehyde and carbon dioxide

Half-life: 50-90 minutes

Signs and Symptoms of Acute Intoxication Diplopia, blurred vision, mydriasis, tachycardia, hypotension, wheezing, dizziness, drowsiness, headache, ataxia, seizures, slurred speech, tremor, coma, asthenia, nausea, vomiting, diarrhea, albuminuria, hematuria, oliguria, anemia, dermal erythema, elevated BUN and creatinine

When to Transport to Hospital Transport any exposed patient

Overdosage/Treatment Decontamination: Inhalation: Move patient out of environment; administer 100% humidified oxygen; symptoms usually abate after 6 hours

Adverse Reactions
 Cardiovascular: Sinus tachycardia
 Respiratory: Primarily from inhalation with a latent period of up to 2 days postinhalation; respiratory depression, nephritis

Reference Range After exposure to 50 ppm, chloromethane breath levels range from 50-80 µg/L; while chloromethane blood levels range from 35-100 µg/L

Drug Interactions Lethargy may be more pronounced in patients also taking a benzodiazepine

Additional Information Colorless gas with a sweet odor
 Lethal concentration: 20,000 ppm
 Toxic symptoms: 200 ppm
 IDLH: 10,000 ppm
 TLV-TWA: 50 ppm

Specific References
 U.S. Department of Health and Human Services, "Toxicological Profile for Chloromethane TP-90/07," Agency for Toxic Substances and Diseases Registry, December 1990.

Chlorothiazide (klor oh THYE a zide)

U.S. Brand Names Diurigen®; Diuril®

Therapeutic Category Diuretic

Use Management of mild to moderate hypertension, or edema associated with congestive heart failure, pregnancy, or nephrotic syndrome in patients unable to take oral hydrochlorothiazide, when a thiazide is the diuretic of choice

Usual Dosage I.V. form not recommended for children and should only be used in adults if unable to take oral in emergency situations:

 Infants <6 months: Oral: 20-40 mg/kg/day in 2 divided doses
 Infants >6 months and Children: Oral: 20 mg/kg/day in 2 divided doses
 Adults: Oral: 500 mg to 2 g/day divided in 1-2 doses
 Elderly: Oral: 500 mg once daily **or** 1 g 3 times/week

Mechanism of Action Inhibits sodium reabsorption in the distal tubules causing increased excretion of sodium and water as well as potassium and hydrogen ions, magnesium, phosphate, calcium

Pharmacodynamics/kinetics
 Absorption: Oral: Poor
 Onset of diuresis: Oral: 2 hours
 Duration of diuretic action: Oral: 6-12 hours
 Half-life: 1-2 hours
 Time to peak serum concentration: Within 4 hours

Signs and Symptoms of Acute Intoxication Hypermotility, diuresis, lethargy, confusion, muscle weakness, coma

When to Transport to Hospital Transport any symptomatic patient

Overdosage/Treatment Following GI decontamination, therapy is supportive with I.V. fluids, electrolytes, and I.V. pressors if needed

Warnings/Precautions Injection must not be administered S.C. or I.M.; may cause hyperbilirubinemia, hypokalemia, alkalosis, hyperglycemia, hyperuricemia; chlorothiazide is minimally effective in patients with a Cl_{cr} <40 mL/minute; this may limit the usefulness of chlorothiazide in the elderly

Adverse Reactions 1% to 10%: Endocrine & metabolic: Hypokalemia, hyponatremia

Drug Interactions
 Decreased effect: NSAIDs + chlorothiazide → decreased antihypertensive effect; decreased absorption of thiazides with cholestyramine resins; chlorothiazide causes a decreased effect of oral hypoglycemics
 (Continued)

Chlorothiazide *(Continued)*

Increased toxicity: Digitalis glycosides, lithium (decreased clearance), probenecid

Dosage Forms
Powder for injection, lyophilized, as sodium: 500 mg
Suspension, oral: 250 mg/5 mL (237 mL)
Tablet: 250 mg, 500 mg

Additional Information Sodium content of injection, 500 mg: 57.5 mg (2 mEq)

Chlorothiazide and Methyldopa

(klor oh THYE a zide & meth il DOE pa)
Synonyms Methyldopa and Chlorothiazide
U.S. Brand Names Aldoclor®
Therapeutic Category Antihypertensive, Combination
Impairment Potential Yes
Dosage Forms Tablet:
150: Chlorothiazide 150 mg and methyldopa 250 mg
250: Chlorothiazide 250 mg and methyldopa 250 mg

Chlorothiazide and Reserpine

(klor oh THYE a zide & re SER peen)
Synonyms Reserpine and Chlorothiazide
Therapeutic Category Antihypertensive, Combination
Impairment Potential Yes
Dosage Forms Tablet:
250: Chlorothiazide 250 mg and reserpine 0.125 mg
500: Chlorothiazide 500 mg and reserpine 0.125 mg

Chlorphed® [OTC] *see* Brompheniramine *on page 84*

Chlorpheniramine (klor fen IR a meen)

Related Information
Hydrocodone and Chlorpheniramine *on page 295*
Synonyms CTM
U.S. Brand Names Aller-Chlor® [OTC]; AL-R® [OTC]; Chlo-Amine® [OTC]; Chlorate® [OTC]; Chlor-Pro® [OTC]; Chlor-Trimeton® [OTC]; Kloromin® [OTC]; Phenetron®; Telachlor®; Teldrin® [OTC]
Therapeutic Category Antihistamine
Impairment Potential Yes
Use Perennial and seasonal allergic rhinitis and other allergic symptoms including rash

Usual Dosage
Children: Oral: 0.35 mg/kg/day in divided doses every 4-6 hours
2-6 years: 1 mg every 4-6 hours, not to exceed 6 mg in 24 hours
6-12 years: 2 mg every 4-6 hours, not to exceed 12 mg/day; sustained release: 8 mg at bedtime
Children >12 years and Adults: Oral: 4 mg every 4-6 hours, not to exceed 24 mg/day; sustained release: 8-12 mg every 8-12 hours, not to exceed 24 mg/day

Adults: Allergic reactions: I.M., I.V., S.C.: 10-20 mg as a single dose; maximum recommended dose: 40 mg/24 hours

Mechanism of Action Competes with histamine for H_1-receptor sites on effector cells in the gastrointestinal tract, blood vessels, and respiratory tract

Pharmacodynamics/kinetics
Onset of action: 20-60 minutes
Duration: 8-12 hours

Absorption: Well from gastrointestinal tract; food in stomach delays absorption but does not affect bioavailability

Metabolism: In the liver

Half-life:

Children: 13 hours

Adults: 20-24 hours

Renal failure: 280-330 hours

Time to peak serum concentration: 2-6 hours

Signs and Symptoms of Acute Intoxication Dry mouth, mydriasis, CNS depression, extrapyramidal reaction, leukopenia, neutropenia, agranulocytosis, granulocytopenia, flushing

When to Transport to Hospital Transport any symptomatic patient

Overdosage/Treatment There is no specific treatment for an antihistamine overdose, however, most of its clinical toxicity is due to anticholinergic effects

Warnings/Precautions Do not administer to premature or full-term neonates; young children may be more susceptible to side effects and CNS stimulation

Adverse Reactions

Genitourinary: Urinary retention, polyuria

Ocular: Diplopia

>10%:

Central nervous system: Slight to moderate drowsiness

Respiratory: Thickening of bronchial secretions

1% to 10%:

Central nervous system: Headache, excitability, fatigue, nervousness, dizziness

Gastrointestinal: Nausea, xerostomia, diarrhea, abdominal pain, appetite increase, weight gain

Neuromuscular & skeletal: Arthralgia, weakness

Respiratory: Pharyngitis

Drug Interactions CNS depressants, monoamine oxidase inhibitors, epinephrine

Dosage Forms

Chlorpheniramine maleate:

Capsule: 12 mg

Capsule, timed release: 8 mg, 12 mg

Injection: 10 mg/mL (1 mL, 30 mL); 100 mg/mL (2 mL)

Syrup: 2 mg/5 mL (120 mL, 473 mL)

Tablet: 4 mg, 8 mg, 12 mg

Tablet:

Chewable: 2 mg

Timed release: 8 mg, 12 mg

Additional Information Not effective for nasal stuffiness

Specific References

Millar K and Wilkinson RT, "The Effects Upon Vigilance and Reaction Speed of the Addition of Ephedrine Hydrochloride to Chlorpheniramine Maleate," *Eur J Clin Pharmacol*, 1981, 20(5):351-7.

Chlorpheniramine and Acetaminophen

(klor fen IR a meen & a seet a MIN oh fen)

U.S. Brand Names Coricidin® [OTC]

Therapeutic Category Antihistamine/Analgesic

Impairment Potential Yes

Dosage Forms Tablet: Chlorpheniramine maleate 2 mg and acetaminophen 325 mg

Chlorpheniramine and Phenylephrine
(klor fen IR a meen & fen il EF rin)

Synonyms Phenylephrine and Chlorpheniramine

U.S. Brand Names Dallergy-D® Syrup; Ed A-Hist® Liquid; Histatab® Plus Tablet [OTC]; Histor-D® Syrup; Rolatuss® Plain Liquid; Ru-Tuss® Liquid

Therapeutic Category Antihistamine/Decongestant Combination

Impairment Potential Yes

Dosage Forms

Capsule, sustained release: Chlorpheniramine maleate 8 mg and phenylephrine hydrochloride 20 mg

Liquid:

Dallergy-D®, Histor-D®, Rolatuss® Plain, Ru-Tuss®: Chlorpheniramine maleate 2 mg and phenylephrine hydrochloride 5 mg per 5 mL

Ed A-Hist® Liquid: Chlorpheniramine maleate 4 mg and phenylephrine hydrochloride 10 mg per 5 mL

Tablet (Histatab® Plus): Chlorpheniramine maleate 2 mg and phenylephrine hydrochloride 5 mg

Chlorpheniramine and Phenylpropanolamine
(klor fen IR a meen & fen il proe pa NOLE a meen)

Synonyms Phenylpropanolamine and Chlorpheniramine

U.S. Brand Names Allerest® 12 Hour Capsule [OTC]; A.R.M.® Caplet [OTC]; Chlor-Rest® Tablet [OTC]; Demazin® Syrup [OTC]; Genamin® Cold Syrup [OTC]; Ornade® Spansule®; Resaid®; Rescon Liquid [OTC]; Silaminic® Cold Syrup [OTC]; Temazin® Cold Syrup [OTC]; Thera-Hist® Syrup [OTC]; Triaminic® Allergy Tablet [OTC]; Triaminic® Cold Tablet [OTC]; Triaminic® Syrup [OTC]; Tri-Nefrin® Extra Strength Tablet [OTC]; Triphenyl® Syrup [OTC]

Therapeutic Category Antihistamine/Decongestant Combination

Abuse Potential Yes

Impairment Potential Yes

Dosage Forms

Capsule, sustained release: Chlorpheniramine maleate 12 mg and phenylpropanolamine hydrochloride 75 mg

Liquid:

Triphenyl®, Genamin®: Chlorpheniramine maleate 1 mg and phenylpropanolamine hydrochloride 6.25 mg per 5 mL

Demazin®, Rescon®, Silaminic®, Temazin®, Thera-Hist®: Chlorpheniramine maleate 2 mg and phenylpropanolamine hydrochloride 12.5 mg per 5 mL

Syrup: Chlorpheniramine maleate 2 mg and phenylpropanolamine hydrochloride 12.5 mg per 5 mL

Tablet

Triaminic® Cold: Chlorpheniramine maleate 2 mg and phenylpropanolamine hydrochloride 12.5 mg

Chlor-Rest®: Chlorpheniramine maleate 2 mg and phenylpropanolamine hydrochloride 18.7 mg

A.R.M.®, Triaminic® Allergy, Tri-Nefrin® Extra Strength: Chlorpheniramine maleate 4 mg and phenylpropanolamine hydrochloride 25 mg

Tablet, sustained release: Chlorpheniramine maleate 12 mg and phenylpropanolamine hydrochloride 75 mg

Chlorpheniramine and Pseudoephedrine
(klor fen IR a meen & soo doe e FED rin)

Synonyms Pseudoephedrine and Chlorpheniramine

U.S. Brand Names Allerest® Maximum Strength [OTC]; Anamine® Syrup [OTC]; Anaplex® Liquid [OTC]; Chlorafed® Liquid [OTC]; Chlor-Trimeton® 4 Hour Relief Tablet [OTC]; Co-Pyronil® 2 Pulvules® [OTC]; Deconamine® SR;

Deconamine® Syrup [OTC]; Deconamine® Tablet [OTC]; Fedahist® Tablet [OTC]; Hayfebrol® Liquid [OTC]; Histalet® Syrup [OTC]; Klerist-D® Tablet [OTC]; Pseudo-Gest Plus® Tablet [OTC]; Rhinosyn® Liquid [OTC]; Rhinosyn-PD® Liquid [OTC]; Ryna® Liquid [OTC]; Sudafed Plus® Liquid [OTC]; Sudafed Plus® Tablet [OTC]

Therapeutic Category Antihistamine/Decongestant Combination

Abuse Potential Yes

Impairment Potential Yes

Dosage Forms

Capsule:

Co-Pyronil® 2 Pulvules®: Chlorpheniramine maleate 4 mg and pseudoephedrine hydrochloride 60 mg

Capsule, sustained release: Chlorpheniramine maleate 4 mg and pseudoephedrine hydrochloride 60 mg; chlorpheniramine maleate 8 mg and pseudoephedrine hydrochloride 120 mg

Liquid:

Anamine®, Anaplex®, Chlorafed®, Deconamine®, Hayfebrol®, Rhinosyn-PD®, Ryna®: Chlorpheniramine maleate 2 mg and pseudoephedrine sulfate 30 mg per 5 mL

Rhinosyn®: Chlorpheniramine maleate 2 mg and pseudoephedrine sulfate 60 mg per 5 mL

Histalet®: Chlorpheniramine maleate 3 mg and pseudoephedrine sulfate 45 mg per 5 mL

Tablet:

Allerest® Maximum Strength: Chlorpheniramine maleate 2 mg and pseudoephedrine hydrochloride 30 mg

Deconamine®, Fedahist®, Klerist-D®, Pseudo-Gest Plus®, Sudafed Plus®: Chlorpheniramine maleate 4 mg and pseudoephedrine hydrochloride 60 mg

Chlor-Trimeton® 4 Hour Relief: Chlorpheniramine maleate 4 mg and pseudoephedrine sulfate 60 mg

Chlorpheniramine, Ephedrine, Phenylephrine, and Carbetapentane

(klor fen IR a meen, e FED rin, fen il EF rin, & kar bay ta PEN tane)

U.S. Brand Names Rentamine®; Rynatuss® Pediatric Suspension; Tri-Tannate Plus®

Therapeutic Category Antihistamine/Decongestant/Antitussive

Abuse Potential Yes

Impairment Potential Yes

Dosage Forms Liquid: Carbetapentane tannate 30 mg, ephedrine tannate 5 mg, phenylephrine tannate 5 mg, and chlorpheniramine tannate 4 mg per 5 mL

Chlorpheniramine, Phenylephrine, and Codeine

(klor fen IR a meen, fen il EF rin, & KOE deen)

U.S. Brand Names Pediacof®; Pedituss®

Therapeutic Category Antihistamine/Decongestant/Antitussive

Abuse Potential Yes

Impairment Potential Yes

Dosage Forms Liquid: Chlorpheniramine maleate 0.75 mg, phenylephrine hydrochloride 2.5 mg, and codeine phosphate 5 mg with potassium iodide 75 mg per 5 mL

Chlorpheniramine, Phenylephrine, and Dextromethorphan

(klor fen IR a meen, fen il EF rin, & deks troe meth OR fan)

U.S. Brand Names Cerose-DM® [OTC]

Therapeutic Category Antihistamine/Decongestant/Antitussive

Abuse Potential Yes

Impairment Potential Yes

Dosage Forms Liquid: Chlorpheniramine maleate 4 mg, phenylephrine hydrochloride 10 mg, and dextromethorphan hydrobromide 15 mg per 5 mL

Chlorpheniramine, Phenylephrine, and Methscopolamine

(klor fen IR a meen, fen il EF rin, & meth skoe POL a meen)

U.S. Brand Names Alersule Forte®; D.A.II® Tablet; Dallergy®; Dura-Vent/DA®; Extendryl® SR; Histor-D® Timecelles®

Therapeutic Category Antihistamine/Decongestant/Anticholinergic

Dosage Forms

Caplet, sustained release: Chlorpheniramine maleate 8 mg, phenylephrine hydrochloride 20 mg, and methscopolamine nitrate 2.5 mg

Capsule, sustained release: Chlorpheniramine maleate 8 mg, phenylephrine hydrochloride 10 mg, and methscopolamine nitrate 2.5 mg

Syrup: Chlorpheniramine maleate 2 mg, phenylephrine hydrochloride 10 mg, and methscopolamine nitrate 0.625 mg per 5 mL

Tablet: Chlorpheniramine maleate 4 mg, phenylephrine hydrochloride 10 mg, and methscopolamine nitrate 1.25 mg

Chlorpheniramine, Phenylephrine, and Phenylpropanolamine

(klor fen IR a meen, fen il EF rin, & fen il proe pa NOLE a meen)

U.S. Brand Names Hista-Vadrin® Tablet

Therapeutic Category Antihistamine/Decongestant Combination

Abuse Potential Yes

Impairment Potential Yes

Dosage Forms Tablet: Chlorpheniramine maleate 6 mg, phenylephrine hydrochloride 5 mg, and phenylpropanolamine hydrochloride 40 mg

Chlorpheniramine, Phenylephrine, and Phenyltoloxamine

(klor fen IR a meen, fen il EF rin, & fen il tole LOKS a meen)

U.S. Brand Names Comhist®; Comhist® LA

Therapeutic Category Antihistamine/Decongestant Combination

Dosage Forms

Capsule, sustained release (Comhist® LA): Chlorpheniramine maleate 4 mg, phenylephrine hydrochloride 20 mg, and phenyltoloxamine citrate 50 mg

Tablet (Comhist®): Chlorpheniramine maleate 2 mg, phenylephrine hydrochloride 10 mg, and phenyltoloxamine citrate 25 mg

Chlorpheniramine, Phenylephrine, Phenylpropanolamine, and Belladonna Alkaloids

(klor fen IR a meen, fen il EF rin, fen il proe pa NOLE a meen, & bel a DON a AL ka loydz)

U.S. Brand Names Atrohist® Plus; Phenahist-TR®; Phenchlor® S.H.A.; Ru-Tuss®; Stahist®

Therapeutic Category Cold Preparation

Abuse Potential Yes

Impairment Potential Yes

Dosage Forms Tablet, sustained release: Chlorpheniramine 8 mg, phenylephrine 25 mg, phenylpropanolamine 50 mg, hyoscyamine 0.19 mg, atropine 0.04 mg, and scopolamine 0.01 mg

Chlorpheniramine, Phenylpropanolamine, and Acetaminophen

(klor fen IR a meen, fen il proe pa NOLE a meen, & a seet a MIN oh fen)

U.S. Brand Names BQ® Tablet [OTC]; Congestant D® [OTC]; Coricidin D® [OTC]; Dapacin® Cold Capsule [OTC]; Duadacin® Capsule [OTC]; Tylenol® Cold Effervescent Medication Tablet [OTC]

Therapeutic Category Antihistamine/Decongestant/Analgesic

Abuse Potential Yes

Impairment Potential Yes

Dosage Forms

Capsule: Chlorpheniramine maleate 2 mg, phenylpropanolamine hydrochloride 12.5 mg, and acetaminophen 325 mg

Tablet: Chlorpheniramine maleate 2 mg, phenylpropanolamine hydrochloride 12.5 mg, and acetaminophen 325 mg

Chlorpheniramine, Phenylpropanolamine, and Dextromethorphan

(klor fen IR a meen, fen il proe pa NOLE a meen, & deks troe meth OR fan)

U.S. Brand Names Triaminicol® Multi-Symptom Cold Syrup [OTC]

Therapeutic Category Antihistamine/Decongestant/Antitussive

Abuse Potential Yes

Impairment Potential Yes

Dosage Forms Liquid: Chlorpheniramine maleate 2 mg, phenylpropanolamine hydrochloride 12.5 mg, and dextromethorphan hydrobromide 10 mg per 5 mL

Chlorpheniramine, Phenyltoloxamine, Phenylpropanolamine, and Phenylephrine

(klor fen IR a meen, fen il tole LOKS a meen, fen il proe pa NOLE a meen, & fen il EF rin)

U.S. Brand Names Naldecon®; Naldelate®; Nalgest®; Nalspan®; New Decongestant®; Par Decon®; Tri-Phen-Chlor®; Uni-Decon®

Therapeutic Category Antihistamine/Decongestant Combination

Abuse Potential Yes

Impairment Potential Yes

Dosage Forms

Drops, pediatric: Chlorpheniramine maleate 0.5 mg, phenyltoloxamine citrate 2 mg, phenylpropanolamine hydrochloride 5 mg, and phenylephrine hydrochloride 1.25 mg per mL

Syrup: Chlorpheniramine maleate 2.5 mg, phenyltoloxamine citrate 7.5 mg, phenylpropanolamine hydrochloride 20 mg, and phenylephrine hydrochloride 5 mg per 5 mL

Syrup, pediatric: Chlorpheniramine maleate 0.5 mg, phenyltoloxamine citrate 2 mg, phenylpropanolamine hydrochloride 5 mg, and phenylephrine hydrochloride 1.25 mg per 5 mL

Tablet, sustained release: Chlorpheniramine maleate 5 mg, phenyltoloxamine citrate 15 mg, phenylpropanolamine hydrochloride 40 mg, and phenylephrine hydrochloride 10 mg

Chlorpheniramine, Pseudoephedrine, and Codeine
(klor fen IR a meen, soo doe e FED rin, & KOE deen)

U.S. Brand Names Codehist® DH; Decohistine® DH; Dihistine® DH; Ryna-C® Liquid

Therapeutic Category Antihistamine/Decongestant/Antitussive

Abuse Potential Yes

Impairment Potential Yes

Dosage Forms Liquid: Chlorpheniramine maleate 2 mg, pseudoephedrine hydrochloride 30 mg, and codeine phosphate 10 mg (120 mL, 480 mL)

Chlorpheniramine, Pyrilamine, and Phenylephrine
(klor fen IR a meen, pye RIL a meen, & fen il EF rin)

U.S. Brand Names Rhinatate® Tablet; R-Tannamine® Tablet; R-Tannate® Tablet; Rynatan® Pediatric Suspension; Rynatan® Tablet; Tanoral® Tablet; Triotann® Tablet; Tri-Tannate® Tablet

Therapeutic Category Antihistamine/Decongestant Combination

Dosage Forms

Liquid: Chlorpheniramine tannate 2 mg, pyrilamine tannate 12.5 mg, and phenylephrine tannate 5 mg per 5 mL

Tablet: Chlorpheniramine tannate 8 mg, pyrilamine maleate 12.5 mg, and phenylephrine tannate 25 mg

Chlorpheniramine, Pyrilamine, Phenylephrine, and Phenylpropanolamine
(klor fen IR a meen, pye RIL a meen, fen il EF rin, & fen il proe pa NOLE a meen)

U.S. Brand Names Histalet® Forte Tablet

Therapeutic Category Antihistamine/Decongestant Combination

Abuse Potential Yes

Impairment Potential Yes

Dosage Forms Tablet: Chlorpheniramine maleate 4 mg, pyrilamine maleate 25 mg, phenylephrine hydrochloride 10 mg, and phenylpropanolamine hydrochloride 50 mg

Chlor-Pro® [OTC] *see* Chlorpheniramine *on page 132*

Chlorpromazine (klor PROE ma zeen)

U.S. Brand Names Amazin®; Bay Clor®; Dozine®; Hibanil®; Largactil®; Ormazine®; Prozil®; Repazine®; Thorazine®

Canadian Brand Names Largactil®; Apo-Chlorpromazine®; Chlorprom®; Chlorpromanyl®; Novo-Chlorpromazine®

Therapeutic Category Antipsychotic Agent; Phenothiazine Derivative

Impairment Potential Yes

Use Treatment of nausea and vomiting; psychoses; Tourette's syndrome; mania; intractable hiccups (adults); behavioral problems (children); tension and vascular headaches

Usual Dosage

Children >6 months:

Psychosis: Oral: 0.5-1 mg/kg/dose every 4-6 hours; older children may require 200 mg/day or higher

Nausea and vomiting:

Oral: 0.5-1 mg/kg/dose every 4-6 hours as needed

Rectal: 1 mg/kg/dose every 6-8 hours as needed

Adults:

Psychosis: Oral: Range: 30-800 mg/day in 1-4 divided doses, initiate at lower doses and titrate as needed; usual dose: 200 mg/day; some patients may require 1-2 g/day

Nausea and vomiting:

Oral: 10-25 mg every 4-6 hours

Rectal: 50-100 mg every 6-8 hours

Mechanism of Action Blocks postsynaptic mesolimbic dopaminergic receptors in the brain; exhibits a strong alpha-adrenergic blocking effect and depresses the release of hypothalamic and hypophyseal hormones; strongly anticholinergic

Pharmacodynamics/kinetics

Onset of action:

Tablet: 30 minutes to 1 hour

Sustained released preparation: 30 minutes to 1 hour

Suppositories: 60 minutes

Duration: of action:

Tablet: 4-6 hours

Sustained release preparation: 10-12 hours

Suppositories: 3-4 hours

Absorption:

Oral: Erratic

I.M.: Rapid

Metabolism: Extensive in the liver to active and inactive metabolites

Half-life:

Biphasic: 30 hours

Phase I: 2 hours

Time to peak serum concentration:

Oral: 2-4 hours

I.M.: 15-20 minutes

Signs and Symptoms of Acute Intoxication Deep sleep, hypoglycemia, coma, night terrors, Q-T prolongation, impotence, hypothermia, hyperprolactinemia, ejaculatory disturbances, toxic epidermal necrolysis, delirium, jaundice, neuroleptic malignant syndrome, photosensitivity, corneal microdeposits, extrapyramidal reaction, appetite (increased), Parkinson's-like symptoms, myasthenia gravis (exacerbation or precipitation of), hyperthermia, abnormal involuntary muscle movements, hypotension or hypertension, hirsutism, vision color changes (brown tinge), vision color changes (yellow tinge); urine discoloration (pink), urine discoloration (red), urine discoloration (red-brown)

When to Transport to Hospital Transport any symptomatic patient

Warnings/Precautions Safety in children <6 months of age has not been established; use with caution in patients with cardiovascular disease or seizures; bone marrow depression, severe liver or cardiac disease; significant hypotension may occur, especially when the drug is administered parenterally; extended release capsules and injection contain benzyl alcohol; injection also contains sulfites which may cause allergic reaction

Adverse Reactions

>10%:

Cardiovascular: Hypotension (especially with I.V. use), tachycardia, arrhythmias, orthostatic hypotension

Central nervous system: Pseudoparkinsonism, akathisia, dystonias, tardive dyskinesia (persistent), dizziness

Gastrointestinal: Constipation

Ocular: Pigmentary retinopathy

Respiratory: Nasal congestion

Miscellaneous: Diaphoresis (decreased)

(Continued)

Chlorpromazine *(Continued)*

1% to 10%:

Dermatologic: Pruritus, rash, increased sensitivity to sun

Endocrine & metabolic: Amenorrhea, galactorrhea, gynecomastia, changes in libido, pain in breasts

Gastrointestinal: GI upset, nausea, vomiting, stomach pain, weight gain, xerostomia

Genitourinary: Dysuria, ejaculatory disturbances, urinary retention

Neuromuscular & skeletal: Trembling of fingers

Ocular: Blurred vision

Reference Range

Therapeutic: 50-300 ng/mL (SI: 157-942 nmol/L)

Toxic: >750 ng/mL (SI: >2355 nmol/L)

Drug Interactions Additive effects with other CNS-depressing agents; epinephrine may cause hypotension in patients receiving chlorpromazine due to phenothiazine-induced alpha-adrenergic blockade and unopposed epinephrine B_2 action; chlorpromazine may increase valproic acid serum concentrations; when given piperazine, seizures may occur; antacids, cimetidine may interfere with chlorpromazine absorption; nortriptyline or propranolol may increase chlorpromazine levels; salicylamide and acetanilide may displace chlorpromazine from its protein binding. H_2 antagonists decrease absorption of chlorpromazine.

Dosage Forms

Chlorpromazine hydrochloride:

Capsule, sustained action: 30 mg, 75 mg, 150 mg, 200 mg, 300 mg

Concentrate, oral: 30 mg/mL (120 mL); 100 mg/mL (60 mL, 240 mL)

Injection: 25 mg/mL (1 mL, 2 mL, 10 mL)

Syrup: 10 mg/5 mL (120 mL)

Tablet: 10 mg, 25 mg, 50 mg, 100 mg, 200 mg

Suppository, rectal, as base: 25 mg, 100 mg

Additional Information Use decreased doses in elderly or debilitated patients; extrapyramidal reaction may be more common in patients with hypocalcemia; extrapyramidal reactions may be more common in pediatric patients, especially those with dehydration or acute illnesses (viral or CNS infections); avoid rectal administration in immunocompromised patients; may be useful in treating headaches due to meningitis

Specific References

Hartley L, Henry T, Couper-Smartt J, "Chlorpromazine and Serial Reacton Performance," *Br J Psychol*, 1978, 69(2):271-6.

Russell SA, Hennes HM, Herson KJ, et al, "Upper Airway Compromise in Acute Chlorpromazine Ingestion," *Am J Emerg Med*, 1996, 14(5):467-8.

Chlorpromazine *see* Methamphetamines, Urine *on page 384*

Chlorpropamide *(klor PROE pa mide)*

U.S. Brand Names Clordiabet®; Diabet®; Diabinese®; Gliconorm®; Glymese®; Hypomide®; Normoglic®

Canadian Brand Names Apo-Chlorpropamide®; Novo-Propamide®

Therapeutic Category Antidiabetic Agent (Oral)

Use Controls blood sugar in adult onset, noninsulin-dependent diabetes (type II)

Usual Dosage The dosage of chlorpropamide is variable and should be individualized based upon the patient's response

Adults:

Initial dose: 250 mg/day in mild to moderate diabetes in middle aged, stable diabetic; elderly patients: 100-125 mg/day

Maintenance dose: 100-250 mg/day; severe diabetics may require 500 mg/day; avoid doses >500 mg/day

Mechanism of Action Stimulates insulin release from the pancreatic beta cells; reduces glucose output from the liver; insulin sensitivity is increased at peripheral target sites

Pharmacodynamics/kinetics

Peak effect: Oral: Within 6-8 hours

Metabolism: Extensive in the liver, ~80%

Half-life: 30-42 hours; prolonged in elderly or with renal disease

Time to peak serum concentration: Within 3-4 hours

Elimination: 10% to 30% excreted in urine as unchanged drug

Signs and Symptoms of Acute Intoxication Hypoglycemia (may be prolonged), jaundice, leukopenia; photosensitivity, hyponatremia, lichenoid eruptions, ataxia, neutropenia; feces discoloration (black); erythema multiforme, agranulocytosis; granulocytopenia; colitis

When to Transport to Hospital Transport any pediatric ingestion, any symptomatic patient, or any ingestion over 500 mg

Warnings/Precautions Patients should be properly instructed in the early detection and treatment of hypoglycemia; long half-life may complicate recovery from excess effects; because of chlorpropamide's long half-life, duration of action, and increased risk for hypoglycemia, not considered a hypoglycemic agent of choice in the elderly. May be porphyrinogenic; use with caution in patients with porphyria.

Adverse Reactions

>10%:

Central nervous system: Headache, dizziness

Gastrointestinal: Anorexia, constipation, heartburn, epigastric fullness, nausea, vomiting, diarrhea

1% to 10%: Dermatologic: Skin rash, urticaria, photosensitivity

Reference Range

Glucose: Adults: 60-115 mg/dL

Elderly fasting glucose: 100-180 mg/dL

Chlorpropamide lethal level: >400 µg/mL in nondiabetic patients

Drug Interactions

Decreased effect: Thiazides and hydantoins (eg, phenytoin), beta-adrenergic blockers, gemfibrozil, isoniazid, rifampin, chlorpromazine, oral contraceptives, thyroid hormone, diazoxide; ↓ chlorpropamide effectiveness → ↑ blood glucose

Increased toxicity: ↑ alcohol-associated disulfiram reactions; ↑ oral anticoagulant effect; salicylates → ↑ chlorpropamide effect → ↓ blood glucose; MAO inhibitors ↑ hypoglycemic response; sulfonamides → ↓ sulfonylureas clearance; indobufen, phenylbutazone, co-trimoxazole, chloramphenicol, monoamine oxidase inhibitors, fluconazole, methyldopa, ranitidine, enalapril, nortriptyline, sulfinpyrazone, miconazole

Dosage Forms Tablet: 100 mg, 250 mg

Specific References

Erickson T, Arora A, Lebby TI, et al, "Acute Oral Hypoglycemic Ingestions," *Vet Hum Toxicol*, 1991, 33(3):256-8.

Chlorprothixene (klor proe THIKS een)

U.S. Brand Names Taractan®; Tarasan®; Truxal®; Truxaletter®

Therapeutic Category Antipsychotic Agent

Use Management of psychotic disorders, emotional disturbances

Usual Dosage

Children >6 years: Oral: 10-25 mg 3-4 times/day

(Continued)

Chlorprothixene *(Continued)*

Adults:
Oral: 25-50 mg 3-4 times/day, to be increased as needed; doses exceeding 600 mg/day are rarely required
I.M.: 25-50 mg up to 3-4 times/day

Mechanism of Action Low anticholinergic activity with similar properties as chlorpromazine

Pharmacodynamics/kinetics
Metabolism: Hepatic
Half-life: 8-12 hours

Signs and Symptoms of Acute Intoxication Deep sleep, coma, impotence, dry eyes, extrapyramidal reaction, Parkinson's-like symptoms, neuroleptic malignant syndrome, ejaculatory disturbances, neutropenia, jaundice, photosensitivity, abnormal involuntary muscle movements, hyperactivity, hypotension, oliguria with azotemia

When to Transport to Hospital Transport any pediatric (<6 years of age) ingestion or any symptomatic patient

Adverse Reactions
>10%:
Cardiovascular: Hypotension (especially with I.V. use), hypotension (orthostatic)
Central nervous system: Tardive dyskinesia, pseudoparkinsonian signs and symptoms, dizziness, akathisia, dystonia
Gastrointestinal: Constipation
Ocular: Retinal pigmentation
Miscellaneous: Diaphoresis (decreased)
<10%:
Cardiovascular: Tachycardia, cardiac arrhythmias, Q-T prolongation, sinus bradycardia, sinus tachycardia
Central nervous system: Sedation, drowsiness, restlessness, anxiety, extrapyramidal reactions, neuroleptic malignant syndrome, seizures, altered central temperature regulation, fever, hyperthermia
Dermatologic: Hyperpigmentation, pruritus, rash, photosensitivity
Endocrine & metabolic: Amenorrhea, galactorrhea, gynecomastia
Gastrointestinal: GI upset, xerostomia, weight gain
Genitourinary: Urinary retention, impotence
Hematologic: Leukopenia/neutropenia (agranulocytosis, granulocytopenia) usually in patients with large doses for prolonged periods; thrombocytopenia, hemolysis, eosinophilia
Hepatic: Cholestatic jaundice
Ocular: **Retinal pigmentation**, diplopia, blurred vision, mydriasis
Miscellaneous: Anaphylactoid reactions, systemic lupus erythematosus

Reference Range
Therapeutic: 0.04-0.30 µg/mL
Fatal: 1.00-2.00 µg/mL

Drug Interactions Ethanol has additive effects

Dosage Forms
Concentrate, oral, as lactate and hydrochloride (fruit flavor): 100 mg/5 mL (480 mL)
Injection, as hydrochloride: 12.5 mg/mL (2 mL)
Tablet: 10 mg, 25 mg, 50 mg, 100 mg

Additional Information Slight amine-like odor

Specific References
Scheithauer W, Ulrich W, Kovarik J, et al, "Acute Oliguria Associated With Chlorprothixene Overdosage," *Nephron*, 1988, 48(1):71-3.

Chlorpyrifos

Synonyms O,O-Diethyl-O-(3,5,6-Trichloro-2-Pyridyl) Phosphorothioate; Phosphorothioic Acid; Trichlorpyriphos (Discontinued)

UN Number 2783

U.S. Brand Names Dursban®; Dursban TC®; Lorsban®; Pyrinex®

Use Broad spectrum insecticide for control of mosquitoes, flies, cockroaches, fleas, and termites (TC formulation); has been used as an ascaricide and a veterinary ectoparasiticide

Toxicodynamics/kinetics

Absorption: Oral: 70%; Dermal: <3%

Metabolism: Hepatic to diethylphosphate, diethylthiophosphate, and 3,5,6-trichloro-2-pyridinol (TCP)

Half-life: 27 hours

Signs and Symptoms of Acute Intoxication Miosis (unreactive to light), mydriasis (rarely), lacrimation, pallor, excessive sweating, confusion, agitation, headache, dysarthria, generalized asthenia, seizures, A-V block, coma, decreased hemoglobin/red blood cell count/platelet count, metabolic acidosis and hyperglycemia (severe intoxication), hypotension, hypertension, bradycardia, tachycardia, Q-T prolongation, heart block, asystole, salivation, bronchorrhea, tachypnea, pulmonary edema, respiratory depression, diaphragmatic paralysis, skeletal muscle fasciculation and flaccid paralysis, nausea, vomiting, abdominal pain, fecal and urinary incontinence; an "intermediate syndrome" of limb asthenia and respiratory paralysis has been reported to occur between 24 and 96 hours postorganophosphate exposure, and is independent of the acute cholinergic crisis; late paresthesia characterized by stocking and glove paresthesia, anesthesia, and asthenia is infrequently observed weeks to months following acute exposure to certain organophosphates; cases of delayed neurotoxicity have been described

When to Transport to Hospital Transport any symptomatic patient

Overdosage/Treatment

Decontamination: Isolation, bagging, and disposal of all contaminated clothing and other articles; all emergency medical workers and hospital staff should follow appropriate precautions regarding exposure to hazardous material including the use of protective clothing, masks, goggles, and respiratory equipment

Dermal: Prompt thorough scrubbing of all affected areas with soap and water, including hair and nails; 5% bleach can also be used

Ocular: Irrigation with copious tepid sterile water or saline

Adverse Reactions

Cardiovascular: Q-T prolongation, sinus bradycardia, sinus tachycardia

Central nervous system: Anxiety, restlessness, dizziness, dystonic reactions, cognitive dysfunction, hypothermia

Dermatologic: Milk skin irritant

Neuromuscular & skeletal: Choreoathetosis

Ocular: Miosis (82%), mydriasis can be present in severely affected individuals; conjunctivitis, photophobia, opsoclonus

Respiratory: Rhinorrhea

Miscellaneous: Diaphoresis

Reference Range Oral dose of 5 mg/kg followed by dermal exposures between 0.5-5 mg/kg 2 weeks later produced blood chlorpyrifos levels <30 µg/L (blood TCP levels were 0.9 mg/L 6 hours after oral ingestion and 0.06 mg/L 24 hours after dermal administration); a single oral dose of 0.5 mg/kg can depress plasma cholinesterase levels by 85%; urinary 3,5,6-trichloro 2-pyridinol (TCP) level of 25 µg/mg creatinine is associated with a 30% decrease of cholinesterase level

(Continued)

Chlorpyrifos (Continued)

Additional Information Red blood cell cholinesterase, and serum pseudocholinesterase may be depressed following acute or chronic organophosphate exposure; RBC cholinesterase is typically not analyzed by in-house laboratories, and is usually not available for consideration during acute management. Pseudocholinesterase levels may be rapidly available from some in-house laboratories, but are not as reliable a marker of organophosphate exposure because of variability secondary to variant genotypes, hepatic disease, oral estrogen use, or malnutrition. Because of this variability, true indication of suppression of either of these enzymes can only be estimated through comparison to pre-exposure values; these enzymes may be useful in measuring a patient's recovery postexposure, especially if the recovery is not progressing as expected. Emits a sulfur (garlic) odor at airborne concentrations exceeding 1 ppb. The intermediate syndrome is not related to delayed neuropathy.

Other information concerning pesticide exposures is available through the EPA-funded National Pesticide Telecommunications Network: 1-800-858-7378 (weekdays, 8 AM to 6 PM, Central Standard time)

Toxic dose: 300 mg/kg

$Q-T_c$ prolongation on EKG in the setting of organophosphate poisoning is associated with a high incidence of respiratory failure and mortality

Atmospheric half-life: 6.34 hours

Estimated daily dietary intake for a 14-16 year old male in the U.S.: ~3.4 ng/kg body weight

EPA tolerance range for agriculture products: 0.05-15 ppm

TLV-TWA: 0.2 mg/m^3

Less likely than other organophosphates to induce organophosphate-induced delayed neuropathy

Specific References
Aiuto LA, Pavlakis SG, and Boxer RA, "Life-Threatening Organophosphate-Induced Delayed Polyneuropathy in a Child After Accidental Chlorpyrifos Ingestion," J Pediatr, 1993, 122(4):658-60.

Chlor-Rest® Tablet [OTC] see Chlorpheniramine and Phenylpropanolamine on page 134

Chlorthalidone (klor THAL i done)

U.S. Brand Names Amaxin®; Hydro-Long®; Hygroton®; Igrotin®; Thalitone®; Urolin®

Canadian Brand Names Apo-Chlorthalidone®; Novo-Thalidone®; Uridon®

Therapeutic Category Diuretic

Use Management of mild to moderate hypertension, used alone or in combination with other agents; treatment of edema associated with congestive heart failure, nephrotic syndrome, or pregnancy

Usual Dosage Oral:
Children: 2 mg/kg 3 times/week or 1-2 mg/kg/day
Adults: 25-100 mg/day or 100 mg 3 times/week

Mechanism of Action Sulfonamide-derived diuretic that inhibits sodium and chloride reabsorption in the kidney

Pharmacodynamics/kinetics
Peak effect: 2-6 hours
Absorption: Oral: 65%
Metabolism: In the liver

Half-life: 35-55 hours; may be prolonged with renal impairment, with anuria: 81 hours

Elimination: ~50% to 65% excreted unchanged in urine; clearance: 1.6 mL/kg/minute

Signs and Symptoms of Acute Intoxication Hypermotility, hyperglycemia, photosensitivity, periarteritis nodosa, diuresis, impotence, LDL (increased), hyponatremia, hypomagnesemia, hypokalemia, hypocalcemia, nocturia, myopia, myasthenia gravis (exacerbation or precipitation of), vision color changes (yellow tinge), hyperuricemia, lethargy, confusion, muscle weakness

When to Transport to Hospital Transport any symptomatic patient or any ingestion over 3 mg/kg

Warnings/Precautions Hypokalemia, renal disease, hepatic disease, gout, lupus erythematosus, diabetes mellitus; use with caution in severe renal diseases

Adverse Reactions 1% to 10%: Endocrine & metabolic: Hypokalemia

Reference Range Peak serum chlorthalidone level of 6.3 mg/L after a single 200 mg dose

Drug Interactions

Decreased effect of oral hypoglycemics; decreased absorption with cholestyramine and colestipol; decreased diuretic effect with naproxen

Increased effect with furosemide and other loop diuretics; increased toxicity/levels of lithium, diazide, pancuronium, calcium salts, vitamin D (increased calcium levels), antineoplastics (leukopenia), digoxin (arrhythmias with electrolyte imbalances); increased incidence of ventricular arrhythmias with ketanserin

Dosage Forms

Tablet:

Hygroton®: 25 mg, 50 mg, 100 mg

Thalitone®: 15 mg, 25 mg

Additional Information Recent studies have found chlorthalidone effective in the treatment of isolated systolic hypertension in the elderly; avoid in breast-feeding mothers

Specific References

Freis ED, "The Efficacy and Safety of Diuretics in Treating Hypertension," *Ann Intern Med*, 1995, 122(3):223-6.

Chlor-Trimeton® [OTC] *see* Chlorpheniramine *on page 132*

Chlor-Trimeton® 4 Hour Relief Tablet [OTC] *see* Chlorpheniramine and Pseudoephedrine *on page 134*

Chlorzoxazone (klor ZOKS a zone)

Synonyms Chlorobenzoxazoline

U.S. Brand Names Biomioran®; Escoflex®; Paraflex®; Paronfon® Forte ESC; Solaxin®

Therapeutic Category Skeletal Muscle Relaxant

Impairment Potential Yes

Use Musculoskeletal pain, muscle spasm

Usual Dosage

Children: 125-500 mg 3-4 times/day

Adult: 250-750 mg 3-4 times/day; maximum tolerated dose: 5 g

Mechanism of Action Precise mechanism is not yet clear, but many effects have been ascribed to its central depressant actions

Pharmacodynamics/kinetics

Duration: 3-4 hours

Metabolism: Hepatic hydroxylation and conjugation to an inactive metabolite

Half-life: 1.1 hours

(Continued)

Chlorzoxazone *(Continued)*

When to Transport to Hospital Transport any patient with a change in mental status

Warnings/Precautions Use with caution in patients with liver dysfunction

Adverse Reactions
>10%: Central nervous system: Drowsiness

1% to 10%:
Cardiovascular: Tachycardia, tightness in chest, flushing of face, syncope
Central nervous system: Mental depression, allergic fever, dizziness, light-headedness, headache, paradoxical stimulation
Dermatologic: Angioedema
Gastrointestinal: Nausea, vomiting, stomach cramps
Neuromuscular & skeletal: Trembling
Ocular: Burning of eyes
Respiratory: Shortness of breath
Miscellaneous: Hiccups

Test Interactions False-positive serum test for aprobarbital can be noted with Toxi-Lab Screen™

Reference Range Peak plasma levels following an oral 750 mg dose: ~36 mg/L at 38 minutes

Drug Interactions Use of alcohol or other central nervous system depressants can have an additive effect

Dosage Forms Tablet: 250 mg, 500 mg

Specific References
Badanowski R and Powell JW, "Previously Unreported Side Effect of Parafon Forte®," *Ann Emerg Med*, 1981, 10:615.

Choledyl® Constant-T® *see* Theophylline Salts *on page 571*

Choline Magnesium Trisalicylate
(KOE leen mag NEE zhum trye sa LIS i late)

U.S. Brand Names Tricosal®; Trilisate®

Therapeutic Category Analgesic, Non-narcotic; Nonsteroidal Anti-Inflammatory Agent (NSAID)

Use Management of osteoarthritis, rheumatoid arthritis, and other arthritides

Usual Dosage Oral (based on total salicylate content):
Children <37 kg: 50 mg/kg/day given in 2 divided doses
Adults: 500 mg to 1.5 g 2-3 times/day; usual maintenance dose: 1-4.5 g/day

Mechanism of Action Inhibits prostaglandin synthesis; acts on the hypothalamus heat-regulating center to reduce fever; blocks the generation of pain impulses

Pharmacodynamics/kinetics
Absorption: From the stomach and small intestine within ~2 hours
Metabolism: Hydrolyzed to salicylate in the liver
Half-life: Dose-dependent ranging from 2-3 hours at low doses to 30 hours at high doses
Time to peak serum concentration: 1-2 hours
Elimination: Urine

Signs and Symptoms of Acute Intoxication Nausea, hyponatremia, wheezing, nephrotic syndrome, cognitive dysfunction, GI upset, GI bleeding, bezoars, hypoglycemia, vomiting, ototoxicity, tinnitus, drowsiness; severe poisoning can manifest with coma, seizures, renal failure and or hepatic failure, hypotension, respiratory depression, hyperthermia, irritability, metabolic acidosis, hyperglycemia, urine discoloration (pink), feces discoloration (black), feces discoloration (pink), feces discoloration (red), feces discoloration (tarry)

When to Transport to Hospital Transport any symptomatic patient or ingestion exceeding 5 g

Warnings/Precautions Use with extreme caution in patients with renal impairment, erosive gastritis, or peptic ulcer; avoid use in patients with suspected varicella or influenza (salicylates have been associated with Reye's syndrome in children <16 years of age when used to treat symptoms of chickenpox or the flu)

Adverse Reactions

>10%: Gastrointestinal: Nausea, heartburn, stomach pains, dyspepsia, epigastric discomfort

1% to 10%:
Central nervous system: Fatigue
Dermatologic: Rash
Gastrointestinal: Gastrointestinal ulceration
Hematologic: Hemolytic anemia
Neuromuscular & skeletal: Weakness
Respiratory: Dyspnea
Miscellaneous: Anaphylactic shock

Test Interactions False-negative results for Clinistix® urine test; false-positive results with Clinitest®

Reference Range

Salicylate blood levels for anti-inflammatory effect: 10-30 mg/dL
Analgesia and antipyretic effect: Up to 10 mg/dL

Drug Interactions Aspirin decreases serum concentrations probably by protein-binding displacement; there is an increased bleeding potential with concomitant warfarin therapy; may increase lithium and methotrexate concentrations by decreasing renal clearance; may decrease diuretic and hypotensive effects of thiazides, loop diuretics, ACE inhibitors, and beta-blockers; may increase nephrotoxicity of cyclosporine

Dosage Forms

Liquid: 500 mg/5 mL [choline salicylate 293 mg and magnesium salicylate 362 mg per 5 mL] (237 mL)
Tablet:
500 mg: Choline salicylate 293 mg and magnesium salicylate 362 mg
750 mg: Choline salicylate 440 mg and magnesium salicylate 544 mg
1000 mg: Choline salicylate 587 mg and magnesium salicylate 725 mg

Additional Information Salicylate salts do not inhibit platelet aggregation and, therefore, should not be substituted for aspirin in the prophylaxis of thrombosis; total dose (mg) multiplied by 0.75 provides aspirin equivalent dose

Specific References

Chapman BJ and Proudfoot AT, "Adult Salicylate Poisoning: Deaths and Outcome in Patients With High Plasma Salicylate Concentrations," *Q J Med*, 1989, 72(268):699-707.

Choline Theophyllinate see Theophylline Salts on page 571

Chromar see Isopropyl Alcohol on page 323

CI-945 see Gabapentin on page 261

Cibalith-S® see Lithium on page 347

Cidan Est® see Streptomycin on page 548

Cimetidine (sye MET i deen)

U.S. Brand Names Antil®; Asaurex®; Beamat®; Dyspamet®; Tagamet®; Zergamet®

Canadian Brand Names Apo-Cimetidine®; Novo-Cimetidine®; Nu-Cimet®; Peptol®

Therapeutic Category Histamine H$_2$ Antagonist
(Continued)

Cimetidine *(Continued)*

Use Short-term treatment of active duodenal ulcers and benign gastric ulcers; long-term prophylaxis of duodenal ulcer; gastric hypersecretory states; gastro-esophageal reflux; prevention of upper gastrointestinal bleeding in critically ill patients; prevention of dapsone-induced methemoglobinemia; used for systemic mastocytosis

Usual Dosage

Neonates: Oral, I.M., I.V.: 10-20 mg/kg/day divided every 4-6 hours

Children: Oral, I.M., I.V.: 20-40 mg/kg/day in divided doses every 4 hours

Adults:

Short-term treatment of active ulcers:

Oral: 300 mg 4 times/day or 800 mg at bedtime or 400 mg twice daily for up to 8 weeks

I.M., I.V.: 300 mg every 6 hours or 37.5 mg/hour by continuous infusion; I.V. dosage should be adjusted to maintain an intragastric pH of ≥5

Prevention of dapsone-induced methemoglobinemia: 400 mg 3 times/day

Patients with an active bleed: Give cimetidine as a continuous infusion (see above)

Duodenal ulcer prophylaxis: Oral: 400-800 mg at bedtime

Gastric hypersecretory conditions: Oral, I.M., I.V.: 300-600 mg every 6 hours; dosage not to exceed 2.4 g/day

Mechanism of Action Competitive inhibition of histamine at H_2-receptors of the gastric parietal cells resulting in reduced gastric acid secretion

Pharmacodynamics/kinetics

Absorption: Oral: ~60% to 75%; may be affected by food

Metabolism: In the liver

Bioavailability: 60% to 70%

Half-life:

Neonates: 3.6 hours

Children: 1.4 hours

Adults:

Normal renal function: 2 hours

Renal insufficiency: 3.7 hours

Time to peak serum concentration: Within 1 hour

Signs and Symptoms of Acute Intoxication Respiratory failure, depression, hyperthermia, impotence, extrapyramidal reaction, ileus, eosinophilia, hyperprolactinemia, galactorrhea, myopathy, myalgia, mania, leukocytosis, A-V block, delirium, disorientation, dementia, cholestatic jaundice, ataxia, bradycardia, mydriasis, coma, parotid pain, dry mouth, slurred speech, sweating, erythema multiforme, leukopenia; neutropenia; agranulocytosis; granulocytopenia

When to Transport to Hospital Transport any symptomatic patient

Warnings/Precautions Modify dosage in patients with renal and/or hepatic impairment

Adverse Reactions 1% to 10%:

Central nervous system: Dizziness, agitation, headache, drowsiness

Gastrointestinal: Diarrhea, nausea, vomiting

Test Interactions May cause a false elevation of serum creatinine due to interference with tubular secretion of creatinine

Reference Range Therapeutic: 0.25-1 μg/mL (SI: 1-4 μmol/L); confusion occurs in levels >2 μg/mL (SI: >8 μmol/L)

Drug Interactions

Decreased elimination of lidocaine, theophylline, phenytoin, metronidazole, triamterene, procainamide, quinidine and propranolol; inhibition of warfarin and morphine metabolism, tricyclic antidepressant metabolism, diazepam elimination and cyclosporine elimination; metoclopramide and propantheline may reduce the absorption of cimetidine

By inhibiting gastric alcohol dehydrogenase, cimetidine can increase the bioavailability and peak concentrations of ethyl alcohol; cimetidine increased peak ethanol levels by 92% with ethanol ingestions (0.15-0.3 g/kg)

Concomitant tacrine and cimetidine administration can result in inhibition of first-pass hepatic extraction of tacrine and thus elevated serum tacrine levels (by ~30%). Cimetidine increases the half-life of tramadol by 19%.

Dosage Forms

Cimetidine hydrochloride:
Infusion, in NS: 300 mg (50 mL)
Injection: 150 mg/mL (2 mL, 8 mL)
Liquid, oral (mint-peach flavor): 300 mg/5 mL with alcohol 2.8% (5 mL, 240 mL)
Tablet: 200 mg, 300 mg, 400 mg, 800 mg

Additional Information Cimetidine is not effective for hepatoprotection in acetaminophen overdose; may inhibit absorption of cobalamin; may increase HDL cholesterol concentrations; may cause phytobezoar formation; at doses >1 g/ day of cimetidine, the risk of developing gynecomastia is 40 times that of nonusers; over-the-counter preparation marketed as Tagamet® HB

Specific References

Krenzelok EP, Litovitz T, Lippold KP, et al, "Cimetidine Toxicity: An Assessment of 881 Cases," *Ann Emerg Med*, 1987, 16(11):1217-21.

Cincofarm® see Oxitriptan on page 451

Cinnamene see Styrene on page 551

Claritin® see Loratadine on page 350

Claritin-D® see Loratadine and Pseudoephedrine on page 351

Claritin-D® 24-Hour see Loratadine and Pseudoephedrine on page 351

Claritine® see Loratadine on page 350

Clarityn® see Loratadine on page 350

Clarityne® see Loratadine on page 350

Clarmyl® see Clobazam on page 151

Clear Away® Disc [OTC] see Salicylic Acid on page 530

Clear Eyes® [OTC] see Naphazoline on page 422

Clear Tussin® 30 see Guaifenesin and Dextromethorphan on page 271

Clemastine (KLEM as teen)

Synonyms Mecloprodin

U.S. Brand Names Aller-eze®; Antihist-1® [OTC]; Tavegil®; Tavist®; Tavist®-1 [OTC]

Therapeutic Category Antihistamine

Use Perennial and seasonal allergic rhinitis and other allergic symptoms including rash

Usual Dosage Oral:
Children: <12 years: 0.4-1 mg twice daily
Children >12 years and Adults: 1.34 mg twice daily to 2.68 mg 3 times/day; do not exceed 8.04 mg/day; lower doses should be considered in patients >60 years; up to 6 mg/day given for angioedema

Mechanism of Action Competes with histamine for H_1-receptor sites on effector cells in the gastrointestinal tract, blood vessels, and respiratory tract

Pharmacodynamics/kinetics
Duration of effect: 10-12 hours
Peak therapeutic effect: Within 5-7 hours
Absorption: Almost 100% from gastrointestinal tract
(Continued)

Clemastine *(Continued)*

Metabolism: In the liver (no enzyme induction)

Elimination: Excreted in urine

When to Transport to Hospital Transport any ingestion over 8 mg or patients exhibiting any change in mental status

Overdosage/Treatment Supportive therapy: There is no specific treatment for an antihistamine overdose, however, most of its clinical toxicity is due to anticholinergic effects. Anticholinesterase inhibitors may be useful by reducing acetylcholinesterase. Anticholinesterase inhibitors include physostigmine, neostigmine, pyridostigmine and edrophonium. For anticholinergic overdose with severe life-threatening symptoms, physostigmine 1-2 mg (0.5 or 0.02 mg/kg for children) I.V., slowly may be given to reverse these effects.

Warnings/Precautions Safety and efficacy have not been established in children <6 years of age; bladder neck obstruction, symptomatic prostate hypertrophy, asthmatic attacks, and stenosing peptic ulcer

Adverse Reactions

>10%:

Central nervous system: Slight to moderate drowsiness

Respiratory: Thickening of bronchial secretions

1% to 10%:

Central nervous system: Headache, fatigue, nervousness, increased dizziness

Gastrointestinal: Appetite increase, weight gain, nausea, diarrhea, abdominal pain, xerostomia

Neuromuscular & skeletal: Arthralgia

Respiratory: Pharyngitis

Drug Interactions Increased toxicity (CNS depression): CNS depressants, MAO inhibitors, tricyclic antidepressants, phenothiazines, biperiden, guanabenz

Dosage Forms

Syrup (citrus flavor): 0.67 mg/5 mL with alcohol 5.5% (120 mL)

Tablet: 1.34 mg, 2.68 mg

Additional Information Clemastine fumarate 1.34 mg = clemastine base 1 mg; offers no significant benefit over other antihistamines except that it may be dosed twice daily (in adults) as compared to other antihistamines with more frequent dosing

Specific References

Kok TH, Taitz LS, Bennett MJ, et al, "Drowsiness Due to Clemastine Transmitted in Breast Milk," *Lancet*, 1982, 1:914-5.

Clemastine and Phenylpropanolamine

(KLEM as teen & fen il proe pa NOLE a meen)

U.S. Brand Names Antihist-D®; Tavist-D®

Therapeutic Category Antihistamine/Decongestant Combination

Abuse Potential Yes

Impairment Potential Yes

Dosage Forms Tablet: Clemastine fumarate 1.34 mg and phenylpropanolamine hydrochloride 75 mg

Clidinium and Chlordiazepoxide

(kli DI nee um & klor dye az e POKS ide)

Synonyms Chlordiazepoxide and Clidinium

U.S. Brand Names Clindex®; Clinoxide®; Clipoxide®; Librax®; Lidox®; Zebrax®

Canadian Brand Names Apo®-Chlorax; Corium®; ProChlorax

Therapeutic Category Anticholinergic Agent

Abuse Potential Yes

Impairment Potential Yes

Use Adjunct treatment of peptic ulcer, treatment of irritable bowel syndrome

Usual Dosage Oral: 1-2 capsules 3-4 times/day, before meals or food and at bedtime

Dosage Forms Capsule: Clidinium bromide 2.5 mg and chlordiazepoxide hydrochloride 5 mg

Climbing Nightshade see Deadly Nightshade on page 178

Clindex® see Clidinium and Chlordiazepoxide on previous page

Clinoril® see Sulindac on page 554

Clinoxide® see Clidinium and Chlordiazepoxide on previous page

Clipoxide® see Clidinium and Chlordiazepoxide on previous page

Clistin® see Carbinoxamine on page 106

Clobazam (KLOE ba zam)

U.S. Brand Names Clarmyl®; Clopax®; Frisium®; Noiafren®; Sederlona®; Urbadan®; Urbanol®; Urbanyl®

Therapeutic Category Anticonvulsant; Antidepressant

Impairment Potential Yes

Use Investigational: Antianxiety, anticonvulsant, and sedative agent

Usual Dosage

Adults: 20-30 mg/day in divided doses or at night; maximum daily dose: 60 mg

Elderly: 10-20 mg/day

Mechanism of Action Facilitates gamma-aminobutyric acid neurotransmission; weak hypnotic agent

Pharmacodynamics/kinetics

Metabolism: Hepatic to active metabolite N-desmethyl clobazam

Half-life: 10-50 hours (parent drug); 77 hours (metabolite)

Peak plasma levels: Within 1.3 hours

Elimination: Renal

When to Transport to Hospital Transport any pediatric patient, any patient who is dizzy, sedated, or confused, or any ingestion over 60 mg

Adverse Reactions May induce systemic lupus erythematosus (SLE)

Cardiovascular: Hypotension (orthostatic), syncope

Central nervous system: Sedation, dizziness, lightheadedness, headache, ataxia, CNS depression, depression

Dermatologic: Toxic epidermal necrolysis

Endocrine & metabolic: Weight gain

Gastrointestinal: Xerostomia

Reference Range After a 40 mg oral dose, peak plasma levels: ~730 µg/L

Dosage Forms

Capsule: 10 mg

Tablet: 10 mg

Additional Information Used to relieve phantom limb pain; similar efficacy as with buspirone in treatment of anxiety/panic disorders; oral ingestion of 300 mg produced mental status changes; reduce dosage in elderly and cirrhosis

Specific References

Bohm C, Placchi M, Stallone F, et al, "A Double-Blind Comparison of Buspirone, Clobazam, and Placebo in Patients With Anxiety Treated in a General Practice Setting," J Clin Psychopharmacol, 1990, 10(3 Suppl):38S-42S.

Clocort® Maximum Strength see Hydrocortisone on page 297

Clomipramine (kloe MI pra meen)

U.S. Brand Names Anafranil®

Canadian Brand Names Apo-Clomipramine®

Therapeutic Category Antidepressant

(Continued)

Clomipramine *(Continued)*

Use Treatment of obsessive-compulsive disorder (OCD)

Usual Dosage Oral: Initial:

Children: 25 mg/day and gradually increase, as tolerated, to a maximum of 3 mg/kg/day or 200 mg/day, whichever is smaller

Adults: 25 mg/day and gradually increase, as tolerated, to 100 mg/day the first 2 weeks, may then be increased to a total of 250 mg/day maximum

Mechanism of Action Clomipramine appears to affect serotonin uptake while its active metabolite, desmethylclomipramine, affects norepinephrine uptake; a tricyclic tertiary amine antidepressant

Pharmacodynamics/kinetics

Onset of action: 2-3 weeks

Absorption: Oral: Rapid

Metabolism: Metabolized to desmethylclomipramine (active) in the liver

Half-life: 20-30 hours; >50 hours in an overdose setting

Signs and Symptoms of Acute Intoxication Agitation, confusion, agranulocytosis, thrombocytopenia, photosensitivity, neuroleptic malignant syndrome, leukopenia, myoclonus, mania, memory loss, lactation, hallucinations, hyperprolactinemia, urinary retention, hyperthermia, hypotension, tachycardia, seizures, apnea

When to Transport to Hospital Transport any symptomatic patient or any ingestion exceeding 300 mg

Warnings/Precautions Seizures are likely and are dose related

Adverse Reactions

>10%:

Central nervous system: Dizziness, drowsiness, headache

Gastrointestinal: Xerostomia, constipation, increased appetite, nausea, unpleasant taste, weight gain

Neuromuscular & skeletal: Weakness

1% to 10%:

Cardiovascular: Arrhythmias, hypotension

Central nervous system: Confusion, delirium, hallucinations, nervousness, restlessness, parkinsonian syndrome, insomnia

Gastrointestinal: Diarrhea, heartburn

Genitourinary: Dysuria, sexual dysfunction

Neuromuscular & skeletal: Fine muscle tremors

Ocular: Blurred vision, eye pain

Miscellaneous: Diaphoresis (excessive)

Reference Range Level of 6560 ng/mL associated with fatality; serum levels may not peak until the fourth day

Drug Interactions

Clomipramine blocks the uptake of guanethidine and clonidine and may prevent the hypotensive effects of these drugs; clomipramine and moclobemide may result in a fatal serotonin syndrome

CNS depressants: Clomipramine may be additive to the effects of CNS depressants

Sympathomimetic agents: Clomipramine potentiates the effects of sympathomimetic agents such as isoproterenol, epinephrine, etc

With MAO inhibitors: Fever, hypertension, tachycardia, seizures, agitation, delirium

Warfarin: Clomipramine may increase prothrombin time in patients stabilized on warfarin

Use with caution with oral contraceptives, may increase plasma concentrations; miconazole may inhibit metabolism of clomipramine; morphine increases availability of clomipramine; concomitant use of clomipramine with alprazolam can result in serotonin syndrome; seizures can result with concomitant clomipramine and fluoxetine or valproic acid therapy; addition of clomipramine to valproic acid in a patient with a stable seizure disorder resulted in status epilepticus

Tachycardia with concomitant fluoxetine

Dosage Forms Capsule, as hydrochloride: 25 mg, 50 mg, 75 mg

Additional Information May also relieve depression, panic attacks, and chronic pain; may be unsafe to use in patients with porphyria; not effective for sleep apnea

Specific References

Dale O and Hole A, "Biphasic Time-Course of Serum Concentrations of Clomipramine and Desmethylclomipramine After a Near-Fatal Overdose," *Vet Hum Toxicol*, 1994, 36(4):309-10.

Clonazepam (kloe NA ze pam)

Related Information

Flunitrazepam *on page 250*
Nitrazepam *on page 435*

U.S. Brand Names Iktorivil®; Klonopin™; Rivotril®

Canadian Brand Names PMS-Clonazepam®; Rivotril®

Therapeutic Category Benzodiazepine

Abuse Potential Yes

Impairment Potential Yes; Plasma clonazepam levels >0.1 mg/L are consistent with impairment. Brief or extended period (up to 1 year) of use is consistent with driving impairment in the elderly; the impairment is greatest in the first 7 days of use.

Baselt RC and Cravey RH, *Disposition of Toxic Drugs and Chemicals in Man*, 4th ed, Foster City, CA: Chemical Toxicology Institute, 1995.

Use Prophylaxis of absence (petit mal), petit mal variant (Lennox-Gastaut), akinetic, and myoclonic seizures

Usual Dosage Oral:

Children <10 years or 30 kg: Initial daily dose: 0.01-0.03 mg/kg/day (maximum: 0.05 mg/kg/day) given in 2-3 divided doses; increase by no more than 0.5 mg every third day until seizures are controlled or adverse effects seen; usual maintenance dose: 0.1-0.2 mg/kg/day divided 3 times/day; not to exceed 0.2 mg/kg/day

Adults: Initial daily dose not to exceed 1.5 mg given in 3 divided doses; may increase by 0.5-1 mg every third day until seizures are controlled or adverse effects seen; usual maintenance dose: 0.05-0.2 mg/kg; do not exceed 20 mg/day

Mechanism of Action Suppresses the spike-and-wave discharge in absence seizures by depressing nerve transmission in the motor cortex

Pharmacodynamics/kinetics

Onset of action: 20-60 minutes

Duration:

Infants and young Children: Up to 6-8 hours

Adults: Up to 12 hours

Absorption: Oral: Well absorbed

Distribution: V_d: Adults: 1.5-4.4 L/kg; distributed widely throughout body; probably crosses blood-brain barrier and placenta

Protein binding: 50% to 85%

Metabolism: Extensive; undergoes nitro-reduction to inactive metabolites; principle metabolite: 7-aminoclonazepam

Half-life:

Children: 22-33 hours

Adults: 19-50 hours

(Continued)

Clonazepam *(Continued)*

Elimination: Metabolites excreted as glucuronide or sulfate conjugates; <2% excreted unchanged in urine

Signs and Symptoms of Acute Intoxication May produce somnolence, gaze nystagmus, purpura, dysarthria, diplopia, confusion, ataxia, diminished reflexes, depression, hyperactivity, neuroleptic malignant syndrome, hirsutism, coma, hypotension, cyanosis, leukopenia; neutropenia; agranulocytosis; granulocytopenia

When to Transport to Hospital Transport any pediatric (<6 years of age) ingestion, any patient with central nervous system changes, or any ingestion over 0.05 mg/kg

Warnings/Precautions Use with caution in patients with chronic respiratory disease or impaired renal function; abrupt discontinuance may precipitate withdrawal symptoms, status epilepticus or seizures

Adverse Reactions

>10%:

Cardiovascular: Tachycardia, chest pain

Central nervous system: Drowsiness, fatigue, ataxia, lightheadedness, memory impairment, insomnia, anxiety, depression, headache

Dermatologic: Rash

Endocrine & metabolic: Decreased libido

Gastrointestinal: Xerostomia, constipation, diarrhea, nausea, increased or decreased appetite, vomiting, decreased salivation

Neuromuscular & skeletal: Dysarthria

Ocular: Blurred vision

Miscellaneous: Diaphoresis

1% to 10%:

Cardiovascular: Syncope, hypotension

Central nervous system: Confusion, nervousness, dizziness, akathisia

Dermatologic: Dermatitis

Gastrointestinal: Weight gain or loss, increased salivation

Neuromuscular & skeletal: Rigidity, tremor, muscle cramps

Otic: Tinnitus

Respiratory: Nasal congestion, hyperventilation

Reference Range

Sample size: 2 mL serum or plasma

Therapeutic: 10-50 ng/mL

Toxic: >80 ng/mL

Timing of serum samples: Peak serum levels occur 1-3 hours after oral ingestion

Drug Interactions CNS depressants, phenytoin, and barbiturates may enhance metabolism

Dosage Forms Tablet: 0.5 mg, 1 mg, 2 mg

Additional Information Ethosuximide or valproic acid may be preferred for treatment of absence (petit mal) seizures; clonazepam-induced behavioral disturbances may be more frequent in mentally handicapped patients; may be effective therapy for tinnitus

Specific References

Khouzam HR and Boutros NN, "The Use of Clonazepam in Psychiatry," *Res Staff Physician*, 1997, 43(6):51-4.

Clonidine *(KLOE ni deen)*

U.S. Brand Names Catapres®; Catapressan®; Catapres-TTS®; Clonistada®; Dixart®; Hyposyn®; Ipotensium®; Isoglaucon®

Canadian Brand Names Apo-Clonidine®; Dixarit®; Novo-Clonidine®; Nu-Clonidine®

Therapeutic Category Alpha-Adrenergic Agonist

Impairment Potential Yes; Doses >0.3 mg associated with sedation in first-time users

Baselt RC and Cravey RH, *Disposition of Toxic Drugs and Chemicals in Man*, 4th ed, Foster City, CA: Chemical Toxicology Institute, 1995, 178.

Use Management of mild to moderate hypertension; either used alone or in combination with other antihypertensives; not recommended for first-line therapy for hypertension; also used for opiates withdrawal and in smoking cessation therapy; other uses may include prophylaxis of migraines, glaucoma, and diabetes-associated diarrhea; epidural use to improve epidural bupivacaine obstetrical anesthesia (can cause a decrease in fetal heart rate)

Usual Dosage

Children: Oral: Initial: 5-10 mcg/kg/day in divided doses every 8-12 hours; increase gradually at 5- to 7-day intervals to 25 mcg/kg/day in divided doses every 6 hours; maximum: 0.9 mg/day

Adults:

Oral: Initial dose: 0.1 mg twice daily, usual maintenance dose: 0.2-1.2 mg/day in 2-4 divided doses; maximum recommended dose: 2.4 mg/day

Transdermal: Apply once every 7 days; for initial therapy start with 0.1 mg and increase by 0.1 mg at 1- to 2-week intervals; dosages >2 x 0.3 mg do not improve efficacy

Mechanism of Action Stimulates alpha$_2$-adrenoreceptors in the brain stem, thus activating an inhibitory neuron, resulting in reduced sympathetic outflow, producing a decrease in vasomotor tone and heart rate

Pharmacodynamics/kinetics

Onset of action: Oral: 30-60 minutes

Peak effect: Within 2-4 hours

Duration: 6-10 hours

Absorption:

Oral: Absorbed well

Transdermal: Absorbed mostly from chest and upper arm and least from thigh; absorbed through skin at a constant rate

Metabolism: Hepatic to inactive metabolites

Bioavailability: Oral: 75% to 95%

Half-life: Adults:

Normal renal function: 6-20 hours

Renal impairment: 18-41 hours

Time to peak serum concentration:

Oral: 3-5 hours

Transdermal: 2-3 days

Signs and Symptoms of Acute Intoxication Bradycardia, hypoglycemia, dry eyes, personality changes, insomnia, impotence, hyponatremia, syncope, A-V block, delirium, dementia, CNS depression, hypotension, ataxia, miosis, coma, dementia, hypotonia, hyporeflexia, hypothermia (usually resolves in 8 hours), nocturia, diarrhea, respiratory depression, apnea, irritability, seizures, paralytic ileus, heart block, hyperglycemia

When to Transport to Hospital Transport any symptomatic patient

Warnings/Precautions Do not abruptly discontinue; rapid increase in blood pressure, and symptoms of sympathetic overactivity (such as increased heart rate, tremor, agitation, anxiety, insomnia, sweating, palpitations) may occur; if need to discontinue, taper dose gradually over more than 1 week; dosage modification may be required in patients with renal impairment (reduce dose with decreased renal function); use with caution in cerebrovascular disease, coronary insufficiency, renal impairment, sinus node dysfunction; use with caution in patients unable to comply with the therapeutic regimen because of the risk of rebound hypertension

(Continued)

Clonidine *(Continued)*

Adverse Reactions
>10%:
Cardiovascular: Orthostatic hypotension (especially with epidural route), rebound hypertension, bradycardia
Central nervous system: Drowsiness, dizziness, confusion, anxiety
Gastrointestinal: Xerostomia, constipation, nausea
Genitourinary: Urinary tract infection

1% to 10%:
Central nervous system: Mental depression, headache, fatigue, hyperaesthesia, pain
Dermatologic: Rash, skin ulcer
Respiratory: Dyspnea, hypoventilation
Cardiovascular: Chest pain
Endocrine & metabolic: Decreased sexual activity, loss of libido
Gastrointestinal: vomiting, constipation
Genitourinary: Nocturia, impotence
Hepatic: Abnormal liver function tests
Neuromuscular & skeletal: Weakness
Otic: Tinnitus

Reference Range Therapeutic: 1-2 ng/mL (SI: 4.4-8.7 nmol/L); ingestion of a clonidine patch in a 14-month old girl resulted in a clonidine serum level of 4 ng/mL with major toxicity noted

Drug Interactions Tricyclic antidepressants antagonize hypotensive effects of clonidine (no effect with maprotiline); beta-blockers may potentiate bradycardia in patients receiving clonidine and may increase the rebound hypertension seen with clonidine withdrawal; discontinue beta-blocker several days before clonidine is tapered off; nonsteroidal anti-inflammatory drugs may reduce clonidine's effect; increased cyclosporin blood levels can occur with concomitant clonidine administration

Dosage Forms
Clonidine hydrochloride:
Injection, preservative free: 100 mcg/mL (10 mL)
Patch, transdermal: 1, 2, and 3 (0.1, 0.2, 0.3 mg/day, 7-day duration)
Tablet: 0.1 mg, 0.2 mg, 0.3 mg

Additional Information Unsafe in patients with porphyria; rebound hypertension upon abrupt withdrawal usually occurs with doses >1.2 mg/day; appears to be the preferred "Mickey Finn" drug used by criminals in Moscow/Russia; addition of clonidine (75-150 µg) increased duration of analgesia produced by epidural morphine (2 mg) for cesarean delivery

Specific References
Nichols MH, King WD, and James LP, "Clonidine Poisoning in Jefferson County, Alabama," *Ann Emerg Med*, 1997, 29(4):511-7.

Clonistada® *see Clonidine on page 154*
Clopax® *see Clobazam on page 151*
ClorazeCaps® *see Clorazepate on this page*

Clorazepate *(klor AZ e pate)*
Related Information
Controlled Substances - Uses and Effects *on page 741*
U.S. Brand Names ClorazeCaps®; ClorazeTabs®; Gen-XENE®; Nansius®; Transene®; Tranxene®; Tranxilium®
Canadian Brand Names Apo-Clorazepate®; Novo-Clopate®
Therapeutic Category Anticonvulsant; Benzodiazepine
Abuse Potential Yes

Impairment Potential Yes; Brief or extended period (up to 1 year) of use is consistent with driving impairment in the elderly. The impairment is greatest in the first 7 days of use.

Use Treatment of generalized anxiety and panic disorders; management of alcohol withdrawal; adjunct anticonvulsant in management of partial seizures

Usual Dosage Oral:

Children 9-12 years: Anticonvulsant: Initial: 3.75-7.5 mg/dose twice daily; increase dose by 3.75 mg at weekly intervals, not to exceed 60 mg/day in 2-3 divided doses

Children >12 years and Adults: Anticonvulsant: Initial: Up to 7.5 mg/dose 2-3 times/day; increase dose by 7.5 mg at weekly intervals; not to exceed 90 mg/day

Adults:

Anxiety: 7.5-15 mg 2-4 times/day, or given as single dose of 11.25 or 22.5 mg at bedtime

Alcohol withdrawal: Initial: 30 mg, then 15 mg 2-4 times/day on first day; maximum daily dose: 90 mg; gradually decrease dose over subsequent days

Mechanism of Action Facilitates gamma aminobutyric acid (GABA)-mediated transmission inhibitory neurotransmitter action, depresses subcortical levels of CNS

Pharmacodynamics/kinetics Studies have shown that the elderly are more sensitive to the effects of benzodiazepines as compared to younger adults.

Onset of action: Depends largely upon absorption rate

Duration: 24 hours

Absorption: Rapidly decarboxylated to desmethyldiazepam (active) in acidic stomach prior to absorption

Metabolism: In the liver to oxazepam (active) and desmethyldiazepam

Half-life: Adults:

Parent compound: >24 hours

Desmethyldiazepam: 48-96 hours

Oxazepam: 6-8 hours

Time to peak serum concentration: Oral: Within 1 hour

Signs and Symptoms of Acute Intoxication Somnolence, confusion, ataxia, diminished reflexes, coma, gaze nystagmus

When to Transport to Hospital Transport any pediatric ingestion (<9 years of age), any symptomatic patient, or any ingestion over 100 mg

Warnings/Precautions Not considered a drug of choice in the elderly; use with caution in patients with hepatic or renal disease; abrupt discontinuation may cause withdrawal symptoms or seizures

Adverse Reactions

>10%:

Cardiovascular: Tachycardia, chest pain

Central nervous system: Drowsiness, fatigue, ataxia, lightheadedness, memory impairment, insomnia, anxiety, headache, depression

Dermatologic: Rash

Endocrine & metabolic: Decreased libido

Gastrointestinal: Xerostomia, constipation, diarrhea, decreased salivation, nausea, vomiting, increased or decreased appetite

Neuromuscular & skeletal: Dysarthria

Ocular: Blurred vision

Miscellaneous: Diaphoresis

1% to 10%:

Cardiovascular: Syncope, hypotension

Central nervous system: Confusion, nervousness, dizziness, akathisia

Dermatologic: Dermatitis

(Continued)

Clorazepate *(Continued)*

Gastrointestinal: Nausea, increased salivation, weight gain or loss
Neuromuscular & skeletal: Rigidity, tremor, muscle cramps
Otic: Tinnitus
Respiratory: Nasal congestion, hyperventilation

Reference Range Therapeutic: 0.12-2.00 µg/mL (SI: 0.36-6.02 µmol/L)

Drug Interactions Cimetidine may decrease hepatic clearance, CNS depressants; antacids may reduce bioavailability; oral contraceptives may inhibit hepatic metabolism

Dosage Forms
Clorazepate dipotassium:
Capsule: 3.75 mg, 7.5 mg, 15 mg
Tablet: 3.75 mg, 7.5 mg, 15 mg
Tablet, single dose: 11.25 mg, 22.5 mg

Additional Information Clorazepate offers no advantage over the other benzodiazepines; can cause fetal malformations

Specific References
Patel DA and Patel AR, "Clorazepate and Congenital Malformations," *JAMA*, 1980, 244(2):135-6.

ClorazeTabs® *see* Clorazepate *on page 156*
Clordiabet® *see* Chlorpropamide *on page 140*

Clove

Synonyms Caryoph; Pentogen (clove oil); Tropical Myrtle
Scientific Name *Caryophyllus aromaticus*
Eugenia caryophyllata
Syzygium aromaticum

Use Carminative; flavoring agent; clove oil contains 85% to 92% eugenol which is effective as a local anesthetic and anesthetic in dentistry; soap fragrance

Usual Dosage Clove oil:
Oral: Toxic dose: Infant: 15 mL (500 mg/kg of eugenol); oil is not used therapeutically in concentrations >0.06%
Therapeutic: 1-2 drops on tooth cavity not more than 4 times/day

Mechanism of Action Eugenol acts similarly to other phenol agents by inhibiting prostaglandin synthesis and causing depression of pain receptors; can also cause uncoupling of oxidative phosphorylation

Pharmacodynamics/kinetics Metabolism: Hepatic

When to Transport to Hospital Transport any symptomatic patient or any ingestion over 10 mL

Overdosage/Treatment
Decontamination:
Oral: Dilute with milk or water; activated charcoal with cathartic may be given; endoscopy may be required within 1 day of ingestion to assess local gastrointestinal mucosal injury
Ocular: Irrigate copiously with saline

Warnings/Precautions
Per Commission E: Oil:
Oral: Alcoholism, anticoagulants, hemophilia, kidney disease, paracetamol, prostatic cancer, SLE
Dermal: Hypersensitive, diseased or damaged skin, all children <2 years of age
Oil in concentrated form may irritate mucous membranes

Adverse Reactions
Dermatologic: Dermatitis, urticaria
Endocrine & metabolic: Hypoglycemia, metabolic acidosis

Gastrointestinal: Vomiting
Hematologic: Disseminated intravascular coagulation (D.I.C.)
Hepatic: Hepatotoxicity
Ocular: Lacrimation
Renal: Proteinuria
Respiratory: Pulmonary edema (when injected)
Miscellaneous: Anaphylaxis, anhidrosis

Clove cigarettes:
Gastrointestinal: Sore throat
Respiratory: Bronchospasm, hemoptysis, pulmonary edema, epistaxis, bronchiectasis, pleural effusion

Additional Information The clove tree grows to ~30 feet and is found in warm climates in the Molucca Islands. The stems, buds and leaves can yield clove oil. Acceptable daily oral intake of eugenol: 2.5 mg/kg. Level of clove in foods does not exceed 0.236%. Clove cigarettes ("Kreteks") contain 60% tobacco and 40% ground clove. The primary components of clove cigarette smoke include eugenol (13 mg), beta-caryophyllene (1.2 mg), eugenol acetate (0.7 mg), alpha-humulene (0.16 mg), and caryophyllene-epoxide (<0.1 mg).

Specific References
Hartnoll G, Moore D, and Douek D, "Near Fatal Ingestion of Oil of Cloves," *Arch Dis Child*, 1993, 69(3):392-3.

Cloxazolam *see* Triazolam *on page 592*

Clozapine (KLOE za peen)
U.S. Brand Names Clozaril®; Leponex®
Therapeutic Category Antipsychotic Agent
Use Management of schizophrenia
Usual Dosage Adults: Oral: 25 mg once or twice daily initially and increased, as tolerated to a target dose of 300-450 mg/day after 2 weeks, but may require doses as high as 600-900 mg/day
Mechanism of Action Tricyclic dibenzodiazepine structure; blocks dopamine receptors
Pharmacodynamics/kinetics
Protein binding: 95%
Metabolism: Hepatic
Half-life: 4.5-7.5 hours; may be as long as 18.5 hours in overdose
Signs and Symptoms of Acute Intoxication Coma, priapism, eosinophilia, seizures, neuroleptic malignant syndrome, salivation, impotence, enuresis, extrapyramidal reaction, delirium, cognitive dysfunction, nausea, hypoglycemia, hypertension, fasciculations, emesis, hypotension, agitation, disorientation, ataxia, torticollis, hypotonicity, Parkinson's-like symptoms, myoclonus, inability to urinate
When to Transport to Hospital Transport any symptomatic patient
Warnings/Precautions Avoid in patients with closed-angle glaucoma, ileus, prostatic enlargement, or pre-existing bone marrow depression
Adverse Reactions
>10%:
Cardiovascular: Tachycardia, hypotension, orthostatic hypotension
Central nervous system: Fever, headache, drowsiness
Gastrointestinal: Constipation, nausea, vomiting, unusual weight gain
1% to 10%:
Cardiovascular: EKG changes, hypertension
Central nervous system: Agitation, akathisia
Gastrointestinal: Abdominal discomfort, heartburn, xerostomia
Ocular: Blurred vision
Miscellaneous: Diaphoresis (increased)
(Continued)

Clozapine *(Continued)*

Test Interactions Nitrazepam can cause a false elevation (about 15%) of clozapine serum levels

Reference Range Therapeutic: 200–400 ng/mL; levels >500 ng/mL associated with change in mental status in children; levels >2000 ng/mL associated with CNS changes in adults; highest reported level with survival: 4400 ng/mL; levels >1300 ng/mL seizures can occur

Drug Interactions Seizure has been reported with concomitant use of erythromycin; myoclonic seizures can result with concomitant fluoxetine and clozapine therapy; syncope can occur with concomitant clozapine and enalapril administration; leukocytosis and increased serum concentrations can occur with concomitant erythromycin and clozapine administration (333 mg 3 times/day); fluoxetine, paroxetine and sertraline increased serum concentrations of clozapine and its major metabolite, norclozapine; elevated serum concentrations with concomitant fluvoxamine (two case reports); agranulocytosis with concomitant risperidone; increased plasma concentrations with concomitant caffeine; increased clozapine levels can occur with concomitant fluvoxamine and/or sertraline; cardiovascular disorders can occur with concomitant cocaine and clozapine administration

Dosage Forms Tablet: 25 mg, 100 mg

Additional Information May be useful in the treatment of neuroleptic-induced vomiting (in doses up to 500 mg/day)

Specific References

Ishii A, Mizoguchi K, Kageoka M, et al, "Nonfatal Suicidal Intoxication by Clozapine," *J Toxicol Clin Toxicol*, 1997, 35(2):195-7.

Clozaril® *see Clozapine on previous page*

CN *see Chloroacetophenone on page 127*

CO *see Carbon Monoxide on page 109*

CO₂ *see Carbon Dioxide on page 107*

Coal Oil *see Kerosene on page 325*

Cocaine *(koe KANE)*

Related Information

Controlled Substances - Uses and Effects *on page 741*

Synonyms Erythroxylon Coca; Methylbenzoylecgonine Hydrochloride

Therapeutic Category Local Anesthetic

Abuse Potential Yes

Impairment Potential Yes; Qualitative urinary positive results for cocaethylene or the parent compound of cocaine is consistent with recent usage

Use Topical anesthesia for mucous membranes

Usual Dosage Use lowest effective dose (contraindications of 1% to 4%); do not exceed 1 mg/kg; patient tolerance, anesthetic technique, vascularity of tissue, and area to be anesthetized will determine dose needed. For topical applications, solutions >4% are not advisable because of increased risk of systemic toxic reactions.

Mechanism of Action Blocks both the initiation and conduction of nerve impulses by decreasing the neuronal membrane's permeability to sodium ions, which results in inhibition of depolarization with resultant blockade of conduction; interferes with the uptake of norepinephrine by adrenergic nerve terminals producing vasoconstriction; a type I antiarrhythmic

Pharmacodynamics/kinetics

Onset of action: Topical: Within 1 minute following administration to mucosa

Peak action: Within 5 minutes

Duration: ≥30 minutes, depending upon route and dosage administered

Absorption: Well absorbed through mucous membranes, limited by drug-induced vasoconstriction, and enhanced by inflammation

Metabolism: In the liver to benzoylecgonine, ecgonine methylester and norcocaine (active)

Bioavailability:
Cocaine Smoked in glass pipes: 70%
Cocaine Smoked in corncob pipes: 60%
Intranasal route: Dose dependent: 25% to 94%
Oral: 30%

Half-life: (Benzoylecgonine from all 3 routes: 3.55-5.79 hours)
Intravenous: 37-41 minutes
Smoked: 58-89 minutes
Intranasal: 73-207 minutes

Elimination: Excreted primarily in urine as metabolites (benzoylecgonine and ecgonine methylester); unchanged drug (<10%)

Signs and Symptoms of Acute Intoxication Apnea, dental erosion, depression, sweating, photophobia, insomnia, hyperreflexia, abdominal pain, nasal congestion, myocardial depression, mania, intracranial hemorrhage, ptosis, extrapyramidal reaction, dry mouth, myalgia, lacrimation, coma, impotence, tachycardia (ventricular), epistaxis, dyspnea, migraine headache (exacerbation of), disorientation, paroxysmal tachycardia (ventricular), cardiomegaly, ataxia, corneal irritation, colitis, seizures, angina, blurred vision, respiratory depression, restlessness, respiratory alkalosis, hyperthermia, delirium, hallucinations, mydriasis, vomiting, muscular spasm, sensory aberrations, rhabdomyolysis, myoglobinuria, CNS hemorrhage, hypertension, chest pain

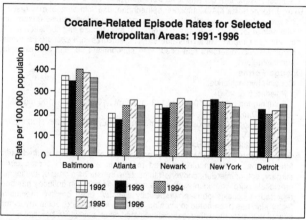

Cocaine-Related Episode Rates for Selected Metropolitan Areas: 1991-1996

From U.S. Department of Health and Human Services Public Health Service, "Annual Trends in Selected Metropolitan Areas," *Preliminary Estimates From the Drug Abuse Warning Network*, 1996, 17:16.

When to Transport to Hospital Transport any symptomatic patient

Warnings/Precautions Cocaine produces an addictive syndrome; use with caution in patients with hypertension, severe cardiovascular disease, or thyrotoxicosis and in infants; use with caution in patients with severely traumatized mucosa and sepsis in the region of intended application

(Continued)

Cocaine *(Continued)*

Adverse Reactions

>10%:

Central nervous system: CNS stimulation

Gastrointestinal: Loss of taste perception

Respiratory: Chronic rhinitis, nasal congestion

Miscellaneous: Loss of smell

1% to 10%:

Cardiovascular: Decreased heart rate with low doses, increased heart rate with moderate doses, hypertension, tachycardia, cardiac arrhythmias

Central nervous system: Nervousness, restlessness, euphoria, excitement, hallucination, seizures

Gastrointestinal: Vomiting

Neuromuscular & skeletal: Tremors and clonic-tonic reactions

Ocular: Sloughing of the corneal epithelium, ulceration of the cornea

Respiratory: Tachypnea, respiratory failure

Reference Range

Therapeutic: 100-500 ng/mL (SI: 330 nmol/L)

Toxic: >1000 ng/mL (SI: >3300 nmol/L)

Blood cocaine levels in "bodypackers" may exceed 50,000 ng/mL

Average blood levels after smoking a standard dose of crack cocaine: 600-700 ng/mL

Average postmortem blood cocaine levels from deceased cocaine abusers: 2500 ng/mL

Highest postmortem cocaine level from bodypacker: 104,000 ng/mL

Drug Interactions MAO inhibitors; epinephrine; use with ethanol may result in a toxic metabolite (cocaethylene) which may have active cardiac effects; use with naloxone; may have caused ventricular arrhythmias and fibrillation (atrial) in one case report; flumazenil has induced seizures in a cocaine rat model; cardiovascular disorders can occur with concomitant cocaine and clozapine administration

Dosage Forms

Cocaine hydrochloride:

Powder: 5 g, 25 g

Solution, topical: 4% [40 mg/mL] (2 mL, 4 mL, 10 mL); 10% [100 mg/mL] (4 mL, 10 mL)

Solution, topical, viscous: 4% [40 mg/mL] (4 mL, 10 mL); 10% [100 mg/mL] (4 mL, 10 mL)

Tablet, soluble, for topical solution: 135 mg

Additional Information May cause cornea to become clouded or pitted, therefore, normal saline should be used to irrigate and protect cornea during surgery; not for injection; converted to cocaine sulfate as a drug of abuse; may precipitate porphyria; increased incidence of anticardiolipin antibody has been reported in cocaine abusers (especially with I.V. use); positive rheumatoid factor also has been noted in cocaine abusers. Incidence of acute myocardial infarction in patients with cocaine-associated chest pain is ~6%; initial EKG is only sensitive for 36% of acute myocardial infarction; ethanol plus cocaine use produces cocaethylene which has a longer half-life (~2 hours) than cocaine; while cocaethylene can produce tachycardia, myocardial depression, and is a competitive muscarinic antagonist, no direct effect on blood pressure is usually seen. Age, cardiac risk factors, inferior infarction, and bradydysrhythmias can predict underlying coronary artery disease in cocaine-induced myocardial infarctions. 142,400 cocaine-related emergency department visits reported to the Drug Abuse Warning Network in 1994 (a 40% increase since 1988). In a rodent model, cocaethylene may continue to form after death but hepatic postmortem cocaethylene production ceases after 1 hour of death. Cocaine is present on 79% of U.S. Currency analyzed in amounts >0.1 µg and in 54% in amounts >1 µg (highest amount recorded was 1327 µg). Anticonvulsants (phenytoin, carbamazepine) have been used to treat cocaine dependence.

Specific References

Byck R, "The Effects of Cocaine on Complex Performance in Humans," *Alcohol, Drugs, and Driving*, 1987, 3(1).

Cone EJ, "Pharmacokinetics and Pharmacodynamics of Cocaine," *J Anal Toxicol*, 1995, 19:459-77.

Cocaine (Cocaine Metabolite), Qualitative

Synonyms Coke; Crack; Snow

Use Evaluate cocaine use

Reference Range Negative (less than cutoff)

Additional Information Cocaine is a highly abused drug which is most frequently detected in the urine as the metabolite, benzoylecgonine and usually as part of a multiclass drug panel. In pre-employment drug screening, the presence of cocaine (benzoylecgonine) should be confirmed by GC/MS.

Cocaine is a central nervous system stimulant. It usually appears as a fine crystal-like powder which is the hydrochloride or sulfate salt and as such is "snorted" (inhaled through the nose). When mixed with sodium bicarbonate and converted to free base, it appears as hard pieces called "crack" which can be smoked. This is currently a very prevalent form of the drug.

The effects of the drug begin within minutes and peak within 15-20 minutes. These effects include dilated pupils, increase in blood pressure, heart rate, breathing rate, and body temperature. The dangers of cocaine use vary, depending on how the drug is taken, the dose, and the individual. Some regular users report feelings of restlessness, irritability, anxiety, and sleeplessness. In some people even low doses of cocaine may create psychological problems. People who use high doses of cocaine over a long period of time may become paranoid or experience what is called a cocaine psychosis. This may include hallucinations of touch, sight, taste, and smell. Cocaine itself has a half-life of 1-2 hours while benzoylecgonine has a half-life of 7-9 hours. Benzoylecgonine is detectable in urine within 2-3 hours and for a period of 2-3 days after a single use.

Positive urine screen due to passive inhalation of cocaine virtually will not occur at cutoff of 300 ng/mL by FPIA, but is possible in children if test by EMIT with a cutoff of 30 ng/mL. Absorption of at least 1 mg of cocaine is usually necessary to produce a cocaine positive urine screen.

Ecgonine urinary levels >50 ng/mL can increase sensitivity of cocaine assays. Urine cocaine metabolites levels may be elevated after a series of sauna treatments. The metabolite anhydroecgonine methyl ester is considered to be a marker for "crack" cocaine use (urine concentration ranges from 5-1477 ng/mL).

Specific References

Cone EJ, Menchen SL, Paul BD, et al, "Validity Testing of Commercial Urine Cocaine Metabolite Assays: I. Assay Detection Times, Individual Excretion Patterns, and Kinetics After Cocaine Administration to Humans," *J Forensic Sci*, 1989, 34(1):15-31.

Cone EJ, Yousefnejad D, Hillsgrove MJ, et al, "Passive Inhalation of Cocaine," *J Anal Toxicol*, 1995, 19(6):399-411.

Codafed® Expectorant *see* Guaifenesin, Pseudoephedrine, and Codeine *on page 275*

Codamine® *see* Hydrocodone and Phenylpropanolamine *on page 296*

Codamine® Pediatric *see* Hydrocodone and Phenylpropanolamine *on page 296*

Codate *see Codeine on this page*

Co-Dax® *see Doxepin on page 211*

Codehist® DH *see Chlorpheniramine, Pseudoephedrine, and Codeine on page 138*

Codeine (KOE deen)

Related Information

Acetaminophen and Codeine *on page 21*
Aspirin and Codeine *on page 58*
Butalbital Compound and Codeine *on page 95*
Controlled Substances - Uses and Effects *on page 741*
Guaifenesin and Codeine *on page 271*

Synonyms Actacode; Codate; Codlin; Methylmorphine; Paveral; Tricodein

Canadian Brand Names Codeine Conhn®; Linctus Codeine Blac; Linctus With Codeine Phosphate; Paveral Stanley Syrup With Codeine Phosphate

Therapeutic Category Analgesic, Narcotic; Antitussive

Abuse Potential Yes

Impairment Potential Yes

Use Treatment of mild to moderate pain; antitussive in lower doses; dextromethorphan has equivalent antitussive activity but has much lower toxicity in accidental overdose

Usual Dosage Doses should be titrated to appropriate analgesic effect; when changing routes of administration, note that oral dose is $^2/_3$ as effective as parenteral dose

Analgesic:
  Children: Oral, I.M., S.C.: 0.5-1 mg/kg/dose every 4-6 hours as needed; maximum: 60 mg/dose
  Adults: Oral, I.M., I.V., S.C.: 30 mg/dose; range: 15-60 mg every 4-6 hours as needed; maximum: 360 mg/24 hours

Antitussive: Oral (for nonproductive cough):
  Children: 1-1.5 mg/kg/day in divided doses every 4-6 hours as needed: Alternative dose according to age:
    2-6 years: 2.5-5 mg every 4-6 hours as needed; maximum: 30 mg/day
    6-12 years: 5-10 mg every 4-6 hours as needed; maximum: 60 mg/day
  Adults: 10-20 mg/dose every 4-6 hours as needed; maximum: 120 mg/day

Mechanism of Action Binds to opiate receptors in the CNS, causing inhibition of ascending pain pathways, altering the perception of and response to pain; causes cough supression by direct central action in the medulla; produces generalized CNS depression; also has a dose-related histamine-releasing effect

Pharmacodynamics/kinetics

Onset of action: Oral: 30-60 minutes
Peak action: Oral: 1-1.5 hours
Duration: 4-6 hours
Absorption: Oral: Adequate
Metabolism: Hepatic to morphine (active) and norcodeine along with other metabolites
Half-life: 3 hours

Signs and Symptoms of Acute Intoxication Somnolence, constipation, miosis, hypocalcemia, vomiting, rhabdomyolysis, ataxia, syncope, erythema multiforme, syndrome of inappropriate antidiuretic hormone (SIADH), myasthenia gravis (exacerbation or precipitation of), respiratory failure, hallucinations, myoglobinuria, urine discoloration (milky)

When to Transport to Hospital Transport any pediatric patient (<6 years of age), any lethargic patient, or any ingestion over 2 mg/kg

Warnings/Precautions Use with caution in patients with hypersensitivity reactions to other phenanthrene-derivative opioid agonists (morphine, hydrocodone, hydromorphone, levorphanol, oxycodone, oxymorphone); respiratory diseases including asthma, emphysema, COPD, or severe liver or renal insufficiency; some preparations contain sulfites which may cause allergic reactions; may be habit-forming

Adverse Reactions
>10%:
Central nervous system: Drowsiness
Gastrointestinal: Constipation
1% to 10%:
Cardiovascular: Tachycardia or bradycardia, hypotension
Central nervous system: Dizziness, lightheadedness, false feeling of well being, malaise, headache, restlessness, paradoxical CNS stimulation, confusion
Dermatologic: Rash, urticaria
Gastrointestinal: Xerostomia, anorexia, nausea, vomiting
Genitourinary: Decreased urination, ureteral spasm
Local: Burning at injection site
Ocular: Blurred vision
Neuromuscular & skeletal: Weakness
Respiratory: Shortness of breath, dyspnea
Miscellaneous: Histamine release

Reference Range Serum:
Therapeutic: Not established
Toxic: >1.1 µg/mL

Drug Interactions
Decreased effect with cigarette smoking
Increased toxicity: CNS depressants, phenothiazines, tricyclic antidepressants, other narcotic analgesics, guanabenz, MAO inhibitors, neuromuscular blockers, quinidine

Dosage Forms
Codeine phosphate:
Injection: 30 mg (1 mL, 2 mL); 60 mg (1 mL, 2 mL)
Tablet, soluble: 30 mg, 60 mg
Codeine sulfate:
Tablet: 15 mg, 30 mg, 60 mg
Tablet, soluble: 15 mg, 30 mg, 60 mg
Solution, oral: 15 mg/5 mL

Specific References
Chesher GB, "Understanding the Opioid Analgesics and Their Effects on Skills Performance," *Alcohol, Drugs, and Driving,* 1989, 5(2).
Linnoila M and Hakkinen S, "Effects of dizepam and Codeine, Alone and in Combination With Alcohol, on Simulated Driving," *Clin Pharmacol Ther,* 1974, 15(4):368-73.

Codeine and Acetaminophen *see* Acetaminophen and Codeine *on page 21*

Codeine and Aspirin *see* Aspirin and Codeine *on page 58*

Codeine and Bromodiphenhydramine *see* Bromodiphenhydramine and Codeine *on page 84*

Codeine and Butalbital Compound *see* Butalbital Compound and Codeine *on page 95*

Codeine and Guaifenesin *see* Guaifenesin and Codeine *on page 271*

Codeine, Urine
Related Information
Opiates, Qualitative, Urine *on page 445*
(Continued)

Codeine, Urine *(Continued)*

Use Evaluate codeine toxicity; detect drug-of-abuse

Reference Range Negative (below cutoff)

Additional Information Codeine, made by the methylation of morphine, is similar to morphine in uses, actions, contraindications, and adverse reactions. About one-sixth to one-tenth as potent as morphine, it is used to manage mild to moderate pain. In low doses, it is an antitussive. After oral dose, the onset of action is 15-30 minutes, and peak levels are reached in 1-1.5 hours. The half-life is 2.5-4 hours. Codeine is excreted mainly in the urine as norcodeine and free and conjugated morphine. Adverse effects of codeine include miosis, increased intracranial pressure, antidiuretic hormone release, and physical and psychological dependence.

Specific References

Barsan W, "Narcotic Agents," *Ann Emerg Med*, 1986, 15:1019-20.

Codiclear® DH *see* Hydrocodone and Guaifenesin *on page 295*

Codimal-A® *see* Brompheniramine *on page 84*

Codlin *see* Codeine *on page 164*

Codoxy® *see* Oxycodone and Aspirin *on page 454*

Cogentin® *see* Benztropine *on page 73*

Co-Gesic® *see* Hydrocodone and Acetaminophen *on page 293*

Co-Hist® [OTC] *see* Acetaminophen, Chlorpheniramine, and Pseudoephedrine *on page 23*

Coke *see* Cocaine (Cocaine Metabolite), Qualitative *on page 163*

Cold & Allergy® Elixir [OTC] *see* Brompheniramine and Phenylpropanolamine *on page 85*

Coldlac-LA® *see* Guaifenesin and Phenylpropanolamine *on page 272*

Coldloc® *see* Guaifenesin, Phenylpropanolamine, and Phenylephrine *on page 274*

Coldrine® [OTC] *see* Acetaminophen and Pseudoephedrine *on page 22*

Collyrium Fresh® [OTC] *see* Tetrahydrozoline *on page 569*

Cologne Spirit *see* Ethyl Alcohol *on page 233*

Comatose Profile *see* Toxicology Drug Screen, Blood *on page 587*

Combivir® *see* Zidovudine and Lamivudine *on page 619*

Comfort® [OTC] *see* Naphazoline *on page 422*

Comhist® *see* Chlorpheniramine, Phenylephrine, and Phenyltoloxamine *on page 136*

Comhist® LA *see* Chlorpheniramine, Phenylephrine, and Phenyltoloxamine *on page 136*

Comizial® *see* Phenobarbital *on page 474*

Common Hops *see* Hops *on page 289*

Compazine® *see* Prochlorperazine *on page 502*

Composition C-4 *see* RDX *on page 522*

Compound 1080® *see* Sodium Monofluoroacetate *on page 542*

Compound 1189® *see* Chlordecone *on page 123*

Compound F *see* Hydrocortisone *on page 297*

Compound W® [OTC] *see* Salicylic Acid *on page 530*

Compoz® Gel Caps [OTC] *see* Diphenhydramine *on page 205*

Compoz® Nighttime Sleep Aid [OTC] *see* Diphenhydramine *on page 205*

Comtrex® Maximum Strength Non-Drowsy [OTC] *see* Acetaminophen, Dextromethorphan, and Pseudoephedrine *on page 23*

Concor® *see* Bisoprolol *on page 78*

Concordin® *see* Protriptyline *on page 515*

Condy't Crustals *see* Potassium Permanganate *on page 491*

Conex® [OTC] *see* Guaifenesin and Phenylpropanolamine *on page 272*

Congess® Jr *see* Guaifenesin and Pseudoephedrine *on page 273*

Congess® Sr *see* Guaifenesin and Pseudoephedrine *on page 273*

Congestac® *see* Guaifenesin and Pseudoephedrine *on page 273*

Congestant D® [OTC] *see* Chlorpheniramine, Phenylpropanolamine, and Acetaminophen *on page 137*

Contac® Cough Formula Liquid [OTC] *see* Guaifenesin and Dextromethorphan *on page 271*

Control® [OTC] *see* Phenylpropanolamine *on page 481*

Controlled Substances - Uses and Effects *see page 741*

Contuss® *see* Guaifenesin, Phenylpropanolamine, and Phenylephrine *on page 274*

Contuss® XT *see* Guaifenesin and Phenylpropanolamine *on page 272*

Converten® *see* Enalapril *on page 217*

Cophene-B® *see* Brompheniramine *on page 84*

Cophene XP® *see* Hydrocodone, Pseudoephedrine, and Guaifenesin *on page 297*

Copperhead Snake

Scientific Name *Agkistrodon contortrix*

Mechanism of Toxic Action Venom; quality and potency vary among species; composition: 90% water with 5-15 enzymes, 3-12 nonenzymatic proteins, as well as other unidentified substances

Signs and Symptoms of Acute Intoxication Local signs include tenderness, edema, erythema, ecchymosis, hemorrhage, bullae, lymphangitis, and rarely a compartment syndrome. Systemic signs and symptoms include hypotension, asthenia, sweating, chills, paresthesia, nausea, vomiting, coagulopathy, fasciculations, and CNS depression; coagulopathies can occur including thrombocytopenia, hypofibrinogenemia, increased PT and PTT. Shock, hypotension, lactic acidosis, hemoconcentration, hypoproteinemia, proteinuria, and hematuria are also potential complications.

When to Transport to Hospital Transport any bite

Overdosage/Treatment Decontamination: Immobilize the area, rapid transport to medical facility. Use negative pressure device to remove venom if available, **do not** incise the wound; constriction band may be applied, **not** a tourniquet Wyeth crotalid polyvalent antivenin; treat moderate to severe envenomations with increments of 5-10 vials at a time; skin test per manufacturer's instructions; if positive skin test develops, may prophylax with H_1- and H_2-receptor blockers; give until local injury has stopped and coagulopathy is reversed; complications include allergic reactions, anaphylaxis, and delayed serum sickness

Additional Information

Family: Crotalidae (Pit Viper)

Range: Eastern U.S. to Southern Texas

Distinguishing characteristics: Facial pits, vertical elliptical pupils, triangular head, single row of subcaudal scales

Case fatality rate: 0.01%; usually there is a relatively benign course

Specific References

Hassen LB, "Reptile and Arthropod Envenomations," *Occup Med*, 1991, 6(3):447-61.

Co-Pyronil® 2 Pulvules® [OTC] *see* Chlorpheniramine and Pseudoephedrine *on page 134*

Cordilox® *see* Verapamil *on page 609*

Coreg® *see* Carvedilol *on page 116*

Corgard® *see* Nadolol *on page 417*

Coricidin® [OTC] *see* Chlorpheniramine and Acetaminophen *on page 133*

Coricidin D® [OTC] *see* Chlorpheniramine, Phenylpropanolamine, and Acetaminophen *on page 137*

CortaGel® [OTC] *see* Hydrocortisone *on page 297*

Cortaid® Maximum Strength [OTC] *see* Hydrocortisone *on page 297*

Cortaid® with Aloe [OTC] *see* Hydrocortisone *on page 297*

Cort-Dome® *see* Hydrocortisone *on page 297*

Cortef® *see* Hydrocortisone *on page 297*

Cortef® Feminine Itch [OTC] *see* Hydrocortisone *on page 297*

Cortenema® *see* Hydrocortisone *on page 297*

Cor Tensobon® *see* Captopril *on page 101*

Corticaine® [OTC] *see* Hydrocortisone *on page 297*

Cortisol *see* Hydrocortisone *on page 297*

Cortizone®-5 [OTC] *see* Hydrocortisone *on page 297*

Cortizone®-10 [OTC] *see* Hydrocortisone *on page 297*

Corynathe Yohimbe *see* Yohimbine *on page 618*

Corynine Hydrochloride *see* Yohimbine *on page 618*

Cotrim® *see* Co-Trimoxazole *on this page*

Cotrim® DS *see* Co-Trimoxazole *on this page*

Co-Trimoxazole (koe trye MOKS a zole)

Synonyms SMZ-TMP; Sulfamethoxazole and Trimethoprim; TMP-SMZ; Trimethoprim and Sulfamethoxazole

U.S. Brand Names Bactrim™; Bactrim™ DS; Cotrim®; Cotrim® DS; Septra®; Septra® DS; Sulfamethoprim®; Sulfatrim®; Sulfatrim® DS; Uroplus® DS; Uroplus® SS

Canadian Brand Names Apo-Sulfatrim®; Novo-Trimel®; Nu-Cotrimox®; Pro-Trin®; Roubac®; Trisulfa®; Trisulfa-S®

Therapeutic Category Sulfonamide

Use Treatment of urinary tract infections; acute otitis media in children; acute exacerbations of chronic bronchitis in adults; prophylaxis of *Pneumocystis carinii* pneumonitis; treatment of documented *Pneumocystis carinii*, empiric treatment of highly suspected *Pneumocystis carinii* in immunocompromised patients; treatment of documented or suspected shigellosis, typhoid fever, or *Nocardia asteroides* infection

Usual Dosage Dosage recommendations are based on the trimethoprim component

Children >2 months:
  Mild to moderate infections: Oral, I.V.: 8 mg TMP/kg/day in divided doses every 12 hours
  Serious infection/*Pneumocystis*: I.V.: 20 mg TMP/kg/day in divided doses every 6 hours
  Urinary tract infection prophylaxis: Oral: 2 mg TMP/kg/dose daily
  Prophylaxis of *Pneumocystis*: Oral, I.V.: 10 mg TMP/kg/day or 150 mg TMP/m²/day in divided doses every 12 hours for 3 days/week; dose should not exceed 320 mg trimethoprim and 1600 mg sulfamethoxazole 3 days/week

Adults:
  Urinary tract infection/chronic bronchitis: Oral: 1 double strength tablet every 12 hours for 10-14 days
  Sepsis: I.V.: 20 TMP/kg/day divided every 6 hours
  Pneumocystis carinii:
    Prophylaxis: Oral, I.V.: 10 mg TMP/kg/day divided every 12 hours for 3 days/week

Treatment: I.V.: 20 mg TMP/kg/day divided every 6 hours

Prevent relapse in patients with Wegener's granulomatosis in remission: 800 mg of sulfamethoxazole with 160 mg of trimethoprim twice daily for 2 years

Mechanism of Action Sulfamethoxazole interferes with bacterial folic acid synthesis and growth via inhibition of dihydrofolic acid formation from para-aminobenzoic acid; trimethoprim inhibits dihydrofolic acid reduction to tetrahydrofolate resulting in sequential inhibition of enzymes of the folic acid pathway

Pharmacodynamics/kinetics

Absorption: Oral: 90% to 100%

Metabolism:

SMX is N-acetylated and glucuronidated in the liver

TMP is metabolized to oxide and hydroxylated metabolites in the liver

Half-life:

SMX: 9 hours

TMP: 6-17 hours, both are prolonged in renal failure

Time to peak serum concentration: Within 1-4 hours

Signs and Symptoms of Acute Intoxication Leukopenia or neutropenia (agranulocytosis, granulocytopenia), blood dyscrasias, jaundice, cholestatic jaundice, coagulopathy, depression, toxic epidermal necrolysis, methemoglobinemia, meningitis, hyperkalemia, hypoglycemia, pseudotumor cerebri, erythema multiforme, colitis

When to Transport to Hospital Transport any patient with dermal reaction or change in mental status

Warnings/Precautions Use with caution in patients with G-6-PD deficiency, impaired renal or hepatic function; adjust dosage in patients with renal impairment; injection vehicle contains benzyl alcohol and sodium metabisulfite; fatalities associated with sulfonamides, although rare, have occurred due to severe reactions including Stevens-Johnson syndrome, toxic epidermal necrolysis, hepatic necrosis, leukopenia; neutropenia; agranulocytosis; granulocytopenia; aplastic anemia and other blood dyscrasias; discontinue use at first sign of rash; elderly patients appear at greater risk for more severe adverse reactions

Adverse Reactions

>10%:

Dermatologic: Allergic skin reactions including rashes and urticaria, photosensitivity

Gastrointestinal: Nausea, vomiting, anorexia

1% to 10%:

Dermatologic: Stevens-Johnson syndrome, toxic epidermal necrolysis

Hematologic: Blood dyscrasias

Hepatic: Hepatitis

Test Interactions Increased serum methotrexate by dihydrofolate reductase method; does not interfere with RIA method; may cause an elevation of serum creatinine due to interference with tubular secretion of creatinine

Reference Range Peak plasma concentrations of 20-50 mg/L (79-198 µmol/L) of SMZ and 0.9-1.9 mg/L (3.1-6.5 µmol/L) of TMP occur after oral ingestion of 800 mg of SMZ and 160 mg of TMP; plasma trimethoprim levels >5 mg/L (17 µmol/L) may be needed to treat *P. carinii* pneumonia

Drug Interactions

Decreased effect of cyclosporines

Increased effect of sulfonylureas and oral anticoagulants

Increased toxicity/levels of phenytoin; increased toxicity by displacing methotrexate from protein binding sites; increased nephrotoxicity of cyclosporines

Simultaneous administration of quinapril and trimethoprim can result in hyperkalemia

Dosage Forms The 5:1 ratio (SMX to TMP) remains constant in all dosage forms:

(Continued)

Co-Trimoxazole *(Continued)*

Injection: Sulfamethoxazole 80 mg and trimethoprim 16 mg per mL (5 mL, 10 mL, 20 mL, 30 mL, 50 mL)

Suspension, oral: Sulfamethoxazole 200 mg and trimethoprim 40 mg per 5 mL (20 mL, 100 mL, 150 mL, 200 mL, 480 mL)

Tablet: Sulfamethoxazole 400 mg and trimethoprim 80 mg

Tablet, double strength: Sulfamethoxazole 800 mg and trimethoprim 160 mg

Additional Information Injection vehicle contains benzyl alcohol and sodium metabisulfite; folinic acid should be given if bone marrow depression occurs; one double-strength tablet of trimethoprim-sulfamethoxazole 5 times/week has been demonstrated to aid in preventing spontaneous bacterial peritonitis in cirrhotic patients

Specific References

Howe RA and Spencer RC, "Co-Trimoxazole. Rationale for Re-Examining Its Indications for Use," *Drug Saf*, 1996, 14(4):213-8.

Crab Louse *see* Lice *on page 343*

Crack *see* Cocaine (Cocaine Metabolite), Qualitative *on page 163*

Creo-Terpin® [OTC] *see* Dextromethorphan *on page 187*

Crispin® *see* Tramadol *on page 589*

Cronus® *see* Zopiclone *on page 621*

CS *see* Chlorobenzylidene Malonitrile *on page 128*

CTM *see* Chlorpheniramine *on page 132*

Cultivated Tobacco *see* Tobacco *on page 585*

Cyanide

Synonyms Carbon Nitride Ion; Isocyanide

UN Number 1588

Commonly Found In Gold and silver ore extraction, electroplating, fumigant, stainless steel manufacture, petroleum refining, rodenticide; plant sources include amygdalin glycodes (such as peach pits), cassava, linium, prunus, sorghum, and bamboo sprouts; also a byproduct of nitroprusside and succinonitrile along with laetrile

Mechanism of Toxic Action Forms a stable complex with ferric ion of cytochrome oxidase enzymes inhibiting cellular respiration; then converted to thiocyanate (less toxic form) by rhodanase enzyme

Toxicodynamics/kinetics

Absorption: By inhalation (58% to 77%), oral (~50%), dermally, and ocular

Distribution: V_d: 0.4 L/kg

Metabolism: Hepatic by rhodanase or 3-mercaptopyruvate to thiocyanate; also combines with hydroxocobalamin to form cyanocobalamin (vitamin B_{12})

Half-life: 0.7-2.1 hours

Elimination: Excreted through the lungs and the kidneys

Signs and Symptoms of Acute Intoxication Tachycardia followed by bradycardia, hypotension, tachypnea, pruritus, headache, metabolic acidosis, hyperventilation, cyanosis, flushing, agitation, bitter almond breath, myoglobinuria, hypothermia, coma, seizures, apnea, mydriasis, pulmonary edema, nausea, vomiting, skin irritation, ototoxicity, tinnitus

When to Transport to Hospital Transport any suspected ingestion or any symptomatic inhalation exposure

Overdosage/Treatment Decontamination: Basic poison management (lavage within 1 hour/activated charcoal); emesis is contraindicated due to rapid course of the neurologic symptoms; give 100% oxygen

Adverse Reactions

Cardiovascular: Myocardial depression, hypotension, sinus bradycardia, angina, chest pain, congestive heart failure, sinus tachycardia, vasodilation

Central nervous system: CNS stimulation followed by CNS depression
Endocrine & metabolic: Goiter, hypothyroidism
Gastrointestinal: Bitter almond, burning taste
Neuromuscular & skeletal: Rhabdomyolysis
Ocular: Blurred vision
Respiratory: Respiratory depression

Reference Range

Whole blood levels: Smoker: ≤0.5 mg/L
Flushing and tachycardia seen at 0.5-1.0 mg/L; obtundation at 1.0-2.5 mg/L
Coma and death occur at >2.5 mg/L
Plasma cyanide:
   Normal: 4-5 µg/L
   Asymptomatic (with metabolic acidosis): 80 µg/L
   Death: >260 µg/L
Red blood cell cyanide:
   Normal: <26 µg/L
   Metabolic acidosis: 1040 µg/L
   Symptomatic: 5200 µg/L
   Fatal: >10,400 µg/L

Additional Information Bitter almond odor, zinc cyanide is odorless; up to 60% of the population may be unable to smell cyanide; parkinsonism has been noted after ingestion of sodium or potassium cyanide; hydroxocobalamin and dicobalt-EDTA used for chelation in Europe; ratio of red blood cell to plasma cyanide concentrations is 60:1
Fatal dose of cyanide: 200-300 mg (adult)
ACGIH-TLV-TWA: 5 mg/m³
IDLH: 50 mg/m³
PEL-TWA: 5 mg/m³
Fatal dose (hydrogen cyanide):
   Dermal: 100 mg/kg
   Inhalation for <1 hour: 110-135 ppm
   Oral: 0.6-1.5 mg/kg

Residence time in atmosphere of hydrogen cyanide: 2 years;
In natural rivers half-life of cyanide: 10-24 days
Daily intake of hydrogen cyanide by inhalation: ~3.8 mcg

Cyanogenic Plants

Plant	Amount of Hydrogen Cyanide Released	Maximum Amygdalin Content (in the seeds or pits)
Apricot seeds	0.1-4.1 mg/g	8%
Peach seeds	0.4-2.6 mg/g	6%
Apple seeds	0.61 mg/g	
Bitter almond seeds	0.9-4.9 mg/g	5%
Cassava (whole root)	0.4 mg/g	
Cassava (dried root)	2.45 mg/g	
Sorphum whole plant (immature)	2.5 mg/g	
Amydalin	59.1 mg/g	
Cotoneaster	15-185 ppm	
Plum		2.5%

(Continued)

Cyanide *(Continued)*

Through drinking water: 0.4-0.7 mcg
Allowable daily intake: ~0.6 mg

Fruit juice typically contains from 1.9-5.3 mg/L of hydrogen cyanide while apricot pits contain 89-2,170 mg/kg (wet weight); inhaled smoke from cigarettes contain from 10-400 mcg/cigarette while sidestream smoke usually runs <27% of mainstream smoke concentrations. Average cyanide emission rate in automobiles varies from 11-14 mg/mile in cars; catalytic converters can reduce cyanide emissions by 90%.

Dermal exposure of 10% sodium cyanide to a large body surface area will cause symptoms within 20 minutes

A 5 g dose of hydroxocobalamin appears to bind all cyanide ions in patients with initial cyanide levels up to 40 μmol/L

Plasma lactate (half-life ~4 hours in treated cyanide poisoning) may be useful in determining treatment efficacy in cyanide poisoning

See table for listing of cyanogenic plants.

Specific References

Yen D, Tsai J, Wang LM, et al, "The Clinical Experience of Acute Cyanide Poisoning," *Am J Emerg Med*, 1995, 13(5):524-8.

Cyanoethylene *see Acrylonitrile on page 27*

Cyanomethane *see Acetonitrile on page 26*

Cyater® *see Terfenadine on page 563*

Cyclizine *(SYE kli zeen)*

U.S. Brand Names Happy-Trip®; Marezine® [OTC]

Therapeutic Category Antihistamine

Abuse Potential Yes

Impairment Potential Yes

Use Prevention and treatment of nausea, vomiting, and dizziness associated with motion sickness; control of postoperative nausea and vomiting

Usual Dosage

Children 6-12 years:
Oral: 25 mg up to 3 times/day
I.M.: Not recommended

Adults:
Oral: 50 mg taken 30 minutes before departure, may repeat in 4-6 hours if needed, up to 200 mg/day
I.M.: 50 mg every 4-6 hours as needed

Pharmacodynamics/kinetics Duration of action: 4-6 hours

Signs and Symptoms of Acute Intoxication Dry mouth, dry nose, euphoria, extrapyramidal reaction, insomnia, diarrhea, cholestatic jaundice, flushing, mydriasis, CNS depression

When to Transport to Hospital Transport any symptomatic patient

Adverse Reactions

>10%:
Central nervous system: Drowsiness
Gastrointestinal: Xerostomia

1% to 10%:
Central nervous system: Headache
Dermatologic: Dermatitis
Gastrointestinal: Nausea
Genitourinary: Urinary retention, polyuria
Ocular: Diplopia

Reference Range Peak serum concentrations of 69 ng/mL after a 50 mg oral dose

Dosage Forms
Injection, as lactate: 50 mg/mL (1 mL)
Tablet, as hydrochloride: 50 mg

Additional Information Commonly abused with opiates for euphoric effects

Specific References
Bassett KE, Schunk JE, and Crouch BI, "Cyclizine Abuse by Teenagers in Utah," *Am J Emerg Med*, 1996, 14(5):472-4.

Cyclobenzaprine (sye kloe BEN za preen)

Synonyms CBZ; Propheptatriene
U.S. Brand Names Flexeril®; Flexiban®; Lisseril®; Yurelax®
Canadian Brand Names Novo-Cycloprine®
Therapeutic Category Skeletal Muscle Relaxant
Impairment Potential Yes

Use Treatment of muscle spasm associated with acute painful musculoskeletal conditions; supportive therapy in tetanus

Usual Dosage Oral: **Note:** Do not use longer than 2-3 weeks
Children: Dosage has not been established
Adults: 20-40 mg/day in 2-4 divided doses; maximum dose: 60 mg/day

Toxic symptoms occur with ingestions >100 mg

Mechanism of Action Reduces tonic somatic motor activity influencing both alpha and gamma motor neurons; structurally related to amitriptyline

Pharmacodynamics/kinetics
Onset of action: Commonly occurs within 1 hour
Absorption: Oral: Completely
Metabolism: Hepatic
Half-life: 1-3 days
Time to peak serum concentration: Within 3-8 hours
Elimination: Excreted renally (50%) as inactive metabolites and in feces (via bile) as unchanged drug

Signs and Symptoms of Acute Intoxication Fever, diaphoresis, ataxia, mania, muscular rigidity, rhabdomyolysis, delirium, mydriasis, myalgia, hallucinations, lethargy (54%), tachycardia (33%), combative (13%); mean time to onset of symptoms: 1.4 hours (all patients should be symptomatic within 4 hours)

When to Transport to Hospital Transport any pediatric exposure, any symptomatic patient, or any ingestion over 100 mg

Warnings/Precautions Hyperthyroidism, congestive heart failure, arrhythmias; cyclobenzaprine shares the toxic potentials of the tricyclic antidepressants; the usual precautions of tricyclic antidepressant therapy should be observed; use with caution in patients with urinary hesitancy or angle-closure glaucoma

Adverse Reactions
>10%:
Central nervous system: Drowsiness, dizziness, lightheadedness
Gastrointestinal: Xerostomia
1% to 10%:
Cardiovascular: Edema of the face/lips, syncope
Gastrointestinal: Bloated feeling
Genitourinary: Problems in urinating, polyuria
Hepatic: Hepatitis
Neuromuscular & skeletal: Problems in speaking, muscle weakness
Ocular: Blurred vision
Otic: Tinnitus
(Continued)

Cyclobenzaprine *(Continued)*

Reference Range Therapeutic serum levels following a 40 mg dose: 10-40 ng/mL; a serum level of 260 ng/mL was associated with lethality

Drug Interactions Do not use concomitantly or within 14 days after MAO inhibitors; can cause fever and seizures

Increased effect/toxicity with alcohol, barbiturates, CNS depressants

Increased toxicity with MAO inhibitors, tricyclic antidepressants, anticholinergics

Can decrease the hypotensive effects of guanethidine

Dosage Forms Tablet, as hydrochloride: 10 mg

Additional Information Has tricyclic antidepressant effect (similar to amitriptyline) at doses of 75-250 mg/day; some antidepressant effects include anticholinergic effects, sedation, reserpine antagonism and norepinephrine potentiation

Specific References

Spiller HA, Winter ML, Mann KV, et al, "Five Year Multicenter Retrospective Review of Cyclobenzaprine Toxicity," *J Emerg Med*, 1995, 13(6):781-5.

Cyclomydril® Ophthalmic *see* Cyclopentolate and Phenylephrine *on this page*

Cyclonite *see* RDX *on page 522*

Cyclopentolate and Phenylephrine

(sye kloe PEN toe late & fen il EF rin)

Synonyms Phenylephrine and Cyclopentolate

U.S. Brand Names Cyclomydril® Ophthalmic

Therapeutic Category Anticholinergic/Adrenergic Agonist

Dosage Forms Solution, ophthalmic: Cyclopentolate hydrochloride 0.2% and phenylephrine hydrochloride 1% (2 mL, 5 mL)

Cycloserine *(sye kloe SER een)*

U.S. Brand Names Seromycin® Pulvules®

Therapeutic Category Antibiotic, Miscellaneous

Use Adjunctive treatment in pulmonary or extrapulmonary tuberculosis; treatment of acute urinary tract infections caused by *E. coli* or *Enterobacter* sp when less toxic conventional therapy has failed or is contraindicated; also is an orphan drug used for Gaucher's disease

Usual Dosage Some of the neurotoxic effects may be relieved or prevented by the concomitant administration of pyridoxine

Tuberculosis: Oral:
  Children: 10-20 mg/kg/day in 2 divided doses up to 1000 mg/day for 18-24 months
  Adults: Initial: 250 mg every 12 hours for 14 days, then give 500 mg to 1 g/day in 2 divided doses for 18-24 months (maximum daily dose: 1 g)

Mechanism of Action Inhibits bacterial cell wall synthesis by competing with amino acid (D-alanine) for incorporation into the bacterial cell wall; bacteriostatic or bactericidal

Pharmacodynamics/kinetics

Absorption: Oral: ~70% to 90% from the GI tract

Half-life: 10 hours in patients with normal renal function

Metabolism: Extensive in liver

Time to peak serum concentration: Oral: Within 3-4 hours

When to Transport to Hospital Transport any symptomatic patient or any ingestion over 1 g

Overdosage/Treatment

Supportive therapy: Neurotoxic effects can be prevented with use of pyridoxine (150-300 mg/day)

Enhanced elimination: Removed by dialysis

Warnings/Precautions Epilepsy, depression, severe anxiety, psychosis, severe renal insufficiency, chronic alcoholism

Adverse Reactions

Cardiovascular: Cardiac arrhythmias, congestive heart failure at doses >1 g/day

Central nervous system: Dizziness, seizures, confusion, paranoia, psychosis, paresis, coma, drowsiness, headache, delirium, absence seizures, catatonia

Dermatologic: Rash, Stevens-Johnson syndrome

Endocrine & metabolic: Vitamin B_{12} deficiency

Hematologic: Folate deficiency

Hepatic: Liver enzymes (elevated)

Neuromuscular & skeletal: Tremor, dysarthria, hyperreflexia

Miscellaneous: Pellagra

Test Interactions May result in assay interference with cyclosporine by HPLC

Reference Range Toxicity is greatly increased at serum levels >30 µg/mL; therapeutic cycloserine serum levels for *Mycobacterium* tuberculosis: 5-20 µg/mL

Drug Interactions Increased toxicity: Alcohol, isoniazid, ethionamide increase toxicity of cycloserine; cycloserine inhibits the hepatic metabolism of phenytoin; cycloserine can increase the effects of oral anticoagulant agents

Dosage Forms Capsule: 250 mg

Specific References

Iseman MD, "Treatment of Multidrug-Resistant Tuberculosis," *N Engl J Med*, 1993, 329(11):784-91.

Cycofed® Pediatric see Guaifenesin, Pseudoephedrine, and Codeine on page 275

Cylert® see Pemoline on page 462

Cylex® [OTC] see Benzocaine on page 70

Cyproheptadine (si proe HEP ta deen)

U.S. Brand Names Klarivitina®; Nuran®; Periactin®; Periactinol®

Canadian Brand Names PMS-Cyproheptadine®

Therapeutic Category Antihistamine

Use Angioedema, pruritus, urticaria (especially cold-induced urticaria), appetite stimulant, atopic dermatitis; useful in treating Cushing's syndrome, blepharospasm; may be useful in treating serotonin syndrome

Usual Dosage

Children: 0.25 mg/kg/day or 8 mg/m²/day in 2-3 doses

Adults: Therapeutic dosage range: 4-20 mg/day; usual adult therapeutic dosage range: 12-16 mg/day; dosage for serotonin syndrome: 4-8 mg initial dose, can repeat every 2-4 hours up to 0.5 mg/kg/day

Maximum daily adult dose: 0.5 mg/kg/day

Mechanism of Action Direct serotonin antagonist with anticholinergic and antihistamine effects

Pharmacodynamics/kinetics

Duration of action: 4-6 hours

Metabolism: Hepatic

Half-life: 16 hours

Elimination: Urine (57%) and feces (26%)

Signs and Symptoms of Acute Intoxication Agitation, confusion, tachycardia, mydriasis, hallucinations, seizures, hypotension, sedation

When to Transport to Hospital Referral and treatment of ingestions >3 times usual dose suggested or any symptomatic patient

Warnings/Precautions Reduce dosage in patients with hepatic insufficiency; use with caution in patients with asthma, hyperthyroidism, stenosing peptic

(Continued)

Cyproheptadine *(Continued)*

ulcer, bladder neck obstruction, gastrointestinal obstruction, hypertension; not to be used in combination with central nervous system depressants, MAO inhibitors, or ethanol

Adverse Reactions

>10%:

Central nervous system: Slight to moderate drowsiness

Respiratory: Thickening of bronchial secretions

1% to 10%:

Central nervous system: Headache, fatigue, nervousness, dizziness

Gastrointestinal: Appetite stimulation, nausea, diarrhea, abdominal pain, xerostomia

Neuromuscular & skeletal: Arthralgia

Respiratory: Pharyngitis

Test Interactions Can cause false-positive serum tricyclic antidepressant screens

Reference Range Postmortem peripheral blood and urine cyproheptadine levels of 0.62 mg/L and 0.75 mg/L noted after an adult cyproheptadine overdose

Drug Interactions

Decreased antidepressant effects of fluoxetine

Increased anticholinergic effect with use of MAO inhibitors

Paranoid delusions with psychosis can develop after administration of cyproheptadine and paroxetine

Dosage Forms

Cyproheptadine hydrochloride:

Syrup: 2 mg/5 mL with alcohol 5% (473 mL)

Tablet: 4 mg

Additional Information Lowers serum prolactin levels; should not be administered during breast-feeding; also has been used to treat serotonin syndrome induced by the combination of sertraline and isocarboxazid at a dose of 4 mg; can cause dependence

Specific References

Levine B, Green-Johnson D, Hogan S, et al, "A Cyproheptadine Fatality," *J Anal Tox*, 1998, 22:72-4.

Cystospaz® *see Hyoscyamine on page 305*

Cystospaz-M® *see Hyoscyamine on page 305*

D.A.II® Tablet *see Chlorpheniramine, Phenylephrine, and Methscopolamine on page 136*

Dalalone® *see Dexamethasone on page 182*

Dalalone D.P.® *see Dexamethasone on page 182*

Dalalone L.A.® *see Dexamethasone on page 182*

Dalcaine® *see Lidocaine on page 345*

Dallergy® *see Chlorpheniramine, Phenylephrine, and Methscopolamine on page 136*

Dallergy-D® Syrup *see Chlorpheniramine and Phenylephrine on page 134*

Dalmane® *see Flurazepam on page 256*

Damason-P® *see Hydrocodone and Aspirin on page 294*

Danlene® *see Dantrolene on next page*

Dantamacrin® *see Dantrolene on next page*

Dantralen® *see Dantrolene on next page*

Dantrium® *see Dantrolene on next page*

Dantrolene (DAN troe leen)

U.S. Brand Names Danlene®; Dantamacrin®; Dantralen®; Dantrium®

Therapeutic Category Skeletal Muscle Relaxant

Use Treatment of malignant hyperthermia, neuroleptic malignant syndrome, and serotonin syndrome; considered possibly beneficial for fever and rigidity due to carbon monoxide, cocaine poisoning, hyperthermia due to baclofen withdrawal

Usual Dosage

Spasticity: Oral:

Children: Initial: 0.5 mg/kg/dose twice daily, increase frequency to 3-4 times/ day at 4- to 7-day intervals, then increase dose by 0.5 mg/kg to a maximum of 3 mg/kg/dose 2-4 times/day up to 400 mg/day

Adults: 25 mg/day to start, increase frequency to 2-4 times/day, then increase dose by 25 mg every 4-7 days to a maximum of 100 mg 2-4 times/ day or 400 mg/day

Malignant hyperthermia: Children and Adults:

Oral: 4-8 mg/kg/day in 4 divided doses

Preoperative prophylaxis: Begin 1-2 days prior to surgery with last dose 3-4 hours prior to surgery

I.V.: 1 mg/kg; may repeat dose up to cumulative dose of 10 mg/kg (mean effective dose is 2.5 mg/kg), then switch to oral dosage

Preoperative: 2.5 mg/kg ~1¼ hours prior to anesthesia and infused over 1 hour with additional doses as needed and individualized

Mechanism of Action Acts directly on skeletal muscle by interfering with release of calcium ion from the sarcoplasmic reticulum; prevents or reduces the increase in myoplasmic calcium ion concentration that activates the acute catabolic processes associated with malignant hyperthermia

Pharmacodynamics/kinetics

Absorption: Slow and incomplete from gastrointestinal tract (70%)

Metabolism: Slow in liver to weakly active metabolites

Half-life: 8.7 hours

Time to peak plasma concentration: 5 hours

Elimination: 25% excreted in urine as metabolites and unchanged drug, 45% to 50% excreted in feces via bile

Signs and Symptoms of Acute Intoxication Lethargy, respiratory depression, pericarditis, nocturia, insomnia, hematuria, disorientation, neutropenia, jaundice, lightheadedness, crystalluria, seizures, hypotension

Warnings/Precautions Use with caution in patients with impaired cardiac function or impaired pulmonary function; has potential for hepatitis; overt hepatitis has been most frequently observed between the third and twelfth month of therapy; hepatic injury appears to be greater in females and in patients >35 years of age

Adverse Reactions

>10%:

Central nervous system: Drowsiness, dizziness, lightheadedness, fatigue

Dermatologic: Rash

Gastrointestinal: Diarrhea (mild), nausea, vomiting

Neuromuscular & skeletal: Muscle weakness

1% to 10%:

Cardiovascular: Pleural effusion with pericarditis

Central nervous system: Chills, fever, headache, insomnia, nervousness, mental depression

Gastrointestinal: Diarrhea (severe), constipation, anorexia, stomach cramps

Ocular: Blurred vision

Respiratory: Respiratory depression

Drug Interactions Increased toxicity with estrogens (hepatitis), CNS depressants (sedation), MAO inhibitors, phenothiazine, clindamycin (↑ neuromuscular (Continued)

Dantrolene *(Continued)*

blockade), verapamil (hyperkalemia and cardiac depression), theophylline (seizures)

Dosage Forms
Capsule: 25 mg, 50 mg, 100 mg
Powder for injection: 20 mg

Additional Information Routine I.V. prophylactic use of dantrolene for malignant hyperthermia is associated with multiple and frequent side effects and thus is **not** recommended

Daonil® *see* Glyburide *on page 267*

Dapacin® Cold Capsule [OTC] *see* Chlorpheniramine, Phenylpropanolamine, and Acetaminophen *on page 137*

Darkene® *see* Flunitrazepam *on page 250*

Darvocet-N® *see* Propoxyphene and Acetaminophen *on page 510*

Darvocet-N® 100 *see* Propoxyphene and Acetaminophen *on page 510*

Darvon® *see* Propoxyphene *on page 508*

Darvon® Compound-65 Pulvules® *see* Propoxyphene and Aspirin *on page 510*

Darvon-N® *see* Propoxyphene *on page 508*

Datolan® *see* Zopiclone *on page 621*

Dayto Himbin® *see* Yohimbine *on page 618*

Deadly Hemlock *see* Poison Hemlock *on page 491*

Deadly Nightshade

Synonyms *Atropa belladonna*; Bittersweet Nightshade; Blue Blindweed; Blue Nightshade; Climbing Nightshade; Devil's Soda Apple; European Bittersweet; Felonwort; Poisonous Nightshade; Scarlet Berry; Violet Bloom; Weedy Nightshade

Scientific Name *Solanum dulcamara*

Abuse Potential Yes

Impairment Potential Yes

Usual Dosage 2-3 green berries or 6 red or black berries should not cause significant toxicity (fatal dose: 200 berries)

Mechanism of Action Contains toxic alkaloids, solanine most significant structurally similar to cardioglycoside, causes hemolytic and hemorrhagic damage to GI tract similar to saponins; some plants may also contain alpha-cholinergic alkaloids

Pharmacodynamics/kinetics Toxicity occurs within 2-24 hours, diarrhea may last 3-6 days, anticholinergic effects may delay GI emptying and produce delayed effects

Signs and Symptoms of Acute Intoxication Nausea, seizures, vomiting, diarrhea, headache, visual changes, drowsiness, fever, sweating, asthenia, mydriasis, hallucinations, anticholinergic effects may or may not be present to varying degrees

When to Transport to Hospital Transport any symptomatic ingestion or ingestion over 10 berries

Adverse Reactions Central nervous system: Psychosis

Additional Information Toxic parts: All parts of plant contain solanine and are regarded as toxic; peak plasma and urine atropine levels 10 hours after ingestion of 6 raw berries and 200 g of cooked berries (and associated with coma) were 217 µg/L and 3092 µg/L respectively

Specific References

Schneider F, Lutun P, Kintz P, et al, "Plasma and Urine Concentrations of Atropine After the Ingestion of Cooked Deadly Nightshade Berries," *J Toxicol Clin Toxicol*, 1996, 34(1):113-7.

Decachloroketone *see* Chlordecone *on page 123*

Decadron® *see* Dexamethasone *on page 182*

Decadron®-LA *see* Dexamethasone *on page 182*

Decadron® Phosphate *see* Dexamethasone *on page 182*

Deca-Durabolin® Injection *see* Nandrolone *on page 421*

Decaject® *see* Dexamethasone *on page 182*

Decaject-LA® *see* Dexamethasone *on page 182*

Decentan® *see* Perphenazine *on page 467*

Decofed® Syrup [OTC] *see* Pseudoephedrine *on page 516*

Decohistine® DH *see* Chlorpheniramine, Pseudoephedrine, and Codeine *on page 138*

Decohistine® Expectorant *see* Guaifenesin, Pseudoephedrine, and Codeine *on page 275*

Deconamine® SR *see* Chlorpheniramine and Pseudoephedrine *on page 134*

Deconamine® Syrup [OTC] *see* Chlorpheniramine and Pseudoephedrine *on page 134*

Deconamine® Tablet [OTC] *see* Chlorpheniramine and Pseudoephedrine *on page 134*

Deconsal® II *see* Guaifenesin and Pseudoephedrine *on page 273*

Deconsal® Sprinkle® *see* Guaifenesin and Phenylephrine *on page 272*

Deep Freeze *see* Chlorobenzylidene Malonitrile *on page 128*

Deer Berry *see* Holly *on page 287*

DEET *see* Diethyltoluamide *on page 197*

Defen-LA® *see* Guaifenesin and Pseudoephedrine *on page 273*

Degest® 2 [OTC] *see* Naphazoline *on page 422*

Dehist® *see* Brompheniramine *on page 84*

Deladumone® Injection *see* Estradiol and Testosterone *on page 229*

Delatest® Injection *see* Testosterone *on page 564*

Delatestryl® *see* Testosterone *on page 564*

Delaxin® *see* Methocarbamol *on page 390*

Delcort® *see* Hydrocortisone *on page 297*

Delgamer® *see* Diethylpropion *on page 196*

Delpral® *see* Tiapride *on page 581*

Delsym® [OTC] *see* Dextromethorphan *on page 187*

Delta-Cortef® *see* Prednisolone *on page 495*

Deltacortisone *see* Prednisone *on page 497*

Deltadehydrocortisone *see* Prednisone *on page 497*

Deltahydrocortisone *see* Prednisolone *on page 495*

Deltasone® *see* Prednisone *on page 497*

Demazin® Syrup [OTC] *see* Chlorpheniramine and Phenylpropanolamine *on page 134*

Demerol® *see* Meperidine *on page 367*

Demetrin® *see* Prazepam *on page 493*

Demorphan *see* Dextromethorphan *on page 187*

Deobase® *see* Kerosene *on page 325*

Deodorized Opium Tincture *see* Opium Tincture *on page 446*

Depakene® *see* Valproic Acid and Derivatives *on page 607*

Depakote® *see* Valproic Acid and Derivatives *on page 607*

depAndrogyn® Injection *see* Estradiol and Testosterone *on page 229*
Deponit® *see* Nitroglycerin *on page 437*
Depo-Testadiol® Injection *see* Estradiol and Testosterone *on page 229*
Depotest® Injection *see* Testosterone *on page 564*
Depotestogen® Injection *see* Estradiol and Testosterone *on page 229*
Depo®-Testosterone Injection *see* Testosterone *on page 564*
Deprax® *see* Trazodone *on page 590*
Deprenyl *see* Selegiline *on page 536*
Deproist® Expectorant with Codeine *see* Guaifenesin, Pseudoephedrine, and Codeine *on page 275*
Deralin® *see* Propranolol *on page 510*
Dermacort® *see* Hydrocortisone *on page 297*
Dermarest Dricort® *see* Hydrocortisone *on page 297*
DermiCort® *see* Hydrocortisone *on page 297*
Dermolate® [OTC] *see* Hydrocortisone *on page 297*
Dermoplast® [OTC] *see* Benzocaine *on page 70*
Dermtex® HC with Aloe *see* Hydrocortisone *on page 297*
Desconex® *see* Loxapine *on page 354*
Déséril® *see* Methysergide *on page 400*
Désernil-Sandoz® *see* Methysergide *on page 400*
Deserril® *see* Methysergide *on page 400*

Desipramine (des IP ra meen)

Synonyms Desmethylimipramine Hydrochloride
U.S. Brand Names Nebril®; Norpramin®; Nortimil®; Pertofrane®; Pertofrin®; Sertofren®
Canadian Brand Names PMS-Desipramine®
Therapeutic Category Antidepressant
Use Treatment of various forms of depression, often in conjunction with psychotherapy; as an analgesic in chronic pain, peripheral neuropathies
Usual Dosage Oral (not recommended for use in children <12 years):
    Adolescents: Initial: 25-50 mg/day; gradually increase to 100 mg/day in single or divided doses; maximum: 150 mg/day
    Adults: Initial: 75 mg/day in divided doses; increase gradually to 150-200 mg/day in divided or single dose; maximum: 300 mg/day
Mechanism of Action Increases the synaptic concentration of serotonin and/or norepinephrine in the central nervous system by inhibition of their reuptake by the presynaptic neuronal membrane
Pharmacodynamics/kinetics
    Onset of action: 2-3 weeks
    Absorption: Well absorbed from gastrointestinal tract
    Metabolism: In the liver (hydroxylation and conjugation)
    Half-life: Adults: 12-57 hours
Signs and Symptoms of Acute Intoxication Agitation, dental erosion, thrombocytopenia, photosensitivity, neuroleptic malignant syndrome, jaundice, hypertension, intraocular pressure (increased), dementia, coma, impotence, eosinophilia, dry mucous membranes, asystole, Q-T prolongation, confusion, hallucinations, hyperthermia, urinary retention, CNS depression, cyanosis, leukopenia, neutropenia, agranulocytosis, granulocytopenia
When to Transport to Hospital Transport any pediatric exposure (<12 years of age), any ingestion over 300 mg, or any symptomatic patient
Warnings/Precautions Some formulations contain tartrazine which may cause allergic reaction; do not discontinue abruptly in patients receiving long-term high-dose therapy; use with caution in patients with cardiovascular

disease, conduction disturbances, urinary retention, seizure disorders, hyperthyroidism, or those receiving thyroid replacement

Adverse Reactions

>10%:

Central nervous system: Dizziness, drowsiness, headache

Gastrointestinal: Xerostomia, constipation, increased appetite, nausea, unpleasant taste, weight gain

Neuromuscular & skeletal: Weakness

1% to 10%:

Cardiovascular: Arrhythmias, hypotension

Central nervous system: Confusion, delirium, hallucinations, nervousness, restlessness, parkinsonian syndrome, insomnia

Gastrointestinal: Diarrhea, heartburn

Genitourinary: Dysuria, sexual dysfunction

Neuromuscular & skeletal: Fine muscle tremors

Ocular: Blurred vision, eye pain

Miscellaneous: Diaphoresis (excessive)

Reference Range

Therapeutic: 150-300 ng/mL (SI: 560-1125 nmol/L)

Possible toxicity: >300 ng/mL (SI: >1070 nmol/L)

Toxic: >1000 ng/mL (SI: >3750 nmol/L)

Drug Interactions May decrease effects of guanethidine and clonidine; may increase effects of CNS depressants, adrenergic agents, anticholinergic agents; with MAO inhibitors, fever, tachycardia, hypertension, seizures, and death may occur; interactions similar to other tricyclics may occur; lower serum tricyclic antidepressant levels may be noted in cigarette smokers due to increased hepatic metabolism; sertraline can inhibit hepatic metabolism of tricyclic antidepressants

Dosage Forms

Desipramine hydrochloride:

Capsule (Pertofrane®): 25 mg, 50 mg

Tablet (Norpramin®): 10 mg, 25 mg, 50 mg, 75 mg, 100 mg, 150 mg

Additional Information May unmask pheochromocytoma; nitroglycerin administration decreases survival time in a rodent model

Specific References

Linnoila M, Johnson J, Dubyoski K, et al, "Effects of Antidepressants on Skilled Performance," *Br J Clin Pharmacol*, 1984, 18(Suppl 1):109S-20S.

Varley CK and McClellan J, "Case Study: Two Additional Sudden Deaths With Tricyclic Antidepressants," *J Am Acad Child Adolesc Psychiatry*, 1997, 36(3):390-4.

Desmethylimipramine Hydrochloride *see* Desipramine *on previous page*

Desoxyephedrine Hydrochloride *see* Methamphetamine *on page 382*

Desoxyn® *see* Methamphetamine *on page 382*

Desoxyphenobarbital *see* Primidone *on page 500*

Desyrel® *see* Trazodone *on page 590*

Detensiel® *see* Bisoprolol *on page 78*

Detussin® Expectorant *see* Hydrocodone, Pseudoephedrine, and Guaifenesin *on page 297*

Devil's Soda Apple *see* Deadly Nightshade *on page 178*

Dexacort® Phosphate in Respihaler *see* Dexamethasone *on next page*

Dexacort® Phosphate Turbinaire® *see* Dexamethasone *on next page*

Dex-A-Diet® [OTC] *see* Phenylpropanolamine *on page 481*

Dexamethasone (deks a METH a sone)

U.S. Brand Names Aeroseb-Dex®; AK-Dex® Ophthalmic; Baldex®; Dalalone®; Dalalone D.P.®; Dalalone L.A.®; Decadron®; Decadron®-LA; Decadron® Phosphate; Decaject®; Decaject-LA®; Dexacort® Phosphate in Respihaler; Dexacort® Phosphate Turbinaire®; Dexasone®; Dexasone® L.A.; Dexone®; Dexone® LA; Dexotic®; Hexadrol®; Hexadrol® Phosphate; I-Methasone®; Maxidex®; Solurex®; Solurex L.A.®

Therapeutic Category Adrenal Corticosteroid

Use Systemically and locally for chronic inflammation, allergic, hematologic, neoplastic, and autoimmune diseases; may be used in management of cerebral edema, as a diagnostic agent, antiemetic; to prevent neurologic sequelae in children with bacterial meningitis due to *Haemophilus influenzae* type b infections; no longer recommended for septic shock; used for thrombocytopenia in AIDS; may reduce peripheral edema due to docetaxel

Usual Dosage

Children:

Antiemetic (prior to chemotherapy): I.V.: 10 mg/m²/dose (maximum: 20 mg) for first dose then 5 mg/m²/dose every 6 hours as needed

Anti-inflammatory immunosuppressant: Oral, I.M., I.V.: 0.08-0.3 mg/kg/day or 2.5-10 mg/m²/day in divided doses every 6-12 hours

Physiologic replacement: Oral, I.M., I.V.: 0.03-0.15 mg/kg/day or 0.6-0.75 mg/m²/day in divided doses every 6-12 hours

Extubation or airway edema: Oral, I.M., I.V.: 0.5-2 mg/kg/day in divided doses every 6 hours beginning 24 hours prior to extubation and continuing for 4-6 doses afterwards

Cerebral edema: Loading dose: Oral, I.M., I.V.: 1-2 mg/kg/dose as a single dose; maintenance: 1-1.5 mg/kg/day (maximum: 16 mg/day) in divided doses every 4-6 hours for 5 days then taper for 5 days, then discontinue

Bacterial meningitis: 0.15 mg/kg within 4 hours of antibiotics and every 6 hours

Inhalation:

Oral: 2 inhalations 3-4 times/day to a maximum of 8 inhalations/day

Intranasal: 6-12 years: 1-2 sprays into each nostril twice daily to a maximum of 8 sprays/day

Adults:

Antiemetic (prior to chemotherapy): I.V.: 10 mg/m²/dose for first dose then 5 mg/m²/dose every 6 hours as needed

Anti-inflammatory: Oral, I.M., I.V. (I.M., I.V. should be sodium phosphate salt): 0.5-9 mg/day in divided doses every 6-12 hours

Cerebral edema: I.V. 10 mg stat, 4 mg I.M./I.V. every 6 hours until response is maximized, then switch to oral regimen, then taper off if appropriate. Dosage may be reduced after 2-4 days and gradually discontinued over 5-7 days

Unresponsive shock: I.V.: 1-6 mg/kg as a single I.V. dose, to 40 mg initially, followed by repeat doses every 2-6 hours while shock persists

Diagnosis for Cushing's syndrome: Oral: 1 mg at 11 PM, draw blood at 8 AM the following day for plasma cortisol determination

Acetate salt:

I.M.: 8-16 mg, may repeat in 1-3 weeks

Intralesional: 0.8-1.6 mg

Intra-articular/soft tissue: 4-16 mg, may repeat in 1-3 weeks

Phosphate salt: Intra-articular, intralesional, or soft tissue: 0.4-6 mg

Inhalation:

Oral: 3 inhalations 3-4 times/day to a maximum of 12 inhalations/day

Intranasal: 2 sprays into each nostril 2-3 times/day to a maximum of 12 sprays/day

Thrombocytopenia in AIDS: 10 mg 4 times/day for 2-4 days

Children and Adults:
 Ophthalmic:
  Ointment: Apply thin coating into conjunctival sac 3-4 times/day, gradually taper dose to discontinue
  Suspension: Instill 2 drops into conjunctival sac every hour during the day and every other hour during the night; gradually reduce dose to every 3-4 hours, then to 3-4 times/day
 Topical: Apply 1-4 times/day
 Peripheral edema due to docetaxel: 4 mg twice daily

Mechanism of Action Decreases inflammation by suppression of migration of polymorphonuclear leukocytes and reversal of increased capillary permeability; suppresses normal immune response

Pharmacodynamics/kinetics
 Time to peak serum concentration: Oral: Within 1-2 hours
 Duration: Metabolic effect can last for 72 hours; acetate is a long-acting repository preparation with a prompt onset of action
 Metabolism: In the liver
 Half-life: 2.4-3.5 hours

When to Transport to Hospital Transport any symptomatic patient

Warnings/Precautions Use with caution in patients with hypothyroidism, cirrhosis, hypertension, congestive heart failure, ulcerative colitis, thromboembolic disorders; fatalities have occurred due to adrenal cortical insufficiency in asthmatic patients during and after transfer from systemic corticosteroids to aerosol steroids; during this period, aerosol steroids do **not** provide the systemic steroid needed to treat patients having trauma, surgery, or infections; may retard bone growth

Adverse Reactions
 >10%:
  Central nervous system: Insomnia, nervousness
  Gastrointestinal: Increased appetite, indigestion
 1% to 10%:
  Dermatologic: Hirsutism
  Endocrine & metabolic: Diabetes mellitus
  Neuromuscular & skeletal: Arthralgia
  Ocular: Cataracts
  Respiratory: Epistaxis

Test Interactions May result in false elevation of digoxin level (by RIA)

Reference Range Dexamethasone suppression test, overnight: 8 AM cortisol <6 μg/100 mL (dexamethasone 1 mg)

Drug Interactions
 Decreased effect with barbiturates, phenytoin, rifampin, aminoglutethimide
 Decreased effect of salicylates, vaccines, toxoids, sulfonylureas
 Decreased phenytoin levels can occur with concomitant dexamethasone administration

Dosage Forms
 Acetate:
  Injection:
   Dalalone L.A.®, Decadron®-LA, Decaject-LA®, Dexasone® L.A., Dexone® LA, Solurex L.A.®: 8 mg/mL (1 mL, 5 mL)
   Dalalone D.P.®: 16 mg/mL (1 mL, 5 mL)
 Base:
  Aerosol, topical:
   Aeroseb-Dex®: 0.01% (58 g)
  Elixir (Decadron®, Hexadrol®): 0.5 mg/5 mL (5 mL, 20 mL, 100 mL, 120 mL, 240 mL, 500 mL)
  Solution, oral: 0.5 mg/5 mL (5 mL, 20 mL, 500 mL)
  Solution, oral concentrate: 0.5 mg/0.5 mL (30 mL)
 (Continued)

Dexamethasone *(Continued)*

Suspension, ophthalmic: 0.1% (5 mL)
Maxidex®: 0.1% (5 mL, 15 mL)
Tablet (Decadron®, Dexone®, Hexadrol®): 0.25 mg, 0.5 mg, 0.75 mg, 1 mg, 1.5 mg, 2 mg, 4 mg, 6 mg
Therapeutic pack: Six 1.5 mg tablets and eight 0.75 mg tablets

Sodium phosphate:

Aerosol, nasal (Dexacort®): 84 mcg/activation [170 metered doses] (12.6 g)
Aerosol, oral (Dexacort®): 84 mcg/activation [170 metered doses] (12.6 g)
Cream (Decadron® Phosphate): 0.1% (15 g, 30 g)
Injection:
Dalalone®, Decadron® Phosphate, Decaject®, Dexasone®, Hexadrol® Phosphate, Solurex®: 4 mg/mL (1 mL, 2 mL, 2.5 mL, 5 mL, 10 mL, 30 mL)
Hexadrol® Phosphate: 10 mg/mL (1 mL, 10 mL); 20 mg/mL (5 mL)
Decadron® Phosphate: 24 mg/mL (5 mL, 10 mL)
Ointment, ophthalmic: 0.05% (3.5 g)
AK-Dex®, Baldex®, Decadron® Phosphate, Maxidex®: 0.05% (3.5 g)
Solution, ophthalmic (AK-Dex®, Baldex®, Decadron® Phosphate, Dexotic®, I-Methasone®): 0.1% (5 mL)

Additional Information Not suitable for every other day dosing due to long duration of effect; intravenous dexamethasone (2 mg I.V.) can impair ethyl alcohol's ability to stimulate sympathetic nerve discharge and thus suppress alcohol-induced high blood pressure in the acute state; nebulization of dexamethasone sodium phosphate (1.5 mg/kg up to 45 mg) may be as effective as oral prednisone in the emergency management of moderately severe asthma in children. Granisetron (3 mg I.V.) is effective when used with dexamethasone to prevent emesis due to chemotherapy

Specific References

Uva JL, "Corticosteroid-Induced Suicide Attempt," *Ann Emerg Med*, 1996, 28(3):376-7.

Dexamyl® *see Dextroamphetamine on page 186*

Dexasone® *see Dexamethasone on page 182*

Dexasone® L.A. *see Dexamethasone on page 182*

Dexatrim® [OTC] *see Phenylpropanolamine on page 481*

Dexbrompheniramine and Pseudoephedrine

(deks brom fen EER a meen & soo doe e FED rin)

Synonyms Pseudoephedrine and Dexbrompheniramine

U.S. Brand Names Disobrom® [OTC]; Disophrol® Chronotabs® [OTC]; Disophrol® Tablet [OTC]; Drixomed®; Drixoral® [OTC]

Therapeutic Category Antihistamine/Decongestant Combination

Abuse Potential Yes

Impairment Potential Yes

Dosage Forms

Tablet (Disophrol®): Dexbrompheniramine maleate 2 mg and pseudoephedrine sulfate 60 mg
Tablet, timed release (Disobrom®, Disophrol® Chrontabs®, Drixomed®, Drixoral®, Histrodrix®, Resporal®): Dexbrompheniramine maleate 6 mg and pseudoephedrine sulfate 120 mg

Dexedrina® *see Dextroamphetamine on page 186*

Dexedrine® *see Dextroamphetamine on page 186*

Dexfenfluramine (deks fen FLURE a meen)
Related Information
Fenfluramine *on page 244*
Synonyms S5614
U.S. Brand Names Adifax®; Dipondal®; Glypolix®; Isomeride®; Redux®
Therapeutic Category Anorexiant
Use Management of obesity (initial body mass >30 kg/m^3 or >27 kg/m^3 with other risk factors such as hypertension, diabetes, or hyperlipidemia); given as an adjunct to dietary restriction; off the U.S. market as of September 15, 1997
Usual Dosage 15 mg 2 times/day with meals
Mechanism of Action Can cause elevation of serotonin in the brain which suppresses appetite for carbohydrates (but not protein-rich foods)
Pharmacodynamics/kinetics
Peak serum levels: 2-4 hours
Metabolism: Hepatic to d-norfenfluramine (active metabolite)
Half-life: Oral:
  Dexfenfluramine: 18 hours
  D-norfenfluramine: 30 hours
When to Transport to Hospital Transport any patient with cardiopulmonary effects or central nervous system complaints
Warnings/Precautions Use with caution in patients with cardiac disease, renal or hepatic insufficiency, porphyria, drug abuse, psychiatric disorder, or organic causes for obesity
Adverse Reactions
>10%:
  Central nervous system: Drowsiness, headache, insomnia
  Gastrointestinal: Abdominal discomfort, xerostomia, diarrhea
  Neuromuscular & skeletal: Weakness
1% to 10%:
  Cardiovascular: Hypotension, primary pulmonary hypertension (18 cases per 1 million users per year), leukocytoclastic vasculitis
  Central nervous system: Fatigue, dizziness, anxiety, depression (reactive), dysphoria
  Dermatologic: Urticaria
  Gastrointestinal: Nausea, vomiting
  Hematologic: Porphyrinogenic
  Renal: Polyuria
Test Interactions Can give a positive urinary immunoassay result for amphetamines but will not confirm by gas chromatography/mass spectrometry
Reference Range After a 20 mg oral dose, peak serum level: ~16 µg/L; peak serum metabolite d-norfenfluramine is 6 µg/L
Dosage Forms Capsule, as hydrochloride: 15 mg
Additional Information On September 12, 1997, the FDA announced new summary information concerning abnormal echocardiogram findings in asymptomatic patients seen in five centers. These patients had been treated with fenfluramine or dexfenfluramine for up to 24 months, most often in combination with phentermine. Abnormal echocardiogram findings were reported in 92 of 291 subjects evaluated, including 80 reports of aortic regurgitation (mild or greater) and 23 reports of mitral regurgitation (moderate or greater). Those requiring further information can call 1-800-892-2718. Questions about returning products can be directed to 1-800-666-7248.
Specific References
Cannistra LB, Davis SM, and Bauman AG, "Valvular Heart Disease Associated With Dexfenfluramine," *N Engl J Med*, 1997, 337(9):636.

Dexone® *see* Dexamethasone *on page 182*

Dexone® LA *see* Dexamethasone *on page 182*
Dexotic® *see* Dexamethasone *on page 182*

Dextroamphetamine (deks troe am FET a meen)

U.S. Brand Names Dexamyl®; Dexedrina®; Dexedrine®; Ferndex®
Therapeutic Category Amphetamine
Abuse Potential Yes
Impairment Potential Yes
Use Treatment of narcolepsy, abnormal behavioral syndrome in children, exogenous obesity
Usual Dosage Oral:
Children:
Narcolepsy: 6-12 years: Initial: 5 mg/day, may increase at 5 mg increments in weekly intervals until side effects appear; maximum dose: 60 mg/day
Attention deficit disorder:
3-5 years: Initial: 2.5 mg/day given every morning; increase by 2.5 mg/day in weekly intervals until optimal response is obtained, usual range: 0.1-0.5 mg/kg/dose every morning with maximum of 40 mg/day
≥6 years: 5 mg once or twice daily; increase in increments of 5 mg/day at weekly intervals until optimal response is reached, usual range: 0.1-0.5 mg/kg/dose every morning (5-20 mg/day) with maximum of 40 mg/day

Adults:
Narcolepsy: Initial: 10 mg/day, may increase at 10 mg increments in weekly intervals until side effects appear; maximum: 60 mg/day
Exogenous obesity: 5-30 mg/day in divided doses of 5-10 mg 30-60 minutes before meals
Mechanism of Action Blocks reuptake of dopamine and norepinephrine from the synapse, thus increases the amount of circulating dopamine and norepinephrine in cerebral cortex to reticular activating system; inhibits the action of monoamine oxidase and causes catecholamines to be released
Pharmacodynamics/kinetics
Onset of action: 1-1.5 hours
Absorption: Food does not delay absorption
Metabolism: In the liver
Half-life: Adults: 34 hours (pH dependent)
Time to peak serum concentration: Oral: Within 3 hours
Signs and Symptoms of Acute Intoxication Tachycardia, bradycardia, mydriasis, hypertension, hypotension, chills, diaphoresis, nausea, vomiting, weight loss, psychomotor agitation or retardation, muscular weakness, respiratory depression, chest pain, cardiac arrhythmias, confusion, seizures, dyskinesia, dystonia, coma
When to Transport to Hospital Transport any pediatric (<6 years of age) exposure, any symptomatic patient, or any ingestion over 60 mg
Warnings/Precautions Use with caution in patients with psychopathic personalities, cardiovascular disease, HTN, angina, and glaucoma; has high potential for abuse; use in weight reduction programs only when alternative therapy has been ineffective; prolonged administration may lead to drug dependence
Adverse Reactions
>10%:
Cardiovascular: Arrhythmia
Central nervous system: False feeling of well being, nervousness, restlessness, insomnia
1% to 10%:
Cardiovascular: Hypertension
Central nervous system: Mood or mental changes, dizziness, lightheadedness, headache

Endocrine & metabolic: Changes in libido

Gastrointestinal: Diarrhea, nausea, vomiting, stomach cramps, constipation, anorexia, weight loss, xerostomia

Ocular: Blurred vision

Miscellaneous: Diaphoresis (increased)

Test Interactions False-positive amphetamine assays may occur from coadministration with ranitidine, phenylpropanolamine, brompheniramine, chlorpromazine, fluspiriline, or pipothiazine

Reference Range Urinary amphetamine concentrations at steady state (30 mg/ day) range from 1100-17,800 ng/mL

Drug Interactions

Decreased effect of methyldopa, ethosuximide; decreased effect with acidifiers, psychotropics, lithium

Increased effect/toxicity of tricyclic antidepressants, phenytoin, MAO inhibitors, phenobarbital, general anesthetics, propoxyphene, norepinephrine, meperidine, acetazolamide, albuterol (cardiac effects)

Dosage Forms

Dextroamphetamine sulfate:

Capsule, sustained release: 5 mg, 10 mg, 15 mg

Elixir: 5 mg/5 mL (480 mL)

Tablet: 5 mg, 10 mg (5 mg tablets contain tartrazine)

Additional Information Illicit preparation may contain up to 24 g per spoon; 5 mg tablets contain tartrazine

Specific References

Poklis A, "Urinary Dextroamphetamine in Adult Attention Deficit/Hyperactivity Disorder," *J Anal Toxicol*, 1997, 21(2):176-7.

Dextroamphetamine and Amphetamine

(deks troe am FET a meen & am FET a meen)

U.S. Brand Names Adderall®

Therapeutic Category Amphetamine

Abuse Potential Yes

Impairment Potential Yes

Dosage Forms Tablet:

10 mg [dextroamphetamine sulfate 2.5 mg, dextroamphetamine saccharate 2.5 mg and amphetamine aspartate 2.5 mg, amphetamine sulfate 2.5 mg]

20 mg [dextroamphetamine sulfate 5 mg, dextroamphetamine saccharate 5 mg and amphetamine aspartate 5 mg, amphetamine sulfate 5 mg]

Dextromethorphan (deks troe meth OR fan)

Synonyms Demorphan; d-Methorphan

U.S. Brand Names Benylin DM® [OTC]; Benylin® Pediatric [OTC]; Children's Hold® [OTC]; Creo-Terpin® [OTC]; Delsym® [OTC]; Drixoral® Cough Liquid Caps [OTC]; Hold® DM [OTC]; Pertussin® CS [OTC]; Pertussin® ES [OTC]; Robitussin® Cough Calmers [OTC]; Robitussin® Pediatric [OTC]; Scot-Tussin DM® Cough Chasers [OTC]; Silphen DM® [OTC]; St. Joseph® Cough Suppressant [OTC]; Sucrets® Cough Calmers [OTC]; Suppress® [OTC]; Trocal® [OTC]; Vicks Formula 44® [OTC]; Vicks Formula 44® Pediatric Formula [OTC]

Therapeutic Category Antitussive

Abuse Potential Yes

Impairment Potential Yes

Use Symptomatic relief of coughs caused by minor viral upper respiratory tract infections or inhaled irritants; most effective for a chronic nonproductive cough

(Continued)

Dextromethorphan *(Continued)*

Usual Dosage Oral:

Children:

2-5 years: 2.5-7.5 mg every 4-8 hours; extended release is 15 mg twice daily (maximum: 30 mg/24 hours)

6-12 years: 5-10 mg every 4 hours or 15 mg every 6-8 hours; extended release is 30 mg twice daily (maximum: 60 mg/24 hours)

Children >12 years and Adults: 10-30 mg every 4-8 hours or 30 mg every 6-8 hours; extended release is 60 mg twice daily (maximum: 120 mg/24 hours)

Mechanism of Action Chemical relative of morphine lacking narcotic properties; controls cough by depressing the medullary cough center; has virtually no analgesic activity; acts through the sigma receptor with little dependence effect

Pharmacodynamics/kinetics

Onset of antitussive action: Within 15-30 minutes

Duration: Up to 6 hours

Metabolism: In the liver to an active metabolite

Half-life: 2-4 hours

Time to peak: 2.5 hours

Elimination: Principally in urine

Signs and Symptoms of Acute Intoxication Excitation, respiratory depression, miosis, insomnia, tachycardia, coma, fever, hypertension, hyperthermia, hyperactivity, ataxia, tremors, dystonic reaction

When to Transport to Hospital Transport any pediatric (<6 years of age) ingestion over 10 mg/kg or any symptomatic patient

Warnings/Precautions Use in children <2 years of age has not been proven safe and effective

Adverse Reactions <1%:

Central nervous system: Drowsiness, dizziness, coma, respiratory depression

Gastrointestinal: Nausea, GI upset, constipation, abdominal discomfort

Test Interactions Can give a false-positive on phencyclidine qualitative immunoassay screen

Reference Range Serum level of 0.1 μg/mL associated with coma

Drug Interactions Administration with monoamine oxidase inhibitors can cause hyperthermia; dextromethorphan can exacerbate theophylline/aminophylline-induced seizures

Dosage Forms

Capsule (Drixoral® Cough Liquid Caps): 30 mg

Liquid:

Creo-Terpin®: 10 mg/15 mL (120 mL)

Pertussin® CS: 3.5 mg/5 mL (120 mL)

Robitussin® Pediatric, St. Joseph® Cough Suppressant: 7.5 mg/5 mL (60 mL, 120 mL, 240 mL)

Pertussin® ES, Vicks Formula 44®: 15 mg/5 mL (120 mL, 240 mL)

Liquid, sustained release, as polistirex (Delsym®): 30 mg/5 mL (89 mL)

Lozenges:

Scot-Tussin DM® Cough Chasers: 2.5 mg

Children's Hold®, Hold® DM, Robitussin® Cough Calmers, Sucrets® Cough Calmers: 5 mg

Suppress®, Trocal®: 7.5 mg

Syrup:

Benylin® Pediatric: 7.5 mg/mL (118 mL)

Benylin DM®, Silphen DM®: 10 mg/5 mL (120 mL, 3780 mL)

Vicks Formula 44® Pediatric Formula: 15 mg/15 mL (120 mL)

Additional Information Monitor for bromide poisoning

Specific References
Pender ES and Parks BR, "Toxicity With Dextromethorphan-Containing Preparations: A Literature Review and Report of Two Additional Cases," *Pediatr Emerg Care*, 1991, 7(3):163-5.

Dextromethorphan and Guaifenesin *see* Guaifenesin and Dextromethorphan *on page 271*

Dextropropoxyphene *see* Propoxyphene *on page 508*

Dey-Dose® Metaproterenol *see* Metaproterenol *on page 376*

Diabet® *see* Chlorpropamide *on page 140*

Diaβeta® *see* Glyburide *on page 267*

Diabetic Tussin DM® [OTC] *see* Guaifenesin and Dextromethorphan *on page 271*

Diabetic Tussin® EX [OTC] *see* Guaifenesin *on page 269*

Diabinese® *see* Chlorpropamide *on page 140*

Diacetylmorphine *see* Heroin *on page 283*

Diamine T.D.® [OTC] *see* Brompheniramine *on page 84*

Diamorphine Hydrochloride *see* Heroin *on page 283*

Diaqua® *see* Hydrochlorothiazide *on page 291*

Diar-aid® [OTC] *see* Loperamide *on page 349*

Diastat® *see* Diazepam *on this page*

Diazemuls® *see* Diazepam *on this page*

Diazepam (dye AZ e pam)
Related Information
Controlled Substances - Uses and Effects *on page 741*

U.S. Brand Names Aliseum®; Alupram®; Atensine®; Diastat®; Diazemuls®; Lamra®; Solis®; Stesolid®; Tensium®; Valium®; Valrelease®; Vatran®; Vivol®; Zetran®

Canadian Brand Names Apo-Diazepam®; Diazemuls®; E Pam®; (Canada); Meval®; Novo-Dipam®; PMS®-Diazepam; Vivol®

Therapeutic Category Benzodiazepine

Abuse Potential Yes

Impairment Potential Yes; Over double-increased risk of injurious auto crash involvement following ingestion ≥20 mg diazepam in elderly drivers. Impairment can also occur at 10 mg doses in younger patients. Brief or extended period (up to 1 year) of use is consistent with driving impairment in the elderly. The impairment is greatest in the first week of use.

Ray WA, Fought RL, and Decker MD, "Psychoactive Drugs and the Risk of Injurious Motor Vehicle Crashes in Elderly Drivers," *Am J Epidemiol*, 1992, 136(7):873-83.

Use Management of general anxiety disorders, panic disorders, and to provide preoperative sedation, light anesthesia, and amnesia; treatment of status epilepticus, alcohol withdrawal symptoms; used as a skeletal muscle relaxant

Usual Dosage Oral absorption is more reliable than I.M.

Children:

Sedation or muscle relaxation or anxiety:

Oral: 0.12-0.8 mg/kg/day in divided doses every 6-8 hours

I.M., I.V.: 0.04-0.3 mg/kg/dose every 2-4 hours to a maximum of 0.6 mg/kg within an 8-hour period if needed

Status epilepticus: I.V.:

Neonates: 0.1-0.3 mg/kg/dose every 15-30 minutes given over 2-3 minutes, not to exceed 2 mg/24 hours

Infants 30 days to 5 years: 0.2-0.5 mg/dose given over 2-3 minutes, every 2-5 minutes to a maximum total dose of 5 mg

(Continued)

Diazepam (Continued)

Children >5 years: 1 mg/dose given over 2-3 minutes, every 2-5 minutes to a maximum total dose of 10 mg

Status epilepticus: Rectal: 0.2-0.5 mg/kg through a 5 French feeding tube with an attached syringe or by lubricated tuberculin syringe inserted 4-5 cm into the rectum

Adults:

Anxiety/sedation/skeletal muscle relaxation:

Oral: 2-10 mg 2-4 times/day

I.M., I.V.: 2-10 mg, may repeat in 3-4 hours if needed

Status epilepticus: I.V.: 5-10 mg every 10-20 minutes or 0.2-0.5 mg/kg/dose every 15-30 minutes, up to 30 mg; may repeat in 2-4 hours if necessary

Mechanism of Action Depresses all levels of the CNS, including the limbic and reticular formation, probably through the increased action of gamma-aminobutyric acid (GABA), which is a major inhibitory neurotransmitter in the brain

Pharmacodynamics/kinetics

Onset of action:

Oral: 30-60 minutes

I.M.: 15-30 minutes

I.V.: 1-5 minutes; onset almost immediate with short duration of action (20-30 minutes) when given I.V. for status epilepticus

Duration:

Oral: ≤3 hours

I.M. 15 minutes to 1 hour

Absorption: Oral: 83% to 100%

Metabolism: In the liver; active major metabolite is desmethyldiazepam; other metabolites are methyl-lorazepam, oxazepam, and temazepam

Half-life:

Increased in neonates, elderly, and those with severe hepatic disorders; desmethyldiazepam: 50-100 hours and can be prolonged in neonates

Adults: 20-50 hours

Signs and Symptoms of Acute Intoxication Somnolence, hiccups, gaze nystagmus, thrombocytopenia, eosinophilia, hypothermia, hyporeflexia, jaundice, memory loss, extrapyramidal reaction, gynecomastia, dysarthria, cognitive dysfunction, rhabdomyolysis, myoglobinuria, confusion, coma, hypoactive reflexes, renal failure, dyspnea, hypotension, slurred speech, ataxia, respiratory depression

When to Transport to Hospital Transport any pediatric patient (<6 years of age) with ingestion over 0.5 mg/kg or any lethargic patient

Warnings/Precautions Do not use in pregnant women; because of its long half-life, not considered a drug of choice in the elderly; use with caution in patients receiving other CNS depressants, patients with low albumin, hepatic dysfunction, and in the elderly and young infants

Adverse Reactions

>10%:

Cardiovascular: Cardiac arrest, hypotension, bradycardia, cardiovascular collapse, tachycardia, chest pain

Central nervous system: Drowsiness, ataxia, amnesia, slurred speech, paradoxical excitement or rage, fatigue, lightheadedness, insomnia, memory impairment, headache, anxiety, depression

Dermatologic: Rash

Endocrine & metabolic: Decreased libido

Gastrointestinal: Xerostomia, changes in salivation, constipation, nausea, vomiting, diarrhea, increased or decreased appetite

Local: Phlebitis, pain with injection

Neuromuscular & skeletal: Dysarthria
Ocular: Blurred vision, diplopia
Respiratory: Decrease in respiratory rate, apnea, laryngospasm
Miscellaneous: Diaphoresis
1% to 10%:
Cardiovascular: Syncope, hypotension
Central nervous system: Confusion, nervousness, dizziness, akathisia
Dermatologic: Dermatitis
Gastrointestinal: Weight gain or loss
Neuromuscular & skeletal: Rigidity, tremor, muscle cramps
Otic: Tinnitus
Respiratory: Nasal congestion, hyperventilation
Miscellaneous: Hiccups

Test Interactions False-negative urinary glucose determinations when using Clinistix® or Diastix®

Reference Range Therapeutic:
Diazepam: 0.2-1.5 µg/mL (SI: 0.7-5.3 µmol/L)
N-desmethyldiazepam (nordiazepam): 0.1-0.5 µg/mL (SI: 0.35-1.8 µmol/L)
Urine drug screens can remain positive for 30 days

Drug Interactions CNS depressants (alcohol, barbiturates, opioids) may enhance sedation and respiratory depression of diazepam; enzyme inducers (nicotine, rifampin) may increase the hepatic metabolism of diazepam, propranolol, omeprazole, oral contraceptives; cimetidine may decrease the metabolism of diazepam; heparin, valproic acid may displace diazepam from binding sites which may result an increase in sedative effects; metoclopramide increases absorption as can antacids; diazepam levels increase with concomitant administration of fluvoxamine; larger doses may be required in smokers to achieve similar sedative effects as in nonsmokers

Dosage Forms
Injection: 5 mg/mL (1 mL, 2 mL, 5 mL, 10 mL)
Injection, emulsified (Dizac®): 5 mg/mL (3 mL)
Solution, oral (wintergreen-spice flavor): 5 mg/5 mL (5 mL, 10 mL, 500 mL)
Solution, oral concentrate: 5 mg/mL (30 mL)
Solution, viscous, rectal (Diastat®): 15 mg
Tablet: 2 mg, 5 mg, 10 mg

Additional Information Benzyl alcohol toxicity can develop after administration of high-dose intravenous diazepam (2.4 mg/kg/hour in 36 hours) in children; oral absorption more reliable than I.M.; intra-arterial injection may cause tissue necrosis. Diazepam is a muscle relaxant and antianxiety drug. Diazepam may exhibit synergism with barbiturates, tricyclic antidepressants, and amine oxidase inhibitors. Toxicity may be additive with other central nervous system depressants, and ethanol enhances the absorption of diazepam itself. Many cases of overdose are seen but few fatalities result from use of this drug alone. A frequent finding is a combination of this drug and ethanol.

Specific References
deGier JJ, Hart BJ, Nelemans FA, et al, "Psychomotor Performance and Real Driving Performance of Outpatients Receiving Diazepam," *Psychopharmacology*, 1981, 73(4):340-4.
Kleinknect RA and Donaldson D, "A Review of the Effects of Diazepam on Cognitive and Psychomotor Performance," *J Nerv Ment Dis*, 1975, 161(6):399-414.
Moskowitz H and Burns M, "The Effects of Alcohol and Valium, Singly and in Combination, Upon Driving-Rleated Skills Performance, *Proceedings*, Heulke DF, ed, Conference of the American Association for Automotive Medicine, 1977, 226-40.
(Continued)

Diazepam *(Continued)*

Moskowitz H and Smiley A, "Effects of Chronically Administered Buspirone and Diazepam on Driving-Related Skills Performance," *J Clin Psychiatry*, 1982, 43(12 Pt 2):45-55.

Murray JB, "Effects of Valium and Librium on Human Psychomotor and Cognitive Functions," *Genet Psychol Monogr*, 1984, 109:167-97.

O'Hanlon JF, Haak TW, Blaauw GJ, et al, "Diazepam Impairs Lateral Position Control in Highway Driving," *Science*, 1982, 217(4554):79-81.

Ziedman K, Smiley A, and Moskowitz H, "Driving Simulator Tests of Diazepam and Secobarbital," *Proceedings*, Human Factors Society 23rd Annual Meeting, 1979, 259-62.

Diazinon

Synonyms O,O-Diethyl O-2-Isopropyl-4-Methyl-6-Pyrimidinyl Thiophosphate

UN Number 2783

U.S. Brand Names Alfa-Tox®; Bazinon®; Diazol®; Gardentox®; Knox-Out®; Spectracide®

Use Marketed as insecticide granules, dusting agent, or spray liquid with or without petroleum derivative as a solvent

Mechanism of Toxic Action Irreversible inhibition of acetylcholinesterase and plasma cholinesterase, resulting in excess accumulation of acetylcholine at muscarinic and nicotinic receptors, and in the central nervous system

Toxicodynamics/kinetics

Absorption: Readily through gastrointestinal (~85%), dermal (3% to 4%), or inhalation

Metabolism: Rapidly metabolized to weakly active compounds through hepatic hydrolysis and other pathways

Half-life: 15 hours

Elimination: Metabolites are excreted in urine

Signs and Symptoms of Acute Intoxication Miosis (unreactive to light), mydriasis (rarely), lacrimation, pallor, excessive sweating, confusion, dementia, agitation, headache, dysarthria, generalized asthenia, seizures, A-V block, coma, decreased hemoglobin/red blood cell count/platelet count, metabolic acidosis and hyperglycemia (severe intoxication), cranial nerve palsies, hypotension, hypertension, bradycardia, tachycardia, Q-T prolongation, heart block, asystole, salivation, bronchorrhea, tachypnea, pulmonary edema, respiratory depression, diaphragmatic paralysis, skeletal muscle fasciculation and flaccid paralysis, nausea, vomiting, abdominal pain, fecal and urinary incontinence; an "intermediate syndrome" of limb asthenia and respiratory paralysis has been reported to occur between 24 and 96 hours postorganophosphate exposure and is independent of the acute cholinergic crisis. Late paresthesia characterized by stocking and glove paresthesia, anesthesia and asthenia is infrequently observed weeks to months following acute exposure to certain organophosphates.

When to Transport to Hospital Transport any ingestion or symptomatic inhalation exposure

Overdosage/Treatment

Decontamination: Isolation, bagging, and disposal of all contaminated clothing and other articles; all emergency medical workers and hospital staff should follow appropriate precautions regarding exposure to hazardous material including the use of protective clothing, masks, goggles, and respiratory equipment

Dermal: Prompt thorough scrubbing of all affected areas with soap and water, including hair and nails; 5% bleach can be used

Ocular: Irrigation with copious tepid sterile water or saline

Warnings/Precautions Significant dermal absorption may occur across intact skin; risk of aspiration pneumonitis exists following oral exposure to agents having a hydrocarbon vehicle; severe laryngeal irritation and violent coughing may result from exposure to dusting powders; exposure to dusting powders and insecticide granules may cause contact dermatitis

Adverse Reactions

>10%: Cardiovascular: Hyperdynamic states (18% to 21%)

<10%:

Cardiovascular: Hypodynamic (~7% to 10%) states, tachycardia, hypertension, Q-T prolongation, sinus bradycardia, sinus tachycardia

Central nervous system: Depression, seizures, hyperactivity, cognitive dysfunction, hypothermia

Endocrine & metabolic: Hypokalemia

Gastrointestinal: Pancreatitis (after ingestion of 1.5 mg/kg), diarrhea

Genitourinary: Urinary incontinence

Neuromuscular & skeletal: Weakness (delayed), paralysis, delayed paresthesia, rhabdomyolysis

Ocular: Miosis

Respiratory: Pulmonary edema, respiratory depression

Miscellaneous: Flu-like symptoms (especially with chronic exposure), diaphoresis

Reference Range Peak plasma diazinon levels in symptomatic patients (who survived) ranged from 0.1-1.7 mg/L

Mild poisoning: Serum cholinesterase is 20% to 50% of normal

Moderate poisoning: Serum cholinesterase is 10% to 20% of normal

Severe poisoning (respiratory distress and coma): Serum cholinesterase is <10%

Drug Interactions Paralysis is potentiated by neuromuscular blockade (ie, pancuronium, vecuronium, succinylcholine, atracurium, doxacurium, mivacurium); inhibition of serum esterase prolongs the half-life of succinylcholine, cocaine, and other ester anesthetics; cholinergic toxicity is potentiated by cholinesterase inhibitors such as physostigmine

Additional Information Yellow to brown liquid; vapor pressure of 0.00014 mm Hg at 20°C; thermal breakdown products include nitrogen and sulfur oxides; red blood cell cholinesterase and serum pseudocholinesterase may be depressed following acute or chronic organophosphate exposure; RBC cholinesterase is typically not analyzed by in-house laboratories, and is usually not available for consideration during acute management. Pseudocholinesterase levels may be rapidly available from some in-house laboratories, but are not as reliable a marker of organophosphate exposure because of variability secondary to variant genotypes, hepatic disease, oral estrogen use, or malnutrition. Because of this variability, true indication of suppression of either of these enzymes can only be estimated through comparison to pre-exposure values; these enzymes may be useful in measuring a patient's recovery postexposure, especially if the recovery is not progressing as expected.

ACGIH TLV: 0.1 mg/m³

PEL-TWA: 0.1 mg/m³

Water solubility: 40 ppm

Water half-life: 3 days to 7.7 weeks (shorter in acidic conditions)

Mean atmospheric diazinon levels in urban areas: 2.1 ng/m³

Oral ingestion of 294 mg/kg of a 10% diazinon formulation associated with fatality; diazinon may prolong the effects of succinylcholine

The intermediate syndrome is not related to delayed neuropathy
(Continued)

Diazinon (Continued)

Other information concerning pesticide exposures is available through the EPA-funded National Pesticide Telecommunications Network: 1-800-858-7378 (weekdays, 8 AM to 6 PM, Central Standard time)

Specific References

Poklis A, Kutz FW, Sperling JF, et al, "A Fatal Diazinon Poisoning," *Forensic Sci Int*, 1980, 15(2):135-40.

Diazol® see Diazinon on page 192

Dibent® see Dicyclomine on this page

1-(2,6-Dichlorobenzylideneamine) Guanidine Acetate see Guanabenz on page 276

Dichlorodifluoromethane see Freon on page 260

Dichloromethane see Methylene Chloride on page 395

Dicyclomine (dye SYE kloe meen)

Related Information

Biperiden on page 77

Synonyms Dicycloverine Hydrochloride

U.S. Brand Names Antispas®; Bemote®; Bentyl® Hydrochloride; Bentylol®; Byclomine®; Dibent®; Di-Spaz®; Formulex®; Lomine®; Neoquess® Injection; Or-Tyl®; Protylol®; Spasmobam®; Spasmoject®

Canadian Brand Names Bentylol®; Formulex®

Therapeutic Category Anticholinergic Agent

Use Treatment of functional disturbances of GI motility such as irritable bowel syndrome

Unlabeled use: Urinary incontinence

Usual Dosage

Oral:

Infants >6 months: 5 mg/dose 3-4 times/day

Children: 10 mg/dose 3-4 times/day

Urinary incontinence: 8 mg/kg/day in 3 divided doses

Adults: Begin with 80 mg/day in 4 equally divided doses, then increase up to 160 mg/day

Urinary incontinence: 60-100 mg/day

I.M. **(should not be used I.V.):** Adults: 80 mg/day in 4 divided doses (20 mg/dose)

Mechanism of Action Blocks the action of acetylcholine at parasympathetic sites in smooth muscle, secretory glands and the CNS

Pharmacodynamics/kinetics

Onset of effect: 1-2 hours

Duration: Up to 4 hours

Absorption: Oral: Well absorbed

Metabolism: Extensive

Half-life:

Initial phase: 1.8 hours

Terminal phase: 9-10 hours

Elimination: In urine (80%) with only a small amount excreted as unchanged drug; 8% excreted fecally

Signs and Symptoms of Acute Intoxication Mydriasis, tachycardia, hyperthermia, ileus, dry mouth, hypertension, urinary retention

When to Transport to Hospital Transport any symptomatic or lethargic patient or any ingestion over 200 mg

Warnings/Precautions Use with caution in patients with hepatic or renal disease, ulcerative colitis, hyperthyroidism, cardiovascular disease, hypertension, tachycardia, GI obstruction, obstruction of the urinary tract. The elderly are at increased risk for anticholinergic effects, confusion and hallucinations.

Adverse Reactions

>10%:

Dermatologic: Dry skin

Gastrointestinal: Constipation, dry throat, xerostomia

Local: Injection site reactions

Respiratory: Dry nose

Miscellaneous: Diaphoresis (decreased)

1% to 10%:

Dermatologic: Increased sensitivity to light

Endocrine & metabolic: Decreased flow of breast milk

Gastrointestinal: Dysphagia

Ocular: Blurred vision

Drug Interactions

Decreased effect: Phenothiazines, anti-Parkinson's drugs, haloperidol, sustained release dosage forms; decreased effect with antacids

Increased toxicity: Anticholinergics, amantadine, narcotic analgesics, type I antiarrhythmics, antihistamines, phenothiazines, TCAs

Enhanced anticholinergic effect with zotepine

Dosage Forms

Dicyclomine hydrochloride:

Capsule: 10 mg, 20 mg

Injection: 10 mg/mL (2 mL, 10 mL)

Syrup: 10 mg/5 mL (118 mL, 473 mL, 946 mL)

Tablet: 20 mg

Specific References

Garriott JC, Rodriguez R, and Norton LE, "Two Cases of Death Involving Dicyclomine in Infants. Measurement of Therapeutic and Toxic Concentrations in Blood," *J Toxicol Clin Toxicol*, 1984, 22(5):455-62.

Dicycloverine Hydrochloride see Dicyclomine *on previous page*

Didrex® see Benzphetamine *on page 72*

5,5-Diethyl-1-Methylbarbituric Acid see Mephobarbital *on page 370*

Diethylamide see Diethyltoluamide *on page 197*

Diethylene Glycol

Synonyms Diglycol; Ethylene Diglycol; Glycol Ether

Commonly Found In Industrial solvents and antifreeze; softening agent in cellophane; in silver sulfadiazine

Impairment Potential Yes

Mechanism of Toxic Action Central nervous system depression and nephrotoxicity with intravascular hemolysis, mechanism unknown

Toxicodynamics/kinetics

Absorption: Small amount may be absorbed dermally; not absorbed by inhalation

Metabolism: Oxidized by alcohol dehydrogenase and aldehyde dehydrogenase to 2-hydroxyethoxy-acetaldehyde and then to 2-hydroxy-ethoxyacetic acid (2-HEAA)

Half-life: 3 hours

Elimination: 70% excreted unchanged; major metabolite is (2-hydroxyethoxy) acetic acid

Signs and Symptoms of Acute Intoxication Hepatic: Hepatotoxicity drowsiness; coma and pulmonary edema can develop, porphyria, feces discoloration

(Continued)

195

Diethylene Glycol *(Continued)*

(black), leukocytosis, jaundice, tachypnea, diarrhea; metabolic acidosis is less common than with ethylene glycol

When to Transport to Hospital Transport any ingestion

Adverse Reactions

Hepatic: Hepatotoxicity

Renal: Renal tubular necrosis (acute); renal failure due to bilateral cortical necrosis

Additional Information Can cause centrilobular necrosis of the liver; diethylene glycol is odorless but has a sweet taste; more toxic than ethylene glycol; radiopaque compound with rapid absorption

Lethal dose: 1 mL/kg

Specific References

Wax PM, "It's Happening Again - Another Diethylene Glycol Mass Poisoning," *Clin Toxicol*, 1996, 34(5):517-20.

Diethylpropion (dye eth il PROE pee on)

Related Information

Controlled Substances - Uses and Effects *on page 741*

Dextroamphetamine *on page 186*

Synonyms Amfepramone

U.S. Brand Names Anorex®; Delgamer®; Linea®; Nobesine®; Regenon®; Tenuate®; Tenuate® Dospan®; Tepanil®

Canadian Brand Names Nobesine®

Therapeutic Category Anorexiant

Use Short-term adjunct in exogenous obesity

Usual Dosage Adults: Oral:

Tablet: 25 mg 3 times/day before meals or food

Tablet, controlled release: 75 mg at midmorning

Mechanism of Action Diethylpropion is used as an anorexiant agent possessing pharmacological and chemical properties similar to those of amphetamines. The mechanism of action of diethylpropion in reducing appetite appears to be secondary to CNS effects, specifically stimulation of the hypothalamus to release catecholamines into the central nervous system; anorexiant effects are mediated via norepinephrine and dopamine metabolism. An increase in physical activity and metabolic effects (inhibition of lipogenesis and enhancement of lipolysis) may also contribute to weight loss.

Pharmacodynamics/kinetics

Duration of effect: 4 hours

Metabolism: Hepatic

Half-life (metabolites): 8 hours

When to Transport to Hospital Transport any pediatric ingestion, any patient with cardipulmonary or central nervous system complaints, or any ingestion over 100 mg

Warnings/Precautions Prolonged administration may lead to dependence; use with caution in patients with mental illness or diabetes mellitus, cardiovascular disease, nephritis, angina pectoris, hypertension, glaucoma, and patients with a history of drug abuse

Adverse Reactions

>10%:

Cardiovascular: Hypertension

Central nervous system: Euphoria, nervousness, insomnia

1% to 10%:

Central nervous system: Confusion, mental depression

Endocrine & metabolic: Changes in libido

    Gastrointestinal: Nausea, vomiting, restlessness, constipation
    Hematologic: Blood dyscrasias
    Neuromuscular & skeletal: Tremor
    Ocular: Blurred vision

Drug Interactions
    Decreased effect of guanethidine; decreased effect with phenothiazines
    Increased effect/toxicity with MAO inhibitors (hypertensive crisis), CNS depressants, general anesthetics (arrhythmias), sympathomimetics

Dosage Forms
    Tablet: 25 mg
    Tablet, controlled release: 75 mg

Specific References
    Silverstone T, "Appetite Suppressants. A Review," *Drugs*, 1992, 43(6):820-36.

Diethyltoluamide

Synonyms Benzamide; DEET; Diethylamide; M-delphene; M-det; M-deta; Metadelphene; 3-Methyl-N,N-Diethylbenzamide; MGK Diethyltoluamide; M-Toluamide; M-Toluic Acid Diethylamide; N,N-Diethyl-3-Methyl-Diethyl-M-Toluamide; N,N-Diethyl-M-Toluamide; N,N-Diethyl-M-Toluic Acid

Commonly Found In Some formulations use as vehicles ethyl and isopropyl alcohols and freon, which may contribute significantly to toxicity

U.S. Brand Names OFF®

Use Insect repellent against mosquitoes, ticks, fleas, leeches, blackflies; used since 1957

Toxicodynamics/kinetics
    Onset of action: Oral: Rapid
    Absorption:
        Oral: Rapid
        Topical: Within 6 hours
    Distribution: Skin and fatty tissues retain DEET and its metabolites for 1-2 months after topical application and may act as reservoirs for DEET
    Metabolism: Occurs in the liver by oxidative enzymes
    Peak plasma concentration: 1 hour

Signs and Symptoms of Acute Intoxication Coma and seizures may occur rapidly within 30-60 minutes after ingestion; hypotension, bradycardia, confusion, ataxia, hypertonicity, clonic jerking, coma, urticaria, seizures, abdominal pain, nausea, vomiting, toxic hepatitis, renal damage, skin irritation, contact rash, bullous eruption/skin necrosis, acute psychosis, cerebral edema, anaphylactic shock; burning sensation of eyes, lips, tongue, and mouth

When to Transport to Hospital Transport any symptomatic patient

Overdosage/Treatment Decontamination: For dermal exposures, wash twice with copious amounts of soap and water, preferably using alcohol-detergent solutions such as "green soap." If irritation or pain persists after washing, consult physician to examine affected area. For eye exposure, irrigate with copious amounts of tepid water for at least 15 minutes; patients should seek medical advice if irritation, pain, swelling, lacrimation, or photophobia persists.

Warnings/Precautions Significant and severe toxicity has occurred following both dermal and oral exposures to large amounts of DEET

Adverse Reactions
    Cardiovascular: Hypotension, bradycardia, Reye's syndrome, sinus bradycardia
    Central nervous system: Psychosis, seizures, coma, drowsiness, headache, mania, slurred speech, ataxia
    Dermatologic: Urticaria, skin necrosis, bullous eruption
    Gastrointestinal: Nausea, vomiting
    Hepatic: Hepatic necrosis, steatosis
    Neuromuscular & skeletal: Tremors, myoclonus, athetosis, hypertonicity
(Continued)

Diethyltoluamide *(Continued)*

Miscellaneous: Anaphylactic shock

Reference Range DEET serum level 8 hours after dermal application: 0.3 mg/dL (0.016 mmol/L) in asymptomatic patient; serum concentration of DEET of 63 mg/L associated with hypotension, lethargy, and EKG changes (S-T abnormalities); serum DEET level of 239 mg/L associated with fatality

Additional Information Severe toxicity occurred in a child 1 year of age following oral ingestion of 25 mL of 50% DEET. Severe toxicity and death occurred following oral ingestion of 50 mL of 100% DEET in adolescents or adults. Extensive daily dermal applications of 10% to 15% solutions for 2 days to 3 months have resulted in encephalopathy in children.

National DEET Registry (Pegus Research, Inc), Salt Lake City, UT, (800)-949-0089

Specific References

Lipscomb JW, Kramer JE, Leikin JB, "Seizure Following Brief Exposure to the Insect Repellent N,N-diethyl-m-toluamide," *Ann Emerg Med*, 1992, 21(3):315-7.

Diflunisal *(dye FLOO ni sal)*

U.S. Brand Names Dolobid®

Canadian Brand Names Apo-Diflunisal®; Novo-Diflunisal®; Nu-Diflunisal®

Therapeutic Category Analgesic, Non-narcotic; Nonsteroidal Anti-Inflammatory Agent (NSAID)

Use Management of inflammatory disorders usually including rheumatoid arthritis and osteoarthritis; can be used as an analgesic for treatment of mild to moderate pain

Usual Dosage Adults: Oral:

Pain: Initial: 500-1000 mg followed by 250-500 mg every 8-12 hours; maximum daily dose: 1.5 g

Inflammatory condition: 500-1000 mg/day in 2 divided doses; maximum daily dose: 1.5 g

Mechanism of Action Inhibits prostaglandin synthesis by decreasing the activity of the enzyme, cyclo-oxygenase, which results in decreased formation of prostaglandin precursors

Pharmacodynamics/kinetics

Onset of analgesia: Within 60 minutes

Duration: 8-12 hours

Absorption: Well absorbed from gastrointestinal tract

Metabolism: Extensive in the liver

Half-life: 8-12 hours, prolonged with renal impairment

Time to peak serum concentration: Within 2-3 hours

Signs and Symptoms of Acute Intoxication Drowsiness, photosensitivity, dermatitis, gastrointestinal bleeding, malaise, depression, wheezing, thrombocytopenia, stomatitis, gastritis; lightheadedness, nephritis, insomnia, toxic epidermal necrolysis, neutropenia, myalgia, erythema multiforme, hyperthermia, nephrotic syndrome, eosinophilia, confusion, coagulopathy, cholestatic jaundice, hematuria, chills, nausea, vomiting, hyperventilation, tachycardia, ototoxicity, tinnitus, stupor, coma, fever

When to Transport to Hospital Transport any pediatric ingestion, any symptomatic patient, or any ingestion over 1.5 g

Warnings/Precautions Peptic ulceration and gastrointestinal bleeding have been reported; platelet function and bleeding time are inhibited by diflunisal at higher doses; ophthalmologic effects; impaired renal function, use lower dosage; peripheral edema; possibility of Reye's syndrome; elevation in liver tests

Adverse Reactions

>10%:
  Central nervous system: Headache
  Endocrine & metabolic: Fluid retention

1% to 10%:
  Cardiovascular: Angina pectoris, arrhythmias
  Central nervous system: Dizziness
  Dermatologic: Rash, itching
  Gastrointestinal: GI ulceration
  Genitourinary: Vaginal bleeding
  Otic: Tinnitus

Test Interactions Increases prothrombin time; decreases uric acid (S); may cross-react with some salicylate assays

Drug Interactions Diflunisal - digoxin leads to increased digoxin plasma concentration; diflunisal - methotrexate may cause increased methotrexate plasma concentrations; diflunisal - anticoagulants leads to increased prothrombin time; hydantoins, sulfonamides, and sulfonylureas may be displayed may cause increase activity; lithium - diflunisal may cause increase lithium level; diflunisal - anticoagulants and thrombolytics increase bleeding without increased PT or PTT but with increased bleeding time; diflunisal - cyclosporine may cause increased cyclosporine toxicity

Dosage Forms Tablet: 250 mg, 500 mg

Specific References
  Arias J, Fernandez-Rivas M, Moral A, et al, "Selective Adverse Reactions to Diflunisal," *Ann Allergy Asthma Immunol*, 1995, 74(2):160-2.

Digacin see Digoxin on this page

Diglycol see Diethylene Glycol on page 195

Digoxin (di JOKS in)

Synonyms Digacin

U.S. Brand Names Allocar®; Cardioreg®; Lanocor®; Lanoxicaps®; Lanoxin®; Lenoxin®; Purgoxin®

Canadian Brand Names Novo-Digoxin®

Therapeutic Category Antiarrhythmic Agent, Miscellaneous; Cardiac Glycoside

Use Treatment of congestive heart failure; slows the ventricular rate in tachyarrhythmias such as fibrillation (atrial), flutter (atrial), tachycardia (ventricular), paroxysmal atrial tachycardia, cardiogenic shock

Usual Dosage When changing from oral (tablets or liquid) or I.M. to I.V. therapy, dosage should be reduced by 20% to 25%

Mechanism of Action Increases the influx of calcium ions, from extracellular to intracellular cytoplasm by inhibition of sodium and potassium ion movement across the myocardial membranes; this increase in calcium ions results in a potentiation of the activity of the contractile heart muscle fibers and an increase in the force of myocardial contraction (positive inotropic effect); inhibits adenosine triphosphatase (ATPase); decreases conduction through the S-A and A-V nodes

Pharmacodynamics/kinetics
  Onset of action: Oral: 1-2 hours
  Peak effect: Oral: 2-8 hours
  Duration: Adults: 3-4 days
  Metabolism: Small amount in the liver and gut by bacteria
  Bioavailability: Dependent upon formulation; elixir: 70% to 85%, tablets: 60% to 80%, capsules: 90% to 100%
  Half-life: Dependent upon age, renal and cardiac function
    Premature: 61-170 hours
  (Continued)

Digoxin *(Continued)*

> Neonates, full-term: 35-45 hours
> Infants: 18-25 hours
> Children: 35 hours
> Adults: 38-48 hours
> > Anephric: >4.5 days

Signs and Symptoms of Acute Intoxication Hyperkalemia, arrhythmias, photophobia, night terrors, heart block, A-V block, impotence, delirium, dementia, depression, hypokalemia, gynecomastia, dysphagia, seizures, neuropathy (peripheral), bowel ischemia, fibrillation (ventricular) or asystole, hypotension, ototoxicity; vision color changes (blue tinge), vision color changes (green tinge), vision color changes (red tinge); vision color changes (orange tinge); tinnitus, tremors

When to Transport to Hospital Transport any pediatric (<6 years of age) ingestion over 0.05 mg/kg, any symptomatic patient, or any acute adult ingestion over 2 mg

Overdosage/Treatment

Decontamination: Lavage (within 1 hour)/activated charcoal; whole bowel irrigation may be useful

Supportive therapy: Antidote: Life-threatening digoxin toxicity is treated with Digibind®; phenytoin, magnesium, and lidocaine are useful for cardiac arrhythmias; atropine is useful for bradycardia; avoid quinidine, bretylium, or cardioversion; ventricular pacing should be reserved for patients not responding to Digibind®; delirium can also respond to Digibind®; torsade de pointes can be treated with magnesium sulfate and overdrive pacing (try to avoid isoproterenol)

Warnings/Precautions Use with caution in patients with hypoxia, hypothyroidism, acute myocarditis, impaired renal function

Adverse Reactions 1% to 10%: Gastrointestinal: Anorexia, nausea, vomiting

Test Interactions Digibind® will increase total serum digoxin level about 50-fold; digoxin-like immunoreactive substance (DLIS) which is an endogenous natriuretic substance may cause false elevation

Reference Range

Therapeutic: 0.5-2.0 ng/mL (SI: 0.6-2.6 nmol/L); Adults: <0.5 ng/mL (SI: <0.6 nmol/L) probably indicates underdigitalization unless there are special circumstances

Toxic: >2.0 ng/mL (SI: >2.6 nmol/L); fatalities associated with levels >3.5 ng/mL (>4.8 nmol/L)

Drug Interactions Antacids, kaolin-pectin, cathartics, neomycin, colestipol, phenytoin, cholestyramine, and metoclopramide may decrease absorption of digoxin; quinidine, indomethacin, verapamil, amiodarone, diltiazem, erythromycin, tetracycline, itraconazole, and spironolactone may increase digoxin serum concentration; penicillamine may decrease digoxin's pharmacologic effects; propantheline and atropine may increase digoxin absorption; digoxin and adenosine can have synergistic effects; administration of clarithromycin or roxithromycin can result in elevated digoxin levels; guar gum can inhibit absorption of digoxin; increased potency/toxicity may occur with long-term use of cascara or senna; use of acarbose and digoxin simultaneously may result in lower serum digoxin levels; elevated serum concentrations and toxicity with concomitant clarithromycin; itraconazole can decrease urinary clearance of digoxin

Dosage Forms

Capsule: 50 mcg, 100 mcg, 200 mcg

Elixir, pediatric (lime flavor): 50 mcg/mL with alcohol 10% (60 mL)

Injection: 250 mcg/mL (1 mL, 2 mL)

Injection, pediatric: 100 mcg/mL (1 mL)

Tablet: 125 mcg, 250 mcg, 500 mcg
Additional Information
Toxic oral dose: 2 mg
Lethal dose:
Children: 4 mg
Adults: 10 mg
Death rate approaches 50% when serum digoxin levels are >6 ng/mL; digoxin-specific antibodies have reversed thrombocytopenia caused by digoxin;
Mean total hospital cost of digoxin toxicity is $4,087.05 ± 2,659.76; mean length of stay: 3.3 ± 1.2 days
Specific References
Keen JH and Huppert P, "Reversing Life-Threatening Cardiac Glycoside Intoxication With Digoxin Immune Fab," *J Emerg Nurs*, 1996, 22(2):136-7.

Dihistine® DH *see* Chlorpheniramine, Pseudoephedrine, and Codeine *on page 138*

Dihistine® Expectorant *see* Guaifenesin, Pseudoephedrine, and Codeine *on page 275*

Dihydrex® Injection *see* Diphenhydramine *on page 205*

Dihydrohydroxycodeinone *see* Oxycodone *on page 452*

Dihydromorphinone *see* Hydromorphone *on page 301*

Dilacor™ XR *see* Diltiazem *on this page*

Diladel® *see* Diltiazem *on this page*

Dilantin® *see* Phenytoin *on page 483*

Dilaudid® *see* Hydromorphone *on page 301*

Dilaudid-HP® *see* Hydromorphone *on page 301*

Dilocaine® *see* Lidocaine *on page 345*

Diltiazem (dil TYE a zem)

Synonyms Latiazem Hydrochloride
U.S. Brand Names Acalix®; Britiazim®; Cardizem®; Cardizem® CD; Cardizem® SR; Dilacor™ XR; Diladel®; Dilzene®; Segontin®; Tildiem®; Zilden®
Canadian Brand Names Apo-Diltiaz®; Novo-Diltazem®; Nu-Diltiaz®; Syn-Diltiazem®
Therapeutic Category Calcium Channel Blocker
Use Management of angina pectoris due to coronary insufficiency, hypertension
Usual Dosage Adults: Oral:
Capsule, sustained release:
Cardizem® CD: 180-300 mg once daily
Cardizem® SR: 60-120 mg twice daily
Dilacor™ XR: 180-240 mg once daily
Tablet: 30-120 mg 3-4 times/day; dosage should be increased gradually, at 1- to 2-day intervals until optimum response is obtained; usual maintenance dose is usually 180-360 mg/day

Toxic dose:
Children: 6 mg/kg
Adults: 2 g
Mechanism of Action A benzodiazepine calcium channel blocker which inhibits calcium ion from entering the "slow channels" or select voltage-sensitive areas of vascular smooth muscle and myocardium during depolarization, producing a relaxation of coronary vascular smooth muscle and coronary vasodilation; increases myocardial oxygen delivery in patients with vasospastic angina
Pharmacodynamics/kinetics
Onset of action:
Extended-release capsules: 2-3 hours
(Continued)

Diltiazem *(Continued)*

Tablets: 30-60 minutes

Duration:

Extended-release capsules: 12 hours

Tablets: 4-8 hours

Absorption: ~40% (90% with long-term therapy)

Metabolism: Extensive in the liver by deacetylation

Bioavailability: ~40% due to a significant first-pass effect following oral administration

Half-life: 4-6 hours (may increase with renal impairment); 36 hours in overdose setting

Time to peak serum concentration: Within 2-3 hours

Signs and Symptoms of Acute Intoxication A-V block, toxic epidermal necrolysis, erythema multiforme, mania, myopathy, purpura, hyperglycemia, gynecomastia, gingival hyperplasia, hypotension, asystole, hypothermia, bradycardia, constipation, congestive heart failure

When to Transport to Hospital Transport any symptomatic patient or ingestion over 5 mg/kg

Warnings/Precautions Use with caution in titrating dosages for impaired renal or hepatic function patients; use with caution in patients with congestive heart failure; may be porphyrinogenic

Adverse Reactions

>10%: Central nervous system: Headache

1% to 10%:

Cardiovascular: Bradycardia, A-V block (first degree), edema, EKG abnormality

Central nervous system: Dizziness

Gastrointestinal: Nausea, vomiting

Neuromuscular & skeletal: Weakness

Reference Range Zero order kinetics are noted with massive ingestion relating to plasma levels >2000 ng/mL; therapeutic serum diltiazem levels: 50-200 ng/mL; peak plasma diltiazem and desacetyldiltiazem plasma levels following a 14.94 g (150 mg/kg) diltiazem overdose were 7044 ng/mL and 1837.55 ng/mL respectively; this was associated with cardiogenic shock and asystole

Drug Interactions The following interactions occur with concomitant use

Adenosine: Prolonged bradycardia

Alfuzosin: Increased serum alfuzosin levels

Amiodarone: Sinus arrest/hypotension

Aspirin: Increased bleeding time

Carbamazepine: Increased carbamazepine levels and neurotoxicity

Cyclosporine: Elevated cyclosporin levels

Diatrizoate: Hypotension

Digoxin/Digitoxin: Increased serum digoxin levels within 1 week

Enflurane: Additive depressive effect on A-V and sinus node

Fluvoxamine: Elevated diltiazem levels

Food: Increased bioavailability by 28%

Imipramine: Increased imipramine levels

Lithium: Increased lithium neurotoxicity (worsening of mania)

Metoprolol: Increased metoprolol serum levels due to increased absorption and decreased clearance

Midazolam: Increased midazolam levels and sedation

Nifedipine: Decreased nifedipine metabolism

Nitroglycerin: Hypotension

Phenobarbital: Decreased diltiazem levels

Phenytoin: Increased phenytoin level

Propranolol: Increased propranolol serum levels due to increased absorption and decreased clearance

Tacrolimus: Increased tacrolimus blood levels

Theophylline: Decreased theophylline clearance

Triazolam, oral: Increased triazolam levels by inhibition of its metabolism

Dosage Forms

Capsule, sustained release:

Cardizem® CD: 120 mg, 180 mg, 240 mg, 300 mg

Cardizem® SR: 60 mg, 90 mg, 120 mg

Dilacor™ XR: 180 mg, 240 mg

Tiazac®: 120 mg, 180 mg, 240 mg, 300 mg, 360 mg

Injection: 5 mg/mL (5 mL, 10 mL)

Cardizem®: 5 mg/mL (5 mL, 10 mL)

Tablet (Cardizem®): 30 mg, 60 mg, 90 mg, 120 mg

Tablet, extended release (Tiamate®): 120 mg, 180 mg, 240 mg

Additional Information Response to atropine may not be observed until after I.V. calcium administration; erythema may precede elevation of liver function tests by 3-5 days; most effective for treating hypertension in African-Americans

Specific References

Kalin JR, Wood KM, and Lee AJ, "A Possible Suicide by Diltiazem Overdose," *J Anal Toxicol*, 1994, 18(3):180-2.

Dilzene® see Diltiazem on page 201

Dimacol® Caplets [OTC] see Guaifenesin, Pseudoephedrine, and Dextromethorphan on page 275

Dima-Fen® see Fenfluramine on page 244

Dimaphen® Elixir [OTC] see Brompheniramine and Phenylpropanolamine on page 85

Dimaphen® Tablets [OTC] see Brompheniramine and Phenylpropanolamine on page 85

Dimenhydrinate (dye men HYE dri nate)

U.S. Brand Names Calm-X® [OTC]; Dimetabs®; Dinate®; Dramamine® [OTC]; Dramilin®; Hydrate®; Marmine® [OTC]; Nico-Vert®; Tega-Cert® [OTC]; TripTone® Caplets® [OTC]; Wehamine®

Therapeutic Category Antihistamine

Impairment Potential Yes

Use Treatment and prevention of nausea, dizziness, and vomiting associated with motion sickness

Usual Dosage

Children:

Oral:

2-5 years: 12.5-25 mg every 6-8 hours, maximum: 75 mg/day

6-12 years: 25-50 mg every 6-8 hours, maximum: 150 mg/day

I.M.: 1.25 mg/kg or 37.5 mg/m² 4 times/day, not to exceed 300 mg/day

Adults: Oral, I.M., I.V.: 50-100 mg every 4-6 hours, not to exceed 400 mg/day

Mechanism of Action Competes with histamine for H_1-receptor sites on effector cells in the gastrointestinal tract, blood vessels, and respiratory tract; blocks chemoreceptor trigger zone, diminishes vestibular stimulation and depresses labyrinthine function through its central anticholinergic activity

Pharmacodynamics/kinetics

Onset of action: Oral: Within 15-30 minutes

Duration: ~4-6 hours

Absorption: Well absorbed from gastrointestinal tract

Metabolism: Extensive in the liver

(Continued)

Dimenhydrinate *(Continued)*

Signs and Symptoms of Acute Intoxication Toxicity may resemble atropine overdosage; CNS depression or CNS stimulation, mydriasis; dry mucous membranes

When to Transport to Hospital Transport any pediatric (<2 years of age) exposure or any symptomatic patient

Warnings/Precautions Use with caution with prostatic hypertrophy, peptic ulcer, narrow-angle glaucoma, bronchial asthma, and cardiac arrhythmias

Adverse Reactions

>10%:

Central nervous system: Slight to moderate drowsiness

Respiratory: Thickening of bronchial secretions

1% to 10%:

Central nervous system: Headache, fatigue, nervousness, dizziness

Gastrointestinal: Appetite increase, weight gain, nausea, diarrhea, abdominal pain, xerostomia

Neuromuscular & skeletal: Arthralgia

Respiratory: Pharyngitis

Drug Interactions CNS depressants, drugs with anticholinergic effects, ototoxic drugs

Dosage Forms

Capsule: 50 mg

Injection: 50 mg/mL (1 mL, 5 mL, 10 mL)

Liquid: 12.5 mg/4 mL

Tablet: 50 mg

Tablet, chewable: 50 mg

Additional Information Dramamine® II contains meclizine

Specific References

Luria SM, Kinney JA, McKay CL, et al, "Effects of Aspirin and Dimenhydrinate (Dramamine®) on Visual Processes," *Br J Clin Pharmacol*, 1979, 7(6):585-93.

Dinate® see Dimenhydrinate on page 203

Dintoina® see Phenytoin on page 483

Diphenacen-50® **Injection** see Diphenhydramine on this page

Diphen® **Cough [OTC]** see Diphenhydramine on this page

Diphenhist® **[OTC]** see Diphenhydramine on this page

Diphenhydramine (dye fen HYE dra meen)

U.S. Brand Names AllerMax® Oral [OTC]; Banophen® Oral [OTC]; Belix® Oral [OTC]; Benadryl® Injection; Benadryl® Oral [OTC]; Benadryl® Topical; Ben-Allergin-50® Injection; Benylin® Cough Syrup [OTC]; Bydramine® Cough Syrup [OTC]; Compoz® Gel Caps [OTC]; Compoz® Nighttime Sleep Aid [OTC]; Dihydrex® Injection; Diphenacen-50® Injection; Diphen® Cough [OTC]; Diphenhist® [OTC]; Dormarex® 2 Oral [OTC]; Dormin® Oral [OTC]; Genahist® Oral; Hydramyn® Syrup [OTC]; Hyrexin-50® Injection; Maximum Strength Nytol® [OTC]; Miles Nervine® Caplets [OTC]; Nidryl® Oral [OTC]; Nordryl® Injection; Nordryl® Oral; Nytol® Oral [OTC]; Phendry® Oral [OTC]; Siladryl® Oral [OTC]; Silphen® Cough [OTC]; Sleep-eze 3® Oral [OTC]; Sleepinal® [OTC]; Sleepwell 2-nite® [OTC]; Sominex® Oral [OTC]; Tusstat® Syrup; Twilite® Oral [OTC]; Uni-Bent® Cough Syrup; 40 Winks® [OTC]

Canadian Brand Names Allerdryl®; Allernix®; Nytol® Extra Strength

Therapeutic Category Antihistamine

Impairment Potential Yes; Impairment occurs at doses exceeding 50 mg

Gengo FM and Manning C, "A Review of the Effects of Antihistamines on Mental Processes Related to Automobile Driving," *J Allergy Clin Immunol*, 1990, 86(2): 1034-9.

Use Reversal of toxin-induced extrapyramidal reactions or serum sickness secondary to antivenin; antitussive; antimotion sickness; sleep-aid; useful in anaphylaxis and allergy treatment

Usual Dosage

Children: Oral, I.M., I.V.: 5 mg/kg/day or 150 mg/m²/day in divided doses every 6-8 hours, not to exceed 300 mg/day

Adults:

Oral: 25-50 mg every 4-6 hours

I.M., I.V.: 10-50 mg in a single dose every 2-4 hours, not to exceed 400 mg/day

Fatal dose: 25 mg/kg

Mechanism of Action Competes with histamine for H_1-receptor sites on effector cells in the gastrointestinal tract, blood vessels, and respiratory tract

Pharmacodynamics/kinetics

Onset of action:

I.M.: 20-30 minutes

Rectal: 30-45 minutes

Duration: 4-7 hours

Absorption: Oral: ~65%

Metabolism: Extensive in the liver and to smaller degrees in the lung and kidney

Half-life: 8 hours (15 hours in cirrhotic patients)

Time to peak serum concentration: Within 2-4 hours

Signs and Symptoms of Acute Intoxication CNS stimulation or depression; overdose may result in death in infants and children; mydriasis, gaze nystagmus, seizures, catatonic stupor (15%), delirium, toxic psychosis, tachycardia, coma; patient may be symptomatic for 2 days, rhabdomyolysis

When to Transport to Hospital Transport any pediatric (<6 years of age) ingestion over 5 mg/kg, any symptomatic patient, or any asymptomatic ingestion over 10 mg/kg

(Continued)

Diphenhydramine *(Continued)*

Warnings/Precautions Use with caution in patients with angle-closure glaucoma, peptic ulcer, urinary tract obstruction, hyperthyroidism; some preparations contain sodium bisulfite; elixir and syrup contain alcohol

Adverse Reactions

>10%:

Central nervous system: Slight to moderate drowsiness

Respiratory: Thickening of bronchial secretions

1% to 10%:

Central nervous system: Headache, fatigue, nervousness

Gastrointestinal: Nausea, vomiting, diarrhea, abdominal pain, xerostomia, appetite increase, weight gain, dry mucous membranes

Neuromuscular & skeletal: Arthralgia

Respiratory: Pharyngitis

Test Interactions False-positive results with methadone or opiate enzyme immunoassay may occur with diphenhydramine or doxylamine

Reference Range Therapeutic: Not established; Toxic: >0.1 µg/mL; plasma diphenhydramine levels >50 µg/L (0.17 µmol/L) associated with sedation; blood diphenhydramine level of 12.8 mg/L associated with fatality

Drug Interactions CNS depressants, monoamine oxidase inhibitors, syrup should not be given to patients taking drugs that can cause disulfiram reactions (ie, metronidazole, chlorpropamide) due to alcohol content; adsorbed by charcoal; haloperidol and diphenhydramine are incompatible in a hypodermic syringe; increase anticholinergic effect with tricyclic antidepressants, MAO inhibitors, or phenothiazines

Dosage Forms

Diphenhydramine hydrochloride:

Capsule: 25 mg, 50 mg

Cream: 1%, 2%

Elixir: 12.5 mg/5 mL (5 mL, 10 mL, 20 mL, 120 mL, 480 mL, 3780 mL)

Injection: 10 mg/mL (10 mL, 30 mL); 50 mg/mL (1 mL, 10 mL)

Lotion: 1% (75 mL)

Solution, topical spray: 1% (60 mL)

Syrup: 12.5 mg/5 mL (5 mL, 120 mL, 240 mL, 480 mL, 3780 mL)

Tablet: 25 mg, 50 mg

Additional Information Has antinauseant and topical anesthetic properties; false-positive results with methadone or opiate enzyme immunoassay may occur with diphenhydramine or doxylamine; liquid preparations may also contain significant amounts of alcohol; topical administration on infants and small children has lead to severe systemic toxicity, particularly in presence of varicella infection

Specific References

Burns M and Moskowitz H, "Antihistamine Effects on Performance: Comparison of Diphenhydramine and Terfenadine," *Alcohol, Drugs and Traffic Safety-T92, Band 2.1*, Utzelmann H, Berghaus G, and Kroz G, eds, Cologne: Verlag TUV Theinland, 1993, 585-90.

Burns M and Moskowitz H, "Effects of Diphenhydramine and Alcohol on Skills Performance," *Eur Clin Pharmacol*, 1980, 17(4):259-66.

Burns M, Shanaman J, and Shellenberger C, "A Laboratory Study With Chronic Allergic Rhinitis Patients: Antihistamine Effects on Skilled Performance," *J Allergy Clin Immunol*, 1994, 93(4):716-24.

Sexton JD and Pronchik DJ, "Diphenhydramine-Induced Psychosis With Therapeutic Doses," *Am J Emerg Med*, 1997, 15(5):548-9.

Diphenhydramine and Pseudoephedrine
(dye fen HYE dra meen & soo doe e FED rin)

U.S. Brand Names Actifed® Allergy Tablet (Night) [OTC]; Banophen® Decongestant Capsule [OTC]; Benadryl® Decongestant Allergy Tablet [OTC]

Therapeutic Category Antihistamine/Decongestant Combination

Abuse Potential Yes

Impairment Potential Yes; Diphenhydramine: Impairment occurs at doses exceeding 50 mg

Gengo FM and Manning C, "A Review of the Effects of Antihistamines on Mental Processes Related to Automobile Driving," *J Allergy Clin Immunol*, 1990, 86(2): 1034-9.

Dosage Forms

Capsule: Diphenhydramine hydrochloride 25 mg and pseudoephedrine hydrochloride 60 mg

Tablet:

Actifed® Allergy (Night): Diphenhydramine hydrochloride 25 mg and pseudoephedrine hydrochloride 30 mg

Benadryl® Decongestant Allergy: Diphenhydramine hydrochloride 25 mg and pseudoephedrine hydrochloride 60 mg

Diphenoxylate and Atropine (dye fen OKS i late & A troe peen)

Synonyms Atropine and Diphenoxylate

U.S. Brand Names Lofene®; Logen®; Lomanate®; Lomodix®; Lomotil®; Lonox®; Low-Quel®

Therapeutic Category Antidiarrheal

Use Treatment of diarrhea with nonbacterial causes

Usual Dosage Use with caution in young children due to variable responses; if there is no response within 48 hours, the drug is unlikely to be effective and should be discontinued. Oral:

Children 2-12 years: 0.3-0.4 mg/kg/day of diphenoxylate in 2-4 divided doses
Adults: 15-20 mg/day of diphenoxylate in 3-4 divided doses

Mechanism of Action Diphenoxylate inhibits excessive gastrointestinal motility and gastrointestinal propulsion (an analogue of meperidine); commercial preparations contain a subtherapeutic amount of atropine to discourage abuse

Pharmacodynamics/kinetics

Onset of action: Within 45-60 minutes
Peak effect: Within 2 hours
Duration: 3-4 hours
Absorption: Oral: Well absorbed
Metabolism: Extensive in the liver to diphenoxylic acid (active)
Half-life: 2.5 hours; difenoxine: 4-7 hours
Time to peak serum concentration: 2 hours

Signs and Symptoms of Acute Intoxication Paralytic ileus

When to Transport to Hospital Transport any patient with changes in mental status or any ingestion over 0.5 mg/kg

Overdosage/Treatment

Decontamination: Lavage (within 1 hour)/activated charcoal
Supportive therapy: Naloxone for respiratory/central nervous system depression

Warnings/Precautions High doses may cause addiction; use with caution in patients with ulcerative colitis, dehydration, and hepatic dysfunction; reduction of intestinal motility may be deleterious in diarrhea resulting from *Shigella*, *Salmonella*, toxigenic strains of *E. coli*, and from pseudomembranous enterocolitis associated with broad spectrum antibiotics; children may develop signs
(Continued)

Diphenoxylate and Atropine *(Continued)*

of atropinism (dryness of skin and mucous membranes, thirst, hyperthermia, tachycardia, urinary retention, flushing) even at the recommended dosages

Adverse Reactions 1% to 10%:

Central nervous system: Nervousness, restlessness, dizziness, drowsiness, headache, mental depression

Gastrointestinal: Paralytic ileus, xerostomia

Genitourinary: Urinary retention and dysuria

Ocular: Blurred vision

Respiratory: Respiratory depression

Reference Range Peak plasma level after 5 mg of diphenoxylate: 0.01 mg/L of diphenoxylate and 0.04 mg/L of difenoxine

Drug Interactions Increased toxicity: MAO inhibitors (hypertensive crisis), CNS depressants, antimuscarinics (paralytic ileus); may prolong half-life of drugs metabolized in liver

Dosage Forms

Solution, oral: Diphenoxylate hydrochloride 2.5 mg and atropine sulfate 0.025 mg per 5 mL (4 mL, 10 mL, 60 mL)

Tablet: Diphenoxylate hydrochloride 2.5 mg and atropine sulfate 0.025 mg

Specific References

McCarron MM, Challoner KR, and Thompson GA, "Diphenoxylate-Atropine (Lomotil®) Overdose in Children: An Update (Report of Eight Cases and Review of the Literature)," *Pediatrics*, 1991, 87(5):694-700.

Diphenylan Sodium® *see* Phenytoin *on page 483*

Diphenylhydantoin *see* Phenytoin *on page 483*

Dipondal® *see* Dexfenfluramine *on page 185*

Diprazinum *see* Promethazine *on page 505*

Dipropyl *see* Hexane *on page 286*

Dipropylacetic Acid *see* Valproic Acid and Derivatives *on page 607*

Dirdalud® *see* Tizanidine *on page 584*

Disobrom® [OTC] *see* Dexbrompheniramine and Pseudoephedrine *on page 184*

Disodium Difluoride *see* Fluoride *on page 251*

***d*-Isoephedrine Hydrochloride** *see* Pseudoephedrine *on page 516*

Disophrol® Chronotabs® [OTC] *see* Dexbrompheniramine and Pseudoephedrine *on page 184*

Disophrol® Tablet [OTC] *see* Dexbrompheniramine and Pseudoephedrine *on page 184*

Di-Spaz® *see* Dicyclomine *on page 194*

Dissenten® *see* Loperamide *on page 349*

Distilled Mustard *see* Mustard Gas *on page 414*

Disulfiram *(dye SUL fi ram)*

U.S. Brand Names Antabuse®

Therapeutic Category Aldehyde Dehydrogenase Inhibitor Agent

Use Management of chronic alcoholics; also used to treat allergic nickel dermatitis and can enhance the elimination of nickel

Usual Dosage Adults: Oral: Maximum daily dose: 500 mg/day in a single dose for 1-2 weeks; average maintenance dose: 250 mg/day; range: 125-500 mg; duration of therapy is to continue until the patient is fully recovered socially and a basis for permanent self control has been established; maintenance therapy may be required for months or even years

Mechanism of Action Disulfiram is a thiuram derivative which interferes with aldehyde dehydrogenase. When taken concomitantly with alcohol, there is an increase in serum acetaldehyde levels. High acetaldehyde causes uncomfortable symptoms, including flushing, nausea, thirst, palpitations, chest pain, dizziness, and hypotension. This reaction is the basis for disulfiram use in postwithdrawal long-term care of alcoholism. May also boost the immune function in HIV patients.

Pharmacodynamics/kinetics
Peak effect: 8-12 hours

Absorption: 80% within 1 hour

Metabolism: To diethyldithiocarbamate (DDC) and methyl-DDC; DDC is then metabolized to diethylamine and carbon disulfide

Half-life:
Disulfiram: 1-12 hours

DDC: 15.5 hours

Methyl-DDC: 22 hours

Diethylamine: 14 hours

Carbon disulfide: 9 hours

Elimination: Renal (<10%), fecal (20%), pulmonary (20% to 30%)

Signs and Symptoms of Acute Intoxication Paresthesia, ataxia, thrombocytopenia, facial flushing, impotence, syncope, ptosis, dysphoria, mania, memory loss, eczema, garlic-like breath, rotten egg breath, dementia, seizures, depression, metallic taste; blindness

When to Transport to Hospital Transport any symptomatic patient or ingestion over 1 g

Warnings/Precautions Should never be administered to a patient when he/she is in a state of alcohol intoxication, or without his/her knowledge; use with caution in patients with diabetes, hypothyroidism, seizure disorders, hepatic cirrhosis or insufficiency

Adverse Reactions
>10%: Central nervous system: Drowsiness

1% to 10%:
Central nervous system: Headache, fatigue, mood changes, neurotoxicity

Dermatologic: Rash

Gastrointestinal: Metallic or garlic-like aftertaste

Genitourinary: Impotence

Disulfiram reaction with alcohol: Flushing, diaphoresis, cardiovascular collapse, myocardial infarction, vertigo, seizures, headache, nausea, vomiting, dyspnea, chest pain, death

Test Interactions Increases acetone levels

Reference Range Peak blood disulfiram level after a 500 mg dose: 0.38 mg/L; peak DDC level is ~1.2 mg/L; peak carbon disulfide level is 14 mg/L; concomitant ethanol levels >0.12 g/dL associated with unconsciousness when ethanol is used with disulfiram

Drug Interactions Increased toxicity of INH, metronidazole, phenytoin, alcohol, warfarin, diazepam, chlordiazepoxide; can cause elevation of theophylline; disulfiram causes a 78% lower methemoglobin level after dapsone use; exposure to vinyl chloride in patients taking Antabuse® may increase the toxicity of vinyl chloride

Dosage Forms Tablet: 250 mg, 500 mg

Specific References
Stransky G, Lambing MK, Simmons GT, et al, "Methemoglobinemia in a Fatal Case of Disulfiram-Ethanol Reaction," *J Anal Toxicol*, 1997, 21(2):178-9.

Ditan® see Phenytoin on page 483

Dithiocarbonic Anhydride see Carbon Disulfide on page 108

Diurigen® see Chlorothiazide on page 131

Diuril® see Chlorothiazide on page 131

Divalproex Sodium see Valproic Acid and Derivatives on page 607

Dixart® see Clonidine on page 154

Dizmiss® [OTC] see Meclizine on page 361

dl-Norephedrine Hydrochloride see Phenylpropanolamine on page 481

d-Methamphetamine see Methamphetamines, Urine on page 384

d-Methorphan see Dextromethorphan on page 187

Dobill's Solution® see Borates on page 80

Doktors® **Nasal Solution [OTC]** see Phenylephrine on page 479

Dolacet® **DuoCet**™ see Hydrocodone and Acetaminophen on page 293

Dolantin® see Meperidine on page 367

Dolantina® see Meperidine on page 367

Dolantine® see Meperidine on page 367

Dolco Mouse Cereal® see Strychnine on page 549

Dolene® see Propoxyphene on page 508

Dolobid® see Diflunisal on page 198

Dolophine® see Methadone on page 379

Dolosal® see Meperidine on page 367

Domnamid® see Estazolam on page 228

Donnatal® see Hyoscyamine, Atropine, Scopolamine, and Phenobarbital on page 306

Dopamet® see Methyldopa on page 393

Dopegyt® see Methyldopa on page 393

Doral® see Quazepam on page 518

Doriden® see Glutethimide on page 266

Dormalin® see Quazepam on page 518

Dormarex® **2 Oral [OTC]** see Diphenhydramine on page 205

Dormicum® see Midazolam on page 402

Dormigen® see Nitrazepam on page 435

Dormin® **Oral [OTC]** see Diphenhydramine on page 205

Doxazosin (doks AYE zoe sin)

U.S. Brand Names Cardura®

Therapeutic Category Alpha-Adrenergic Blocking Agent

Use Alpha-blocking agent for treatment of hypertension; treatment of benign prostatic hyperplasia (BPH)

Usual Dosage Adults: Oral: 1 mg once daily, may be increased to 2 mg once daily thereafter up to 4, 8, and 16 mg if needed

Mechanism of Action Doxazosin is a long-acting selective inhibitor of postjunctional alpha$_1$-adrenoceptors as demonstrated in isolated animal tissues and anesthetized healthy animals. Doxazosin is a water soluble quinazoline analogue of prazosin, and on a weight-for-weight basis is approximately half as potent as prazosin in postsynaptic alpha$_1$-adrenoceptor inhibition in animals and man. Inhibition of these alpha$_1$-adrenergic receptors in the peripheral vasculature prevents vasoconstriction from adrenergic stimulation; therefore, allowing vasodilation and a reduction in blood pressure. Because of doxazosin's and similar alpha$_1$-adrenergic blockers specificity, they preserve feedback control of transmitter norepinephrine release and, therefore, cause minimal reflex activation.

Pharmacodynamics/kinetics Increased age does not significantly affect the pharmacodynamics of doxazosin

Maximal effect: 2-6 hours after a dose

Duration of action: 24 hours

Metabolism: Extensive in the liver

Half-life: 10-22 hours (no difference in renal failure)

Time to peak serum concentration: 2.3 hours

Signs and Symptoms of Acute Intoxication Severe hypotension, light-headedness, drowsiness, tachycardia

When to Transport to Hospital Transport any pediatric exposure, any symptomatic patient, or any asymptomatic ingestion over 20 mg

Warnings/Precautions Can cause marked hypotension and syncope with sudden loss of consciousness with the first few doses. Anticipate a similar effect if therapy is interrupted for a few days, if dosage is increased rapidly, or if another antihypertensive drug is introduced. Use with caution in patients with renal impairment, patients receiving first dose, or dosage increase of doxazosin.

Adverse Reactions

>10%: Central nervous system: Dizziness

1% to 10%:

Cardiovascular: Palpitations, arrhythmia

Central nervous system: Vertigo, nervousness, somnolence, anxiety

Endocrine & metabolic: Decreased libido

Gastrointestinal: Nausea, vomiting, xerostomia, diarrhea, constipation

Neuromuscular & skeletal: Shoulder, neck, back pain

Ocular: Abnormal vision

Respiratory: Rhinitis

Reference Range 8 mg dose is associated with a serum level of 60 ng/mL

Drug Interactions Other hypotensive agents

Dosage Forms Tablet: 1 mg, 2 mg, 4 mg, 8 mg

Specific References

Evans M, Perera PW, and Donaghue J, "Drug Induced Psychosis With Doxazosin," *Br Med J*, 1997, 314:1869.

Doxepin (DOKS e pin)

U.S. Brand Names Adapin®; Co-Dax®; Novoxapin®; Sinequan®; Triadapin®

Canadian Brand Names Apo-Doxepin®; Novo-Doxepin®; Triadapin®

Therapeutic Category Antidepressant

Impairment Potential Yes; Single oral doses of 25 mg can prolong choice reaction time

Stromberg C, Seppala T, and Mattila MJ, "Acute Effects of Maprotiline, Doxepin, and Zimeldine With Alcohol in Healthy Volunteers," *Arch Int Pharmacodyn Ther*, 1988, 291:217-28.

Use Treatment of various forms of depression, usually in conjunction with psychotherapy; treatment of anxiety disorders; analgesic for certain chronic and neuropathic pain; topical preparation is used for pruritus

Usual Dosage

Oral (entire daily dose may be given at bedtime):

Adolescents: Initial: 25-50 mg/day in single or divided doses; gradually increase to 100 mg/day

Adults: Initial: 30-150 mg/day at bedtime or in 2-3 divided doses; may gradually increase up to 300 mg/day; single dose should not exceed 150 mg; select patients may respond to 25-50 mg/day

Topical: Adults: Apply in a thin film 4 times/day (with at least a 3- to 4-hour interval between applications); chronic use beyond 8 days may result in higher systemic levels

Mechanism of Action Increases the synaptic concentration of serotonin and/or norepinephrine in the central nervous system by inhibition of their reuptake by the presynaptic neuronal membrane; also an H_2-receptor antagonist

Pharmacodynamics/kinetics

Peak effect: Antidepressant effects usually occur after more than 2 weeks; anxiolytic effects may occur sooner

(Continued)

Doxepin *(Continued)*

Absorption: Oral: Rapidly and well absorbed from gastrointestinal tract

Metabolism: Hepatically metabolized to metabolites, including desmethyldoxepin (active)

Half-life: Adults: 6-8 hours

Time to peak serum concentration: 2-4 hours

Signs and Symptoms of Acute Intoxication Confusion, dental erosion, priapism, photosensitivity, gynecomastia, hallucinations, ataxia, ejaculatory disturbances, extrapyramidal reaction, galactorrhea, seizures, rhabdomyolysis, myoglobinuria, urinary retention, hypoglycemia, hypothermia, hypotension, tachycardia, cyanosis, Q-T prolongation, respiratory depression

When to Transport to Hospital Transport any symptomatic patient or ingestion over 150 mg

Warnings/Precautions Do not discontinue abruptly in patients receiving chronic high-dose therapy; use with caution in patients with cardiovascular disease, conduction disturbances, seizure disorders, urinary retention, hyperthyroidism or those receiving thyroid replacement; avoid use during lactation; use with caution in pregnancy

Adverse Reactions

>10%:

Central nervous system: Sedation, drowsiness, dizziness, headache

Gastrointestinal: Xerostomia, constipation, increased appetite, nausea, unpleasant taste, weight gain

Neuromuscular & skeletal: Weakness

1% to 10%:

Cardiovascular: Hypotension, arrhythmias

Central nervous system: Confusion, delirium, hallucinations, nervousness, restlessness, parkinsonian syndrome, insomnia

Gastrointestinal: Diarrhea, heartburn

Genitourinary: Sexual dysfunction, dysuria

Neuromuscular & skeletal: Fine muscle tremors

Ocular: Blurred vision, eye pain

Miscellaneous: Diaphoresis (excessive)

Reference Range

Therapeutic: 110-250 ng/mL

Toxic: >500 ng/mL

Drug Interactions MAO inhibitors, guanethidine, clonidine, cimetidine inhibits elimination of doxepin; dextropropoxyphene inhibits metabolism of doxepin; tamoxifen may cause a decrease serum concentration of doxepin

Dosage Forms

Doxepin hydrochloride:

Capsule: 10 mg, 25 mg, 50 mg, 75 mg, 100 mg, 150 mg

Concentrate, oral: 10 mg/mL (120 mL)

Cream: 5% (30 g)

Additional Information Entire daily dose may be given at bedtime; avoid unnecessary exposure to sunlight; found in a 5% concentration in Zonalon® topical cream for pruritus; toxic reactions can occur due to percutaneous absorption

Specific References

Vo MY, Williamsen AR, Wasserman GS, et al, "Toxic Reaction From Topically Applied Doxepin in a Child With Eczema," *Arch Dermatol*, 1995, 131(12):1467-8.

Doxoline® *see* Loxapine *on page 354*

Dozic® *see* Haloperidol *on page 280*

Dozine® *see* Chlorpromazine *on page 138*

DPA see Valproic Acid and Derivatives on page 607

DPH see Phenytoin on page 483

Dramamine® [OTC] see Dimenhydrinate on page 203

Dramilin® see Dimenhydrinate on page 203

Dri-Ear® [OTC] see Boric Acid on page 80

Dristan® Cold Caplets [OTC] see Acetaminophen and Pseudoephedrine on page 22

Dristan® Sinus Caplets [OTC] see Pseudoephedrine and Ibuprofen on page 517

Drixomed® see Dexbrompheniramine and Pseudoephedrine on page 184

Drixoral® [OTC] see Dexbrompheniramine and Pseudoephedrine on page 184

Drixoral® Cough & Congestion Liquid Caps [OTC] see Pseudoephedrine and Dextromethorphan on page 517

Drixoral® Cough Liquid Caps [OTC] see Dextromethorphan on page 187

Drixoral® Cough & Sore Throat Liquid Caps [OTC] see Acetaminophen and Dextromethorphan on page 21

Drixoral® Syrup [OTC] see Brompheniramine and Pseudoephedrine on page 86

Dromia® see Oxitriptan on page 451

Dromoran® see Levorphanol on page 342

Dronabinol (droe NAB i nol)

Synonyms Tetrahydrocannabinol; THC

U.S. Brand Names Marinol®

Therapeutic Category Antiemetic

Abuse Potential Yes

Impairment Potential Yes

Use When conventional antiemetics fail to relieve the nausea and vomiting associated with cancer chemotherapy, AIDS-related anorexia

Usual Dosage Oral:

Children: NCI protocol recommends 5 mg/m² starting 6-8 hours before chemotherapy and every 4-6 hours after to be continued for 12 hours after chemotherapy is discontinued

Adults: 5 mg/m² 1-3 hours before chemotherapy, then administer 5 mg/m²/dose every 2-4 hours after chemotherapy for a total of 4-6 doses/day; dose may be increased up to a maximum of 15 mg/m²/dose if needed (dosage may be increased by 2.5 mg/m² increments)

Appetite stimulant (AIDS-related): Initial: 2.5 mg twice daily (before lunch and dinner); titrate up to a maximum of 20 mg/day

Mechanism of Action Not well defined, probably inhibits the vomiting center in the medulla oblongata

Pharmacodynamics/kinetics

Absorption: Oral: Erratic

Metabolism: In the liver to several metabolites, some of which are active

Half-life: 19-24 hours

Time to peak serum concentration: Within 2-3 hours

Elimination: In feces and urine

Signs and Symptoms of Acute Intoxication Tachycardia, hypertension, and hypotension

When to Transport to Hospital Transport any symptomatic patient or any ingestion over 20 mg

Warnings/Precautions Use with caution in patients with heart disease, hepatic disease, or seizure disorders; reduce dosage in patients with severe hepatic impairment

(Continued)

Dronabinol *(Continued)*

Adverse Reactions

>10%: Central nervous system: Drowsiness, dizziness, detachment, anxiety, difficulty concentrating, mood change

1% to 10%:

Cardiovascular: Orthostatic hypotension, tachycardia

Central nervous system: Ataxia, depression, headache, vertigo, hallucinations, memory lapse

Gastrointestinal: Xerostomia

Neuromuscular & skeletal: Paresthesia, weakness

Test Interactions ↓ FSH, ↓ LH, ↓ growth hormone, ↓ testosterone

Reference Range Antinauseant effects: 5-10 ng/mL

Drug Interactions Increased toxicity (drowsiness) with alcohol, barbiturates, benzodiazepines

Dosage Forms Capsule: 2.5 mg, 5 mg, 10 mg

Specific References

Lane M, Smith FE, Sullivan RA, et al, "Dronabinol and Prochlorperazine Alone and in Combination as Antiemetic Agents for Cancer Chemotherapy," *Am J Clin Oncol*, 1990, 13(6):480-4.

Droperidol *(droe PER i dole)*

Related Information

Droperidol and Fentanyl *on next page*

U.S. Brand Names Inapsine®

Therapeutic Category Antipsychotic Agent

Impairment Potential Yes

Use Tranquilizer and antiemetic in surgical and diagnostic procedures; antiemetic for cancer chemotherapy; preoperative medication; has good antiemetic effect as well as sedative and antianxiety effects

Usual Dosage Titrate carefully to desired effect

Children 2-12 years:

Premedication: I.M.: 0.1-0.15 mg/kg; smaller doses may be sufficient for control of nausea or vomiting

Adjunct to general anesthesia: I.V. induction: 0.088-0.165 mg/kg

Nausea and vomiting: I.M., I.V.: 0.05-0.06 mg/kg/dose every 4-6 hours as needed

Adults:

Premedication: I.M.: 2.5-10 mg 30 minutes to 1 hour preoperatively

Adjunct to general anesthesia: I.V. induction: 0.22-0.275 mg/kg; maintenance: 1.25-2.5 mg/dose

Alone in diagnostic procedures: I.M.: Initial: 2.5-10 mg 30 minutes to 1 hour before; then 1.25-2.5 mg if needed

Nausea and vomiting: I.M., I.V.: 2.5-5 mg/dose every 3-4 hours as needed

Mechanism of Action Alters the action of dopamine in the CNS, at subcortical levels, to produce sedation; reduces emesis by blocking dopamine stimulation of the chemotrigger zone

Pharmacodynamics/kinetics

Metabolism: In the liver

Half-life: Adults: 2.3 hours

Signs and Symptoms of Acute Intoxication Hypotension, tachycardia, hallucinations, extrapyramidal symptoms

When to Transport to Hospital Transport any pediatric (<2 years of age) exposure, any symptomatic patient, or any parenteral exposure over 15 mg

Warnings/Precautions Safety in children <6 months of age has not been established; use with caution in patients with seizures, bone marrow suppression, or severe liver disease

Significant hypotension may occur, especially when the drug is administered parenterally; injection contains benzyl alcohol; injection also contains sulfites which may cause allergic reaction

Tardive dyskinesia: Prevalence rate may be 40% in elderly; development of the syndrome and the irreversible nature are proportional to duration and total cumulative dose over time. May be reversible if diagnosed early in therapy.

Extrapyramidal reactions are more common in elderly with up to 50% developing these reactions after 60 years of age. Drug-induced **Parkinson's syndrome** occurs often. **Akathisia** is the most common extrapyramidal reaction in elderly.

Increased confusion, memory loss, psychotic behavior, and agitation frequently occur as a consequence of anticholinergic effects

Orthostatic hypotension is due to alpha-receptor blockade, the elderly are at greater risk for orthostatic hypotension

Antipsychotic associated sedation in nonpsychotic patients is extremely unpleasant due to feelings of depersonalization, derealization, and dysphoria

Life-threatening arrhythmias have occurred at therapeutic doses of antipsychotics

Adverse Reactions
>10%:
    Cardiovascular: Mild to moderate hypotension, tachycardia
    Central nervous system: Postoperative drowsiness
1% to 10%:
    Cardiovascular: Hypertension
    Central nervous system: Extrapyramidal reactions
    Respiratory: Respiratory depression

Drug Interactions Increased toxicity: CNS depressants, fentanyl and other analgesics increased blood pressure; conduction anesthesia decreased blood pressure; epinephrine decreased blood pressure; atropine, lithium

Dosage Forms Injection: 2.5 mg/mL (1 mL, 2 mL, 5 mL, 10 mL)

Specific References
Rosen C, Ratliff AF, Wolfe RW, et al, "The Efficacy of Droperidol in the Prehospital Setting," *Acad Emerg Med*, 1995, 2:446.

Droperidol and Fentanyl (droe PER i dole & FEN ta nil)

Related Information
Controlled Substances - Uses and Effects *on page 741*
Droperidol *on previous page*
Fentanyl *on page 247*

Synonyms Fentanyl and Droperidol

U.S. Brand Names Innovar®

Therapeutic Category Analgesic, Narcotic

Dosage Forms Injection: Droperidol 2.5 mg and fentanyl 50 mcg per mL (2 mL, 5 mL)

Dr Scholl's® Disk [OTC] *see* Salicylic Acid *on page 530*

Dr Scholl's® Wart Remover [OTC] *see* Salicylic Acid *on page 530*

Drug Screen, Comprehensive Panel or Analysis *see* Toxicology Drug Screen, Blood *on page 587*

Drug Screen, Comprehensive Panel or Analysis, Urine *see* Toxicology Drug Screen, Urine *on page 588*

Drug Screen, Meconium *see* Meconium Drug Screen *on page 363*

Dry Cleaning Safety Solvent *see* Stoddard Solvent *on page 547*

Dry Ice *see* Carbon Dioxide *on page 107*

DTO *see* Opium Tincture *on page 446*

Duadacin® Capsule [OTC] *see* Chlorpheniramine, Phenylpropanolamine, and Acetaminophen *on page 137*

Duboisine *see* Hyoscyamine *on page 305*

Dull-C® [OTC] *see* Ascorbic Acid *on page 53*

Duo-Cyp® Injection *see* Estradiol and Testosterone *on page 229*

DuoFilm® [OTC] *see* Salicylic Acid *on page 530*

DuoPlant® Gel [OTC] *see* Salicylic Acid *on page 530*

Duo-Trach® *see* Lidocaine *on page 345*

Duradalat® *see* Nifedipine *on page 433*

Duragesic™ *see* Fentanyl *on page 247*

Dura-Gest® *see* Guaifenesin, Phenylpropanolamine, and Phenylephrine *on page 274*

Duramorph® *see* Morphine Sulfate *on page 410*

Duranifin® *see* Nifedipine *on page 433*

Duraphyl™ *see* Theophylline Salts *on page 571*

Durapindol® *see* Pindolol *on page 488*

Duratest® Injection *see* Testosterone *on page 564*

Duratestrin® Injection *see* Estradiol and Testosterone *on page 229*

Durathate® Injection *see* Testosterone *on page 564*

Duratuss-G® *see* Guaifenesin *on page 269*

Dura-Vent® *see* Guaifenesin and Phenylpropanolamine *on page 272*

Dura-Vent/DA® *see* Chlorpheniramine, Phenylephrine, and Methscopolamine *on page 136*

Durrax® *see* Hydroxyzine *on page 303*

Dursban® *see* Chlorpyrifos *on page 143*

Dursban TC® *see* Chlorpyrifos *on page 143*

Dyazide® *see* Hydrochlorothiazide and Triamterene *on page 293*

Dymelor® *see* Acetohexamide *on page 24*

Dynafed®, Maximum Strength [OTC] *see* Acetaminophen and Pseudoephedrine *on page 22*

Dynalert® *see* Pemoline *on page 462*

Dynef® *see* Enalapril *on next page*

Dyspamet® *see* Cimetidine *on page 147*

Easprin® *see* Aspirin *on page 56*

EB *see* Ethylbenzene *on page 236*

Economycin® *see* Tetracycline *on page 568*

Econopred® *see* Prednisolone *on page 495*

Econopred® Plus *see* Prednisolone *on page 495*

Ecotrin® [OTC] *see* Aspirin *on page 56*

Ecotrin® Low Adult Strength [OTC] *see* Aspirin *on page 56*

Ectasule® *see* Ephedrine *on page 220*

Ectodex® *see* Amitraz *on page 39*

Ed A-Hist® Liquid *see* Chlorpheniramine and Phenylephrine *on page 134*

E.E.S.® Oral *see* Erythromycin *on page 226*

Efedron® *see* Ephedrine *on page 220*

Effexor® *see* Venlafaxine *on page 608*

Egazil Duretter® *see* Hyoscyamine *on page 305*

Elaldehyde *see* Paraldehyde *on page 456*

Elavil® *see* Amitriptyline *on page 40*

Eldecort® *see* Hydrocortisone *on page 297*

Eldepryl® *see* Selegiline *on page 536*

Elisal® *see* Sulthiame *on page 555*

Elixophyllin® *see* Theophylline Salts *on page 571*

Elixophyllin® SR *see* Theophylline Salts *on page 571*

Embafume® *see* Methyl Bromide *on page 393*

Emconcor® *see* Bisoprolol *on page 78*

Emcor® *see* Bisoprolol *on page 78*

Emdopa® *see* Methyldopa *on page 393*

Emeside® *see* Ethosuximide *on page 232*

Empirin® [OTC] *see* Aspirin *on page 56*

Empirin® With Codeine *see* Aspirin and Codeine *on page 58*

Emulsoil® [OTC] *see* Castor Oil *on page 118*

E-Mycin® Oral *see* Erythromycin *on page 226*

Enalapril (e NAL a pril)

Synonyms Enalaprilat; MK-421; N-(1-Ethoxycarbonyl-3-Phenylpropyl)-l-Anal-l-Proline Hydrogen Maleate

U.S. Brand Names Converten®; Dynef®; Enapren®; Innovace®; Pres®; Reniten®; Vasotec®; Xanef®

Canadian Brand Names Apo-Enalapril®

Therapeutic Category Angiotensin-Converting Enzyme (ACE) Inhibitors

Use Management of mild to severe hypertension and congestive heart failure

Usual Dosage Use lower listed initial dose in patients with hyponatremia, hypovolemia, severe congestive heart failure, decreased renal function, or in those receiving diuretics

Children: Investigational initial oral doses of **enalapril** of 0.1 mg/kg/day increasing over 2 weeks to 0.12-0.43 mg/kg/day have been used to treat severe congestive heart failure in infants (n=8)

Adults: Oral: **Enalapril**: 2.5-5 mg/day then increase as required, usual therapeutic dose for hypertension: 10-40 mg/day in 1-2 divided doses; usual therapeutic dose for heart failure: 5-20 mg/day

Mechanism of Action Competitive inhibitor of angiotensin-converting enzyme (ACE); prevents conversion of angiotensin I to angiotensin II, a potent vasoconstrictor; results in lower levels of angiotensin II which causes an increase in plasma renin activity and a reduction in aldosterone secretion

Pharmacodynamics/kinetics

Onset of action: Oral: ~1 hour

Peak effect: Occurs in 4-8 hours

Duration: 12-24 hours

Absorption: Oral: 55% to 75% (enalapril) from gastrointestinal tract

Protein binding: 50% to 60%

Metabolism: Enalapril is a prodrug and undergoes biotransformation to enalaprilat in the liver (70% conversion of enalapril to enalaprilat)

Half-life:

Enalapril:

Healthy adults: 1.3 hours

CHF adults: 3.4-5.8 hours

Enalaprilat:

Infants 6 weeks to 8 months: 6-10 hours

Adults: 35-38 hours

Time to peak serum concentration: Within 30 minutes to 1.5 hours, while peak serum levels of enalaprilic acid (active) occur within 3-4.5 hours

Signs and Symptoms of Acute Intoxication Hypotension is usually not severe in overdose patients and manifests itself within 1 hour with a maximal effect at 4 hours; bradycardia, hypoglycemia, eosinophilia, azotemia, ototoxicity; tinnitus, pemphigus, thrombocytopenia, deafness, depression, insomnia, coagulopathy

(Continued)

217

Enalapril (Continued)

When to Transport to Hospital Transport any asymptomatic pediatric patient (<6 years of age) with ingestion of 1 mg/kg or patients with cardiopulmonary symptoms

Warnings/Precautions Use with caution and modify dosage in patients with renal impairment (especially renal artery stenosis), hyponatremia, hypovolemia, severe congestive heart failure or with coadministered diuretic therapy; experience in children is limited

Adverse Reactions 1% to 10%:

Cardiovascular: Chest pain, palpitations, tachycardia, syncope

Central nervous system: Insomnia, headache, dizziness, fatigue, malaise

Dermatologic: Rash

Gastrointestinal: Abnormal taste, abdominal pain, vomiting, nausea, diarrhea, anorexia, constipation

Neuromuscular & skeletal: Paresthesia, weakness

Respiratory: Bronchitis, cough, dyspnea

Test Interactions May cause false-positive results in urine acetone determinations using sodium nitroprusside reagent

Reference Range Enalaprilat plasma level of 40 µg/L (104 mmol/L) can produce a mean blood pressure reduction of 12 mm Hg

Drug Interactions Use with potassium-sparing diuretics may cause a additive hyperkalemic effect; hypotensive agent or diuretics leads to an increase of hypotensive effect; indomethacin may decrease hypotensive effect; may increase plasma concentrations of lithium; syncope can occur with concomitant clozapine and enalapril administration; see table.

Drug-Drug Interactions With ACEIs

Precipitant Drug	Drug (Category) and Effect	Description
Antacids	ACE Inhibitors: decreased	Decreased bioavailability of ACEIs. May be more likely with captopril. Separate administration times by 1-2 hours.
NSAIDs (indomethacin)	ACEIs: decreased	Reduced hypotensive effects of ACEIs. More prominent in low renin or volume dependent hypertensive patients.
Phenothiazines	ACEIs: increased	Pharmacologic effects of ACEIs may be increased.
ACEIs	Allopurinol: increased	Higher risk of hypersensitivity reaction possible when given concurrently. Three case reports of Stevens-Johnson syndrome with captopril.
ACEIs	Digoxin: increased	Increased plasma digoxin levels.
ACEIs	Lithium: increased	Increased serum lithium levels and symptoms of toxicity may occur.
ACEIs	Potassium preps/ potassium sparing diuretics increased	Coadministration may result in elevated potassium levels.

Dosage Forms

Injection, as enalaprilat: 1.25 mg/mL (1 mL, 2 mL)

Tablet, as maleate: 2.5 mg, 5 mg, 10 mg, 20 mg

Additional Information Severe hypotension may occur in patients who are sodium and/or volume depleted, initiate lower doses and monitor closely when starting therapy in these patients; reduces albuminuria in sickle cell anemia by up to 70%

Specific References

Lau CP, "Attempted Suicide With Enalapril," *N Engl J Med*, 1986, 315(3):197

Enalapril and Hydrochlorothiazide

(e NAL a pril & hye droe klor oh THYE a zide)

U.S. Brand Names Vaseretic® 10-25

Canadian Brand Names Vaseretic®

Therapeutic Category Antihypertensive, Combination

Dosage Forms Tablet: Enalapril maleate 10 mg and hydrochlorothiazide 25 mg

Enalaprilat *see* Enalapril *on page 217*

Enapren® *see* Enalapril *on page 217*

Endak® *see* Carteolol *on page 115*

Endal® *see* Guaifenesin and Phenylephrine *on page 272*

Endolor® *see* Butalbital Compound *on page 93*

Endone® *see* Oxycodone *on page 452*

English-Oregon-American-Christmas-Indian Holly *see* Holly *on page 287*

Enomine® *see* Guaifenesin, Phenylpropanolamine, and Phenylephrine *on page 274*

Entex® *see* Guaifenesin, Phenylpropanolamine, and Phenylephrine *on page 274*

Entex® LA *see* Guaifenesin and Phenylpropanolamine *on page 272*

Entex® PSE *see* Guaifenesin and Pseudoephedrine *on page 273*

Epanutin® *see* Phenytoin *on page 483*

Ephedra

Synonyms Joint Fir; Ma-Huang; Mormon Tea (*Ephedra nevadensis*); Squaw Tea; Teamsters' Tea; Yellow Horse

Abuse Potential Yes

Impairment Potential Yes

Use Herbal medicinal uses include treatment for asthma, bronchitis, edema, arthritis, headache, fever, urticaria; also used for weight reduction and for euphoria

Usual Dosage

E. sinica extracts (with 10% alkaloid content): 125-250 mg 3 times/day

As a tea: Steeping 1 heaping teaspoon in 240 mL of boiling water for 10 minutes (equivalent to 15-30 mg of ephedrine)

Per Commission E: Single dose: Herb preparation corresponds to 15-30 mg total alkaloid (calculation as ephedrine)

Mechanism of Action An alpha- and beta-adrenergic stimulant; most species contain ephedrine and/or pseudoephedrine although *E. nevadensis* may not contain any ephedrine; tannin contributes to its bitter taste

Signs and Symptoms of Acute Intoxication Dysrhythmias, CNS depression, depression, insomnia, dry skin, respiratory depression, vomiting, respiratory alkalosis, seizures, mydriasis

When to Transport to Hospital Transport any symptomatic patient

Warnings/Precautions AHPA warning as of March 1994 for ephedra product labels: "Seek advice from 2 health care professionals prior to use if you are pregnant or nursing, or if you have high blood pressure, heart or thyroid disease, diabetes, difficulty in urination due to prostate enlargement, or if taking 2 MAO inhibitors or any other prescription drug. Reduce or discontinue use if nervousness, tremor, sleeplessness, loss of appetite, or nausea occur. Not intended for use by persons <18 years of age. Keep out of reach of children."

Adverse Reactions

>10%: Central nervous system: Nervousness, restlessness, insomnia

(Continued)

Ephedra *(Continued)*

<10%:

Cardiovascular: Hypertension, cardiomyopathy, vasculitis, cardiomegaly, palpitations, vasoconstriction

Central nervous system: CNS-stimulating effects, anxiety, fear, psychosis, tension, agitation, excitation, irritability, auditory and visual hallucinations, sympathetic storm

Gastrointestinal: Nausea, anorexia

Neuromuscular & skeletal: Tremors, weakness

Reference Range Therapeutic serum level of ephedrine: 0.04-0.08 µg/mL

Drug Interactions Per Commission E: May potentiate with MAO inhibitors in combination with cardiac glycosides or halothane; arrhythmias; with guanethidine: Enhancement of sympathomimetic effect; with MAO inhibitors: Potentiates sympathomimetic effect of ephedrine

Additional Information Limit daily consumption to 120 mg total ephedra alkaloids in 4 equal doses. Consists of dried young branches of *Ephedra sinica*, *Ephedra equisetina* and *Ephedra gerardiana*

Erect evergreen shrubs growing up to 6 feet in height with rounded flowers blooming in early spring; while the fruits are nearly alkaloid free, the green stems and twigs contain the highest amount of ephedrine and pseudoephedrine; Mormon tea (*Ephedra nevadensis*) contains large amount of tannin, no ephedrine (but possibly t-norpseudoephedrine, a CNS stimulant) and can produce a mild diuresis along with constipation; in fact North and Central American ephedra species lack sympathomimetic alkaloids

Specific References

Doyle H and Kargin M, "Herbal Stimulant Containing Ephedrine Has Also Caused Psychosis," *BMJ*, 1996, 313(7059):756.

Israelson L, "Ephedra: An Insider's Perspective," *Herbs Health*, July/August, 1997, 50-1.

Ephedrine *(e FED rin)*

Related Information

Ephedra *on previous page*

U.S. Brand Names Ectasule®; Efedron®; Ephedsol®; Fedrine®; Vicks Vatronol®

Therapeutic Category Adrenergic Agonist Agent

Abuse Potential Yes

Impairment Potential Yes

Use Bronchial asthma; nasal congestion; acute wheezing; acute hypotensive states

Usual Dosage

Children: Oral, I.V., S.C.: 3 mg/kg/day or 100 mg/m^2/day in 4-6 divided doses

Adults: Oral: 25-50 mg every 3-4 hours as needed

Mechanism of Action Releases tissue stores of epinephrine and thereby produces an alpha- and beta-adrenergic stimulation

Pharmacodynamics/kinetics

Onset of action: Oral: Bronchodilation within 15-60 minutes

Duration: 3-6 hours

Absorption: Rapid after administration

Metabolism: Little hepatic metabolism

Half-life: 2.5-3.6 hours

Signs and Symptoms of Acute Intoxication Dysrhythmias, CNS depression, depression, insomnia, dry skin, respiratory depression, vomiting, respiratory alkalosis, seizures, mydriasis

When to Transport to Hospital Transport any pediatric (<6 years of age) ingestion over 2 mg/kg or any symptomatic ingestion

Ephedrine products are marketed under a variety of packaging gimmicks and names. The following products are marketed as natural versions of illegal drugs:

Herbal Ecstasy

Herbal X GWM

Cloud 9

Fat burner

Herbal Bliss

Ritual Spirit

Thermoslim

Truck stop ephedrine products include the following:

357 Magnum

Efedrin

GoPower

Heads Up

Max Alert

Maxephedrine

Mini-Thins

Thin-Edrine

Turbo Tabs

Many products contain a form of ephedrine called ma huang, with ephedrine concentrations as much as 16 times higher than the naturally occurring levels. These include:

AM Trim and Firm

Blasting Caps

Chi Powder

Cyber genics

Dextrate

Diet Max

Diet Max LiquidGels

Diet Now

Diet Pep

Ephedra 850

Excell Ultra High Energy Performance

Excell Energy

Formula One

Herbal Fuel

Kickers Instant Energy Caplets

Mega Ripped

Mega Ripped

New Zest

New Zest Plus

Now

Nura One

Performance Energy

Power Trim

Pro Ripped

Ripped Fuel Tea

Quick Shot Energel

Super Day Trim

Summit Select

Super Fat Burners

Smart Body

Thermo Diet

Thermo Slim

Thermogenics

Thermojetics

Thinline III

Trim Time Tea

Ultra Diet Pep

Up Your Gas

Warnings/Precautions Blood volume depletion should be corrected before ephedrine therapy is instituted; use with caution in patients with hypertension or hyperthyroidism; may cause hypertension

Adverse Reactions

>10%: Central nervous system: CNS stimulating effects, nervousness, anxiety, apprehension, fear, tension, agitation, excitation, restlessness, irritability, insomnia, hyperactivity

1% to 10%:

Cardiovascular: Hypertension, tachycardia, palpitations, elevation or depression of blood pressure, unusual pallor

Central nervous system: Dizziness, headache

Gastrointestinal: Xerostomia, nausea, anorexia, GI upset, vomiting

Genitourinary: Painful urination

(Continued)

Ephedrine *(Continued)*

Neuromuscular & skeletal: Trembling, tremor (more common in the elderly), weakness

Miscellaneous: Diaphoresis (increased)

Reference Range Postmortem blood level of 11 mg/L associated with a fatal ephedrine overdose; therapeutic serum level: 0.04-0.08 µg/mL

Drug Interactions Do not administer with other sympathomimetic agents; MAO inhibitors, general anesthetics, alpha- and beta-adrenergic blocking agents, cardiac glycosides, atropine, theophylline; moclobemide potentiates effect of ephedrine

Dosage Forms

Ephedrine sulfate:

Capsule: 25 mg, 50 mg

Injection: 25 mg/mL (1 mL); 50 mg/mL (1 mL, 10 mL)

Spray (Pretz-D®): 0.25% (15 mL)

Drops (Vicks Vatronol®): 0.5% (30 mL)

Jelly, as alkaloid (Kondon's Nasal®): 1% (20 g)

Additional Information For I.V. administration, give undiluted injection slowly; additional I.V. doses may be given in 5-10 minutes if needed; do not exceed adult parenteral dose of 150 mg/24 hours; do not exceed pediatric dose of 3 mg/kg/24 hours; use the smallest effective dose; ephedrine is a precursor in the illicit manufacture of methamphetamine; ephedrine is extracted by dissolving ephedrine tablets in water or alcohol (50,000 tablets can result in 1 kg of ephedrine); conversion to methamphetamine occurs at a rate of 50% to 70% of the weight of ephedrine; ephedrine is synthesized by the reductive condensation of L-1-phenyl-1-acetylcarbinol with methylamine

Specific References

Backer R, Tautman D, Lowry S, et al, "Fatal Ephedrine Intoxication," *J Forensic Sci*, 1996, 42(1):157-9.

Ephedrone *see* Methcathinone *on page 389*

Ephedsol® *see* Ephedrine *on page 220*

Epilim® *see* Valproic Acid and Derivatives *on page 607*

Epimorph Dolcontin® *see* Morphine Sulfate *on page 410*

Epinat® *see* Phenytoin *on page 483*

Epitrol® *see* Carbamazepine *on page 103*

Epivir® *see* Lamivudine *on page 333*

EPO *see* Epoetin Alfa *on this page*

Epoetin Alfa (e POE e tin AL fa)

Synonyms EPO; Erythropoietin; rHuEPO-α

U.S. Brand Names Epogen®; Epoxitin®; Eprex®; Globuren®; Procrit®; Recormon®

Therapeutic Category Colony Stimulating Factor

Usual Dosage In patients on dialysis, epoetin alfa usually has been administered as an I.V. bolus 3 times/week. While the administration is independent of the dialysis procedure, it may be administered into the venous line at the end of the dialysis procedure to obviate the need for additional venous access; in patients with CRF not on dialysis, epoetin alfa may be given either as an I.V. or S.C. injection.

Dosing recommendations:

Dosing schedules need to be individualized and careful monitoring of patients receiving the drug is mandatory

rHuEPO-α may be ineffective if other factors such as iron or B₁₂/folate deficiency limit marrow response

Initial dose: I.V., S.C.: 50-150 units/kg 3 times/week

Dose should be reduced when the hematocrit reaches the target range of 30% to 33% (maximum: 36%) or a hematocrit increase of >4 points over any 2-week period

Dose should be held if the hematocrit exceeds 36% and until the hematocrit decreases to the target range (30% to 33%)

Dose should be increased by 25 units/kg 3 times/week if the hematocrit does not increase by 5-6 points after 8 weeks of therapy and hematocrit is below the target range; further increases of 25 units/kg 3 times/week may be made at 4- to 6-week intervals until the desired response is obtained. Doses exceeding 300 units/kg 3 times/week are not recommended because a greater biological response is not observed.

Maintenance dose: Should be individualized to maintain the hematocrit within the 30% to 33% target range

Anemia of prematurity: S.C.: 25-100 units/kg/dose 3 times/week

Zidovudine-treated HIV patients (available evidence indicates patients with endogenous serum erythropoietin levels >500 mU/mL are unlikely to respond); target hematocrit range: 36% to 40%

Cancer patients on chemotherapy (treatment of patients with endogenous serum erythropoietin levels >200 mU/mL is not recommended); target hematocrit range: 36% to 40%

Mechanism of Action Induces erythropoiesis by stimulating the division and differentiation of committed erythroid progenitor cells; induces the release of reticulocytes from the bone marrow into the blood stream, where they mature to erythrocytes. There is a dose response relationship with this effect. This results in an increase in reticulocyte counts followed by a rise in hematocrit and hemoglobin levels. Studies in lab animals suggest that epoetin may have an effect on megakaryoblast development, and increased platelet counts have been noted in dialysis patients receiving epoetin.

Pharmacodynamics/kinetics

Bioavailability: 20% to 30% (S.C. injection)

Half-life: 9.3 hours (initial); 6.2 hours (multiple dose)

Elimination: 2.8 mL/kg/hour

When to Transport to Hospital Transport any hallucinating or agitated patient

Warnings/Precautions Use with caution in patients with history of epilepsy or seizures, thrombocytosis, chronic liver failure, malignancy, ischemic vascular disease, porphyria, hypertension; prior to and during therapy, iron stores must be evaluated

Pretherapy parameters:

Serum ferritin >100 ng/dL

Transferrin saturation (serum iron/iron binding capacity x 100) of >20%

Iron supplementation (usual oral dosing of 325 mg 2-3 times/day) should be given during therapy to provide for increased requirements during expansion of the red cell mass secondary to marrow stimulation by EPO.

For patients with endogenous serum EPO levels which are inappropriately low for hemoglobin level, documentation of the serum EPO level will help indicate which patients may benefit from EPO therapy.

Adverse Reactions

>10%:

Cardiovascular: Hypertension

Central nervous system: Fatigue, headache, fever

1% to 10%:

Cardiovascular: Edema, chest pain

Central nervous system: Dizziness, seizures

(Continued)

Epoetin Alfa *(Continued)*

    Gastrointestinal: Nausea, vomiting, diarrhea

    Hematologic: Clotted access

    Neuromuscular & skeletal: Arthralgia, weakness

Reference Range Transferrin soluble receptor (TSR) protein levels >3000 ng/mL in plasma associated with exogenous erythropoietin use (normal range: 1000-2000 ng/mL)

Dosage Forms Injection, preservative free: 2000 units (1 mL); 3000 units (1 mL); 4000 units (1 mL); 10,000 units (1 mL)

Additional Information May require supplemental iron to keep ferritin levels >100 ng/dL; frequently used by athletes for "blood doping"; response to erythropoietin of metastatic renal cell carcinoma has been reported; high ratio of soluble transferrin to ferritin may be indicative of exogenous erythropoietin use

Specific References

    Steinberg H, "Erythropoietin and Visual Hallucinations," *N Engl J Med*, 1991, 325(4):285.

Epogen® *see* Epoetin Alfa *on page 222*

Epoxitin® *see* Epoetin Alfa *on page 222*

Eprex® *see* Epoetin Alfa *on page 222*

Eptadone® *see* Methadone *on page 379*

Eptastatin *see* Pravastatin *on page 492*

Equagesic® *see* Aspirin and Meprobamate *on page 58*

Equanil® *see* Meprobamate *on page 371*

Equibral® *see* Chlordiazepoxide *on page 124*

Equilium® *see* Tiapride *on page 581*

Ercaf® *see* Ergotamine *on this page*

Ergenyl® *see* Valproic Acid and Derivatives *on page 607*

Ergomar® *see* Ergotamine *on this page*

Ergostat® *see* Ergotamine *on this page*

Ergotamine *(er GOT a meen)*

U.S. Brand Names Cafatine®; Cafatine-PB®; Cafergot®; Cafetrate®; Ercaf®; Ergomar®; Ergostat®; Lanatrate®; Medihaler Ergotamine™; Migergot®; Wigraine®

Canadian Brand Names Ergomar®; Gynergen®

Therapeutic Category Ergot Alkaloid

Use Vascular headache, such as migraine or cluster

Usual Dosage Adults:

    Oral:

        Cafergot®: 2 tablets at onset of attack; then 1 tablet every 30 minutes as needed; maximum: 6 tablets per attack; do not exceed 10 tablets/week

        Ergostat®: 1 tablet under tongue at first sign, then 1 tablet every 30 minutes, 3 tablets/24 hours, 5 tablets/week

    Rectal (Cafergot® suppositories, Wigraine® suppositories, Cafatine® PB suppositories): 1 at first sign of an attack; follow with second dose after 1 hour, if needed; maximum: 2 per attack; do not exceed 5/week

    Inhalation: Initial: 1 inhalation, followed by repeat inhalations 5 minutes apart to a maximum of 6 inhalations/24 hours or 15 inhalations/1 week

Mechanism of Action Ergot alkaloid alpha-adrenergic blocker directly stimulates vascular smooth muscle to vasoconstrict peripheral and cerebral vessels; may also have antagonist effects on serotonin

Pharmacodynamics/kinetics

    Onset of action: Variable usually within 1-2 hours

Absorption: Oral, rectal: Erratic; absorption is enhanced by caffeine coadministration

Metabolism: Extensive in the liver

Bioavailability: <5%; rectal suppositories are ~20 times increased bioavailability than oral forms

Half-life: ~2 hours

Time to peak serum concentration: Within 30 minutes to 3 hours

Signs and Symptoms of Acute Intoxication Vasospastic effects, colitis, nausea, vomiting, drowsiness, impaired mental function, myalgia, asthenia, hypotension, chest pain, hypertension, bradycardia, vision color changes (red tinge), unconsciousness, seizures, shock and death

When to Transport to Hospital Transport any pediatric (<6 years of age) ingestion over 1 mg/kg or any symptomatic patient

Warnings/Precautions Avoid during pregnancy; avoid prolonged administration or excessive dosage because of the danger of ergotism and gangrene

Adverse Reactions

>10%:

Cardiovascular: Tachycardia, bradycardia, arterial spasm, claudication and vasoconstriction; rebound headache may occur with sudden withdrawal of the drug in patients on prolonged therapy; localized edema, peripheral vascular effects (numbness and tingling of fingers and toes)

Central nervous system: Drowsiness, dizziness

Gastrointestinal: Nausea, vomiting, diarrhea, xerostomia

1% to 10%:

Cardiovascular: Transient tachycardia or bradycardia, precordial distress and pain

Neuromuscular & skeletal: Weakness in the legs, abdominal or muscle pain, muscle pains in the extremities, paresthesia

Reference Range Serum levels >1.8 ng/mL are toxic

Drug Interactions

Propranolol: One case of severe vasoconstriction with pain and cyanosis has been reported

Erythromycin: Monitor for signs of ergot toxicity; troleandomycin

Ritonavir: Inhibition of ergotamine metabolism by ergotamine

Dosage Forms

Suppository, rectal (Cafatine®, Cafergot®, Cafetrate®, Wigraine®): Ergotamine tartrate 2 mg and caffeine 100 mg (12s)

Tablet (Ercaf®, Wigraine®): Ergotamine tartrate 1 mg and caffeine 100 mg

Tablet:

Extended release:

Bellergal-S®: Ergotamine tartrate 0.6 mg with belladonna alkaloids 0.2 mg, and phenobarbital 40 mg

Cafatine-PB®: Ergotamine tartrate 1 mg with belladonna alkaloids 0.125 mg, caffeine 100 mg, and pentobarbital 30 mg

Sublingual (Ergomar®, Ergostat®): Ergotamine tartrate 2 mg

Additional Information

Ergotamine tartrate: Ergostat®

Ergotamine tartrate and caffeine: Cafergot®

Ergotamine, caffeine, belladonna alkaloids and pentobarbital: Cafatine® P-B

Specific References

Meyler WJ, "Side Effects of Ergotamine," *Cephalalgia*, 1996, 16(1):5-10.

Eryc® Oral see Erythromycin on next page

EryPed® Oral see Erythromycin on next page

Ery-Tab® Oral see Erythromycin on next page

Erythrocin® Oral see Erythromycin on next page

Erythromycin (er ith roe MYE sin)

U.S. Brand Names E.E.S.® Oral; E-Mycin® Oral; Eryc® Oral; EryPed® Oral; Ery-Tab® Oral; Erythrocin® Oral; Ilosone® Oral; PCE® Oral; Wyamycin® S Oral

Canadian Brand Names Apo-Erythro® E-C; Diomycin®; Erybid®; Erythro-Base®; Novo-Rythro® Encap; PMS®-Erythromycin

Therapeutic Category Macrolide (Antibiotic)

Use Treatment of susceptible bacterial infections including *M. pneumoniae*, *Legionella* pneumonia, diphtheria, pertussis, chancroid, *Chlamydia*, and *Campylobacter* gastroenteritis; used in conjunction with neomycin for decontaminating the bowel

Unlabeled use: Gastroparesis

Usual Dosage

Neonates:

Postnatal age <7 days: Oral: 10 mg/kg/dose every 12 hours

Postnatal age >7 days: Oral:

<1200 g: 10 mg/kg/dose every 12 hours

≥1200 g: 10 mg/kg/dose every 8 hours

Ophthalmic: Prophylaxis of neonatal gonococcal or chlamydial conjunctivitis: 0.5-1 cm ribbon of ointment should be instilled into each conjunctival sac

Infants and Children:

Oral: Do not exceed 2 g/day

Base and ethylsuccinate: 30-50 mg/kg/day divided every 6-8 hours

Estolate: 30-50 mg/kg/day divided every 8-12 hours

Stearate: 20-40 mg/kg/day divided every 6 hours

Children and Adults:

Ophthalmic: Instill ½" (1.25 cm) 2-8 times/day depending on the severity of the infection

Topical:

Gel/Solution: Apply twice daily to affected areas

Ointment: Apply every 3 hours 6 times/day for 1 week

Adults:

Oral:

Base: 333 mg every 8 hours

Estolate, stearate or base: 250-500 mg every 6-12 hours

Ethylsuccinate: 400-800 mg every 6-12 hours

Mechanism of Action Inhibits RNA-dependent protein synthesis at the chain elongation step; binds to the 50S ribosomal subunit resulting in blockage of transpeptidation

Pharmacodynamics/kinetics

Absorption: Oral: 18% to 45%; variable but better with salt forms than with base form

Metabolism: In the liver by demethylation

Half-life: 1.5-2 hours (peak), prolonged with reduced renal function (5-6 hours)

Time to peak serum concentration: 4 hours for the base, 3 hours for the stearate, 0.5-2.5 hours for the ethylsuccinate, 2-4 hours for the estolate; delayed in the presence of food except when using the estolate; due to differences in absorption, 400 mg erythromycin ethylsuccinate produces the same serum levels as erythromycin base or estolate

When to Transport to Hospital Transport any patient exhibiting cardiopulmonary or central nervous systems changes

Warnings/Precautions Should not be administered concurrently with astemizole, terfenadine; use with caution in patients with hepatic dysfunction; hepatic impairment with or without jaundice has occurred chiefly in older children and adults; it may be accompanied by malaise, nausea, vomiting, abdominal colic, and fever; discontinue use if these occur; avoid using erythromycin lactobionate in neonates since formulations may contain benzyl alcohol which is associated with toxicity in neonates

Adverse Reactions

>10%: Gastrointestinal: Abdominal pain, cramping, nausea, vomiting

1% to 10%:

Gastrointestinal: Oral candidiasis

Hepatic: Cholestatic jaundice

Local: Phlebitis at the injection site

Miscellaneous: Hypersensitivity reactions

Reference Range Peak plasma level after 500 mg dose is 0.3-1.9 µg/mL

Drug Interactions Increased effect/toxicity/levels of alfentanil, anticoagulants, astemizole, terfenadine, loratadine, bromocriptine, carbamazepine, cyclosporine, digoxin, disopyramide, theophylline, and triazolam; erythromycin coadministered with quinidine may reduce quinidine clearance; deafness reported with concomitant cimetidine; concomitant use of quinidine and erythromycin can result in increased quinidine levels; increased toxicity with ergots, methylprednisolone; odds ratio for Q-T_c prolongation with concomitant erythromycin and terfenadine use is 2.33; increased tacrolimus levels can occur with concomitant administration of erythromycin or rifampin; neutropenia and muscle pain can result if vinblastine and erythromycin are used together; increased clozapine serum concentrations and leukocytosis can occur with concomitant erythromycin and clozapine administration (333 mg 3 times/day); increased toxicity of carbamazepine when given with erythromycin; behavioral disorders with concomitant risperidone and clomipramine; use of pimozide with macrolide antibiotics can result in sudden death due to increased pimozide plasma levels and resultant cardiac arrhythmia

Dosage Forms

Erythromycin base:

Capsule, delayed release: 250 mg

Capsule, delayed release, enteric coated pellets (Eryc®): 250 mg

Tablet:

Delayed release: 333 mg

Enteric coated (E-Mycin®, Ery-Tab®, E-Base®): 250 mg, 333 mg, 500 mg

Film coated: 250 mg, 500 mg

Polymer coated particles (PCE®): 333 mg, 500 mg

Erythromycin estolate:

Capsule (Ilosone® Pulvules®): 250 mg

Suspension, oral (Ilosone®): 125 mg/5 mL (480 mL); 250 mg/mL (480 mL)

Tablet (Ilosone®): 500 mg

Erythromycin ethylsuccinate:

Granules for oral suspension (EryPed®): 400 mg/5 mL (60 mL, 100 mL, 200 mL)

Powder for oral suspension (E.E.S.®): 200 mg/5 mL (100 mL, 200 mL)

Suspension, oral (E.E.S.®, EryPed®): 200 mg/5 mL (5 mL, 100 mL, 200 mL, 480 mL); 400 mg/5 mL (5 mL, 60 mL, 100 mL, 200 mL, 480 mL)

Suspension, oral [drops] (EryPed®): 100 mg/2.5 mL (50 mL)

Tablet (E.E.S.®): 400 mg

Tablet, chewable (EryPed®): 200 mg

Erythromycin gluceptate: Injection: 1000 mg (30 mL)

Erythromycin lactobionate: Powder for injection, I.V.: 500 mg, 1000 mg

Erythromycin stearate: Tablet, film coated (Eramycin®, Erythrocin®, Wyamycin® S): 250 mg, 500 mg

Specific References

Orban Z, MacDonald LL, Peters MA, et al, "Erythromycin-Induced Cardiac Toxicity," *Am J Cardiol*, 1995, 75(12):859-61.

Erythromycin and Sulfisoxazole
(er ith roe MYE sin & sul fi SOKS a zole)
Synonyms Sulfisoxazole and Erythromycin
U.S. Brand Names Eryzole®; Pediazole®
Therapeutic Category Macrolide (Antibiotic); Sulfonamide
Dosage Forms Suspension, oral: Erythromycin ethylsuccinate 200 mg and
sulfisoxazole acetyl 600 mg per 5 mL (100 mL, 150 mL, 200 mL, 250 mL)

Erythropoietin see Epoetin Alfa on page 222

Erythroxylon Coca see Cocaine on page 160

Eryzole® see Erythromycin and Sulfisoxazole on this page

Escoflex® see Chlorzoxazone on page 145

Escopon® see Opium Alkaloids (Hydrochlorides) on page 445

Esgic® see Butalbital Compound on page 93

Esgic-Plus® see Butalbital Compound on page 93

Esidrix® see Hydrochlorothiazide on page 291

Esilgan® see Estazolam on this page

Eskalith® see Lithium on page 347

Eskalith® CR see Lithium on page 347

Eskazina® see Trifluoperazine on page 596

Estazolam (es TA zoe lam)
U.S. Brand Names Domnamid®; Esilgan®; Eurodin®; Nuctalon®; ProSom™
Therapeutic Category Benzodiazepine
Abuse Potential Yes
Impairment Potential Yes
Use Short-term management of insomnia
Usual Dosage Adults: Oral: 1 mg at bedtime, some patients may require 2 mg;
start at doses of 0.5 mg in debilitated or small elderly patients
Mechanism of Action Has not been fully elucidated in humans; the most
promising hypothesis involves GABA transmission. GABA is a major inhibitory
transmitter in the CNS. Benzodiazepines may exert their pharmacologic effect
through potentiation of the inhibitory activity of GABA. Specific benzodiazepine
receptors have been identified in the rat brain located in proximity to dense
areas of GABA receptors, primarily in the frontal and occipital cortex. Benzodiazepines do not alter the synthesis, release, reuptake, or enzymatic degradation of GABA.
Pharmacodynamics/kinetics Studies have shown that the elderly are more
sensitive to the effects of benzodiazepines as compared to younger adults
Metabolism: Rapid and extensive in the liver to inactive metabolites (1-oxo-
estazolam)
Half-life: 8-31 hours (no significant changes in the elderly) (mean: 17 hours)
Time to peak serum concentration: Within 0.5-6 hours
Signs and Symptoms of Acute Intoxication Somnolence, confusion, coma,
diminished reflexes, mydriasis, respiratory depression, gaze nystagmus
When to Transport to Hospital Transport any pediatric exposure, any patient
with change in mental status, or any ingestion over 3 mg
Warnings/Precautions Abrupt discontinuance may precipitate withdrawal or
rebound insomnia; has the potential for drug dependence and abuse
Adverse Reactions
>10%:
Cardiovascular: Tachycardia, chest pain
Central nervous system: Drowsiness, fatigue, ataxia, lightheadedness,
memory impairment, insomnia, anxiety, depression, headache
Dermatologic: Rash

Endocrine & metabolic: Decreased libido
Gastrointestinal: Xerostomia, constipation, decreased salivation, nausea, vomiting, diarrhea, increased or decreased appetite
Neuromuscular & skeletal: Dysarthria
Ocular: Blurred vision
Miscellaneous: Diaphoresis
1% to 10%:
Cardiovascular: Syncope, hypotension
Central nervous system: Confusion, nervousness, dizziness, akathisia
Dermatologic: Dermatitis
Gastrointestinal: Weight gain or loss, increased salivation
Neuromuscular & skeletal: Rigidity, tremor, muscle cramps
Otic: Tinnitus
Respiratory: Nasal congestion, hyperventilation
Drug Interactions CNS depressants may increase CNS adverse effects; cimetidine may decrease and enzyme inducers may increase the metabolism of estazolam
Dosage Forms Tablet: 1 mg, 2 mg
Specific References
Busto U, Bendayan R, and Sellers EM, "Clinical Pharmacokinetics of Nonopiate Abuse Drugs," *Clin Pharmacokinet*, 1989, 16(1):1-26.

Estivin® II [OTC] *see Naphazoline on page 422*

Estradiol and Testosterone (es tra DYE ole & tes TOS ter one)
Synonyms Estradiol Cypionate and Testosterone Cypionate; Estradiol Valerate and Testosterone Enanthate; Testosterone and Estradiol
U.S. Brand Names Andro/Fem® Injection; Deladumone® Injection; depAndrogyn® Injection; Depo-Testadiol® Injection; Depotestogen® Injection; Duo-Cyp® Injection; Duratestrin® Injection; Valertest No.1® Injection
Therapeutic Category Estrogen and Androgen Combination
Abuse Potential Yes - testosterone component
Dosage Forms Injection:
Andro/Fem®, DepAndrogyn®, Depo-Testadiol®, Depotestogen®, Duo-Cyp®, Duratestrin®: Estradiol cypionate 2 mg and testosterone cypionate 50 mg per mL in cottonseed oil (1 mL, 10 mL)
Androgyn L.A.®, Deladumone®, Estra-Testrin®, Valertest No.1®: Estradiol valerate 4 mg and testosterone enanthate 90 mg per mL in sesame oil (5 mL, 10 mL)

Estradiol Cypionate and Testosterone Cypionate *see Estradiol and Testosterone on this page*

Estradiol Valerate and Testosterone Enanthate *see Estradiol and Testosterone on this page*

Estratest® *see Estrogens and Methyltestosterone on next page*

Estratest® H.S. *see Estrogens and Methyltestosterone on next page*

Estrogens and Medroxyprogesterone
(ES troe jenz & me DROKS ee proe JES te rone)
U.S. Brand Names Premphase™; Prempro™
Therapeutic Category Estrogen and Progestin Combination
Dosage Forms
Premphase™: Two separate tablets in therapy pack: Conjugated estrogens 0.625 mg [Premarin®] (28s) taken orally for 28 days and medroxyprogesterone acetate [Cycrin®] 5 mg (14s) which are taken orally with a Premarin® tablet on days 15 through 28
Prempro™: Conjugated estrogens 0.625 mg and medroxyprogesterone acetate 2.5 mg (14s)

Estrogens and Methyltestosterone
(ES troe jenz & meth il tes TOS te rone)

U.S. Brand Names Estratest®; Estratest® H.S.; Premarin® With Methyltestosterone

Therapeutic Category Estrogen and Androgen Combination

Abuse Potential Yes - Methyltestosterone component

Dosage Forms Tablet:

Estratest®, Menogen®: Esterified estrogen 1.25 mg and methyltestosterone 2.5 mg

Estratest® H.S., Menogen H.S.®: Esterified estrogen 0.625 mg and methyltestosterone 1.25 mg

Premarin® With Methyltestosterone: Conjugated estrogen 0.625 mg and methyltestosterone 5 mg; conjugated estrogen 1.25 mg and methyltestosterone 10 mg

Ethambutol (e THAM byoo tole)

U.S. Brand Names Myambutol®

Canadian Brand Names Etibl®

Therapeutic Category Antimycobacterial Agent

Use Treatment of tuberculosis and other mycobacterial diseases in conjunction with other antituberculosis agents

Usual Dosage Oral (not recommended in children <12 years of age):

Children >12 years: 15 mg/kg/day once daily

Adolescents and Adults: 15-25 mg/kg/day once daily, not to exceed 2.5 g/day

Mechanism of Action Suppresses mycobacteria multiplication by interfering with RNA synthesis

Pharmacodynamics/kinetics

Absorption: Oral: ~80%

Metabolism: 20% by the liver to inactive metabolite

Half-life: 2.5-3.6 hours (up to 15 hours with renal impairment)

Time to peak serum concentration: Within 2-4 hours

Elimination: ~50% excreted in urine and 20% excreted in feces as unchanged drug

Signs and Symptoms of Acute Intoxication Mental confusion, eosinophilia, disorientation, purpura, hyperuricemia, blindness, neutropenia, hallucinations, jaundice, nausea, vomiting, neuropathy (peripheral), optic neuropathy, fever, visual changes, anorexia, arthralgia, numbness of the extremities, toxic epidermal necrolysis, alopecia

When to Transport to Hospital Transport any pediatric (<12 years of age) exposure or any symptomatic patient

Adverse Reactions 1% to 10%:

Central nervous system: Headache, confusion, disorientation

Endocrine & metabolic: Acute gout or hyperuricemia

Gastrointestinal: Abdominal pain, anorexia, nausea, vomiting

Reference Range Peak plasma ethambutol level after a dose of 25 mg/kg: ~5 µg/mL

Drug Interactions Aluminum salts; aluminum hydroxide can decrease intestinal absorption of fluoride

Dosage Forms Tablet, as hydrochloride: 100 mg, 400 mg

Additional Information Incidence of optic neuropathy increases significantly with dosages above 15 mg/kg/day but may be idiosyncratic

Specific References

Pickles RW and Spelman DW, "Suspected Ethambutol-Induced Mania," *Med J Aust*, 1996, 164(7):445-6.

Ethanal see Acetaldehyde on page 19

ETH and C see Terpin Hydrate and Codeine on page 564
Ethanoic Acid see Vinyl Acetate on page 613
Ethanol see Ethyl Alcohol on page 233
Ethanol, Blood see Alcohol, Serum on page 33

Ethchlorvynol (eth klor VI nole)
Related Information
  Controlled Substances - Uses and Effects on page 741
U.S. Brand Names Placidyl®
Therapeutic Category Hypnotic, Nonbarbiturate
Impairment Potential Yes
Use Short-term management of insomnia
Usual Dosage Adults: Oral: 500-1000 mg at bedtime
Mechanism of Action A chlorinated acetylenic carbinol which causes nonspecific depression of the reticular activating system
Pharmacodynamics/kinetics
  Onset of action: 15-60 minutes
  Duration: 5 hours
  Absorption: Rapid from gastrointestinal tract
  Distribution: V_d: 3-4 L/kg
  Protein binding: 35% to 50%
  Metabolism: In the liver
  Half-life: 10-20 hours; over 100 hours in overdose
  Time to peak serum concentration: 1.5 hours
  Elimination: ~10% of the drug is normally excreted in 4 hours in a normal patient
Signs and Symptoms of Acute Intoxication Hypotension, cough, pleural effusion, prolonged coma lasting over 100 hours, respiratory depression, ataxia, myopathy, numbness, pulmonary edema, rhabdomyolysis, hypothermia, bradycardia; bullous skin lesions
When to Transport to Hospital Transport any pediatric exposure, any patient with cardiopulmonary or central nervous system abnormalities, or any ingestion over 1.5 g
Warnings/Precautions Administer with caution to depressed or suicidal patients or to patients with a history of drug abuse; intoxication symptoms may appear with prolonged daily doses of as little as 1 g; withdrawal symptoms may be seen upon abrupt discontinuation; use with caution in the elderly and in patients with hepatic or renal dysfunction; use with caution in patients who have a history of paradoxical restlessness to barbiturates or alcohol; some products may contain tartrazine
Adverse Reactions
  >10%:
    Central nervous system: Dizziness
    Gastrointestinal: Indigestion, nausea, stomach pain, unpleasant aftertaste
    Neuromuscular & skeletal: Weakness
    Ocular: Blurred vision
  1% to 10%:
    Central nervous system: Nervousness, excitement, ataxia, confusion, drowsiness (daytime)
    Dermatologic: Rash
Reference Range
  Therapeutic: 2-8 μg/mL
  Toxic: >13 μg/mL
Drug Interactions
  Decreased effect of oral anticoagulants
  (Continued)

Ethchlorvynol *(Continued)*

Increased toxicity (CNS depression) with alcohol, CNS depressants, MAO inhibitors, tricyclic antidepressants (delirium)

Dosage Forms Capsule: 200 mg, 500 mg, 750 mg

Specific References

Yell RP, "Ethchlorvynol Overdose," *Am J Emerg Med*, 1990, 8(3):246-50.

Ethenylbenzene *see* Styrene *on page 551*

Ethenyl Ester *see* Vinyl Acetate *on page 613*

Ethosuximide *(eth oh SUKS i mide)*

Synonyms 2-ethyl-2-methylsuccinmide

U.S. Brand Names Emeside®; Zarontin®

Therapeutic Category Anticonvulsant

Impairment Potential Yes

Use Management of absence (petit mal) seizures, myoclonic seizures, and akinetic epilepsy

Usual Dosage Oral:

Children 3-6 years: Initial: 250 mg/day (or 15 mg/kg/day) in 2 divided doses; increase every 4-7 days; usual maintenance dose: 15-40 mg/kg/day in 2 divided doses

Children >6 years and Adults: Initial: 250 mg twice daily; increase by 250 mg as needed every 4-7 days up to 1.5 g/day in 2 divided doses; usual maintenance dose: 20-40 mg/kg/day in 2 divided doses

Mechanism of Action Increases the seizure threshold and suppresses paroxysmal spike-and-wave pattern in absence seizures; depresses nerve transmission in the motor cortex

Pharmacodynamics/kinetics

Absorption: Rapid and complete

Metabolism: ~80% in the liver to three inactive hydroxylated metabolites

Half-life:

Children: 30 hours

Adults: 50-60 hours

Time to peak serum concentration:

Children: 3-7 hours

Capsule: Within 2-4 hours

Syrup: <2-4 hours

Signs and Symptoms of Acute Intoxication Acute overdosage can cause CNS depression, ataxia, stupor, coma, hypotension; chronic overdose can cause skin rash, confusion, albuminuria, erythema multiforme, hepatic dysfunction, extrapyramidal reaction, dementia, hematuria, leukopenia; neutropenia; agranulocytosis; granulocytopenia; myasthenia gravis (exacerbation or precipitation of), insomnia

When to Transport to Hospital Transport any symptomatic patient or any ingestion over 50 mg/kg

Warnings/Precautions When used alone in mixed seizures, ethosuximide may increase the frequency of tonic-clonic seizures. When patients with absence seizures also have tonic-clonic seizures, other anticonvulsants such as phenytoin or phenobarbital must be used in combination with ethosuximide. Avoid abrupt discontinuation of therapy; dosage should be reduced slowly to avoid precipitation of seizures. Use with caution in patients with hepatic or renal disease; may impair mental alertness and coordination.

Adverse Reactions
>10%:
  Central nervous system: Ataxia, drowsiness, sedation, dizziness, lethargy, euphoria, hallucinations, insomnia, agitation, behavioral changes, headache
  Dermatologic: Stevens-Johnson syndrome
  Gastrointestinal: Weight loss, nausea, vomiting, anorexia, abdominal pain
  Miscellaneous: Hiccups, SLE syndrome
1% to 10%:
  Central nervous system: Aggressiveness, mental depression, nightmares, fatigue
  Neuromuscular & skeletal: Weakness

Reference Range
Therapeutic: 40-100 µg/mL (SI: 280-710 µmol/L)
Toxic: >150 µg/mL (SI: >1062 µmol/L); at steady-state, each 1 mg/kg will result in a serum rise of 2 µg/mL

Drug Interactions Phenytoin, carbamazepine, primidone, phenobarbital may increase the hepatic metabolism of ethosuximide; isoniazid may inhibit hepatic metabolism with a resultant increase in ethosuximide serum concentrations

Dosage Forms
Capsule: 250 mg
Syrup (raspberry flavor): 250 mg/5 mL (473 mL)

Additional Information Considered to be drug of choice for simple absence seizures

Specific References
Marbury TC, Lee CS, Perchalski RJ, et al, "Hemodialysis Clearance of Ethosuximide in Patients With Chronic Renal Disease," *Am J Hosp Pharm*, 1981, 38(11):1757-60.

2-ethyl-2-methylsuccinmide *see* Ethosuximide *on previous page*

Ethyl Alcohol (ETH il AL koe hol)
Synonyms Beer; Cologne Spirit; Ethanol; EtOH; Liquers; Liquor; Spirits; Wine
UN Number 1170
U.S. Brand Names AHD 2000®; Lavacol® [OTC]
Therapeutic Category Intravenous Nutritional Therapy; Pharmaceutical Aid
Abuse Potential Yes
Impairment Potential Yes; see chart
Use Topical anti-infective; pharmaceutical aid; as an antidote for ethylene glycol overdose; as antidote for methanol overdose; may also be useful in propylene glycol
Usual Dosage I.V. doses of 100-125 mg/kg/hour to maintain blood levels of 100 mg/dL are recommended after a loading dose of 0.6 g/kg; maximum dose: 400 mL of a 5% solution within 1 hour
Mechanism of Action Central nervous system depressant
Pharmacodynamics/kinetics Metabolism: Hepatic to acetaldehyde by alcohol dehydrogenase at a rate of 10-30 mg/dL/hour
Signs and Symptoms of Acute Intoxication Atrial tachycardia, chorea (extrapyramidal), cardiomyopathy, tremors, thrombocytopenia, myocardial depression, impotence, acetone breath, dementia, depression, sedation, encephalopathy, leukocytosis, myopathy, hypocalcemia, hyporeflexia, hypophosphatemia, hyperuricemia, optic neuropathy, dysphagia, seizures, myoclonus, diplopia, apnea, lymphopenia, hyperventilation, numbness, respiratory depression, CNS depression, acidosis, hypokalemia, paresthesia, hypomagnesemia, hypothermia, gynecomastia, rhabdomyolysis, myoglobinuria, hyponatremia, fever, hypotension, methemoglobinemia, mydriasis, gaze nystagmus, porphyria, ototoxicity, tinnitus, hypoglycemia (3.4%)
(Continued)

Ethyl Alcohol *(Continued)*

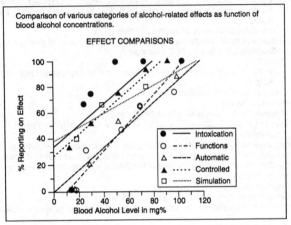

Comparison of various categories of alcohol-related effects as function of blood alcohol concentrations.

From Brain Information Service, Brain Research Institute, University of California, Los Angeles, CA 900024-1746.

When to Transport to Hospital Transport any pediatric exposure or any patient with decreased mental status

Warnings/Precautions Administer only by slow I.V. infusion

Adverse Reactions

Cardiovascular: Tachycardia, hypertension, fibrillation (atrial), flutter (atrial), cardiomegaly, angina, chest pain, congestive heart failure, sinus tachycardia, tachycardia (supraventricular), arrhythmias (ventricular), vasodilation

Central nervous system: Ataxia, dementia, Wernicke-Korsakoff syndrome, amnesia, paranoia, hyperthermia

Gastrointestinal: Nausea, diarrhea, abdominal pain, dyspepsia, vomiting, gastrointestinal hemorrhage, anorexia, pancreatitis, esophageal sphincter tone (decreased)

Hematologic: Porphyria, megaloblastic anemia

Hepatic: Hepatic cirrhosis, fatty degeneration of liver, hepatic steatosis, impaired gluconeogenesis

Neuromuscular & skeletal: Dysarthria, neuropathy (peripheral)

Miscellaneous: Impaired judgment, hiccups, breast cancer

Test Interactions Increases ammonia (B), creatine phosphokinase (CPK) (S), serum osmolarity gap increases an average of 20 for every 100 mg/dL of ethanol; decreases glucose, magnesium

Reference Range Levels >100 mg/dL can cause nausea and vomiting; levels >300 mg/dL can be associated with coma and fatalities

Drug Interactions Chloral hydrate, disulfiram, guanethidine, methotrexate, metronidazole, nitroglycerin, phenytoin, CNS depressants enhance effect; may exacerbate acetaminophen toxicity; may increase nifedipine levels; probably no relevant clinical effect with H_2 blockers; disulfiram causes nausea/vomiting and hypotension; increases serum levels of phenytoin; shortens the half lives of tolbutamide, isoniazid, and warfarin; combination of methamphetamine with ethanol can increase heart rate and cardiac work

Ethanol Content

Beverages	Percent Ethanol
7-Up (diet)	0.077
7-Up (Cherry, diet)	0.017
Ale	5-8
Beer	4-6
Bourbon	40-50
Brandy	35-40
Calistoga Lemon Flavor	0.096
Cognac	40-41
Coca-Cola (Caffeine-free, diet)	0.005
Coca-Cola	0.004
Distilled liquors	22-50
Dr. Pepper (diet)	0.024
Fruit Punch (Hawaiian Punch orange creme)	0.040
Fruit Punch (Tropicana)	0.096
Fruit Punch (Veryfine papaya)	0.058
Gin	40-47
Ginger ale (Canada Dry)	0.065
Lemonade (Elliott's)	0.037
Light beer	2.5-3.5
Mountain Dew	0.024
Root beer (A&W)	0.004
Rum	40-41
Scotch	40-50
Second Wind (sports drink)	0.025
Slice (lemon-lime)	0.056
Sprite (diet)	0.054
Tea (Elliott's Brewed Ice)	0.017
Tequila	40-46
Vodka	40-41
Whiskey	40-45
Wine	10-18

Non-medicinal	Ethanol Content (%)
Colognes and perfumes	40-60
Cements	7-30
Gasohol	10
Glass cleaners	10
Hair tonics	25-65
Paint stripper	25
Liquid hand-washing detergent	1-10

Medicinal (Oral)	
Mouthwashes	14-27
Cough/cold preparations	3-25
Vitameatavegamin	23
Homeopathic/herbal medicine	Varies

Ethyl Alcohol *(Continued)*

By inhibiting gastric alcohol dehydrogenase, aspirin, ranitidine, cimetidine, and nizatidine can increase the bioavailability and peak concentrations of ethyl alcohol; aspirin (1 g) has been shown to increase bioavailability of ethanol (0.3 g/kg) in the fed state but not in the fasting state; ranitidine (150 mg twice daily) increased peak ethanol concentrations by 34% and cimetidine increased peak ethanol levels by 92% with similar ethanol ingestions (0.15-0.3 g/kg); nizatidine also increased peak ethanol levels after a 0.75 g/kg ethanol dose after a meal. While these interactions are of statistical significance, they are probably of little clinical significance in that most serum ethanol levels achieved were <40.9 mg/dL (8.89 mmol/L); famotidine had no effect on absorption of ethanol. Ethyl alcohol can potentiate the severity of benzene-induced hematological abnormalities. Concurrent intake of ethanol and aspirin can reduce the peak aspirin concentration by 25%.

Dosage Forms
Injection, absolute: 2 mL
Liquid, topical, denatured: 70% (473 mL)
Solution, inhalation: 20%, 40%

Additional Information Energy content of ethanol: 7.1 kcal (29.7 kg) per g

Highest serum level recorded with full recovery: 1510 mg/dL (327.8 mmol/L) in an adult; in an adolescent it is 757 mg/dL; children who ingest a significant amount of alcohol should be monitored hourly for up to 6 hours; elevated serum lactate and lactate dehydrogenase levels may interfere with enzymatic ethanol assays; intravenous dexamethasone (2 mg I.V.) can impair ethyl alcohols ability to stimulate sympathetic nerve discharge and thus suppress alcohol-induced high blood pressure in the acute state

Moderate drinking is defined as not more than 2 drinks (28 g) of ethanol daily in men and only 1 drink (14 g) daily in women. Corpus callosum atrophy can occur in the brain with chronic ethyl alcohol intake; daily ingestion of 40-60 g of ethanol in men and 20 g of ethanol in women can significantly increase the incidence of cirrhosis in individuals who are well nourished.

While the reduced risk for coronary heart disease by ethanol appears to be related to elevation of high density lipoprotein (HDL cholesterol) levels, the maximal benefit appears to be at the amount of one drink daily. Hepatic toxicity can occur at lower ethanol amounts in women as opposed to men. Serum selenium levels are significantly lower (24 ng/mL versus 39 ng/mL in control patients) in chronic alcohol abuse patients.

Odor threshold: 10 ppm
TLV-TWA: 1000 ppm

Specific References
Holloway FA, "Low-Dose Alcohol Effects on Human Behavior and Performance," *Alcohol, Drugs and Driving*, 1995, 11(1):39-56.

Ethyl Alcohol, Blood *see* Alcohol, Serum *on page 33*

Ethyl Alcohol, Urine *see* Alcohol, Semiquantitative, Urine *on page 33*

Ethyl Aldehyde *see* Acetaldehyde *on page 19*

Ethyl Aminobenzoate *see* Benzocaine *on page 70*

Ethylbenzene

Synonyms EB; Ethylbenzol; Phenylethane

UN Number 1175

Impairment Potential Yes

Use Solvent which is found in asphalt, fuels, and naphtha; used in the products of styrene and other organic chemicals; used in paint thinners and as a degreaser

Mechanism of Toxic Action Aromatic hydrocarbon with mucosal irritant effects; central nervous system depression can occur at very high concentrations

Toxicodynamics/kinetics
Absorption: Rapid from inhalation (57%) and skin (rate of 20-33 mg/cm²/hour)
Metabolism: Hepatic to mandelic acid and phenylglyoxylated acid
Elimination: Renal

Signs and Symptoms of Acute Intoxication Dizziness, gaze nystagmus, ataxia, slurred speech, unsteady gait, lethargy, depressed reflexes, psychomotor retardation, tremor, generalized muscle weakness, blurred vision or diplopia, stupor, coma, euphoria

When to Transport to Hospital Transport any patient with cough, dizziness, or skin irritation

Adverse Reactions
Central nervous system: Dizziness at levels >2000 ppm
Dermatologic: Dermal irritant at levels of 200 ppm
Hematologic: Anemia (long-term exposure)
Hepatic: Hepatotoxicity
Ocular: Eye irritation with lacrimation at levels >1000 ppm
Respiratory: Upper respiratory tract irritation at levels >2000 ppm

Reference Range Ethylbenzene blood levels of 61 µg/L associated with anemia; at 100 ppm exposure of ethylbenzene, it has been estimated that urinary phenylglyoxylic acid and mandelic acid concentrations would be 95 mg/L and 395 mg/L respectively

Additional Information Not associated with cancer; carbon monoxide and ethanol inhibit metabolism of ethylbenzene in rodents; does not bioaccumulate
IDLH: 2000 ppm; TLV-PEL: 100 ppm
BEI (urinary mandelic acid) at the end of shift at the end of work week: 2 g/L or 1.5 g/g creatinine
Frequently found in ground water at hazardous waste sites (average concentration: 0.65 ppm)
Minimal uptake of fluorescein on ocular exposure

Specific References
U.S. Department of Health and Human Services, "Toxicological Profile for Ethylbenzene TP-90/15," Agency for Toxic Substances and Diseases Registry, December 1990.

Ethylbenzol see Ethylbenzene on previous page
Ethylene Alcohol see Ethylene Glycol on this page
Ethylenediamine see Theophylline Salts on page 571
Ethylene Diglycol see Diethylene Glycol on page 195
Ethylene Dihydrate see Ethylene Glycol on this page

Ethylene Glycol
Synonyms Ethylene Alcohol; Ethylene Dihydrate; Glycol Alcohol; Monoethylene Glycol
Impairment Potential Yes
Use Automotive radiator antifreeze and coolants, solvent
Mechanism of Toxic Action Metabolized into glycolic acid and oxalate via the alcohol dehydrogenase pathway (ADH), thus producing profound metabolic acidosis
Toxicodynamics/kinetics
Specific gravity: 1.11 g/mL
Absorption:
Oral, percutaneous: Rapid
Inhalation: Not well absorbed
(Continued)

Ethylene Glycol *(Continued)*

Metabolism: Liver with principle toxic metabolites including glycolic acid (96%) and oxalic acid (2.3%); see figure

Metabolic Pathway for Oxidation of Ethylene Glycol*

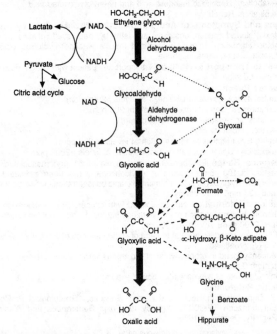

Adapted from the U.S. Department of Health and Human Services, "Technical Report for Ethylene Glycol/Propylene Glycol," Agency for Toxic Substances and Disease Registry, May 1993.

Half-life, elimination:
    No ethanol therapy: 3 hours
    During ethanol therapy: 17 hours
    During ethanol therapy and hemodialysis: 2^1/2 hours
    During 4-methylpyrazole therapy: 13 hours
Elimination: Renal clearance 3.2 mL/kg/minute

Signs and Symptoms of Acute Intoxication Similar to methanol ingestion, ethylene glycol can initially result in inebriation; the toxicity of ethylene glycol can be divided into three stages:

Stage I (30 minutes to 12 hours after ingestion): Inebriation, ataxia, and metabolic acidosis with resulting respiratory compensation (Kussmaul's breathing), seizures, hypocalcemia, cranial nerve palsies, calcium oxaluria (4-8 hours after ingestion), and myoclonus; coma can occur, and death is usually due to cerebral edema during this stage

Stage II (12-36 hours after ingestion): Respiratory status deteriorates, with tachypnea, tachycardia, cyanosis, dyspnea, and pulmonary edema with cardiomegaly developing; death is usually due to cardiovascular causes or bronchopneumonia during this stage

Stage III (36-72 hours after ingestion): Renal failure dominates this phase, with acute tubular necrosis, hematuria, oliguria, albuminuria, or anuria occurring; noncardiogenic pulmonary edema may occur in this stage

When to Transport to Hospital Transport any ingestion or significant inhalation

Overdosage/Treatment

Decontamination: Avoid emesis with ipecac; activated charcoal is not effective at a 5:1 ratio (charcoal:toxin); higher doses of activated charcoal may be needed, but this is of unproven benefit.

Dermal: Wash with soap and water

Ocular: Irrigate copiously with saline

Supportive therapy: Ethanol therapy should be initiated at ethylene glycol level 20 mg/dL, severe acidosis or electrolyte abnormality present, or renal failure; treat acidosis with I.V. sodium bicarbonate; administer thiamine and pyridoxine, 100 mg once a day for 2 days for both drugs. Calcium chloride or calcium gluconate can be given for hypocalcemia. 4-Methylpyrazole (4-MP) use (at a dose of 20 mg/kg/day) is investigational. 4-MP is a specific antagonist of alcohol dehydrogenase.

Enhancement of elimination: Hemodialysis should be considered if ethylene glycol level is >20 mg/dL or if metabolitic acidosis is present; continuous arteriovenous or veno-venous hemodiafiltration may be useful

Adverse Reactions

Cardiovascular: Myocarditis, Q-T prolongation, sinus tachycardia

Central nervous system: Cranial nerve palsies, ataxia, anisocoria, slurred speech, seizures, coma, headache, cranial nerve dysfunction (6th nerve)

Endocrine & metabolic: Metabolic acidosis, hypocalcemia, osmolal gap

Gastrointestinal: Feces discoloration (black)

Hematologic: Porphyria

Neuromuscular & skeletal: Hyperreflexia, rhabdomyolysis

Ocular: Mydriasis, diplopia, optic neuropathy, gaze nystagmus

Renal: Renal tubular damage progressing to renal insufficiency, myoglobinuria

Respiratory: Hyperventilation, respiratory irritation/cough on inhalation

Miscellaneous: Breast cancer

Reference Range

Toxic: Plasma level of 20 mg/dL

Fatal: Levels >85 mg/dL

Additional Information Sweet tasting liquid

Atmospheric half-life: 24-50 hours

Water half-life: 3-5 days

Lethal dose: 100 mL (1.5 mL/kg)

Contribution of a serum concentration level of 100 mg/dL to elevation of osmolar gap: 16

Existence of propionic acid through inborn errors of metabolism can give a false-positive ethylene glycol level

Specific References

Pincus KT, Shinn BW, and Frock JT, "Ethylene Glycol Poisoning Revisited," *Hosp Pharm*, 1996, 31(5):536-41.

Ethylene Glycol Monobutyl Ether *see* 2-Butoxyethanol *on page 96*

Ethylene Monochloride *see* Vinyl Chloride *on page 613*

Ethyl Methyl Ketone *see* Methyl Ethyl Ketone *on page 396*

Etodolac (ee toe DOE lak)

U.S. Brand Names Lodine®

Therapeutic Category Analgesic, Non-narcotic; Nonsteroidal Anti-Inflammatory Agent (NSAID)

Use Acute and long-term use in the management of signs and symptoms of osteoarthritis and management of pain; rheumatoid arthritis

Usual Dosage Single dose of 76-100 mg is comparable to the analgesic effect of aspirin 650 mg; in patients ≥65 years, no substantial differences in the pharmacokinetics or side-effects profile were seen compared with the general population

Adults: Oral:

Acute pain: 200-400 mg every 6-8 hours, as needed, not to exceed total daily doses of 1200 mg; for patients weighing <60 kg, total daily dose should not exceed 20 mg/kg/day

Osteoarthritis: Initial: 800-1200 mg/day given in divided doses: 400 mg 2 or 3 times/day; 300 mg 2, 3 or 4 times/day; 200 mg 3 or 4 times/day; total daily dose should not exceed 1200 mg; for patients weighing <60 kg, total daily dose should not exceed 20 mg/kg/day

Mechanism of Action Inhibits prostaglandin synthesis by decreasing the activity of the enzyme, cyclo-oxygenase, which results in decreased formation of prostaglandin precursors

Pharmacodynamics/kinetics

Absorption: Oral: Well absorbed

Half-life: 7 hours

Time to peak serum concentration: Within 1 hour

Signs and Symptoms of Acute Intoxication Nausea, flatulence, wheezing, vomiting, dysuria, hematuria, cognitive dysfunction, conjunctivitis, gastrointestinal bleeding, gastritis; nephrotic syndrome, ototoxicity, tinnitus, drowsiness; severe poisoning can manifest with coma, seizures, renal failure and or hepatic failure, hypotension, respiratory depression, leukocytes

When to Transport to Hospital Transport any pediatric exposure or any symptomatic patient

Warnings/Precautions Risk of gastrointestinal ulceration, bleeding, and perforation with therapy

Adverse Reactions

>10%:

Central nervous system: Dizziness

Dermatologic: Rash

Gastrointestinal: Abdominal cramps, heartburn, indigestion, nausea

1% to 10%:

Central nervous system: Headache, nervousness

Dermatologic: Itching

Endocrine & metabolic: Fluid retention

Gastrointestinal: Vomiting

Otic: Tinnitus

Reference Range After a 200 mg oral dose, peak plasma levels are ~12-16 mg/L; after a 400 mg oral dose, peak plasma level is ~21 mg/L

Drug Interactions Aspirin decreases serum concentrations probably by protein-binding displacement; there is an increased bleeding potential with concomitant warfarin therapy; may increase lithium and methotrexate concentrations by decreasing renal clearance; may decrease diuretic and hypotensive effects of thiazides, loop diuretics, ACE inhibitors, and beta-blockers; may increase nephrotoxicity of cyclosporine

Dosage Forms

Capsule: 200 mg, 300 mg

Tablet: 500 mg

Specific References
   Boldy DA, Hale KA, and Vale JA, "Etodolac Overdose," *Hum Toxicol*, 1988, 7(2):203-4.

EtOH *see Alcohol, Serum on page 33*

EtOH *see Ethyl Alcohol on page 233*

Etrafon® *see Amitriptyline and Perphenazine on page 42*

Eucalyptamint® *see Eucalyptus Oil on this page*

Eucalyptus Oil
   Scientific Name *Eucalyptus globulus*
   U.S. Brand Names Bosisto's® Eucalyptus Spray; Eucalyptamint®; Gelodurat®
   Use A volatile oil often used as a liniment; taken orally for treatment of cough or catarrh
   Usual Dosage
      Therapeutic: Oral: ~0.5 mL/dose
      Liniments: Concentrations as high as 25% eucalyptus oil
      Fatal dose: ~3.5 mL
   Mechanism of Action Contains as much as 70% of the substance citronellal which is an irritant. Obtained from the leaves and terminal branches of the Eucalyptus (Myrtaceae) dives or Eucalyptus radiata
   Pharmacodynamics/kinetics Elimination: Lungs/GI tract
   Signs and Symptoms of Acute Intoxication Miosis, tachycardia, apnea, coma, seizures, hyporeflexia, pulmonary edema, cyanosis, slurred speech, respiratory depression
   When to Transport to Hospital Transport any symptomatic patient or ingestion over 1 mL
   Adverse Reactions
      Central nervous system: Fever, dizziness, ataxia
      Dermatologic: Contact dermatitis (allergic and irritant)
      Gastrointestinal: Nausea, vomiting, diarrhea
      Respiratory: Bronchospasm, cough, tachypnea, lipoid pneumonia
   Additional Information Specific gravity: 0.9; camphor-like odor; after ingestion, the patient's breath may continue to elicit this odor for as long as 2 weeks; oil solution can cause a lipoid pneumonia
   Specific References
      Spoerke DG, Vandenberg SA, Smolinske SC, et al, "Eucalyptus Oil: 14 Cases of Exposure," *Vet Hum Toxicol*, 1989, 31(2):166-8.

Eudal-SR® *see Guaifenesin and Pseudoephedrine on page 273*

Eukodal® *see Oxycodone on page 452*

Euphypnos® *see Temazepam on page 559*

Euradal® *see Bisoprolol on page 78*

Eurodin® *see Estazolam on page 228*

European Bittersweet *see Deadly Nightshade on page 178*

European Hops *see Hops on page 289*

Eventin® *see Propylhexedrine on page 513*

Everone® Injection *see Testosterone on page 564*

E-Vista® *see Hydroxyzine on page 303*

Excedrin®, Extra Strength [OTC] *see Acetaminophen, Aspirin, and Caffeine on page 23*

Excedrin® IB [OTC] *see Ibuprofen on page 308*

Excedrin® P.M. [OTC] *see Acetaminophen and Diphenhydramine on page 22*

Exhaust Gas *see Carbon Monoxide on page 109*

EXP-126 *see Rimantadine on page 526*

Extendryl® SR see Chlorpheniramine, Phenylephrine, and Methscopolamine on page 136

Extra Action Cough Syrup [OTC] see Guaifenesin and Dextromethorphan on page 271

Extra Strength Adprin-B® [OTC] see Aspirin on page 56

Extra Strength Bayer® Enteric 500 Aspirin [OTC] see Aspirin on page 56

Extra Strength Bayer® Plus [OTC] see Aspirin on page 56

Eye Bright see Indian Tobacco on page 312

Eye-Zine® [OTC] see Tetrahydrozoline on page 569

Ezide® see Hydrochlorothiazide on page 291

Factitious Air see Nitrous Oxide on page 439

Famodil® see Famotidine on this page

Famotidine (fa MOE ti deen)

U.S. Brand Names Famodil®; Gaster®; Pepcid®; Pepcidine®; Pepdul®; Pepdulmite®

Canadian Brand Names Apo-Famotidine®; Novo-Famotidine®; Nu-Famotidine®

Therapeutic Category Histamine H_2 Antagonist

Use Therapy and treatment of duodenal ulcer, gastric ulcer, control gastric pH in critically ill patients, symptomatic relief in gastritis, gastroesophageal reflux, active benign ulcer, and pathological hypersecretory conditions; decrease incidence of gastric or duodenal ulcer due to NSAID therapy

Usual Dosage
Children: Oral, I.V.: Doses of 1-2 mg/kg/day have been used; maximum dose: 40 mg
Adults: Oral:
Duodenal ulcer, gastric ulcer: 40 mg/day at bedtime for 4-8 weeks
Hypersecretory conditions: Initial: 20 mg every 6 hours, may increase up to 160 mg every 6 hours
GERD: 20 mg twice daily for 6 weeks
Prophylaxis of NSAID-induced ulcers: 40 mg 2 times/day

Mechanism of Action Competitive inhibition of histamine at H_2-receptors of the gastric parietal cells, which inhibits gastric acid secretion

Pharmacodynamics/kinetics
Onset of action: Gastrointestinal effects can be observed within 60 minutes following oral administration
Duration: 10-12 hours
Metabolism: ~30% to 35% by the liver
Bioavailability: Oral: 40% to 50%
Half-life: 2.5-3.5 hours (increases with renal impairment; oliguric half-life: 20 hours)
Time to peak serum concentration: 1-3 hours

Signs and Symptoms of Acute Intoxication Hypotension, tachycardia, neutropenia, depression, dry skin, insomnia, impotence, abdominal pain, seizures, A-V block, vomiting, CNS depression, confusion

When to Transport to Hospital Transport any symptomatic patient or any ingestion over 5 mg/kg

Warnings/Precautions Reduce dosage in decreased renal function

Adverse Reactions
1% to 10%:
Central nervous system: Dizziness, headache
Gastrointestinal: Constipation, diarrhea

Reference Range Serum level of 13 ng/mL will produce 50% inhibition of gastric acid secretion

Drug Interactions Chlorpromazine absorption decreases; famotidine has no effect on absorption of ethanol

Dosage Forms
Infusion, premixed in NS: 20 mg (50 mL)
Injection: 10 mg/mL (2 mL, 4 mL)
Powder for oral suspension (cherry-banana-mint flavor): 40 mg/5 mL (50 mL)
Tablet, film coated: 20 mg, 40 mg
Pepcid® AC Acid Controller: 10 mg

Additional Information The expensive parenteral route should only be used when a patient is unable to take oral medication; less antiandrogenic than cimetidine; over-the-counter preparation marketed as Pepcid® AC

Specific References
Howden CW and Tytgat GN, "The Tolerability and Safety Profile of Famotidine," *Clin Ther*, 1996, 18(1):36-54.

Fannoform see Formaldehyde on page 259
Fargan see Promethazine on page 505
Fasciolin® see Carbon Tetrachloride on page 113
Fastin® see Phentermine on page 478
Fedahist® Expectorant [OTC] see Guaifenesin and Pseudoephedrine on page 273
Fedahist® Expectorant Pediatric [OTC] see Guaifenesin and Pseudoephedrine on page 273
Fedahist® Tablet [OTC] see Chlorpheniramine and Pseudoephedrine on page 134
Fedrine® see Ephedrine on page 220
Feldene® see Piroxicam on page 489
Felonwort see Deadly Nightshade on page 178
Femcet® see Butalbital Compound on page 93
Femiron® see Iron on page 318

Femoxetine (fe MOX e teen)

Therapeutic Category Antidepressant
Use Investigational: Antidepressant, narcolepsy, tension headache
Usual Dosage
Depression: 300-600 mg in 3 divided doses; start at the lower dose
Narcolepsy: 300 mg twice daily
Tension headache: 100 mg 4 times/day
Mechanism of Action Selectively inhibits reuptake of serotonin
Pharmacodynamics/kinetics
Metabolism: Hepatic to inactive metabolites
Bioavailability: 5% to 10%
Half-life: ~20 hours
Elimination: Primarily renal
When to Transport to Hospital Transport any patient with palpitations or cardiopulmonary symptoms or ingestion over 1 g
Warnings/Precautions Use with caution in patients with previous hypersensitivity to this class of agents, patients with epilepsy, and in patients with hepatic disorders
Adverse Reactions
Cardiovascular: Palpitations
Central nervous system: Nervousness, anxiety, insomnia, dizziness, headache
Dermatologic: Urticaria
Gastrointestinal: Nausea, dry mouth, constipation
Genitourinary: Dysuria
Hepatic: Hepatitis
(Continued)

Femoxetine (Continued)

Neuromuscular & skeletal: Tremor
Respiratory: Nasal congestion
Miscellaneous: Diaphoresis

Reference Range Peak serum levels following a 500-600 mg dose: 120 ng/mL

Drug Interactions Concomitant administration with cimetidine can result in increased femoxetine levels

Additional Information Does not appear to be as effective as propranolol for migraine prophylaxis

Specific References

Aunsholt NA and Agnholt J, "Toxic Hepatitis Due to Femoxetine," *Acta Pharmacol Toxicol*, 1986, 58(4):253-4.

Fenamon® see Nifedipine on page 433

Fenesin™ see Guaifenesin on page 269

Fenesin DM® see Guaifenesin and Dextromethorphan on page 271

Fenfluramine (fen FLURE a meen)

Related Information

Dexfenfluramine on page 185

U.S. Brand Names Dima-Fen®; Pesos®; Ponderax®; Pondimin®; Ponflural®

Therapeutic Category Adrenergic Agonist Agent; Anorexiant

Use Anorectic agent; off the U.S. market as of September 15, 1997

Usual Dosage

Children: 1.5 mg/kg/day
Adults: 20 mg 3 times/day to a maximum of 40 mg 3 times/day
Minimum: <200 mg to 28.7 mg/kg
Maximum: <200 mg to 1600 mg
Symptoms usually at 4.6-6.2 mg/kg

Pharmacodynamics/kinetics

Duration of action: 4-6 hours
Absorption: Rapid in gastrointestinal tract
Metabolism: Mainly in liver to N-triclyoromethylhippuric acid (66% to 92%); norfenfluramine (2% to 22%)
Half-life: 11 hours at a urinary pH of 5; 20 hours at a lower urinary pH
Time to peak: Within 1-2 hours

Signs and Symptoms of Acute Intoxication Rapid onset of symptoms with relative short time between ingestion and death with a lack of response to normal supportive measures; tachycardia, mydriasis, seizures, occur within 30 minutes to 3½ hours postingestion; severe respiratory and/or cardiovascular complications occur within the first 4 hours; symptoms may last 2-3 days; arrhythmias reported are tachycardia, extrasystoles, asystole, and fibrillation (ventricular); facial flushing, sweating, night terrors, shivering, mania and hyperventilation have been reported; neurologic changes include tremors, seizures, ataxia, dementia, depression, diplopia, agitation, hypertension, impotence, hyperthermia, confusion, hyperreflexia, clonus, coma, hallucination, and psychosis; hallucinations (visual) and porphyrinogenic; insomnia

When to Transport to Hospital Transport any pediatric (<6 years of age) patient with ingestion over 10 mg/kg or any symptomatic patient

Overdosage/Treatment

Decontamination: **Do not** induce emesis; lavage within 2 hours of ingestion/ activated charcoal

Supportive therapy: Treatment of symptoms; seizures can be treated with benzodiazepines; seizures can occur in ingestions >5 mg/kg; treat hypotension with intravenous crystalloid solutions; vasopressors can be used for refractory cases; propranolol (1 mg/dose in adults or 0.01-0.1 mg/kg/dose in children over 10 minutes) or esmolol can be used to treat tachycardia; lidocaine can be used to treat ventricular arrhythmia; hyperpyrexia can be treated with external (passive) cooling

Enhancement of elimination: Dialysis may help if renal function is impaired

Adverse Reactions

>10%:

Cardiovascular: Hypertension

Central nervous system: Euphoria, nervousness, insomnia

1% to 10%:

Central nervous system: Confusion, mental depression, restlessness

Endocrine & metabolic: Changes in libido

Gastrointestinal: Nausea, vomiting, constipation

Hematologic: Blood dyscrasia

Neuromuscular & skeletal: Tremor

Ocular: Blurred vision

Test Interactions Can give a positive urinary immunoassay result for amphetamines but will not confirm by gas chromatography/mass spectrometry

Reference Range Therapeutic plasma fenfluramine levels: 0.05-0.15 µg/mL; fatalities can occur with postmortem blood levels >6.5 µg/mL

Lethal dose: 2 g

Drug Interactions General anesthesia with halothane may have produced a fatal cardiac arrest in a patient taking fenfluramine; fenfluramine may potentiate effects of insulin causing hypoglycemia; this may be delayed in onset; increased lethargy with amitriptyline or imipramine; combined fenfluramine and phentermine therapy may result in ischemic colitis, valvular heart disease or psychotic mania

Fenfluramine/phentermine potential interaction: As of July 8, 1997, there have been 33 cases reported to the FDA of unusual cardiac valvular morphology and regurgitation involving the mitral, aortic and/or tricuspid valves (usually multivalvular) with 6 of these patients requiring surgical intervention. About half of the women also had pulmonary hypertension. The mean age was 43.3 years (range: 35-72) with the mean duration of combination therapy of fenfluramine/phentermine of 10 months. Further cases should be reported to the FDA's MEDWATCH Program (800)FDA-1088.

Dosage Forms Tablet, as hydrochloride: 20 mg

Additional Information On September 12, 1997, the FDA announced new summary information concerning abnormal echocardiogram findings in asymptomatic patients seen in five centers. These patients had been treated with fenfluramine or dexfenfluramine for up to 24 months, most often in combination with phentermine. Abnormal echocardiogram findings were reported in 92 of 291 subjects evaluated, including 80 reports of aortic regurgitation (mild or greater) and 23 reports of mitral regurgitation (moderate or greater). Those requiring further information can call 1-800-892-2718. Questions about returning products can be directed to 1-800-666-7248.

Specific References

Raison CL and Klein HM, "Psychotic Mania Associated With Fenfluramine and Phentermine Use," *Am J Psychiatry*, 1997, 154(5):711.

Fenilcal® *see* Phenobarbital *on page 474*

Fenitoina *see* Phenytoin *on page 483*

Fenoprofen (fen oh PROE fen)

U.S. Brand Names Nalfon®

Therapeutic Category Analgesic, Non-narcotic; Nonsteroidal Anti-Inflammatory Agent (NSAID)

(Continued)

Fenoprofen *(Continued)*

Use Symptomatic treatment of acute and chronic rheumatoid arthritis and osteo-arthritis; relief of mild to moderate pain

Usual Dosage Adults: Oral:

Rheumatoid arthritis: 300-600 mg 3-4 times/day up to 3.2 g/day

Mild to moderate pain: 200 mg every 4-6 hours as needed

Mechanism of Action Inhibits prostaglandin synthesis by decreasing the activity of the enzyme, cyclo-oxygenase, which results in decreased formation of prostaglandin precursors; propionic acid derivative (like ibuprofen)

Pharmacodynamics/kinetics

Onset of action: Within 15-30 minutes

Duration: ~4-6 hours

Absorption: Rapid (to 80%) from upper gastrointestinal tract

Metabolism: Extensive in the liver

Half-life: 2.5-3 hours

Time to peak serum concentration: Within 2 hours

Signs and Symptoms of Acute Intoxication Nausea, vomiting, azotemia, wheezing, nephrotic syndrome, erythema multiforme, gastrointestinal bleeding, gastritis; cognitive dysfunction, coagulopathy, ototoxicity, tinnitus, drowsiness; severe poisoning can manifest with coma, seizures, renal failure and or hepatic failure, hypotension, respiratory depression, tachycardia, leukopenia, neutropenia, agranulocytosis, granulocytopenia, hypothermia

When to Transport to Hospital Transport any pediatric exposure, any symptomatic patient, or any ingestion over 1 g

Warnings/Precautions Use with caution in patients with congestive heart failure, hypertension, decreased renal or hepatic function, history of gastrointestinal disease, or those receiving anticoagulants

Adverse Reactions

>10%:

Central nervous system: Dizziness

Dermatologic: Rash

Gastrointestinal: Abdominal cramps, heartburn, indigestion, nausea

1% to 10%:

Central nervous system: Headache, nervousness

Dermatologic: Itching

Endocrine & metabolic: Fluid retention

Gastrointestinal: Vomiting

Otic: Tinnitus

Test Interactions Can yield false-positive for benzodiazepine and barbiturate assay

Reference Range Therapeutic: 20-65 µg/mL (SI: 82-268 µmol/L)

Drug Interactions Aspirin decreases serum concentrations probably by protein-binding displacement of fenoprofen; there is an increased bleeding potential with concomitant warfarin therapy; may increase lithium and methotrexate concentrations by decreasing renal clearance; may decrease diuretic and hypotensive effects of thiazides, loop diuretics, ACE inhibitors, and beta-blockers; may increase nephrotoxicity of cyclosporine

Dosage Forms

Fenoprofen calcium:

Capsule: 200 mg, 300 mg

Tablet: 600 mg

Additional Information Generally nontoxic ingestions

Specific References

Stotts JS, Fang ML, Dannaker CJ, et al, "Fenoprofen-Induced Toxic Epidermal Necrolysis," *J Am Acad Dermatol*, 1988, 18(4 Pt 1):755-7.

Fentanest® see Fentanyl *on this page*

Fentanyl (FEN ta nil)
Related Information
Controlled Substances - Uses and Effects *on page 741*
Droperidol and Fentanyl *on page 215*

Synonyms Phentanyl

U.S. Brand Names Duragesic™; Fentanest®; Fentanyl Oralet®; Leptanal®; Sublimaze®; Tanyl®

Therapeutic Category Analgesic, Narcotic; General Anesthetic

Abuse Potential Yes

Impairment Potential Yes

Use Sedation, relief of pain, preoperative medication, adjunct to general or regional anesthesia, management of chronic pain (transdermal product)

Usual Dosage Doses should be titrated to appropriate effects; wide range of doses, dependent upon desired degree of analgesia/anesthesia

Children 1-12 years:
  Sedation for minor procedures/analgesia:
    I.M., I.V.: 1-2 mcg/kg/dose; may repeat at 30- to 60-minute intervals. **Note:** Children 18-36 months of age may require 2-3 mcg/kg/dose
    Transmucosal: 5 mcg/kg, if child is not fearful, fearful children and some younger children may require doses of 5-15 mcg/kg (which also carries an increased risk of hypoventilation); drug effect begins within 10 minutes, with sedation beginning shortly thereafter
  Continuous sedation/analgesia: Initial I.V. bolus: 1-2 mcg/kg then 1 mcg/kg/hour; titrate upward; usual: 1-3 mcg/kg/hour
  Pain control: Transdermal: Not recommended
Children >12 years and Adults:
  Sedation for minor procedures/analgesia:
    I.M., I.V.: 0.5-1 mcg/kg/dose; higher doses are used for major procedures
    Transmucosal: 5 mcg/kg, suck on lozenge vigorously approximately 20-40 minutes before the start of procedure, drug effect begins within 10 minutes, with sedation beginning shortly thereafter
  Preoperative sedation, adjunct to regional anesthesia, postoperative pain: I.M., I.V.: 50-100 mcg/dose
  Adjunct to general anesthesia: I.M., I.V.: 2-50 mcg/kg
  General anesthesia without additional anesthetic agents: I.V. 50-100 mcg/kg with O_2 & skeletal muscle relaxant
  Pain control: Transdermal: Initial: 25 mcg/hour system; if currently receiving opiates, convert to fentanyl equivalent and administer equianalgesic

Equianalgesic Doses of Opioid Agonists

Drug	Equianalgesic Dose (mg)	
	I.M.	P.O.
Codeine	130	200
Hydromorphone	1.5	7.5
Levorphanol	2	4
Meperidine	75	—
Methadone	10	20
Morphine	10	60
Oxycodone	15	30
Oxymorphone	1	10 (PR)

From *N Engl J Med*, 1985, 313:84-95.

(Continued)

Fentanyl *(Continued)*

dosage titrated to minimize the adverse effects and provide analgesia. To convert patients from oral or parenteral opioids to Duragesic™, the previous 24-hour analgesic requirement should be calculated. This analgesic requirement should be converted to the equianalgesic oral morphine dose. See tables.

Corresponding Doses of Oral/Intramuscular Morphine and Duragesic™

Oral 24-Hour Morphine (mg/d)	I.M. 24-Hour Morphine (mg/d)	Duragesic™ Dose (mcg/h)
45-134	8-22	25
135-224	28-37	50
225-314	38-52	75
315-404	53-67	100
405-494	68-82	125
495-584	83-97	150
585-674	98-112	175
675-764	113-127	200
765-854	128-142	225
855-944	143-157	250
945-1034	158-172	275
1035-1124	173-187	300

Product information, Duragesic™— Janssen Pharmaceutica, January, 1991.

The dosage should not be titrated more frequently than every 3 days after the initial dose or every 6 days thereafter. The majority of patients are controlled on every 72-hour administration, however, a small number of patients require every 48-hour administration.

Elderly >65 years: Transmucosal: Dose should be reduced to 2.5-5 mcg/kg; elderly have been found to be twice as sensitive as younger patients to the effects of fentanyl

Adults: Lethal dose: I.V.: 1 mg

Mechanism of Action Binds with stereospecific receptors at many sites within the CNS, increases pain threshold, alters pain reception, inhibits ascending pain pathways

Pharmacodynamics/kinetics Respiratory depressant effect may last longer than analgesic effect

I.M.:
  Onset of analgesia: 7-15 minutes
  Duration: 1-2 hours
I.V.:
  Onset of analgesia: Almost immediate
  Duration: 0.5-1 hour
Transmucosal:
  Onset of effect: 5-15 minutes with a maximum reduction in activity/fear
  Peak analgesia: Within 20-30 minutes
  Duration: Related to blood level of the drug
Absorption: Transmucosal: Rapid, ~25% from the buccal mucosa; 75% swallowed with saliva and slowly absorbed from gastrointestinal tract
Metabolism: In the liver (N-dealkylation and hydroxylation); metabolites not active

Bioavailability: Transmucosal: ~50% (range: 36% to 71%)
Half-life: 2-4 hours
    Transmucosal: 6.6 hours (range: 5-15 hours)
Elimination: Excreted in urine primarily as metabolites and 10% as unchanged drug

Signs and Symptoms of Acute Intoxication Apnea, flatulence, hypertension, pseudotumor cerebri, depression, confusion, hypertonia, laryngospasm, exfoliative dermatitis, coma, dyspnea, chest pain, respiratory depression (especially with doses >200 mcg), hiccups, hypotension, seizures, miosis

When to Transport to Hospital Transport any exposure

Warnings/Precautions Fentanyl shares the toxic potentials of opiate agonists, and precautions of opiate agonist therapy should be observed; use with caution in patients with bradycardia; rapid I.V. infusion may result in skeletal muscle and chest wall rigidity → impaired ventilation → respiratory distress → apnea, bronchoconstriction, laryngospasm; inject slowly over 3-5 minutes; nondepolarizing skeletal muscle relaxant may be required; use transmucosal product with caution in patients with hepatic or renal disease, chronic obstructive pulmonary disease, patients with decreased respiratory reserve, and others with potentially compromised respiration; transmucosal product is not recommended for use in those who have received MAO inhibitors within 14 days; should be used with caution in patients with myasthenia gravis.

Adverse Reactions
>10%:
    Cardiovascular: Hypotension, bradycardia
    Central nervous system: CNS depression, drowsiness, sedation
    Gastrointestinal: Nausea, vomiting, constipation
    Respiratory: Respiratory depression
1% to 10%:
    Cardiovascular: Cardiac arrhythmias, orthostatic hypotension
    Central nervous system: Confusion, CNS depression
    Gastrointestinal: Biliary tract spasm
    Ocular: Miosis

Reference Range
Therapeutic: 2-200 µg/L
Fatal: Serum level of 17.7 µg/L has been correlated with fatality

Drug Interactions Increased toxicity with CNS depressants, cimetidine, thiopental, phenothiazine, tricyclic antidepressants, benzodiazepines; with midazolam, hypotension and respiratory depression have been noted. Decreased effect of epidural fentanyl when given with chloroprocaine.

Dosage Forms
Injection, as citrate: 0.05 mg/mL (2 mL, 5 mL, 10 mL, 20 mL, 50 mL)
Lozenge, oral transmucosal (raspberry flavored): 200 mcg, 300 mcg, 400 mcg
Transdermal system: 25 mcg/hour [10 cm^2]; 50 mcg/hour [20 cm^2]; 75 mcg/hour [30 cm^2]; 100 mcg/hour [40 cm^2] (all available in 5s)

Specific References
Berens AI, Voets AJ, and Demedts P, "Illicit Fentanyl in Europe," *Lancet*, 1996, 347(9011):1334-5.

Fentanyl and Droperidol *see* Droperidol and Fentanyl *on page 215*
Fentanyl Oralet® *see* Fentanyl *on page 247*
Fentazin® *see* Perphenazine *on page 467*
Fenytoin® *see* Phenytoin *on page 483*
Feosol® *see* Iron *on page 318*
Feostat® *see* Iron *on page 318*
Feratab® *see* Iron *on page 318*
Fergon® *see* Iron *on page 318*

Fer-In-Sol® *see* Iron *on page 318*
Fer-Iron® *see* Iron *on page 318*
Ferndex® *see* Dextroamphetamine *on page 186*
Fero-Gradumet® *see* Iron *on page 318*
Ferospace® *see* Iron *on page 318*
Ferralet® *see* Iron *on page 318*
Ferralyn® Lanacaps® *see* Iron *on page 318*
Ferra-TD® *see* Iron *on page 318*
Ferro-Sequels® *see* Iron *on page 318*
Feverall™ [OTC] *see* Acetaminophen *on page 20*
Feverall™ Sprinkle Caps [OTC] *see* Acetaminophen *on page 20*
"Fiddle Back" Spider *see* Brown Recluse Spider *on page 87*
Fiorgen PF® *see* Butalbital Compound *on page 93*
Fioricet® *see* Butalbital Compound *on page 93*
Fiorinal® *see* Butalbital Compound *on page 93*
Fiorinal® With Codeine *see* Butalbital Compound and Codeine *on page 95*
Fire Damp *see* Methane *on page 385*
Flavorcee® [OTC] *see* Ascorbic Acid *on page 53*
Fleet® Flavored Castor Oil [OTC] *see* Castor Oil *on page 118*
Flexartal® *see* Carisoprodol *on page 114*
Flexeril® *see* Cyclobenzaprine *on page 173*
Flexiban® *see* Cyclobenzaprine *on page 173*
Flue Gas *see* Carbon Monoxide *on page 109*
Flukoids® *see* Carbon Tetrachloride *on page 113*
Flumadine® *see* Rimantadine *on page 526*

Flunitrazepam (floo nye TRAZ e pam)
Related Information
Clonazepam *on page 153*
Nitrazepam *on page 435*
Synonyms RO5-4200
U.S. Brand Names Darkene®; Hypnoderm®; Hypnor®; Narcozep®; Noriel®; Rohipnol®; Rohypnol®; Roipnol®; Valsera®
Therapeutic Category Benzodiazepine
Abuse Potential Yes
Impairment Potential Yes
Use Not marketed in United States, but is encountered in the U.S. as a drug of abuse; used for insomnia and sedation (short-term therapy) and anesthesia induction or supplementation in Europe
Usual Dosage
Anesthesia induction: I.V.: 0.015-0.03 mg/kg slowly over 30-60 seconds
Premedication for anesthesia: I.M.: 0.015-0.03 mg/kg slowly over 30-60 seconds
Anesthesia maintenance: I.V.: 0.2-0.5 mg (0.005-0.01 mg/kg) 2-3 hours after anesthesia induction
Insomnia: Oral: 0.5-2 mg nightly; in elderly, 0.5 mg dose should be initiated
Mechanism of Action Intermediate to long-acting benzodiazepine, this agent facilitates the gamma-aminobutyric acid-mediated neuroreceptors
Pharmacodynamics/kinetics
Onset: 20 minutes
Peak sedation: 1-2 hours
Duration of sedation: 8-12 hours
Absorption: Food can reduce absorption by 50%
Metabolism: Hepatic to 7-aminoflunitrazepam and other metabolites

Bioavailability: 80% to 90%
Half-life: 19-22 hours
Elimination: Renal

Signs and Symptoms of Acute Intoxication Hypotension, apnea, coma, ataxia, slurred speech, unsteady gait, gaze nystagmus, impairment in attention or memory, stupor, hypothermia

When to Transport to Hospital Transport any suspected exposure

Warnings/Precautions Use with caution in patients with porphyria, myasthenia gravis, cardiovascular disease, or hepatic/renal insufficiency; reduce dosage in elderly; dependence may occur

Adverse Reactions
Cardiovascular: Tachycardia, myocardial depression, hypotension, shock, congestive heart failure, sinus tachycardia
Central nervous system: Lethargy, dizziness, ataxia, headache, night terrors, amnesia (anterograde), cognitive dysfunction
Gastrointestinal: Nausea, diarrhea
Hematologic: Porphyria
Neuromuscular & skeletal: Tremor
Respiratory: Cough, apnea
Miscellaneous: Hiccups

Reference Range Peak plasma levels after a 2 mg oral dose: 10-15 ng/mL; may be detectable in urine for 3 days postingestion

Drug Interactions Enhances sedative effects of ethanol and general anesthesias; with succinylcholine, increased intraovular pressure can occur; theophylline antagonizes sedative effects

Dosage Forms
Injection: 2 mg/mL
Tablet: 0.5 mg, 1 mg, 2 mg

Additional Information About 10 times as potent as diazepam; insoluble in water; a growing drug of abuse in Europe and in the U.S. due to its euphoric producing qualities and low street price; usually several tablets are required for a euphoric effect; oral dose of 28 mg associated with fatality; psychomotor effects may last for 12 hours postdose; often abused in combination with heroin, ethanol, cocaine, or methamphetamine; not detectable on urine assays by EMIT for most benzodiazepine tests. Hoffman-LaRoche can assist in analyzing urine specimens (1-800-608-6540) with a turnaround time of 1 week. General phone number for information (1-800-720-1076).

Specific References
Anglin D, Spears KL, and Hutson HR, "Flunitrazepam and Its Involvement in Date or Acquaintance Rape," *Acad Emerg Med*, 1997, 4(4):323-6.

Fluohydric Acid see Hydrogen Fluoride *on page 300*

Fluopromazine see Triflupromazine *on page 597*

Fluoride (FLOR ide)

Synonyms Acidulated Phosphate Fluoride; Disodium Difluoride; Sodium Fluoride; Sodium Hydrofluoride; Stannous Fluoride

UN Number 1690

U.S. Brand Names ACT® [OTC]; Fluorigard® [OTC]; Fluorinse®; Fluoritab®; Flura®; Flura-Drops®; Flura-Loz®; Gel Kam®; Gel-Tin® [OTC]; Karidium®; Karigel®; Karigel®-N; Listermint® With Fluoride [OTC]; Luride®; Luride® Lozi-Tab®; Luride®-SF Lozi-Tab®; Minute-Gel®; Pediaflor®; Pharmaflur®; Phos-Flur®; Point-Two®; Prevident®; Stop® [OTC]

Therapeutic Category Mineral, Oral

Use Prevention of dental caries

Usual Dosage Dental rinse or gel: Oral:
(Continued)

251

Fluoride *(Continued)*

Children 6-12 years: 5-10 mL rinse or apply to teeth and spit daily after brushing

Adults: 10 mL rinse or apply to teeth and spit daily after brushing

Mechanism of Action Derived from hydrofluoric acid, reduces acid production by dental bacteria; increases tooth resistance to acid dissolution

Pharmacodynamics/kinetics

Absorption: Absorbed in gastrointestinal tract, lungs, and skin; calcium, iron, or magnesium may delay absorption

Half-life: 2-9 hours

Signs and Symptoms of Acute Intoxication Gastrointestinal hemorrhage, delirium, apnea, slurred speech, tremors, tetany, seizures, abdominal pain, hematuria, osteomalacia, hypothyroidism, hypotension, hypocalcemia, hypomagnesemia, hyperkalemia, fibrillation (ventricular), esophageal stricture, respiratory paralysis, mydriasis, urine discoloration (milky), nausea, vomiting, epigastric pain, diarrhea

When to Transport to Hospital Transport any pediatric (<6 years of age) ingestion over 8 mg/kg or any symptomatic patient

Warnings/Precautions Prolonged ingestion with excessive doses may result in dental fluorosis and osseous changes; do **not** exceed recommended dosage; some products contain tartrazine

Adverse Reactions <1%:

Dermatologic: Rash

Gastrointestinal: Nausea, vomiting, products containing stannous fluoride may stain the teeth

Reference Range Normal serum level of fluoride: 1.9-7.6 µg/dL (SI: 1-4 µmol/L); toxic urine fluoride level is >10 mg/L

Drug Interactions Decreased effect/absorption with magnesium-, calcium-, and aluminum-containing products

Dosage Forms Fluoride ion content listed in brackets

Drops, oral, as sodium:

Fluoritab®, Flura-Drops®: 0.55 mg/drop [0.25 mg/drop] (22.8 mL, 24 mL)

Karidium®, Luride®: 0.275 mg/drop [0.125 mg/drop] (30 mL, 60 mL)

Pediaflor®: 1.1 mg/mL [0.5 mg/mL] (50 mL)

Gel, topical:

Acidulated phosphate fluoride (Minute-Gel®): 1.23% (480 mL)

Sodium fluoride (Karigel®, Karigel®-N, PreviDent®): 1.1% [0.5%] (24 g, 30 g, 60 g, 120 g, 130 g, 250 g)

Stannous fluoride (Gel Kam®, Gel-Tin®, Stop®): 0.4% [0.1%] (60 g, 65 g, 105 g, 120 g)

Lozenge, as sodium (Flura-Loz®) (raspberry flavor): 2.2 mg [1 mg]

Rinse, topical, as sodium:

ACT®, Fluorigard®: 0.05% [0.02%] (90 mL, 180 mL, 300 mL, 360 mL, 480 mL)

Fluorinse®, Point-Two®: 0.2% [0.09%] (240 mL, 480 mL, 3780 mL)

Listermint® with Fluoride: 0.02% [0.01%] (180 mL, 300 mL, 360 mL, 480 mL, 540 mL, 720 mL, 960 mL, 1740 mL)

Solution, oral, as sodium (Phos-Flur®): 0.44 mg/mL [0.2 mg/mL] (250 mL, 500 mL, 3780 mL)

Tablet, as sodium: Chewable:

Fluoritab®, Luride® Lozi-Tab®, Pharmaflur®: 1.1 mg [0.5 mg]

Fluoritab®, Karidium®, Luride® Lozi-Tab®, Luride®-SF Lozi-Tab®, Pharmaflur®: 2.2 mg [1 mg]

Flura®, Karidium®: 2.2 mg [1 mg]

Additional Information Odorless; not flammable; seafood can contain large amounts of fluoride (up to 28 mg/kg); tea can contain 0.5 mg/cup

PEL-TWA: 2.5 mg/m³
IDLH: 500 mg/m³
Total daily intake of fluoride: 2.1-2.4 mg (diet) and 2.8-5.9 mg (water)

In pediatrics, the therapeutic fluoride dosage is 0.05-0.07 mg/kg/day; fluorosis can develop at daily fluoride doses exceeding 0.1 mg/kg; fluoride supplementation should occur at age 6 months at a dose of 0.25 mg/day if their formulas or water contains <0.3 mg/L (0.3 ppm); this increases to daily supplementation of 0.5 mg at age 3 years and 1 mg at 6 years. Children >3 years of age require 0.25 mg/day of fluoride (0.5 mg/day at 6 years) if water fluoride ion level is 0.3-0.6 mg/L (0.3-0.6 ppm); fluoride levels in drinking water >0.6 mg/L (0.6 ppm) require no supplementation. Most fluoridated toothpastes contain ~1000 ppm of fluoride; thus, the daily dose of fluoride by brushing teeth is 0.134 mg from brushing once daily and 0.268 mg brushing twice daily. 53% of U.S. population drinks artificially fluoridated water at an optimal level of 1 mg/L (maximum allowable level 4 mg/L); carbonated beverages contain ~0.74 ppm of fluoride while tea contains ~2.6 ppm. Patients with skeletal fluorosis may exhibit lower serum testosterone levels

Specific References

McIvor ME, "Acute Fluoride Toxicity. Pathophysiology and Management," *Drug Saf*, 1990, 5(2):79-85.

Fluorigard® [OTC] *see* Fluoride *on page 251*

Fluorinated Hydrocarbons *see* Freon *on page 260*

Fluorinse® *see* Fluoride *on page 251*

Fluoritab® *see* Fluoride *on page 251*

Fluoroacetic Acid (Sodium Salt) *see* Sodium Monofluoroacetate *on page 542*

Fluoxetine (floo OKS e teen)

Synonyms Fontex; LY-110140

U.S. Brand Names Prozac®

Therapeutic Category Antidepressant

Use Treatment of major depression, premenstrual dysphoria

Usual Dosage Oral:

Children <18 years: Dose not established

Adults: 20 mg/day in the morning; may increase after several weeks by 20 mg/day increments; maximum: 80 mg/day; doses >20 mg should be divided into morning and noon doses
Note: Lower doses of 5 mg/day have been used for initial treatment
Premenstrual dysphoria: 20 mg/day

Mechanism of Action Inhibits CNS neuron serotonin uptake; minimal or no effect on reuptake of norepinephrine or dopamine; does not significantly bind to alpha-adrenergic, histamine or cholinergic receptors; may therefore be useful in patients at risk from sedation, hypotension and anticholinergic effects of tricyclic antidepressants

Pharmacodynamics/kinetics

Onset of action: 1-4 weeks

Peak effect: Antidepressant effects usually occur after more than 4 weeks; due to long half-life, resolution of adverse reactions after discontinuation may be slow

Absorption: Oral: Well absorbed

Metabolism: To norfluoxetine (active)

Half-life:

Fluoxetine: 2-3 days (range: 1-9 days)

Norfluoxetine: 7-9 days (range: 3-15 days)

Time to peak serum concentration: Within 4-8 hours

(Continued)

Fluoxetine *(Continued)*

Signs and Symptoms of Acute Intoxication Nausea, cystitis, hirsutism, tachycardia (ventricular), Q-T prolongation, insomnia, vasculitis, A-V block, myoclonus, eosinophilia, extrapyramidal reaction, cognitive dysfunction, light-headedness, leukocytosis, depression, delirium, hallucinations, hyponatremia, hypokalemia, hypoglycemia, spontaneous vomiting, gout, rhabdomyolysis, myoglobinuria, agitation, hypomania, mania, generalized seizures, drowsiness, bradycardia

When to Transport to Hospital Transport any pediatric exposure, any symptomatic patient, or any adult ingestion over 100 mg

Warnings/Precautions Avoid alcoholic beverages; due to limited experience, use with caution in patients with renal or hepatic impairment; seizure disorders; cardiac dysfunction; diabetes mellitus; use with caution in patients at high risk for suicide

Adverse Reactions Predominant adverse effects are CNS and GI

>10%:

Central nervous system: Headache, nervousness, insomnia, drowsiness

Gastrointestinal: Nausea, diarrhea, xerostomia

1% to 10%:

Central nervous system: Anxiety, dizziness, fatigue, sedation

Dermatologic: Rash, pruritus

Endocrine & metabolic: SIADH, hypoglycemia, hyponatremia (elderly or volume-depleted patients)

Gastrointestinal: Anorexia, dyspepsia, constipation

Neuromuscular & skeletal: Tremor

Miscellaneous: Diaphoresis (excessive)

Test Interactions Increases albumin in urine; fluoxetine can interfere with bupropion quantitation by HPLC analysis in plasma or serum

Reference Range Therapeutic:

Fluoxetine: 100-800 ng/mL (SI: 289-2314 nmol/L); serum level of 1956 ng/mL (norfluoxetine level of 416 ng/mL) associated with seizure

Norfluoxetine: 100-600 ng/mL (SI: 289-1735 nmol/L)

Drug Interactions With MAO inhibitors, fever, tremor, seizures, delirium, coma can occur; with tryptophan or selegiline may cause increased CNS and gastrointestinal toxic effects; fluoxetine may inhibit metabolism and increase effects of tricyclic antidepressants, trazodone, warfarin and possibly diazepam; may antagonize buspirone effects and may displace highly protein bound drugs; over 500 mg of fluoxetine combined with ethanol can lead to tachycardia, hypertension, and decrease in the level of consciousness; concomitant use of clarithromycin with fluoxetine can result in fluoxetine intoxication manifesting as delirium; seizures can result with concomitant clomipramine and fluoxetine therapy; myoclonic seizures can result with concomitant fluoxetine and clozapine therapy; increased cyclosporine serum levels can occur after coadministration with fluoxetine; prolonged Q-T interval can occur with concomitant terfenadine/fluoxetine therapy; anorexia may develop with concomitant fluoxetine and itraconazole therapy; galactorrhea with concomitant pimozide; inappropriate antidiuretic hormone secretion (SIADH) can occur with coadministration of paroxetine with fluoxetine; fluoxetine, paroxetine and sertraline increased serum concentrations of clozapine and its major metabolite, norclozapine; panic with concomitant amfebutamone; sympathetic hyperstimulation can occur with concomitant fluoxetine and phentermine; metabolism of imipramine to desipramine is blocked by fluoxetine and therefore imipramine levels may be increased; may inhibit oxidative metabolism of diazepam and warfarin

Dosage Forms
Fluoxetine hydrochloride:
Capsule: 10 mg, 20 mg
Liquid (mint flavor): 20 mg/5 mL (120 mL)

Additional Information EKG may reveal S-T segment depression; not shown to be teratogenic in rodents; plasma levels may be reliable in reflecting drug concentration in whole blood. Buspirone (15-60 mg/day) may be useful in treatment of sexual dysfunction during treatment with a selective serotonin reuptake inhibitor.

Specific References
Moskowitz H and Burns M, "The Effects of Performance of Two Antidepressants, Alone and in Combination With Diazepam," *Prog Neuropsychopharmacol Biol Psychiatry*, 1988, 12(5):783-92.

Fluphenazine (floo FEN a zeen)

U.S. Brand Names Moditen®; Permitil®; Prolixin®

Canadian Brand Names Modecate® [Fluphenazine Decanoate]; Modecate® Enanthate [Fluphenazine Enanthate]; Apo-Fluphenazine® [Hydrochloride]; Moditen® Hydrochloride; PMS-Fluphenazine® [Hydrochloride]

Therapeutic Category Antipsychotic Agent; Phenothiazine Derivative

Use Management of manifestations of psychotic disorders

Usual Dosage Adults:
Oral: 0.5-10 mg/day in divided doses at 6- to 8-hour intervals; some patients may require up to 40 mg/day
I.M.: 2.5-10 mg/day in divided doses at 6- to 8-hour intervals (parenteral dose is $\frac{1}{3}$ to $\frac{1}{2}$ the oral dose for the hydrochloride salts)
I.M., S.C. (decanoate): 12.5 mg every 3 weeks
Conversion from hydrochloride to decanoate I.M. 0.5 mL (12.5 mg) decanoate every 3 weeks is approximately equivalent to 10 mg hydrochloride/ day
I.M., S.C. (enanthate): 12.5-25 mg every 3 weeks

Mechanism of Action Blocks postsynaptic mesolimbic dopaminergic receptors in the brain; exhibits a strong alpha-adrenergic blocking effect and depresses the release of hypothalamic and hypophyseal hormones

Pharmacodynamics/kinetics
Onset of action: I.M. or S.C.: 24-72 hours
Peak neuroleptic effects: 48-96 hours; effects, onset, and duration are derivative dependent; the hydrochloride salt acts quickly and persist briefly, while the decanoate last the longest and requires more time for onset; following hydrochloride derivative administration, the onset of activity occurs within 1 hour yet persists for only 6-8 hours
Absorption: Varies with route of administration
Metabolism: In the liver
Half-life: Half-life is derivative dependent:
Enanthate: 84-96 hours
Hydrochloride: 33 hours
Decanoate: 163-232 hours

Signs and Symptoms of Acute Intoxication Deep sleep, enuresis, hypotension or hypertension, photosensitivity, gynecomastia, lactation, neuroleptic malignant syndrome, ejaculatory disturbances, hyponatremia, depression, hypothermia, dystonic reactions, seizures, extrapyramidal reaction, respiratory failure, Parkinson's-like symptoms, hyperthermia, vision color changes (brown tinge), vision color changes (yellow tinge); Q-T (prolongation), urine discoloration (pink), urine discoloration (red), urine discoloration (red-brown)

When to Transport to Hospital Transport any pediatric patient, any symptomatic patient, or any ingestion over 50 mg
(Continued)

Fluphenazine (Continued)

Warnings/Precautions Watch for hypotension when administering I.M. or I.V.; safety in children <6 months of age has not been established; use with caution in patients with cardiovascular disease or seizures; benefits of therapy must be weighed against risks of therapy; adverse effects may be of longer duration with depot form

Adverse Reactions

>10%:

Cardiovascular: Orthostatic hypotension, hypotension, tachycardia, arrhythmias

Central nervous system: Parkinsonian symptoms, akathisia, dystonias, tardive dyskinesia (persistent), dizziness

Gastrointestinal: Constipation

Ocular: Pigmentary retinopathy

Respiratory: Nasal congestion

Miscellaneous: Diaphoresis (decreased)

1% to 10%:

Dermatologic: Increased sensitivity to sun, rash

Endocrine & metabolic: Changes in menstrual cycle, breast pain, amenorrhea, galactorrhea, gynecomastia, changes in libido

Gastrointestinal: Weight gain, nausea, vomiting, stomach pain

Genitourinary: Dysuria, ejaculatory disturbances

Neuromuscular & skeletal: Trembling of fingers

Reference Range Therapeutic: 5-20 ng/mL (SI: 10-40 nmol/L)

Drug Interactions Decreases barbiturate levels and decreases fluphenazine effectiveness when given together; with ethanol effects of both drugs may be increased; EPSEs and other CNS effects may be increased when coadministered with lithium; may potentiate the effects of narcotics including apnea; clonidine administration with fluphenazine may cause delirium

Dosage Forms

Fluphenazine hydrochloride:

Concentrate:

Permitil®: 5 mg/mL with alcohol 1% (118 mL)

Prolixin®: 5 mg/mL with alcohol 14% (120 mL)

Elixir (Prolixin®): 2.5 mg/5 mL with alcohol 14% (60 mL, 473 mL)

Injection (Prolixin®): 2.5 mg/mL (10 mL)

Tablet:

Permitil®: 2.5 mg, 5 mg, 10 mg

Prolixin®: 1 mg, 2.5 mg, 5 mg, 10 mg

Injection, as decanoate (Prolixin Decanoate®): 25 mg/mL (1 mL, 5 mL)

Injection, as enanthate (Prolixin Enanthate®): 25 mg/mL (5 mL)

Additional Information Oral liquid to be diluted in the following only: water, saline, 7-UP®, homogenized milk, carbonated orange beverages, pineapple, apricot, prune, orange, V8® juice, tomato, and grapefruit juices; benztropine can be used to treat nausea/vomiting

Specific References

Cheung HK and Yu EC, "Effect of 1050 mg Fluphenazine Decanoate Given Intramuscularly Over Six Days," *Br Med J (Clin Res)*, 1983, 286(6370):1016-7.

Flura® *see* Fluoride *on page 251*

Flura-Drops® *see* Fluoride *on page 251*

Flura-Loz® *see* Fluoride *on page 251*

Flurazepam (flure AZ e pam)

Related Information

Controlled Substances - Uses and Effects *on page 741*

U.S. Brand Names Benozil®; Dalmane®; Staurodorm®

Canadian Brand Names Apo-Flurazepam®; Somnol®; Som Pam®; Novo-Flupam®; PMS-Flupam®

Therapeutic Category Benzodiazepine

Abuse Potential Yes

Impairment Potential Yes; A 15 mg ingestion of flurazepam at bedtime has been demonstrated to result in driving impairment the next morning. Brief or extended period (up to 1 year) of use is consistent with driving impairment in the elderly. The impairment is greatest in the first week of use.

Betts TA and Birtle J, "Effect of Two Hypnotic Drugs on Actual Driving Performances Next Morning," *Br Med J*, 1982, 285(6345):852.

Use Short-term treatment of insomnia

Usual Dosage Oral:

Children:
   <15 years: Dose not established
   >15 years: 15 mg at bedtime
Adults: 15-30 mg at bedtime

Mechanism of Action Depresses all levels of the CNS, including the limbic and reticular formation, probably through the increased action of gamma-aminobutyric acid (GABA), which is a major inhibitory neurotransmitter in the brain

Pharmacodynamics/kinetics

Onset of action: 15-20 minutes
Peak effect: 3-6 hours
Duration: 7-8 hours
Absorption: Rapid through gastrointestinal tract
Metabolism: In the liver to N-desalkylflurazepam (active)
Half-life: Adults: 40-114 hours; N-desalkylflurazepam: 47-100 hours

Signs and Symptoms of Acute Intoxication Apnea, respiratory depression, hyporeflexia, hypoactive reflexes, asterixis, unsteady gait, metallic taste, hypotension, coma, hyperactivity, drowsiness, ataxia, mydriasis, adult respiratory distress syndrome, gaze nystagmus

When to Transport to Hospital Transport any pediatric exposure or any symptomatic adult patient

Warnings/Precautions Do not use in pregnant women; may cause drug dependency; safety and efficacy have not been established in children <15 years of age; use with caution in patients receiving other CNS depressants, patients with low albumin, hepatic dysfunction and in the elderly

Adverse Reactions

>10%:
   Cardiovascular: Tachycardia, chest pain
   Central nervous system: Drowsiness, fatigue, ataxia, lightheadedness, memory impairment, insomnia, anxiety, depression, headache
   Dermatologic: Rash
   Endocrine & metabolic: Decreased libido
   Gastrointestinal: Xerostomia, constipation, decreased salivation, nausea, vomiting, diarrhea, increased or decreased appetite
   Neuromuscular & skeletal: Dysarthria
   Ocular: Blurred vision
   Miscellaneous: Diaphoresis
1% to 10%:
   Cardiovascular: Syncope, hypotension
   Central nervous system: Confusion, nervousness, dizziness, akathisia
   Dermatologic: Dermatitis
   Gastrointestinal: Weight gain or loss, increased salivation
   Neuromuscular & skeletal: Rigidity, tremor, muscle cramps
(Continued)

Flurazepam *(Continued)*

    Otic: Tinnitus
    Respiratory: Hyperventilation, nasal congestion

Reference Range
    Therapeutic: 0-4 ng/mL (SI: 0-9 nmol/L)
    Metabolite N-desalkylflurazepam: 20-110 ng/mL (SI: 43-240 nmol/L)
    Toxic: >0.12 µg/mL

Drug Interactions Additive CNS depression with other CNS depressants, cimetidine may decrease and enzyme inducers may increase metabolism of flurazepam

Dosage Forms Capsule, as hydrochloride: 15 mg, 30 mg

Specific References
    Ruff RL, Kutt H, and Hafler D, "Prolonged Benzodiazepine Coma," *N Y State J Med*, 1981, 81(5):776-7.

Fluvoxamine *(floo VOKS ah meen)*

U.S. Brand Names Luvox®

Therapeutic Category Antidepressant

Use Treatment of major depression and obsessive-compulsive disorder (OCD)

Usual Dosage Initiate at 50 mg/day; usual therapeutic dose: 100-300 mg/day in divided doses

Mechanism of Action Serotonin reuptake inhibitor

Pharmacodynamics/kinetics
    Absorption: Rapid and complete
    Metabolism: Extensive to inactive metabolites
    Half-life, elimination: 15 hours, increased in elderly
    Time to peak concentration: 5 hours

Signs and Symptoms of Acute Intoxication Insomnia, coma, tachycardia, amenorrhea, mania, toxic epidermal necrolysis, depression, bradycardia, syndrome of inappropriate antidiuretic hormone (SIADH), hypotension, elevated liver function tests, seizures

When to Transport to Hospital Transport any pediatric exposure or symptomatic adult patient

Warnings/Precautions Use with caution in patients with seizures

Adverse Reactions
    >10%: Gastrointestinal: Nausea
    1% to 10%:
        Cardiovascular: Palpitations
        Central nervous system: Somnolence, headache, insomnia, dizziness, nervousness, mania, hypomania, vertigo, abnormal thinking, agitation, anxiety, malaise, amnesia
        Endocrine & metabolic: Decreased libido
        Gastrointestinal: Xerostomia, abdominal pain, vomiting, dyspepsia, constipation, diarrhea, abnormal taste, anorexia
        Neuromuscular & skeletal: Tremors, weakness
        Miscellaneous: Diaphoresis

Drug Interactions Fluvoxamine inhibits cytochrome P450 IIID$_6$, P450 IIIA$_4$, and may increase propranolol, warfarin, amitriptyline, clomipramine, imipramine, diazepam, alprazolam, terfenadine, astemizole; hepatic metabolism of theophylline, maprotiline, antipyrine and methadone is also inhibited by fluvoxamine; use with MAO inhibitors or other serotonin reuptake inhibitors, hyperpyrexia, tachycardia, seizures, death can occur; use with lithium has been associated with seizures; discontinuation of fluvoxamine in patients receiving methadone (for maintenance therapy) has been associated with increase methadone blood levels along with increased opioid effects; use with lithium has been associated with seizures; ethanol can increase fluvoxamine absorption by 19%; concomitant use of phenytoin with fluvoxamine can result in increased phenytoin levels; increased clozapine levels can occur with concomitant fluvoxamine

Dosage Forms Tablet: 50 mg, 100 mg

Additional Information Rate of serotonin syndrome-like symptoms: ~0.04-0.006/100 treatment days

Specific References

Benfield P, and Ward A, "Fluvoxamine: A Review of Its Pharmacodynamic and Pharmacokinetic Properties, and Therapeutic Efficacy in Depressive Illness," *Drugs*, 1986, 32(4):313-34.

Flying Saucers see Morning Glory on page 409

Foille® [OTC] see Benzocaine on page 70

Foille Medicated First Aid® [OTC] see Benzocaine on page 70

Foltran® see Zopiclone on page 621

Fontex see Fluoxetine on page 253

Formaldehyde

Synonyms Fannoform; Formic Aldehyde, Formalin; Fyde; Hoch; Morbicid; Paraform; Trioxane; Veracur

UN Number 1198 (solution); 2209 (formalin)

Impairment Potential Yes

Use In embalming, fireproofing, glues/adhesives, lacquers, electrical insulation, tannery products

Mechanism of Toxic Action Covalently binds to proteins and causes cell necrosis; mucous membrane irritant

Toxicodynamics/kinetics

Absorption: Well absorbed from the gastrointestinal tract and by inhalation; to a lesser extent, absorbed through the skin

Metabolism: Rapidly (within 1.5 minutes) to formic acid which is then metabolized to carbon dioxide and water

Half-life: Formate: 1.5 hours

Signs and Symptoms of Acute Intoxication Dizziness, urticaria, dyspnea, hyposmia, cough, drowsiness, ataxia, coma, gastritis

When to Transport to Hospital Transport any symptomatic patient

Adverse Reactions

Cardiovascular: Cardiovascular collapse, hypotension

Central nervous system: CNS depression, panic attacks

Dermatologic: Contact dermatitis, dermal irritation, nonimmunologic contact urticaria, immunologic contact urticaria

Endocrine & metabolic: Metabolic acidosis

Gastrointestinal: Coagulation necrosis on ingestion, vomiting, diarrhea, feces discoloration (black), throat irritation

Renal: Nephritis, renal failure

Respiratory: Wheezing, tachypnea, bronchospasm, sino-nasal cancer

Miscellaneous: Multiple chemical sensitivity syndrome

Reference Range Blood formaldehyde levels of 4.8 mg/L and 11 mg/L associated with fatality due to ingestion

Additional Information Implicated in squamous cell carcinoma of the nasopharynx (probable human carcinogen)

30 mL (of a 37% solution) may cause fatalities

TLV-TWA: 1 ppm

IDLH: 100 ppm

PEL-TWA: 3 ppm

Formalin contains 37% formaldehyde and 12% to 15% methanol

(Continued)

Formaldehyde *(Continued)*

Specific References
Council on Scientific Affairs, "Formaldehyde," *JAMA*, 1989, 261(8):1183-7.

Formic Aldehyde, Formalin *see* Formaldehyde *on previous page*

Formistin® *see* Cetirizine *on page 120*

Formosa Camphor *see* Camphor *on page 99*

Formulex® *see* Dicyclomine *on page 194*

Formyl Trichloride *see* Chloroform *on page 129*

Fortal® *see* Pentazocine *on page 463*

Fortral® *see* Pentazocine *on page 463*

Fortulgesic® *see* Pentazocine *on page 463*

Fortunan® *see* Haloperidol *on page 280*

Fortwin® *see* Pentazocine *on page 463*

Four-O'Clock

Synonyms Mirakelblomst
Scientific Name *Mirabilis jalapa*
Usual Dosage Not established
Signs and Symptoms of Acute Intoxication Handling the roots or seeds may result in dermatitis; ingestion may cause nausea, vomiting, diarrhea, and abdominal pain; smoking or eating the seeds is rumored to result in hallucinogenic effects
When to Transport to Hospital Transport any symptomatic patient
Additional Information
Toxin: Trigonelline
Range: Native to Mexico and Central and South America, cultivated throughout the U.S.
Toxic part: Roots and seeds

Freezone® Solution [OTC] *see* Salicylic Acid *on page 530*

Freon

Synonyms Dichlorodifluoromethane; Fluorinated Hydrocarbons; Halon
Abuse Potential Yes
Impairment Potential Yes
Use Refrigerant and in fire extinguishers/propellant
Mechanism of Toxic Action Can cause cold injury to surface on contact, sensitizer of myocardium to catecholamines
Toxicodynamics/kinetics
Absorption: Immediate
Half-life: 75 minutes
Signs and Symptoms of Acute Intoxication Conjunctivitis, dyspnea, dizziness, hemoptysis, ataxia, slurred speech, drowsiness, coma, seizures, tremor, bradycardia, diarrhea, gaze nystagmus
When to Transport to Hospital Transport any symptomatic patient
Overdosage/Treatment Decontamination: Basic poison management, avoid emesis, avoid catecholamines
Adverse Reactions
Cardiovascular: Myocardial depression, arrhythmias, sinus bradycardia, congestive heart failure
Dermatologic: Contact dermatitis
Respiratory: Pulmonary edema, bronchoconstriction
Miscellaneous: Multiple chemical sensitivity syndrome
Additional Information Odor of "fresh cut grass;" levels peak almost immediately after inhalation; heating may produce phosgene

Specific References
Voge VM, "Secondary Arterial Hypertension Linked to Freon Exposure," *South Med J*, 1996, 89(5):516-8.

Freon 10® *see* Carbon Tetrachloride *on page 113*
Freon 20 *see* Chloroform *on page 129*
Freon 30 *see* Methylene Chloride *on page 395*
Freon 40 *see* Chloromethane *on page 130*
Frisium® *see* Clobazam *on page 151*
Fristamin® *see* Loratadine *on page 350*
Fuel Oil Number 1 *see* Kerosene *on page 325*
Fumasorb® *see* Iron *on page 318*
Fumerin® *see* Iron *on page 318*
"Fungus" Japonicus *see* Kombucha *on page 330*
Furazosin *see* Prazosin *on page 494*
Fyde *see* Formaldehyde *on page 259*
G-1® *see* Butalbital Compound *on page 93*

Gabapentin (GA ba pen tin)

Synonyms CI-945
U.S. Brand Names Neurontin®
Therapeutic Category Anticonvulsant
Use Partial or secondary generalized seizures; possibly useful for pain relief due to reflex sympathetic dystrophy
Usual Dosage Children >12 years and Adults: Oral: 900-1800 mg/day administered in 3 divided doses; therapy is initiated with a rapid titration, beginning with 300 mg on day 1, 300 mg twice daily on day 2, and 300 mg 3 times/day on day 3
Mechanism of Action Structural analog to gamma amino butyric acid (GABA). Binds to gabapentin receptors in hippocampus. No effect on GABA system.
Pharmacodynamics/kinetics
Absorption: Oral: 50% to 60%
Distribution: V_d: 0.6-0.8 L/kg
Protein binding: 0%
Half-life: 5-6 hours
Elimination: Renal (56% to 80%)
When to Transport to Hospital Transport any pediatric (<12 years of age) exposure, any symptomatic patient, or any ingestion over 2 g
Adverse Reactions
>10%: Central nervous system: Somnolence, dizziness, ataxia, fatigue
1% to 10%:
　Cardiovascular: Peripheral edema
　Central nervous system: Nervousness, amnesia, depression, anxiety, abnormal coordination
　Dermatologic: Pruritus
　Gastrointestinal: Dyspepsia, dry throat, xerostomia, nausea, constipation, appetite stimulation (weight gain)
　Genitourinary: Impotence
　Hematologic: Leukopenia
　Neuromuscular & skeletal: Back pain, myalgia, dysarthria, tremor
　Ocular: Diplopia, blurred vision, gaze nystagmus
　Respiratory: Rhinitis, bronchospasm
　Miscellaneous: Hiccups
Reference Range Peak plasma level: 2 µg/mL 1.5-3 hours after a 200 mg dose
Drug Interactions Slight reduction in absorption with antacids
Dosage Forms Capsule: 100 mg, 300 mg, 400 mg
(Continued)

Gabapentin *(Continued)*

Additional Information Not effective for absence seizures; benign pancreatic tumors noted in rodents administered high doses, ingestion of 48.9 g resulted in minimal symptoms; gabapentin levels 5 times over therapeutic limit result in minimal clinical effects; proposed use for amyotrophic lateral sclerosis

Specific References

Fischer JH, Barr AN, Rogers SL, et al, "Lack of Serious Toxicity Following Gabapentin Overdose," *Neurology*, 1994, 44(5):982-3.

Gallopamil *(gal LOP a mil)*

U.S. Brand Names Algocor®; Procurum®

Therapeutic Category Neuromuscular Blocker Agent, Nondepolarizing; Skeletal Muscle Relaxant

Use Angina, hypertension

Usual Dosage Oral:

Angina: 50-75 mg 3 times/day days

Hypertension: 50 mg 2-3 times/day; reduce dose by 50% to 75% in liver disease

Mechanism of Action Second generation calcium antagonist with actions very similar to verapamil, but about 8 times as potent

Pharmacodynamics/kinetics

Peak serum level: 1-2 hours; sustained release: 4 hours

Metabolism: Hepatic

Half-life: 4-8 hours; cirrhotic patients: 5-20 hours

Bioavailability: 25%

Signs and Symptoms of Acute Intoxication Atrioventricular dissociations

When to Transport to Hospital Transport any pediatric exposure or any patient exhibiting cardiopulmonary symptoms

Warnings/Precautions Use with caution in patients hypersensitive to verapamil, patients with bradycardia, heart failure, aortic stenosis, liver disease, patients taking calcium supplements or beta-blocking agents

Adverse Reactions

Cardiovascular: Bradycardia, palpitations, edema, flushing, sinus bradycardia, angina, chest pain

Central nervous system: Headache, drowsiness, dizziness

Gastrointestinal: Constipation

Hepatic: Cholestatic jaundice

Reference Range Mean serum level 2 hours after a 50 mg dose: ~40 ng/mL

Drug Interactions Enhances hypotensive effects of moxonidine; can increase anti-ischemic effect of isosorbide mononitrate

Specific References

Brogden RN and Benfield P, "Gallopamil: A Review of Its Pharmacodynamic and Pharmacokinetic Properties and Therapeutic Potential in Ischemic Heart Disease," *Drugs*, 1994, 47(1):93-115.

Gamma Hydroxybutyric Acid

(GAM a hye DROX ee byoo TIR ik AS id)

Synonyms GHB; 4-Hydroxybutyrate; Sodium Oxybate

U.S. Brand Names Gamma-OH®; Somatomax PM®; Somsanit®

Therapeutic Category General Anesthetic

Abuse Potential Yes

Impairment Potential Yes; Ingestion >100 mg/kg or urinary gamma/hydroxybutyrate levels >2000 mg/L are consistent with driving impairment

Stephens BG and Baselt RC, "Driving Under the Influence of GHB?" *J Anal Toxicol*, 1994, 18(6):357-8.

Use Narcolepsy; anesthetic agent

Usual Dosage
  Analgesia/amnesia: 10-20 mg
  General anesthesia: 50 mg/kg
  Intoxicating dose: 15 mg/kg
  Lethal dose: ~4 g

Mechanism of Action Central nervous system depressant which has anesthetic action; possible role as a neurotransmitter particularly in the substantia nigra influencing dopamine release

Pharmacodynamics/kinetics
  Onset of action:
    Oral: 15-30 minutes
    I.V.: 2-15 minutes
  Duration of action: 3 hours
  Metabolism: Metabolized to succinic acid and carbon dioxide
  Half-life: 0.3-1 hour

When to Transport to Hospital Transport any suspected exposure

Adverse Reactions
  Cardiovascular: Bradycardia, hypertension, hypotension
  Central nervous system: Confusion, seizures, coma, dizziness, relaxation, euphoria, amnesia, hypotonia (dose related), ataxia, extrapyramidal reaction
  Gastrointestinal: Fecal incontinence, excessive salivation
  Genitourinary: Urinary incontinence
  Hematologic: Porphyria
  Neuromuscular & skeletal: Tremors
  Ocular: Gaze nystagmus
  Respiratory: Apnea, respiratory depression

Test Interactions Increases growth hormone and prolactin levels with a dose as little as 3 g; sodium salt can cause hypernatremia; hypokalemia has also been reported

Reference Range 4-butyrolactone plasma levels >2.5 mmol/L are associated with coma; oral doses (in mg/kg) approximate plasma levels (in mcg/mL); following an oral dose of 100 mg, peak urinary GHB concentrations are approximately 1100 mg/L; urinary levels are undetectable in 12 hours

Additional Information Recalled by the FDA in November 1990; found in certain ripe fruits such as guava; can be synthesized by titrating gamma butyryl lactone with sodium hydroxide to a pH of 6-7; withdrawal symptoms (insomnia, anxiety, tremors) may last 3-12 days; more commonly sold as a liquid form in its sodium salt form dissolved in ethanol or water. As of July 1996, two states (Rhode Island and Georgia) have state-controlled GHB as a schedule I substance. GHB can increase plasma growth hormone levels up to 40 ng/mL.

Sources for GHB analysis include: Kathleen Andrews, DEA Western Laboratory, 390 Main Street, Room #700, San Francisco, CA 94105, (415) 744-7051 ext 33; Adrian Krawczeniuk, DEA Northeast Laboratory, 99 Tenth Avenue, Suite 721, New York, NY 10011, (212) 620-3684; Peter K Poole, DEA North Central Laboratory, 536 South Clark Street, Room 8, Chicago IL 60605, (312) 353-3640 ext 1601

GHB cases can be reported to the DEA through: Tom Diberardino, Office of Diversion Control, Drug and Chemical Evaluation Section, E 62491, Drug Enforcement Administration, Washington, DC 20537, (202) 307-7207

Gamma-OH® see Gamma Hydroxybutyric Acid *on previous page*

Gardenale® see Phenobarbital *on page 474*

Garden Heliotrope see Valerian *on page 606*

Gardentox® see Diazinon *on page 192*

Garranil® see Captopril *on page 101*

Gasoline

Synonyms Mogas; Motor Fuel; Motor Spirit; Natural Gasoline; Petrol

UN Number 1203; 1257

Abuse Potential Yes

Impairment Potential Yes

Use Fuel for internal combustion engines

Mechanism of Toxic Action A volatile hydrocarbon with central nervous system depressant and arrhythmogenic effects

Toxicodynamics/kinetics

Half-life: 17 hours

Elimination: Pulmonary/renal

Signs and Symptoms of Acute Intoxication Death due to ingestion usually due to aspiration; symptoms occur at 1000 ppm after 1 hour; euphoria, confusion, hallucinations (visual, auditory and tactile), vertigo, headache, dysarthria, tremor, ataxia, mania, delirium

Inhalation: Pulmonary edema, intra-alveolar hemorrhage, cardiac arrhythmia, muscle cramps, nausea, vomiting, drowsiness, dizziness, hallucinations, ataxia, myoclonus, paresthesias, insomnia

Ingestion: Pulmonary congestion, belching, hypotension, hemolysis, elevated hepatic enzymes, oliguria, aspiration, hematuria, disseminated intravascular coagulation can occur

When to Transport to Hospital Transport any symptomatic patient or any suspected ingestion

Adverse Reactions

Cardiovascular: Sinus bradycardia

Central nervous system: Panic attacks with inhalation

Neuromuscular & skeletal: Rhabdomyolysis

Reference Range Urinary phenol (for benzene measurement) >40 mg/L consistent with gasoline exposure in gasoline pump workers; blood 2 methylpentane levels >50 mg/L associated with fatality

Additional Information Highly lipid soluble; gasoline contains a mixture of benzene (0.5%-2.5%), toluene, xylene, ethyl benzene, and possible lead (tetraethyl lead); other additives include ethylene dichloride and ethylene dibromide; lead poisoning is unusual from inhalation of gasoline containing tetraethyl lead

Odor threshold of gasoline: 0.25 ppm

Lethal inhalation concentration: 5000 ppm

Lethal ingestion concentration: 5 g/kg (12 oz)

Ambient level of gasoline at service stations is usually <100 ppm

Specific References

Cox MJ, Hwang JC, Himel HN, et al, "Severe Burn Injury From Recreational Gasoline Use," *Am J Emerg Med*, 1996, 14(1):39-42.

Gaster® *see* Famotidine *on page 242*

Gastrosed™ *see* Hyoscyamine *on page 305*

Gee Gee® [OTC] *see* Guaifenesin *on page 269*

Gel Kam® *see* Fluoride *on page 251*

Gelodurat® *see* Eucalyptus Oil *on page 241*

Gelpirin® [OTC] *see* Acetaminophen, Aspirin, and Caffeine *on page 23*

Gel-Tin® [OTC] *see* Fluoride *on page 251*

Gemonil® *see* Metharbital *on page 389*

Genagesic® *see* Guaifenesin and Phenylpropanolamine *on page 272*

Genahist® Oral *see* Diphenhydramine *on page 205*

Genamin® Cold Syrup [OTC] *see* Chlorpheniramine and Phenylpropanolamine *on page 134*

Genamin® Expectorant [OTC] *see* Guaifenesin and Phenylpropanolamine *on page 272*

Genapap® [OTC] *see* Acetaminophen *on page 20*

Genatap® Elixir [OTC] *see* Brompheniramine and Phenylpropanolamine *on page 85*

Genatuss® [OTC] *see* Guaifenesin *on page 269*

Genatuss DM® [OTC] *see* Guaifenesin and Dextromethorphan *on page 271*

Genpril® [OTC] *see* Ibuprofen *on page 308*

Gen-XENE® *see* Clorazepate *on page 156*

GG *see* Guaifenesin *on page 269*

GG-Cen® [OTC] *see* Guaifenesin *on page 269*

GHB *see* Gamma Hydroxybutyric Acid *on page 262*

Glibenclamide *see* Glyburide *on page 267*

Glibenese® *see* Glipizide *on this page*

Gliconorm® *see* Chlorpropamide *on page 140*

Glifonox® *see* Glyphosate *on page 269*

Glipizide (GLIP i zide)

Synonyms Glydiazinamide

U.S. Brand Names Glibenese®; Glucotrol®; Mindiab®; Minidiab®; Minodiab®

Therapeutic Category Antidiabetic Agent (Oral)

Use Management of noninsulin-dependent diabetes mellitus (type II)

Usual Dosage Oral (allow several days between dose titrations; administer 30 minutes before a meal for greatest reduction in postprandial hyperglycemia):

Adults: 2.5-40 mg/day; doses larger than 15-20 mg/day should be divided and given twice daily

Elderly: Initial: 2.5-5 mg/day; increase by 2.5-5 mg/day every 1-2 weeks

Mechanism of Action Sulfonylurea which stimulates insulin release from the pancreatic beta cells; reduces glucose output from the liver; insulin sensitivity is increased at peripheral target sites

Pharmacodynamics/kinetics

Duration of action: 12-24 hours

Peak blood glucose reductions: Within 1.5-2 hours

Absorption: Delayed when given with food; impaired in patients with hyperglycemia

Protein binding: 92% to 99%

Metabolism: In the liver with metabolites (91% to 97%)

Half-life: 3-4 hours

Elimination: Metabolites (91% to 97%) excreted in urine (60% to 80%) and feces (11%)

When to Transport to Hospital Transport any pediatric exposure or any symptomatic patient

Warnings/Precautions Use with caution in patients with severe hepatic disease; a useful agent since few drug to drug interactions and not dependent upon renal elimination of active drug

Adverse Reactions

>10%:

Central nervous system: Headache

Gastrointestinal: Anorexia, nausea, vomiting, diarrhea, epigastric fullness, constipation, heartburn

1% to 10%: Dermatologic: Rash, urticaria, photosensitivity

Reference Range Glucose: Adults: 80-140 mg/dL; Elderly: 100-180 mg/dL

Drug Interactions

Increased effect: Histamine H_2 antagonists, anticoagulants, androgens, fluconazole, salicylates, gemfibrozil, sulfonamides, tricyclic antidepressants, (Continued)

Glipizide *(Continued)*

probenecid, MAO inhibitors, methyldopa, digitalis glycosides, urinary acidifiers

Decreased effect: Beta-blockers, cholestyramines, hydantoins, rifampin, thiazide diuretics, urinary alkalines, charcoal

Dosage Forms

Tablet: 5 mg, 10 mg

Tablet, extended release: 5 mg, 10 mg

Additional Information Exhibits more of a diuretic action than chlorpropamide

Specific References

Frederick KA and Wang RY, "Delayed Hypoglycemia in a Child After Ingestion of a Single Glipizide Tablet," *Vet Hum Toxicol*, 1994, 35:365.

Globuren® *see Epoetin Alfa on page 222*

Glonoin *see Nitroglycerin on page 437*

Glucolon® *see Glyburide on next page*

Glucophage® *see Metformin on page 377*

Glucose, Random

Use Evaluate carbohydrate metabolism, acidosis and ketoacidosis, dehydration; work up alcoholism, or apparent alcoholism; work-up of coma, neuroglycopenia. Hypoglycemia if present should be investigated with insulin levels as well. For the diagnosis of diabetes mellitus in nonpregnant adult subjects, random glucose >200 mg/dL (SI: >11.1 mmol/L) is required. Other criteria exist. Determination of blood glucose on admission in patients who have had an out-of-hospital cardiac arrest can serve as a predictor of neurologic recovery. Higher levels are indicative of more severe brain ischemia and difficult resuscitation. In pregnant women, a value >105 mg/dL usually prompts further investigation.

Reference Range Dependent on time and content of last meal. Glucose of >200 mg/dL (SI: >11.1 mmol/L) in a nonstressed, ambulatory subject supports the diagnosis of diabetes mellitus. Values in term neonates are published.

Additional Information Recall that **blood glucose** values are not equivalent to **plasma glucose**. If glucose is >400 mg/dL (SI: >22.2 mmol/L), an acetone (ketone body) examination probably should be done. A fasting and a 2-hour postprandial specimen is preferable to a random specimen for evaluation of possible diabetes mellitus. The incidence of hypoglycemia in hospitalized patients appears to be significant, but may be better controlled if frequent monitoring of glucose levels is employed. Wider utilization of bedside glucose testing may allow for closer patient monitoring, but the establishment of uniform quality control procedures is necessary to ensure valid results from this type of testing. Evaluation of glycated hemoglobin and self-monitoring of blood glucose are two relatively new means of assessing glycemia which have become widely available.

May cause a false elevation of serum creatinine through interference with laboratory determination

Specific References

Palardy J, Havrankova J, Lepage R, et al, "Blood Glucose Measurements During Symptomatic Episodes in Patients With Suspected Postprandial Hypoglycemia," *N Engl J Med*, 1989, 321(21):1421-5.

Glucotrol® *see Glipizide on previous page*

Glutethimide *(gloo TETH i mide)*

Related Information

Controlled Substances - Uses and Effects *on page 741*

U.S. Brand Names Doriden®

Therapeutic Category Hypnotic, Nonbarbiturate

Abuse Potential Yes

Impairment Potential Yes; Blood glutethimide levels >5 mg/L associated with intoxication

Chazan JA and Garella S, "Glutethimide Intoxication. A Prospective Study of 70 Patients Treated Conservatively Without Hemodialysis," *Arch Int Med*, 1971, 128(2):215-9.

Use Short-term treatment of insomnia

Usual Dosage Oral:

Adults: 250-500 mg at bedtime, dose may be repeated but not less than 4 hours before intended awakening; maximum: 1 g/day

Elderly/debilitated patients: Total daily dose should not exceed 500 mg

Mechanism of Action Central nervous system depressant with hypnotic action of phenobarbital and antimuscarinic effects

Pharmacodynamics/kinetics

Protein binding: 50%

Metabolism: Hepatic to an active metabolite (4-hydroxy-2-ethyl-2-phenyl-glutarimide); significant enterohepatic recirculation

Half-life: 5-22 hours

Signs and Symptoms of Acute Intoxication Slurred speech, ataxia, unsteady gait, gaze nystagmus, impairment in attention or memory, stupor, coma

When to Transport to Hospital Transport any pediatric ingestion, any symptomatic patient, or any adult ingestion exceeding 1 g

Adverse Reactions

>10%: Central Nervous System: Daytime drowsiness

1% to 10%:

Central nervous system: Confusion, headache

Dermatologic: Skin rash

Gastrointestinal: Nausea, vomiting

Ocular: Blurred vision

Reference Range

Therapeutic: 2-6 µg/mL

Toxic: >6 µg/mL

Drug Interactions Decreased effect of anticoagulants

Dosage Forms Tablet: 250 mg

Glyate® [OTC] *see* Guaifenesin *on page 269*

Glyben® *see* Glyburide *on this page*

Glybenzcyclamide *see* Glyburide *on this page*

Glyburide (GLYE byoor ide)

Synonyms Glibenclamide; Glybenzcyclamide

U.S. Brand Names Calabren®; Daonil®; Diaβeta®; Glucolon®; Glyben®; Glynase™ PresTab™; Melix®; Micronase®

Canadian Brand Names Albert® Glyburide; Apo-Glyburide®; Euglucon®; Gen-Glybe®; Novo-Glyburide®; Nu-Glyburide®

Therapeutic Category Antidiabetic Agent (Oral)

Use Management of noninsulin-dependent diabetes mellitus (type II)

Usual Dosage Oral:

Adults: 1.25-5 mg to start then increase at weekly intervals to 1.25-20 mg maintenance dose/day divided in 1-2 doses

Elderly: Initial: 1.25-2.5 mg/day, increase by 1.25-2.5 mg/day every 1-3 weeks

PresTab™: Initial: 0.75-3 mg/day, increase by 1.5 mg/day in weekly intervals, maximum: 12 mg/day

(Continued)

Glyburide (Continued)

Mechanism of Action A sulfonylurea which stimulates insulin release from the pancreatic beta cells; reduces glucose output from the liver; insulin sensitivity is increased at peripheral target sites

Pharmacodynamics/kinetics

Onset of action: Oral: Insulin levels in the serum begin to increase within 15-60 minutes after a single dose

Duration: Up to 24 hours

Metabolism: To one moderately active and several inactive metabolites

Half-life: 3 hours; may be prolonged with renal insufficiency or hepatic insufficiency

Time to peak serum concentration: Adults: Within 2-4 hours

Elimination: 50% feces, 50% urine

Signs and Symptoms of Acute Intoxication Leukopenia or neutropenia (agranulocytosis, granulocytopenia); enuresis, eosinophilia, hyponatremia, photosensitivity, nocturia, exfoliative dermatitis, hypoglycemia, diuresis, coagulopathy

When to Transport to Hospital Transport any pediatric exposure or any symptomatic patient

Warnings/Precautions Use with caution in patients with hepatic impairment. Elderly: Rapid and prolonged hypoglycemia (>12 hours) despite hypertonic glucose injections have been reported; age and hepatic and renal impairment are independent risk factors for hypoglycemia; dosage titration should be made at weekly intervals.

Adverse Reactions

>10%:

Central nervous system: Headache, dizziness

Gastrointestinal: Nausea, epigastric fullness, heartburn, constipation, diarrhea, anorexia

Ocular: Blurred vision

1% to 10%: Dermatologic: Pruritus, rash, urticaria, photosensitivity reaction

Reference Range

Normal fasting glucose:

Adults: 80-140 mg/dL

Elderly: 100-180 mg/dL

Therapeutic glyburide level: 40-50 ng/mL

Drug Interactions

Decreased effect: Thiazides and beta-blockers may decrease effectiveness of glyburide

Increased effect: Increased hypoglycemia with phenylbutazone, oral anticoagulants, hydantoins, salicylates, NSAIDs, MAO inhibitors

Increased toxicity: Increased disulfiram reactions with alcohol

Concomitant administration of glyburide and aspirin can cause an increase of insulin levels resulting in transient hypoglycemia

Dosage Forms

Tablet (Diaβeta®, Micronase®): 1.25 mg, 2.5 mg, 5 mg

Tablet, micronized (Glynase™ PresTab™): 1.5 mg, 3 mg

Additional Information More diuretic effect than chlorpropamide; glyburide-microsed dust may cause hypoglycemia by inhalation

Specific References

Gavin JR 3d, "Glyburide: New Insights Into Its Effects on the Beta Cell and Beyond," *Am J Med*, 1990, 89(Suppl 2A):1S-2S.

Glycel® see Glyphosate on next page

Glycerol Guaiacolate see Guaifenesin on next page

Glycerol-T® see Theophylline and Guaifenesin on page 571

Glyceryl Trinitrate see Nitroglycerin on page 437

Glycofed® see Guaifenesin and Pseudoephedrine on page 273

Glycol Alcohol see Ethylene Glycol on page 237

Glycol Ether see Diethylene Glycol on page 195

Glycotuss® [OTC] see Guaifenesin on this page

Glycotuss-dM® [OTC] see Guaifenesin and Dextromethorphan on page 271

Glydiazinamide see Glipizide on page 265

Glymese® see Chlorpropamide on page 140

Glynase™ PresTab™ see Glyburide on page 267

Glyphosate

Synonyms N-(Phosphonomethyl) glycine: GlySH

U.S. Brand Names Bronco®; Glifonox®; Glycel®; Glyphotox®; Kleen-up®; Network® Rodeo®; Roundup®; Weedoff®

Abuse Potential Yes

Impairment Potential Yes

Use Herbicide

Mechanism of Toxic Action The surfactant (polyoxyethyleneamine) may cause uncoupling of oxidative phosphorylation (although this mechanism is in question); additionally is a mucosal irritant and a myocardial depressant

Toxicodynamics/kinetics Absorption: May be absorbed dermally (<2%)

Signs and Symptoms of Acute Intoxication Drowsiness, oral mucosal ulceration, dysphagia, salivation, esophagitis, gastritis, emesis, gaze nystagmus, excessive hematemesis, diarrhea, respiratory failure, hyperkalemia, bronchospasm, cough, dyspnea, hypotension, piloerection, oliguria, anuria, hematuria, metabolic acidosis (78% of cases), leukocytosis (average 14,300 cells/mm^3), noncardiogenic pulmonary edema (5% to 13%), acute tubular necrosis (10%)

When to Transport to Hospital Transport any exposure

Overdosage/Treatment Dilute ingestions with milk or water

Reference Range Serum glyphosate levels over 1000 ppm associated with severe symptoms

Additional Information Patients >40 years who ingest >150 mL are at highest risk for death; minimal lethal dose: 60 mL (in an 84 year old man)

Specific References

Chen K-W, Huang J-H, Sung J-M, et al, "Clinical Experience of Glyphosate-Surfactant Herbicide Intoxication: A Review of 100 Cases," *Ann Emerg Med*, 1995, 26(6):722.

Glyphotox® see Glyphosate on this page

Glypolix® see Dexfenfluramine on page 185

Glytuss® [OTC] see Guaifenesin on this page

Goody's® Headache Powders see Acetaminophen, Aspirin, and Caffeine on page 23

Gordofilm® Liquid see Salicylic Acid on page 530

Grass see Cannabinoids, Qualitative on page 100

Guaifed® [OTC] see Guaifenesin and Pseudoephedrine on page 273

Guaifed®-PD see Guaifenesin and Pseudoephedrine on page 273

Guaifenesin (gwye FEN e sin)

Related Information

Guaifenesin and Codeine on page 271

Synonyms GG; Glycerol Guaiacolate

U.S. Brand Names Anti-Tuss® Expectorant [OTC]; Breonesin® [OTC]; Diabetic Tussin® EX [OTC]; Duratuss-G®; Fenesin™; Gee Gee® [OTC]; Genatuss® (Continued)

Guaifenesin *(Continued)*

[OTC]; GG-Cen® [OTC]; Glyate® [OTC]; Glycotuss® [OTC]; Glytuss® [OTC]; Guaifenex® LA; GuiaCough® Expectorant [OTC]; Guiatuss® [OTC]; Halotussin® [OTC]; Humibid® L.A.; Humibid® Sprinkle; Hytuss® [OTC]; Hytuss-2X® [OTC]; Liquibid®; Malotuss® [OTC]; Medi-Tuss® [OTC]; Monafed®; Muco-Fen-LA®; Mytussin® [OTC]; Naldecon® Senior EX [OTC]; Organidin® NR; Pneumomist®; Respa-GF®; Robitussin® [OTC]; Scot-Tussin® [OTC]; Siltussin® [OTC]; Sinumist®-SR Capsulets®; Touro Ex®; Tusibron® [OTC]; Uni-tussin® [OTC]

Canadian Brand Names Balminil® Expectorant; Calmylin® Expectorant

Therapeutic Category Expectorant

Use Temporary control of cough due to minor throat and bronchial irritation

Usual Dosage Oral:

Children:

<2 years: 12 mg/kg/day in 6 divided doses

2-5 years: 50-100 mg (2.5-5 mL) every 4 hours, not to exceed 600 mg/day

6-11 years: 100-200 mg (5-10 mL) every 4 hours, not to exceed 1.2 g/day

Children >12 years and Adults: 200-400 mg (10-20 mL) every 4 hours to a maximum of 2.4 g/day (120 mL/day)

Mechanism of Action Thought to act as an expectorant by irritating the gastric mucosa and stimulating respiratory tract secretions, thereby increasing respiratory fluid volumes and decreasing phlegm viscosity

Pharmacodynamics/kinetics

Absorption: Well absorbed from gastrointestinal tract

Metabolism: Hepatic, 60%

Half-life: 1 hour

Signs and Symptoms of Acute Intoxication Vomiting, lethargy, coma, respiratory depression, nausea

When to Transport to Hospital Transport any symptomatic patient or any ingestion over 12 mg/kg

Warnings/Precautions Not for persistent cough such as occurs with smoking, asthma, or emphysema or cough accompanied by excessive secretions

Adverse Reactions 1% to 10%:

Central nervous system: Drowsiness, headache

Dermatologic: Rash

Gastrointestinal: Nausea, vomiting, stomach pain

Test Interactions Possible color interference with determination of 5-HIAA and VMA; decreases serum uric acid (uricosuric)

Reference Range 600 mg oral dose results in a peak guaifenesin blood level of 1.4 mg/L

Drug Interactions Disulfiram, MAO inhibitors, metronidazole, procarbazine

Dosage Forms

Caplet, sustained release (Touro Ex®): 600 mg

Capsule (Breonesin®, GG-Cen®, Hytuss-2X®): 200 mg

Capsule, sustained release (Humibid® Sprinkle): 300 mg

Liquid:

Diabetic Tussin® EX, Organidin® NR, Tusibron®: 100 mg/5 mL (118 mL)

Naldecon® Senior EX: 200 mg/5 mL (118 mL, 480 mL)

Syrup (Anti-Tuss® Expectorant, Genatuss®, Glyate®, GuiaCough® Expectorant, Guiatuss®, Halotussin®, Malotuss®, Medi-Tuss®, Mytussin®, Robitussin®, Scot-tussin®, Siltussin®, Tusibron®, Uni-Tussin®): 100 mg/5 mL with alcohol 3.5% (30 mL, 120 mL, 240 mL, 473 mL, 946 mL)

Tablet:

Duratuss-G®: 1200 mg

Gee Gee®, Glytuss®, Organidin® NR: 200 mg

Glycotuss®, Hytuss®: 100 mg

Sustained release:
Fenesin™, Guaifenex® LA, Humibid® L.A., Liquibid®, Monafed®, Muco-Fen-LA®, Pneumomist®, Respa-GF®, Sinumist®-SR Capsulets®: 600 mg

Specific References
Kuhn JJ, Hendley JO, Adams DF, et al, "Antitussive Effect of Guaifenesin in Young Adults With Natural Colds," *Chest*, 1982, 6:713-8.

Guaifenesin and Codeine (gwye FEN e sin & KOE deen)
Related Information
Codeine *on page 164*
Controlled Substances - Uses and Effects *on page 741*
Guaifenesin *on page 269*
Synonyms Codeine and Guaifenesin
U.S. Brand Names Brontex® Liquid; Brontex® Tablet; Cheracol®; Guaituss AC® Guiatussin® with Codeine; Mytussin® AC; Robafen® AC; Robitussin® A-C; Tussi-Organidin® NR
Therapeutic Category Antitussive/Expectorant
Dosage Forms
Liquid [C-V] (Brontex®): Guaifenesin 75 mg and codeine phosphate 2.5 mg per 5 mL

Syrup [C-V] (Cheracol®, Guaituss AC®, Guiatussin® with Codeine, Mytussin® AC, Robafen® AC, Robitussin® A-C, Tussi-Organidin® NR): Guaifenesin 100 mg and codeine phosphate 10 mg per 5 mL (60 mL, 120 mL, 480 mL)

Tablet [C-III] (Brontex®): Guaifenesin 300 mg and codeine phosphate 10 mg

Guaifenesin and Dextromethorphan
(gwye FEN e sin & deks troe meth OR fan)
Synonyms Dextromethorphan and Guaifenesin
U.S. Brand Names Benylin® Expectorant [OTC]; Cheracol® D [OTC]; Clear Tussin® 30; Contac® Cough Formula Liquid [OTC]; Diabetic Tussin DM® [OTC]; Extra Action Cough Syrup [OTC]; Fenesin DM®; Genatuss DM® [OTC]; Glycotuss-dM® [OTC]; Guaifenex® DM; GuiaCough® [OTC]; Guiatuss-DM® [OTC]; Halotussin® DM [OTC]; Humibid® DM [OTC]; Iobid DM®; Kolephrin® GG/DM [OTC]; Monafed® DM; Muco-Fen-DM®; Mytussin® DM [OTC]; Naldecon® Senior DX [OTC]; Phanatuss® Cough Syrup [OTC]; Phenadex® Senior [OTC]; Respa-DM®; Rhinosyn-DMX® [OTC]; Robafen DM® [OTC]; Robitussin®-DM [OTC]; Safe Tussin® 30 [OTC]; Scot-Tussin® Senior Clear [OTC]; Siltussin DM® [OTC]; Synacol® CF [OTC]; Syracol-CF® [OTC]; Tolu-Sed® DM [OTC]; Tusibron-DM® [OTC]; Tuss-DM® [OTC]; Tussi-Organidin® DM NR; Uni-tussin® DM [OTC]; Vicks® 44E [OTC]; Vicks® Pediatric Formula 44E [OTC]
Therapeutic Category Antitussive/Expectorant
Abuse Potential Yes
Impairment Potential Yes
Dosage Forms
Syrup:
Benylin® Expectorant: Guaifenesin 100 mg and dextromethorphan hydrobromide 5 mg per 5 mL (118 mL, 236 mL)

Cheracol® D, Clear Tussin® 30, Genatuss DM®, Mytussin® DM, Robitussin®-DM, Siltussin DM®, Tolu-Sed® DM, Tussi-Organidin® DM NR: Guaifenesin 100 mg and dextromethorphan hydrobromide 10 mg per 5 mL (5 mL, 10 mL, 120 mL, 240 mL, 360 mL, 480 mL, 3780 mL)

Contac® Cough Formula Liquid: Guaifenesin 67 mg and dextromethorphan hydrobromide 10 mg per 5 mL (120 mL)

Extra Action Cough Syrup, GuiaCough®, Guiatuss DM®, Halotussin® DM, Rhinosyn-DMX®, Tusibron-DM®, Uni-tussin® DM: Guaifenesin 100 mg and
(Continued)

Guaifenesin and Dextromethorphan *(Continued)*

dextromethorphan hydrobromide 15 mg per 5 mL (120 mL, 240 mL, 480 mL)

Kolephrin® GG/DM: Guaifenesin 150 mg and dextromethorphan hydrobromide 10 mg per 5 mL (120 mL)

Naldecon® Senior DX: Guaifenesin 200 mg and dextromethorphan hydrobromide 15 mg per 5 mL (118 mL, 480 mL)

Phanatuss®: Guaifenesin 85 mg and dextromethorphan hydrobromide 10 mg per 5 mL

Vicks® 44E: Guaifenesin 66.7 mg and dextromethorphan hydrobromide 6.7 mg per 5 mL

Tablet:

Extended release

Guaifenex® DM, Iobid DM®, Fenesin DM®, Humibid® DM, Monafed® DM, Respa-DM®: Guaifenesin 600 mg and dextromethorphan hydrobromide 30 mg

Glycotuss-dM®: Guaifenesin 100 mg and dextromethorphan hydrobromide 10 mg

Queltuss®: Guaifenesin 100 mg and dextromethorphan hydrobromide 15 mg

Syracol-CF®: Guaifenesin 200 mg and dextromethorphan hydrobromide 15 mg

Tuss-DM®: Guaifenesin 200 mg and dextromethorphan hydrobromide 10 mg

Guaifenesin and Hydrocodone *see* Hydrocodone and Guaifenesin *on page 295*

Guaifenesin and Phenylephrine *(gwye FEN e sin & fen il EF rin)*
U.S. Brand Names Deconsal® Sprinkle®; Endal®; Sinupan®
Therapeutic Category Cold Preparation
Dosage Forms

Capsule, sustained release:

Deconsal® Sprinkle®: Guaifenesin 300 mg and phenylephrine hydrochloride 10 mg

Sinupan®: Guaifenesin 200 mg and phenylephrine hydrochloride 40 mg

Tablet, timed release (Endal®): Guaifenesin 300 mg and phenylephrine hydrochloride 20 mg

Guaifenesin and Phenylpropanolamine
(gwye FEN e sin & fen il proe pa NOLE a meen)
Synonyms Phenylpropanolamine and Guaifenesin
U.S. Brand Names Ami-Tex LA®; Coldlac-LA®; Conex® [OTC]; Contuss® XT; Dura-Vent®; Entex® LA; Genagesic®; Genamin® Expectorant [OTC]; Guaifenex® PPA 75; Guaipax®; Myminic® Expectorant [OTC]; Naldecon-EX® Children's Syrup [OTC]; Nolex® LA; Partuss® LA; Phenylfenesin® L.A.; Profen II®; Profen LA®; Rymed-TR®; Silaminic® Expectorant [OTC]; Sildicon-E® [OTC]; Snaplets-EX® [OTC]; Theramin® Expectorant [OTC]; Triaminic® Expectorant [OTC]; Tri-Clear® Expectorant [OTC]; Triphenyl® Expectorant [OTC]; ULR-LA®; Vicks® DayQuil® Sinus Pressure & Congestion Relief [OTC]
Therapeutic Category Expectorant/Decongestant
Abuse Potential Yes
Impairment Potential Yes
Dosage Forms

Caplet:

Vicks® DayQuil® Sinus Pressure & Congestion Relief: Guaifenesin 200 mg and phenylpropanolamine hydrochloride 25 mg

Rymed-TR®: Guaifenesin 400 mg and phenylpropanolamine hydrochloride 75 mg

Drops:
  Sildicon-E®: Guaifenesin 30 mg and phenylpropanolamine hydrochloride 6.25 mg per mL (30 mL)
Granules (Snaplets-EX®): Guaifenesin 50 mg and phenylpropanolamine hydrochloride 6.25 mg (pack)
Liquid:
  Conex®, Genamin® Expectorant, Myminic® Expectorant, Silaminic® Expectorant, Theramine® Expectorant, Triaminic® Expectorant, Tri-Clear® Expectorant, Triphenyl® Expectorant: Guaifenesin 100 mg and phenylpropanolamine hydrochloride 12.5 mg per 5 mL (120 mL, 240 mL, 480 mL, 3780 mL)
  Naldecon-EX® Children's Syrup: Guaifenesin 100 mg and phenylpropanolamine hydrochloride 6.25 mg per 5 mL (120 mL)
Tablet, extended release:
  Ami-Tex LA®, Contuss® XT, Entex® LA, Guaipax®, Nolex® LA, Partuss® LA, Phenylfenesin® L.A., ULR-LA®: Guaifenesin 400 mg and phenylpropanolamine hydrochloride 75 mg
  Dura-Vent®, Profen LA®: Guaifenesin 600 mg and phenylpropanolamine hydrochloride 75 mg
  Coldlac-LA®, Guaifenex® PPA 75, Profen II®: Guaifenesin 600 mg and phenylpropanolamine hydrochloride 37.5 mg

Guaifenesin and Pseudoephedrine
(gwye FEN e sin & soo doe e FED rin)

Synonyms Pseudoephedrine and Guaifenesin

U.S. Brand Names Congess® Jr; Congess® Sr; Congestac®; Deconsal® II; Defen-LA®; Entex® PSE; Eudal-SR®; Fedahist® Expectorant [OTC]; Fedahist® Expectorant Pediatric [OTC]; Glycofed®; Guaifed® [OTC]; Guaifed®-PD; Guaifenex® PSE; GuaiMAX-D®; Guaitab®; Guaivent®; Guai-Vent/PSE®; Guiatuss PE® [OTC]; Halotussin® PE [OTC]; Histalet® X; Nasabid™; Respa-1st®; Respaire®-60 SR; Respaire®-120 SR; Robitussin-PE® [OTC]; Robitussin® Severe Congestion Liqui-Gels [OTC]; Ru-Tuss® DE; Rymed®; Sinufed® Timecelles®; Touro LA®; Tuss-LA®; V-Dec-M®; Versacaps®; Zephrex®; Zephrex LA®

Therapeutic Category Expectorant/Decongestant

Abuse Potential Yes

Impairment Potential Yes

Dosage Forms
Capsule:
  Guaivent®: Guaifenesin 250 mg and pseudoephedrine hydrochloride 120 mg
  Robitussin® Severe Congestion Liqui-Gels: Guaifenesin 200 mg and pseudoephedrine hydrochloride 30 mg
  Rymed®: Guaifenesin 250 mg and pseudoephedrine hydrochloride 30 mg
Capsule, extended release:
  Congess® Jr: Guaifenesin 125 mg and pseudoephedrine hydrochloride 60 mg
  Nasabid®: Guaifenesin 250 mg and pseudoephedrine hydrochloride 90 mg
  Congess® Sr, Guaifed®, Respaire®-120 SR,: Guaifenesin 250 mg and pseudoephedrine hydrochloride 120 mg
  Guaifed®-PD, Sinufed® Timecelles®, Versacaps®: Guaifenesin 300 mg and pseudoephedrine hydrochloride 60 mg
  Respaire®-60 SR: Guaifenesin 200 mg and pseudoephedrine hydrochloride 60 mg
  Tuss-LA® Capsule: Guaifenesin 500 mg and pseudoephedrine hydrochloride 120 mg
Drops, oral (Fedahist® Expectorant Pediatric): Guaifenesin 40 mg and pseudoephedrine hydrochloride 7.5 mg per mL (30 mL)
(Continued)

Guaifenesin and Pseudoephedrine *(Continued)*

Syrup:
  Fedahist® Expectorant, Guaifed®: Guaifenesin 200 mg and pseudoephedrine hydrochloride 30 mg per 5 mL (120 mL, 240 mL)
  Guiatuss® PE, Halotussin® PE, Robitussin-PE®, Rymed®: Guaifenesin 100 mg and pseudoephedrine hydrochloride 30 mg per 5 mL (120 mL, 240 mL, 480 mL)
  Histalet® X: Guaifenesin 200 mg and pseudoephedrine hydrochloride 45 mg per 5 mL (473 mL)
Tablet:
  Congestac®, Guaitab®, Zephrex®: Guaifenesin 400 mg and pseudoephedrine hydrochloride 60 mg
  Glycofed®: Guaifenesin 100 mg and pseudoephedrine hydrochloride 30 mg
Tablet, extended release:
  Deconsal® II, Defen-LA®, Respa-1st®: Guaifenesin 600 mg and pseudoephedrine hydrochloride 60 mg
  Entex® PSE, Guaifenex® PSE, GuaiMAX-D®, Guai-Vent/PSE®, Ru-Tuss® DE, Sudex®, Zephrex LA®: Guaifenesin 600 mg and pseudoephedrine hydrochloride 120 mg
  Eudal-SR®, Histalet® X, Touro LA®: Guaifenesin 400 mg and pseudoephedrine hydrochloride 120 mg
  Tuss-LA® Tablet, V-Dec-M®: Guaifenesin 5mg and pseudoephedrine hydrochloride 120 mg

Guaifenesin, Phenylpropanolamine, and Dextromethorphan

(gwye FEN e sin, fen il proe pa NOLE a meen, & deks troe meth OR fan)
U.S. Brand Names Anatuss® [OTC]; Guiatuss CF® [OTC]; Naldecon® DX Adult Liquid [OTC]; Profen II DM®; Robafen® CF [OTC]; Robitussin-CF® [OTC]; Siltussin-CF® [OTC]
Therapeutic Category Antitussive/Decongestant/Expectorant
Abuse Potential Yes
Impairment Potential Yes
Dosage Forms
Syrup:
  Anatuss®: Guaifenesin 100 mg, phenylpropanolamine hydrochloride 25 mg, and dextromethorphan hydrobromide 15 mg per 5 mL (120 mL, 473 mL)
  Guiatuss® CF, Robafen® CF, Robitussin-CF®: Guaifenesin 100 mg, phenylpropanolamine hydrochloride 12.5 mg, and dextromethorphan hydrobromide 10 mg per 5 mL (120 mL, 240 mL, 360 mL, 480 mL)
  Naldecon® DX Adult: Guaifenesin 200 mg, phenylpropanolamine hydrochloride 12.5 mg, and dextromethorphan hydrobromide 10 mg per 5 mL (120 mL, 473 mL)
  Siltussin-CF®: Guaifenesin 100 mg, phenylpropanolamine hydrochloride 12.5 mg, and dextromethorphan hydrobromide 10 mg per 5 mL
Tablet: Anatuss®: Guaifenesin 100 mg, phenylpropanolamine hydrochloride 25 mg, and dextromethorphan hydrobromide 15 mg
  Timed release (Profen II DM®): Guaifenesin 600 mg, phenylpropanolamine hydrochloride 37.5 mg, and dextromethorphan hydrobromide 30 mg

Guaifenesin, Phenylpropanolamine, and Phenylephrine

(gwye FEN e sin, fen il proe pa NOLE a meen, & fen il EF rin)
U.S. Brand Names Coldloc®; Contuss®; Dura-Gest®; Enomine®; Entex®; Guaifenex®; Guiatex®

Therapeutic Category Expectorant/Decongestant

Abuse Potential Yes

Impairment Potential Yes

Dosage Forms

Capsule (Contuss®, Dura-Gest®, Enomine®, Entex®, Guiatex®): Guaifenesin 200 mg, phenylpropanolamine hydrochloride 45 mg, and phenylephrine hydrochloride 5 mg

Liquid (Coldloc®, Contuss®, Entex®, Guiafenex®): Guaifenesin 100 mg, phenylpropanolamine hydrochloride 20 mg, and phenylephrine hydrochloride 5 mg per 5 mL (118 mL, 480 mL)

Tablet (Respinol-G®): Guaifenesin 200 mg, phenylpropanolamine hydrochloride 45 mg, and phenylephrine hydrochloride 5 mg

Guaifenesin, Pseudoephedrine, and Codeine

(gwye FEN e sin, soo doe e FED rin, & KOE deen)

U.S. Brand Names Codafed® Expectorant; Cycofed® Pediatric; Decohistine® Expectorant; Deprost® Expectorant with Codeine; Dihistine® Expectorant; Guiatuss DAC®; Guiatussin® DAC; Halotussin® DAC; Isoclor® Expectorant; Mytussin® DAC; Nucofed®; Nucofed® Pediatric Expectorant; Nucotuss®; Phenhist® Expectorant; Robitussin®-DAC; Ryna-CX®; Tussar® SF Syrup

Therapeutic Category Antitussive/Decongestant/Expectorant

Abuse Potential Yes

Impairment Potential Yes

Dosage Forms Liquid:

C-III: Nucofed®, Nucotuss®: Guaifenesin 200 mg, pseudoephedrine hydrochloride 60 mg, and codeine phosphate 20 mg per 5 mL (480 mL)

C-V: Codafed® Expectorant, Cycofed® Pediatric, Decohistine® Expectorant, Deprost® Expectorant with Codeine, Dihistine® Expectorant, Guiatuss DAC®, Guiatussin® DAC, Halotussin® DAC, Isoclor® Expectorant, Mytussin® DAC, Nucofed® Pediatric Expectorant, Phenhist® Expectorant, Robitussin®-DAC, Ryna-CX®, Tussar® SF: Guaifenesin 100 mg, pseudoephedrine hydrochloride 30 mg, and codeine phosphate 10 mg per 5 mL (120 mL, 480 mL, 4000 mL)

Guaifenesin, Pseudoephedrine, and Dextromethorphan

(gwye FEN e sin, soo doe e FED rin, & deks troe meth OR fan)

U.S. Brand Names Anatuss® DM [OTC]; Dimacol® Caplets [OTC]; Rhinosyn-X® Liquid [OTC]; Ru-Tuss® Expectorant [OTC]; Sudafed® Cold & Cough Liquid Caps [OTC]

Therapeutic Category Cold Preparation

Abuse Potential Yes

Impairment Potential Yes

Dosage Forms

Caplets (Dimacol®): Guaifenesin 100 mg, pseudoephedrine hydrochloride 30 mg, and dextromethorphan hydrobromide 10 mg

Capsule (Sudafed® Cold & Cough Liquid Caps): Guaifenesin 100 mg, pseudoephedrine hydrochloride 30 mg, and dextromethorphan hydrobromide 10 mg

Liquid (Anatuss® DM, Rhinosyn-X® Liquid, Ru-Tuss® Expectorant): Guaifenesin 100 mg, pseudoephedrine hydrochloride 30 mg, and dextromethorphan hydrobromide 10 mg per 5 mL

Guaifenex® see Guaifenesin, Phenylpropanolamine, and Phenylephrine on previous page

Guaifenex® DM see Guaifenesin and Dextromethorphan on page 271

Guaifenex® LA see Guaifenesin on page 269

Guaifenex® PPA 75 *see* Guaifenesin and Phenylpropanolamine *on page 272*

Guaifenex® PSE *see* Guaifenesin and Pseudoephedrine *on page 273*

GuaiMAX-D® *see* Guaifenesin and Pseudoephedrine *on page 273*

Guaipax® *see* Guaifenesin and Phenylpropanolamine *on page 272*

Guaitab® *see* Guaifenesin and Pseudoephedrine *on page 273*

Guaituss AC® Guiatussin® with Codeine *see* Guaifenesin and Codeine *on page 271*

Guaivent® *see* Guaifenesin and Pseudoephedrine *on page 273*

Guai-Vent/PSE® *see* Guaifenesin and Pseudoephedrine *on page 273*

Guanabenz (GWAHN a benz)

Synonyms 1-(2,6-Dichlorobenzylideneamine) Guanidine Acetate; WY-8678

U.S. Brand Names Rexitene®; Wytensin®

Therapeutic Category Alpha-Adrenergic Agonist

Impairment Potential Yes

Use Management of mild to moderate hypertension

Usual Dosage Adults: Oral: Initial: 4 mg twice daily, increase in increments of 4-8 mg/day every 1-2 weeks to a maximum of 32 mg twice daily

Mechanism of Action Stimulates alpha$_2$-adrenoreceptors in the brain stem, thus activating an inhibitory neuron, resulting in reduced sympathetic outflow, producing a decrease in vasomotor tone and heart rate

Pharmacodynamics/kinetics

Onset of action: Antihypertensive effects occur within 60 minutes

Duration: 12 hours

Absorption: Oral: ~75% from gastrointestinal tract

Metabolism: Extensive

Bioavailability: Very low

Half-life: 7-10 hours

Time to peak serum concentration: 2-5 hours

Signs and Symptoms of Acute Intoxication CNS depression, dyspnea, depression, impotence, gynecomastia, hypothermia, apnea, myalgia, bradycardia, drowsiness, diarrhea, hypotension, miosis, hyperglycemia and hypoglycemia

When to Transport to Hospital Transport any pediatric exposure or symptomatic ingestion

Warnings/Precautions Not considered a drug of choice in the elderly; do not abruptly discontinue this medication

Adverse Reactions

>10%:

Central nervous system: Drowsiness or sedation, dizziness

Gastrointestinal: Xerostomia

Neuromuscular & skeletal: Weakness

1% to 10%:

Cardiovascular: Chest pain, edema

Central nervous system: Headache

Endocrine & metabolic: Decreased sexual ability

Gastrointestinal: Nausea

Drug Interactions Other hypotensive agents

Dosage Forms Tablet, as acetate: 4 mg, 8 mg

Additional Information Guanabenz is considered an alternate to clonidine; it causes less sodium retention than clonidine or methyldopa

Specific References

Hall AH, Smolinske SC, Kulig KW, et al, "Guanabenz Overdose," *Ann Intern Med*, 1985, 102(6):787-8.

Rogers SJ, "Guanabenz Overdose," *Ann Intern Med*, 1986, 104(3):445.

Guanadrel (GWAHN a drel)

U.S. Brand Names Hylorel®

Therapeutic Category Alpha-Adrenergic Agonist

Impairment Potential Yes

Use Step 2 agent in stepped-care treatment of hypertension, usually with a diuretic

Usual Dosage Adults: Oral: Initial: 10 mg/day (5 mg twice daily); adjust dosage until blood pressure is controlled, usual dosage: 20-75 mg/day, given twice daily

Mechanism of Action Acts as a false neurotransmitter that blocks the adrenergic actions of norepinephrine; it displaces norepinephrine form its presynaptic storage granules and thus exposes it to degradation; it thereby produces a reduction in total peripheral resistance and therefore blood pressure

Pharmacodynamics/kinetics

Onset of action: 2 hours

Peak effect: Within 4-6 hours

Duration: 4-14 hours, average of 9 hours

Absorption: Oral: Rapid from gastrointestinal tract

Metabolism: Hepatic

Half-life: Initial: 1-4 hours, terminal: 5-45 hours

Time to peak serum concentration: Within 90-120 minutes

Signs and Symptoms of Acute Intoxication Hypotension, blurred vision, ejaculatory disturbances, dizziness, nocturia, nausea, vomiting

When to Transport to Hospital Transport any pediatric ingestion or any symptomatic patient

Warnings/Precautions Not considered a drug of choice in the elderly

Adverse Reactions

>10%:

Cardiovascular: Palpitations, chest pain, peripheral edema

Central nervous system: Fatigue, headache, faintness, drowsiness, confusion

Gastrointestinal: Increased bowel movements, gas pain, constipation, anorexia, weight gain/loss

Genitourinary: Nocturia, polyuria, ejaculation disturbances

Neuromuscular & skeletal: Paresthesia, aching limbs, leg cramps, backache, arthralgia

Ocular: Visual disturbances

Respiratory: Shortness of breath, coughing

1% to 10%:

Cardiovascular: Orthostatic hypotension

Central nervous system: Psychological problems, depression, sleep disorders

Gastrointestinal: Increased bowel movements, glossitis, nausea, vomiting, xerostomia

Genitourinary: Impotence

Renal: Hematuria

Drug Interactions Tricyclic antidepressants, sympathomimetics, vasodilators, alpha- or beta-blocking agents, reserpine, other hypotensive agents

Dosage Forms Tablet: 10 mg, 25 mg

Additional Information Considered an alternative to guanethidine

Specific References

Finnerty FA Jr and Brogden RN, "Guanadrel: A Review of Its Pharmacodynamic and Pharmacokinetic Properties and Therapeutic Use in Hypertension," *Drugs*, 1985, 30(1):22-31.

Guanethidine (gwahn ETH i deen)

Synonyms Guanetidine

U.S. Brand Names Ismelin®

Canadian Brand Names Apo-Guanethidine®

Therapeutic Category Alpha-Adrenergic Agonist

Impairment Potential Yes

Use Treatment of moderate to severe hypertension; also useful in treating vasopressin extravasation

Usual Dosage Oral:

Children: Initial: 0.2 mg/kg/day, increase by 0.2 mg/kg/day at 7- to 10-day intervals to a maximum of 3 mg/kg/day

Adults:

Ambulatory patients: Initial: 10 mg/day, increase at 5- to 7-day intervals to a maximum of 25-50 mg/day

Hospitalized patients: Initial: 25-50 mg/day, increase by 25-50 mg/day or every other day to desired therapeutic response

Vasopressin extravasation: 10 mg in 0.9% saline (10 mL) with 1000 units of heparin either through offending I.V. cannulas or through multiple S.C. injections after removal of catheter; apply ice to affected area

Mechanism of Action Acts as a false neurotransmitter that blocks the adrenergic actions of norepinephrine; it displaces norepinephrine from its presynaptic storage granules and thus exposes it to degradation; it thereby produces a reduction in total peripheral resistance and therefore blood pressure

Pharmacodynamics/kinetics

Onset of action: 0.5-2 hours

Peak effect: 6-8 hours

Duration: 24-48 hours

Absorption: Oral: Irregular (3% to 55%)

Protein binding: None

Metabolism: Hepatic metabolism to inactive metabolites

Half-life: 5-10 days

Signs and Symptoms of Acute Intoxication Hypotension, ejaculatory disturbances, blurred vision, periarteritis nodosa, nocturia, ptosis, impotence, dizziness, syncope, nausea, vomiting

When to Transport to Hospital Transport any symptomatic patient or any ingestion over 3 mg/kg

Overdosage/Treatment Supportive therapy: Hypotension usually responds to I.V. fluids or Trendelenburg positioning. If unresponsive to these measures, the use of a parenteral vasoconstrictor may be required (eg, dopamine at 2-5 mcg/kg/minute titrated to 10 mcg/kg/minute). Treatment is primarily supportive and symptomatic; overdose symptoms usually last for 72 hours.

Warnings/Precautions Orthostatic hypotension can occur frequently; avoid the use of guanethidine in the elderly

Adverse Reactions

>10%:

Cardiovascular: Palpitations, chest pain, peripheral edema

Central nervous system: Fatigue, headache, faintness, drowsiness, confusion

Gastrointestinal: Increased bowel movements, gas pain, constipation, anorexia, weight gain/loss

Genitourinary: Nocturia, polyuria, impotence, ejaculation disturbances

Neuromuscular & skeletal: Paresthesia, aching limbs, leg cramps, backache, arthralgia

Ocular: Visual disturbances

Respiratory: Shortness of breath, coughing

1% to 10%:
    Cardiovascular: Orthostatic hypotension
    Central nervous system: Psychological problems, depression, sleep disorders
    Gastrointestinal: Increased bowel movements, glossitis, nausea, vomiting, xerostomia
    Renal: Hematuria

Reference Range Adrenergic blockade at plasma concentrations of 8 ng/mL

Drug Interactions Tricyclic antidepressants, phenothiazines, anorexiants, haloperidol, maprotiline, methylphenidate and MAO inhibitors decrease antihypertensive efficacy, sympathomimetics (metaraminol, ephedrine)

Dosage Forms Tablet, as monosulfate: 10 mg, 25 mg

Specific References

Kalmanovitch DV and Hardwick PB, "Hypotension After Guanethidine Block," *Anaesthesia*, 1988, 43(3):256.

Guanetidine see Guanethidine *on previous page*

GuiaCough® [OTC] see Guaifenesin and Dextromethorphan *on page 271*

GuiaCough® Expectorant [OTC] see Guaifenesin *on page 269*

Guiatex® see Guaifenesin, Phenylpropanolamine, and Phenylephrine *on page 274*

Guiatuss® [OTC] see Guaifenesin *on page 269*

Guiatuss CF® [OTC] see Guaifenesin, Phenylpropanolamine, and Dextromethorphan *on page 274*

Guiatuss DAC® see Guaifenesin, Pseudoephedrine, and Codeine *on page 275*

Guiatuss-DM® [OTC] see Guaifenesin and Dextromethorphan *on page 271*

Guiatussin® DAC see Guaifenesin, Pseudoephedrine, and Codeine *on page 275*

Guiatuss PE® [OTC] see Guaifenesin and Pseudoephedrine *on page 273*

Gum Camphor see Camphor *on page 99*

Gum Spirits see Turpentine Oil *on page 603*

GVG see Vigabatrin *on page 612*

Gynecort® [OTC] see Hydrocortisone *on page 297*

Habitrol™ Patch see Nicotine *on page 431*

Halazepam (hal AZ e pam)

Related Information
    Controlled Substances - Uses and Effects *on page 741*

U.S. Brand Names Paxipam®

Therapeutic Category Benzodiazepine

Abuse Potential Yes

Impairment Potential Yes

Use Management of anxiety disorders; short-term relief of the symptoms of anxiety

Usual Dosage Adults: Oral: 20-40 mg 3 or 4 times daily

Mechanism of Action Benzodiazepines appear to potentiate the effects of GABA and other inhibitory neurotransmitters by binding to specific benzodiazepine-receptor sites in various areas of the CNS

Pharmacodynamics/kinetics
Half-life:
    Parent: 14 hours
    Active metabolite (desmethyldiazepam): 50-100 hours
Peak level: 1-3 hours
(Continued)

Halazepam *(Continued)*

Signs and Symptoms of Acute Intoxication Slurred speech, ataxia, unsteady gait, gaze nystagmus, impairment in attention or memory, stupor, coma

When to Transport to Hospital Transport any pediatric exposure or any patient exhibiting change in mental status

Overdosage/Treatment Treatment for benzodiazepine overdose is supportive; rarely is mechanical ventilation required; flumazenil has been shown to selectively block the binding of benzodiazepines to CNS receptors, resulting in a reversal of benzodiazepine-induced sedation; however, its use may not alter the course of overdose

Warnings/Precautions Safety and efficacy in children <18 years of age have not been established

Adverse Reactions

>10%:

Cardiovascular: Chest pain

Central nervous system: Drowsiness, fatigue, impaired coordination, light-headedness, memory impairment, insomnia, dysarthria, headache, anxiety, depression

Dermatologic: Rash

Endocrine & metabolic: Decreased libido

Gastrointestinal: Xerostomia, constipation, diarrhea, decreased salivation, nausea, vomiting, increased or decreased appetite

Miscellaneous: Diaphoresis

1% to 10%:

Cardiovascular: Tachycardia, hypotension

Central nervous system: Confusion, nervousness, syncope, dizziness, akathisia

Dermatologic: Dermatitis

Gastrointestinal: Weight gain or loss, increased salivation

Neuromuscular & skeletal: Rigidity, tremor, muscle cramps

Ocular: Blurred vision

Otic: Tinnitus

Respiratory: Nasal congestion, hyperventilation

Drug Interactions Benzodiazepines may increase digoxin concentrations and may decrease the effect of levodopa

Decreased metabolism: Cimetidine, fluoxetine

Increased metabolism: Rifampin

Increased toxicity: CNS depressants, alcohol

Dosage Forms Tablet: 20 mg, 40 mg

Additional Information Halazepam offers no significant advantage over other benzodiazepines

Halcion® *see* Triazolam *on page 592*

Haldol® *see* Haloperidol *on this page*

Haldol® Decanoate *see* Haloperidol *on this page*

Halenol® Childrens [OTC] *see* Acetaminophen *on page 20*

Halfprin® 81® [OTC] *see* Aspirin *on page 56*

Hallucinogenic Snuff *see* Bufotenine *on page 88*

Halon *see* Freon *on page 260*

Halon 104® *see* Carbon Tetrachloride *on page 113*

Haloneural® *see* Haloperidol *on this page*

Haloperidol *(ha loe PER i dole)*

U.S. Brand Names Dozic®; Fortunan®; Haldol®; Haldol® Decanoate; Haloneural®; Serenace®

Therapeutic Category Antipsychotic Agent

Abuse Potential Yes

Impairment Potential Yes

Use Treatment of psychoses, Tourette's disorder, and severe behavioral problems in children; may be used for the emergency sedation of severely agitated or delirious patients

Usual Dosage

Children:

3-6 years (15-40 kg): Oral: Initial: 0.25-0.5 mg/day given in 2-3 divided doses; increase by 0.25-0.5 mg every 5-7 days; usual maintenance:

Agitation or hyperkinesia: 0.01-0.03 mg/kg/day once daily

Nonpsychotic disorders: 0.05-0.075 mg/kg/day in 2-3 divided doses

Psychotic disorders: 0.05-0.15 mg/kg/day in 2-3 divided doses

6-12 years:

Oral: Initial: 0.5-1.5 mg/day and increase gradually by 0.5 mg/24 hour increments to maintenance of 2-4 mg/24 hours

I.M. (as lactate): 1-3 mg/dose every 4-8 hours to a maximum of 0.1 mg/kg/day; change over to oral therapy as soon as able

Adults:

Oral: 0.5-5 mg 2-3 times/day; maximum: 100 mg/day

I.M. (as lactate): 2-5 mg every 4-8 hours as needed

I.M. (as decanoate): Initial: 10-15 times the daily oral dose administered at 4-week intervals

Haloperidol lactate may also be administered intravenously

Mechanism of Action Competitive blockade of postsynaptic dopamine receptors in the mesolimbic dopaminergic system; depresses cerebral cortex and hypothalamus; exhibits a strong alpha-adrenergic and anticholinergic-blocking activity

Pharmacodynamics/kinetics

Peak effect: Peak pharmacologic action and control of psychotic manifestation occurs within 30-40 minutes; decanoate form: Peak concentrations occur within about 6-7 days (range: 1-9 days)

Absorption: Well absorbed from the gastrointestinal tract

Metabolism: In the liver to inactive compounds

Bioavailability: Oral: 60%

Half-life: 20 hours; Decanoate: 3 weeks

Time to peak serum concentration:

Oral: 3-6 hours

I.M.: 10-20 minutes

I.M. (long-acting): 3-9 days

Signs and Symptoms of Acute Intoxication Deep sleep, hyperthermia, impotence, dementia, hyperreflexia, hyperprolactinemia, ejaculatory disturbances, chorea (extrapyramidal), hyperglycemia, ptosis, memory loss, lactation, hypopigmented hair, Parkinson's-like symptoms, confusion, dementia, gynecomastia, neuroleptic malignant syndrome, gaze nystagmus, myasthenia gravis (exacerbation or precipitation of), hypoglycemia, hypothermia, disorientation, dysphagia, dystonic reactions, agitation, pulmonary edema, hypokalemia, arrhythmias, extrapyramidal reaction, Q-T prolongation, dry mouth, alopecia, bradycardia, fever, urine discoloration (pink), urine discoloration (red), urine discoloration (red-brown); cardiac conduction abnormalities can occur if daily dose intravenously exceeds 50 mg

When to Transport to Hospital Transport any symptomatic patient or any ingestion over 0.2 mg/kg

Warnings/Precautions Safety and efficacy have not been established in children <3 years of age; watch for hypotension when administering I.M. or I.V.; use with caution in patients with cardiovascular disease or seizures; benefits

(Continued)

281

Haloperidol *(Continued)*

of therapy must be weighed against risks of therapy; decanoate form should never be given I.V. Some tablets contain tartrazine which may cause allergic reactions; use caution in patients receiving anticonvulsant agents and in those with a history of seizures or EEG abnormalities.

Adverse Reactions EKG changes, retinal pigmentation are more common than with chlorpromazine

>10%:

Central nervous system: Restlessness, anxiety, extrapyramidal reactions, dystonic reactions, pseudoparkinsonian signs and symptoms, tardive dyskinesia, neuroleptic malignant syndrome (NMS), seizures, altered central temperature regulation, akathisia

Endocrine & metabolic: Edema of the breasts

Gastrointestinal: Weight gain, constipation

1% to 10%:

Cardiovascular: Hypotension (especially orthostatic), tachycardia, arrhythmias, abnormal T waves with prolonged ventricular repolarization

Central nervous system: Hallucinations, sedation, drowsiness, persistent tardive dyskinesia

Gastrointestinal: Nausea, vomiting

Genitourinary: Dysuria

Reference Range

Therapeutic: 5-15 ng/mL (SI: 10-30 nmol/L) (psychotic disorders - less for Tourette's and mania)

Toxic: >28 ng/mL (SI: >56 nmol/L)

Drug Interactions CNS depressants may increase adverse effects; epinephrine may cause hypotension, carbamazepine and phenobarbital may increase metabolism and decrease effectiveness of haloperidol; haloperidol and anticholinergic agents may cause an increase in intraocular pressure; concurrent use with lithium has occasionally caused acute encephalopathy-like syndrome; ethanol potentiates haloperidol's depressive action in isolated rat heart model; haloperidol and diphenhydramine are incompatible in a hypodermic syringe; reduced plasma levels of haloperidol when given with rifampin; increased plasma concentrations with concomitant itraconazole; urinary retention with concomitant fluoxetine; urinary retention with concomitant venlafaxine

Dosage Forms

Injection, as decanoate: 50 mg/mL (1 mL, 5 mL); 100 mg/mL (1 mL, 5 mL)

Haloperidol lactate:

Concentrate, oral: 2 mg/mL (5 mL, 10 mL, 15 mL, 120 mL, 240 mL)

Injection: 5 mg/mL (1 mL, 2 mL, 2.5 mL, 10 mL)

Tablet: 0.5 mg, 1 mg, 2 mg, 5 mg, 10 mg, 20 mg

Additional Information 5 mg of haloperidol (I.V.) followed by a bolus of 1 L of normal saline has been used to treat migraine headaches; may be used for the emergency sedation of severely psychotic agitated patients (5 mg I.M. with 2 mg of lorazepam I.M.)

Specific References

Mahutte CK, Nakasato SK, and Light RW, "Haloperidol and Sudden Death Due to Pulmonary Edema," *Arch Intern Med*, 1982, 142(10):1951-2.

Halotussin® [OTC] *see* Guaifenesin *on page 269*

Halotussin® DAC *see* Guaifenesin, Pseudoephedrine, and Codeine *on page 275*

Halotussin® DM [OTC] *see* Guaifenesin and Dextromethorphan *on page 271*

Halotussin® PE [OTC] *see* Guaifenesin and Pseudoephedrine *on page 273*

Haltran® [OTC] *see* Ibuprofen *on page 308*

Happy-Trip® *see* Cyclizine *on page 172*

Hashish see Cannabinoids, Qualitative on page 100

Hayfebrol® Liquid [OTC] see Chlorpheniramine and Pseudoephedrine on page 134

hCG, Slide Test, Stat see Pregnancy Test on page 499

hCG, Urine see Pregnancy Test on page 499

HCTZ see Hydrochlorothiazide on page 291

HD see Mustard Gas on page 414

He see Helium on this page

Head Louse see Lice on page 343

Heavenly Blue see Morning Glory on page 409

Heitrin® see Terazosin on page 560

Helium

Synonyms He

UN Number 1046

Use Often used as an inhalant of misuse; also may be a byproduct in welding; a balloon filler heating medium; used in neon signs and mixed-gas sea diving

Mechanism of Toxic Action Can cause arterial gas embolism

Signs and Symptoms of Acute Intoxication Coma, nausea, dizziness, seizures, paresthesia, headache, blurriness, clonus, neck pain, limb weakness; all symptoms of cerebral gas embolism; also can cause dermal burns upon skin contact; laryngeal changes can occur

When to Transport to Hospital Transport any suspected exposure

Overdosage/Treatment

Decontamination: Inhalation: Humidified 100% oxygen

Supportive therapy: Hyperbaric oxygen may be useful if signs of arterial gas embolism develop

Additional Information Liquid helium is a colorless, tasteless, odorless liquid which is easily vaporized; atmospheric concentrations exceeding 20 mg/dL can cause symptoms

Specific gravity: 0.15

Vapor density: 0.14

Specific References

Pao BS and Hayden SR, "Cerebral Gas Embolism Resulting From Inhalation of Pressurized Helium," Ann Emerg Med, 1996, 28:363-6.

Hemlock see Poison Hemlock on page 491

Hemocyte® see Iron on page 318

Hemp see Cannabinoids, Qualitative on page 100

Hemril-HC™ see Hydrocortisone on page 297

Herb and Al see Cannabinoids, Qualitative on page 100

Heroin (HAIR oh in)

Synonyms Acetomorphine; Diacetylmorphine; Diamorphine Hydrochloride

Therapeutic Category Analgesic, Narcotic

Abuse Potential Yes

Impairment Potential Yes

Use Most commonly a drug of abuse in the United States; used as an analgesic agent or cough suppressant in Britain

Usual Dosage

Analgesia (in Europe):

Oral: 5-10 mg

I.M., S.C.: 5 mg (usually I.V. dose)

As a drug of abuse: Nasal insufflation, I.V., S.C.: Up to 200 mg; usual dose: ~2 mg

(Continued)

Heroin *(Continued)*

Mechanism of Action Acetylated morphine derivative with CNS depressant effects

Pharmacodynamics/kinetics

Peak plasma level: 10 minutes after I.M. absorption

Metabolism: Deacetylation to 6-acetylmorphine and then to morphine in the liver (both active metabolites)

Half-life: 3-20 minutes

Elimination: Urine (as morphine glucuronides); total clearance: 31 mL/kg/minute

Estimated Number of Emergency Department Heroin/Morphine Mentions, by Metropolitan Area by Year, 1991-1996

	Total 1991	Total 1992	Total 1993	Total 1994	Total 1995*	Total 1996*
Total U.S.	35,898	48,003	63,232	64,013	72,229*	70,463*
Atlanta	157	232	250	456	446	455
Baltimore	3,892	5,106	5,719	7,510	8,220	7,845
Boston (NECMA)	1,165	2,061	2,319	2,527	2,821	2,467
Buffalo	155	172	279	355	416	404
Chicago	2,262	2,958	3,581	4,787	4,852	6,100
Dallas	234	276	297	237	301	379
Denver	109	123	276	495	622	361
Detroit	1,828	1,843	2,380	2,106	2,422	3,117
Los Angeles - LB	1,674	2,944	3,724	2,949	3,097	3,099
Miami - Hialeah	145	181	251	264	339	389
Minneapolis - SP	76	94	138	78	99	115
New Orleans	223	152	140	197	283	332
New York	6,019	8,382	11,351	11,185	11,048	9,837
Newark	2,328	2,868	4,526	4,498	5,684	5,492
Philadelphia	2,424	2,364	2,478	2,440	3,759	3,598
Phoenix	348	324	487	483	488	624
St Louis - MO, IL	177	204	215	408	409	507
San Diego	773	1,022	842	695	682	881
San Francisco	3,140	3,131	3,694	3,555	3,474	3,491
Seattle	789	1,100	1,727	2,092	2,095	2,405
Washington DC	1,480	1,512	1,414	1,261	1,301	1,492
Z-NAT Panel	6,502	10,956	17,146	15,437	19,369	17,083

* Estimates for this time period are preliminary. Final estimates will be produced later and may be higher or lower than preliminary estimates due to nonresponse adjustment and other factors.

Note: These estimates are based on a representative sample of non-federal short stay hospitals with 24-hour Emergency Departments.

From SAMHSA, Drug Abuse Warning Network, April 1997 files.

Signs and Symptoms of Acute Intoxication Amenorrhea, delirium, tongue discoloration, hypothermia, photophobia, pemphigus, nephrotic syndrome, myopathy, myocardial depression, impotence, extrapyramidal reaction, encephalopathy, miosis, dry mouth, dysphoria, disorientation, constipation, coma, respiratory depression, dyspnea

When to Transport to Hospital Transport any symptomatic patient

Overdosage/Treatment

Decontamination: Oral: Activated charcoal; for asymptomatic body packers, whole bowel irrigation with polyethylene glycol (PEG) solution is recommended

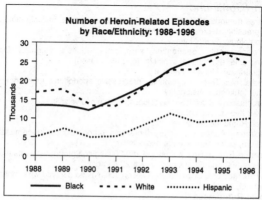

From U.S. Department of Health and Human Services Public Health Service, "Annual Trends in Heroin-Related Episodes," *Preliminary Estimates From the Drug Abuse Warning Network,* 1996, 17:10.

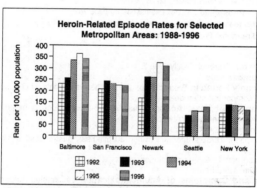

From U.S. Department of Health and Human Services Public Health Service, "Annual Trends In Selected Metropolitan Areas, *Preliminary Estimates From the Drug Abuse Warning Network,*" 1996, 17:17.

Supportive therapy: Antidote of choice is naloxone (bolus: 0.4-2 mg I.V.); a continuous infusion may be required, especially in the management of a body stuffer/packer

Warnings/Precautions May provoke hypertension and tachycardia in patients with pheochromocytoma; diarrhea associated with antibiotics; pulmonary disease, gallbladder disease, hypothyroidism, inflammatory bowel disease, prostatic hypertrophy, increased intracranial pressure

Adverse Reactions

Cardiovascular: Hypotension, congestive heart failure
(Continued)

Heroin *(Continued)*

Central nervous system: Lethargy, coma, euphoria, hallucinations, CNS depression, depression, paranoia

Dermatologic: Pemphigus

Gastrointestinal: Constipation, xerostomia, nausea, vomiting, Ogilvie's syndrome, esophageal sphincter tone (decreased)

Genitourinary: Urinary retention

Hematologic: Thrombocytopenia, progressive spongiform leukoencephalopathy, leukoencephalopathy

Neuromuscular & skeletal: Myoclonus, rhabdomyolysis

Ocular: Miosis, photophobia

Renal: Renal failure, proteinuria

Respiratory: Apnea, respiratory depression, bronchospasm (upon nasal insufflation), pulmonary edema, aspiration

Reference Range Heroin doses of 150-200 mg can produce plasma morphine levels of 300 ng/mL; analgesic level: 20-65 ng/mL

Drug Interactions Subcutaneous absorption may be delayed when coadministered with cocaine

Specific References

Sporer KA, Firestone J, and Isaacs SM, "Out-of-Hospital Treatment of Opioid Overdoses in an Urban Setting," *Acad Emerg Med*, 1996, 3(7):660-7.

Heroin *see* Opiates, Qualitative, Urine *on page 445*

Hexacycline® *see* Tetracycline *on page 568*

Hexadrol® *see* Dexamethasone *on page 182*

Hexadrol® Phosphate *see* Dexamethasone *on page 182*

Hexahydrodesoxyephedrine *see* Propylhexedrine *on page 513*

Hexamidinum *see* Primidone *on page 500*

Hexane

Synonyms Dipropyl; Skellysolve B

UN Number 1208

Commonly Found In Production of glues, adhesives, paints, shoes, and furniture; component of crude oil

Mechanism of Toxic Action Metabolite 2,5-hexanedione is neurotoxic; 2-methyl pentone leads to hexone

Toxicodynamics/kinetics

Absorption: Through the skin (within 30 minutes), gastrointestinal tract, and lungs

Metabolism: To 2,5-hexanedione

Half-life: 1.5-2 hours

Signs and Symptoms of Acute Intoxication Lacrimation, upper airway irritation, dyspnea, muscle cramps, ototoxicity, tinnitus, blurred vision; peripheral muscles are affected first; peripheral sensorimotor neuropathy

When to Transport to Hospital Transport any suspected exposure

Overdosage/Treatment Decontamination:

Oral exposure: Dilute with 4-8 oz of milk or water

Dermal: Irrigate skin with soap and water

Adverse Reactions

Cardiovascular: Tachycardia, sinus tachycardia

Central nervous system: CNS depression

Respiratory: Respiratory depression

Miscellaneous: Multiple chemical sensitivity syndrome

Reference Range Urine concentration of 2,5-hexanedione should be <5 mg/L; background blood hexane concentrations in unexposed adults range from 0.02-7.7 µg/L (average: 0.6 µg/L)

Additional Information Parkinsonism may occur with chronic exposure along with a sensory polyneuropathy and memory deficits

TLV-TWA: 50 ppm

Specific References

Couri DC and Milks MM, "Hexacarbon Neuropathy: Tracking a Toxin," *Neurotoxicology*, 1985, 6(4):65-72.

Hexogen *see RDX on page 522*

Hexolite *see RDX on page 522*

Hibanil® *see Chlorpromazine on page 138*

Hi-Cor 1.0® *see Hydrocortisone on page 297*

Hi-Cor-2.5® *see Hydrocortisone on page 297*

Hismanal® *see Astemizole on page 59*

Histaject® *see Brompheniramine on page 84*

Histalet® **Forte Tablet** *see Chlorpheniramine, Pyrilamine, Phenylephrine, and Phenylpropanolamine on page 138*

Histalet® **Syrup [OTC]** *see Chlorpheniramine and Pseudoephedrine on page 134*

Histalet® **X** *see Guaifenesin and Pseudoephedrine on page 273*

Histatab® **Plus Tablet [OTC]** *see Chlorpheniramine and Phenylephrine on page 134*

Hista-Vadrin® **Tablet** *see Chlorpheniramine, Phenylephrine, and Phenylpropanolamine on page 136*

Histerone® **Injection** *see Testosterone on page 564*

Histor-D® **Syrup** *see Chlorpheniramine and Phenylephrine on page 134*

Histor-D® **Timecelles**® *see Chlorpheniramine, Phenylephrine, and Methscopolamine on page 136*

Hoch *see Formaldehyde on page 259*

Hold® **DM [OTC]** *see Dextromethorphan on page 187*

Holly

Synonyms Appalachian Tea; Cassena; Deer Berry; English-Oregon-American-Christmas-Indian Holly; Indian Black Drink; Kristtorn; Yanpon

Scientific Name *Ilex aquifolium*

Ilex opaca

Ilex vomitoria

Use Native Americans used the plant as an emetic and cardiac stimulant

Usual Dosage Not well established; apparently berries must be eaten in quantity to produce toxic symptoms

Mechanism of Toxic Action Irritation of the gastrointestinal tract

Signs and Symptoms of Acute Intoxication Nausea, vomiting, and diarrhea

When to Transport to Hospital Transport any patient ingesting over 5 berries or any patient exhibiting gastrointestinal symptoms

Overdosage/Treatment

Decontamination: One dose of cathartic may be given if symptoms have not begun; gastric decontamination emesis with ipecac within 30 minutes or lavage within 1 hour for ingestions over six berries

Supportive therapy: Replace fluids and electrolytes as needed to prevent dehydration

Additional Information

Range: Found throughout the Eastern and Southern U.S.

Toxin: Ilexanthin, ilex acid, tannic acid, ilicin

Toxic part: Berries are toxic in quantity

(Continued)

Holly *(Continued)*
Specific References
Rodrigues TD, Johnson PN, and Jeffrey LP, "Holly Berry Ingestion: Case Report," *Vet Hum Toxicol*, 1984, 26(2):157-8.

Holy Mushroom *see* Reishi Mushroom *on page 523*

Homatropine *(hoe MA troe peen)*
Related Information
Hydrocodone and Homatropine *on page 295*
U.S. Brand Names AK-Homatropine®; Isopto® Homatropine
Therapeutic Category Anticholinergic Agent
Use Producing cycloplegia and mydriasis for refraction; treatment of acute inflammatory conditions of the uveal tract
Usual Dosage
Children:
  Mydriasis and cycloplegia for refraction: Instill 1 drop of 2% solution immediately before the procedure; repeat at 10-minute intervals as needed
  Uveitis: Instill 1 drop of 2% solution 2-3 times/day
Adults:
  Mydriasis and cycloplegia for refraction: Instill 1-2 drops of 2% solution or 1 drop of 5% solution before the procedure; repeat at 5- to 10-minute intervals as needed
  Uveitis: Instill 1-2 drops of 2% or 5% 2-3 times/day up to every 3-4 hours as needed
Mechanism of Action Blocks response of iris sphincter muscle and the accommodative muscle of the ciliary body to cholinergic stimulation resulting in dilation and loss of accommodation
Pharmacodynamics/kinetics
Onset of accommodation and pupil effect: Ophthalmic:
  Maximum mydriatic effect: Within 10-30 minutes
  Maximum cycloplegic effect: Within 30-90 minutes
Duration:
  Mydriasis: 6 hours to 4 days
  Cycloplegia: 10-48 hours
Signs and Symptoms of Acute Intoxication Blurred vision, urinary retention, tachycardia
When to Transport to Hospital Transport any symptomatic patient
Warnings/Precautions Use with caution in patients with hypertension, cardiac disease, or increased intraocular pressure; safety and efficacy not established in infants and young children, therefore, use with extreme caution due to susceptibility of systemic effects; use with caution in obstructive uropathy, paralytic ileus, ulcerative colitis, unstable cardiovascular status in acute hemorrhage
Adverse Reactions
>10%: Ocular: Blurred vision, photophobia
1% to 10%:
  Local: Stinging, local irritation
  Ocular: Increased intraocular pressure
  Respiratory: Congestion
Dosage Forms
Homatropine hydrobromide:
  Solution, ophthalmic:
    2% (1 mL, 5 mL); 5% (1 mL, 2 mL, 5 mL)
    AK-Homatropine®: 5% (15 mL)
    Isopto® Homatropine 2% (5 mL, 15 mL); 5% (5 mL, 15 mL)

Specific References
Barker DB and Solomon DA, "The Potential for Mental Status Changes Associated With Systemic Absorption of Anticholinergic Ophthalmic Medications: Concerns in the Elderly," *DICP Ann Pharmacother*, 1990, 24(9):847-50.

Homatropine and Hydrocodone *see* Hydrocodone and Homatropine *on page 295*

Hops

Synonyms Common Hops; European Hops; Lupulin
Scientific Name *Humulus lupulus*
Use In herbal medicine as a sleep aid (sometimes combined with valerian root)
Mechanism of Toxic Action Contains several bitter acids (lupulone, myrcene, humulone) which may have antimicrobial activity, inhibit smooth muscle activity and exhibit CNS depression; probable dermal irritant
When to Transport to Hospital Transport any patient with central nervous system depression
Overdosage/Treatment Decontamination: Dermal: Wash with soap and water
Adverse Reactions Dermatologic: Contact dermatitis (upon exposure to extracts)
Additional Information A perennial, climbing vine with heights up to 25 feet found in Germany and Pacific Northwest; loses most of its activity (85%) after 9 months of storage; not to be confused with Wild Hops (*Bryonia*)

Hortetracin® *see* Tetracycline *on page 568*
5-HTP *see* Oxitriptan *on page 451*
Huile de Camphre *see* Camphor *on page 99*
Human Chorionic Gonadotropin, Urine *see* Pregnancy Test *on page 499*
Humex® *see* Carbinoxamine *on page 106*
Humibid® DM [OTC] *see* Guaifenesin and Dextromethorphan *on page 271*
Humibid® L.A. *see* Guaifenesin *on page 269*
Humibid® Sprinkle *see* Guaifenesin *on page 269*
Humulin® *see* Insulin Preparations *on page 314*
Hurricaine® *see* Benzocaine *on page 70*
Hybolin™ Decanoate Injection *see* Nandrolone *on page 421*
Hybolin™ Improved Injection *see* Nandrolone *on page 421*
HycoClear Tuss® *see* Hydrocodone and Guaifenesin *on page 295*
Hycodan® *see* Hydrocodone and Homatropine *on page 295*
Hycomine® *see* Hydrocodone and Phenylpropanolamine *on page 296*
Hycomine® Compound *see* Hydrocodone, Chlorpheniramine, Phenylephrine, Acetaminophen, and Caffeine *on page 296*
Hycomine® Pediatric *see* Hydrocodone and Phenylpropanolamine *on page 296*
Hycort® *see* Hydrocortisone *on page 297*
Hycotuss® Expectorant Liquid *see* Hydrocodone and Guaifenesin *on page 295*
Hydeltrasol® *see* Prednisolone *on page 495*
Hydeltra-T.B.A.® *see* Prednisolone *on page 495*

Hydralazine (hye DRAL a zeen)

U.S. Brand Names Apresoline®
Canadian Brand Names Apo-Hydralazine®; Novo-Hylazin®; Nu-Hydral®
Therapeutic Category Vasodilator
Use Management of moderate to severe hypertension, congestive heart failure, hypertension secondary to pre-eclampsia/eclampsia; has been used to treat primary pulmonary hypertension
(Continued)

289

Hydralazine *(Continued)*

Usual Dosage Titrate dosage to patient's response

Children:

Oral: Initial: 0.75-1 mg/kg/day in 2-4 divided doses, not to exceed 25 mg/dose; increase over 3-4 weeks to maximum of 7.5 mg/kg/day in 2-4 divided doses; maximum daily dose: 200 mg/day

I.M., I.V.: 0.1-0.5 mg/kg/dose (initial dose not to exceed 20 mg) every 4-6 hours as needed

Adults:

Oral: Initial: 10 mg 4 times/day, increase by 10-25 mg/dose every 2-5 days to maximum of 300 mg/day

I.M., I.V.:

Hypertensive initial: 10-20 mg/dose every 4-6 hours as needed, may increase to 40 mg/dose; change to oral therapy as soon as possible

Pre-eclampsia/eclampsia: 5 mg/dose then 5-10 mg every 20-30 minutes as needed

Mechanism of Action Direct vasodilation of arterioles (with little effect on veins) with decreased systemic resistance

Pharmacodynamics/kinetics

Onset of action:

Oral: 20-30 minutes

I.V.: 5-20 minutes

Duration:

Oral: 2-4 hours

I.V.: 2-6 hours

Absorption: Well absorbed

Bioavailability: 30% to 50%

Half-life: 0.44-0.47 hours

Time to peak serum concentration: Oral: 60 minutes

Elimination:

Renal: 2% to 14% unchanged

Feces: 3% to 12%

Signs and Symptoms of Acute Intoxication Hypotension, erythema multiforme, wheezing, lacrimation, impotence, cholestatic jaundice, tachycardia, thrombocytopenia, neuropathy (peripheral), hyperthermia, arrhythmias, shock, hypokalemia, lactic acidosis, leukopenia; neutropenia; agranulocytosis; granulocytopenia

When to Transport to Hospital Transport any symptomatic patient or ingestions exceeding 1 mg/kg

Warnings/Precautions Discontinue hydralazine in patients who develop SLE-like syndrome or positive ANA. Use with caution in patients with severe renal disease or cerebral vascular accidents. Some formulations may contain tartrazines or sulfites.

Adverse Reactions

>10%:

Cardiovascular: Palpitations, flushing, tachycardia, angina pectoris

Central nervous system: Headache

Gastrointestinal: Nausea, vomiting, diarrhea, anorexia

1% to 10%:

Cardiovascular: Hypotension, redness or flushing of face

Gastrointestinal: Constipation

Ocular: Lacrimation

Respiratory: Dyspnea, nasal congestion

Note: Because of blunted beta-receptor response, the elderly are less likely to experience reflex tachycardia; this puts them at greater risk for orthostatic hypotension

Drug Interactions MAO inhibitors may significantly decrease blood pressure; indomethacin may decrease hypotensive effects

Dosage Forms
Injection: 20 mg/mL (1 mL)
Tablet: 10 mg, 25 mg, 50 mg, 100 mg

Additional Information Slow acetylators, patients with decreased renal function and patients receiving >200 mg/day (chronically) are at higher risk for systemic lupus erythematosus (SLE). Usually administered with diuretic and a beta-blocker to counteract side effects of sodium and water retention and reflex tachycardia although the beta-blocker may not be necessary in the elderly; odorless, bitter-tasting powder.

Specific References
Smith BA and Ferguson DB, "Acute Hydralazine Overdose: Marked ECG Abnormalities in a Young Adult," *Ann Emerg Med*, 1992, 21(3):326-30.

Hydralazine and Hydrochlorothiazide
(hye DRAL a zeen & hye droe klor oh THYE a zide)
Synonyms Hydrochlorothiazide and Hydralazine
U.S. Brand Names Apresazide®
Therapeutic Category Antihypertensive, Combination
Dosage Forms Capsule:
25/25: Hydralazine hydrochloride 25 mg and hydrochlorothiazide 25 mg
50/50: Hydralazine hydrochloride 50 mg and hydrochlorothiazide 50 mg
100/50: Hydralazine hydrochloride 100 mg and hydrochlorothiazide 50 mg

Hydralazine, Hydrochlorothiazide, and Reserpine
(hye DRAL a zeen, hye droe klor oh THYE a zide, & re SER peen)
U.S. Brand Names Hydrap-ES®; Marpres®; Ser-Ap-Es®
Therapeutic Category Antihypertensive, Combination
Impairment Potential Yes
Dosage Forms Tablet: Hydralazine 25 mg, hydrochlorothiazide 15 mg, and reserpine 0.1 mg

Hydramyn® Syrup [OTC] *see* Diphenhydramine *on page 205*
Hydrap-ES® *see* Hydralazine, Hydrochlorothiazide, and Reserpine *on this page*
Hydrate® *see* Dimenhydrinate *on page 203*
Hydrocet® *see* Hydrocodone and Acetaminophen *on page 293*

Hydrochlorothiazide (hye droe klor oh THYE a zide)
Synonyms HCTZ
U.S. Brand Names Aquazide-H®; Diaqua®; Esidrix®; Ezide®; HydroDIURIL®; Hydro-Par®; Hydro-T®; Mictrin®; Oretic®
Canadian Brand Names Apo-Hydro®; Diuchlor®; Neo-Codema®; Novo-Hydrazide®; Urozide®
Therapeutic Category Diuretic
Use Management of mild to moderate hypertension; treatment of edema in congestive heart failure and nephrotic syndrome; diabetes insipidus, hypercalciuria
Usual Dosage In pediatric patients, chlorothiazide may be preferred as there are more dosage forms (ie, suspension)

Oral (effect of drug may be decreased when used every day):
Children (daily dosages should be decreased if used with other antihypertensives):
<6 months: 2-3 mg/kg/day in 2 divided doses
>6 months: 2 mg/kg/day in 2 divided doses
Adults: 25-50 mg/day in 1-2 doses; maximum: 200 mg/day
(Continued)

Hydrochlorothiazide *(Continued)*

Mechanism of Action Inhibits sodium reabsorption in the distal tubules causing increased excretion of sodium and water as well as potassium and hydrogen ions; at high doses may inhibit carbonic anhydrase

Pharmacodynamics/kinetics

Onset of diuretic action: Oral: Within 2 hours

Peak effect: 4 hours

Duration: 6-12 hours

Absorption: Oral: ~60% to 80%

Half-life: 10-12 hours (may be up to 29 hours in patients with heart failure)

Signs and Symptoms of Acute Intoxication A-V block, cystitis, impotence, photosensitivity, hypokalemia, hyperuricemia, hyperglycemia, myocarditis, myalgia, diabetes insipidus, diuresis, nocturia, myasthenia gravis (exacerbation or precipitation of), vision color changes (yellow tinge), hyponatremia, pancreatitis, hyperperistalsis, hypercalcemia, leukopenia; neutropenia; agranulocytosis; granulocytopenia; fever

When to Transport to Hospital Transport any symptomatic patient or ingestions over 3 mg/kg

Warnings/Precautions Use with caution in renal disease, hepatic disease, gout, lupus erythematosus, diabetes mellitus; some products may contain tartrazine

Adverse Reactions 1% to 10%: Endocrine & metabolic: Hypokalemia

Test Interactions Hydrochlorothiazide may cause false increase in acetaminophen assay by HPLC method

Reference Range Serum level of 2 µg/mL associated with peak diuretic effect

Drug Interactions

Decreased effect of oral hypoglycemics; decreased absorption with cholestyramine and colestipol

Increased effect with furosemide and other loop diuretics

Increased toxicity/levels of lithium; increases amantadine toxicity

Hyponatremia associated with trimethoprim or carbamazepine; calcium salt administration may result in milk-alkali syndrome; can produce elevation of plasma triglyceride concentrations when used with beta-blocking agents

Dosage Forms

Solution, oral (mint flavor): 50 mg/5 mL (50 mL)

Tablet: 25 mg, 50 mg, 100 mg

Additional Information Inhibits insulin secretion/vitamin D synthesis

Specific References

Zahid M, Krumlovsky FA, Roxe D, et al, "Central Nervous System and Cardiac Manifestations of Hydrochlorothiazide Overdosage; Treatment With Hemodialysis," *Am J Kidney Dis*, 1988, 11(6):508-11.

Hydrochlorothiazide and Hydralazine *see* Hydralazine and Hydrochlorothiazide *on previous page*

Hydrochlorothiazide and Methyldopa *see* Methyldopa and Hydrochlorothiazide *on page 395*

Hydrochlorothiazide and Reserpine

(hye droe klor oh THYE a zide & re SER peen)

Synonyms Reserpine and Hydrochlorothiazide

U.S. Brand Names Hydropres®; Hydro-Serp®; Hydroserpine®

Therapeutic Category Antihypertensive, Combination

Impairment Potential Yes

Dosage Forms Tablet: 50: Hydrochlorothiazide 50 mg and reserpine 0.125 mg

Hydrochlorothiazide and Triamterene
(hye droe klor oh THYE a zide & trye AM ter een)

U.S. Brand Names Dyazide®; Maxzide®

Canadian Brand Names Apo-Triazide®; Novo-Triamzide®; Nu-Triazide®

Therapeutic Category Antihypertensive, Combination

Dosage Forms

Capsule (Dyazide®): Hydrochlorothiazide 25 mg and triamterene 37.5 mg

Tablet:

Maxzide®-25: Hydrochlorothiazide 25 mg and triamterene 37.5 mg

Maxzide®: Hydrochlorothiazide 50 mg and triamterene 75 mg

Hydrocodone and Acetaminophen
(hye droe KOE done & a seet a MIN oh fen)

Related Information

Acetaminophen *on page 20*

Controlled Substances - Uses and Effects *on page 741*

Synonyms Acetaminophen and Hydrocodone

U.S. Brand Names Anexsia®; Anodynos-DHC®; Bancap HC®; Co-Gesic®; Dolacet®; DuoCet™; Hydrocet®; Hydrogesic®; Hy-Phen®; Lorcet® Lorcet®-HD; Lorcet® Plus; Lortab®; Margesic® H; Medipain 5® Norcet®; Stagesic®; T-Gesic®; Vicodin®; Vicodin® ES HP; Zydone®

Canadian Brand Names Vapocet®

Therapeutic Category Analgesic, Narcotic

Abuse Potential Yes

Impairment Potential Yes; Blood hydrocodone levels >0.13 mg/L associated with driving impairment

Baselt RC and Cravey RH, *Disposition of Toxic Drugs and Chemicals in Man*, 4th ed, Foster City, CA: Chemical Toxicology Institute, 1995, 381.

Use Relief of moderate to severe pain; antitussive (hydrocodone)

Usual Dosage Oral (doses should be titrated to appropriate analgesic effect):

Children:

Antitussive (hydrocodone): 0.6 mg/kg/day in 3-4 divided doses

A single dose should not exceed 10 mg in children >12 years, 5 mg in children 2-12 years, and 1.25 mg in children <2 years of age

Analgesic (acetaminophen): Refer to Acetaminophen monograph

Adults: Analgesic: 1-2 tablets or capsules every 4-6 hours or 5-10 mL solution every 4-6 hours as needed for pain

Signs and Symptoms of Acute Intoxication Hepatic necrosis, blood dyscrasias, respiratory depression, miosis, bradycardia, hypotension, sedation, drowsiness, ptosis, fatigue, vomiting, slow and raspy speech

Adverse Reactions

>10%:

Cardiovascular: Hypotension

Central nervous system: Lightheadedness, dizziness, sedation, drowsiness, fatigue

Neuromuscular & skeletal: Weakness

1% to 10%:

Cardiovascular: Bradycardia

Central nervous system: Confusion

Gastrointestinal: Nausea, vomiting

Genitourinary: Decreased urination

Respiratory: Shortness of breath, dyspnea

Drug Interactions

Decreased effect with phenothiazines

Increased effect with dextroamphetamine

(Continued)

293

Hydrocodone and Acetaminophen *(Continued)*

Increased toxicity with CNS depressants, TCAs

Dosage Forms

Capsule: Bancap HC®, Dolacet®, Hydrocet®, Hydrogesic®, Lorcet®-HD, Margesic® H, Medipain 5®, Norcet®, Stagesic®, T-Gesic®, Zydone®: Hydrocodone bitartrate 5 mg and acetaminophen 500 mg

Elixir (tropical fruit punch flavor) (Lortab®): Hydrocodone bitartrate 2.5 mg and acetaminophen 167 mg per 5 mL with alcohol 7% (480 mL)

Solution, oral (tropical fruit punch flavor) (Lortab®): Hydrocodone bitartrate 2.5 mg and acetaminophen 167 mg per 5 mL with alcohol 7% (480 mL)

Tablet:

Lortab® 2.5/500: Hydrocodone bitartrate 2.5 mg and acetaminophen 500 mg

Anexsia® 5/500, Anodynos-DHC®, Co-Gesic®, DuoCet™, DHC®; Hy-Phen®, Lorcet®, Lortab®® 5/500, Vicodin®: Hydrocodone bitartrate 5 mg and acetaminophen 500 mg

Lortab® 7.5/500: Hydrocodone bitartrate 7.5 mg and acetaminophen 500 mg

Anexsia® 7.5/650, Lorcet® Plus: Hydrocodone bitartrate 7.5 mg and acetaminophen 650 mg

Vicodin® ES: Hydrocodone bitartrate 7.5 mg and acetaminophen 750 mg

Lortab® 10/500: Hydrocodone bitartrate 10 mg and acetaminophen 500 mg

Lorcet® 10/650: Hydrocodone bitartrate 10 mg and acetaminophen 650 mg

Vicodin® HP: Hydrocodone bitartrate 10 mg and acetaminophen 660 mg

Additional Information Abrupt discontinuation after sustained use (generally >10 days) may cause withdrawal symptoms

Hydrocodone and Aspirin *(hye droe KOE done & AS pir in)*

Related Information

Aspirin *on page 56*

Controlled Substances - Uses and Effects *on page 741*

U.S. Brand Names Alor® 5/500; Azdone®; Damason-P®; Lortab® ASA; Panasal® 5/500

Therapeutic Category Analgesic, Narcotic

Abuse Potential Yes

Impairment Potential Yes; Blood hydrocodone levels >0.13 mg/L associated with driving impairment

Baselt RC and Cravey RH, *Disposition of Toxic Drugs and Chemicals in Man*, 4th ed, Foster City, CA: Chemical Toxicology Institute, 199, 381.

Use Relief of moderate to moderately severe pain

Usual Dosage Adults: Oral: 1-2 tablets every 4-6 hours as needed for pain

Mechanism of Action Refer to individual agents

Signs and Symptoms of Acute Intoxication Miosis, bradycardia, hypotension, sedation, drowsiness, ptosis, fatigue, vomiting, slow and raspy speech

Overdosage/Treatment Antidote is naloxone for codeine. Naloxone 2 mg I.V. (0.01 mg/kg for children) with repeat administration as necessary up to a total of 10 mg. Treatment can also be based upon symptomatology; see Aspirin.

Warnings/Precautions Use with caution in patients with impaired renal function, erosive gastritis, or peptic ulcer disease; children and teenagers should not use for chickenpox or flu symptoms before a physician is consulted about Reye's syndrome

Adverse Reactions

>10%:

Cardiovascular: Hypotension

Central nervous system: Lightheadedness, dizziness, sedation, drowsiness, fatigue

Gastrointestinal: Nausea, heartburn, stomach pains, dyspepsia, epigastric discomfort

Neuromuscular & skeletal: Weakness

1% to 10%:

Cardiovascular: Bradycardia

Central nervous system: Confusion

Dermatologic: Rash

Gastrointestinal: Vomiting, gastrointestinal ulceration

Genitourinary: Decreased urination

Hematologic: Hemolytic anemia

Respiratory: Shortness of breath, dyspnea

Miscellaneous: Anaphylactic shock

Test Interactions Urine glucose, urinary 5-HIAA, serum uric acid

Drug Interactions Increased toxicity with CNS depressants, warfarin (bleeding)

Dosage Forms Tablet: Hydrocodone bitartrate 5 mg and aspirin 500 mg

Hydrocodone and Chlorpheniramine

(hye droe KOE done & klor fen IR a meen)

Related Information

Chlorpheniramine *on page 132*

Controlled Substances - Uses and Effects *on page 741*

U.S. Brand Names Tussionex®

Therapeutic Category Antihistamine/Antitussive

Dosage Forms Syrup, alcohol free: Hydrocodone polistirex 10 mg and chlorpheniramine polistirex 8 mg per 5 mL (480 mL, 900 mL)

Hydrocodone and Guaifenesin

(hye droe KOE done & gwye FEN e sin)

Synonyms Guaifenesin and Hydrocodone

U.S. Brand Names Codiclear® DH; HycoClear Tuss®; Hycotuss® Expectorant Liquid; Kwelcof®

Therapeutic Category Antitussive/Expectorant

Abuse Potential Yes

Impairment Potential Yes; Blood hydrocodone levels >0.13 mg/L associated with driving impairment

Baselt RC and Cravey RH, *Disposition of Toxic Drugs and Chemicals in Man*, 4th ed, Foster City, CA: Chemical Toxicology Institute, 1995, 381.

Dosage Forms Liquid: Hydrocodone bitartrate 5 mg and guaifenesin 100 mg per 5 mL (120 mL, 480 mL)

Hydrocodone and Homatropine

(hye droe KOE done & hoe MA troe peen)

Related Information

Controlled Substances - Uses and Effects *on page 741*

Homatropine *on page 288*

Synonyms Homatropine and Hydrocodone

U.S. Brand Names Hycodan®; Hydromet®; Hydropane®; Hydrotropine®; Tussigon®

Therapeutic Category Antitussive

Dosage Forms

Syrup (Hycodan®, Hydromet®, Hydropane®, Hydrotropine®): Hydrocodone bitartrate 5 mg and homatropine methylbromide 1.5 mg per 5 mL (120 mL, 480 mL, 4000 mL)

Tablet (Hycodan®, Tussigon®): Hydrocodone bitartrate 5 mg and homatropine methylbromide 1.5 mg

Hydrocodone and Ibuprofen
(hye droe KOE done & eye byoo PROE fen)
U.S. Brand Names Vicoprofen®
Therapeutic Category Analgesic, Narcotic
Abuse Potential Yes
Impairment Potential Yes; Blood hydrocodone levels >0.13 mg/L associated with driving impairment

Baselt RC and Cravey RH, *Disposition of Toxic Drugs and Chemicals in Man*, 4th ed, Foster City, CA: Chemical Toxicology Institute, 1995, 381.

Dosage Forms Tablet: Hydrocodone bitartrate 7.5 mg and ibuprofen 200 mg

Hydrocodone and Phenylpropanolamine
(hye droe KOE done & fen il proe pa NOLE a meen)
Synonyms Phenylpropanolamine and Hydrocodone
U.S. Brand Names Codamine®; Codamine® Pediatric; Hycomine®; Hycomine® Pediatric; Hydrocodone PA® Syrup
Therapeutic Category Antitussive/Decongestant
Abuse Potential Yes
Impairment Potential Yes; Blood hydrocodone levels >0.13 mg/L associated with driving impairment

Baselt RC and Cravey RH, *Disposition of Toxic Drugs and Chemicals in Man*, 4th ed, Foster City, CA: Chemical Toxicology Institute, 1995, 381.

Dosage Forms Syrup:
Codamine®, Hycomine®: Hydrocodone bitartrate 5 mg and phenylpropanolamine hydrochloride 25 mg per 5 mL (480 mL, 3780 mL)
Codamine® Pediatric, Hycomine® Pediatric: Hydrocodone bitartrate 2.5 mg and phenylpropanolamine hydrochloride 12.5 mg per 5 mL (480 mL, 3780 mL)

Hydrocodone, Chlorpheniramine, Phenylephrine, Acetaminophen, and Caffeine
(hye droe KOE done, klor fen IR a meen, fen il EF rin, a seet a MIN oh fen, & KAF een)
U.S. Brand Names Hycomine® Compound
Therapeutic Category Antitussive
Abuse Potential Yes
Impairment Potential Yes; Blood hydrocodone levels >0.13 mg/L associated with driving impairment

Baselt RC and Cravey RH, *Disposition of Toxic Drugs and Chemicals in Man*, 4th ed, Foster City, CA: Chemical Toxicology Institute, 1995, 381.

Dosage Forms Tablet: Hydrocodone bitartrate 5 mg, chlorpheniramine maleate 2 mg, phenylephrine hydrochloride 10 mg, acetaminophen 250 mg, and caffeine 30 mg

Hydrocodone PA® Syrup *see* Hydrocodone and Phenylpropanolamine *on this page*

Hydrocodone, Phenylephrine, Pyrilamine, Phenindamine, Chlorpheniramine, and Ammonium Chloride
(hye droe KOE done, fen il EF rin, peer IL a meen, fen IN da meen, klor fen IR a meen, & a MOE nee um KLOR ide)
U.S. Brand Names P-V-Tussin®
Therapeutic Category Antihistamine/Decongestant/Antitussive
Abuse Potential Yes

Impairment Potential Yes; Blood hydrocodone levels >0.13 mg/L associated with driving impairment

Baselt RC and Cravey RH, *Disposition of Toxic Drugs and Chemicals in Man*, 4th ed, Foster City, CA: Chemical Toxicology Institute, 1995, 381.

Hydrocodone, Pseudoephedrine, and Guaifenesin
(hye droe KOE done, soo doe e FED rin, & gwye FEN e sin)

U.S. Brand Names Cophene XP®; Detussin® Expectorant; SRC® Expectorant; Tussafin® Expectorant

Therapeutic Category Antitussive/Decongestant/Expectorant

Abuse Potential Yes

Impairment Potential Yes; Blood hydrocodone levels >0.13 mg/L associated with driving impairment

Baselt RC and Cravey RH, *Disposition of Toxic Drugs and Chemicals in Man*, 4th ed, Foster City, CA: Chemical Toxicology Institute, 1995, 381.

Dosage Forms Liquid: Hydrocodone bitartrate 5 mg, pseudoephedrine hydrochloride 60 mg, and guaifenesin 200 mg per 5 mL with alcohol 12.5% (480 mL)

Hydrocort® *see* Hydrocortisone *on this page*

Hydrocortisone (hye droe KOR ti sone)

Synonyms Compound F; Cortisol

U.S. Brand Names Acticort™; Aeroseb-HC®; A-HydroCort®; Ala-Cort®; Ala-Scalp®; Anucort-HC®; Anumed HC™; Anusol-HC® [OTC]; Caldecort® Anti-Itch Spray [OTC]; Caldecort® [OTC]; Cetacort® [OTC]; Clocort® Maximum Strength; CortaGel® [OTC]; Cortaid® Maximum Strength [OTC]; Cortaid® with Aloe [OTC]; Cort-Dome®; Cortef®; Cortef® Feminine Itch [OTC]; Cortenema®; Corticaine® [OTC]; Cortizone®-5 [OTC]; Cortizone®-10 [OTC]; Delcort®; Dermacort®; Dermarest Dricort®; DermiCort®; Dermolate® [OTC]; Dermtex® HC with Aloe; Eldecort®; Gynecort® [OTC]; Hemril-HC™; Hi-Cor 1.0®; Hi-Cor-2.5®; Hycort®; Hydrocort®; Hydrocortone® Acetate; Hydrocortone® Phosphate; HydroSKIN®; Hydro-Tex® [OTC]; Hytone®; LactiCare-HC® [OTC]; Lanacort® [OTC]; Locoid®; Maximum Strength Bactine™ [OTC]; Nutracort®; Orabase® HCA; Penecort®; Proctocort™; ProctoCream-HC™; Scalpicin®; Solu-Cortef®; S-T Cort®; Synacort®; Tegrin®-HC; Texacort™; U-Cort™ Cortifoam®; Westcort®

Therapeutic Category Adrenal Corticosteroid; Corticosteroid, Topical

Use Management of adrenocortical insufficiency; relief of inflammation of corticosteroid-responsive dermatoses (low and medium potency topical corticosteroid); adjunctive treatment of ulcerative colitis

Usual Dosage Dose should be based on severity of disease and patient response

Acute adrenal insufficiency: I.M., I.V.:
 Infants and young Children: Succinate: 1-2 mg/kg/dose bolus, then 25-150 mg/day in divided doses every 6-8 hours
 Older Children: Succinate: 1-2 mg/kg bolus then 150-250 mg/day in divided doses every 6-8 hours
 Adults: Succinate: 100 mg I.V. bolus, then 300 mg/day in divided doses every 8 hours or as a continuous infusion for 48 hours; once patient is stable change to oral, 50 mg every 8 hours for 6 doses, then taper to 30-50 mg/day in divided doses

Chronic adrenal corticoid insufficiency: Adults: Oral: 20-30 mg/day

Anti-inflammatory or immunosuppressive:
 Infants and Children:
  Oral: 2.5-10 mg/kg/day **or** 75-300 mg/m²/day every 6-8 hours
  I.M., I.V.: Succinate: 1-5 mg/kg/day **or** 30-150 mg/m²/day divided every 12-24 hours
(Continued)

Hydrocortisone *(Continued)*

Adolescents and Adults: Oral, I.M., I.V.: Succinate: 15-240 mg every 12 hours

Congenital adrenal hyperplasia: Oral: Initial: 30-36 mg/m²/day with ⅓ of dose every morning and ⅔ every evening or ¼ every morning and mid-day and ½ every evening; maintenance: 20-25 mg/m²/day in divided doses

Physiologic replacement: Children:
Oral: 0.5-0.75 mg/kg/day **or** 20-25 mg/m²/day every 8 hours
I.M.: Succinate: 0.25-0.35 mg/kg/day **or** 12-15 mg/m²/day once daily

Shock: I.M., I.V.: Succinate:
Children: Initial: 50 mg/kg, then repeated in 4 hours and/or every 24 hours as needed; maximum I.V. recommended daily dose: 50 mg/kg
Adolescents and Adults: 500 mg to 2 g every 2-6 hours

Status asthmaticus: Children and Adults: I.V.: Succinate: 1-2 mg/kg/dose every 6 hours for 24 hours, then maintenance of 0.5-1 mg/kg every 6 hours

Rheumatic diseases:
Adults: Intralesional, intra-articular, soft tissue injection: Acetate:
Large joints: 25 mg (up to 37.5 mg)
Small joints: 10-25 mg
Tendon sheaths: 5-12.5 mg
Soft tissue infiltration: 25-50 mg (up to 75 mg)
Bursae: 25-37.5 mg
Ganglia: 12.5-25 mg

Dermatosis: Children >2 years and Adults: Topical: Apply to affected area 3-4 times/day

Ulcerative colitis: Adults: Rectal: 10-100 mg 1-2 times/day for 2-3 weeks

Mechanism of Action Decreases inflammation by suppression of migration of polymorphonuclear leukocytes and reversal of increased capillary permeability

Pharmacodynamics/kinetics

Absorption: Rapid by all routes, except rectally
Metabolism: In the liver
Bioavailability:
Oral: 96%
Rectal: 2%
Half-life, biologic: 8-12 hours
Hydrocortisone acetate salt has a slow onset but long duration of action when compared with more soluble preparations
Hydrocortisone sodium phosphate salt is a water soluble salt with a rapid onset but short duration of action
Hydrocortisone sodium succinate salt is a water soluble salt with is rapidly active

Signs and Symptoms of Acute Intoxication Muscle weakness (systemic), osteoporosis (systemic) all with long-term use only. When consumed in excessive quantities for prolonged periods, systemic hypercorticism and adrenal suppression may occur. In those cases, discontinuation and withdrawal of the corticosteroid should be done judiciously.

When to Transport to Hospital Transport any patient with muscle weakness or exhibiting agitation

Warnings/Precautions

Use with caution in patients with hyperthyroidism, cirrhosis, nonspecific ulcerative colitis, hypertension, osteoporosis, thromboembolic tendencies, CHF, convulsive disorders, myasthenia gravis, thrombophlebitis, peptic ulcer, diabetes

Acute adrenal insufficiency may occur with abrupt withdrawal after long-term therapy or with stress; young pediatric patients may be more susceptible to adrenal axis suppression from topical therapy

Because of the risk of adverse effects, systemic corticosteroids should be used cautiously in the elderly, in the smallest possible dose, and for the shortest possible time

Adverse Reactions

>10%:

Central nervous system: Insomnia, nervousness
Gastrointestinal: Increased appetite, indigestion

1% to 10%:

Dermatologic: Hirsutism
Endocrine & metabolic: Diabetes mellitus
Neuromuscular & skeletal: Arthralgia
Ocular: Cataracts
Respiratory: Epistaxis

Reference Range Therapeutic: AM: 5-25 µg/dL (SI: 138-690 nmol/L), PM: 2-9 µg/dL (SI: 55-248 nmol/L) depending on test, assay

Drug Interactions

Inducer of cytochrome P-450 enzymes
Cytochrome P-450 3A enzyme substrate

Decreased effect:

Insulin decreases hypoglycemic effect
Phenytoin, phenobarbital, ephedrine, carbamazepine, and rifampin increase metabolism of hydrocortisone and decrease steroid blood level

Increased toxicity:

Oral anticoagulants change prothrombin time; potassium-depleting diuretics increase risk of hypokalemia
Cardiac glucosides increase risk of arrhythmias or digitalis toxicity secondary to hypokalemia
Enhances potassium depletion caused by amphotericin B

Dosage Forms

Hydrocortisone acetate:

Cream, topical: 0.5% (15 g, 22.5 g, 30 g); 1% (15 g, 30 g, 120 g)
Ointment, topical: 0.5% (15 g, 30 g); 1% (15 g, 21 g, 30 g)
Injection, suspension: 25 mg/mL (5 mL, 10 mL); 50 mg/mL (5 mL, 10 mL)
Suppositories, rectal: 10 mg, 25 mg

Hydrocortisone base:

Aerosol, topical: 0.5% (45 g, 58 g); 1% (45 mL)
Cream, rectal: 1% (30 g); 2.5% (30 g)
Cream, topical: 0.5% (15 g, 30 g, 60 g, 120 g, 454 g); 1% (15 g, 20 g, 30 g, 60 g, 90 g, 120 g, 240 g, 454 g); 2.5% (15 g, 20 g, 30 g, 60 g, 120 g, 240 g, 454 g)
Gel, topical: 0.5% (15 g, 30 g); 1% (15 g, 30 g)
Lotion, topical: 0.25% (120 mL); 0.5% (30 mL, 60 mL, 120 mL); 1% (60 mL, 118 mL, 120 mL); 2% (30 mL) ; 2.5% (60 mL, 120 mL)
Ointment, rectal: 1% (30 g)
Ointment, topical: 0.5% (30 g) ; 1% (15 g, 20 g, 28 g, 30 g, 60 g, 120 g, 240 g, 454 g); 2.5% (20 g, 30 g)
Suspension, rectal: 100 mg/60 mL (7s)
Tablet, oral: 5 mg, 10 mg, 20 mg

Hydrocortisone cypionate:

Suspension, oral: 10 mg/5 mL (120 mL)

Hydrocortisone sodium phosphate:

Injection, IM/IV/SC: 50 mg/mL (2 mL, 10 mL)

Hydrocortisone sodium succinate:

Injection, IM/IV: 100 mg, 250 mg, 500 mg, 1000 mg

(Continued)

Hydrocortisone *(Continued)*

Hydrocortisone valerate:
Cream, topical: 0.2% (15 g, 45 g, 60 g)
Ointment, topical: 0.2% (15 g, 45 g, 60 g, 120 g)

Additional Information
Sodium content of 1 g (sodium succinate injection): 47.5 mg (2.07 mEq)
Hydrocortisone base topical cream, lotion, and ointments in concentrations of 0.25%, 0.5%, and 1% may be OTC or prescription depending on the product labeling
Food reduces absorption

Specific References
Ramsahoye BH, Davies SV, el-Gaylani N, et al, "The Mineralcorticoid Effects of High Dose Hydrocortisone," *BMJ*, 1995, 310(6980):656-7.

Hydrocortone® Acetate *see Hydrocortisone on page 297*

Hydrocortone® Phosphate *see Hydrocortisone on page 297*

HydroDIURIL® *see Hydrochlorothiazide on page 291*

Hydrofluoric Acid *see Hydrogen Fluoride on this page*

Hydrogen Fluoride

Synonyms Fluohydric Acid; Hydrofluoric Acid

UN Number 1052; 1786; 1790

Commonly Found In Automotive cleaning products; production of integrated circuits

Use In etching and cleaning of glass and porcelain; produce computer screen, fluorescent bulbs; refine high octane gasoline

Mechanism of Toxic Action Corrosive, produces heat when exposed to water; binds calcium, potassium, and magnesium; dissociates in tissue to free H^+ and F^- ions; fluoride anion inhibits Na^+/K^+ ATPase enzyme

Toxicodynamics/kinetics
Onset of action: Immediate corrosive effects although symptoms may be delayed 12-24 hours
Absorption: Inhalation and dermal routes
Half-life: 2-9 hours

Signs and Symptoms of Acute Intoxication Erythema of skin, blistering, pain, burns, vomiting (with ingestion), pulmonary edema, nausea (22%), diarrhea (22%), bone pain

When to Transport to Hospital Transport any suspected exposure

Overdosage/Treatment Decontamination: Dilute with milk or water; emesis is contraindicated. As first aid, affected extremity can be irrigated with water and bathed in an iced solution of 25% magnesium sulfate; give 300 mL of magnesium citrate orally for oral ingestion; give 20 mL 10% calcium gluconate I.V. for oral ingestion; nebulized calcium gluconate (4 mL of a 2.5% solution mixed in normal saline and delivered with 100% oxygen as a nebulized treatment) for inhalation exposures or infiltrate with subcutaneous injection of 0.5 mL of 10% calcium gluconate or 10% magnesium sulfate with a 30-gauge needle not greater than 0.5 mL/cm²; magnesium sulfate may also given I.V. (**Do not** use calcium chloride for injection.) 2.5% calcium gluconate gel can also be utilized.

Adverse Reactions
Cardiovascular: Fibrillation (ventricular)
Dermatologic: Dermal burns, onycholysis
Gastrointestinal: Vomiting (with ingestion)
Respiratory: Pneumonitis, hemorrhagic pulmonary edema, reactive airways disease syndrome

Reference Range Normal plasma fluoride levels are <0.1 µg/L; postmortem blood fluoride concentration following a fatal oral ingestion of 10% hydrofluoric acid compound was 13 mg/mL

Additional Information A commercial 2.5% calcium gluconate gel (as "H-F Antidote Gel") is available in 25 g tubes from Pharmascience, Inc, Montreal, Quebec (514-340-1114)

Latex gloves are not protective; as little as 7 mL of anhydrous topical hydrogen fluoride can cause profound hypocalcemia; a 2.5% total body surface burn can be fatal; colorless

To make calcium gel for dermal exposure to hydrogen fluoride, 3.5 g of calcium gluconate can be added to 5 oz tube of a surgical lubricant (water soluble such as K-Y® Jelly); alternatively can be ground into a fine powder and added to 20 mL of surgical lubricant (water soluble such as K-Y® Jelly), resulting in a 32.5% slurry. Calcium chloride should not be used for these purposes.

Odor threshold: 0.03 mg/m³
Minimum lethal exposure: 1.5 g
TLV-ceiling: 3 ppm
IDLH: 20 ppm
PEL-TWA: 3 ppm

Specific References
O'Neil K, "A Fatal Hydrogen Fluoride Exposure," *J Emerg Nurs*, 1994, 20(6):451-3.

Hydrogesic® see Hydrocodone and Acetaminophen *on page 293*
Hydro-Long® see Chlorthalidone *on page 144*
Hydromet® see Hydrocodone and Homatropine *on page 295*

Hydromorphone (hye droe MOR fone)
Related Information
Controlled Substances - Uses and Effects *on page 741*
Synonyms Dihydromorphinone
U.S. Brand Names Dilaudid®; Dilaudid-HP®
Canadian Brand Names Hydromorph Contin®; PMS-Hydromorphone®
Therapeutic Category Analgesic, Narcotic
Abuse Potential Yes
Impairment Potential Yes
Use Management of moderate to severe pain; antitussive at lower doses
Usual Dosage
Doses should be titrated to appropriate analgesic effects; when changing routes of administration, note that oral doses are less than half as effective as parenteral doses (may be only one-fifth as effective)

Pain: Older Children and Adults:
Oral, I.M., I.V., S.C.: 1-4 mg/dose every 4-6 hours as needed; usual adult dose: 2 mg/dose
Rectal: 3 mg every 6-8 hours
Antitussive: Oral:
Children 6-12 years: 0.5 mg every 3-4 hours as needed
Children >12 years and Adults: 1 mg (5 mL) every 3-4 hours as needed
Mechanism of Action Binds to opiate receptors in the CNS, causing inhibition of ascending pain pathways, altering the perception of and response to pain; causes cough supression by direct central action in the medulla; produces generalized CNS depression
Pharmacodynamics/kinetics
Onset of analgesic effect: Within 15-30 minutes
Peak effect: Within 30-60 minutes
(Continued)

Hydromorphone *(Continued)*

Duration: 4-5 hours
Metabolism: Primarily in the liver
Bioavailability: 62%
Half-life: 2-3 hours

Signs and Symptoms of Acute Intoxication Apnea, respiratory depression, myasthenia gravis (exacerbation or precipitation of), coma, syndrome of inappropriate antidiuretic hormone (SIADH), flaccidity, hypotension, bradycardia, confusion, miosis

When to Transport to Hospital Transport any symptomatic patient or ingestion over 5 mg/kg

Warnings/Precautions Tablet and cough syrup contain tartrazine which may cause allergic reactions; hydromorphone shares toxic potential of opiate agonists, and precaution of opiate agonist therapy should be observed; extreme caution should be taken to avoid confusing the highly concentrated injection with the less concentrated injectable product, injection contains benzyl alcohol; use with caution in patients with hypersensitivity to other phenanthrene opiates, in patients with respiratory disease, or severe liver or renal failure

Adverse Reactions

Endocrine & metabolic: Antidiuretic hormone release
Gastrointestinal: Biliary tract spasm
Genitourinary: Urinary tract spasm
Ocular: Miosis
Sensitivity reactions: Histamine release
Miscellaneous: Physical and psychological dependence

>10%:
Cardiovascular: Palpitations, hypotension, peripheral vasodilation
Central nervous system: Dizziness, lightheadedness, drowsiness
Gastrointestinal: Anorexia

1% to 10%:
Cardiovascular: Tachycardia, bradycardia, flushing of face
Central nervous system: CNS depression, increased intracranial pressure, fatigue, headache, nervousness, restlessness
Gastrointestinal: Nausea, vomiting, constipation, stomach cramps, xerostomia
Genitourinary: Decreased urination, ureteral spasm
Neuromuscular & skeletal: Trembling, weakness
Respiratory: Respiratory depression, dyspnea, shortness of breath

Test Interactions ↑ aminotransferase [ALT (SGPT)/AST (SGOT)] (S)

Reference Range 0.001-0.032 mg/L

Drug Interactions Increased toxicity with CNS depressants, phenothiazines, tricyclic antidepressants, MAO inhibitors, guanabenz, skeletal muscle relaxants (eg, tubocurarine)

Dosage Forms

Injection: 1 mg/mL (1 mL); 2 mg/mL (1 mL, 20 mL); 3 mg/mL (1 mL); 4 mg/mL (1 mL); 10 mg/mL (1 mL, 2 mL, 5 mL)
Suppository, rectal: 3 mg
Tablet: 1 mg, 2 mg, 3 mg, 4 mg

Additional Information Equianalgesic doses: Morphine 10 mg I.M. = hydromorphone 1.5 mg I.M.

Specific References

Inturrisi CE, "Narcotic Drugs," *Med Clin North Am*, 1982, 66(5):1061-71.

Hydropane® see Hydrocodone and Homatropine *on page 295*

Hydro-Par® see Hydrochlorothiazide *on page 291*

Hydrophed® see Theophylline, Ephedrine, and Hydroxyzine *on page 571*

Hydropres® see Hydrochlorothiazide and Reserpine *on page 292*
Hydro-Serp® see Hydrochlorothiazide and Reserpine *on page 292*
Hydroserpine® see Hydrochlorothiazide and Reserpine *on page 292*
HydroSKIN® see Hydrocortisone *on page 297*
Hydro-T® see Hydrochlorothiazide *on page 291*
Hydro-Tex® [OTC] see Hydrocortisone *on page 297*
Hydrotropine® see Hydrocodone and Homatropine *on page 295*

Hydroxyamphetamine (hye droks ee am FET a meen)
U.S. Brand Names Paredrine®
Therapeutic Category Adrenergic Agonist Agent
Use Produce mydriasis in diagnostic eye examination
Usual Dosage Instill 1-2 drops into conjunctival sac
Dosage Forms Solution, as hydrobromide: 1%

4-Hydroxybutyrate see Gamma Hydroxybutyric Acid *on page 262*
3-hydroxydiazepam see Temazepam *on page 559*

Hydroxyzine (hye DROKS i zeen)
U.S. Brand Names Anxanil®; Atarax®; Atazina®; Atozine®; Durrax®; E-Vista®; Hy-Pam®; Hyzine-50®; Masmoran®; Multipax®; Neucalm®; Quiess®; Rezine®; Ucerax®; Vamate®; Vistacon-50®; Vistaject-25®; Vistaject-50®; Vistaquel®; Vistaril®; Vistazine®
Canadian Brand Names Apo-Hydroxyzine®; Multipax®; Novo-Hydroxyzine®; PMS®-Hydroxyzine
Therapeutic Category Antiemetic; Antihistamine
Impairment Potential Yes; Impairment occurs (over about a 6-hour period) at doses of 25 mg

Gengo FM and Manning C, "A Review of the Effects of Antihistamines on Mental Processes Related to Automobile Driving," *J Allergy Clin Immunol*, 1990 86(2):1034-9.

Use Treatment of anxiety, as a preoperative sedative, an antipruritic, an antiemetic, and in alcohol withdrawal symptoms
Usual Dosage
Children:
  Oral: 0.6 mg/kg/dose every 6 hours
  I.M.: 0.5-1 mg/kg/dose every 4-6 hours as needed
Adults:
  Antiemetic: I.M.: 25-100 mg/dose every 4-6 hours as needed
  Anxiety: Oral: 25-100 mg 4 times/day; maximum dose: 600 mg/day
  Preoperative sedation:
    Oral: 50-100 mg
    I.M.: 25-100 mg
  Management of pruritus: Oral: 25 mg 3-4 times/day
Mechanism of Action A piperazine compound which competes with histamine for H_1-receptor sites on effector cells in the gastrointestinal tract, blood vessels, and respiratory tract
Pharmacodynamics/kinetics
Onset of effect: Within 15-30 minutes
Duration: 6-24 hours
Absorption: Oral: Rapid
Metabolism: Exact metabolic fate is unknown
Half-life:
  Children: 7 hours
  Adults: 20 hours
  Elderly: 29 hours (25 hours citrizine)
(Continued)

Hydroxyzine *(Continued)*

Biliary cirrhosis patients: 37 hours

Time to peak serum concentration: Within 2 hours

Signs and Symptoms of Acute Intoxication Seizures, sedation, myalgia, depression, insomnia, impotence, hypotension

When to Transport to Hospital Transport any symptomatic patient or any ingestion over 3 mg/kg

Warnings/Precautions Should be used with caution in patients with angle-closure glaucoma, prostatic hypertrophy, and bladder neck obstruction; should also be used with caution in patients with asthma or COPD; subcutaneous, intra-arterial and I.V. administration **not** recommended since thrombosis and digital gangrene can occur; extravasation can result in sterile abscess and marked tissue induration

Adverse Reactions

>10%:

Central nervous system: Slight to moderate drowsiness

Respiratory: Thickening of bronchial secretions

1% to 10%:

Central nervous system: Headache, fatigue, nervousness, dizziness

Gastrointestinal: Appetite increase, weight gain, nausea, diarrhea, abdominal pain, xerostomia

Neuromuscular & skeletal: Arthralgia

Respiratory: Pharyngitis

Reference Range Plasma hydroxyzine level of 5.6-41.8 µg/dL (13.2-102.0 nmol/L) therapeutic for pruritus in children; peak plasma level is 73 µg/L after 0.7 mg/kg dose in adults

Drug Interactions Increased effect/toxicity: CNS depressants, anticholinergics

Dosage Forms

Hydroxyzine hydrochloride:

Injection:

Vistaject-25®, Vistaril®: 25 mg/mL (1 mL, 2 mL, 10 mL)

E-Vista®, Hyzine-50®, Neucalm®, Quiess®, Vistacon-50®, Vistaject-50®, Vistaquel®, Vistaril®, Vistazine®: 50 mg/mL (1 mL, 2 mL, 10 mL)

Syrup (Atarax®): 10 mg/5 mL (120 mL, 480 mL, 4000 mL)

Tablet:

Anxanil®: 25 mg

Atarax®: 10 mg, 25 mg, 50 mg, 100 mg

Atozine®: 10 mg, 25 mg, 50 mg

Durrax®: 10 mg, 25 mg

Rezine®: 10 mg, 25 mg

Hydroxyzine pamoate:

Capsule:

Hy-Pam®: 25 mg, 50 mg

Vamate®: 25 mg, 50 mg, 100 mg

Vistaril®: 25 mg, 50 mg, 100 mg

Suspension, oral (Vistaril®:) 25 mg/5 mL (120 mL, 480 mL)

Specific References

Simons FE, et al, "Adverse Central Nervous System Effects of Older Antihistamines in Children," *Pediatr Allergy Immunol*, 1996, 7:22-7.

Hygroton® *see* Chlorthalidone *on page 144*

Hylorel® *see* Guanadrel *on page 277*

Hyoscine *see* Scopolamine *on page 532*

Hyoscyamine (hye oh SYE a meen)

Synonyms *l*-Hyoscyamine Sulfate

U.S. Brand Names Anaspaz®; Cystospaz®; Cystospaz-M®; Duboisine; Egazil Duretter®; Gastrosed™; Levsin®; Levsinex®; Neoquess®; Peptard®

Therapeutic Category Anticholinergic Agent

Use Treatment of gastrointestinal tract disorders caused by spasm, adjunctive therapy for peptic ulcers; also has been used in parkinsonism

Usual Dosage

Children: Oral, S.L.: Dose as per table repeated every 4 hours as needed

Hyoscyamine

Weight (kg)	Dose (mcg)	Maximum 24-Hour Dose (mcg)
Children <2 y		
2.3	12.5	75
3.4	16.7	100
5	20.8	125
7	25	150
10	31.3-33.3	200
15	45.8	275
Children 2-10 y		
10	31.3-33.3	Do not exceed 0.75 mg
20	62.5	
40	93.8	
50	125	

Adults:

Oral or S.L.: 0.125-0.25 mg 3-4 times/day before meals or food and at bedtime

Oral: 0.375-0.75 mg (timed release) every 12 hours

I.M., I.V., S.C.: 0.25-0.5 mg every 6 hours

Mechanism of Action Blocks the action of acetylcholine at parasympathetic sites in smooth muscle, secretory glands and the CNS; increases cardiac output, dries secretions, antagonizes histamine and serotonin, antimuscarinic agent; found in the plant *Hyoscyamus niger*

Pharmacodynamics/kinetics

Onset of effect: 2-3 minutes

Duration: 4-6 hours

Absorption: Oral: Absorbed well

Metabolism: In the liver

Half-life: 13% to 38%

Signs and Symptoms of Acute Intoxication Dilated unreactive pupils; impotence, blurred vision; facial flushing; dryness of mucous membranes; dysphagia, memory loss, foul breath, intraocular pressure (increased), diminished or absent bowel sounds, urinary retention, ileus, photophobia, tachycardia, lightheadedness, rhabdomyolysis, hyperthermia, hypertension, respiratory rate (increased), hallucinations (lilliputian), seizures, ataxia, coma, myoglobinuria

When to Transport to Hospital Transport any symptomatic patient

Warnings/Precautions Use with caution in children with spastic paralysis; use with caution in elderly patients. Low doses cause a paradoxical decrease in heart rates. Some commercial products contain sodium metabisulfite, which (Continued)

Hyoscyamine *(Continued)*

can cause allergic-type reactions. May accumulate with multiple inhalational administration, particularly in the elderly. Heat prostration may occur in hot weather. Use with caution in patients with autonomic neuropathy, prostatic hypertrophy, hyperthyroidism, congestive heart failure, cardiac arrhythmias, chronic lung disease, biliary tract disease

Adverse Reactions

>10%:
Dermatologic: Dry skin
Gastrointestinal: Dry throat, xerostomia
Local: Irritation at injection site
Respiratory: Dry nose
Miscellaneous: Diaphoresis (decreased)
1% to 10%:
Dermatologic: Photosensitivity
Gastrointestinal: Constipation, dysphagia
Ocular: Blurred vision, mydriasis

Drug Interactions

Decreased effect with antacids
Increased toxicity with amantadine, antimuscarinics, haloperidol, phenothiazines, tricyclic antidepressants, MAO inhibitors

Dosage Forms

Capsule, timed release (Cystospaz-M®, Levsinex®): 0.375 mg
Elixir (Levsin®): 0.125 mg/5 mL with alcohol 20% (480 mL)
Injection (Levsin®): 0.5 mg/mL (1 mL, 10 mL)
Solution, oral (Gastrosed™, Levsin®): 0.125 mg/mL (15 mL)
Tablet:
Anaspaz®, Gastrosed™, Levsin®, Neoquess®: 0.125 mg
Cystospaz®: 0.15 mg

Specific References

Shutt LE and Bowes JB, "Atropine and Hyoscine," *Anaesthesia*, 1979, 34(5):476-90.

Hyoscyamine, Atropine, Scopolamine, and Phenobarbital

(hye oh SYE a meen, A troe peen, skoe POL a meen & fee noe BAR bi tal)
U.S. Brand Names Barbidonna®; Donnatal®; Hyosophen®; Malatal®; Spasmolin®

Therapeutic Category Anticholinergic Agent

Abuse Potential Yes

Impairment Potential Yes

Dosage Forms

Capsule (Donnatal®, Spasmolin®): Hyoscyamine sulfate 0.1037 mg, atropine sulfate 0.0194 mg, scopolamine hydrobromide 0.0065 mg, and phenobarbital 16.2 mg
Elixir (Donnatal®, Hyosophen®, Spasmophen®): Hyoscyamine sulfate 0.1037 mg, atropine sulfate 0.0194 mg, scopolamine hydrobromide 0.0065 mg, and phenobarbital 16.2 mg per 5 mL (120 mL, 480 mL, 4000 mL)
Tablet:
Barbidonna®: Hyoscyamine hydrobromide 0.1286 mg, atropine sulfate 0.025 mg, scopolamine hydrobromide 0.0074 mg, and phenobarbital 16 mg
Barbidonna® No. 2: Hyoscyamine hydrobromide 0.1286 mg, atropine sulfate 0.025 mg, scopolamine hydrobromide 0.0074 mg, and phenobarbital 32 mg

Donnatal®, Hyosophen®: Hyoscyamine sulfate 0.1037 mg, atropine sulfate 0.0194 mg, scopolamine hydrobromide 0.0065 mg, and phenobarbital 16.2 mg

Long-acting (Donnatal®): Hyoscyamine sulfate 0.3111 mg, atropine sulfate 0.0582 mg, scopolamine hydrobromide 0.0195 mg, and phenobarbital 48.6 mg

Spasmophen®: Hyoscyamine sulfate 0.1037 mg, atropine sulfate 0.0194 mg, scopolamine hydrobromide 0.0065 mg, and phenobarbital 15 mg

Hyoscyamine, Atropine, Scopolamine, Kaolin, and Pectin

(hye oh SYE a meen, A troe peen, skoe POL a meen, KAY oh lin & PEK tin)

Therapeutic Category Anticholinergic Agent

Abuse Potential Yes

Impairment Potential Yes

Dosage Forms Suspension, oral: Hyoscyamine sulfate 0.1037 mg, atropine sulfate 0.0194 mg, scopolamine hydrobromide 0.0065 mg, kaolin 6 g, and pectin 142.8 mg per 30 mL

Hyoscyamine, Atropine, Scopolamine, Kaolin, Pectin, and Opium

(hye oh SYE a meen, A troe peen, skoe POL a meen, KAY oh lin, PEK tin, & OH pee um)

Therapeutic Category Anticholinergic Agent

Abuse Potential Yes

Impairment Potential Yes

Dosage Forms Suspension, oral: Hyoscyamine sulfate 0.1037 mg, atropine sulfate 0.0194 mg, scopolamine hydrobromide 0.0065 mg, kaolin 6 g, pectin 142.8 mg, and powdered opium 24 mg per 30 mL with alcohol 5%

Hyosophen® see Hyoscyamine, Atropine, Scopolamine, and Phenobarbital on previous page

Hy-Pam® see Hydroxyzine on page 303

Hypercal® see Rauwolfia Serpentina on page 521

Hy-Phen® see Hydrocodone and Acetaminophen on page 293

Hypnoderm® see Flunitrazepam on page 250

Hypnor® see Flunitrazepam on page 250

Hypnotics and Tranquilizers, Toxicology, Blood see Toxicology, Hypnotics and Tranquilizers, Serum on page 588

Hypnovel® see Midazolam on page 402

Hypolag® see Methyldopa on page 393

Hypomide® see Chlorpropamide on page 140

Hyposyn® see Clonidine on page 154

Hypovase® see Prazosin on page 494

Hyrexin-50® Injection see Diphenhydramine on page 205

Hytone® see Hydrocortisone on page 297

Hytrin® see Terazosin on page 560

Hytrinex® see Terazosin on page 560

Hytuss® [OTC] see Guaifenesin on page 269

Hytuss-2X® [OTC] see Guaifenesin on page 269

Hyzaar® see Losartan and Hydrochlorothiazide on page 353

Hyzine-50® see Hydroxyzine on page 303

Ibidomide Hydrochloride see Labetalol on page 331

Ibuprin® [OTC] *see* Ibuprofen *on this page*

Ibuprofen (eye byoo PROE fen)

Synonyms *p*-Isobutylhydratropic Acid

U.S. Brand Names Advil® [OTC]; Excedrin® IB [OTC]; Genpril® [OTC]; Haltran® [OTC]; Ibuprin® [OTC]; Ibuprohm® [OTC]; Ibu-Tab®; Medipren® [OTC]; Menadol® [OTC]; Midol® 200 [OTC]; Motrin®; Motrin® IB [OTC]; Nuprin® [OTC]; Pamprin IB® [OTC]; PediaProfen™; Rufen®; Saleto-200® [OTC]; Saleto-400®; Trendar® [OTC]; Uni-Pro® [OTC]

Canadian Brand Names Actiprofen®; Apo-Ibuprofen®; Novo-Profen®; Nu-Ibuprofen®

Therapeutic Category Analgesic, Non-narcotic; Antipyretic; Nonsteroidal Anti-Inflammatory Agent (NSAID)

Use Inflammatory diseases and rheumatoid disorders including juvenile rheumatoid arthritis; mild to moderate pain; fever; dysmenorrhea; gout

Investigational: May prevent patent ductus arteriosus in premature neonates

Usual Dosage

Neonates, premature: I.V.: Prevention of patent ductus arteriosus (ibuprofen lysine): 10 mg/kg within 3 hours of age followed by 5 mg/kg at 1 and 2 days of age

Children: Oral:

Antipyretic: 6 months to 12 years: Temperature <102.5°F (39°C): 5 mg/kg/dose; temperature >102.5°F: 10 mg/kg/dose given every 6-8 hours; maximum daily dose: 40 mg/kg/day

Juvenile rheumatoid arthritis: 30-70 mg/kg/24 hours divided every 6-8 hours
<20 kg: Maximum: 400 mg/day
20-30 kg: Maximum: 600 mg/day
30-40 kg: Maximum: 800 mg/day
>40 kg: Adult dosage

Start at lower end of dosing range and titrate upward; maximum: 2.4 g/day

Analgesic: 4-10 mg/kg/dose every 6-8 hours

Adults: Oral:

Inflammatory disease: 400-800 mg/dose 3-4 times/day; maximum dose: 3.2 g/day

Analgesia/pain/fever/dysmenorrhea: 200-400 mg/dose every 4-6 hours; maximum daily dose: 3.4 g

Mechanism of Action Inhibits prostaglandin synthesis by decreasing the activity of the enzyme, cyclo-oxygenase, which results in decreased formation of prostaglandin precursors

Pharmacodynamics/kinetics

Onset of action: 30 minutes

Duration: 4-6 hours

Absorption: Oral: Rapid (85%) from gastrointestinal tract

Metabolism: In the liver by oxidation

Half-life: 2 hours

Time to peak serum concentration: Within 1-2 hours

Elimination: Urine (1% as free drug); some biliary excretion occurs; clearance: 0.045 L/hour/kg

Signs and Symptoms of Acute Intoxication Nausea, vomiting, azotemia, wheezing, purpura, thrombocytopenia, nephrotic syndrome, hyperthermia, photosensitivity, depression, gastrointestinal bleeding, mental confusion, light-headedness, hyponatremia, leukocytosis, hypoglycemia, gastritis; flatulence, erythema multiforme, cognitive dysfunction, coagulopathy, ototoxicity; tinnitus, drowsiness; severe poisoning can manifest with coma, seizures, renal and or hepatic failure, hypotension, hypothermia, respiratory depression, apnea, metabolic acidosis; more significant exposures associated with ingestions of

>400 mg/kg, alopecia, fever, urine discoloration (red), urine discoloration (red-purple), feces discoloration (tarry)

When to Transport to Hospital Transport any symptomatic patient or any ingestion over 200 mg/kg

Adverse Reactions
>10%:
  Central nervous system: Dizziness, fatigue
  Dermatologic: Rash, urticaria
  Gastrointestinal: Abdominal cramps, heartburn, indigestion, nausea
1% to 10%:
  Central nervous system: Headache, nervousness
  Dermatologic: Itching
  Endocrine & metabolic: Fluid retention
  Gastrointestinal: Dyspepsia, vomiting, abdominal pain, peptic ulcer, GI bleed, GI perforation
  Otic: Tinnitus

Reference Range Plasma concentrations >200 µg/mL (971 µmol/L) may be associated with severe toxicity; not readily available, thus not recommended; antipyretic effect can occur at plasma concentrations of 10 µg/mL (48 µmol/L)

Drug Interactions Aspirin decreases serum concentrations probably by protein-binding displacement; there is an increased bleeding potential with concomitant warfarin therapy; may increase lithium and methotrexate concentrations by decreasing renal clearance; may decrease diuretic and hypotensive effects of thiazides, loop diuretics, ACE inhibitors, and beta-blockers; may increase nephrotoxicity of cyclosporine

Dosage Forms
Injection: Not available in U.S.
Suspension, oral: 100 mg/5 mL (120 mL, 480 mL)
Tablet: 200 mg [OTC], 300 mg, 400 mg, 600 mg, 800 mg

Additional Information Each 5 mL of suspension contains 2.5 g of sucrose; nomogram available but relative lack of significant toxicity and inaccessibility of laboratory assay precludes use (see nomogram in the text preceding this chapter); high-dose ibuprofen may be effective in treating lung disease in cystic fibrosis; largest ibuprofen ingested reported was 72 g in an adult; while hyperkalemia, metabolic acidosis, and rhabdomyolysis was noted, the patient did well with supportive therapy and did not require dialysis

Specific References
Hall AH, Smolinske SC, Conrad FL, et al, "Ibuprofen Overdose: 126 Cases," *Ann Emerg Med*, 1986, 15(11):1308-13.

Ibuprohm® [OTC] *see* Ibuprofen *on previous page*
Ibu-Tab® *see* Ibuprofen *on previous page*
Igrotin® *see* Chlorthalidone *on page 144*
Ikacor® *see* Verapamil *on page 609*
Iktorivil® *see* Clonazepam *on page 153*
Ilosone® Oral *see* Erythromycin *on page 226*
Imagotan® *see* Mesoridazine *on page 375*
I-Methasone® *see* Dexamethasone *on page 182*
Imex® *see* Tetracycline *on page 568*
Imigran® *see* Sumatriptan Succinate *on page 556*

Imipramine (im IP ra meen)

U.S. Brand Names Berkomine®; Dimipressin®; Iprogen®; Janimine®; Presamine®; SK-Pramine®; Tofranil®; Tofranil-PM®
Canadian Brand Names Apo-Imipramine®; Novo-Pramine®; PMS-Imipramine®
(Continued)

Imipramine *(Continued)*

Therapeutic Category Antidepressant

Use Treatment of various forms of depression, often in conjunction with psychotherapy; enuresis in children; analgesic for certain chronic and neuropathic pain

Usual Dosage Maximum antidepressant effect may not be seen for 2 or more weeks after initiation of therapy

Children: Oral:

Depression: 1.5 mg/kg/day with dosage increments of 1 mg/kg every 3-4 days to a maximum dose of 5 mg/kg/day in 1-4 divided doses; monitor carefully especially with doses ≥3.5 mg/kg/day

Enuresis: ≥6 years: Initial: 10-25 mg at bedtime; if inadequate response still seen after 1 week of therapy, increase by 25 mg/day; dose should not exceed 2.5 mg/kg/day or 50 mg at bedtime if 6-12 years of age or 75 mg at bedtime if ≥12 years of age

Adjunct in the treatment of cancer pain: Initial: 0.2-0.4 mg/kg at bedtime; dose may be increased by 50% every 2-3 days up to 1-3 mg/kg/dose at bedtime

Adolescents: Oral: Initial: 25-50 mg/day; increase gradually; maximum: 100 mg/day in single or divided doses

Adults:

Oral: Initial: 25 mg 3-4 times/day, increase dose gradually, total dose may be given at bedtime; maximum: 300 mg/day

I.M.: Initial: Up to 100 mg/day in divided doses; change to oral as soon as possible

Mechanism of Action Increases the synaptic concentration of serotonin, norepinephrine, and/or dopamine in the central nervous system by inhibition of their reuptake by the presynaptic neuronal membrane; peripheral alpha-receptor blockade may be the cause of hypotension (orthostatic).

Pharmacodynamics/kinetics

Maximum antidepressant effect: Usually after 2 weeks or more

Absorption: Oral: Well absorbed from gastrointestinal tract

Metabolism: In the liver by microsomal enzymes to desipramine (active) and other metabolites; significant first-pass metabolism; undergoes enterohepatic recirculation

Half-life: 6-18 hours

Time to peak serum concentration:

Oral: 1-2 hours

I.M.: 30 minutes

Elimination: Almost all compounds following metabolism are excreted in urine; ~27% of the drug is normally excreted in 4 hours in a normal patient

Signs and Symptoms of Acute Intoxication Confusion, dental erosion, depression, impotence, eosinophilia, disorientation, colitis, jaundice, mania, lactation, ejaculatory disturbances, hypoglycemia, Q-T prolongation, hallucinations, hyponatremia, hyperthyroidism, intraocular pressure (increased), seizures, (within 3 hours of ingestion), myasthenia gravis (exacerbation or precipitation of), hypotension, galactorrhea, cardiac arrhythmias, conduction defects; constipation, cyanosis, dementia, tachycardia (sinus); QRS prolongation, with rightward terminal 40 millisecond frontal plane of QRS vector, coma (mean duration: 6 hours); myoclonus, respiratory depression, pulmonary edema, leukopenia; neutropenia; agranulocytosis; granulocytopenia; alopecia, ototoxicity; tinnitus

When to Transport to Hospital Transport any symptomatic patient or any ingestion over 5 mg/kg

Warnings/Precautions Do not discontinue abruptly in patients receiving long-term high-dose therapy; some oral preparations contain tartrazine and injection contains sulfites both of which can cause allergic reactions; use with caution in patients with cardiovascular disease, conduction disturbances, seizure disorders, urinary retention, hyperthyroidism or those receiving thyroid replacement

Adverse Reactions Less sedation and anticholinergic effects than amitriptyline

>10%:
  Central nervous system: Dizziness, drowsiness, headache
  Gastrointestinal: Increased appetite, nausea, unpleasant taste, weight gain, xerostomia, constipation
  Genitourinary: Urinary retention
  Neuromuscular & skeletal: Weakness

1% to 10%:
  Cardiovascular: Postural hypotension, arrhythmias, tachycardia, sudden death
  Central nervous system: Confusion, delirium, hallucinations, nervousness, restlessness, parkinsonian syndrome, insomnia
  Endocrine & metabolic: Sexual dysfunction
  Gastrointestinal: Diarrhea, heartburn
  Genitourinary: Dysuria
  Neuromuscular & skeletal: Fine muscle tremors
  Ocular: Blurred vision, eye pain
  Miscellaneous: Diaphoresis (excessive)

Test Interactions EMIT assays may give false-positive in presence of diphenhydramine, thioridazine, chlorpromazine, alimenazine, carbamazepine, cyclobenzaprine, or perphenazine

Reference Range
  Therapeutic:
    Imipramine and desipramine 150-250 ng/mL (SI: 530-890 nmol/L)
    Desipramine 150-300 ng/mL (SI: 560-1125 nmol/L)
  Metabolism may be impaired in elderly patients; toxic: >300 ng/mL (SI: >1070 nmol/L); serious symptoms are associated with levels >1000 ng/mL (SI: >3566 nmol/L)

Drug Interactions May decrease or reverse effects of guanethidine and clonidine; may increase effects of CNS depressants, adrenergic agents, anticholinergic agents; with MAO inhibitors, fever, tachycardia, hypertension, seizures and death may occur; similar interactions as with other tricyclics may occur; carbamazepine enhances metabolism of imipramine; lower serum tricyclic antidepressant levels may be noted in cigarette smokers due to increased hepatic metabolism; metabolism of imipramine to desipramine is blocked by fluoxetine and therefore imipramine levels may be increased; increased serum concentrations with concomitant thioridazine

Dosage Forms
  Imipramine hydrochloride:
    Injection (Tofranil®): 12.5 mg/mL (2 mL)
    Tablet (Janimine®, Tofranil®): 10 mg, 25 mg, 50 mg
  Capsule, as pamoate (Tofranil-PM®): 75 mg, 100 mg, 125 mg, 150 mg

Additional Information Imipramine hydrochloride: Tofranil®, Janimine® Imipramine Pamoate: Tofranil-PM®; monoclonal anti-imipramine antibodies are investigational

Specific References
  Tribble J, Weinhouse E, Garland J, et al, "Treatment of Severe Imipramine Poisoning Complicated by a Negative History of Drug Ingestion," *Pediatr Emerg Care*, 1989, 5(4):234-7.

Imitrex® *see* Sumatriptan Succinate *on page 556*

Immenoctal® *see* Secobarbital *on page 534*

Imodium® *see* Loperamide *on page 349*

Imodium® A-D [OTC] *see* Loperamide *on page 349*

Imosec® *see* Loperamide *on page 349*
Imovan® *see* Zopiclone *on page 621*
Imovane® *see* Zopiclone *on page 621*
I-Naphline® *see* Naphazoline *on page 422*
Inapsine® *see* Droperidol *on page 214*
Inderal® *see* Propranolol *on page 510*
Inderal® LA *see* Propranolol *on page 510*
Inderide® *see* Propranolol and Hydrochlorothiazide *on page 513*
Indian Black Drink *see* Holly *on page 287*

Indian Tobacco

Synonyms Asthma Weed; Bladder Pod; Eye Bright; "Puke Weed"; "Vomit Wort"; Wild Tobacco

Scientific Name *Lobelia inflata*

Use Variety of purposes over the years; the extract has been used as an emetic; lobeline sulfate has been used as an aid to stop smoking

Usual Dosage Lobeline content may vary, specific toxic amounts of plant material is unknown most poisonings have been from herbal preparations

Mechanism of Toxic Action Contains lobeline alkaloids which have nicotinic-like action and other piperidine alkaloids

Signs and Symptoms of Acute Intoxication Nausea, vomiting, diarrhea, abdominal pain, hypertension, bradycardia, paralysis, tremor, seizures, coma, and euphoria; dermatitis has also been reported

When to Transport to Hospital Transport any symptomatic patient

Adverse Reactions Cardiovascular: Sinus bradycardia

Additional Information Other related toxic species are *Lobelia cardinalis*, *Lobelia siphilitica*, and *Lobelia berlandieri*; *Eriogonum umbellatum* is also known as Indian tobacco and is considered nontoxic
Family: Campanulaceae
Range: Grows extensively throughout the U.S.
Toxic parts: All parts, especially roots and seeds
Toxic dose: 50 mg of dried herb; poisoning is more transient than that of nicotine

Specific References
Siegel RK, "Herbal Intoxication. Psychoactive Effects From Herbal Cigarettes, Tea, and Capsules," *JAMA*, 1976, 236(5):473-6.

Indocin® *see* Indomethacin *on this page*
Indometacin *see* Indomethacin *on this page*

Indomethacin (in doe METH a sin)

Synonyms Indometacin

U.S. Brand Names Indocin®

Canadian Brand Names Apo-Indomethacin®; Indocid®; Indocid-SR®; Novo-Methacin®; Nu-Indo®; Pro-Indo®

Therapeutic Category Analgesic, Non-narcotic; Nonsteroidal Anti-Inflammatory Agent (NSAID)

Use Management of inflammatory diseases and rheumatoid disorders; moderate pain; acute gouty arthritis; I.V. form used as alternative to surgery for closure of patent ductus arteriosus in neonates

Usual Dosage
Patent ductus arteriosus: Neonates: I.V.: Initial: 0.2 mg/kg; followed with: 2 doses of 0.1 mg/kg at 12- to 24-hour intervals if age <48 hours at time of first dose; 0.2 mg/kg 2 times if 2-7 days old at time of first dose; or 0.25 mg/kg 2 times if over 7 days at time of first dose; discontinue if significant adverse effects occur. Dose should be withheld if patient has anuria or oliguria.

Analgesia:

Children: Oral: Initial: 1-2 mg/kg/day in 2-4 divided doses; maximum: 4 mg/kg/day; not to exceed 150-200 mg/day

Adults: Oral, rectal: 25-50 mg/dose 2-3 times/day; maximum dose: 200 mg/day; extended release capsule should be given on a 1-2 times/day schedule

Mechanism of Action Inhibits prostaglandin synthesis by decreasing the activity of the enzyme, cyclo-oxygenase, which results in decreased formation of prostaglandin precursors

Pharmacodynamics/kinetics

Onset of action: Within 30 minutes

Duration: 4-6 hours

Absorption: Prompt and extensive from gastrointestinal tract

Metabolism: In the liver with significant enterohepatic recycling

Half-life: $4^1/_2$ hours (longer in neonates)

Time to peak serum concentration: Within 3-4 hours

Signs and Symptoms of Acute Intoxication Nausea, colitis, wheezing, pseudotumor cerebri, gastrointestinal bleeding, photosensitivity, dementia, azotemia, impotence, hyponatremia, gastrointestinal hypoglycemia, esophageal ulceration; upset; syndrome of inappropriate antidiuretic hormone (SIADH), corneal microdeposits, hematuria, cholestatic jaundice, coagulopathy, vomiting, ototoxicity; tinnitus, drowsiness; severe poisoning can manifest with coma, seizures, blurred vision, renal and or hepatic failure, hypotension, respiratory depression, blindness, thrombocytopenia, hyperglycemia, urine discoloration (green), feces discoloration (green)

When to Transport to Hospital Transport any symptomatic patient or any ingestion over 5 mg/kg

Warnings/Precautions Use with caution in patients with cardiac dysfunction, hypertension, renal or hepatic impairment, epilepsy, patients receiving anticoagulants and for treatment of JRA in children (fatal hepatitis has been reported)

Adverse Reactions

>10%:

Central nervous system: Dizziness

Dermatologic: Rash

Gastrointestinal: Nausea, epigastric pain, abdominal pain, anorexia, GI bleeding, ulcers, perforation, abdominal cramps, heartburn, indigestion

1% to 10%:

Central nervous system: Headache, nervousness

Dermatologic: Itching

Endocrine & metabolic: Fluid retention

Gastrointestinal: Vomiting

Otic: Tinnitus

Reference Range Therapeutic: 0.3-3.0 mg/L (0.8-8.0 μmol/L)

Drug Interactions Aspirin decreases serum concentrations probably by protein-binding displacement; there is an increased bleeding potential with concomitant warfarin therapy; may increase lithium and methotrexate concentrations by decreasing renal clearance; may decrease diuretic and hypotensive effects of thiazides, loop diuretics, ACE inhibitors, and beta-blockers; may increase nephrotoxicity of cyclosporine; cimetidine reduces absorption

Dosage Forms

Capsule: 25 mg, 50 mg

Capsule, sustained release: 75 mg

Powder for injection, as sodium trihydrate: 1 mg

Suppository, rectal: 50 mg

Suspension, oral: 25 mg/5 mL (237 mL, 500 mL)

(Continued)

Indomethacin *(Continued)*

Additional Information May affect platelet and renal function in neonates; misoprostol (200 µg) can reverse indomethacin-induced renal dysfunction in patients with stable alcoholic cirrhosis

Specific References

Hoppmann RA, Peden JG, and Ober SK, "Central Nervous System Side Effects of Nonsteroidal Anti-inflammatory Drugs. Aseptic Meningitis, Psychosis, and Cognitive Dysfunction," *Arch Intern Med*, 1991, 151(7):1309-13.

Infants Feverall™ [OTC] *see* Acetaminophen *on page 20*

Infants' Silapap® [OTC] *see* Acetaminophen *on page 20*

InFed™ Injection *see* Iron *on page 318*

Inflamase® *see* Prednisolone *on page 495*

Inflamase® Mild *see* Prednisolone *on page 495*

INH *see* Isoniazid *on page 322*

Initard® *see* Insulin Preparations *on this page*

Innovace® *see* Enalapril *on page 217*

Innovar® *see* Droperidol and Fentanyl *on page 215*

Inomnium® LF *see* Zopiclone *on page 621*

Insoma® *see* Nitrazepam *on page 435*

Insomnium® NF *see* Zopiclone *on page 621*

Insulatard® NPH *see* Insulin Preparations *on this page*

Insulin Preparations (IN su lin prep a RAY shuns)

Synonyms Insulinum; Lente®; NPH; Semilente®; Ultralente®

U.S. Brand Names Actrafan® HM; Actrap® MC; Beef NPH Iletin® II; Beef Regular Iletin® II; Humulin®; Initard®; Insulatard® NPH; Lente® Iletin® I; Lente® Iletin® II; Lente® Purified Pork Insulin; Mixtard®; Neulente®; Novolin®; NPH Iletin® I; Pork NPH Iletin® II; Pork Regular Iletin® II; Regular Iletin® I; Regular [Concentrated] Iletin® II U-500; Semilente® Iletin® I; Ultralente® Iletin® I; Ultratard; Velosulin®; Velosulin® BR

Therapeutic Category Antidiabetic Agent, Parenteral

Use Treatment of insulin-dependent diabetes mellitus, also noninsulin-dependent diabetes mellitus unresponsive to treatment with diet and/or oral hypoglycemics; to assure proper utilization of glucose and reduce glucosuria in nondiabetic patients receiving parenteral nutrition whose glucosuria cannot be adequately controlled with infusion rate adjustments or those who require assistance in achieving optimal caloric intakes; used to treat hyperkalemia

Usual Dosage May administer I.V. (regular), I.M., S.C.

Diabetes mellitus:

Children and Adults: 0.5-1 unit/kg/day

Adolescents (growth spurts): 0.8-1.2 units/kg/day

Adjust dose to maintain premeal and bedtime blood glucose of 80-140 mg/dL (children <5 years: 100-200 mg/dL)

Hyperkalemia: Give calcium gluconate and $NaHCO_3$ first then 50% dextrose at 0.5-1 mL/kg and insulin 1 unit for every 4-5 g dextrose given

Diabetic ketoacidosis: Children and Adults: I.V. loading dose: 0.1 unit/kg, then maintenance continuous infusion: 0.1 unit/kg/hour (range: 0.05-0.2 units/kg/hour depending upon the rate of decrease of serum glucose - too rapid decrease of serum glucose may lead to cerebral edema).

Optimum rate of decrease (serum glucose): 80-100 mg/dL/hour

Note: Newly diagnosed patients with JODM presenting in DKA and patients with blood sugars <800 mg/dL may be relatively "sensitive" to insulin and should receive loading and initial maintenance doses approximately $\frac{1}{2}$ of those indicated above.

Mechanism of Action Replacement therapy for persons unable to produce the hormone naturally or in insufficient amounts to maintain glycemic control

Pharmacodynamics/kinetics

Onset and duration of hypoglycemic effects depend upon preparation administered; see table.

Insulin Preparations

Preparation	Onset of Action	Peak	Duration	pH
Regular	30 min	2.5-5 h	5-8 h	2.5-3.5
Semilente®	1-2 h	3-10 h	10-16 h	6.9-7.5
Lente®	2.5 h	7-15 h	18-23 h	6.9-7.5
NPH	90 min	10-20 h	24 h	6.9-7.5
PZI	4-8 h	14-24 h	<36 h	7.1-7.4
70/30	30 min	6-12 h	24 h	7.0-7.8
Isophane/Regular	6 h	4-8 h	24 h	6.9-7.5

Onset and duration: Biosynthetic NPH human insulin shows a more rapid onset and shorter duration of action than corresponding porcine insulins; human insulin and purified porcine regular insulin are similarly efficacious following S.C. administration. The duration of action of highly purified porcine insulins is shorter than that of conventional insulin equivalents. Duration depends on type of preparation and route of administration as well as patient related variables. In general, the larger the dose of insulin, the longer the duration of activity.

Absorption: Biosynthetic regular human insulin is absorbed from the S.C. injection site more rapidly than insulins of animal origin (60-90 minutes peak vs 120-150 minutes peak respectively) and lowers the initial blood glucose much faster.

Metabolism: Hepatic

Bioavailability: Medium-acting S.C. Lente®-type human insulins did not differ from the corresponding porcine insulins

Signs and Symptoms of Acute Intoxication Hepatomegaly, seizures, dysarthria, numbness, parotid pain, ataxia, hypothermia, hyperglycemia, apnea, mydriasis, coma, periarteritis nodosa, noncardiogenic pulmonary edema, hypokalemia, hypoglycemia

When to Transport to Hospital Transport any symptomatic patient

Overdosage/Treatment

Decontamination: Excision of tissue near insulin injection site can be performed

Supportive therapy: 50 mL $D_{50}W$ given intravenously; if no I.V. is available, glucagon 0.5-1 mg S.C. or I.M.; give 300 g of carbohydrates orally when patient awakens; insulin-induced peripheral and sacral edema has been successfully treated with oral ephedrine (15 mg every 8 hours); for most insulin overdoses, anticipate a need of 400-600 mg of glucose/kg/hour; continuous infusions of glucose with concentrations exceeding 20% should be given by central venous line

Warnings/Precautions Any change of insulin should be made cautiously; changing manufacturers, type and/or method of manufacture, may result in the need for a change of dosage; use with caution in patients with a previous hypersensitivity reaction; S.C. doses used in insulin-resistant patients must be reduced if given I.V., only regular insulin should be given I.V.

(Continued)

315

Insulin Preparations (Continued)

Adverse Reactions

1% to 10%:

Cardiovascular: Palpitation, tachycardia, pallor

Central nervous system: Fatigue, mental confusion, loss of consciousness, headache, hypothermia

Dermatologic: Urticaria, redness

Endocrine & metabolic: Hypoglycemia

Gastrointestinal: Hunger, nausea, numbness of mouth

Local: Itching, edema, stinging, or warmth at injection site, atrophy or hypertrophy of S.C. fat tissue

Neuromuscular & skeletal: Muscle weakness, paresthesia, tremors

Ocular: Transient presbyopia or blurred vision, blurred vision

Miscellaneous: Diaphoresis, anaphylaxis

Reference Range

Therapeutic, serum insulin (fasting): 5-20 μIU/mL (SI: 35-145 pmol/L)

Glucose:

Newborns: 20-80 mg/dL

Adults: 60-115 mg/dL

Elderly: 100-180 mg/dL

Peptide fragments are low (<0.5 ng/mL) in cases of exogenous insulin administration but high in insulinoma or sulfonylurea ingestion

Drug Interactions See table.

Environmental/Drug Interactions With Insulin Injection

Decrease Hypoglycemic Effect of Insulin	Increase Hypoglycemic Effect of Insulin	Unstable or Mixed Hypoglycemic Effect of Insulin
Chlorpromazine	Alcohol	Alcohol
Contraceptives, oral	Alpha-blockers	Beta-blockers
Corticosteroids	Anabolic steroids	Cyclophosphamide
Dextrothyroxine	Beta-blockers*	Isoniazid
Diltiazem	Captopril	Smoking
Dobutamine	Clofibrate	
Epinephrine	Enalapril	
Niacin	Fenfluramine	
Smoking	Guanethidine	
Thiazide diuretics	Hot baths	
Thyroid hormone	MAO inhibitors	
	Mebendazole	
	Pentamidine	
	Phenylbutazone	
	Salicylates	
	Sauna	
	Sulfinpyrazone	
	Tetracyclines	

*Nonselective beta-blockers may delay recovery from hypoglycemic episodes and mask signs/symptoms of hypoglycemia. Cardioselective agents may be alternatives.

Dosage Forms All insulins are 100 units/mL (10 mL) except where indicated:
Rapid-acting:
  Regular beef and pork (Regular Iletin® I)
  Regular beef (purified) (Beef Regular Iletin® II)
  Regular human:
    rDNA (Humulin® R)
    rDNA, buffered (Humulin® BR)
    Semisynthetic: Novolin® R, Novolin® R PenFil® (1.5 mL), Velosulin®
  Regular pork:
    Purified (Pork Regular Iletin® II, Velosulin®)
    Purified, concentrated (Regular [Concentrated] Iletin® II U-500): 500 units/
      mL (20 mL)
    Regular Insulin
  Zinc suspension, prompt:
    Beef (Semilente® Insulin)
    Beef and pork (Semilente® Iletin® I)
Intermediate-acting:
  Isophane suspension:
    Beef (NPH Insulin)
    Beef and pork (NPH Iletin® I)
    Beef (purified) (Beef NPH Iletin® II)
    Human (rDNA) (Humulin® N)
    Human (semisynthetic) (Novolin® N, Novolin® N PenFil®) (1.5 mL)
    Pork (purified) (NPH Purified, Pork NPH Iletin® II, Insulatard® NPH)
  Zinc suspension:
    Beef (Lente® Insulin)
    Beef and pork (Lente® Iletin® I)
    Beef (purified) (Lente® Iletin® II)
    Human (rDNA) (Humulin® L)
    Human (semisynthetic) (Novolin® L)
    Pork (purified) (Lente® Iletin® II, Lente® Purified Pork Insulin)
Long-acting:
  Zinc suspension, extended:
    Beef (Ultralente® Insulin)
    Beef and pork (Ultralente® Iletin® I)
    Human (rDNA) (Humulin® U)
Combinations:
  Isophane insulin suspension (50%) and insulin injection (50%) human
    (rDNA) (Humulin® 50/50)
  Isophane insulin suspension (70%) and insulin injection (30%) human
    (rDNA) (Humulin® 70/30)
  Isophane insulin suspension (70%) and insulin injection (30%) human (semi-
    synthetic) (Mixtard® Human 70/30, Novolin® 70/30)
  Isophane insulin suspension (70%) and insulin injection (30%) human (semi-
    synthetic) (Novolin® 70/30 PenFil®): 1.5 mL
  Isophane insulin suspension (70%) and insulin injection (30%) pork (purified)
    (Mixtard®)
Additional Information The term "purified" refers to insulin preparations containing no more than 10 ppm proinsulin (purified and human insulins are less immunogenic). Insulin abuse can be identified by presence of anti-insulin antibodies or decreased plasma C-peptide concentration; aspirin may be useful in alleviating hypersensitivity reactions; gas gangrene may occur secondary to S.C. insulin injection
Specific References
  Davidson J and Paterson KR, "Insulin-Adverse Reactions and Clinical Problems," *Adv Drug React Toxicol Rev*, 1996, 15(4):79-91.

Insulinum *see* Insulin Preparations *on page 314*

Iobid DM® *see* Guaifenesin and Dextromethorphan *on page 271*

Iofed® *see* Brompheniramine and Pseudoephedrine *on page 86*

Iofed® PD *see* Brompheniramine and Pseudoephedrine *on page 86*

Ionamin® *see* Phentermine *on page 478*

Ipersed® *see* Nitrazepam *on page 435*

I-Phrine® Ophthalmic Solution *see* Phenylephrine *on page 479*

Ipotensium® *see* Clonidine *on page 154*

Iproveratril Hydrochloride *see* Verapamil *on page 609*

Ircon® *see* Iron *on this page*

Iron (EYE ern)

Synonyms Iron Dextran Complex

Commonly Found In Ferrous sulfate, ferrous gluconate, ferrous fumarate, ferrous chloride, ferrous carbonate, ferrous chloride

U.S. Brand Names Femiron®; Feosol®; Feostat®; Feratab®; Fergon®; Fer-In-Sol®; Fer-Iron®; Fero-Gradumet®; Ferospace®; Ferralet®; Ferralyn® Lanacaps®; Ferra-TD®; Ferro-Sequels®; Fumasorb®; Fumerin®; Hemocyte®; InFeD™ Injection; Ircon®; Mol-Iron®; Nephro-Fer™; Simron®; Slow FE®; Span-FF®

Therapeutic Category Electrolyte Supplement

Use Prevention and/or treatment of iron deficiency anemias; prenatal supplementation

Usual Dosage Oral (dose expressed in terms of elemental iron):

Recommended daily allowance:

Male: 10 mg

Female: 18 mg

Pregnancy and lactation: 30-60 mg

Iron replacement:

Infants: 10-25 mg/day in 3-4 divided doses

Children:

6 months to 2 years: Up to 6 mg/kg/day in 3-4 divided doses

2-12 years: 3 mg/kg/day given 3-4 times/day

Adults: 2-3 mg/kg/day given 3 times/day

Mechanism of Action Essential component of hemoglobin, myoglobin, and multiple enzymes; supplementation is given to replenish lost iron stores

Pharmacodynamics/kinetics Total body stores are 3-4 g

Absorption: In ferrous state (Fe^{2+}) in duodenum and jejunum

Distribution: 70% as ferrous state in hemoglobin, 25% in ferric state as ferritin or hemosiderin, 0.1% in ferric state in plasma

Elimination: ~1 mg/day of iron is lost via urinary excretion, skin desquamation; this may increase to 2 mg/day when iron accumulates

Signs and Symptoms of Acute Intoxication Fever, hypoglycemia, coagulopathy, hematuria, hyperventilation, bezoars, urine discoloration (black), hyperthermia, feces discoloration (black), feces discoloration (green); acute gastrointestinal irritation, esophageal ulceration; sweating, erosion of gastrointestinal mucosa, hepatic and renal impairment, sedation, coma, hematemesis, drowsiness, acidosis

There are essentially five stages of iron poisoning:

Stage I (30 minutes to 6 hours): Predominately gastrointestinal irritation, due primarily to the corrosive effect of iron; nausea, vomiting, epigastric pain, gastrointestinal bleeding, drowsiness, and hypotension may occur; a metabolic acidosis, leukocytosis, or hyperglycemia may be present (due to vasodilatation)

318

Stage II (6-24 hours): A latent period of symptom quiescence during which symptomatic improvement may be noted; in severe poisonings, there may be no latent period

Stage III (6-48 hours): Metabolic and systemic derangement occur with cardiovascular collapse, coma, seizures, and coagulopathy (inhibition of thrombin and fibrinogen); pulmonary edema may occur due to cardiac failure

Stage IV (2-7 days): Hepatotoxicity (jaundice) and coagulopathy occur; metabolic acidosis is present, and renal insufficiency may occur

Stage V (1-8 weeks): Primarily delayed gastrointestinal complications, including gastric/duodenal fibrosis resulting in obstructive pattern; achlorhydria may develop

When to Transport to Hospital Transport any pediatric (<6 years of age) ingestion over 20 mg/kg or any symptomatic patient

Warnings/Precautions Some products contain tartrazine which may cause allergic reactions

Adverse Reactions
Cardiovascular: Cardiovascular collapse, hypotension
Dermatologic: Urticaria
Hematologic: Leukocytosis

>10%:
Cardiovascular: Flushing
Central nervous system: Dizziness, fever, headache, pain
Gastrointestinal: Nausea, vomiting, metallic taste
Local: Staining of skin at the site of I.M. injection, phlebitis,
Miscellaneous: Diaphoresis

1% to 10%:
Gastrointestinal: Diarrhea
Genitourinary: Discoloration of urine

Note: Diaphoresis, urticaria, arthralgia, fever, chills, dizziness, headache, and nausea may be delayed 24-48 hours after I.V. administration or 3-4 days after I.M. administration

Anaphylactoid reactions: Respiratory difficulties and cardiovascular collapse have been reported and occur most frequently within the first several minutes of administration

Test Interactions Measured serum iron concentrations will be lowered in face of deferoxamine therapy; high serum iron may falsely increase total iron binding capacity (TIBC) for most common assay; Hemoccult® and Gastroccult® tests can be unreliable in detecting gastrointestinal bleeding in iron overdoses treated with whole bowel irrigation (ferrous sulfate/ferrous gluconate: false-positive; ascorbic acid: false-negative)

Reference Range Levels >450-500 µg/dL associated with toxicity; consider treatment with levels ≥350 µg/dL; peak values are 2-4 hours after ingestion; standard measurement of total iron binding capacity (IBC) are unreliable and should not be used to assess the patient

Therapeutic:
Male: 75-175 µg/dL (SI: 13.4-31.3 µmol/L)
Female: 65-165 µg/dL (SI: 11.6-29.5 µmol/L); iron levels >300 µg/dL can be considered toxic and should be treated as an overdose

Drug Interactions Antacids decrease iron absorption; vitamin C increases gastrointestinal absorption; iron can inhibit tetracycline and penicillamine absorption

Dosage Forms Amount of elemental iron is listed in brackets
Ferrous fumarate:
Capsule, controlled release (Span-FF®): 325 mg [106 mg]
(Continued)

Iron (Continued)

    Drops (Feostat®): 45 mg/0.6 mL [15 mg/0.6 mL] (60 mL)
    Suspension, oral (Feostat®): 100 mg/5 mL [33 mg/5 mL] (240 mL)
    Tablet: 325 mg [106 mg]
        Chewable (chocolate flavor) (Feostat®): 100 mg [33 mg]
        Femiron®: 63 mg [20 mg]
        Fumerin®: 195 mg [64 mg]
        Fumasorb®, Ircon®: 200 mg [66 mg]
        Hemocyte®: 324 mg [106 mg]
        Nephro-Fer™: 350 mg [115 mg]
        Timed release (Ferro-Sequels®): Ferrous fumarate 150 mg [50 mg] and docusate sodium 100 mg

Ferrous gluconate:
    Capsule, soft gelatin (Simron®): 86 mg [10 mg]
    Elixir (Fergon®): 300 mg/5 mL [34 mg/5 mL] with alcohol 7% (480 mL)
    Tablet: 300 mg [34 mg]; 325 mg [38 mg]
        Fergon®, Ferralet®: 320 mg [37 mg]
        Sustained release (Ferralet® Slow Release): 320 mg [37 mg]

Ferrous sulfate:
    Capsule:
        Exsiccated (Fer-In-Sol®): 190 mg [60 mg]
        Exsiccated, timed release (Feosol®): 159 mg [50 mg]
        Exsiccated, timed release (Ferralyn® Lanacaps®, Ferra-TD®): 250 mg [50 mg]
        Ferospace®: 250 mg [50 mg]
    Drops, oral:
        Fer-In-Sol®: 75 mg/0.6 mL [15 mg/0.6 mL] (50 mL)
        Fer-Iron®: 125 mg/mL [25 mg/mL] (50 mL)
    Elixir (Feosol®): 220 mg/5 mL [44 mg/5 mL] with alcohol 5% (473 mL, 4000 mL)
    Powder for injection: Deferoxamine: 500 mg vials
    Syrup (Fer-In-Sol®): 90 mg/5 mL [18 mg/5 mL] with alcohol 5% (480 mL)
    Tablet: 324 mg [65 mg]
        Exsiccated (Feosol®) 200 mg [65 mg]
        Exsiccated, timed release (Slow FE®): 160 mg [50 mg]
        Feratab®: 300 mg [60 mg]
        Mol-Iron®: 195 mg [39 mg]
        Timed release (Fero-Gradumet®): 525 mg [105 mg]
    Iron dextran complex: InFed™ injection: 50 mg/mL (2 mL, 10 mL)

Specific References
    Chyka PA, Butler AY, and Holley JE, "Serum Iron Concentrations and Symptoms of Acute Iron Poisoning in Children," *Pharmacotherapy*, 1996, 16(6):1053-8.

Iron Dextran Complex *see* Iron *on page 318*
Ismelin® *see* Guanethidine *on page 278*
Isoamyl Nitrite *see* Amyl Nitrite *on page 49*
Isobamate *see* Carisoprodol *on page 114*

Isocarboxazid (eye soe kar BOKS a zid)

    U.S. Brand Names Marplan®
    Therapeutic Category Antidepressant
    Use Symptomatic treatment of atypical, nonendogenous or neurotic depression
    Usual Dosage Adults: Oral: 10 mg 3 times/day; reduce to 10-20 mg/day in divided doses when condition improves

Mechanism of Action Thought to act by increasing endogenous concentrations of epinephrine, norepinephrine, dopamine, and serotonin through inhibition of the enzyme (monoamine oxidase) responsible for the breakdown of these neurotransmitters

When to Transport to Hospital Transport any pediatric exposure or any symptomatic patient

Warnings/Precautions Avoid tyramine-containing foods: red wine, cheese (except cottage, ricotta, and cream), smoked or pickled fish, beef or chicken liver, dried sausage, fava or broad bean pods, yeast vitamin supplements; avoid use with patients <16 or >60 years of age

Adverse Reactions

>10%:

Cardiovascular: Hypotension

Central nervous system: Drowsiness

Ocular: Blurred vision

<10%:

Cardiovascular: Hypertension, edema, EKG changes (peaked T waves), palpitations, vasoconstriction

Central nervous system: Excitement, mania, coma, hallucinations, seizures, delirium, hyperthermia

Dermatologic: Skin rash, hyperhidrosis

Endocrine & metabolic: Syndrome of inappropriate antidiuretic hormone

Gastrointestinal: Dry mouth, constipation, nausea

Genitourinary: Urinary retention, ejaculatory disturbances

Ocular: Photophobia, ptosis, diplopia, mydriasis, "ping-pong" gaze

Neuromuscular & skeletal: Muscle rigidity, hyperreflexia

Renal: Myoglobinuria leading to renal failure

Respiratory: Tachypnea

Miscellaneous: Sweating

Drug Interactions

Decreased effect of antihypertensives

Increased toxicity with disulfiram (possible seizures), fluoxetine (and other serotonin active agents), tricyclic antidepressants (cardiovascular instability), meperidine (cardiovascular instability), phenothiazines (hyperpyretic crisis), levodopa, sympathomimetics (hyperpyretic crisis), barbiturates, rauwolfia alkaloids (eg, reserpine), dextroamphetamine (psychoses), foods containing tyramine (hypertension, headache, seizures); theophylline/caffeine (hyperthermia), cyclobenzaprine (fever/seizures)

Potentiation of hypoglycemia with oral hypoglycemic agents

Dosage Forms Tablet: 10 mg

Specific References

Erich JL, Shih RD, and O'Connor R, "Ping-Pong Gaze Associated With Monoamine Oxidase Inhibitor Overdose," *Vet Hum Toxicol*, 1994, 36:371.

Isoclor® Expectorant see Guaifenesin, Pseudoephedrine, and Codeine on page 275

Isocom® see Acetaminophen, Isometheptene, and Dichloralphenazone on page 24

Isocyanide see Cyanide on page 170

Isoethadione see Paramethadione on page 458

Isoglaucon® see Clonidine on page 154

Isollyl Improved® see Butalbital Compound on page 93

Isomeride® see Dexfenfluramine on page 185

Isoniazid (eye soe NYE a zid)

Synonyms INH; Isonicotinic Acid Hydrazide

U.S. Brand Names Laniazid®; Niconyl®; Nydrazid®; Triniad®; Uniad®

Canadian Brand Names PMS-Isoniazid®

Therapeutic Category Antitubercular Agent

Use Treatment of susceptible tuberculosis infections and prophylactically to those individuals exposed to tuberculosis

Usual Dosage Oral, I.M. (recommendations often change due to resistant strains and newly developed information; consult *MMWR Morb Mortal Wkly Rep* for current CDC recommendations):

Children: 10-20 mg/kg/day in 1-2 divided doses (maximum: 300 mg total dose)
  Prophylaxis: 10 mg/kg/day (up to 300 mg total dose) for 12 months
Adults: 5 mg/kg/day (usual dose is 300 mg)
  Disseminated disease: 10 mg/kg/day in 1-2 divided doses
  Treatment should be continued for 9 months with rifampin or for 6 months with rifampin and pyrazinamide
  Prophylaxis: 300 mg/day for 12 months
American Thoracic Society and CDC currently recommend twice weekly therapy as part of a short-course regimen which follows 1-2 months of daily treatment for uncomplicated pulmonary tuberculosis in compliant patients
Children: 20-40 mg/kg/dose (up to 900 mg) twice weekly
Adults: 15 mg/kg/dose (up to 900 mg) twice weekly

Toxic dose: 1.5 g
Lethal dose: 80-150 mg/kg

Mechanism of Action Inhibits myocolic acid synthesis resulting in disruption of the bacterial cell wall; inhibits pyridoxine use as a cofactor in production of gamma-aminobutyric acid (GABA), an inhibitory neurotransmitter in the brain

Pharmacodynamics/kinetics

Absorption: Oral, I.M.: Rapid and complete; rate of absorption can be slowed when administered with food
Metabolism: By the liver
Half-life: Varies from 30-90 minutes to 2-5 hours
  Half-life may be prolonged in patients with impaired hepatic function or severe renal impairment

Signs and Symptoms of Acute Intoxication Nausea, exfoliative dermatitis, eosinophilia, hyperreflexia, memory loss, hyperthermia, arthralgia, encephalopathy, deafness, vomiting, neuropathy (peripheral), myoglobinuria, myoclonus, hypoglycemia, slurred speech, dizziness, rhabdomyolysis, meningitis, metabolic acidosis, hyperglycemia, fever, blurred vision, hallucinations, paresthesia, hyperkalemia, stupor, coma, intractable seizures in acute; chronic overdosage has similar toxicities, though early signs of acute overdosage (nausea, vomiting) may not occur, leukopenia, neutropenia, agranulocytosis, granulocytopenia; tachycardia, hypotension, leukocytosis

When to Transport to Hospital Transport any pediatric (<6 years of age) ingestion over 10 mg/kg or any symptomatic patient

Warnings/Precautions Severe and sometimes fatal hepatitis may occur or develop even after many months of treatment; patients must report any prodromal symptoms of hepatitis, such as fatigue, asthenia, malaise, anorexia, nausea, or vomiting; use with caution in patients with renal impairment and chronic liver disease

Adverse Reactions

>10%:
  Gastrointestinal: Loss of appetite, nausea, vomiting, stomach pain
  Hepatic: Hepatitis
  Neuromuscular & skeletal: Weakness, peripheral neuritis

1% to 10%:
  Central nervous system: Dizziness, slurred speech, lethargy
  Neuromuscular & skeletal: Hyper-reflexia
Drug Interactions Phenytoin, carbamazepine, ketoconazole, fluconazole, diazepam, prednisone, disulfiram, aluminum salts, cycloserine, ethionamide; due to mild inhibition of monoamine oxidase by isoniazid, a potential reaction with selective serotonin-reuptake inhibitors may occur
Dosage Forms
  Injection: 100 mg/mL (10 mL)
  Syrup (orange flavor): 50 mg/5 mL (473 mL)
  Tablet: 50 mg, 100 mg, 300 mg
Additional Information Due to mild inhibition of monoamine oxidase by isoniazid, an interaction with tyramine containing foods may occur; children with low milk and low meat intake should receive concomitant pyridoxine therapy; most combination antituberculin products contain INH which generally should be regarded as the more significant toxin

Toxic dose: 1.5 g
Specific References
  Wilcox WD, Hacker YE, and Geller RJ, "Acute Isoniazid Overdose in a Compliant Adolescent Patient," *Clin Pediatr (Phila)*, 1996, 35:213-4.

Isonicotinic Acid Hydrazide see Isoniazid *on previous page*

Isonipecaine Hydrochloride see Meperidine *on page 367*

Isopap® see Acetaminophen, Isometheptene, and Dichloralphenazone *on page 24*

Isopropanol see Isopropyl Alcohol *on this page*

Isopropyl Alcohol
Synonyms Alcojel; Chromar; Dimethyl Carbinol; Isopropanol; Propol
UN Number 1219
Commonly Found In Rubbing alcohol, secondary propyl alcohol, solvents in perfumes, paint thinners, cleaners, disinfectants, racing fuels
Impairment Potential Yes; Serum acetone level of 100 mg/dL is consistent with mild signs of intoxication and driving impairment

Rich J, Scheife RT, Katz N, et al, "Isopropyl Alcohol Intoxication," *Arch Neurol*, 1990, 47(3):322-4.
Mechanism of Toxic Action Metabolized by alcohol dehydrogenase to acetone which contributes to central nervous system depression
Toxicodynamics/kinetics
  Specific gravity: 0.79 g/mL
  Absorption: Rapid from gastrointestinal tract or by inhalation; little absorption through intact skin
  Metabolism: In the liver; 15% metabolized to acetone
  Half-life:
    Isopropyl alcohol: 2.9-16.2 hours
    Acetone: 7.6-26.2 hours
Signs and Symptoms of Acute Intoxication Lethargy, aplastic anemia, coma, vomiting, myoglobinuria, hypotension, tachycardia, hypothermia, hyperglycemia, porphyria, feces discoloration (black), hypotension due to myocardial depression, hemolytic anemia, rhabdomyolysis
When to Transport to Hospital Transport any ingestion or any symptomatic patient having inhalation or dermal contact
Adverse Reactions
  Cardiovascular: Congestive heart failure, sinus tachycardia, Reye's-like syndrome
  Central nervous system: Depression, drowsiness, ataxia, headache
(Continued)

Isopropyl Alcohol *(Continued)*

    Dermatologic: Immunologic contact urticaria

    Hepatic: Impaired gluconeogenesis

    Neuromuscular & skeletal: Areflexia

Reference Range Toxic: >50 mg/dL; death can occur at 150 mg/dL

Additional Information No long-term sequelae; twice as lethal as ethanol; spirituous odor but a clean colorless liquid; bitter taste; can cause skin burns when used topically on premature infants

    Contribution of a serum concentration level of 100 mg/dL to elevation of osmolar gap: 17

    Lethal dose in adults: 250 mL; serious illness can occur with ingestion of 10 mL

Isopropylmeprobamate *see* Carisoprodol *on page 114*

Isoptin® *see* Verapamil *on page 609*

Isopto® Carpine *see* Pilocarpine *on page 486*

Isopto® Frin Ophthalmic Solution *see* Phenylephrine *on page 479*

Isopto® Homatropine *see* Homatropine *on page 288*

Isopto® Hyoscine *see* Scopolamine *on page 532*

Italprid® *see* Tiapride *on page 581*

Jacob's Ladder *see* Valerian *on page 606*

Janimine® *see* Imipramine *on page 309*

Jellyfish

Scientific Name Aurelia aurita

Mechanism of Toxic Action Stings

Signs and Symptoms of Acute Intoxication Pain, burning, urticaria, regional lymph node involvement, skin ulceration, anaphylactic shock (rare)

When to Transport to Hospital Transport any patient with suspected exposure

Overdosage/Treatment

    Decontamination: Immediately rinse with seawater, should then prevent further envenomation by applying acetic acid 5% (vinegar) to any tentacles still adhering to tissue; if acetic acid is not available, use isopropyl alcohol 40% to 70% or finally may use aluminum sulfate; shave envenomated area after initial treatment, then repeat local decontamination therapy. Ocular exposures are to be decontaminated by water irrigation only. **Do not** rub affected area. Wear gloves during decontamination. Meat tenderizers have been used, however, they are not preferred decontamination measures and should not have prolonged contact times (>10 minutes).

    Supportive therapy: Local symptoms persisting after the initial treatment may be treated with antihistamines, local anesthetics, or steroid lotion; tetanus prophylaxis should be given according to patient's immunization status

Adverse Reactions Severe stings may include hematuria, syncope, paralysis, renal insufficiency, hypotension, cardiorespiratory failure

    Central nervous system: Fever, chills

    Dermatologic: Nonimmunologic contact urticaria

    Neuromuscular & skeletal: Muscle spasms

Additional Information

    Class: Scyphozoa

    Range: All oceans

Specific References

    Auerbach PS, "Marine Envenomations," *N Engl J Med*, 1991, 325(7): 486-93.

Jesuit's Tea *see* Maté *on page 360*

Jet Fuel-4

Synonyms JP-4

UN Number 1863

Applies to MIL-T-5624-L-Amd 1

Use Aviation turbine fuel used by the U.S. military (constitutes 85% of turbine fuel used by Department of Defense)

Mechanism of Toxic Action A mixture of alkanes (43%), cycloalkanes (11%), alkylbenzenes (12%), and naphthalenes (2%) which can cause CNS depression

Overdosage/Treatment

Decontamination:

Oral: **Do not** induce emesis or lavage due to risk of aspiration pneumonia; activated charcoal can adsorb benzene

Dermal: Wash with soap and water

Ocular: Flush with saline or water for at least 15 minutes

Inhalation: Administer 100% humidified oxygen

Supportive therapy: Benzodiazepines for seizure control; avoid use of catecholamines due to risk of ventricular arrhythmia

Adverse Reactions

Central nervous system: Neurologic: headache, dizziness, polyneuropathy (on long-term exposure), ataxia, panic attacks, muscle asthenia (at inhalation levels between 3000-7000 ppm)

Dermatologic: Dermal irritant

Gastrointestinal: Nausea

Additional Information

Odor threshold: 1 ppm

PEL-TWA: 400 ppm

Specific References

Davis NE, "Jet Fuel Intoxication," *Aerospace Med*, 1964, 35:481-2.

U.S. Department of Health and Human Services, "Toxicological Profile for Jet Fuels JP-4 and JP-7," Agency for Toxic Substances and Diseases Registry, May, 1993.

Joint Fir *see* Ephedra *on page 219*

JP-4 *see* Jet Fuel-4 *on this page*

Jumex® *see* Selegiline *on page 536*

Jumexal® *see* Selegiline *on page 536*

Junior Strength Panadol® [OTC] *see* Acetaminophen *on page 20*

Kalma® *see* Tryptophan *on page 602*

Kampfer *see* Camphor *on page 99*

Kaopectate® II [OTC] *see* Loperamide *on page 349*

Kargasok "Tea" *see* Kombucha *on page 330*

Karidium® *see* Fluoride *on page 251*

Karigel® *see* Fluoride *on page 251*

Karigel®-N *see* Fluoride *on page 251*

Katopil® *see* Captopril *on page 101*

Kendol® *see* Lorazepam *on page 351*

Kepone® *see* Chlordecone *on page 123*

Kerlone® *see* Betaxolol *on page 76*

Kerosene

Synonyms Coal Oil; Fuel Oil Number 1; Kerosine; Range Oil; Straight Run Kerosene

UN Number 1223

U.S. Brand Names Deobase®; Mobil Oil Cooling System Cleaner

(Continued)

Kerosene *(Continued)*

Abuse Potential Yes

Impairment Potential Yes

Use Originally produced for jet fuel engine; domestic heating; illuminating fuel; a vehicle in pesticides and lighter fluid; solvent in paints

Mechanism of Toxic Action A product of straight-run distillation of crude petroleum, kerosene is a hydrocarbon with low viscosity and low volatility which can produce a pneumonitis upon aspiration

Toxicodynamics/kinetics Absorption: Dermal, oral and inhalation absorption can occur

Signs and Symptoms of Acute Intoxication Tachycardia, cardiomegaly, cyanosis, chest pain, fatigue, sleep disturbances, dizziness, headache, coma, fever, irritability, ataxia, cognitive dysfunction, erythema, bullae, pruritus, blisters, acne, eczema, vomiting, hematemesis, abdominal pain, leukocytosis, hepatotoxicity, cirrhosis, pneumonitis, aspiration pneumonia, pleural effusion, lipoidal pneumonia, pneumothorax, emphysema, cough, dyspnea

When to Transport to Hospital Transport any suspected ingestion or any symptomatic patient

Overdosage/Treatment Decontamination:

Dermal: Wash liberally with soap and water

Ocular: Irrigate eyes copiously with saline or water

Gastrointestinal: Very controversial; certainly it is generally agreed that in ingestions of small amounts (under 30 mL in children), no gastrointestinal decontamination should occur

Drug Interactions May increase sedative properties of hexobarbital

Additional Information Maximum tolerated oral exposure: 1700 mg/kg; minimum lethal oral dose: 1890 mg/kg; oral ingestion of 10-30 mL can result in pulmonary complications in 2% to 3% of individuals

Note that use of kerosene space heaters can result in increased emission rates of carbon monoxide (average of 7.4 ppm)

Odor threshold: 0.08-1 ppm

Specific gravity: 0.8

Toxic inhalation dosage: 0.1-0.2 mL

Specific References

Nagi NA and Abdulallah ZA, "Kerosene Poisoning in Children in Iraq," *J Postgrad Med*, 1995, 71:419-22.

Kerosine *see Kerosene on previous page*

Ketaject® *see Ketamine on this page*

Ketalar® Injection *see Ketamine on this page*

Ketamine *(KEET a meen)*

U.S. Brand Names Ketaject®; Ketalar® Injection; Ketanest®; Ketavet®

Therapeutic Category General Anesthetic

Abuse Potential Yes

Impairment Potential Yes

Use Induction of anesthesia; short surgical procedures; dressing changes

Usual Dosage

Anesthetic induction dose:

Oral: 4-5 mg/kg

I.M.: 5-10 mg/kg

I.V.: 1-2 mg/kg

Maintenance dose is ¹/₂, up to total induction dose as needed to maintain anesthesia

Duration of unconsciousness: 1 hour

Duration of amnesia: 2 hours

Mechanism of Action An N-methyl-D-aspartate (NMDA) brain neuroreceptor antagonist; some opiate agonist effect; while analgesic effect is rapid, laryngeal reflexes, muscle tone, and cardiopulmonary function is usually not affected; structurally related to phencyclidine

Pharmacodynamics/kinetics Duration of action (following a single dose):
Unconsciousness: 10-15 minutes
Analgesia: 30-40 minutes
Amnesia: May persist for 1-2 hours
Metabolism: Hepatic to the active metabolite norketamine and dehydronorketamine
Half-life: 2.5 hours

Signs and Symptoms of Acute Intoxication Seizures, apnea, delirium, fasciculations, extrapyramidal reaction, lacrimation, laryngospasm, insomnia, hyperglycemia, seizures, polyneuropathy, coma, cardiac arrest, gaze nystagmus

When to Transport to Hospital Transport any patient with suspected ingestion

Warnings/Precautions Should be used by or under the direct supervision of physicians experienced in administering general anesthetics and in maintenance of an airway, and in the control of respiration. Resuscitative equipment should be available for use.

Postanesthetic emergence reactions which can manifest as vivid dreams, hallucinations and/or frank delirium occur in 12% of patients; these reactions are less common in patients >65 years of age and when given I.M.; emergence reactions, confusion, or irrational behavior may occur up to 24 hours postoperatively and may be reduced by minimization of verbal, tactile, and visual patient stimulation during recovery or by pretreatment with a benzodiazepine.

Adverse Reactions
>10%:
Cardiovascular: Hypertension, tachycardia, increased cardiac output, paradoxical direct myocardial depression
Central nervous system: Increased intracranial pressure, vivid dreams, visual hallucinations
Neuromuscular & skeletal: Tonic-clonic movements, tremors
Miscellaneous: Emergence reactions, vocalization
1% to 10%:
Cardiovascular: Bradycardia, hypotension
Dermatologic: Pain at injection site, skin rash
Gastrointestinal: Vomiting, anorexia, nausea
Ocular: Gaze nystagmus, diplopia
Respiratory: Respiratory depression

Reference Range An I.V. dose of 2.5 mg/kg produces an average serum ketamine concentration of 1 mg/L at 12 minutes and 0.5 mg/L at 30 minutes, while doses of 4 mg/kg can produce a peak serum ketamine level of 6.3 mg/L

Drug Interactions Elimination half-life and serum levels may be increased with concomitant administration of diazepam; thyroid therapy may enhance hypertensive effect; can enhance the effect of tubocurarine; naloxone can reverse the analgesia but not any other effect (ie, apnea); flumazenil can cause an increase in unpleasant emergence reactions when used with ketamine

Dosage Forms Injection: 10 mg/mL (20 mL, 25 mL, 50 mL); 50 mg/mL (10 mL); 100 mg/mL (5 mL)

Specific References
Awuonda M, "Swedes Alarmed at Ketamine Misuse," *Lancet*, 1996, 348:122.

Ketanest® *see* Ketamine *on previous page*
Ketavet® *see* Ketamine *on previous page*

Ketoprofen (kee toe PROE fen)

U.S. Brand Names Actron®; Orudis®; Orudis® KT

Canadian Brand Names Orafen; Apo-Keto®; Apo-Keto-E®; Novo-Keto-EC®; Nu-Ketoprofen®; Nu-Ketoprofen-E®; Rhodis®; Rhodis-EC®; PMS-Ketoprofen®

Therapeutic Category Analgesic, Non-narcotic; Nonsteroidal Anti-Inflammatory Agent (NSAID)

Use Acute or long-term treatment of rheumatoid arthritis and osteoarthritis; primary dysmenorrhea; mild to moderate pain

Usual Dosage Oral:

Children 3 months to 14 years: Fever: 0.5-1 mg/kg every 6-8 hours

Children >12 years and Adults:

Rheumatoid arthritis or osteoarthritis: 50-75 mg 3-4 times/day up to a maximum of 300 mg/day

Mild to moderate pain: 25-50 mg every 6-8 hours up to a maximum of 300 mg/day

Mechanism of Action Inhibits prostaglandin synthesis by decreasing the activity of the enzyme, cyclo-oxygenase, which results in decreased formation of prostaglandin precursors thus decreasing inflammatory response

Pharmacodynamics/kinetics

Absorption: Almost completely from gastrointestinal tract

Metabolism: In the liver

Half-life: 1-4 hours

Time to peak serum concentration: Within 30 minutes to 2 hours

Signs and Symptoms of Acute Intoxication Nausea, wheezing, insomnia, purpura, pseudotumor cerebri, photosensitivity, nephrotic syndrome, depression, conjunctivitis, gastrointestinal bleeding, impotence, myalgia, gastritis; exfoliative dermatitis, eczema, dyspnea, confusion, vomiting, cognitive dysfunction, ototoxicity; tinnitus, drowsiness; severe poisoning can manifest with coma, seizures, renal failure and or hepatic failure, hypotension, respiratory depression, apnea, metabolic acidosis; leukocytosis

When to Transport to Hospital Transport any symptomatic patient

Warnings/Precautions Use with caution in patients with congestive heart failure, hypertension, decreased renal or hepatic function, history of gastrointestinal disease (bleeding or ulcers), or those receiving anticoagulants

Adverse Reactions

>10%:

Central nervous system: Dizziness

Dermatologic: Rash

Gastrointestinal: Abdominal cramps, heartburn, indigestion, nausea

1% to 10%:

Central nervous system: Headache, nervousness

Dermatologic: Itching

Endocrine & metabolic: Fluid retention

Gastrointestinal: Vomiting

Otic: Tinnitus

Drug Interactions Aspirin decreases serum concentrations probably by protein-binding displacement; there is an increased bleeding potential with concomitant warfarin therapy; may increase lithium and methotrexate concentrations by decreasing renal clearance; may decrease diuretic and hypotensive effects of thiazides, loop diuretics, ACE inhibitors, and beta-blockers; may increase nephrotoxicity of cyclosporine

Dosage Forms

Capsule (Orudis®): 25 mg, 50 mg, 75 mg

Capsule, extended release (Oruvail®): 100 mg, 150 mg, 200 mg

Tablet [OTC]: 12.5 mg

Specific References

Moore N, Vuillemin N, Abiteboul M, et al, "Large Scale Safety Study of Keto-profen 25 mg (Toprec®) in Febrile and Painful Conditions," *Pharmacoepidemiol Drug Saf*, 1996, 5:295-302.

Ketorolac Tromethamine (KEE toe role ak troe METH a meen)

U.S. Brand Names Toradol®

Therapeutic Category Analgesic, Non-narcotic; Nonsteroidal Anti-Inflammatory Agent (NSAID)

Use Short-term management of pain; first parenteral NSAID for analgesia

Usual Dosage

Adults (pain relief usually begins within 10 minutes):

I.M., I.V.: Initial: 30-60 mg, then 15-30 mg every 6 hours as needed for up to 5 days maximum; maximum dose in the first 24 hours: 150 mg with 120 mg/24 hours for up to 5 days total

Oral (use of oral ketorolac is only indicated as continuation therapy to parenteral ketorolac): 10 mg every 4-6 hours as needed for a maximum of 40 mg/day; on day of transition from I.M. to oral: maximum oral dose: 40 mg (or 120 mg combined oral and I.M.); maximum 5 days administration

Ophthalmic: Instill 1 drop in eye(s) 4 times/day

Elderly >65 years: Renal insufficiency or weight <50 kg:

I.M., I.V.: 15-30 mg, then 15 mg every 6 hours (parenteral) up to a maximum daily dose of 60 mg

Oral dosage should not exceed daily amounts of 40 mg; maximum daily dose (including parenteral) should not exceed 120 mg

Mechanism of Action Inhibits prostaglandin synthesis by decreasing the activity of the enzyme, cyclo-oxygenase, which results in decreased formation of prostaglandin precursors

Pharmacodynamics/kinetics

Peak effect: Within 75-150 minutes

Duration: 6-8 hours

Absorption: Oral: Well absorbed

Metabolism: In the liver

Half-life: 5-6 hours, increased 30% to 50% in the elderly

Signs and Symptoms of Acute Intoxication Nausea, chills, wheezing, nephrotic syndrome, gastrointestinal bleeding, cognitive dysfunction, dry mouth, vomiting, coagulopathy, ototoxicity; tinnitus, drowsiness; severe poisoning can manifest with coma, seizures, renal and or hepatic failure, hypotension, respiratory depression

When to Transport to Hospital Transport any pediatric exposure or any symptomatic patient

Warnings/Precautions Use of ketorolac at recommended doses for longer than 5 days is associated with an increased frequency and severity of adverse events; use extra caution and reduce dosages in the elderly because it is cleared renally somewhat slower and the elderly are also more sensitive to the renal effects of NSAIDs

Adverse Reactions

Genitourinary: Renal impairment

Hematologic: Wound bleeding (with I.M.), postoperative hematomas

1% to 10%:

Cardiovascular: Edema

Central nervous system: Drowsiness, dizziness, headache, pain

Gastrointestinal: Nausea, dyspepsia, diarrhea, gastric ulcers, indigestion

Local: Pain at injection site

Miscellaneous: Diaphoresis (increased)

(Continued)

Ketorolac Tromethamine *(Continued)*

Reference Range
Peak plasma level after a 60 mg dose (I.M.): 4-4.5 µg/mL
Serum concentration:
  Therapeutic: 0.3-5.0 µg/mL
  Toxic: >5.0 µg/mL

Drug Interactions Aspirin decreases serum concentrations probably by protein-binding displacement; there is an increased bleeding potential with concomitant warfarin therapy; may increase lithium and methotrexate concentrations by decreasing renal clearance; may decrease diuretic and hypotensive effects of thiazides, loop diuretics, ACE inhibitors, and beta-blockers; may increase nephrotoxicity of cyclosporine; concomitant administration of lithium and ketorolac can result in elevated lithium levels

Dosage Forms
Injection: 15 mg/mL (1 mL); 30 mg/mL (1 mL, 2 mL)
Solution, ophthalmic: 0.5% (5 mL)
Tablet: 10 mg

Additional Information 30 mg provides the analgesia comparable to 12 mg of morphine or 100 mg of meperidine; postmarketing surveillance of ketorolac indicated that the risk of clinically serious gastrointestinal bleeding was dose-dependent, particularly in elderly patients, who received doses exceeding 60 mg/day. No addictive effect.

Specific References
Hoppmann RA, Peden JG, and Ober SK, "Central Nervous System Side Effects of Nonsteroidal Anti-inflammatory Drugs. Aseptic Meningitis, Psychosis, and Cognitive Dysfunction," *Arch Intern Med*, 1991, 151(7):1309-13.

Key-Pred® *see* Prednisolone *on page 495*

Key-Pred-SP® *see* Prednisolone *on page 495*

Khat *see* Cathinone *on page 119*

Klarivitina® *see* Cyproheptadine *on page 175*

Kleen-up® *see* Glyphosate *on page 269*

Klerist-D® Tablet [OTC] *see* Chlorpheniramine and Pseudoephedrine *on page 134*

Klonopin™ *see* Clonazepam *on page 153*

Kloral® *see* Chloral Hydrate *on page 122*

Kloral Hydrat *see* Chloral Hydrate *on page 122*

Kloromin® [OTC] *see* Chlorpheniramine *on page 132*

Knox-Out® *see* Diazinon *on page 192*

Kolephrin® GG/DM [OTC] *see* Guaifenesin and Dextromethorphan *on page 271*

Kombucha

Synonyms "Fungus" Japonicus; Kargasok "Tea"; Kombucha Mushroom; Kombucha Tea; Kwassan; Manchurian "Fungus"; Manchurian Tea; T'Chai from the Sea; Teekwass

Use Folk/herbal remedy used to relieve arthritis; treat insomnia, hypertension, ache; stimulate hair growth; used by AIDS patients to stimulate the immune (T-cell) system (all these actions are unproven); other claims include elimination of wrinkles and cleansing the gallbladder; has been used in alternative medicine for HIV therapy although its use has markedly decreased

Usual Dosage 4-8 ounces/day

Mechanism of Toxic Action Unknown bacterial products may affect gut's bacterial flora

Signs and Symptoms of Acute Intoxication Hepatotoxicity (usually resolves within a month), abdominal cramping, chest pain, cough, erythematous rash, anorexia, thrombocytopenia, hepatomegaly, nausea, elevated prothrombin time, allergic symptoms

When to Transport to Hospital Transport any symptomatic patient

Overdosage/Treatment Symptoms are usually self limited

Adverse Reactions

Central nervous system: Coma

Dermatologic: Erythematous rash

Endocrine & metabolic: Severe metabolic acidosis

Gastrointestinal: Anorexia

Hepatic: Hepatotoxicity, hepatitis, hepatomegaly

Hematologic: Thrombocytopenia, disseminated intravascular coagulopathy

Respiratory: Cough (nonproductive)

Additional Information Due to acidic nature of the tea (pH is ~1.8), it should not be prepared or stored in ceramic or lead crystal containers. During fermentation process, ethanol (up to 1.5%), ethyl acetate, acetic acid, lactic acid, glucuronic acid, heparin, hyaluronic acid, chondroitin sulfate acid, mukoitin sulfate, or lactic acid may be produced. Found as a gray, flat patty (3" in diameter) which is fermented in black tea and sugar. A 6" wide gray fungus that is often ingested in sugared tea after fermentation; production of 0.5% alcohol, glucuronic acid, hyaluronic acid, chondroitin sulfate acid, usnic acid, mukoitin sulfate, heparin, lactic acid along with *Acetobacter* ketogenum and pichia fermentans has been associated with the tea; not a fungus but a fungal symbiot that is a 6" patty which has been used in Asia and Europe as an unproven therapeutic agent for rheumatism, intestinal disorders, and premenstrual syndrome

Usually referred to as a mushroom, several species of yeast and bacteria are held together by a thin membrane. Some species associated with the Kombucha colony include *S. ludwigii*, *S. pombe*, *Bacterium xylinum*, *Acetobacter ketogenum*, *S. gluconicum*, *B. xylinoides*, *B. katogenum*, *Picha fermentans*, and *Torula* sp, *Saccharomyces cerevisiae*, and *Candida valida*. In addition, contamination with *Aspergillus* may be present.

Specific References

Perron AD, Patterson JA, and Yanofsky NN, "Kombucha 'Mushroom' Hepatotoxicity," *Ann Emerg Med*, 1995, 26(5):660-1.

Kombucha Mushroom *see Kombucha on previous page*

Kombucha Tea *see Kombucha on previous page*

Komex® *see Boric Acid on page 80*

Kredex® *see Carvedilol on page 116*

Kristtorn *see Holly on page 287*

Kwassan *see Kombucha on previous page*

Kwelcof® *see Hydrocodone and Guaifenesin on page 295*

Kwells® *see Scopolamine on page 532*

Kwik-kil® *see Strychnine on page 549*

L-5-Hydroxytryptophan *see Oxitriptan on page 451*

LAAM *see Levomethadyl Acetate Hydrochloride on page 341*

Labetalol (la BET a lole)

Synonyms Ibidomide Hydrochloride

U.S. Brand Names Labrocol®; Normodyne®; Trandate®

Therapeutic Category Alpha-/Beta- Adrenergic Blocker

Use Treatment of mild to severe hypertension; I.V. for hypertensive emergencies (Continued)

Labetalol *(Continued)*

Usual Dosage Due to limited documentation of its use, labetalol should be initiated cautiously in pediatric patients with careful dosage adjustment and blood pressure monitoring

Children:

Oral: Limited information regarding labetalol use in pediatric patients is currently available in literature. Some centers recommend initial oral doses of 4 mg/kg/day in 2 divided doses. Reported oral doses have started at 3 mg/kg/day and 20 mg/kg/day and have increased up to 40 mg/kg/day.

I.V., intermittent bolus doses of 0.3-1 mg/kg/dose have been reported.

For treatment of pediatric hypertensive emergencies, initial continuous infusions of 0.4-1 mg/kg/hour with a maximum of 3 mg/kg/hour have been used.

Adults:

Oral: Initial: 100 mg twice daily, may increase as needed every 2-3 days by 100 mg until desired response is obtained; usual dose: 200-400 mg twice daily; not to exceed 2.4 g/day

I.V.: 20 mg or 1-2 mg/kg whichever is lower, IVP over 2 minutes, may give 40-80 mg at 10-minute intervals, up to 300 mg total dose

I.V. infusion: Initial: 0.5-2 mg/minute; titrate to response up to 300 mg total dose

Mechanism of Action Blocks alpha-, beta$_1$-, and beta$_2$-adrenergic receptor sites; elevated renins are reduced; beta- to alpha-blocking ratio is 7:1 (I.V.) and 3:1 (oral)

Pharmacodynamics/kinetics

Onset of action:

Oral: 20 minutes to 2 hours

I.V.: 2-5 minutes

Peak effect:

Oral: 1-4 hours

I.V.: 5-15 minutes

Duration:

Oral: 8-24 hours (dose-dependent)

I.V.: 2-4 hours

Absorption: Oral: Rapid and complete

Metabolism: In liver

Bioavailability: Oral: 25%; increased bioavailability with liver disease, elderly and concurrent cimetidine

Half-life: 5.5-8 hours

Signs and Symptoms of Acute Intoxication Hypotension, claudication, priapism, cholestatic jaundice, night terrors, impotence, lightheadedness, ejaculatory disturbances, hypoglycemia, dyspepsia, depression, heart failure, wheezing, oliguric renal failure, bradycardia, leukopenia; neutropenia; agranulocytosis; granulocytopenia

When to Transport to Hospital Transport any pediatric ingestion over 5 mg/kg or any symptomatic patient

Warnings/Precautions Orthostatic hypotension may occur with I.V. administration; patient should remain supine during and for up to 3 hours after I.V. administration; paradoxical increase in blood pressure has been reported with treatment of pheochromocytoma or clonidine withdrawal syndrome; use with extreme caution in patients with hyper-reactive airway disease, congestive heart failure, diabetes mellitus, hepatic dysfunction

Adverse Reactions

1% to 10%:

Cardiovascular: Congestive heart failure, arrhythmia, reduced peripheral circulation, orthostatic hypotension

Central nervous system: Mental depression, dizziness, drowsiness
Dermatologic: Itching, numbness of skin
Endocrine & metabolic: Decreased sexual ability
Gastrointestinal: Nausea, vomiting, stomach discomfort, abnormal taste
Neuromuscular & skeletal: Weakness
Respiratory: Dyspnea, nasal congestion

Test Interactions A labetalol metabolite (3-amino-1-phenylbutane or APB) may cause a false-positive result with amphetamine/methamphetamine by thin-layer chromatography or immunoassay

Reference Range Toxic: Serum levels >500 ng/mL

Drug Interactions Cimetidine may potentiate labetalol action, additive hypotensive effects with other hypotensive drugs, halothane used concurrently may further decrease blood pressure, glutethimide may decrease labetalol concentrations. An increased incidence of tremor may be seen with concomitant tricyclic antidepressant use.

Dosage Forms
Injection: 5 mg/mL (20 mL, 40 mL, 60 mL)
Tablet: 100 mg, 200 mg, 300 mg

Additional Information Not shown to be effective for cocaine-cardiovascular toxicity

Specific References
Zell-Kanter M and Leikin JB, "Oral Labetalol in Hypertensive Urgencies," *Am J Emerg Med*, 1991, 9(2):136-8.

LaBID® Phyllocontin® *see Theophylline Salts on page 571*

Labrocol® *see Labetalol on page 331*

LactiCare-HC® *see Hydrocortisone on page 297*

LAM *see Levomethadyl Acetate Hydrochloride on page 341*

Lamictal® *see Lamotrigine on next page*

Lamivudine (la MI vyoo deen)

Synonyms 3TC; 3-Thiacytidine

U.S. Brand Names Epivir®

Therapeutic Category Antiviral Agent

Use In combination with zidovudine for treatment of HIV infection when therapy is warranted based on clinical and/or immunological evidence of disease progression; has also demonstrated positive effects in the treatment of hepatitis B; also used in chronic hepatitis B infection

Usual Dosage Oral:
Children 3 months to 12 years: 4 mg/kg twice daily (maximum: 150 mg twice daily) with zidovudine
Adolescents 12-16 years and Adults: 15 mg twice daily with zidovudine
Adults <50 kg: 2 mg/kg twice daily with zidovudine

Mechanism of Action *In vitro*, lamivudine is phosphorylated to its active 5'-triphosphate metabolite (L-TP), which inhibits HIV reverse transcription via viral DNA chain termination; L-TP also inhibits the RNA- and DNA-dependent DNA polymerase activities of reverse transcriptase

Pharmacodynamics/kinetics
Absorption: Oral: Rapid in HIV-infected patients
Bioavailability:
Children: 66%
Adults: 87% (oral solution); 66% (tablet)
Half-life:
Children: 2 hours
Adults: 5-7 hours

When to Transport to Hospital Transport any symptomatic patient
(Continued)

Lamivudine (Continued)

Warnings/Precautions A decreased dosage is recommended in patients with renal dysfunction since AUC, C_{max}, and half-life increased with diminishing renal function; use with extreme caution in children with history of pancreatitis or risk factors for development of pancreatitis; hepatic; neutropenia/thrombocytopenia; use with caution in patients with epilepsy, peripheral neuropathy or other CNS disorders

Adverse Reactions

>10%:

Central nervous system: Headache, insomnia, malaise, fatigue, pain

Gastrointestinal: Nausea, diarrhea, vomiting

Neuromuscular & skeletal: Peripheral neuropathy, paresthesia

Respiratory: Nasal signs and symptoms, cough

1% to 10%:

Central nervous system: Dizziness, depression, fever, chills

Dermatologic: Rashes

Gastrointestinal: Anorexia, abdominal pain, dyspepsia, elevated amylase

Hematologic: Neutropenia, anemia

Hepatic: Elevated AST, ALT

Neuromuscular & skeletal: Myalgia, arthralgia

Reference Range Peak serum concentrations after a 8 mg/kg I.V. and oral dose: 10,560 ng/mL and 5815 ng/mL respectively

Drug Interactions Increased effect: Zidovudine concentrations increase significantly (~39%) with coadministration with lamivudine; trimethoprim/sulfamethoxazole increases lamivudine's AUC and decreases its renal clearance by 44% and 29%, respectively; although the AUC was not significantly affected, absorption of lamivudine was slowed and C_{max} was 40% lower when administered to patients in the fed versus the fasted state; increased absorption when given with trimethoprim-sulfamethoxazole

Dosage Forms

Solution, oral: 10 mg/mL (240 mL)

Tablets: 150 mg

Additional Information There are, as yet, no results from clinical trials evaluating the effect of lamivudine, in combination with zidovudine, on progression of HIV infection (eg, incidence of opportunistic infections or survival). Patients may continue to develop infections and other complications of HIV infection and should remain under close physician observation.

Specific References

van Leeuwen R, Katlama C, Kitchen V, et al, "Evaluation of Safety and Efficacy of 3TC (Lamivudine) in Patients With Asymptomatic or Mildly Symptomatic Human Immunodeficiency Virus Infection: A Phase I/II Study," *J Infect Dis*, 1995, 171(5):1166-71.

Lamotrigine (la MOE tri jeen)

Synonyms BW-430-C; LTG

U.S. Brand Names Lamictal®

Therapeutic Category Anticonvulsant

Use Partial/secondary generalized seizures, childhood epilepsy

Usual Dosage

Initial dose: 50-100 mg/day then titrate to daily maintenance dose of 100-400 mg/day in 1-2 divided daily doses

With concomitant valproic acid therapy: Start initial dose at 25 mg/day then titrate to maintenance dose of 50-200 mg/day in 1-2 divided daily doses

Mechanism of Action Triazine derivative which inhibits release of glutamate (an excitatory amino acid) in the brain

Pharmacodynamics/kinetics
Metabolism: Hepatic and renal
Bioavailability: 97.6% (oral)
Half-life: 24 hours; increases to 59 hours with concomitant valproic acid therapy; decreases with concomitant phenytoin or carbamazepine therapy to 15 hours
Elimination: Hepatic and renal

When to Transport to Hospital Transport any pediatric exposure or any patient exhibiting sedation or dizziness

Adverse Reactions 1% to 10%:
Central nervous system: Dizziness, sedation, ataxia
Dermatologic: Hypersensitivity rash, Stevens-Johnson syndrome, angioedema
Ocular: Diplopia
Renal: Hematuria

Reference Range Therapeutic: 2-4 µg/mL

Drug Interactions
Decreased effectiveness when given with acetaminophen (increased renal clearance)
Increased serum concentration and encephalopathy with concomitant valproic acid
Valproate can increase the half-life of lamotrigine

Additional Information Low water solubility

Specific References
Brodie MJ, "Lamotrigine," *Lancet*, 1992, 339(8806):1397-400.

Lamra® *see Diazepam on page 189*
Lanacane® [OTC] *see Benzocaine on page 70*
Lanacort® [OTC] *see Hydrocortisone on page 297*
Lanatrate® *see Ergotamine on page 224*
Laniazid® *see Isoniazid on page 322*
Lanocor® *see Digoxin on page 199*
Lanorinal® *see Butalbital Compound on page 93*
Lanoxicaps® *see Digoxin on page 199*
Lanoxin® *see Digoxin on page 199*
Laractone® *see Spironolactone on page 544*
Largactil® *see Chlorpromazine on page 138*
Latiazem Hydrochloride *see Diltiazem on page 201*
Latycin® *see Tetracycline on page 568*
Laudanum *see Opium Tincture on page 446*
Laughing Gas *see Nitrous Oxide on page 439*
Laurel Camphor *see Camphor on page 99*
Lavacol® [OTC] *see Ethyl Alcohol on page 233*
Laxopol® *see Castor Oil on page 118*
L-Deprenyl *see Selegiline on page 536*

Lead

Related Information
Gasoline *on page 264*

UN Number 1616; 2291; 2811

Impairment Potential Yes; Mean blood levels >50 µg/dL probably result in decrements in reaction time, visual motor performance, hand dexterity, and cognitive performance

Bleecker ML and Hansen JA, *Occupational Neurology and Clinical Neurotoxicology*, Baltimore, MD: Williams & Wilkins, 1994, 215.
(Continued)

Lead *(Continued)*

Use Lead is available in 19 inorganic and 2 organic compounds; common sources (especially for children) are air, water, soil, and leaded paint chips. Use of tap water (as "first-drawn" or with excessive boiling or stored in lead-based kettles) in reconstituting infant formulas for infants; additional sources/uses include leaded foreign bodies such as bullet fragments, numerous imported Asian products, herbal/folk remedies, Mexican remedies for "empacho" and home abortifacients; recreational sources include lead-based cosmetics, contamination of illicitly distilled alcohols or illicit intravenous drug products, leaded gasoline "sniffing", and even chewing colored plastic wires.

Mechanism of Toxic Action Lead's effects are mediated by its ability to complex sulfhydryl groups and other ligands, in enzyme systems throughout the body

Toxicodynamics/kinetics

Absorption: Pulmonary absorption is 30% to 85%; gastric absorption is 5% to 15% in adults and up to 40% in children; gastric absorption can increase to 50% in the presence of calcium, iron, and zinc deficiencies and is also increased in pregnancy

Distribution: Three compartment model predominantly stored in bones (90%), lead is also found in brain, kidney, and liver tissue; blood lead (<1% body stores) is 95% intracellular

Half-life, blood: 28-36 days

Signs and Symptoms of Acute Intoxication

Mild toxicity: Myalgia or paresthesia, mild fatigue, irritability, drowsiness, occasional abdominal discomfort

Moderate toxicity: Arthralgia, general fatigue, difficulty concentrating, muscular exhaustibility, deafness, tremor, headache, diffuse abdominal pain, vomiting, weight loss, constipation

Severe toxicity: Paresis or paralysis, cranial nerve palsies, blindness, encephalopathy (may abruptly lead to seizures, changes in consciousness, coma, and death), lead line (blue-black) on gingival tissue, colic (intermittent, severe abdominal cramps)

When to Transport to Hospital Transport any pediatric ingestion or any symptomatic patient

Warnings/Precautions After chelation, especially in chronic toxicity, redistribution of lead into blood and soft tissues leads to a "rebound" in lead concentrations; also failure to remove the patient from the source(s) of lead will prevent adequate response to chelation therapy

Adverse Reactions Lead toxicity occurs in the acute, acute-on-chronic, or chronic settings secondary to environmental, occupational, intentional, or recreational activities. Acute exposures are commonly associated with symptoms of malaise, nausea, vomiting, myoclonus, metallic taste, fasciculations, abdominal pain; severe exposures can result in encephalopathy, and death; chronic exposures manifest with neuropsychiatric symptoms, anemia, renal dysfunction/chronic failure, hypertension, arthralgias, teratogenesis, and impotence. See chart.

<10%:

Cardiovascular: Sinus bradycardia, cardiomyopathy, cardiomegaly, vasoconstriction, Reye's-like syndrome

Central nervous system: Ataxia, encephalopathy, headache, learning disabilities, drowsiness, dementia, mood and/or mental status changes, seizures, memory disturbance, catatonia, CNS depression, depression, psychosis

Endocrine & metabolic: Growth suppression, syndrome of inappropriate antidiuretic hormone (SIADH), hypermineralization

Gastrointestinal: Abdominal pain, colic, constipation, nausea, vomiting

Hematologic: Anemia (at lead levels >40 µg/dL), hemolysis

Hepatic: Hepatitis
Neuromuscular & skeletal: Arthralgia, paresthesia, rhabdomyolysis
Ocular: Blurred vision, diplopia, optic neuropathy, color vision abnormalities
Renal: Proteinuria, hematuria, chronic renal failure due to interstitial nephritis, acute tubular necrosis
Miscellaneous: Multiple chemical sensitivity syndrome

Effects of Inorganic Lead on Children and Adults-- Lowest Observable Adverse Effect Levels

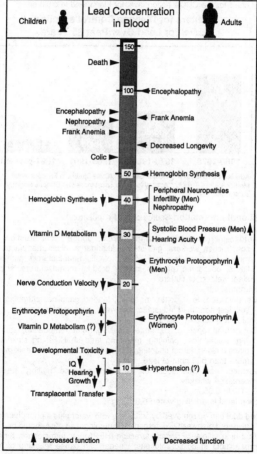

Adapted from U.S. Department of Health and Human Services, "Case Studies in Environmental Medicine: Lead Toxicity," Agency for Toxic Substances and Disease Registry, June 1990.

(Continued)

Lead *(Continued)*

Reference Range Asymptomatic and whole blood lead concentrations of >10-25 μg/dL is an indication for the initiation of community prevention programs, 25-50 μg/dL with positive LMT is an indication for EDTA, >45 μg/dL is an indication for succimer, and >50 μg/dL is an indication for BAL and EDTA; lead mobilization test (LMT); this test is performed by administering 500 mg/m² of $CaNA_2$-ethylenediaminetetra-acetic acid (EDTA) and then collecting urine for 8 hours; a positive result is defined as determining a ratio of urinary lead/dose EDTA >0.6 or a total urinary excretion of >200 μg of lead

See chart for the CDC's action level for blood lead in children.

Centers for Disease Control's Action Level for Lead Over Past 35 Years

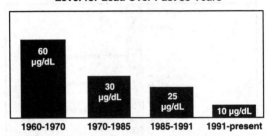

Adapted from Health and Human Services, "Case Studies in Environmental Medicine: Lead Toxicity," Agency for Toxic Substances and Disease Registry, June 1990.

Additional Information Source of lead exposure:

Occupational:

Auto repairers, battery manufacturers, bridge reconstruction workers, construction workers, gas station attendants, glass manufacturers, lead miners, lead smelters and refiners, plastic manufacturers, plumbers, pipe fitters, policemen, printers, rubber product manufacturers, shipbuilders, steel welders or cutters

Environmental:

Ceramicware, lead containing paint, leaded gasoline, plumbing leachate, soil/dust near lead industries, roadways, lead painted homes

Hobbies & related activities:

Car or boat repair, glazed pottery making, home remodeling, lead soldering (eg, electronics), painting, preparing lead shot, fishing sinkers, stained glass making, target shooting at firing ranges; pool cue chalk may contain more than 500 ppm of lead

Substance use: Cosmetics, folk remedies, gasoline "huffing", health foods, moonshine whiskey

PEL-TWA: 0.05 mg/m³

Action level in drinking water: 0.015 mg/L

Lead dust can be removed by scrubbing with water plus a phosphate detergent or powdered dishwasher detergent. Vacuuming lead dust should be performed with a high efficiency particle arresting (HEPA) vacuum cleaner. Since lead is more soluble in acidic solutions, vinegar can cause leaching of lead from leaded containers or bottles.

Action level for home water lead amounts are 15 ppb for first draw water and 5 ppb for purged-line water (water that has run for at least 1 minute)

The Environmental Protection Agency lowered the amount of lead used in gasoline from 1.1 g of lead/gallon to 0.1 g of lead/gallon in 1985

OSHA requires removal of any adult employee with blood lead levels ≥50 μg/dL

OSHA Interim Final Standard for Lead in Construction (permissible lead exposure limit) is 50 μg/m³

Between 1976 and 1991, mean blood lead levels in pediatric patients have decreased from 13 μg/dL (0.66 μmol/L) to 3.2 μg/dL (0.15 μmol/L). Prevalence of blood lead levels >10 μg/dL (0.48 μmol/L) in nonhispanic blacks is estimated to be ~21%.

1 μg/dL = 0.0483 μmol/L

Suggestion of an association between gliomas and occupational lead exposure (blood lead levels >1.4 μmol/L) has recently been noted

Current CDC recommendations for allowable lead concentration:
 Surface paint: ≤.06% lead
 Household soil and dust: <1000 ppm lead
 Tap water: <15 ppm lead
 Household floor dust: 200 μg/f²
 Household windowsill dust: 500 μg/f²
 Household window well dust: 800 μg/f²

Long-term lead exposure can lead to renal impairment and hypertension in middle-aged men

Some types of imported plastic miniblinds contain as much as 2,874 μg of lead per square foot (Federal Housing and Urban Development Child-Safety limit is 500 μg of lead dust per square foot of window sill); other sources for lead include imported (from China) crayons, bulk water tanks, wrappers from certain brands of Mexican candy, pool cue chalk and folk-remedy powders (ie, azarcon, greta)

Specific References
 Paloucek FP, "Lead Poisoning," *Am Pharm*, 1993, NS33(11):81-8.

Lemiserp® *see* Reserpine *on page 523*

Lenoxin® *see* Digoxin *on page 199*

Lente® *see* Insulin Preparations *on page 314*

Lente® Iletin® I *see* Insulin Preparations *on page 314*

Lente® Iletin® II *see* Insulin Preparations *on page 314*

Lente® Purified Pork Insulin *see* Insulin Preparations *on page 314*

Leponex® *see* Clozapine *on page 159*

Leptanal® *see* Fentanyl *on page 247*

Leptilan® *see* Valproic Acid and Derivatives *on page 607*

Lergefin® *see* Carbinoxamine *on page 106*

Lesten® *see* Rauwolfia Serpentina *on page 521*

Lethobard® *see* Pentobarbital *on page 464*

Levanxol® *see* Temazepam *on page 559*

Levodopa and Carbidopa (lee voe DOE pa & kar bi DOE pa)
Related Information
 Carbidopa *on page 105*
Synonyms Carbidopa and Levodopa
U.S. Brand Names Sinemet®
Therapeutic Category Anti-Parkinson's Agent; Dopaminergic Agent (Antiparkinson's)
(Continued)

Levodopa and Carbidopa *(Continued)*

Use Treatment of parkinsonian syndrome; 50-100 mg/day of carbidopa is needed to block the peripheral conversion of levodopa to dopamine. "On-off" can be managed by giving smaller, more frequent doses of Sinemet® or adding a dopamine agonist or selegiline; when adding a new agent, doses of Sinemet® should usually be decreased.

Usual Dosage Oral:

Adults: Initial: 25/100 2-4 times/day, increase as necessary to a maximum of 200/2000 mg/day

Elderly: Initial: 25/100 twice daily, increase as necessary

Conversion from Sinemet® to Sinemet® CR (50/200): (Sinemet® [total daily dose of levodopa] / Sinemet® CR)

300-400 mg / 1 tablet twice daily

500-600 mg / 1½ tablets twice daily or one 3 times/day

700-800 mg / 4 tablets in 3 or more divided doses

900-1000 mg / 5 tablets in 3 or more divided doses

Intervals between doses of Sinemet® CR should be 4-8 hours while awake

Mechanism of Action Parkinson's symptoms are due to a lack of striatal dopamine; levodopa circulates in the plasma to the blood-brain-barrier (BBB), where it crosses, to be converted by striatal enzymes to dopamine; carbidopa inhibits the peripheral plasma breakdown of levodopa by inhibiting its decarboxylation, and thereby increases available levodopa at the BBB

Pharmacodynamics/kinetics

Carbidopa:

Absorption: Oral: 40% to 70%

Half-life: 1-2 hours

Levodopa:

Absorption: May be decreased if given with a high protein meal

Half-life: 1.2-2.3 hours

Signs and Symptoms of Acute Intoxication Palpitations, arrhythmias, spasms, hypotension; may cause hypertension or hypotension

When to Transport to Hospital Transport any pediatric exposure or any symptomatic patient

Overdosage/Treatment Treatment is supportive; initiate gastric lavage, administer I.V. fluids judiciously and monitor EKG; use fluids judiciously to maintain pressures; may precipitate a variety of arrhythmias

Warnings/Precautions Use with caution in patients with history of myocardial infarction, arrhythmias, asthma, wide angle glaucoma, peptic ulcer disease; sudden discontinuation of levodopa may cause a worsening of Parkinson's disease; some tablets may contain tartrazine. The elderly may be more sensitive to the CNS effects of levodopa. Protein in the diet should be distributed throughout the day to avoid fluctuations in levodopa absorption.

Adverse Reactions

>10%:

Cardiovascular: Orthostatic hypotension, palpitations, cardiac arrhythmias

Central nervous system: Confusion, nightmares, dizziness, anxiety

Gastrointestinal: Nausea, vomiting, anorexia, constipation

Neuromuscular & skeletal: Dystonic movements, "on-off", choreiform and involuntary movements

Ocular: Blepharospasm

Renal: Dysuria

1% to 10%:

Central nervous system: Headache

Gastrointestinal: Diarrhea, xerostomia

Genitourinary: Discoloration of urine

Neuromuscular & skeletal: Muscle twitching

    Ocular: Eyelid spasms
    Miscellaneous: Discoloration of sweat
Drug Interactions
  Decreased effect:
    Hydantoins, pyridoxine
    Phenothiazines and hypotensive agents may decrease effects of levodopa
  Increased toxicity with antacids
    Monoamine oxidase inhibitors → hypertensive reactions
Dosage Forms
  Tablet:
    10/100: Carbidopa 10 mg and levodopa 100 mg
    25/100: Carbidopa 25 mg and levodopa 100 mg
    25/250: Carbidopa 25 mg and levodopa 250 mg
    Sustained release: Carbidopa 25 mg and levodopa 100 mg; carbidopa 50 mg
      and levodopa 200 mg
Specific References
  Koller WC, Silver DE, and Lieberman A, "An Algorithm for the Management of
    Parkinson's Disease," *Neurology*, 1994, 44(12 Suppl 10):S1-52.

Levo-Dromoran® *see Levorphanol on next page*

Levomethadyl Acetate Hydrochloride
  (lee voe METH a dil AS e tate hye droe KLOR ide)
Related Information
  Controlled Substances - Uses and Effects *on page 741*
Synonyms LAAM; LAM; L-Methadyl Acetate
U.S. Brand Names ORLAAM®
Therapeutic Category Analgesic, Narcotic
Abuse Potential Yes
Impairment Potential Yes
Use Management of opiate dependence
Usual Dosage Adults: Oral: 20-40 mg 3 times/week, with ranges of 10 mg to as
  high as 140 mg 3 times/week; always dilute before administration and mix with
  diluent prior to dispensing
Mechanism of Action Derivative of methadone but with a longer half-life
Pharmacodynamics/kinetics
  Protein binding: 80%
  Metabolism: Hepatic
  Half-life: 35-60 hours
  Time to peak serum concentration: 1.5-6 hours
Signs and Symptoms of Acute Intoxication Bradycardia, hypotension,
  syndrome of inappropriate antidiuretic hormone (SIADH), coma, miosis
When to Transport to Hospital Transport any pediatric exposure or any
  symptomatic patient
Warnings/Precautions Not recommended for uses outside of the treatment of
  opiate addiction; shall be dispensed only by treatment programs approved by
  FDA, DEA, and the designated state authority. Approved treatment programs
  shall dispense and use levomethadyl in oral form only and according to the
  treatment requirements stipulated in federal regulations. Failure to abide by
  these requirements may result in injunction precluding operation of the
  program, seizure of the drug supply, revocation of the program approval, and
  possible criminal prosecution.
Adverse Reactions
  >10%:
    Cardiovascular: Bradycardia, hypotension
    Central nervous system: Drowsiness
    Gastrointestinal: Nausea, vomiting
(Continued)

Levomethadyl Acetate Hydrochloride *(Continued)*

Respiratory: Respiratory depression

1% to 10%:

Cardiovascular: Peripheral vasodilation, orthostatic hypotension, increased intracranial pressure

Central nervous system: Dizziness/vertigo, CNS depression, confusion, sedation

Endocrine & metabolic: Antidiuretic hormone release

Gastrointestinal: Constipation, biliary tract spasm

Genitourinary: Urinary tract spasm

Ocular: Miosis, blurred vision

Test Interactions Can cause positive opiate urine screen

Reference Range A 60 mg dose can result in a peak serum level of 130 ng/mL; at 24 hours, it is 50 ng/mL

Drug Interactions Decreased effect/levels with phenobarbital

Dosage Forms Solution, oral: 10 mg/mL (474 mL)

Specific References

Blaine JD, Renault PR, Thomas DB, et al, "Clinical Status of Methadyl Acetate (LAAM)," *Ann N Y Acad Sci*, 1981, 362:101-15.

Levorphanol *(lee VOR fa nole)*

Synonyms Levorphan Tartrate

U.S. Brand Names Dromoran®; Levo-Dromoran®

Therapeutic Category Analgesic, Narcotic

Abuse Potential Yes

Impairment Potential Yes

Use Relief of moderate to severe pain; also used parenterally for preoperative sedation and an adjunct to nitrous oxide/oxygen anesthesia; 2 mg levorphanol produces analgesia comparable to that produced by 10 mg of morphine

Usual Dosage Adults:

Oral: 2 mg every 6-24 hours as needed

S.C.: 2 mg, up to 3 mg if necessary, every 6-8 hours

Mechanism of Action Levorphanol tartrate is a synthetic opioid agonist that is classified as a morphinan derivative. Opioids interact with stereospecific opioid receptors in various parts of the central nervous system and other tissues. Analgesic potency parallels the affinity for these binding sites. These drugs do not alter the threshold or responsiveness to pain, but the perception of pain.

Pharmacodynamics/kinetics

Onset of action: Analgesic effect: 10-30 minutes

Duration: 8 hours

Half-life: 12-16 hours

Signs and Symptoms of Acute Intoxication Miosis, bradycardia, hypotension, sedation, drowsiness, ptosis, fatigue, vomiting, slow and raspy speech

When to Transport to Hospital Transport any pediatric exposure or any adult symptomatic patient

Warnings/Precautions Use with caution in patients with hypersensitivity reactions to other phenanthrene derivative opioid agonists (morphine, hydrocodone, hydromorphone, levorphanol, oxycodone, oxymorphone); respiratory diseases including asthma, emphysema, COPD or severe liver or renal insufficiency; some preparations contain sulfites which may cause allergic reactions; may be habit-forming; dextromethorphan has equivalent antitussive activity but has much lower toxicity in accidental overdose

Adverse Reactions
>10%:
  Cardiovascular: Palpitations, hypotension, bradycardia, peripheral vasodilation
  Central nervous system: CNS depression, fatigue, drowsiness, dizziness
  Dermatologic: Pruritus
  Gastrointestinal: Nausea, vomiting
  Neuromuscular & skeletal: Weakness
1% to 10%:
  Central nervous system: Nervousness, headache, restlessness, anorexia, malaise, confusion
  Gastrointestinal: Stomach cramps, xerostomia, constipation
  Endocrine & metabolic: Antidiuretic hormone release
  Gastrointestinal: Biliary tract spasm
  Genitourinary: Decreased urination, urinary tract spasm
  Local: Pain at injection site
  Ocular: Miosis
  Respiratory: Respiratory depression

Drug Interactions
Increased effect with methylphenidate (↑ efficacy, ↓ respiratory depression)
Increased toxicity with CNS depressants (CNS depression); may potentiate toxicity (hyperthermia) of MAO inhibitors

Dosage Forms
Levorphanol tartrate:
  Injection: 2 mg/mL (1 mL, 10 mL)
  Tablet: 2 mg

Specific References
Sinclair JG and Lo GF, "The Blockade of Serotonin Uptake and the Meperidine-Monoamine Oxidase Inhibitor Interaction," *Proc West Pharmacol Soc,* 1977, 20:373-4.

Levorphan Tartrate see Levorphanol *on previous page*
Levothym® see Oxitriptan *on page 451*
Le Votonine® see Oxitriptan *on page 451*
Levsin® see Hyoscyamine *on page 305*
Levsinex® see Hyoscyamine *on page 305*
l-Hyoscyamine Sulfate see Hyoscyamine *on page 305*
Librax® see Clidinium and Chlordiazepoxide *on page 150*
Libritabs® see Chlordiazepoxide *on page 124*
Librium® see Chlordiazepoxide *on page 124*

Lice

Synonyms Body Louse; Crab Louse; Head Louse
Scientific Name *Pediculus humanus*
Phthirus pubis
Mechanism of Toxic Action Requires human blood to survive; an ectoparasite
Signs and Symptoms of Acute Intoxication Pruritus, erythema: Secondary impetiginization can occur; small macules may be seen in *Phthirus pubis* (maculae cerulea)
Overdosage/Treatment General principles of treating pediculosis include discarding or carefully laundering clothing, discarding infested combs or hats, and laundering bedsheets. In general, clothes and bedsheets can be effectively decontaminated by dry cleaning or by machine washing and drying in a hot cycle. Secondary bacterial infections of the skin are common and generally respond to antibiotics effective against *Staphylococcus aureus* (dicloxacillin, (Continued)

Lice *(Continued)*

erythromycin, and others). Pruritus is typically quite severe and may be alleviated by hydroxyzine (Atarax®), diphenhydramine (Benadryl®), and/or topical steroid creams. Treatment guidelines are as follows:

1. Pediculosis corporis: Since the louse resides mainly in the creases of clothes and not on the host, the infection can often be eradicated by delousing contaminated items and maintaining careful hygiene.

2. Pediculosis capitis: Several agents are effective: 1% lindane (Kwell®) shampoo to the scalp, pyrethrin liquid (RID), or permethrin creme rinse (Nix™) These insecticides are probably equal in efficacy. Only lindane requires a prescription. **Caution:** Lindane has been associated with seizures and other nervous system toxicities. However, the risk of serious adverse effects during treatment for pediculosis is small due to its minimal systemic absorption. Nevertheless, lindane should be avoided in pregnancy and in lactating women.

3. Pediculosis pubis: The treatment recommendations are the same as for *P. capitis*. In addition, sexual partners should be identified and treated in the same manner. Pediculosis involving the eyelashes should **not** be treated with insecticides. Instead, occlusive ophthalmic ointment should be applied to the eyelashes twice daily for at least 8 days in an attempt to smother the parasites.

Patients should be seen in follow-up if symptoms persist 1 week after treatment. A second application may be necessary. Some clinicians routinely instruct patients to reapply the insecticide at the 1 week point.

Additional Information Transmitted through body contact

Family: *Anoplura*

Pediculus humanus corporis (head louse, body louse); *Phthirus pubis* (crab louse)

Microbiology: Human lice are ectoparasites and thus tend to live on or in the skin of the host. They belong to the insect class *Hexapoda*. There are three species important in human infection. *Pediculus humanus* var. *corporis* is the human body louse, *Pediculus humanus* var. *capitis* is the human head louse, and *Phthirus pubis* is the crab louse. The body and head louse have similar appearances and are about 4 mm long. The pubic louse is much wider and has a crab-like appearance from which its name is derived; the eggs adhere to human hair and to clothing, and are termed nits.

Epidemiology: Humans are the reservoir for lice. Infestations have been described worldwide especially in areas of overcrowding. The incubation period is about 1-4 weeks following exposure. Individuals are communicable until all the lice and eggs have been treated and destroyed. Pediculosis capitis is a particular problem with school-aged children, where the practice of sharing combs or brushes facilitates epidemic transmission. All socioeconomic backgrounds are at risk for head lice. In contrast, pediculosis corporis is seen mainly in areas of poor sanitation. The body louse resides almost exclusively in soiled clothing, rather than the skin, and only leaves the clothing for a blood meal from the host. Pediculosis corporis also transmits the rickettsial infection epidemic typhus, as well as several others. *Phthirus pubis* is usually sexually transmitted, although spreading via infested bedding or clothing can occur.

Clinical Syndromes:

• **Pediculosis corporis:** Typically, the patient complains of severe pruritus, and small, erythematous papules are found on the body. Often extensive self-induced excoriations across the trunk are noted. If left untreated for long periods, hyperpigmentation and scarring may occur, called "vagabond's disease."

- **Pediculosis capitis:** The most common presentation is intractable scalp pruritus. On examination there may be evidence of secondary bacterial infection of the scalp from excoriations. At times, an "id reaction" occurs, characterized by a dramatic skin eruption over the arms and trunk, felt to be a hypersensitivity reaction.
- *Pediculus pubis*: Most patients present with pruritus in the region of the pubic hairs, but other areas may be involved including the eyelashes and hairs in the axilla; secondary bacterial infections are less common

Diagnosis: The diagnosis of pediculosis is often suspected when an individual presents with severe pruritus. On some occasions, the patient may have identified lice themselves or have had a recent contact history. The diagnosis is confirmed by finding lice (1-4 mm long, depending on species) and/or the "nits" (usually 1 mm or less, attached to hairs).

Specific References

Forsman KE, "Pediculosis and Scabies. What to Look for in Patients Who are Crawling With Clues," *Postgrad Med*, 1995, 98(6):89-90, 93-5, 99-100.

Lidocaine (LYE doe kane)

Synonyms Lignocaine Hydrochloride

U.S. Brand Names Anestacon®; Baylocaine®; Dalcaine®; Dilocaine®; Duo-Trach®; LidoPen®; Nervocaine®; Norocaine®; Octocaine®; Xylocaine®

Canadian Brand Names PMS®-Lidocaine Viscous; Xylocard®

Therapeutic Category Analgesic, Topical; Antiarrhythmic Agent, Class I-B; Local Anesthetic

Use Local anesthetic and acute treatment of ventricular arrhythmias from myocardial infarction, cardiac manipulation, digitalis intoxication; suppression of tinnitus

Investigational: Intranasal use for acute migraine headache

Usual Dosage

Topical: Apply to affected area as needed; maximum: 3 mg/kg/dose; do not repeat within 2 hours

Injectable local anesthetic: Varies with procedure, degree of anesthesia needed, vascularity of tissue, duration of anesthesia required, and physical condition of patient; maximum: 4.5 mg/kg/dose; do not repeat within 2 hours

Acute migraine headache:

Unilateral: 0.5 mL of 4% solution dripped into nostril of affected side by a 1 mL syringe with head hyperextended 45 degrees and rotated 30 degrees to the side of headache

Bilateral: Repeat procedure with other nostril; second dose may be given after 2 minutes

Mechanism of Action An antiarrhythmic agent; suppresses automaticity of cardiac conduction tissue; blocks both the initiation and conduction of nerve impulses by decreasing the neuronal membrane's permeability to sodium ions, which results in inhibition of depolarization with resultant blockade of conduction

Pharmacodynamics/kinetics

Onset of action: 45-90 seconds (single bolus dose)

Duration: 10-20 minutes

Absorption: Oral: 30%

Metabolism: 95% in liver

Half-life: Biphasic: Alpha: 7-30 minutes; Beta (terminal) adults: 1.5-2 hours; (terminal) premature infants: 3.2 hours; increased half-life with CHF, liver disease, shock, severe renal disease

Signs and Symptoms of Acute Intoxication Convulsions, asystole, methemoglobinemia, numbness, disorientation, respiratory failure, ptosis, mydriasis, A-V block, tachycardia (ventricular), diplopia, heart block, myoclonus, tremors, myasthenia gravis (exacerbation or precipitation of), delirium, slurred speech, (Continued)

Lidocaine *(Continued)*

agitation, coma, bradycardia, hypotension, cardiovascular collapse, euphoria, hypokalemia, ototoxicity; tinnitus

When to Transport to Hospital Transport any symptomatic patient

Warnings/Precautions Do not use preparations containing preservatives for spinal or epidural (including caudal) anesthesia; hepatic disease; heart failure, marked hypoxia, severe respiratory depression; hypovolemia or shock; incomplete heart block or bradycardia, fibrillation (atrial), renal dysfunction

Adverse Reactions 1% to 10%:
Cardiovascular: Hypotension
Central nervous system: Positional headache
Miscellaneous: Shivering

Test Interactions Falsely lowered if blood makes contact with stopper of tube

Reference Range
Therapeutic: 1.5-4.0 µg/mL (SI: 6.4-17.1 µmol/L), up to 6.0 µg/mL (SI: 25.6 µmol/L) if necessary
Therapeutic level for tinnitus: 1.5-2.5 µg/mL
Toxic: >8.0 µg/mL (SI: >34.2 µmol/L)
Fatal: >15.0 µg/mL

Drug Interactions Concomitant cimetidine or propranolol may result in increased serum concentrations of lidocaine with resultant toxicity; highly lipid soluble beta-blockers may impair lidocaine clearance

Dosage Forms
Cream: 2% (56 g)
Injection: 0.5% [5 mg/mL] (50 mL); 1% [10 mg/mL] (2 mL, 5 mL, 10 mL, 20 mL, 30 mL, 50 mL); 1.5% [15 mg/mL] (20 mL); 2% [20 mg/mL] (2 mL, 5 mL, 10 mL, 20 mL, 30 mL, 50 mL); 4% [40 mg/mL] (5 mL); 10% [100 mg/mL] (10 mL); 20% [200 mg/mL] (10 mL, 20 mL)
Injection:
I.M. use: 10% [100 mg/mL] (3 mL, 5 mL)
Direct I.V.: 1% [10 mg/mL] (5 mL, 10 mL); 20 mg/mL (5 mL)
I.V. admixture, preservative free: 4% [40 mg/mL] (25 mL, 30 mL); 10% [100 mg/mL] (10 mL); 20% [200 mg/mL] (5 mL, 10 mL)
I.V. infusion, in D₅W: 0.2% [2 mg/mL] (500 mL); 0.4% [4 mg/mL] (250 mL, 500 mL, 1000 mL); 0.8% [8 mg/mL] (250 mL, 500 mL)
Jelly, topical: 2% (30 mL)
Liquid, viscous: 2% (20 mL, 100 mL)
Ointment, topical: 2.5% [OTC], 5% (35 g)
Solution, topical: 2% [20 mg/mL] (15 mL, 240 mL); 4% [40 mg/mL] (50 mL)

Additional Information Odorless, bitter taste; intranasal use of 4% solution is 55% effective for migraine; child-resistant packaging ordered by the U.S. Consumer Product Safety Commission for products containing more than 5 mg of lidocaine

Specific References
Amitai Y, Whitesell L, and Lovejoy FH Jr, "Death Following Accidental Lidocaine Overdose in a Child," *N Engl J Med*, 1986, 314(3):181-2.

Lidone® *see Molindone on page 407*

LidoPen® *see Lidocaine on previous page*

Lidox® *see Clidinium and Chlordiazepoxide on page 150*

Lignocaine Hydrochloride *see Lidocaine on previous page*

Limbitrol® DS 10-25 *see Amitriptyline and Chlordiazepoxide on page 41*

Limovan® *see Zopiclone on page 621*

Linea® *see Diethylpropion on page 196*

Lioresal® *see Baclofen on page 63*

Lipostat® *see Pravastatin on page 492*

Liquers see Ethyl Alcohol on page 233

Liquibid® see Guaifenesin on page 269

Liquid Pred® see Prednisone on page 497

Liquiprin® [OTC] see Acetaminophen on page 20

Liquor see Ethyl Alcohol on page 233

Lisino® see Loratadine on page 350

Lisinopril and Hydrochlorothiazide
(lyse IN oh pril & hye droe klor oh THYE a zide)

U.S. Brand Names Prinzide®; Zestoretic®

Therapeutic Category Antihypertensive, Combination

Dosage Forms Tablet:
Lisinopril 10 mg and hydrochlorothiazide 12.5 mg
[12.5]-Lisinopril 20 mg and hydrochlorothiazide 12.5 mg
[25]-lisinopril 20 mg and hydrochlorothiazide 25 mg

Lisseril® see Cyclobenzaprine on page 173

Listermint® With Fluoride [OTC] see Fluoride on page 251

Lithane® see Lithium on this page

Lithium (LITH ee um)

U.S. Brand Names Cibalith-S®; Eskalith®; Eskalith® CR; Lithane®; Lithobid®; Lithonate®; Lithotabs®; PFI-Lith®; Phasal®

Therapeutic Category Antimanic Agent

Abuse Potential Yes

Impairment Potential Yes

Use Management of acute manic episodes, bipolar disorders, and depression; industrial use: lubricants, alkaline storage batteries, nuclear reactors, alloys

Usual Dosage Oral: Monitor serum concentrations and clinical response (efficacy and toxicity) to determine proper dose

Children 6-12 years: 15-60 mg/kg/day in 3-4 divided doses; dose not to exceed usual adult dosage

Adults: 300-600 mg 3-4 times/day; usual maximum maintenance dose: 2.4 g/day or 450-900 mg of sustained release twice daily

Mechanism of Action Alters cation transport across cell membrane in nerve and muscle cells and influences reuptake of serotonin and/or norepinephrine

Pharmacodynamics/kinetics

Absorption: Rapid

Metabolism: None

Half-life:

Adolescents: 18 hours

Adults: 24 hours

Terminal: 18-24 hours, can increase to more than 36 hours

Elderly or patients with renal impairment: Up to 36 hours

Time to peak serum concentration: Within 30 minutes to 2 hours

Time to peak CSF concentration: 24 hours

Signs and Symptoms of Acute Intoxication Sedation, ataxia, cognitive dysfunction, impotence, hypothyroidism, hypothermia, hepatic failure, A-V block, encephalopathy, chorea (extrapyramidal), downbeat nystagmus, dementia, parotid pain, nocturia, hypokalemia, dysosmia, hypoglycemia, hyperthyroidism, hypertonia, hyperglycemia, neuroleptic malignant syndrome, mania, fever, photophobia, confusion, seizures, Graves' disease, thrombocytosis, rhabdomyolysis, myoglobinuria, hypercalcemia, ototoxicity, Parkinson's-
(Continued)

347

Lithium *(Continued)*

like symptoms, tinnitus, heart block, tremors, arthralgia, leukopenia, neutropenia, agranulocytosis, granulocytopenia, visual changes, bradycardia, ventricular arrhythmia, myocardial infarction, hyperkalemia, polyuria, blurred vision, alopecia, hypotension; see table.

Lithium (Acute Ingestion)

Serum Level	Symptom
1.5-2.5 mEq/L	Polyuria, blurred vision, weakness, lethargy, dizziness, increased reflexes, fasiculations
2.5-3.0 mEq/L	Myoclonic twitching, incontinence, stupor, restlessness, coma
>3.0 mEq/L	Seizures, hypotension, cardiac arrhythmias

When to Transport to Hospital Transport any pediatric exposure (<6 years of age) or any acute ingestions over 1 g

Warnings/Precautions Lithium toxicity is closely related to serum levels and can occur at therapeutic doses; serum lithium determinations are required to monitor therapy; concomitant use of lithium with thiazide diuretics may decrease renal excretion and enhance lithium toxicity; diuretic dosage may need to be reduced by 30%; do not crush or chew, slow or extended release dosage form, swallow whole; use with caution in patients with cardiovascular or thyroid disease

Adverse Reactions

>10%:
   Endocrine & metabolic: Polydipsia, stress
   Gastrointestinal: Nausea, diarrhea, abnormal taste
   Neuromuscular & skeletal: Trembling
1% to 10%:
   Central nervous system: Fatigue
   Dermatologic: Rash
   Gastrointestinal: Bloated feeling, weight gain
   Neuromuscular & skeletal: Muscle twitching, weakness

Test Interactions Increases calcium (S), glucose, magnesium, potassium (S); decreases thyroxine (S); serum bicarbonate, urea levels elevated, serum bromide levels decreased; causes leukopenia, thrombocytopenia

Reference Range

Therapeutic: 0.6-1.2 mEq/L (SI: 0.6-1.2 mmol/L), for acute mania; 0.8-1.0 mEq/L (SI: 0.8-1.0 mmol/L) for protection against future episodes in most patients with bipolar disorder. A higher rate of relapse is described in subjects who are maintained below 0.4 mEq/L (SI: 0.4 mmol/L).

Toxic: >1.5 mEq/L (SI: >1.5 mmol/L); highest survival level: 14.6 mEq/L

Dosage Forms

Lithium carbonate:
   Capsule: 150 mg, 300 mg, 600 mg
   Tablet: 300 mg
   Tablet:
      Controlled release: 450 mg
      Slow release: 300 mg
Syrup, as citrate: 300 mg/5 mL (5 mL, 10 mL, 480 mL)

Additional Information Lithium blood levels increase during caffeine withdrawal

Lithium citrate: Cibalith-S®

Lithium carbonate: Eskalith®, Lithane®, Lithobid®, Lithonate®, Lithotabs®

Specific References
Groleau G, "Lithium Toxicity," *Emerg Med Clin North Am*, 1994, 12(2):511-31.

Lithobid® *see Lithium on page 347*
Lithonate® *see Lithium on page 347*
Lithotabs® *see Lithium on page 347*
Liticon® *see Pentazocine on page 463*
L-Methadyl Acetate *see Levomethadyl Acetate Hydrochloride on page 341*
l-Methamphetamine *see Methamphetamines, Urine on page 384*
Locoid® *see Hydrocortisone on page 297*
Lodine® *see Etodolac on page 240*
Lodis® *see Loperamide on this page*
Lodosyn® *see Carbidopa on page 105*
Lofene® *see Diphenoxylate and Atropine on page 207*
Logen® *see Diphenoxylate and Atropine on page 207*
Lomanate® *see Diphenoxylate and Atropine on page 207*
Lomine® *see Dicyclomine on page 194*
Lomodix® *see Diphenoxylate and Atropine on page 207*
Lomotil® *see Diphenoxylate and Atropine on page 207*
Loniten® *see Minoxidil on page 404*
Lonox® *see Diphenoxylate and Atropine on page 207*
Lontanyl® *see Testosterone on page 564*
Lopemid® *see Loperamide on this page*

Loperamide (loe PER a mide)
U.S. Brand Names Arret®; Blox®; Brek®; Diar-aid® [OTC]; Dissenten®; Imodium®; Imodium® A-D [OTC]; Imosec®; Kaopectate® II [OTC]; Lodis®; Lopemid®; Loperyl®; Orulop®; Pepto® Diarrhea Control [OTC]
Canadian Brand Names PMS-Loperamide®
Therapeutic Category Antidiarrheal
Use Treatment of acute nonspecific diarrhea (including traveler's diarrhea) and chronic diarrhea associated with inflammatory bowel disease; decrease the volume of ileostomy discharge; also used as a prophylaxis for chemotherapy-induced diarrhea
Usual Dosage Oral:
Children:
Acute diarrhea: 0.4-0.8 mg/kg/day divided every 6-12 hours, maximum: 2 mg/dose
Chronic diarrhea: 0.08-0.24 mg/kg/day divided 2-3 times/day, maximum: 2 mg/dose
Adults: Initial: 4 mg (2 capsules), followed by 2 mg after each loose stool, up to 16 mg/day (8 capsules)
Toxic dose: 2 mg/kg
Mechanism of Action Acts directly on intestinal muscles to inhibit peristalsis and prolong transit time
Pharmacodynamics/kinetics
Onset of action: Oral: Within 0.5-1 hour
Absorption: Oral: 40%; levels in breast milk expected to be very low
Metabolism: Hepatic (>50%) to inactive compounds
Half-life: 7-15 hours
Signs and Symptoms of Acute Intoxication CNS and respiratory depression, personality changes, dry mouth, dystonic reactions, gastrointestinal cramping, ileus, constipation, miosis
(Continued)

Loperamide *(Continued)*

When to Transport to Hospital Transport any pediatric (<6 years of age) ingestion over 0.4 mg/kg, any symptomatic patient, or any adult ingestion over 1 mg/kg

Overdosage/Treatment Supportive therapy: Naloxone is useful to reverse CNS or apnea; dystonic reaction can be managed with benztropine (1-2 mg I.V.) or diphenhydramine (1 mg/kg up to 50 mg I.V.)

Warnings/Precautions Large first-pass metabolism, use with caution in hepatic dysfunction and ulcerative colitis; should not be used if diarrhea accompanied by high fever, blood in stool

Adverse Reactions

Cardiovascular: Bradycardia

Central nervous system: Sedation, psychosis, restlessness, fatigue, dizziness, delirium

Dermatologic: Rash

Gastrointestinal: Nausea, vomiting, constipation, abdominal pain, abdominal cramping, dry mouth, appendicitis, pancreatitis

Genitourinary: Urinary retention, toxic megacolon

Drug Interactions Increased toxicity with CNS depressants, phenothiazines, tricyclic antidepressants

Dosage Forms

Caplet: 2 mg

Capsule: 2 mg

Liquid, oral: 1 mg/5 mL (60 mL, 90 mL, 120 mL)

Tablet: 2 mg

Additional Information If clinical improvement is not achieved after 16 mg/day for 10 days, control is unlikely with further use. Continue use if diet or other treatment does not control. Elderly are particularly sensitive to fluid and electrolyte loss. This generally results in lethargy, weakness, and confusion. Repletion and maintenance of electrolytes and water are essential in the treatment of diarrhea. Drug therapy must be limited in order to avoid toxicity with this agent.

Specific References

Schwartz RH and Rodriquez WJ, "Toxic Delirium Possibly Caused by Loperamide," *J Pediatr*, 1991, 118(4 Pt 1):656-7.

Loperyl® *see* Loperamide *on previous page*

Lopressor® *see* Metoprolol *on page 400*

Loram® *see* Lorazepam *on next page*

Loratadine *(lor AT a deen)*

Synonyms SCH-29851

U.S. Brand Names Claritin®; Claritine®; Clarityn®; Clarityne®; Fristamin®; Lisino®

Therapeutic Category Antihistamine

Use Relief of nasal and non-nasal symptoms of seasonal allergic rhinitis with little sedative properties; urticaria (chronic); idiopathic chronic urticaria

Usual Dosage Children >12 years and Adults: Oral: 10 mg/day on an empty stomach

Chronic idiopathic urticaria: 10 mg once daily

Mechanism of Action Long-acting tricyclic antihistamine with selective peripheral histamine H_1 receptor antagonist properties; derived from azatadine

Pharmacodynamics/kinetics

Onset of action: Within 1-3 hours

Peak effect: 8-12 hours

Duration: >24 hours

Absorption: Rapid

Metabolism: Extensive to an active metabolite (descarboethoxyloratadine)
Half-life: 12-15 hours
Elderly: 18 hours
Descarboethoxyloratadine: 18 hours

Signs and Symptoms of Acute Intoxication Coma

When to Transport to Hospital Transport any pediatric exposure, any sedated patient, or any ingestion over 30 mg

Warnings/Precautions Patients with liver impairment should start with a lower dose (10 mg every other day), since their ability to clear the drug will be reduced; use with caution in lactation, safety in children <12 years of age has not been established

Adverse Reactions
>10%:
Central nervous system: Headache, somnolence, fatigue
Gastrointestinal: Xerostomia
1% to 10%:
Cardiovascular: Hypotension, hypertension, palpitations, tachycardia
Central nervous system: Anxiety, depression
Endocrine & metabolic: Breast pain
Neuromuscular & skeletal: Hyperkinesia, arthralgias
Respiratory: Nasal dryness, pharyngitis, dyspnea
Miscellaneous: Diaphoresis

Reference Range Peak serum level of 18 ng/mL 1 hour after a single 40 mg dose

Drug Interactions Although there have not been any reports of interactions with triazole antifungals, cimetidine, ranitidine, theophylline, or macrolide antibiotics, extreme caution is still warranted when concurrently administered with these agents

Increased toxicity: Procarbazine, other antihistamines, alcohol

Dosage Forms Tablet: 10 mg

Specific References
Bradley CM and Nicholson AN, "Studies of the Central Effects of the H1-Antagonist, Loratadine," *Eur J Clin Pharmacol*, 1987, 32:419-21.
Wilkinson CJ and Moskowitz H, "Acute Effects of Loratadine, Diphenhydramine, and Placebo, Alone and With Alcohol, on Skills Performance," *Alcohol, Drugs, and Traffic Safety - T89*, Perrine MW, ed, (Proceedings of the 11th International Conference on Alcohol, Drugs and Traffic Safety), Chicago: National Safety Council, 1990, 476-82.

Loratadine and Pseudoephedrine
(lor AT a deen & soo doe e FED rin)
U.S. Brand Names Claritin-D®; Claritin-D® 24-Hour
Canadian Brand Names Chlor-Tripolon N.D.®; Claritin® Extra
Therapeutic Category Antihistamine/Decongestant Combination
Abuse Potential Yes
Impairment Potential Yes
Dosage Forms
Tablet: Loratadine 5 mg and pseudoephedrine sulfate 120 mg
Tablet, extended release: Loratadine 10 mg and pseudoephedrine sulfate 240 mg

Loraz® *see* Lorazepam *on this page*

Lorazepam (lor A ze pam)
Related Information
Controlled Substances - Uses and Effects *on page 741*
(Continued)

Lorazepam *(Continued)*

U.S. Brand Names Ativan®; Kendol®; Loram®; Loraz®; Noxaben®; Punktyl®; Titus®

Canadian Brand Names Apo-Lorazepam®; Novo-Lorazepam®; Nu-Loraz®; PMS-Lorazepam®; Pro-Lorazepam®

Therapeutic Category Benzodiazepine

Abuse Potential Yes

Impairment Potential Yes; Cognitive and psychomotor impairment occur in the elderly following acute single dose (0.5 and 1 mg) effects of oral lorazepam

Pomara N, Tun H, DaSilva D, et al, "Benzodiazepine Use and Crash Risk in Older Patients," *JAMA*, 1998, 279(2):113-4.

Use Management of anxiety, status epilepticus, delirium tremors, preoperative sedation, and amnesia, pain due to black widow spider bites

Usual Dosage

Antiemetic:
  Children 2-15 years: I.V.: 0.05 mg/kg (up to 2 mg/dose) prior to chemotherapy
  Adults: Oral, I.V.: 0.5-2 mg every 4-6 hours as needed

Anxiety and sedation:
  Infants and Children: Oral, I.V.: Usual: 0.05 mg/kg/dose (range: 0.02-0.09 mg/kg) every 4-8 hours
  Adults: Oral: 1-10 mg/day in 2-3 divided doses; usual dose: 2-6 mg/day in divided doses

Insomnia: Adults: Oral: 2-4 mg at bedtime

Status epilepticus: I.V.:
  Neonates: 0.05 mg/kg over 2-5 minutes; may repeat in 10-15 minutes (see warning regarding benzyl alcohol)
  Infants and Children: 0.1 mg/kg slow I.V. over 2-5 minutes, do not exceed 4 mg/single dose; may repeat second dose of 0.05 mg/kg slow I.V. in 10-15 minutes if needed
  Adolescents: 0.07 mg/kg slow I.V. over 2-5 minutes; maximum: 4 mg/dose; may repeat in 10-15 minutes
  Adults: 4 mg/dose given slowly over 2-5 minutes; may repeat in 10-15 minutes; usual maximum dose: 8 mg

Mechanism of Action Depresses all levels of the CNS, including the limbic and reticular formation, probably through the increased action of gamma-aminobutyric acid (GABA), which is a major inhibitory neurotransmitter in the brain

Pharmacodynamics/kinetics Studies have shown that the elderly are more sensitive to the effects of benzodiazepines as compared to younger adults
  Onset of action: I.M.: Hypnosis occurs in ~20-30 minutes; has been delayed in overdosage up to 7 hours
  Duration: 6-8 hours
  Metabolism: In the liver to inactive compounds (piperazine N-oxide)
  Half-life:
    Neonates: 40 hours
    Adults: 10-16 hours; one study found the half-life in the elderly to be 15.9 hours as compared to 14.1 hours in younger adults

Signs and Symptoms of Acute Intoxication Symptoms of overdosage may be delayed for up to 7 hours; confusion, hypoactive reflexes, hyporeflexia, disorientation, rhabdomyolysis, gaze nystagmus, myalgia, acute myoglobinuria, depression, visual and auditory hallucinations, dyspnea, labored breathing, "alpha" coma (alpha frequency rhythm on EEG), ataxia; onset of effects delayed as long as 7 hours in acute overdosage

When to Transport to Hospital Transport any pediatric patient (<2 years of age) or any symptomatic patient

Warnings/Precautions Dilute injection prior to I.V. use with equal volume of compatible diluent (D_5W, 0.9% sodium chloride, sterile water for injection); do **not** inject intra-arterially, arteriospasm and gangrene may occur; injection contains benzyl alcohol 2%, polyethylene glycol and propylene glycol; use caution in patients with renal or hepatic impairment, organic brain syndrome, myasthenia gravis or Parkinson's disease

Adverse Reactions

Respiratory: Decrease in respiratory rate, apnea, laryngospasm

>10%:

Cardiovascular: Tachycardia, chest pain

Central nervous system: Drowsiness, confusion, ataxia, amnesia, slurred speech, paradoxical excitement, rage, headache, depression, anxiety, fatigue, lightheadedness, insomnia

Dermatologic: Rash

Endocrine & metabolic: Decreased libido

Gastrointestinal: Xerostomia, constipation, diarrhea, nausea, vomiting, increased or decreased appetite, decreased salivation

Local: Phlebitis, pain with injection

Neuromuscular & skeletal: Dysarthria

Ocular: Blurred vision, diplopia

Miscellaneous: Diaphoresis

1% to 10%:

Cardiovascular: Cardiac arrest, hypotension, bradycardia, cardiovascular collapse, syncope

Central nervous system: Confusion, nervousness, dizziness, akathisia

Neuromuscular & skeletal: Rigidity, tremor, muscle cramps

Dermatologic: Dermatitis

Gastrointestinal: Weight gain or loss

Otic: Tinnitus

Respiratory: Nasal congestion, hyperventilation

Reference Range Therapeutic: 50-240 ng/mL (SI: 156-746 nmol/L)

Drug Interactions Alcohol: Additive CNS depression, excessive or chronic alcohol ingestion should be avoided; probenecid inhibits clearance

Dosage Forms

Injection: 2 mg/mL (1 mL, 10 mL); 4 mg/mL (1 mL, 10 mL)

Solution, oral concentrated, alcohol and dye free: 2 mg/mL (30 mL)

Tablet: 0.5 mg, 1 mg, 2 mg

Additional Information Injectable form has a longer duration of action than diazepam; provides an amnestic effect

Specific References

Lapierre YD and Labelle A, "Manic-Like Reaction Induced by Lorazepam Withdrawal," *Can J Psychiatry*, 1987, 32(8):697-8.

Lorcet® Lorcet®-HD *see* Hydrocodone and Acetaminophen *on page 293*

Lorcet® Plus *see* Hydrocodone and Acetaminophen *on page 293*

Lorsban® *see* Chlorpyrifos *on page 143*

Lortab® *see* Hydrocodone and Acetaminophen *on page 293*

Lortab® ASA *see* Hydrocodone and Aspirin *on page 294*

Losartan and Hydrochlorothiazide

(loe SAR tan & hye droe klor oh THYE a zide)

U.S. Brand Names Hyzaar®

Therapeutic Category Antihypertensive, Combination

Dosage Forms Tablet: Losartan potassium 50 mg and hydrochlorothiazide 12.5 mg

Losna *see* Wormwood *on page 617*

Lotensin® see Benazepril on page 67
Lotensin HCT® see Benazepril and Hydrochlorothiazide on page 68
Lotrel™ see Amlodipine and Benazepril on page 42

Lovastatin (LOE va sta tin)

Synonyms Mevinolin; Mevlor; Monacolin K
U.S. Brand Names Mevacor®; Mevinacor®
Therapeutic Category HMG-CoA Reductase Inhibitor
Use Adjunct to dietary therapy to decrease elevated serum total and LDL cholesterol concentrations in primary hypercholesterolemia
Usual Dosage Adults: Oral: Initial: 20 mg with evening meal, then adjust at 4-week intervals; maximum dose: 80 mg/day
Mechanism of Action Lovastatin acts by competitively inhibiting 3-hydroxyl-3-methylglutaryl-coenzyme A (HMG-CoA) reductase, the enzyme that catalyzes the rate-limiting step in cholesterol biosynthesis

Pharmacodynamics/kinetics
Onset of effect: 3 days of therapy required for LDL cholesterol concentration reductions
Absorption: Oral: 30%
Bioavailability: <5%
Half-life: 1.1-1.7 hours
Time to peak serum concentration: Oral: 2-4 hours

Signs and Symptoms of Acute Intoxication Myoglobinuria, rhabdomyolysis, dyspepsia, myalgia, hyperthermia, gynecomastia, cholestatic jaundice

When to Transport to Hospital Transport any pediatric exposure, any symptomatic patient, or any ingestion over 100 mg

Warnings/Precautions May elevate aminotransferases; LFTs should be performed before and every 4- 6 weeks during the first 12-15 months of therapy and periodically thereafter; can cause myalgia and rhabdomyolysis; use with caution in patients who consume large quantities of alcohol or who have a history of liver disease

Adverse Reactions 1% to 10%:
Central nervous system: Headache, dizziness
Dermatologic: Rash, pruritus
Endocrine & metabolic: Elevated creatine phosphokinase (CPK)
Gastrointestinal: Flatulence, abdominal pain, cramps, diarrhea, pancreatitis, constipation, nausea, dyspepsia, heartburn
Neuromuscular & skeletal: Myalgia

Drug Interactions
Increased effect/toxicity of levothyroxine (hyper-/hypothyroidism)
Increased toxicity with gemfibrozil (musculoskeletal effects such as myopathy, myalgia and/or muscle asthenia accompanied by markedly elevated CK concentrations, rash and/or pruritus); clofibrate, niacin (myopathy), erythromycin, cyclosporine, oral anticoagulants (increased PT)

Dosage Forms Tablet: 10 mg, 20 mg, 40 mg

Specific References
The Lovastatin Study Group II, "Therapeutic Response to Lovastatin (Mevinolin) in Nonfamilial Hypercholesterolemia: A Multicenter Study," *JAMA*, 1986, 256(20):2829-34.

Low-Quel® see Diphenoxylate and Atropine on page 207
Loxapac® see Loxapine on this page

Loxapine (LOKS a peen)

Synonyms Oxilapine Succinate
U.S. Brand Names Desconex®; Doxoline®; Loxapac®; Loxitane®
Canadian Brand Names Loxapac®

Therapeutic Category Antipsychotic Agent

Impairment Potential Yes

Use Management of psychotic disorders

Usual Dosage Adults:

Oral: 10 mg twice daily, increase dose until psychotic symptoms are controlled; usual dose range: 60-100 mg/day in divided doses 2-4 times/day; dosages >250 mg/day are not recommended

I.M.: 12.5-50 mg every 4-6 hours or longer as needed and change to oral therapy as soon as possible

Mechanism of Action Unclear mechanism of action; a dibenzoxazepine thought to be similar to chlorpromazine

Pharmacodynamics/kinetics

Onset of action: Oral: Neuroleptic effects occur within 20-30 minutes

Peak effect: 90-180 minutes

Duration of effect: ~12 hours

Absorption: Completely from gastrointestinal tract

Metabolism: Hepatic to amoxapine

Half-life:

Biphasic, initial: 5 hours

Terminal: 12-19 hours

Signs and Symptoms of Acute Intoxication Deep sleep, Parkinson's-like symptoms, dysphagia, gynecomastia, dystonic reactions, syncope, neuroleptic malignant syndrome, rhabdomyolysis, agitation, CNS depression, ptosis, leukocytosis, sinus tachycardia, arrhythmias, extrapyramidal reaction, hypothermia, hypertension followed by hypotension, seizures, myoglobinuria, renal failure (acute), leukopenia; neutropenia; agranulocytosis; granulocytopenia

When to Transport to Hospital Transport any pediatric exposure, any symptomatic patient, or any ingestion over 200 mg

Warnings/Precautions Watch for hypotension when administering I.M. or I.V.; safety in children <6 months of age has not been established; use with caution in patients with cardiovascular disease or seizures; benefits of therapy must be weighed against risks of therapy

Adverse Reactions

>10%:

Cardiovascular: Orthostatic hypotension

Central nervous system: Drowsiness, extrapyramidal effects (parkinsonian), confusion, persistent tardive dyskinesia

Gastrointestinal: Xerostomia

Ocular: Blurred vision

1% to 10%:

Dermatologic: Rash

Endocrine & metabolic: Enlargement of breasts

Gastrointestinal: Constipation, nausea, vomiting

Test Interactions EMIT assays may give false-positive in presence of diphenhydramine, thioridazine, chlorpromazine, alimenazine, carbamazepine, cyclobenzaprine, or perphenazine

Drug Interactions Other CNS depressants, anticonvulsants, lithium, metrizamide

Dosage Forms

Capsule, as succinate: 5 mg, 10 mg, 25 mg, 50 mg

Concentrate, oral, as hydrochloride: 25 mg/mL (120 mL dropper bottle)

Injection: 50 mg/mL (1 mL)

Additional Information

Loxapine hydrochloride: Loxitane® C oral concentrate, Loxitane® IM

Loxapine succinate: Loxitane® capsule

(Continued)

Loxapine *(Continued)*

Specific References
Peterson CD, "Seizures Induced by Acute Loxapine Overdose," *Am J Psychiatry*, 1981, 138(8):1089-91.

Loxitane® *see Loxapine on page 354*

LSD *see Lysergic Acid Diethylamide on this page*

L-Sodium Glutamate *see Monosodium Glutamate Food Poisoning on page 409*

LTG *see Lamotrigine on page 334*

L-Tryptophan *see Tryptophan on page 602*

Lude *see Methaqualone Level on page 389*

Ludiomil® *see Maprotiline on next page*

Luminal® *see Phenobarbital on page 474*

Lumirelax® *see Methocarbamol on page 390*

Lupulin *see Hops on page 289*

Luride® *see Fluoride on page 251*

Luride® Lozi-Tab® *see Fluoride on page 251*

Luride®-SF Lozi-Tab® *see Fluoride on page 251*

Luvox® *see Fluvoxamine on page 258*

Luxoben® *see Tiapride on page 581*

LY-110140 *see Fluoxetine on page 253*

LY170053 *see Olanzapine on page 443*

Lysanxia® *see Prazepam on page 493*

Lysergic Acid Diethylamide

Related Information
Controlled Substances - Uses and Effects *on page 741*

Synonyms LSD

Therapeutic Category Hallucinogen

Abuse Potential Yes

Impairment Potential Yes; Blood LSD levels >0.002 mg/L associated with cognitive dysfunction

Baselt RC and Cravey RH, *Disposition of Toxic Drugs and Chemicals in Man*, 4th ed, Foster City, CA: Chemical Toxicology Institute, 1995, 436.

Toxic Dose
Hallucinogenic dose:
Oral: 100-750 mcg
I.V.: 50-500 mcg
Lethal dose: 0.2-1 mg/kg

Mechanism of Toxic Action Agonist at 5-hydroxytryptamine presynaptic receptor in midbrain

Toxicodynamics/kinetics
Onset of action: 20-90 minutes (10 minutes I.V.)
Duration: 6-8 hours
Metabolism: To 2-oxylysergic acid diethylamide
Half-life: 3-5 hours

Signs and Symptoms of Acute Intoxication Rhabdomyolysis, fear, tremors, delirium, hyperglycemia, leukocytosis, ataxia, psychosis, mydriasis, fever, sweating, flushing, tachycardia, hyperreflexia, hallucinations (auditory and visual), vision color changes (increased color perception), euphoria, hypertonia, neuroleptic malignant syndrome, lacrimation, nausea, vomiting, diarrhea, hyperthermia, coma, seizures, tachypnea, respiratory arrest

When to Transport to Hospital Transport any ptient with mental status changes

Adverse Reactions

Cardiovascular: Sinus tachycardia

Central nervous system: Palinopsia, dysphoria, memory disturbance, psychosis

Ocular: Color vision abnormalities

Reference Range Dose of 500 mcg orally resulted in peak plasma levels of 4.2 ng/mL

Drug Interactions When combined with lithium and fluoxetine, can cause seizures; sertraline or paroxetine can incite occurrence of LSD flashback episodes (primarily visual)

Additional Information May be given as sugar cube, on filter or blotting paper, as a tablet or capsule; flashbacks may be induced by alcohol; urine may be positive for up to 120 hours by radioimmunoassay; odorless, colorless, tasteless

Specific References

Kulig K, "LSD," *Emerg Med Clin North Am*, 1990, 8(3):551-8.

MACE *see* Chloroacetophenone *on page 127*

Magace® *see* Megestrol Acetate *on page 365*

Magnacide H® *see* Acrolein *on page 27*

Magnesium Perborate *see* Borates *on page 80*

Mahi Mahi Flush *see* Scombroid Food Poisoning *on page 532*

Ma-Huang *see* Ephedra *on page 219*

Maigret-50 *see* Phenylpropanolamine *on page 481*

Malatal® *see* Hyoscyamine, Atropine, Scopolamine, and Phenobarbital *on page 306*

Mallorol® *see* Thioridazine *on page 578*

Malogex® *see* Testosterone *on page 564*

Malotuss® [OTC] *see* Guaifenesin *on page 269*

Manchurian "Fungus" *see* Kombucha *on page 330*

Manchurian Tea *see* Kombucha *on page 330*

Manerix® *see* Moclobemide *on page 406*

Mapap® [OTC] *see* Acetaminophen *on page 20*

Maprotiline (ma PROE ti leen)

U.S. Brand Names Ludiomil®

Therapeutic Category Antidepressant

Impairment Potential Yes

Use Treatment of depression and anxiety associated with depression

Usual Dosage Oral:

Children 6-14 years: 10 mg/day, increase to a maximum daily dose of 75 mg

Adults: 75 mg/day to start, increase by 25 mg every 2 weeks up to 150-225 mg/day; given in 3 divided doses or in a single daily dose

Mechanism of Action Increases the synaptic concentration of serotonin and/or norepinephrine in the central nervous system by inhibition of their reuptake by the presynaptic neuronal membrane

Pharmacodynamics/kinetics

Onset of action: For desired therapeutic effect, up to 2-3 weeks, but sometimes within 7 days

Absorption: Slow

Metabolism: In the liver to active and inactive compounds

Half-life: 51-58 hours

Time to peak serum concentration: Within 12 hours

(Continued)

Maprotiline *(Continued)*

Signs and Symptoms of Acute Intoxication Agitation, confusion, Q-T prolongation, photosensitivity, A-V block, dental erosion, vasculitis, intraocular pressure (increased), bradycardia, eosinophilia, delirium, hypnopompic hallucinations, mania, urinary retention, hypothermia, hypotension, seizures, tachycardia, torsade de pointes, respiratory depression, leukopenia; neutropenia; agranulocytosis; granulocytopenia

When to Transport to Hospital Transport any pediatric (<6 years of age) exposure, any symptomatic patient, or any ingestion over 200 mg

Warnings/Precautions Maprotiline should not be abruptly discontinued in patients receiving high doses for prolonged periods; do not drink alcoholic beverages; use with caution in patients with cardiac conduction disturbances, history of hyperthyroid; safe use of tricyclic antidepressants in children <12 years of age has not been established

Adverse Reactions

>10%:
  Cardiovascular: Orthostatic hypotension
  Central nervous system: Drowsiness
  Dermatologic: Rash
  Gastrointestinal: Xerostomia
  Genitourinary: Urinary retention
  Neuromuscular & skeletal: Weakness

1% to 10%:
  Central nervous system: Insomnia
  Gastrointestinal: Constipation, nausea, vomiting, increased appetite and weight gain or loss
  Neuromuscular & skeletal: Trembling

Reference Range Therapeutic: 100-150 ng/mL (SI: 361-540 nmol/L); levels >237 ng/mL can be associated with seizures

Drug Interactions CNS depression synergism with ethanol use

Maprotiline blocks the uptake of guanethidine and thus prevents the hypotensive effect of guanethidine; maprotiline may be additive with or may potentiate the action of other CNS depressants such as sedatives or hypnotics; maprotiline potentiates the pressor and cardiac effects of sympathomimetic agents such as isoproterenol, epinephrine, etc

With MAO inhibitors, fever, hypertension, tachycardia, confusion, seizures, and death have been reported

Additive anticholinergic effects seen with other anticholinergic agents

Cimetidine reduces the hepatic metabolism of maprotiline

Maprotiline may increase the prothrombin time in patients stabilized on warfarin

Dosage Forms Tablet: 25 mg, 50 mg, 75 mg

Additional Information Odorless, bitter tasting; seizures rarely seen 5-30 hours postdrug ingestion

Specific References

Bergman RN and Watson WA, "Cardiac Toxicity Associated With Acute Maprotiline Self Poisoning," *Am J Emerg Med*, 1983, 2(2):144-6.

Maranox® [OTC] *see* Acetaminophen *on page 20*

Marax® *see* Theophylline, Ephedrine, and Hydroxyzine *on page 571*

Marbaxin® *see* Methocarbamol *on page 390*

Marcillin® *see* Ampicillin *on page 48*

Marezine® [OTC] *see* Cyclizine *on page 172*

Margesic® H *see* Hydrocodone and Acetaminophen *on page 293*

Marijuana *see* Cannabinoids, Qualitative *on page 100*

Marijuana (Cannabis)

Related Information

Controlled Substances - Uses and Effects *on page 741*

Scientific Name *Cannabis sativa*

Abuse Potential Yes

Impairment Potential Yes; Mean detection time for marijuana metabolites using a 100 ng/mL urinary cutoff by immunoassay is about 24 hours. Delta-9-THC blood levels as low as 2 ng/mL is consistent with recent usage and probably impairment. Studies have demonstrated that 94% of drivers with delta-9-THC levels over 25 ng/mL have failed standard roadside sobriety testing. Pilots exposed to marijuana demonstrated impaired flying skills as long as 24 hours postexposure.

Mechanism of Toxic Action Antiemetic for therapeutic uses/hallucinogen; derived from the hemp plant *Cannabis sativa* (which contains 2% to 6% tetra-hydrocannabinol) and which is psychotropically active in the (-) enantiometric form; affects serotonin release along with increasing catecholaminergic effect while inhibiting parasympathetic effects

Pharmacodynamics/kinetics

Onset of action:

Inhalation: 6-12 minutes

Oral: 30-120 minutes

Duration of acute effect: 0.5-3 hours

Absorption:

Smoking: 18% to 50%

Ingestion: 5% to 20%

Metabolism: Major metabolite is 11-hydroxy-tetrahydrocannabinol

Half-life: 28 hours (first-time users); 56 hours (chronic users)

Signs and Symptoms of Acute Intoxication Relaxation, fatigue, sense of well being, perceptual alterations, impaired recall, mood swings, memory deficits, depersonalization, slurred speech, impaired coordination, hallucinations, delusions, paranoia, conjunctival injection, tachycardia, increased appetite, dry mouth

When to Transport to Hospital Transport any patient with fever, fast heart rate, or decreased mental status

Overdosage/Treatment

Decontamination: Ingestion: Lavage (within 1 hour)/activated charcoal with cathartic

Supportive therapy: Benzodiazepines for agitation; hypotension can be treated with Trendelenburg/crystalloid infusion; tachycardia can be treated with beta-blockers

Adverse Reactions

Cardiovascular: Dose-related tachycardia, sinus tachycardia

Central nervous system: Irritability, disorientation, euphoria, short-term memory disturbance, distortion of time and space, dysphoria, hyperthermia, synesthesia, hypothermia, psychosis

Gastrointestinal: Constipation

Genitourinary: Urinary retention, impotence

Neuromuscular & skeletal: Trismus, fine tremor

Ocular: Mydriasis, injected conjunctival vessels

Respiratory: Bronchial irritation

Miscellaneous: Thirst

Specific References

Burns M and Moskowitz H, "Alcohol, Marijuana and Skills Performance," *Alcohol, Drugs and Traffic Safety*, Goldberg L, ed, Stockholm: Almquist and Wiksell, 1981.

Moskowitz H, "Marihuana and Driving," *Accid Anal Prev*, 1976, 8:21-6.

Marinol® *see* Dronabinol *on page 213*

Marmine® [OTC] *see* Dimenhydrinate *on page 203*

Marnal® *see* Butalbital Compound *on page 93*

Marplan® *see* Isocarboxazide *on page 320*

Marpres® *see* Hydralazine, Hydrochlorothiazide, and Reserpine *on page 291*

Marsh Gas *see* Methane *on page 385*

Masmoran® *see* Hydroxyzine *on page 303*

Maté

Synonyms Jesuit's Tea; Paraguay Tea; South American Holly; St. Bartholomew's Tea; Yerba de Mate; Yerba Maté

Scientific Name *Ilex paraguariensis*

Use Herbal medicine as a depurative, stimulant and diuretic

Usual Dosage One cup of maté (6 ounces) is equivalent to 25-50 mg of caffeine

Mechanism of Toxic Action Plant contains caffetanin; leaves contain rutin, alpha-amyrin, trigonelline, choline and ursolic acid; teas contain caffeine; may also contain belladonna alkaloids as a contamination

When to Transport to Hospital Transport any symptomatic patient

Adverse Reactions

Cardiovascular: Tachycardia

Central nervous system: Fever, disorientation

Dermatologic: Flushed skin

Gastrointestinal: Dry mouth

Genitourinary: Urinary retention

Ocular: Mydriasis

Miscellaneous: Incidence of esophageal cancer and bladder cancer (increased) when used with tobacco, for chronic users

Additional Information A climbing evergreen shrub which can grow to 20 feet; native to South American countries; greenish white flowers with small deep red berries; leaves contain as much as 2% caffeine along with theophylline (0.05%); apnea has occurred in an infant after breast-feeding from a mother ingesting maté; teas should be used with caution in patients with elevated blood pressure, diabetes or ulcer disease; teas should be used with caution in patients with elevated blood pressure, diabetes or ulcer disease

Specific References

DeAnnutis GJ, Fill S, Meggs WJ, et al, "Anticholinergic Poisoning from Para-guay Tea: A Need for Further Regulation," *Vet Hum Toxicol*, 1994, 36:359.

Matricaria Camphor *see* Camphor *on page 99*

Maxidex® *see* Dexamethasone *on page 182*

Maximum Strength Anbesol® [OTC] *see* Benzocaine *on page 70*

Maximum Strength Bactine™ [OTC] *see* Hydrocortisone *on page 297*

Maximum Strength Nytol® [OTC] *see* Diphenhydramine *on page 205*

Maximum Strength Orajel® [OTC] *see* Benzocaine *on page 70*

Maxzide® *see* Hydrochlorothiazide and Triamterene *on page 293*

Maygace® *see* Megestrol Acetate *on page 365*

Mazanor® *see* Mazindol *on this page*

Mazindol (MAY zin dole)

Related Information

Controlled Substances - Uses and Effects *on page 741*

Dextroamphetamine *on page 186*

U.S. Brand Names Mazanor®; Sanorex®; Téronac®

Therapeutic Category Anorexiant

Use Short-term adjunct in exogenous obesity
  Investigational: Narcolepsy, Duchenne muscular dystrophy
Usual Dosage Oral:
  Obesity: Adults: Initial dose: 1 mg once daily, adjust to patient response; usual dose: 1 mg 3 times/day, 1 hour before meals, or 2 mg once daily, 1 hour before lunch; take with meals to avoid GI discomfort
  Narcolepsy:
    Children: 1-2 mg/day
    Adults: 3-8 mg/day
Pharmacodynamics/kinetics Half-life: 33-55 hours
Signs and Symptoms of Acute Intoxication Hyperthermia, hypertension, tachycardia
When to Transport to Hospital Transport any symptomatic patient
Adverse Reactions
  >10%:
    Cardiovascular: Hypertension
    Central nervous system: Euphoria, nervousness, insomnia
  <10%:
    Cardiovascular: Tachycardia, arrhythmias, palpitations
    Central nervous system: Confusion, restlessness, headache, auditory hallucinations, psychosis, CNS depression
    Dermatologic: Alopecia
    Endocrine & metabolic: Libido (changes in)
    Gastrointestinal: Nausea, vomiting, constipation, diarrhea, abdominal cramps
    Genitourinary: Dysuria, testicular pain
    Hematologic: Blood dyscrasias
    Neuromuscular & skeletal: Tremor, myalgia
    Ocular: Blurred vision
    Renal: Dyspnea, polyuria
    Miscellaneous: Sweating (increased)
Drug Interactions When given with lithium, can result in lithium toxicity; enhances lethal actions and seizures when given with cocaine in rodents
Dosage Forms
  Tablet:
    Mazanor®: 1 mg
    Sanorex®: 1 mg, 2 mg
Specific References
  Allsopp MR and Zaiwalla Z, "Narcolepsy," *Arch Dis Child*, 1992, 67(3):302-6.

MCB see Chlorobenzene on page 128
M-delphene see Diethyltoluamide on page 197
M-det see Diethyltoluamide on page 197
M-deta see Diethyltoluamide on page 197
MDL-71754 see Vigabatrin on page 612
MDMA see Methamphetamine on page 382
Meballymal see Secobarbital on page 534
Mebaral® see Mephobarbital on page 370

Meclizine (MEK li zeen)

U.S. Brand Names Antivert®; Antrizine®; Bonine® [OTC]; Dizmiss® [OTC]; Meni-D®; Ru-Vert-M®
Therapeutic Category Antihistamine
Use Prevention and treatment of motion sickness; management of dizziness with diseases affecting the vestibular system
Usual Dosage Children >12 years and Adults: Oral:
  (Continued)

Meclizine *(Continued)*

Motion sickness: 25-50 mg 1 hour before travel, repeat dose every 24 hours as needed

Vertigo: 25-100 mg/day in divided doses

Mechanism of Action Has central anticholinergic action by blocking chemoreceptor trigger zone; decreases excitability of the middle ear labyrinth and blocks conduction in the middle ear vestibular-cerebellar pathways

Pharmacodynamics/kinetics

Onset of action: Within 1-2 hours

Duration: 8-24 hours

Distribution: Well distributed throughout the body

Metabolism: In the liver

Half-life: 6 hours

Elimination: Excreted as metabolites in urine and as unchanged drug in feces

Signs and Symptoms of Acute Intoxication Excitation alternating with drowsiness, disorientation, confusion, respiratory depression, memory loss, hallucinations, flushing, mydriasis

When to Transport to Hospital Transport any pediatric patient (<12 years of age), any ingestion over 100 mg, or if patient is hallucinating

Warnings/Precautions Use with caution in patients with angle-closure glaucoma or prostatic hypertrophy

Adverse Reactions

>10%:

Central nervous system: Slight to moderate drowsiness

Respiratory: Thickening of bronchial secretions

1% to 10%:

Central nervous system: Headache, fatigue, nervousness, dizziness

Gastrointestinal: Appetite increase, weight gain, nausea, diarrhea, abdominal pain, xerostomia

Neuromuscular & skeletal: Arthralgia

Respiratory: Pharyngitis

Reference Range Serum level of 10 ng/mL 12 hours after an oral dose of 75 mg

Drug Interactions CNS depressants, alcohol increases sedation

Dosage Forms

Meclozine hydrochloride:

Capsule: 15 mg, 25 mg, 30 mg

Tablet: 12.5 mg, 25 mg, 50 mg

Tablet:

Chewable: 25 mg

Film coated: 25 mg

Specific References

Oosterveld WJ, "Vertigo: Current Concepts in Management," *Drugs*, 1985, 30(3):275-83.

Meclofenamate *(me kloe fen AM ate)*

U.S. Brand Names Meclomen®

Therapeutic Category Analgesic, Non-narcotic; Nonsteroidal Anti-Inflammatory Agent (NSAID)

Use Treatment of inflammatory disorders

Usual Dosage Children >14 years and Adults: Oral:

Mild to moderate pain: 50 mg every 4-6 hours, not to exceed 400 mg/day

Rheumatoid arthritis/osteoarthritis: 200-400 mg/day in 3-4 equal doses

Mechanism of Action Inhibits prostaglandin synthesis by decreasing the activity of the enzyme, cyclo-oxygenase, which results in decreased formation of prostaglandin precursors

Pharmacodynamics/kinetics
Duration of action: 2-4 hours
Absorption: Rapid and complete from gastrointestinal tract
Metabolism: In the liver
Half-life: 2-3.3 hours
Time to peak serum concentration: Within 30-90 minutes

Signs and Symptoms of Acute Intoxication Nausea, vomiting, wheezing, nephrotic syndrome, gastrointestinal bleeding, gastritis; cognitive dysfunction, ototoxicity; tinnitus, drowsiness; severe poisoning can manifest with coma, seizures, renal and or hepatic failure, hypotension, respiratory depression

When to Transport to Hospital Transport any pediatric (<14 years of age) exposure, any patient with tachypnea, seizures, decreased mental status, or any ingestion over 400 mg

Adverse Reactions
>10%:
Central nervous system: Dizziness
Dermatologic: Rash
Gastrointestinal: Abdominal cramps, heartburn, indigestion, nausea
1% to 10%:
Central nervous system: Headache, nervousness
Dermatologic: Itching
Endocrine & metabolic: Fluid retention
Gastrointestinal: Vomiting
Otic: Tinnitus

Reference Range Steady-state meclofenamate plasma levels range from 10-20 µg/mL at a dose of 100 mg 3 times/day; one 100 mg dose results in a peak plasma level of 8-9 µg/mL

Drug Interactions Aspirin decreases serum concentrations probably by protein-binding displacement; there is an increased bleeding potential with concomitant warfarin therapy; may increase lithium and methotrexate concentrations by decreasing renal clearance; may decrease diuretic and hypotensive effects of thiazides, loop diuretics, ACE inhibitors, and beta-blockers; may increase nephrotoxicity of cyclosporine

Dosage Forms
Capsule: 50 mg, 100 mg
Tablet: 50 mg, 100 mg

Specific References
Smolinske SC, Hall AH, Vandenberg SA, et al, "Toxic Effects of Nonsteroid Anti-inflammatory Drugs in Overdose. An Overview of Recent Evidence on Clinical Effects and Dose-Response Relationships," *Drug Saf*, 1990, 5(4):252-74.

Meclomen® see Meclofenamate *on previous page*
Mecloprodin see Clemastine *on page 149*

Meconium Drug Screen
Synonyms Drug Screen, Meconium
Use Drugs of abuse screen (amphetamines, opiates, cocaine, marijuana, phencyclidine)
Additional Information Can detect maternal drug usage during the final 20 weeks of gestation. May detect three times higher rate of drugs of abuse then maternal urinary screening at time of birth. Cocaethylene can also be detected.
Specific References
Ostrea EM Jr, Brady MJ, Parks PM, et al, "Drug Screening of Meconium in Infants of Drug-Dependent Mothers: An Alternative to Urine Testing," *J Pediatr*, 1989, 115(3):474-7.

Medical Legal Specimens *see* Chain-of-Custody Protocol *on page 121*

Medigesic® *see* Butalbital Compound *on page 93*

Medihaler Ergotamine™ *see* Ergotamine *on page 224*

Medipain 5® Norcet® *see* Hydrocodone and Acetaminophen *on page 293*

Mediplast® Plaster [OTC] *see* Salicylic Acid *on page 530*

Medipren® [OTC] *see* Ibuprofen *on page 308*

Medi-Tuss® [OTC] *see* Guaifenesin *on page 269*

Medomet® *see* Methyldopa *on page 393*

Meetco® *see* Methyl Ethyl Ketone *on page 396*

Mefenamic Acid (me fe NAM ik AS id)

U.S. Brand Names Ponstel®

Canadian Brand Names Ponstan®

Therapeutic Category Analgesic, Non-narcotic; Nonsteroidal Anti-Inflammatory Agent (NSAID)

Use Short-term relief of mild to moderate pain including primary dysmenorrhea

Usual Dosage Children >14 years and Adults: Oral: 500 mg to start then 250 mg every 4 hours as needed; maximum therapy: 1 week

Seizuregenic dose:
   Children: 2 g
   Adults: 6 g

Mechanism of Action Inhibits prostaglandin synthesis by decreasing the activity of the enzyme, cyclo-oxygenase, which results in decreased formation of prostaglandin precursors

Pharmacodynamics/kinetics

Onset of action: Within 2-4 hours

Duration: Up to 6 hours

Absorption: Slow from gastrointestinal tract

Metabolism: Conjugated in the liver

Half-life: 3.5 hours

Time to peak serum concentration:
   250 mg dose: 2.5 hours
   100 mg dose: 2-4 hours

Signs and Symptoms of Acute Intoxication Nausea, vomiting, wheezing, nephrotic syndrome, thrombocytopenia, gastrointestinal bleeding, torticollis, insomnia, gastritis; cognitive dysfunction, colitis, bullous skin disease/pemphigoid, ototoxicity; tinnitus, drowsiness; severe poisoning can manifest with coma, seizures (38%), renal and or hepatic failure, hypotension, respiratory depression

When to Transport to Hospital Transport patients with change in mental status, seizures, or any ingestion over 1 g

Adverse Reactions

>10%:
   Central nervous system: Dizziness
   Dermatologic: Rash
   Gastrointestinal: Abdominal cramps, heartburn, indigestion, nausea

1% to 10%:
   Central nervous system: Headache, nervousness
   Dermatologic: Itching
   Endocrine & metabolic: Fluid retention
   Gastrointestinal: Vomiting
   Otic: Tinnitus

Drug Interactions Aspirin decreases serum concentrations probably by protein-binding displacement; there is an increased bleeding potential with concomitant warfarin therapy; may increase lithium and methotrexate concentrations by decreasing renal clearance; may decrease diuretic and hypotensive effects of thiazides, loop diuretics, ACE inhibitors, and beta-blockers; may increase nephrotoxicity of cyclosporine

Dosage Forms Capsule: 250 mg

Specific References

Gossinger H, Hruby K, Haubenstock A, et al, "Coma in Mefenamic Acid Poisoning," *Lancet*, 1982, 2(8294):384.

Megace® *see* Megestrol Acetate *on this page*

Megeron® *see* Megestrol Acetate *on this page*

Megestrol Acetate (me JES trole AS e tate)

U.S. Brand Names Magace®; Maygace®; Megace®; Megeron®; Niagestin®; Ovaban®; Volplan®

Therapeutic Category Antineoplastic Agent; Progestin

Use Palliative treatment of breast and endometrial carcinomas, appetite stimulation, and promotion of weight gain in cachexia (especially in patients with AIDS)

Usual Dosage Adults: Oral (**refer to individual protocols**):

Female:

Breast carcinoma: 40 mg 4 times/day; maximum daily dose: 1600 mg

Endometrial: 40-320 mg/day in divided doses; use for 2 months to determine efficacy; maximum doses used have been up to 800 mg/day

Uterine bleeding: 40 mg 2-4 times/day

Male and Female: HIV-related cachexia: Initial dose: 800 mg/day; daily doses of 400 and 800 mg/day were found to be clinically effective

Mechanism of Action A synthetic progestin with antiestrogenic properties which disrupt the estrogen receptor cycle. Megace® interferes with the normal estrogen cycle and results in a lower LH titer. May also have a direct effect on the endometrium. Megestrol is an antineoplastic progestin thought to act through an antileutenizing effect mediated via the pituitary.

Pharmacodynamics/kinetics

Onset of action: At least 2 months of continuous therapy is necessary

Absorption: Oral: Well absorbed

Metabolism: Completely metabolized in the liver to free steroids and glucuronide conjugates

Time to peak serum concentration: Oral: Within 1-3 hours

Half-life, elimination: 13-105 hours (mean: 34 hours)

Signs and Symptoms of Acute Intoxication Nausea, vomiting

When to Transport to Hospital Transport any pediatric ingestion or any patient exhibiting gastrointestinal complaints

Warnings/Precautions The U.S. Food and Drug Administration (FDA) currently recommends that procedures for proper handling and disposal of antineoplastic agents be considered. Use during the first 4 months of pregnancy is not recommended. Use with caution in patients with a history of thrombophlebitis. Elderly females may have vaginal bleeding or discharge and need to be forewarned of this side effect and inconvenience.

Adverse Reactions

>10%:

Cardiovascular: Edema

Endocrine & metabolic: Breakthrough bleeding and amenorrhea, spotting, changes in menstrual flow

Neuromuscular & skeletal: Weakness

1% to 10%:

Central nervous system: Insomnia, depression, fever, headache

Dermatologic: Allergic rash with or without pruritus, melasma or chloasma, rash, and rarely alopecia

(Continued)

Megestrol Acetate *(Continued)*

Endocrine & metabolic: Changes in cervical erosion and secretions, increased breast tenderness, amenorrhea, changes in vaginal bleeding pattern, edema, fluid retention, hyperglycemia

Gastrointestinal: Weight gain (not attributed to edema or fluid retention), nausea, vomiting, stomach cramps

Hepatic: Cholestatic jaundice, hepatotoxicity

Hematologic: Myelosuppressive:

WBC: None

Platelets: None

Local: Thrombophlebitis

Neuromuscular & skeletal: Carpal tunnel syndrome

Respiratory: Hyperpnea

Reference Range Following a single 40 mg oral dose, peak plasma levels range from 10-56 ng/mL

Dosage Forms

Suspension, oral: 40 mg/mL with alcohol 0.06% (236.6 mL)

Tablet: 20 mg, 40 mg

Specific References

Schacter L, Rozencweig M, Canetta R, et al, "Megestrol Acetate: Clinical Experience," *Can Treat Rev*, 1989, 16:49-63.

MEK *see* Methyl Ethyl Ketone *on page 396*

Melatonin *(mel ah TOE nin)*

Synonyms N-Acetyl-5-methoxytryptamine

Therapeutic Category Hormone

Use Sleep disorders (insomnia), circadian rhythm disturbances (ie, jet lag); only FDA approval (as an orphan drug) is for treatment of circadium rhythm sleep disorders in blind people with no light perception

Usual Dosage Oral:

Jet lag: 5 mg/day (at 1800 hours) for 1 week starting 3 days before the flight

Hypnotic effects: Oral: 0.1-0.3 mg (daytime); 1-10 mg (nighttime)

Insomnia: 5-75 mg at night have been used

Mechanism of Action A hormone produced and secreted in the pineal gland causes an increase in hypothalamus aminobutyric acid and serotonin. Increased secretion occurs during dark hours; decreases neopterin release; counteracts apoptosis; increases thymus activity

Pharmacodynamics/kinetics

Absorption: Rapid

Peak plasma level: 1 hour

Signs and Symptoms of Acute Intoxication Drowsiness, ataxia

When to Transport to Hospital Transport any pediatric exposure or any patient exhibiting sedation or ataxia

Adverse Reactions

Central nervous system: Drowsiness, dysphoria, giddiness

Gastrointestinal: Nausea

Reference Range Mean baseline melatonin serum levels 80 pg/mL (range: 0-200) between 0200-0400 hours. Elevated endogenous levels seen after 0900 hours; after a 2.5 mg oral dose, plasma melatonin level may be as high as 8.50 pg/mL.

Dosage Forms

Tablet: 3 mg

Tablet, sublingual: 2.5 mg

Specific References

Arendt J, "Clinical Perspectives for Melatonin and Its Agonists," *Biol Psychiatry*, 1994, 35(1):1-2.

Meleretten® *see* Thioridazine *on page 578*

Melix® *see* Glyburide *on page 267*

Mellaril® *see* Thioridazine *on page 578*

Mellaril-S® *see* Thioridazine *on page 578*

Menadol® [OTC] *see* Ibuprofen *on page 308*

Meni-D® *see* Meclizine *on page 361*

Mentholatum® Vapor Rub *see* Camphor *on page 99*

Mepergan® *see* Meperidine and Promethazine *on page 369*

Meperidine (me PER i deen)

Related Information

Controlled Substances - Uses and Effects *on page 741*

Synonyms Isonipecaine Hydrochloride; Pethidine Hydrochloride

U.S. Brand Names Centralgine®; Demerol®; Dolantin®; Dolantina®; Dolantine®; Dolosal®

Therapeutic Category Analgesic, Narcotic

Abuse Potential Yes

Impairment Potential Yes

Use Management of moderate to severe pain; adjunct to anesthesia and preoperative sedation; relieves shaking or shivering after general anesthesia or during amphotericin B infusion

Usual Dosage Doses should be titrated to appropriate analgesic effect; when changing route of administration, note that oral doses are about half as effective as parenteral dose. Oral, I.M., I.V., S.C.:

Children: 1-1.5 mg/kg/dose every 3-4 hours as needed; 1-2 mg/kg as a single dose preoperative medication may be used; maximum: 100 mg/dose

Adults: 50-150 mg/dose every 3-4 hours as needed

Relief of shaking or shivering during amphotericin B infusion: 25-50 mg

Mechanism of Action Binds to opiate receptors in the CNS, causing inhibition of ascending pain pathways, altering the perception of and response to pain; produces generalized CNS depression; a cogener of atropine

Pharmacodynamics/kinetics

Oral, I.M., S.C.:

Onset of analgesic effect: Within 10-15 minutes

Peak effect: Within 1 hour

Duration: 2-4 hours

I.V.: Onset of effect: Within 5 minutes

Protein binding: 55% to 75% in healthy patients

Metabolism: In the liver to normeperidine

Half-life:

Parent drug: Terminal phase:

Neonates: 23 hours; range: 12-39 hours

Adults: 2.5-4 hours

Adults with liver disease: 7-11 hours

Normeperidine (active metabolite):

Neonates: 20-80 hours

Adults: 15-30 hours; is dependent on renal function and can accumulate with high doses or in patients with decreased renal function

Signs and Symptoms of Acute Intoxication Myoglobinuria, rhabdomyolysis, ejaculatory disturbances, syndrome of inappropriate antidiuretic hormone (SIADH), seizures

(Continued)

Meperidine (Continued)

When to Transport to Hospital Transport any patient with decreased mental status or any ingestion exceeding 3 mg/kg

Warnings/Precautions Use with caution in patients with pulmonary, hepatic, renal disorders, or increased intracranial pressure; use with caution in patients with renal failure or seizure disorders or those receiving high-dose meperidine; normeperidine (an active metabolite and CNS stimulant) may accumulate and precipitate twitches, tremors, or seizures; some preparations contain sulfites which may cause allergic reaction

Adverse Reactions

>10%:

Cardiovascular: Hypotension

Central nervous system: Fatigue, drowsiness, dizziness

Gastrointestinal: Nausea, vomiting, constipation

Neuromuscular & skeletal: Weakness

Miscellaneous: Histamine release

1% to 10%:

Central nervous system: Nervousness, headache, restlessness, malaise, confusion

Gastrointestinal: Anorexia, stomach cramps, xerostomia, biliary spasm

Genitourinary: Ureteral spasms, decreased urination

Local: Pain at injection site

Respiratory: Dyspnea, shortness of breath

Reference Range

Meperidine:

Therapeutic: 70-500 ng/mL (SI: 283-2020 nmol/L)

Toxic: >1000 ng/mL (SI: >4043 nmol/L)

Normeperidine: Toxic: >450 ng/mL

Drug Interactions

Decreased effect with phenytoin (↑ toxicity of meperidine and normeperidine concurrently)

Increased effect/toxicity of isoniazid (hypotension); increased effect/toxicity with MAO inhibitors (can be fatal), serotonin reuptake inhibitors (eg, fluoxetine), CNS depressants, tricyclic antidepressants, chlorpromazine, phenothiazines, barbiturates, amphetamines, cimetidine

Increased neurotoxicity with acyclovir

Depressive or excitatory reactions can occur with concomitant MAO inhibitors, selegiline or furazolidone use; phenytoin can increase meperidine clearance by 25% and decrease oral bioavailability of meperidine by 20%; primidone and barbiturates can also accelerate meperidine metabolism

Animal studies have shown that use of naloxone or metoclopramide may attenuate the hyperthermia caused by interaction of tranylcypromine and meperidine

Dosage Forms

Injection:

Multiple-dose vials: 50 mg/mL (30 mL); 100 mg/mL (20 mL)

Single dose: 10 mg/mL (5 mL, 10 mL, 30 mL); 25 mg/dose (0.5 mL, 1 mL); 50 mg/dose (1 mL); 75 mg/dose (1 mL, 1.5 mL); 100 mg/dose (1 mL)

Syrup: 50 mg/5 mL (500 mL)

Tablet: 50 mg, 100 mg

Additional Information Decrease the dose in patients with renal or hepatic impairment; equianalgesic doses: morphine 10 mg I.M. is equivalent to meperidine 75-100 mg I.M.

I.V. incompatible with barbiturates

Specific References

Korttila R and Linnoila M, "Psychomotor Skills Related to Driving After Intramuscular Administration of Diazepam and Meperidine," *Anesthesiology*, 1975, 42(6):685-91.

Meperidine and Promethazine

(me PER i deen & proe METH a zeen)

U.S. Brand Names Mepergan®

Therapeutic Category Analgesic, Narcotic

Abuse Potential Yes

Impairment Potential Yes

Dosage Forms

Capsule: Meperidine hydrochloride 50 mg and promethazine hydrochloride 25 mg

Injection: Meperidine hydrochloride 25 mg and promethazine hydrochloride 25 per mL (2 mL, 10 mL)

Mephenytoin (me FEN i toyn)

Related Information

Phenytoin *on page 483*

Synonyms Methoin; Methylphenylethylhydantoin; Phenantoin

U.S. Brand Names Mesantoin®; Sedantoinal®

Therapeutic Category Anticonvulsant

Abuse Potential Yes

Impairment Potential Yes

Use Treatment of tonic-clonic and partial seizures in patients who are uncontrolled with less toxic anticonvulsants

Usual Dosage Oral:

Children: 3-15 mg/kg/day in 3 divided doses; usual maintenance dose: 100-400 mg/day in 3 divided doses

Adults: Initial dose: 50-100 mg/day given daily; increase by 50-100 mg at weekly intervals; usual maintenance dose: 200-600 mg/day in 3 divided doses; maximum: 800 mg/day

Mechanism of Action Stabilizes neuronal membranes and decreases seizure activity by increasing efflux or decreasing influx of sodium ions across cell membranes in the motor cortex during generation of nerve impulses; prolongs effective refractory period and suppresses ventricular pacemaker automaticity, shortens action potential in the heart

Pharmacodynamics/kinetics

Onset of action: 30 minutes

Duration: 24-48 hours

Absorption: Oral: Rapid

Protein binding:

Mephenytoin: 60%

5-phenyl-5-ethylhydantoin: 68%

Metabolism: In the liver to 5-phenyl-5-ethylhydantoin and 4-hydroxymephenytoin

Half-life: Chronic therapy:

Mephenytoin: ~17 hours

5-phenyl-5-ethylhydantoin: 112 hours

Elimination: In urine

When to Transport to Hospital Transport any symptomatic patient

Warnings/Precautions Fatal irreversible aplastic anemia has occurred; abrupt withdrawal may precipitate seizures; may increase frequency of petit mal seizures; use with caution in patients with liver disease or porphyria; usually (Continued)

Mephenytoin *(Continued)*

listed in combination with other anticonvulsants; discontinue drug if neutrophil count falls <1600

Adverse Reactions

>10%:
Central nervous system: Psychiatric changes, slurred speech, dizziness, drowsiness
Gastrointestinal: Constipation, nausea, vomiting
Neuromuscular & skeletal: Trembling

<10%:
Cardiovascular: Hypotension, bradycardia, cardiac arrhythmias, cardiovascular collapse
Central nervous system: Headache, insomnia, confusion, fever, ataxia, psychotic episodes, complex partial epilepsy, simple partial epilepsy, tonic-clonic epilepsy
Dermatologic: Skin rash, Stevens-Johnson syndrome or SLE-like syndrome, alopecia, urticaria, purpura
Gastrointestinal: Anorexia, weight loss, gingival hyperplasia (less common than with phenytoin)
Hematologic: Blood dyscrasias (neutropenia, thrombocytopenia, leukopenia, pancytopenia), aplastic anemia, Hodgkin's disease-like syndrome
Hepatic: Hepatitis, jaundice
Local: Venous irritation and pain, thrombophlebitis
Neuromuscular & skeletal: Paresthesia, neuropathy (peripheral)
Ocular: Diplopia, gaze nystagmus, blurred vision, photophobia, conjunctivitis
Renal: Nephrotic syndrome, proteinuria, serum creatinine (elevated)
Respiratory: Pulmonary fibrosis
Miscellaneous: Lymphadenopathy, serum sickness, periarteritis nodosa

Reference Range Total mephenytoin (mephenytoin plus 5-ethyl-5-phenylhydantoin) of 25-40 µg/mL produces optimal seizure control; serum levels >40 µg/mL can produce central nervous system effects or exacerbate seizures

Drug Interactions

Decreased effect with carbamazepine, TCAs, calcium antacids; chronic ethanol abuse, decreased effect of oral anticoagulants, oral contraceptives, steroids, quinidine, vitamin D, vitamin K, doxycycline, furosemide, TCAs
Increased effect/toxicity with alcohol (acute), sulfonamides, chloramphenicol, cimetidine, isoniazid, disulfiram, phenothiazines, benzodiazepines

Dosage Forms Tablet: 100 mg

Additional Information Usually used in combination with other anticonvulsants

Mephobarbital *(me foe BAR bi tal)*

Synonyms 5,5-Diethyl-1-Methylbarbituric Acid; Methylphenobarbital

U.S. Brand Names Mebaral®

Therapeutic Category Barbiturate

Abuse Potential Yes

Impairment Potential Yes

Use Prophylactic management of tonic-clonic (grand mal) seizures and absence (petit mal) seizures

Usual Dosage Oral:

Epilepsy:
Children: 6-12 mg/kg/day in 2-4 divided doses
Adults: 200-600 mg/day in 2-4 divided doses
Sedation:
Children:
<5 years: 16-32 mg 3-4 times/day

>5 years: 32-64 mg 3-4 times/day
Adults: 32-100 mg 3-4 times/day

Mechanism of Action Increases seizure threshold in the motor cortex; depresses monosynaptic and polysynaptic transmission in the CNS

Pharmacodynamics/kinetics
Onset of action: 20-60 minutes
Duration: 6-8 hours
Absorption: Oral: ~70%
Metabolism: Demethylated by the liver to phenobarbital (15%)
Half-life: 48-52 hours

Signs and Symptoms of Acute Intoxication CNS depression, respiratory depression, gaze nystagmus, bradycardia, hypothermia, tachycardia, hypotension, vision color changes (green tinge), vision color changes (yellow tinge); ptosis, renal failure, cyclic coma

When to Transport to Hospital Transport any ingestion over 10 mg/kg or any patient with decreased mental status

Warnings/Precautions Use with caution in patients with renal impairment and pulmonary insufficiency; avoid abrupt discontinuation of mephobarbital

Adverse Reactions
>10%: Central nervous system: Dizziness, lightheadedness, drowsiness, "hangover" effect
1% to 10%:
    Central nervous system: Confusion, mental depression, unusual excitement, nervousness, faint feeling, headache, insomnia, nightmares
    Gastrointestinal: Constipation, nausea, vomiting

Reference Range Phenobarbital level should be in the range of 15-40 µg/mL; levels of >80 µg/mL correlate with decreased mental status

Drug Interactions Mephobarbital is converted to phenobarbital in the liver; phenobarbital induces the liver enzyme involved with warfarin and doxycycline metabolism; ethanol and antihistamines may enhance adverse neurological effects

Dosage Forms Tablet: 32 mg, 50 mg, 100 mg

Additional Information Sometimes used in specific patients who have excessive sedation or hyperexcitability from phenobarbital; avoid abrupt discontinuation

Meprobam see Meprobamate on this page

Meprobamate (me proe BA mate)

Related Information
Carisoprodol on page 114
Controlled Substances - Uses and Effects on page 741

Synonyms Meprobam

U.S. Brand Names Equanil®; Meprospan®; Miltown®; Neuramate®; Tenavoid®

Canadian Brand Names Apo-Meprobamate®; Meditran®; Novo-Mepro®

Therapeutic Category Antianxiety Agent

Abuse Potential Yes

Impairment Potential Yes; Serum meprobamate levels >60 mg/L associated with impairment

Baselt RC and Cravey RH, *Disposition of Toxic Drugs and Chemicals in Man*, 4th ed, Foster City, CA: Chemical Toxicology Institute, 1995, 460.

Use Management of anxiety disorders

Usual Dosage Oral:
Children 6-12 years: 100-200 mg 2-3 times/day
    Sustained release: 200 mg twice daily
Adults: 400 mg 3-4 times/day, up to 2400 mg/day
(Continued)

Meprobamate *(Continued)*

Sustained release; 400-800 mg twice daily

Mechanism of Action Precise mechanisms are not yet clear, but many effects have been ascribed to its central depressant actions

Pharmacodynamics/kinetics

Onset of action: Oral: Within 60 minutes

Absorption: Oral: Well absorbed from gastrointestinal tract

Metabolism: Promptly in the liver

Half-life: 10 hours; in overdose setting: >24 hours

Time to peak serum concentration: 1-3 hours

Signs and Symptoms of Acute Intoxication Drowsiness, bradycardia, drowsiness, wheezing, hyporeflexia, coma, respiratory depression, syncope, gaze nystagmus, stupor, ataxia, areflexia, hypotension, tachycardia, bezoars, porphyria, leukopenia; neutropenia; agranulocytosis; granulocytopenia

When to Transport to Hospital Transport any pediatric (<6 years of age) exposure, any patient with ingestion over 1 g, or patients with decreased mental status

Warnings/Precautions Physical and psychological dependence and abuse may occur; not recommended in children <6 years of age; allergic reaction may occur in patients with history of dermatological condition (usually by fourth dose)

Adverse Reactions

>10%: Central nervous system: Drowsiness, ataxia

1% to 10%:

Central nervous system: Dizziness

Dermatologic: Rashes

Gastrointestinal: Diarrhea, vomiting

Ocular: Blurred vision

Respiratory: Wheezing

Reference Range

Therapeutic: 6-12 µg/mL (SI: 28-55 µmol/L)

Toxic: >60 µg/mL (SI: >275 µmol/L); coma is associated with levels >70 µg/mL

Fatal: Fatalities can occur with levels >142 µg/mL

Drug Interactions CNS depressants, anticoagulants (not clinically significant), alcohol

Dosage Forms

Capsule, sustained release: 200 mg, 400 mg

Tablet: 200 mg, 400 mg, 600 mg

Additional Information Can cause bezoars

Specific References

Volturo GA, "Meprobamate and Bezoar Formation," *Ann Emerg Med*, 1987, 16(4):472-3.

Meprobamate and Aspirin see Aspirin and Meprobamate on page 58

Meprospan® see Meprobamate on previous page

Mercury

UN Number 2809; 2024; 2025; 1629

Commonly Found In Inorganic mercury salts; organic mercury; elemental mercury; found in thimerosal; used by amalgam makers, jewelers, paint manufacturers, laboratorians, taxidermists, fireworks, embalmers, button batteries, dye makers, fur processors, photographers, electroplaters

Mechanism of Toxic Action Causes cell membrane damage; elemental and organic mercury are CNS toxins; inorganic is a corrosive; organic mercury causes teratogenicity; high-binding affinity of divalent cation form of mercury to thiol or sulfhydryl protein groups occur

Toxicodynamics/kinetics

Absorption: Elemental mercury is poorly absorbed orally and well absorbed by inhalation while inorganic and organic mercury are well absorbed orally; metallic mercury is minimally absorbed dermally (0.024 ng of mercury absorbed per cm^2 of skin)

Distribution: Elemental to CNS, kidney, liver, and heart; inorganic mercury concentrates in the kidney; organic mercury (alkyl mercury groups) distribute throughout the body while methylmercury concentrates in blood and CNS

Metabolism: Metallic/inorganic mercury: Oxidized to an inorganic divalent form in the red blood cells (note that ethanol can inhibit this step)

Half-life:
  Elemental and inorganic: 40-60 days; organic: 70 days
  Organic: Converted to divalent cation form in tissues

Elimination:
  Metallic: Urine, feces, and lung
  Inorganic: Urine, feces
  Organic: Primarily feces

Signs and Symptoms of Acute Intoxication Elemental mercury is poorly absorbed orally with minimal adverse effects; inhalation acutely can cause chemical pneumonitis, noncardiogenic pulmonary edema, and gingivostomatitis; chronic exposure to mercury vapor will cause tremor, hematuria, leukocytosis, fatigue, proteinuria, alopecia, fasciculations, insomnia, loss of memory, and acrodynia

Inorganic mercury: After oral administration, will develop abdominal pain, gastrointestinal irritation, gastrointestinal bleeding, shock, renal failure, and ATN; possible CNS toxicity

Organic mercury: Causes CNS toxicity including ataxia, dysarthria, paresthesias, hearing and visual loss, and gastrointestinal distress

When to Transport to Hospital Transport any suspected exposure; treat the scene as a hazardous material site

Overdosage/Treatment

Decontamination:
  Inhalation: Patients should be monitored for pulmonary edema and pneumonitis; give oxygen if necessary
  Dermal: Wash with tincture of green soap and water
  Ocular: Copious irrigation with saline

Adverse Reactions

Cardiovascular: Hypertension, tachycardia, hypotension, cranial nerve palsies, cardiomyopathy, cardiomegaly, palpitations, Q-T prolongation, sinus tachycardia, arrhythmias (ventricular), vasoconstriction

Central nervous system: Dementia, hyperthermia, encephalopathy, ataxia, Jarisch-Herxheimer reaction, CNS depression, depression

Dermatologic: Dermal granuloma, skin granuloma, systemic contact dermatitis

Gastrointestinal: Salivation, metallic taste

Hematologic: Thrombocytopenia, eosinophilia

Neuromuscular & skeletal: Tremor, myoclonus, neuritis, rhabdomyolysis

Ocular: Diplopia, photophobia

Otic: Deafness

Renal: Glomerulonephritis

Respiratory: Hyposmia

Miscellaneous: Toxic shock-like syndrome

Reference Range Urinary and whole blood levels can be obtained; normally urinary values are <10 µg/dL and whole blood <2 µg/dL; whole blood levels <50 µg/dL are usually associated with gastroenteritis and acute tubular necrosis; urinary levels for organic mercury are not useful since 90% is eliminated through bile in the feces; urinary mercury levels >56µg/L can result in neurotoxic effects (due to elemental mercury)

(Continued)

373

Mercury (Continued)

Additional Information

Ambient atmospheric mercury levels range from 10-20 ng/m³

Estimated daily intake of mercury from air: 0.2 mcg; from drinking water: 0.1 mcg

Residence atmospheric time of elemental mercury: 6-24 months

Average methyl mercury content in tuna: 0.17 ppm

Chinese herbal balls may contain from 7.8-621.3 mg of mercury and from 0.1-36.6 mg of arsenic

Specific References

Aks SE, Erickson T, Branches FJ, et al, "Fractional Mercury Levels in Brazilian Gold Refiners and Miners," *J Toxicol Clin Toxicol*, 1995, 33(1):1-10.

Merex® *see* Chlordecone *on page 123*

Mesantoin® *see* Mephenytoin *on page 369*

Mescal Buttons *see* Mescaline *on this page*

Mescaline

Related Information

Controlled Substances - Uses and Effects *on page 741*

Peyote *on page 469*

Synonyms Mescal Buttons

Scientific Name *Lophophora williamsii*

Abuse Potential Yes

Impairment Potential Yes

Usual Dosage Hallucinogenic dose: Oral: 5 mg/kg

Mechanism of Toxic Action Hallucinogenic methoxylated amphetamine stimulating both serotonin and dopamine receptors in the central nervous system

Pharmacodynamics/kinetics

Duration of effect: Psychic effects last 6-12 hours

Metabolism: Hepatic to inactive metabolites

Half-life: 6 hours

Signs and Symptoms of Acute Intoxication Hypertension, chest pain, bradycardia, psychosis, hallucinations, headache, dizziness, ataxia, tremor, coma, fever, flushing, sweating, flashbacks, vomiting, mydriasis, tachypnea, hyperreflexia, myoglobinuria, rhabdomyolysis

When to Transport to Hospital Transport any pediatric exposure or any patient with bradycardia, psychosis, fever, or chest pain

Overdosage/Treatment Benzodiazepines are useful for agitation; haloperidol or chlorpromazine can be used if psychiatric symptoms are not responsive to benzodiazepines; do not use phenothiazines for treatment of flashback

Adverse Reactions

Cardiovascular: Sinus bradycardia, angina

Endocrine & metabolic: Hyperprolactinemia

Drug Interactions Flashbacks may be exacerbated by phenothiazines

Additional Information

Active ingredient in the peyote cactus (*Lophophora williamsii*). Available as whole dried cactus tops ("buttons"); peyote contains 1% to 6% mescaline; each "button" contains about 45 mg of mescaline.

Range: Found in the Southwestern U.S. and Mexico

Hallucinogenic effects occur at blood levels of mescaline of 1.5-14.8 µg/mL; peak blood level after an oral 500 mg dose: 3.8 mg/mL at 2 hours postingestion and 1.5 mg/L at 7 hours postingestion; after a 5 mg/kg intravenous dose, peak blood mescaline level was 14.8 µg/mL 15 minutes postdose

Specific References

Reynolds PC and Jindrich EJ, "A Mescaline Associated Fatality," *J Anal Toxicol*, 1985, 9(4):183-4.

Mesoridazine (mez oh RID a zeen)

U.S. Brand Names Imagotan®; Serentil®

Therapeutic Category Antipsychotic Agent; Phenothiazine Derivative

Impairment Potential Yes

Use Symptomatic management of psychotic disorders, including schizophrenia, behavioral problems, alcoholism as well as reducing anxiety and tension occurring in neurosis

Usual Dosage Concentrate may be diluted just prior to administration with distilled water, acidified tap water, orange or grape juice; do not prepare and store bulk dilutions

Adults:

Oral: 25-50 mg 3 times/day; maximum: 100-400 mg/day

I.M.: 25 mg initially, repeat in 30-60 minutes as needed; optimal dosage range: 25-200 mg/day

Mechanism of Action Blockade of postsynaptic CNS dopamine receptors; a metabolite of thioridazine

Pharmacodynamics/kinetics

Onset of action: 30 minutes to 1 hour

Duration: 4-6 hours

Absorption: Very erratic, oral liquids are much more dependable

Metabolism: Hepatic

Half-life: 24-48 hours

Time to peak serum concentration: 2-4 hours; steady-state serum levels: 4-7 days

Signs and Symptoms of Acute Intoxication Deep sleep, coma, priapism, photophobia, impotence, enuresis, extrapyramidal reaction, neuroleptic malignant syndrome, ejaculatory disturbances, gynecomastia, Parkinson's-like symptoms, galactorrhea, abnormal involuntary muscle movements, hypotension, cardiac arrhythmias, QRS prolongation, vision color changes (brown tinge), vision color changes (yellow tinge); urine discoloration (pink), urine discoloration (red), urine discoloration (red-brown), leukopenia; neutropenia; agranulocytosis; granulocytopenia

When to Transport to Hospital Transport any symptomatic patient

Warnings/Precautions Safety in children <6 months of age has not been established; use with caution in patients with cardiovascular disease or seizures; benefits of therapy must be weighed against risks of therapy

Adverse Reactions

>10%:

Cardiovascular: Hypotension, orthostatic hypotension

Central nervous system: Pseudoparkinsonism, akathisia, dystonias, tardive dyskinesia (persistent), dizziness

Gastrointestinal: Constipation

Ocular: Pigmentary retinopathy

Respiratory: Nasal congestion

Miscellaneous: Diaphoresis (decreased)

1% to 10%:

Dermatologic: Increased sensitivity to sun, rash

Endocrine & metabolic: Changes in menstrual cycle, changes in libido, breast pain

Gastrointestinal: Weight gain, nausea, vomiting, stomach pain

Genitourinary: Dysuria, ejaculatory disturbances

Neuromuscular & skeletal: Trembling of fingers

(Continued)

375

Mesoridazine (Continued)

Test Interactions May give false-positive when testing for tricyclic antidepressants through EMIT system

Drug Interactions
Other CNS depressants: Increased central nervous system depression
Anticonvulsants: Decreased mesoridazine levels
Lithium: Oral solutions are incompatible when mixed
Metrizamide: Increases risk of seizures

Dosage Forms
Injection: 25 mg/mL (1 mL)
Liquid, oral: 25 mg/mL (118 mL)
Tablet: 10 mg, 25 mg, 50 mg, 100 mg

Specific References
Marrs-Simon PA, Zell-Kanter M, Kendzierski DL, et al, "Cardiotoxic Manifestations of Mesoridazine Overdose," *Ann Emerg Med*, 1988, 17(10):1074-8.

Metabisulfites see Sulfite Food Poisoning on page 553

Metacortandralone see Prednisolone on page 495

Metadelphene see Diethyltoluamide on page 197

Metandren® see Methyltestosterone on page 398

Metaprel® see Metaproterenol on this page

Metaproterenol (met a proe TER e nol)

Synonyms Orciprenaline Sulfate

U.S. Brand Names Alupent®; Arm-a-Med® Metaproterenol; Dey-Dose® Metaproterenol; Metaprel®; Prometa®

Therapeutic Category Adrenergic Agonist Agent

Use Bronchodilator in reversible airway obstruction due to asthma or COPD; because of its delayed onset of action (one hour) and prolonged effect (4 or more hours), this may not be the drug of choice for assessing response to a bronchodilator

Usual Dosage
Oral:
Children:
<6 years: 0.3-0.5 mg/kg/dose every 6-8 hours
6-9 years, <60 lbs: 10 mg 3-4 times/day
Children >9 years, >60 lbs and Adults: 20 mg 3-4 times/day
Inhalation: Children >12 years and Adults: 2-3 inhalations every 3-4 hours, up to 12 inhalations in 24 hours
Nebulizer:
Infants and Children: 0.01-0.02 mL/kg of 5% solution; minimum dose: 0.1 mL; maximum dose: 1 mL diluted in 2-3 mL normal saline every 4-6 hours (may be given more frequently according to need)
Adolescents and Adults: 5-20 breaths of full strength 5% metaproterenol **or** 0.2-0.3 mL of 5% metaproterenol in 2.5-3 mL normal saline until nebulized every 4-6 hours (can be given more frequently according to need)

Mechanism of Action Relaxes bronchial smooth muscle by action on beta$_2$-receptors with very little effect on heart rate

Pharmacodynamics/kinetics
Onset of action: Oral: Bronchodilation occurs within 15 minutes
Peak effect: Within 1 hour
Duration:
Oral: Up to 4 hours
Inhalation, aerosol: 1-5 hours
Inhalation, handbulb nebulizer or IPPB: 2-6 hours
Absorption: Well from gastrointestinal tract

Metabolism: In the liver

Time to peak serum concentration:
Inhalation, aerosol: ~1 hour
Oral: Within 1 hour

Signs and Symptoms of Acute Intoxication Angina, cardiac arrhythmias, tremors, dry mouth, insomnia

When to Transport to Hospital Transport any pediatric (<6 years of age) exposure or any patient exhibiting tremors, dry mouth, or cardiopulmonary symptoms

Warnings/Precautions Excessive or prolonged use may lead to tachyphylaxis; use with caution in patients with cardiovascular disorders, hyperthyroidism, seizure disorders, or diabetes mellitus; excessive use may result in cardiac arrest and death; do not use concurrently with other sympathomimetic bronchodilators

Adverse Reactions

>10%:

Central nervous system: Nervousness

Neuromuscular & skeletal: Tremor

1% to 10%:

Cardiovascular: Tachycardia, palpitations, hypertension

Central nervous system: Headache, dizziness

Gastrointestinal: Nausea, vomiting, bad taste

Neuromuscular & skeletal: Trembling, muscle cramps, weakness

Respiratory: Coughing

Miscellaneous: Diaphoresis (increased)

Test Interactions Increases potassium (S)

Drug Interactions Other sympathomimetic agents exacerbate cardiac effects

Dosage Forms

Aerosol, oral: 0.65 mg/dose (5 mL, 10 mL)

Solution for inhalation: 0.4% [4 mg/mL] (2.5 mL); 0.6% [6 mg/mL] (2.5 mL); 5% [50 mg/mL] (0.3 mL, 10 mL, 30 mL)

Syrup: 10 mg/5 mL (480 mL)

Tablet: 10 mg, 20 mg

Additional Information Because of its delayed onset of action (1 hour) and prolonged effect (4 or more hours), this may not be the drug of choice for assessing response to a bronchodilator

Specific References

Jerrard DA, Olshaker J, Welebob E, et al, "Efficacy and Safety of a Rapid-Sequence Metaproterenol Protocol in the Treatment of Acute Adult Asthma," *Am J Emerg Med*, 1995, 13(4):392-5.

Metasedin® *see* Methadone *on page 379*

Metformin (met FOR min)

U.S. Brand Names Glucophage®

Canadian Brand Names Novo-Metformin®

Therapeutic Category Antidiabetic Agent (Oral)

Use Management of noninsulin-dependent diabetes mellitus (type II) as monotherapy when hyperglycemia cannot be managed on diet alone. May be used concomitantly with a sulfonylurea when diet and metformin or sulfonylurea alone do not result in adequate glycemic control.

Investigational: Data suggests that some patients with NIDDM with secondary failure to sulfonylurea therapy may obtain significant improvement in metabolic control when metformin in combination with insulin and a sulfonylurea is used in lieu of insulin alone

(Continued)

Metformin *(Continued)*

Usual Dosage Oral (allow 1-2 weeks between dose titrations):

Adults:

500 mg tablets: Initial: 500 mg twice daily (given with the morning and evening meals). Dosage increases should be made in increments of one tablet every week, given in divided doses, up to a maximum of 2,500 mg/day. Doses of up to 2000 mg/day may be given twice daily. If a dose of 2,500 mg/day is required, it may be better tolerated 3 times/day (with meals).

850 mg tablets: Initial: 850 mg once daily (given with the morning meal). Dosage increases should be made in increments of one tablet every OTHER week, given in divided doses, up to a maximum of 2550 mg/day. The usual maintenance dose is 850 mg twice daily (with the morning and evening meals). Some patients may be given 850 mg 3 times/day (with meals).

Elderly patients: The initial and maintenance dosing should be conservative, due to the potential for decreased renal function. Generally, elderly patients should not be titrated to the maximum dose of metformin.

Transfer from other antidiabetic agents: No transition period is generally necessary except when transferring from chlorpropamide. When transferring from chlorpropamide, care should be exercised during the first 2 weeks because of the prolonged retention of chlorpropamide in the body, leading to overlapping drug effects and possible hypoglycemia.

Concomitant metformin and oral sulfonylurea therapy: If patients have not responded to 4 weeks of the maximum dose of metformin monotherapy, consideration to a gradual addition of an oral sulfonylurea while continuing metformin at the maximum dose, even if prior primary or secondary failure to a sulfonylurea has occurred.

Mechanism of Action Decreases hepatic glucose production, decreasing intestinal absorption of glucose and improves insulin sensitivity (increases peripheral glucose uptake and utilization)

Pharmacodynamics/kinetics Half-life, plasma elimination: 6.2 hours

Signs and Symptoms of Acute Intoxication Hypoglycemia has not been observed with ingestions of up to 85 g of metformin, although lactic acidosis has occurred in such circumstances

When to Transport to Hospital Transport any pediatric exposure or any symptomatic patient

Warnings/Precautions Administration of oral antidiabetic drugs has been reported to be associated with increased cardiovascular mortality as compared to treatment with diet alone or diet plus insulin. Metformin is substantially excreted by the kidney - the risk of accumulation and lactic acidosis increases with the degree of impairment of renal function. Patients with renal function below the limit of normal for their age should not receive metformin. In elderly patients, renal function should be monitored regularly. Use of concomitant medications that may affect renal function (ie, affect tubular secretion) may affect metformin disposition. Therapy should be suspended for any surgical procedures. Avoid use in patients with impaired liver function.

Adverse Reactions

>10%: Gastrointestinal: Anorexia, nausea, vomiting, diarrhea, epigastric fullness, constipation, heartburn

1% to 10%:

Dermatologic: Rash, urticaria, photosensitivity

Miscellaneous: Decreased vitamin B_{12} levels

Reference Range Target range: Adults:

Fasting blood glucose: <120 mg/dL

Glycosylated hemoglobin: <7%

Drug Interactions

Decreased effects: Drugs which tend to produce hyperglycemia (eg, diuretics, corticosteroids, phenothiazines, thyroid products, estrogens, oral contraceptives, phenytoin, nicotinic acid, sympathomimetics, calcium channel blocking drugs, isoniazid) may lead to a loss of glycemic control

Increased effects: Furosemide increased the metformin plasma and blood C_{max} without altering metformin renal clearance in a single dose study

Increased toxicity:

Cationic drugs (eg, amiloride, digoxin, morphine, procainamide, quinidine, quinine, ranitidine, triamterene, trimethoprim, and vancomycin) which are eliminated by renal tubular secretion could have the potential for interaction with metformin by competing for common renal tubular transport systems

Cimetidine increases (by 60%) peak metformin plasma and whole blood concentrations

Dosage Forms Tablet, as hydrochloride: 500 mg, 850 mg

Specific References

Bailey CJ and Turner RC, "Metformin," *N Engl J Med*, 1996, 334(9):574-97.

Methadone (METH a done)

Related Information

Controlled Substances - Uses and Effects *on page 741*

U.S. Brand Names Dolophine®; Eptadone®; Metasedin®; Physeptone®; Symoron®

Canadian Brand Names Methadose®

Therapeutic Category Analgesic, Narcotic

Abuse Potential Yes

Impairment Potential Yes; No apparent impairment in complex tasks noted in patients on daily methadone maintenance (60-100 mg)

Moskowitz H and Robinson CD, "Methadone Maintenance and Tracking Performance," *Alcohol Drugs and Traffic Safety*, Kaye S and Meier GW, eds, Univ Puerto Rico, 1985, 995-1004.

Use Management of severe pain, used in narcotic detoxification maintenance programs

Usual Dosage Doses should be titrated to appropriate effects

Children: Analgesia:

Oral, I.M., S.C.: 0.7 mg/kg/24 hours divided every 4-6 hours as needed or 0.1-0.2 mg/kg every 4-12 hours as needed; maximum: 10 mg/dose

I.V.: 0.1 mg/kg every 4 hours initially for 2-3 doses, then every 6-12 hours as needed; maximum: 10 mg/dose

Adults:

Analgesia: Oral, I.M., I.V., S.C.: 2.5-10 mg every 3-8 hours as needed, up to 5-20 mg every 6-8 hours

Detoxification: Oral: 15-40 mg/day; should not exceed 21 days and may not be repeated earlier than 4 weeks after completion of preceding course

Maintenance dose: Oral: 20-120 mg/day

Mechanism of Action Binds to opiate receptors in the CNS, causing inhibition of ascending pain pathways, altering the perception of and response to pain; produces generalized CNS depression

Pharmacodynamics/kinetics

Oral:

Onset of action: Within 30-60 minutes

Duration: 6-8 hours; with repeated doses, increases to 22-48 hours

Parenteral:

Onset of action: Within 10-20 minutes

Peak effect: Within 1-2 hours

(Continued)

Methadone *(Continued)*

Enhanced analgesia has been seen in elderly patients on therapeutic doses of narcotics; duration of action may be increased.

Absorption: Absorbed well from gastrointestinal tract

Protein binding: 80% to 89%

Metabolism: Liver metabolism (N-demethylation)

Bioavailability, oral: 92%

Half-life: 15-29 hours, half-life may be prolonged with alkaline pH

Signs and Symptoms of Acute Intoxication Pulmonary edema, ejaculatory disturbances, respiratory depression, impotence, coma, miosis

When to Transport to Hospital Transport any pediatric ingestion over 10 mg or any patient with decreased mental status

Overdosage/Treatment Naloxone hydrochloride (0.4-2 mg I.V., S.C., or through an endotracheal tube); a continuous infusion (at $^2/_3$ the response dose/hour) may be required; opioid-induced myoclonus may respond to dantrolene (50-150 mg/day)

Warnings/Precautions Tablets are to be used only for oral administration and **must not** be used for injection; use with caution in patients with respiratory diseases including: asthma, emphysema, or COPD and in patients with severe liver disease; because methadone's effects on respiration last much longer than its analgesic effects, the dose must be titrated slowly

Adverse Reactions

Central nervous system: CNS depression

Endocrine & metabolic: Antidiuretic hormone release

Ocular: Miosis

Respiratory: Respiratory depression

>10%:

Cardiovascular: Palpitations, hypotension, bradycardia, peripheral vasodilation

Central nervous system: Fatigue, drowsiness, dizziness

Gastrointestinal: Nausea, vomiting, constipation

Neuromuscular & skeletal: Weakness

Miscellaneous: Histamine release

1% to 10%:

Central nervous system: Nervousness, headache, restlessness, anorexia, malaise, confusion, increased intracranial pressure

Gastrointestinal: Stomach cramps, xerostomia, biliary tract spasm

Genitourinary: Decreased urination, urinary tract spasm

Local: Pain at injection site

Respiratory: Dyspnea, shortness of breath

Reference Range

Therapeutic: 0.1-0.4 ng/mL (SI: 0.32-1.29 µmol/L)

Toxic: >2.0 µg/mL (SI: >6.46 µmol/L)

Drug Interactions

Decreased effect with phenytoin (increases withdrawal), rifampin (causes withdrawal), pentazocine (causes withdrawal)

Increased effect/toxicity with CNS depressants, phenothiazines, tricyclic antidepressants, MAO inhibitors, cimetidine, diazepam

Discontinuation of fluvoxamine in patients receiving methadone (for maintenance therapy) has been associated with increase methadone blood levels along with increased opioid effects

Dosage Forms

Injection: 10 mg/mL (1 mL, 10 mL, 20 mL)

Solution: Oral: 5 mg/5 mL (5 mL, 500 mL); 10 mg/5 mL (500 mL)

Solution, oral concentrate: 10 mg/mL (30 mL)

Tablet: 5 mg, 10 mg

Tablet, dispersible: 40 mg

Additional Information Not detected as an opioid in most urine immunoassays

Specific References

De Vos JW, Geerlings PJ, Van Den Brink W, et al, "Pharmacokinetics of Methadone and Its Primary Metabolite in 20 Opiate Addicts," *Eur J Clin Pharmacol*, 1995, 48:361-6.

Gordon NB and Appel PW, "Functional Potential of the Methadone-Maintained Person," *Alcohol, Drugs, and Driving*, 1995, Vol 11, No 1.

Methadone, Quantitative, Serum

Synonyms Phenadone, Serum

Use Monitor patient compliance; evaluate toxicity

Reference Range For narcotic stabilization: 0.3-1.0 µg/mL

Additional Information Methadone is a synthetic diphenylheptane derivative. It produces less sedation and euphoria than morphine and its effects are cumulative. Methadone is highly addictive, but the withdrawal symptoms are less intense. This drug is used in the management of severe pain and in narcotic detoxification maintenance programs. Onset of action is 30-60 minutes after oral dose and 10-20 minutes following parenteral administration. The half-life is 15-25 hours. Adverse effects include marked sedation after repeated administration, CNS and respiratory depression, nausea and vomiting, bradycardia, hypotension, increased intracranial pressure, miosis, antidiuretic hormone release, and physical and psychological dependence.

Specific References

Marquet P, Mura P, Lotfi H, et al, "Salivary Excretion Kinetics and Saliva-Plasma Ratios of Methadone and Metabolite (EDDP) in Humans," *J Anal Toxicol*, 1997, 21:82.

Methadone, Urine

Use Evaluate toxicity; detect drugs of abuse

Reference Range Negative (less than cutoff); when used therapeutically for pain, plasma levels are in the range of 0.05-0.10 µg/mL

Additional Information Methadone is a synthetic diphenylheptane derivative. It produces less sedation and euphoria than morphine and its effects are cumulative. Methadone is highly addictive, but the withdrawal symptoms are less intense. This drug is used in the management of severe pain and in narcotic detoxification maintenance programs. Onset of action is 30-60 minutes after oral dose and 10-20 minutes following parenteral administration. The half-life is 15-25 hours. Adverse effects include marked sedation after repeated administration, CNS and respiratory depression, nausea and vomiting, bradycardia, hypotension, increased intracranial pressure, miosis, antidiuretic hormone release, and physical and psychological dependence. Methadone is a drug of abuse. Patients on methadone maintenance protocols will test above cutoff in urine drug screens.

Specific References

Calsyn DA, Saxon AJ, and Barndt DC, "Urine Screening Practices in Methadone Maintenance Clinics. A Survey of How the Results Are Used," *J Nerv Ment Dis*, 1991, 179(4):222-7.

Wolff K, Hay AW, and Raistrick D, "Plasma Methadone Measurements and Their Role in Methadone Detoxification Programs," *Clin Chem*, 1992, 38(3):420-5.

Methaminodiazepoxide Hydrochloride *see* Chlordiazepoxide *on page 124*

Methampex® *see* Methamphetamine *on next page*

Methamphetamine (meth am FET a meen)

Related Information
Controlled Substances - Uses and Effects *on page 741*

Synonyms Desoxyephedrine Hydrochloride; MDMA

U.S. Brand Names Desoxyn®; Methampex®

Therapeutic Category Amphetamine

Abuse Potential Yes

Impairment Potential Yes; Blood methamphetamine levels >0.1 mg/L associated with driving impairment (typical driving behaviors noted include speeding, weaving, drifting, out of lane of travel, and erratic driving).

Logan BK, "Methamphetamine and Driving Impairment," *J Forensic Sci*, 1996, 41(3):457-64.

Use Treatment of narcolepsy, exogenous obesity, abnormal behavioral syndrome in children (minimal brain dysfunction)

Usual Dosage Oral:
Attention deficit disorder: Children >6 years: 2.5-5 mg 1-2 times/day, may increase by 5 mg increments weekly until optimum response is achieved, usually 20-25 mg/day
Exogenous obesity: Children >12 years and Adults: 5 mg, 30 minutes before each meal; long-acting formulation: 10-15 mg in morning; treatment duration should not exceed a few weeks

Pharmacodynamics/kinetics
Duration of action: 6-12 hours
Metabolism: In liver to amphetamine (4% to 7%) and other metabolites
Half-life: 12-34 hours
Elimination: Renal

Signs and Symptoms of Acute Intoxication Pulmonary edema, mydriasis, respiratory alkalosis, gynecomastia, insomnia, hypertension, tachycardia or reflex bradycardia, periarteritis nodosa, tachypnea, delirium, rhabdomyolysis, confusion, mania, rigors, myoclonus, myoglobinuria, tremors, alopecia, feces discoloration (black)

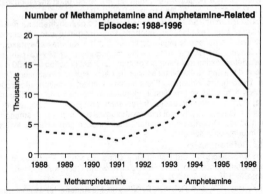

Number of Methamphetamine and Amphetamine-Related Episodes: 1988-1996

From U.S. Department of Health and Human Services Public Health Service, "Annual Trends in Other Illicit Drug-Related Episodes," *Preliminary Estimates From the Drug Abuse Warning Network*, 1996, 17:13.

When to Transport to Hospital Transport any pediatric (<6 years of age) exposure, any febrile patients, or any patient with cardiac or central nervous system abnormalities

Warnings/Precautions Cardiovascular disease, nephritis, angina pectoris, hypertension, glaucoma, patients with a history of drug abuse

Adverse Reactions

>10%:

Cardiovascular: Arrhythmia

Central nervous system: False feeling of well being, nervousness, restlessness, insomnia

1% to 10%:

Cardiovascular: Hypertension

Central nervous system: Mood or mental changes, dizziness, lightheadedness, headache

Endocrine & metabolic: Changes in libido

Gastrointestinal: Diarrhea, nausea, vomiting, stomach cramps, constipation, anorexia, weight loss, xerostomia

Ocular: Blurred vision

Miscellaneous: Diaphoresis (increased)

Test Interactions A labetalol metabolite (3-amino-1-phenylbutane or APB) may cause a false-positive result with amphetamine/methamphetamine by thin-layer chromatography or immunoassay; false-positives by immunoassay can be seen with ranitidine, phenylpropanolamine, brompheniramine, chlorpromazine, fluspirilene or pipothiazine coingestion; alum (25 g/L) can elicit a false-negative urinary assay for methamphetamine; urine will be acidic in these cases

Reference Range Therapeutic: 20-30 ng/mL

Drug Interactions Increased toxicity with MAO inhibitors (hypertensive crisis); combination of methamphetamine with ethanol can increase heart rate and cardiac work

Dosage Forms

Tablet: 5 mg

Tablet, extended release (Gradumet®): 5 mg, 10 mg, 15 mg

Additional Information

Typical Driving Behaviors in 28 Methamphetamine-Positive Drivers

Leaving lane of travel	13
Pulled out into oncoming traffic	4
Speeding	7
Failed to stop at stop sign	2
General erratic driving	5
Rear ended another vehicle	1

Reprinted with permission from Logan BK, "Methamphetamine and Driving Impairment," *J Forensic Sci*, 1996, 41:457-64.

Illicit methamphetamine may contain lead; alkalinizing urine can result in longer methamphetamine half-life and elevated blood level; ephedrine is a precursor in the illicit manufacture of methamphetamine; ephedrine is extracted by dissolving ephedrine tablets in water or alcohol (50,000 tablets can result in 1 kg of ephedrine); conversion to methamphetamine occurs at a rate of 50% to 70% of the weight of ephedrine.

(Continued)

Methamphetamine *(Continued)*

Examples of Withdrawal Effects From Low Dose and High Dose Drug Use

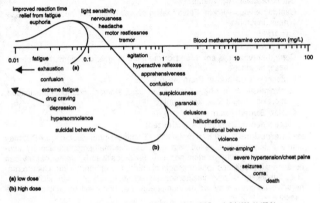

Used with permission from Logan BK, "Methamphetamine and Driving Impairment," *J Forensic Sci*, 1996, 41:457-64.

Specific References
Milroy CM, Clark JC, and Forrest AR, "Pathology of Deaths Associated With "Ecstasy" and "Eve" Misuse," *J Clin Pathol*, 1996, 49(2):149-53.

Methamphetamines, Serum

Use Evaluate toxicity; detect abuse

Reference Range Therapeutic: 20-30 ng/mL

Additional Information Methamphetamine is sympathomimetic amine chemically related to ephedrine and amphetamine. It is used in the management of obesity, to treat certain depressive reactions, and as adjunctive therapy for narcolepsy, epilepsy, attention deficit disorders, and postencephalitic parkinsonism. Methamphetamine is readily absorbed by the GI tract and the effects last from 6-12 hours. Adverse effects include tremor, insomnia, nervousness, anxiety, euphoria or dysphoria, hyper- or hypotension, arrhythmias, circulatory collapse, and nausea and vomiting.

Methamphetamines, Urine

Applies to Chlorpromazine; d-Methamphetamine; l-Methamphetamine; Methylenedioxymethamphetamine; Phentermine; Phenylpropanolamine; Pseudoephedrine; Ranitidine

Use Evaluate for drug abuse; assess toxicity

Reference Range Negative (less than cutoff)

Additional Information The most abused drug in this class is d-methampheta-mine. The optical isomer, L-methamphetamine, has less pronounced central effects and is used as a nasal decongestant in Vicks Inhaler® (legal, over-the-counter). Amphetamine isomers are present in Dexedrine® and Benzedrine®. These drugs are self-administered orally, I.V., or by smoking. Half-life is 10-20 hours and it can be detected in urine within 3 hours of use. The parent drugs are the substances detected by the screening tests. Over-the-counter medica-tion for colds and allergies (Contac®, Dimetapp®, Sine-Off®, Sudafed®) contain phenylpropanolamine or pseudoephedrine which give a positive EIA screening test when the polyclonal antibody is used. This antibody also detects methylenedioxymethamphetamine (MDMA), a controlled substance classed as an hallucinogen and "designer" drug. With the monoclonal EIA test, the above medications are not detected, but phentermine (Adipex®, Fastin®), ranitidine (Zantac®), and chlorpromazine (Thorazine®) give a positive test. Confirmation by GC/MS rules out these false-positives. In order to rule out the false-positive given by L-methamphetamine (legal nasal decongestant), a chiral column or procedure, which separates the "L" and "D" isomers, must be used in the GC/MS confirmation. Famprofazone (which metabolizes to methamphetamine and amphetamine) can give a positive immunoassay and GC/MS assay for meth-amphetamine for up to 56 hours.

Methamphetamine is a sympathomimetic amine chemically related to ephed-rine and amphetamine. It is used in the management of obesity, to treat certain depressive reactions, and as adjunctive therapy for narcolepsy, epilepsy, atten-tion deficit disorders, and postencephalitic parkinsonism. Methamphetamine is readily absorbed by the GI tract and the effects last from 6-12 hours. Adverse effects include tremor, insomnia, nervousness, anxiety, euphoria or dysphoria, hyper- or hypotension, arrhythmias, circulatory collapse, and nausea and vomiting.

Specific References

Derlet RW and Heischober G, "Methamphetamine. Stimulant of the 1990s?" *West J Med*, 1990, 153(6):625-8.

Methane

Synonyms Fire Damp; Marsh Gas; Methyl Hydride; Natural Gas (85% Methane)

UN Number 1971

Commonly Found In Sludge digestion; produced through natural breakdown of sewage; raw material for hydrogen, ammonia, or acetylene production; found in mining industry

Abuse Potential Yes

Impairment Potential Yes

Mechanism of Toxic Action Asphyxiant - Displaces oxygen from the atmos-phere

Signs and Symptoms of Acute Intoxication Tachypnea, cough, tachy-cardia, blurred or decreased vision, unconsciousness, CNS depression

When to Transport to Hospital Transport any patient with tachypnea or respiratory symptoms

Overdosage/Treatment Supportive therapy: 100% humidified oxygen

Adverse Reactions

Cardiovascular: Sinus tachycardia

Respiratory: Hypoxia, hyperventilation; no direct lung damage

Additional Information Colorless, odorless

TLV-TWA: No limits as long as sufficient atmospheric oxygen is available. Usually when asphyxiant is 33% of atmosphere, symptoms will develop; methane is flammable at concentrations of 5%

Death can occur at 75% concentration

(Continued)

Methane *(Continued)*

Specific References
Kizer KW, "Toxic Inhalations," *Emerg Med Clin North Am*, 1984, 2(3):649-66.

Methane Dichloride *see* Methylene Chloride *on page 395*

Methane Trichloride *see* Chloroform *on page 129*

Methanol

Synonyms Carbinol; Methyl Alcohol; Wood Alcohol; Wood Naphtha

UN Number 1230

Commonly Found In Industrial and household solvent

Use Fuel, paint remover; also is an additive to gasoline

Mechanism of Toxic Action Slowly metabolized to formaldehyde and then converted rapidly to formic acid which accounts for the acidosis and ocular toxicity

Toxicodynamics/kinetics
Specific gravity: 0.79 g/mL

Absorption: Dermally (enhanced with gasoline mixtures), by inhalation (58%), and through the gastrointestinal tract (~100%)

Distribution: V_d: 0.6 L/kg

Metabolism: Slowly in the liver by alcohol dehydrogenase to formaldehyde and then to formic acid; see figure

Peak serum concentration: Within 1 hour; found in higher concentrations in ocular and cerebrospinal fluids

Half-life, elimination: 8-28 hours (8 mg/dL/hour); with hemodialysis: 2 hours

Elimination: ~3% excreted unchanged renally and 12% by the lungs; ~22% of the drug is normally excreted in 4 hours in a normal patient

Signs and Symptoms of Acute Intoxication Blurred vision or diplopia progressing to blindness in about 33% of patients, feces discoloration (black), porphyria, headache, dyspnea, coma, seizures, hypomagnesemia, extrapyramidal symptoms, visual changes, hyperventilation, bilateral basal ganglia, metabolic acidosis, gaze nystagmus, hemorrhage, and renal failure can develop, parkinsonism, hypotension, paresthesia, myoglobinuria, ototoxicity, dementia, tinnitus, hypophosphatemia, bradycardia; symptoms may not occur for 24 hours

When to Transport to Hospital Transport any patient with any amount of ingestion

Overdosage/Treatment Decontamination:
Dermal: Wash with soap and water
Ocular: Irrigate copiously with saline

Adverse Reactions
Cardiovascular: Sinus bradycardia

Endocrine & metabolic: Anion gap metabolic acidosis (lactic acidosis)

Neuromuscular & skeletal: Rhabdomyolysis

Ocular: Visual abnormalities, blindness with edematous optic disk, photophobia, optic neuropathy

Renal: Hematuria, osmolal gap

Reference Range
Blood methanol level >50 mg/dL is associated with severe toxicity; minimal lethal level without treatment: 80 mg/dL; baseline methanol level from endogenous and dietary sources: <0.15 mg/dL

Central nervous system toxicity usually appears at methanol blood levels of 20 mg/dL; ocular symptoms occur at 100 mg/dL; fatalities can occur at blood methanol levels >150 mg/dL; serum formate levels >20 mg/dL are consistent with ocular symptoms and metabolic acidosis

Methanol Metabolism to Toxic
Intermediates—Formaldehyde and Formic Acid (Formate)

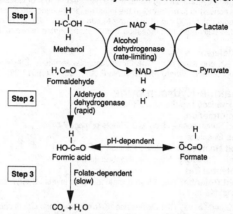

Discovery of methanol's metabolic pathway has led to several practical treatments; among them are the therapeutic administration of ethanol and folic acid. Alcohol dehydrogenase, the enzyme responsible for the first step of methanol metabolism, has an approximately ninefold greater affinity for ethanol than for methanol. Administration of ethanol blocks the oxidation of methanol, preventing the lethal synthesis of formaldehyde and formic acid and increasing the amount of methanol that is eliminated unchanged (now approximately equal amounts in urine and exhaled breath). Administration of folic acid and its analogues, which affect Step 3, enhances the conversion of toxic formic acid to carbon dioxide and water.

Adapted from Shusterman D and Osterloh JD, "Methanol Toxicity," *Case Studies in Environmental Medicine*, U.S. Department of Health and Human Services, Agency for Toxic Substances and Disease Registry, July 1992.

Endogenous serum formate concentrations: 0.6-1.6 mg/L; inhalation of methanol at concentrations of 200 ppm for 4 hours (or roughly 4 mg/kg) can result in peak serum and urine methanol levels of 6.5 mg/L and 0.9 mg every 4 hours respectively

Additional Information Parkinson syndrome has been described; methanol has $\frac{1}{3}$ the intoxicating effect of ethanol; discontinue ethanol therapy if methanol level is <10 mg/dL, or acidosis or central nervous system abnormalities have resolved; headaches can occur at air methanol levels in the range of 200-375 ppm; 4-Methylpyrazole has been used to treat methanol poisoning in Europe; bilateral basal ganglion lesions along with symmetrical putamen necrosis may be noted on CT scan or MRI; reduction of serum pH and development of acidosis may take 6-8 hours

Minimum oral lethal exposure: ~50 mL with blindness occurring at 10 mL

Contribution of a serum concentration level of 100 mg/dL to elevation of osmolar gap: 31

Odor threshold: 100-250 ppm

TLV-TWA: 200 ppm

Dose of methanol that will saturate the folate pathway is ~210 mg/kg. Methanol content in fruits, vegetables, and fruit juices can approach 140 mg/L; in (Continued)

Methanol *(Continued)*

fermented beverages it can be up to 1.5 g/L; since ~10% of ingested aspartame is converted to methanol in the intestine, a 12-ounce can of carbonated soda (containing 200 mg of aspartame) can produce ~20 mg of methanol; estimated daily methanol ingestion from noncarbonated drinks: 0.3-1.1 mg/kg

Specific References

Burkhart KK and Kulig KW, "The Other Alcohols: Methanol, Ethylene Glycol, and Isopropanol," *Emerg Med Clin North Am*, 1990, 8(4):913-28.

Methaqualone Hydrochloride

(meth A kwa lone hye droe KLOR ide)

Related Information

Controlled Substances - Uses and Effects *on page 741*

Synonyms Quaalude®

U.S. Brand Names Normi-Nox®; Pallidan®; Somnomed®

Therapeutic Category Hypnotic, Nonbarbiturate

Abuse Potential Yes

Impairment Potential Yes; Plasma methaqualone levels >2 mg/L associated with erratic driving

Baselt RC and Cravey RH, *Disposition of Toxic Drugs and Chemicals in Man*, 4th ed, Foster City, CA: Chemical Toxicology Institute, 1995, 484.

Use Europeans use for insomnia; taken off the U.S. market in 1984

Toxic Dose

Insomnia: 150-300 mg at night

Lethal dose: 8 g

Mechanism of Toxic Action Nonbarbiturate hypnosedative

Toxicodynamics/kinetics

Absorption: Complete within 2 hours

Metabolism: Hepatic

Half-life: 33-40 hours

Elimination: ~8% of the drug is normally excreted in 4 hours in a normal patient

Signs and Symptoms of Acute Intoxication Hypotension, coma, hematuria, hyperreflexia, A-V block, erythema multiforme, dyspnea, hyperthermia, vision color changes (yellow tinge); respiratory depression, apnea, seizures, myoclonus, gaze nystagmus

When to Transport to Hospital Transport any patient with change in mental status or any ingestion over 1 g

Adverse Reactions

Cardiovascular: Tachycardia, sinus tachycardia

Central nervous system: Euphoria, slurred speech, salivation, ataxia, electroencephalogram abnormalities

Dermatologic: Bullous lesions

Gastrointestinal: Vomiting, necrotizing cystitis

Ocular: Gaze nystagmus

Renal: Hematuria

Respiratory: Aspiration

Reference Range A 600 mg dose will yield a peak plasma level of 7 mg/L; plasma level of methaqualone >20 mg/L is consistent with toxicity

Drug Interactions Enhances codeine analgesia

Additional Information Mandrax® also contains diphenhydramine

Specific References

Kulberg A, "Substance Abuse: Clinical Identification and Management," *Pediatr Clin North Am*, 1986, 33(2):325-61.

Methaqualone Level

Synonyms Lude

Use Evaluate for toxicity; evaluate for drug abuse

Reference Range Urine: negative (less than cutoff); serum: 1-5 µg/mL (SI: 4-20 nmol/L)

Additional Information Methaqualone is a nonbarbiturate sedative-hypnotic. It is rapidly absorbed from the GI tract. Hyperexcitability, coma, and cardiovascular and respiratory depression characterize overdosage. It is a common drug of abuse, and "street" preparations may be adulterated with other pharmacoactive substances. Half-life is 20-60 hours. It is extensively metabolized and screening methods must detect metabolites. Enzyme-multiplied immunoassay technique (EMIT) detects four of the most common metabolites.

Specific References

Beebe DK and Walley E, "Substance Abuse: The Designer Drugs," *Am Fam Physician*, 1991, 43(5):1689-98.

Buckner JC and Mandell W, "Risk Factors for Depressive Symptomatology in a Drug Using Population," *Am J Public Health*, 1990, 80(5):580-5.

Metharbital (meth AR bi tal)

Synonyms Metharbitone

U.S. Brand Names Gemonil®

Therapeutic Category Anticonvulsant

Abuse Potential Yes

Impairment Potential Yes

Use Control of grand mal, petit mal, myoclonic and mixed types of seizures

Usual Dosage Oral:

Children: 5-15 mg/kg/day or 50 mg 1-3 times/day

Adults: 100 mg 1-3 times/day, adjust dosage to obtain optimal effect

Pharmacodynamics/kinetics

Metabolism: Demethylated to barbital (active)

Elimination: Renal, 1% excreted unchanged; 9% excreted as barbital

Signs and Symptoms of Acute Intoxication Slurred speech, ataxia, unsteady gait, gaze nystagmus, impairment in attention or memory, stupor, coma

When to Transport to Hospital Transport any symptomatic patient or any ingestion over 15 mg/kg

Adverse Reactions

Cardiovascular: Hypotension, circulatory collapse

Central nervous system: Drowsiness, paradoxical excitement, hyperkinetic activity, cognitive impairment, defects in general comprehension, short-term memory deficits, decreased attention span, ataxia

Dermatologic: Skin eruptions, skin rash, exfoliative dermatitis

Hematologic: Megaloblastic anemia

Hepatic: Hepatitis

Ocular: Vision color changes (yellow tinge), ptosis

Respiratory: Apnea (especially with rapid I.V. use), respiratory depression

Miscellaneous: Psychological and physical dependence

Dosage Forms Tablet: 100 mg

Additional Information Faint, aromatic odor

Metharbitone *see* Metharbital *on this page*

Methcathinone

Related Information

Cathinone *on page 119*

Synonyms Ephedrone; N-Methyl-Cathinone

(Continued)

Methchathinone *(Continued)*

Abuse Potential Yes

Impairment Potential Yes

Usual Dosage Estimated to be 80-250 mg by intranasal use (can be used I.V.); typical daily dose: 500-1000 mg

Pharmacodynamics/kinetics Metabolism: To ephedrine and phenylpropanolamine (norephedrine)

Signs and Symptoms of Acute Intoxication Tachycardia (dose-related), hypertension (dose related), agitation, tremor, slurred speech, paranoia, auditory hallucinations, back pain, headache, abdominal pain, leukocytosis, anorexia, constipation, visual hallucinations, sweating, fever, myoglobinuria, rhabdomyolysis, mydriasis

When to Transport to Hospital Transport any patient with changes in mental status

Adverse Reactions Cardiovascular: Sinus tachycardia

Test Interactions Does not cause a positive amphetamine result on urine immunoassays

Additional Information Ephedrine, pseudoephedrine, and phenylpropanone may turn up positive in drug testing in that these chemicals are used in the production of methcathinone

Reference range: Reference levels of methcaninone in symptomatic individuals were measured at 56 ng/mL and 78 ng/mL

Specific References

Emerson TS and Cisek JE, "Methcathinone: A Russian Designer Amphetamine Infiltrates the Rural Midwest," *Ann Emerg Med*, 1993, 22(12):1897-903.

Methocarbamol *(meth oh KAR ba mole)*

U.S. Brand Names Delaxin®; Lumirelax®; Marbaxin®; Relax Llano®; Robaxin®; Robomol®; Traumacut®; Tresortil®

Therapeutic Category Skeletal Muscle Relaxant

Use Treatment of muscle spasm associated with acute painful musculoskeletal conditions; supportive therapy in tetanus, Iatrodectism

Usual Dosage

Children: Recommended **only** for use in tetanus I.V.: 15 mg/kg/dose or 500 mg/m²/dose, may repeat every 6 hours if needed; maximum dose: 1.8 g/m²/day for 3 days only

Adults: Muscle spasm:

Oral: 1.5 g 4 times/day for 2-3 days, then decrease to 4-4.5 g/day in 3-6 divided doses

I.M., I.V.: 1 g every 8 hours if oral not possible

Mechanism of Action Causes skeletal muscle relaxation by reducing the transmission of impulses from the spinal cord to skeletal muscle

Pharmacodynamics/kinetics

Onset of action: Oral: Within 0.5 hours

Absorption: Rapid and complete

Metabolism: In the liver

Half-life: 1-2 hours

Time to peak serum concentration: Within 1 hour

Signs and Symptoms of Acute Intoxication Cardiac arrhythmias, nausea, vomiting, drowsiness, hypotension, apnea, coma, urine discoloration (black), urine discoloration (blue), urine discoloration (brown), urine discoloration (green)

When to Transport to Hospital Transport any patient with changes in mental status

Adverse Reactions
>10%: Central nervous system: Drowsiness, dizziness, lightheadedness
1% to 10%:
Cardiovascular: Flushing of face, bradycardia
Dermatologic: Allergic dermatitis
Gastrointestinal: Nausea, vomiting
Respiratory: Nasal congestion
Reference Range Peak serum level after 2 g: 25.8 mg/L; peak serum levels after 4 g: 41 mg/L; blood levels >320 mg/L have been associated with fatalities
Drug Interactions Potentiated with ethanol; will potentiate antimuscarinics and psychotropic agents
Dosage Forms
Injection: 100 mg/mL in polyethylene glycol 50% (10 mL)
Tablet: 500 mg, 750 mg
Specific References
Preston KL, Guarino JJ, Kirk WT, et al, "Evaluation of the Abuse Potential of Methocarbamol," *J Pharmacol Exp Ther*, 1989, 248(3):1146-57.

Methocarbamol and Aspirin (meth oh KAR ba mole & AS pir in)
U.S. Brand Names Robaxisal®
Therapeutic Category Skeletal Muscle Relaxant
Dosage Forms Tablet: Methocarbamol 400 mg and aspirin 325 mg

Methohexital (meth oh HEKS i tal)
U.S. Brand Names Brevital® Sodium
Therapeutic Category Barbiturate
Impairment Potential Yes
Use Induction and maintenance of general anesthesia for short procedures
Usual Dosage Doses must be titrated to effect
Children 3-12 years:
I.M.: Preop: 5-10 mg/kg/dose
I.V.: Induction: 1-2 mg/kg/dose
Rectal: Preop/induction: 20-35 mg/kg/dose; usual 25 mg/kg/dose; give as 10% aqueous solution
Adults: I.V.: Induction: 50-120 mg to start; 20-40 mg every 4-7 minutes

Lethal dose: 1-2 g
Mechanism of Action Ultra short-acting I.V. barbiturate anesthetic
Pharmacodynamics/kinetics
Duration of action: 0.3 hours
Half-life: 1-2 hours
Signs and Symptoms of Acute Intoxication Apnea, tachycardia, ptosis, vision color changes (green tinge), vision color changes (yellow tinge); wheezing, hypotension
When to Transport to Hospital Transport any patient with mental status changes
Warnings/Precautions Use with extreme caution in patients with liver impairment, asthma, cardiovascular instability
Adverse Reactions
>10%: Local: Pain on I.M. injection
1% to 10%: Gastrointestinal: Cramping, diarrhea, rectal bleeding
Drug Interactions CNS depressants; seizures possible with concurrent use with paroxetine
Dosage Forms Injection: 500 mg, 2.5 g, 5 g
(Continued)

Methohexital *(Continued)*

Specific References

Lerman B, Yoshida D, and Levitt MA, "A Prospective Evaluation of the Safety and Efficacy of Methohexital in the Emergency Department," *Am J Emerg Med*, 1996, 14:351-54.

Methoin *see* Mephenytoin *on page 369*

Methsuximide *(meth SUKS i mide)*

U.S. Brand Names Celontin®

Therapeutic Category Anticonvulsant

Impairment Potential Yes

Use Control of absence (petit mal) seizures; useful adjunct in refractory, partial complex (psychomotor) seizures

Usual Dosage Oral:

Children: Initial: 10-15 mg/kg/day in 3-4 divided doses; increase weekly up to maximum of 30 mg/kg/day

Adults: 300 mg/day for the first week; may increase by 300 mg/day at weekly intervals up to 1.2 g/day in 2-4 divided doses/day

Mechanism of Action Increases the seizure threshold and suppresses paroxysmal spike-and-wave pattern in absence seizures; depresses nerve transmission in the motor cortex of the brain

Pharmacodynamics/kinetics

Absorption: Rapidly and completely

Metabolism: Rapidly demethylated in the liver to N-desmethylmethsuximide (active metabolite)

Half-life: 2-4 hours; N-desmethylmethsuximide half-life may be 28-57 hours

Time to peak serum concentration: Within 1-4 hours

Signs and Symptoms of Acute Intoxication Dizziness, ataxia, hiccups, insomnia, dysarthria, stupor, relapsing coma, leukopenia; neutropenia; agranulocytosis; granulocytopenia

When to Transport to Hospital Transport any patient with mental status changes

Warnings/Precautions Use with caution in patients with hepatic or renal disease; avoid abrupt withdrawal of methsuximide

Adverse Reactions

>10%:

Central nervous system: Ataxia, dizziness, drowsiness, headache

Dermatologic: Stevens-Johnson syndrome

Gastrointestinal: Anorexia, nausea, vomiting, weight loss

Miscellaneous: Hiccups, SLE syndrome

1% to 10%:

Central nervous system: Aggressiveness, mental depression, nightmares, fatigue

Neuromuscular & skeletal: Weakness

Test Interactions Increases alkaline phosphatase (S); decreases calcium (S)

Reference Range

Therapeutic (normethsuximide): 10-40 µg/mL (SI: 53-212 µmol/L)

Toxic: >40 µg/mL (SI: >212 µmol/L); N-desmethylmethsuximide levels >150 µg/mL (SI: >738 µmol/L) associated with coma

Dosage Forms Capsule: 150 mg, 300 mg

Specific References

Karch SB, "Methsuximide Overdose: Delayed Onset of Profound Coma," *JAMA*, 1973, 223(13):1463-5.

Methyl Acetone *see* Methyl Ethyl Ketone *on page 396*

Methyl Alcohol *see* Methanol *on page 386*

Methyl Benzene *see* Toluene *on page 586*
Methylbenzoylecgonine Hydrochloride *see* Cocaine *on page 160*

Methyl Bromide

Synonyms Bercema; Bromomethane; Monobromomethane
UN Number 1062
U.S. Brand Names Embafume®; Terabol®
Use Degreasing wool, extracting oils, insect fumigant, fire extinguishers
Mechanism of Toxic Action Intense vesicant (blister agent)
Toxicodynamics/kinetics
  Absorption: By inhalation or through the skin
  Metabolism: Hepatic, metabolites to methanol and bromide ion
  Half-life: Probably <1 hour
Signs and Symptoms of Acute Intoxication Dermal burns, myoclonus, acetone breath, coma, seizures, difficulty in focusing, hyperthermia, dyspnea, dizziness, hyposmia, drowsiness, headache, nausea, vomiting, anorexia, distal neuritis, loss of ankle reflexes
When to Transport to Hospital Transport any symptomatic patient or patients with a burn
Overdosage/Treatment Decontamination: Basic poison management; **do not** induce vomiting; dilute with 4-8 oz of milk or water. For inhalation, give 100% humidified oxygen.
Adverse Reactions
  Cardiovascular: Myocardial irritability, Reye's-like syndrome
  Central nervous system: CNS depression, extrapyramidal signs, cerebellar ataxia, headache, confusion, seizures, psychosis, amnesia
  Hepatic: Liver injury, hepatomegaly
  Neuromuscular & skeletal: Tremors
  Ocular: Blurred vision, diplopia, mydriasis
  Renal: Nephritis, oliguria, albuminuria
  Respiratory: Pulmonary edema, pulmonary hemorrhage
  Miscellaneous: Potentially carcinogenic
Reference Range Toxicity may occur at serum bromine levels >24 µg/mL
Additional Information Permanent neurological sequelae include depression, paralysis, ataxia, myoclonus; colorless, odorless gas; burning taste; readily penetrates leather
  TLV-TWA: 5 ppm
  IDLH: 2000 ppm
  PEL-TWA: 5 ppm
Specific References
  Michalodimitrakis MN, Tsatsakis AM, Christakis-Hampsas MG, et al, "Death Following Intentional Methyl Bromide Poisoning: Toxicological Data and Literature Review," *Vet Hum Toxicol*, 1996, 39(1):30-4.

Methyl Chloride *see* Chloromethane *on page 130*
Methyl Chloroform *see* Trichloroethane *on page 594*
Methyl Cyanide *see* Acetonitrile *on page 26*

Methyldopa (meth il DOE pa)

U.S. Brand Names Aldomet®; Dopamet®; Dopegyt®; Emdopa®; Hypolag®; Medomet®; Mopatil®; Novomedopa®
Canadian Brand Names Apo-Methyldopa®; Dopamet®; Medimet®; Novo-Medopa®; Nu-Medopa®
Therapeutic Category Alpha-Adrenergic Blocking Agent
Impairment Potential Yes
Use Management of moderate to severe hypertension
(Continued)

Methyldopa *(Continued)*

Usual Dosage

Children:

Oral: Initial: 10 mg/kg/day in 2-4 divided doses; increase every 2 days as needed to maximum dose of 65 mg/kg/day; do not exceed 3 g/day

I.V.: 5-10 mg/kg/dose every 6-8 hours up to a total dose of 65 mg/kg/24 hours or 3 g/24 hours

Adults:

Oral: Initial: 250 mg 2-3 times/day; increase every 2 days as needed; usual dose 1-1.5 g/day in 2-4 divided doses; maximum dose: 3 g/day

I.V.: 250-1000 mg every 6-8 hours; maximum dose: 1 g every 6 hours

Mechanism of Action Stimulation of alpha-adrenergic receptors by a false transmitter that results in a decreased sympathetic outflow to the heart, kidneys and peripheral vasculature (similar to clonidine)

Pharmacodynamics/kinetics

Onset of action: Oral, parenteral: Peak hypotensive effects occur within 3-6 hours

Duration: Variable: Oral: 12-24 hours

Absorption: From gastrointestinal tract is variable but averages ~50%

Metabolism: Intestinally and in the liver

Half-life: 75-80 minutes

Signs and Symptoms of Acute Intoxication Hypotension, hiccups, encephalopathy, photosensitivity, A-V block, hyperprolactinemia, gynecomastia, hyperthermia, ejaculatory disturbances, hypertension, dementia, depression, delirium, memory loss, lichenoid eruptions, galactorrhea, parotid pain, eczema, dermatitis, colitis, cognitive dysfunction, circulatory collapse, cholestatic jaundice, sedation, Parkinson's-like symptoms, bradycardia, dizziness, constipation or diarrhea, flatus, nausea, vomiting, hypothermia, CNS depression, leukopenia; neutropenia; agranulocytosis; granulocytopenia; alopecia, impotence, urine discoloration (black), urine discoloration (brown), urine discoloration (red), urine discoloration (red-brown)

When to Transport to Hospital Transport any symptomatic patient

Warnings/Precautions May rarely produce hemolytic anemia and liver disorders; perform periodic CBCs; sedation usually transient may occur during initial therapy or whenever the dose is increased. Use with caution in patients with previous liver disease or dysfunction, the active metabolites of methyldopa accumulate in uremia. Patients with impaired renal function may respond to smaller doses. Elderly patients may experience syncope (avoid by giving smaller doses). Tolerance may occur usually between the second and third month of therapy. Adding a diuretic or increasing the dosage of methyldopa frequently restores blood pressure control.

Adverse Reactions

>10%: Cardiovascular: Peripheral edema

1% to 10%:

Central nervous system: Drug fever, mental depression, anxiety, nightmares, drowsiness, headache

Gastrointestinal: Xerostomia

Test Interactions Methyldopa interferes with the following laboratory tests: urinary uric acid, serum creatinine (alkaline picrate method), AST (colorimetric method), and urinary catecholamines (falsely high levels)

Reference Range

Therapeutic: 1-5 µg/mL (SI: 4.7-23.7 µmol/L)

Toxic: >7 µg/mL (SI: >33.0 µmol/L)

Drug Interactions Iron supplements can interact and cause a significant **increase** in blood pressure; methyldopa administration with lithium may cause increased lithium toxicity

Dosage Forms
Injection, as methyldopate hydrochloride: 50 mg/mL (5 mL, 10 mL)
Suspension, oral: 250 mg/5 mL (5 mL, 473 mL)
Tablet: 125 mg, 250 mg, 500 mg

Specific References
Shnaps Y, Almog S. Halkin H, et al, "Methyldopa Poisoning," *J Toxicol Clin Toxicol*, 1982, 19(5):501-3.

Methyldopa and Chlorothiazide see Chlorothiazide and Methyldopa on page 132

Methyldopa and Hydrochlorothiazide
(meth il DOE pa & hye droe klor oh THYE a zide)
Synonyms Hydrochlorothiazide and Methyldopa
U.S. Brand Names Aldoril®
Canadian Brand Names Aldoril®-15; Aldoril®-25; Apo®-Methazide; Novo-Doparil®; PMS-Dopazide®
Therapeutic Category Antihypertensive, Combination
Impairment Potential Yes
Dosage Forms Tablet:
15: Methyldopa 250 mg and hydrochlorothiazide 15 mg
25: Methyldopa 250 mg and hydrochlorothiazide 25 mg
D50: Methyldopa 500 mg and hydrochlorothiazide 50 mg

Methylene Chloride
Synonyms Dichloromethane; Freon 30; Methane Dichloride
UN Number 1593
Commonly Found In Paint and varnish removers, fire extinguishers, and fumigants
Mechanism of Toxic Action Solvent-induced central nervous system depression/carbon monoxide effects
Toxicodynamics/kinetics
Absorption: Inhalation (70% to 75%), oral (98% within 20 minutes), and dermal
Metabolism: Converted hepatically to carbon monoxide (30%) and carbon dioxide (70%)
Half-life: 40 minutes
Elimination: Primarily pulmonary (carbon monoxide/carbon dioxide)
Signs and Symptoms of Acute Intoxication Eye irritation, skin irritation, dyspnea, encephalopathy, dermal burns, lightheadedness, dizziness, tremor
When to Transport to Hospital Transport any symptomatic inhalation exposure or any ingestion
Overdosage/Treatment
Decontamination: Basic poison management; induce vomiting only in large ingestions
Supportive therapy: 100% humidified oxygen; hyperbaric oxygen has been advocated for patients with neurological abnormalities
Adverse Reactions
Central nervous system: Anesthesia, memory disturbance, chest pain
Renal: Tubular necrosis (acute)
Miscellaneous: Multiple chemical sensitivity syndrome
Reference Range Blood levels of 2 mg/L correlate with exposure of 200 ppm; carboxyhemoglobin levels usually in the range of 8% to 20%
Additional Information Colorless fluid, pleasant odor; not flammable nor explosive
TLV-TWA: 50 ppm
IDLH: 5000 ppm
PEL-TWA: 500 ppm
(Continued)

Methylene Chloride *(Continued)*

Atmospheric half-life: 100-500 days

Mean concentrations in drinking water: Usually <1 mcg/L

Odor threshold (sweet): Water: 9.1 ppm; air: 160-620 ppm

Minimum lethal oral dose: 0.5-5.0 mL/kg

Specific References

Leikin JB, Kaufman D, Lipscomb JW, et al, "Methylene Chloride: Report of Five Exposures and Two Deaths," *Am J Emerg Med*, 1990, 8(6):534-7.

Methylenedioxymethamphetamine *see* Methamphetamines, Urine *on page 384*

Methyl Ethyl Ketone

Synonyms 2-Butanone; Ethyl Methyl Ketone; MEK; Methyl Acetone; 2-Oxobutane

UN Number 1193; 1232

U.S. Brand Names Meetco®

Use In production of drugs of abuse; used as a solvent for coatings, adhesives, magnetic tapes, printing inks, paint remover, vinyl films, polystyrene, polyurethane; also used in manufacture of aluminum foil and synthetic leather

Mechanism of Toxic Action Mucosal irritant and central nervous system depressant

Toxicodynamics/kinetics

Absorption: Inhalation: 41% to 56%

Metabolism: Hepatic

Half-life: 49-96 minutes

Elimination: Lungs

When to Transport to Hospital Transport any symptomatic patient

Adverse Reactions

Cardiovascular: Hypotension, tachycardia

Central nervous system: Headache at 300 ppm; coma, dizziness, fatigue, panic attacks

Dermatologic: Urticaria, immunologic contact urticaria

Endocrine & metabolic: Metabolic acidosis, hyperglycemia

Hematologic: Methemoglobinemia

Gastrointestinal: Nausea

Neuromuscular & skeletal: Paresthesia

Ocular: Eye irritant at 200 ppm; can cause conjunctival irritation, mydriasis

Respiratory: Irritant at 100 ppm; hyperventilation

Reference Range Plasma 2-butanone level of 95 mg/100 mL consistent with coma in an oral ingestion

Additional Information Colorless liquid with acetone odor

Odor threshold: <10 ppm

OSHA-PEL: 200 ppm

OSHA-STEL: 300 ppm

BEI: 2 mg MEK/L

Specific References

Varigos GA and Nurse DS, "Contact Urticaria From Methyl Ethyl Ketone," *Contact Dermatitis*, 1986, 15(4):259-60.

Methyl Glycol *see* Propylene Glycol *on page 513*

Methyl Hydride *see* Methane *on page 385*

Methylmorphine *see* Codeine *on page 164*

3-Methyl-N,N-Diethylbenzamide *see* Diethyltoluamide *on page 197*

Methylphenidate (meth il FEN i date)

Related Information
Controlled Substances - Uses and Effects *on page 741*

U.S. Brand Names Ritalin®; Ritalin-SR®; Rubifen

Canadian Brand Names PMS-Methylphenidate®

Therapeutic Category Central Nervous System Stimulant, Nonamphetamine

Abuse Potential Yes

Impairment Potential Yes

Use Treatment of attention deficit disorder and symptomatic management of narcolepsy; many unlabeled uses

Usual Dosage Oral:
Children ≥6 years: Attention deficit disorder: Initial: 0.3 mg/kg/dose or 2.5-5 mg/dose given before breakfast and lunch; increase by 0.1 mg/kg/dose or by 5-10 mg/day at weekly intervals; usual dose: 0.5-1 mg/kg/day; maximum dose: 2 mg/kg/day or 60 mg/day
Adults: Narcolepsy: 10 mg 2-3 times/day, up to 60 mg/day

Discontinue periodically to re-evaluate or if no improvement occurs within 1 month

Mechanism of Action Blocks the reuptake mechanism of dopaminergic neurons, appears to act at the cerebral cortex and subcortical structures

Pharmacodynamics/kinetics
Immediate release tablet:
Peak cerebral stimulation effect: Within 2 hours
Duration: 3-6 hours
Sustained release tablet:
Peak effect: Within 4-7 hours
Duration: 8 hours
Absorption: Slow and incomplete from gastrointestinal tract
Metabolism: In liver via hydroxylation to ritolinic acid
Half-life: Oral: 2-4 hours
Time to peak: 1-3 hours postingestion

Signs and Symptoms of Acute Intoxication Tachypnea, seizures, agitation, insomnia, coma, mydriasis

When to Transport to Hospital Transport any pediatric (<6 years of age) ingestion over 1 mg/kg or any symptomatic patient (especially agitated patient)

Warnings/Precautions Use with caution in patients with hypertension, seizures; has high potential for abuse; use with caution in patients with glaucoma, motor tics, Tourette's syndrome, patients with marked agitation, tension, and anxiety

Adverse Reactions
>10%:
Cardiovascular: Tachycardia
Central nervous system: Nervousness, insomnia
Gastrointestinal: Anorexia
1% to 10%:
Central nervous system: Dizziness, drowsiness
Gastrointestinal: Stomach pain
Miscellaneous: Hypersensitivity reactions

Test Interactions False-positives by immunoassay can be seen with ranitidine, phenylpropanolamine, brompheniramine, chlorpromazine, fluspirilene or pipothiazine coingestion

Reference Range Therapeutic: 5-40 ng/mL

Drug Interactions
Increased effect with MAO inhibitors; increased effect of guanethidine, bretylium
(Continued)

Methylphenidate *(Continued)*

Increased serum concentrations of tricyclic antidepressants, warfarin, phenytoin, phenobarbital and primidone

Dosage Forms

Tablet: 5 mg, 10 mg, 20 mg

Tablet, sustained release: 20 mg

Additional Information Chewing tablets instead of swallowing can lead to decreased efficacy and increase in side effects

Specific References

Corrigall R and Ford T, "Methylphenidate Euphoria," *J Am Acad Child Adolesc Psychiatr*, 1996, 35:1421.

Methylphenobarbital *see* Mephobarbital *on page 370*

Methylphenylethylhydantoin *see* Mephenytoin *on page 369*

Methyltestosterone (meth il tes TOS te rone)

U.S. Brand Names Android®; Metandren®; Oreton® Methyl; Testred®; Virilon®

Therapeutic Category Androgen

Abuse Potential Yes

Use

Male: Hypogonadism; delayed puberty; impotence and climacteric symptoms

Female: Palliative treatment of metastatic breast cancer; postpartum breast pain and/or engorgement

Usual Dosage Adults (buccal absorption produces twice the androgenic activity of oral tablets):

Male:

Oral: 10-40 mg/day

Buccal: 5-25 mg/day

Female:

Breast pain/engorgement:

Oral: 80 mg/day for 3-5 days

Buccal: 40 mg/day for 3-5 days

Breast cancer:

Oral: 50-200 mg/day

Buccal: 25-100 mg/day

Mechanism of Action Stimulates receptors in organs and tissues to promote growth and development of male sex organs and maintains secondary sex characteristics in androgen-deficient males

Pharmacodynamics/kinetics

Absorption: From GI tract and oral mucosa

Metabolism: Hepatic

Half-life: 2.5-3 hours

Elimination: In urine

When to Transport to Hospital Transport symptomatic patients

Warnings/Precautions Use with extreme caution in patients with liver, epilepsy, migraine headaches, or kidney disease or serious heart disease; may accelerate bone maturation without producing compensatory gain in linear growth

Adverse Reactions

>10%:

Cardiovascular: Edema

Males: Virilism, priapism

Females: Virilism, menstrual problems (amenorrhea), breast soreness

Dermatologic: Acne

1% to 10%:

Males: Prostatic hypertrophy, prostatic carcinoma, impotence, testicular

Females: Hirsutism (increase in pubic hair growth) atrophy
Gastrointestinal: GI irritation, nausea, vomiting
Hepatic: Hepatic dysfunction
Reference Range Peak serum concentrations following a 10 mg ingestion: 24-39 ng/mL
Drug Interactions Increased effect: Oral anticoagulant effect or insulin requirements may be increased
Dosage Forms
Capsule: 10 mg
Tablet: 10 mg, 25 mg
Tablet, buccal: 5 mg, 10 mg
Specific References
Akhter J, Hyder S, and Ahmed, "Cerebrovascular Accident Associated With Anabolic Steroid Use in a Young Man," *Neurology*, 1994, 44:2405-6.

Methyltoluene *see* Xylene *on page 617*

Methyprylon (meth i PRYE lon)
Related Information
Controlled Substances - Uses and Effects *on page 741*
U.S. Brand Names Noludar®
Therapeutic Category Hypnotic, Nonbarbiturate
Abuse Potential Yes
Impairment Potential Yes
Usual Dosage
Usual daily dose: 200-400 mg at night
Minimum lethal dose: 6 g
Mechanism of Action Similar to glutethimide; it is a piperidineclione which has sedative/hypnotic properties
Pharmacodynamics/kinetics
Metabolism: Hepatic
Half-life: 4-16 hours (in overdose: 50 hours)
Signs and Symptoms of Acute Intoxication Leukopenia or neutropenia (agranulocytosis, granulocytopenia); hypothermia, gaze nystagmus
When to Transport to Hospital Transport any pediatric exposure or any symptomatic patient
Adverse Reactions
Cardiovascular: Tachycardia, hypotension, sinus tachycardia
Central nervous system: Headache, coma, dementia, seizures, hypothermia, hyperthermia
Gastrointestinal: Nausea, vomiting, diarrhea
Hematologic: Thrombocytopenia, neutropenia, porphyria, porphyrinogenic
Hepatic: Jaundice, liver function tests (mild elevation)
Neuromuscular & skeletal: Hyperreflexia
Respiratory: Respiratory failure, apnea, pulmonary edema
Reference Range Therapeutic: 1 mg/dL; respiratory arrest can occur at plasma levels exceeding 6 mg/dL
Drug Interactions Ethanol potentiates sedative nature
Dosage Forms
Capsule: 300 mg
Tablet: 50 mg, 200 mg
Specific References
Mandelbaum JM and Simon NM, "Severe Methyprylon Intoxication Treated by Hemodialysis," *JAMA*, 1971, 216(1):139-40.

Methysergide (meth i SER jide)
Related Information
Ergotamine on page 224
U.S. Brand Names Déséril®; Désernil-Sandoz®; Deserril®; Sansert®
Therapeutic Category Ergot Alkaloid
Use Prophylaxis of vascular headache; has been used to treat profuse diarrhea due to carcinoid syndrome
Usual Dosage Adults: Oral: 4-8 mg/day with meals; if no improvement is noted after 3 weeks, drug is unlikely to be beneficial; must not be given continuously for longer than 6 months, and a drug-free interval of 3-4 weeks must follow each 6-month course
Mechanism of Action Ergotamine congener, however actions appear to differ; methysergide has minimal ergotamine-like oxytocic or vasoconstrictive properties, and has significantly greater serotonin-like properties in the brainstem but is a serotonin antagonist peripherally
Pharmacodynamics/kinetics
Metabolism: Undergoes liver metabolism
Half-life, serum: 90 minutes
Signs and Symptoms of Acute Intoxication Hyperactivity, spasms in limbs, impaired mental function, impaired circulation
When to Transport to Hospital Transport any pediatric exposure or any symptomatic patient
Warnings/Precautions Patients receiving long-term therapy may develop retroperitoneal fibrosis, pleuropulmonary fibrosis and fibrotic thickening of the cardiac valves. Fibrosis occurs rarely when therapy is interrupted for 3-4 weeks every 6 months. Use caution in patients with impairment of renal of hepatic function; some products may contain tartrazine. Use with caution in patients with peptic ulcer disease.
Adverse Reactions
>10%:
Cardiovascular: Postural hypotension, peripheral ischemia
Central nervous system: Insomnia
Gastrointestinal: Nausea, vomiting, abdominal pain, diarrhea
1% to 10%:
Cardiovascular: Peripheral edema, tachycardia, bradycardia
Dermatologic: Rash
Gastrointestinal: Heartburn
Drug Interactions Arterial occlusion can develop with simultaneous administration of ergotamine with methysergide; arterial vasoconstriction can also occur with concomitant administration of propranolol
Dosage Forms Tablet: 2 mg
Additional Information Every patient on methysergide should have an annual I.V. pyelogram
Specific References
Vanghan-Lane T, "Gangrene Induced by Methysergide and Ergotamine: A Case Report," *J Bone Joint Surg*, 1979, 61B:213.

Meticorten® *see* Prednisone *on page 497*

Metoprolol (me toe PROE lole)
U.S. Brand Names Beloc®; Beprolo®; Betaloc®; Lopressor®; Metoros®; Prelis®; Selokeen®; Selo-Zok®; Toprol XL®
Canadian Brand Names Apo-Metoprolol® (Type L); Betaloc®; Betaloc Durules®; Novo-Metoprolol®; Nu-Metop®
Therapeutic Category Beta-Adrenergic Blocker

Use Treatment of hypertension and angina pectoris; prevention of myocardial infarction; selective inhibitor of beta$_1$-adrenergic receptors; migraine prophylaxis

Usual Dosage Safety and efficacy in children have not been established

Children: Oral: 1-5 mg/kg/24 hours divided twice daily; allow 3 days between dose adjustments

Adults:

Oral: 100-450 mg/day in 2-3 divided doses, begin with 50 mg twice daily and increase doses at weekly intervals to desired effect

Sustained release: 50-100 mg once daily; maximum: 400 mg/day

I.V.: 5 mg every 2 minutes for 3 doses in early treatment of myocardial infarction; thereafter give 50 mg orally every 6 hours 15 minutes after last I.V. dose and continue for 48 hours; then administer a maintenance dose of 100 mg twice daily

Mechanism of Action Selective inhibitor of beta$_1$-adrenergic receptors; competitively blocks beta$_1$-receptors, with little or no effect on beta$_2$-receptors at doses <100 mg

Pharmacodynamics/kinetics

Onset of action: Oral: Peak antihypertensive effects occur within 1.5-4 hours

Duration: 10-20 hours

Absorption: Rapid and completely from gastrointestinal tract (90%)

Distribution: Widely distributed to body tissues; highest concentrations in heart, liver, lungs, and saliva; crosses the blood-brain barrier; distributes into breast milk, lipid solubility is moderate

Metabolism: Extensively metabolized in the liver

Half-life: 3-4 hours

Time to peak serum concentration: 1½ to 4 hours

Signs and Symptoms of Acute Intoxication Bradycardia, hypotension, ataxia, seizures, insomnia, impotence, hyperreflexia, confusion, night terrors, heart failure, A-V block, asystole, cyanosis, wheezing, apnea, respiratory arrest, metabolic acidosis

When to Transport to Hospital Transport any symptomatic patient

Warnings/Precautions Use with caution in patients with inadequate myocardial function; acute withdrawal may exacerbate symptoms; use with caution in patients undergoing anesthesia, bronchospastic disease, hyperthyroidism, and impaired hepatic function

Adverse Reactions

>10%:

Central nervous system: Mental depression, fatigue, dizziness

Neuromuscular & skeletal: Weakness

1% to 10%:

Cardiovascular: Bradycardia, arrhythmia, reduced peripheral circulation

Gastrointestinal: Heartburn

Respiratory: Wheezing

Reference Range Therapeutic: 20-340 ng/mL; survival has occurred with levels as high as 7,140 ng/mL

Drug Interactions Diuretics or other hypotensive drugs may increase the hypotensive effect of metoprolol; oral contraceptives may increase plasma metoprolol levels; cimetidine reduces clearance of metoprolol; cardiogenic shock and complete heart block has occurred with concomitant use of verapamil and metoprolol (oral) in an elderly patient

Dosage Forms

Injection: 1 mg/mL (5 mL)

Tablet: 50 mg, 100 mg

Tablet, sustained release: 50 mg, 100 mg, 200 mg

(Continued)

Metoprolol *(Continued)*

Specific References

Hoeper MM and Boeker KH, "Overdose of Metoprolol Treated With Enoximone," *N Engl J Med*, 1996, 335:1538.

Metoros® *see Metoprolol on page 400*

Metreton® *see Prednisolone on page 495*

Mevacor® *see Lovastatin on page 354*

Mevinacor® *see Lovastatin on page 354*

Mevinolin *see Lovastatin on page 354*

Mevlor *see Lovastatin on page 354*

MG *see Mustard Gas on page 414*

MGK Diethyltoluamide *see Diethyltoluamide on page 197*

Micronase® *see Glyburide on page 267*

Mictrin® *see Hydrochlorothiazide on page 291*

Midazol *see Midazolam on this page*

Midazolam *(MID aye zoe lam)*

Related Information

Controlled Substances - Uses and Effects *on page 741*

Synonyms Midazol

U.S. Brand Names Dormicum®; Hypnovel®; Versed®

Therapeutic Category Benzodiazepine

Abuse Potential Yes

Impairment Potential Yes

Use Preoperative sedation and provide conscious sedation prior to diagnostic or radiographic procedures

Investigational: Status epilepticus

Usual Dosage The dose of midazolam needs to be individualized based on the patient's age, underlying diseases, and concurrent medications. Personnel and equipment needed for standard respiratory resuscitation should be immediately available during midazolam administration.

Children:

Preoperative sedation:

I.M.: 0.07-0.08 mg/kg 30-60 minutes presurgery

I.V.: 0.035 mg/kg/dose, repeat over several minutes as required to achieve the desired sedative effect up to a total dose of 0.1-0.2 mg/kg

Rectal: 0.3 mg/kg diluted in 5 mL of saline

Adjunct use in anesthesia: Intranasal: 0.2-0.3 mg/kg

Conscious sedation during mechanical ventilation: I.V.: Loading dose: 0.05-0.2 mg/kg then follow with initial continuous infusion: 1-2 mcg/kg/minute; titrate to the desired effect; usual range: 0.4-6 mcg/kg/minute

Conscious sedation for procedures:

Oral, Intranasal: 0.2-0.4 mg/kg (maximum: 15 mg) 30-45 minutes before the procedure

I.V.: 0.05 mg/kg 3 minutes before procedure

Adolescents >12 years: I.V.: 0.5 mg every 3-4 minutes until effect achieved

Adults:

Preoperative sedation: I.M.: 0.07-0.08 mg/kg 30-60 minutes presurgery; usual dose: 5 mg

Conscious sedation: I.V.: Initial: 0.5-2 mg slow I.V. over at least 2 minutes; slowly titrate to effect by repeating doses every 2-3 minutes if needed; usual total dose: 2.5-5 mg; use decreased doses in elderly; status epilepticus: I.M.: 5 mg

Healthy Adults <60 years: Some patients respond to doses as low as 1 mg; no more than 2.5 mg should be administered over a period of 2 minutes. Additional doses of midazolam may be administered after a 2-minute waiting period and evaluation of sedation after each dose increment. A total dose >5 mg is generally not needed. If narcotics or other CNS depressants are administered concomitantly, the midazolam dose should be reduced by 30%.

Mechanism of Action A short-acting triazolobenzodiazepine which depresses all levels of the CNS, including the limbic and reticular formation, probably through the increased action of gamma-aminobutyric acid (GABA), which is a major inhibitory neurotransmitter in the brain

Pharmacodynamics/kinetics

Onset of action (sedation):

I.M.: Within 15 minutes

I.V.: Within 1-5 minutes

Peak effect: I.M.: 30-60 minutes

Duration: I.M.: Mean: 2 hours, up to 6 hours

Metabolism: Extensive in the liver (microsomally)

Half-life: 1-4 hours; increased half-life with cirrhosis, CHF, obesity, elderly

Time to peak serum concentration: I.M.: 15-60 minutes

Signs and Symptoms of Acute Intoxication Apnea, cough, chills, encephalopathy, hypothermia, hyperactivity, euphoria, dyspnea, respiratory depression, seizures, hypotension, coma, stupor, confusion, cardiovascular arrest, gaze nystagmus

When to Transport to Hospital Transport any suspected exposure

Warnings/Precautions Midazolam may cause respiratory depression/arrest; deaths and hypoxic encephalopathy have resulted when these were not promptly recognized and treated appropriately. The danger of apnea or underventilation is greater in the elderly; the peak effect may take longer; reduce dosage increments and slow the rate of injection. Impaired metabolism with cirrhosis. Use with caution in patients with congestive heart failure, renal impairment, pulmonary disease, hepatic dysfunction.

Adverse Reactions

>10%:

Local: Pain and local reactions at injection site (severity less than diazepam)

Miscellaneous: Hiccups

1% to 10%:

Cardiovascular: Cardiac arrest, hypotension, bradycardia

Central nervous system: Drowsiness, ataxia, amnesia, dizziness, paradoxical excitement, sedation, headache

Gastrointestinal: Nausea, vomiting

Ocular: Blurred vision, diplopia

Respiratory: Respiratory depression, apnea, laryngospasm, bronchospasm

Miscellaneous: Physical and psychological dependence with prolonged use

Drug Interactions CNS depressants, leads to increased sedation and apnea; doses of anesthetic agents should be reduced when used in conjunction with midazolam; cimetidine may increase midazolam serum concentrations; theophylline may antagonize the sedative effects of midazolam; rifampin reduces the plasma concentration of oral midazolam by >90%; carbamazepine and phenytoin may increase hepatic metabolism of midazolam; grapefruit juice delays absorption and increases bioavailability of oral midazolam by inhibiting midazolam metabolism

Dosage Forms Injection: 1 mg/mL (2 mL, 5 mL, 10 mL); 5 mg/mL (1 mL, 2 mL, 5 mL, 10 mL)

Additional Information Each mL contains 0.14 mEq of sodium

(Continued)

Midazolam *(Continued)*

Specific References

Ziegler G, Ludwig L, and Klotz U, "Relationships Between Plasma Levels and Psychological Effects of Benzodiazepines," *Pharmacopsychiatria*, 1983, 16(3):71-6.

Midchlor® *see* Acetaminophen, Isometheptene, and Dichloralphenazone *on page 24*

Midol® 200 [OTC] *see* Ibuprofen *on page 308*

Midol® PM [OTC] *see* Acetaminophen and Diphenhydramine *on page 22*

Midrin® *see* Acetaminophen, Isometheptene, and Dichloralphenazone *on page 24*

Migergot® *see* Ergotamine *on page 224*

Migratine® *see* Acetaminophen, Isometheptene, and Dichloralphenazone *on page 24*

Mikelan® *see* Carteolol *on page 115*

Miles Nervine® Caplets [OTC] *see* Diphenhydramine *on page 205*

Milontin® *see* Phensuximide *on page 477*

MIL-T-5624-L-Amd 1 *see* Jet Fuel-4 *on page 325*

Miltown® *see* Meprobamate *on page 371*

Mindiab® *see* Glipizide *on page 265*

Mineral Naphtha *see* Benzene *on page 69*

Minidiab® *see* Glipizide *on page 265*

Minipress® *see* Prazosin *on page 494*

Minitran® *see* Nitroglycerin *on page 437*

Minodiab® *see* Glipizide *on page 265*

Minodyl® *see* Minoxidil *on this page*

Minoxidil *(mi NOKS i dil)*

U.S. Brand Names Loniten®; Minodyl®; Rogaine® for Men [OTC]; Rogaine® for Women [OTC]

Therapeutic Category Topical Skin Product; Vasodilator

Use Management of severe hypertension (usually in combination with a diuretic and beta-blocker); treatment of male pattern baldness (alopecia androgenetica)

Usual Dosage

Children <12 years: Hypertension: Oral: Initial: 0.1-0.2 mg/kg once daily; maximum: 5 mg/day; increase gradually every 3 days; usual dosage: 0.25-1 mg/kg/day in 1-2 divided doses; maximum: 50 mg/day

Children >12 years and Adults:

Hypertension: Oral: Initial: 5 mg once daily, increase gradually every 3 days; usual dose: 10-40 mg/day in 1-2 divided doses; maximum: 100 mg/day

Alopecia: Topical: Apply twice daily; 4 months of therapy may be necessary for hair growth

Elderly: Initial: 2.5 mg once daily; increase gradually

Mechanism of Action Produces vasodilation by directly relaxing arteriolar smooth muscle, with little effect on veins; effects may be mediated by cyclic AMP; stimulation of hair growth is secondary to vasodilation, increased cutaneous blood flow and stimulation of resting hair follicles

Pharmacodynamics/kinetics

Onset of hypotensive effect: Oral: Within 30 minutes

Peak effect: Within 2-8 hours

Duration: Up to 2-5 days

Metabolism: In the liver

Half-life: Adults: 3.5-4.2 hours

Signs and Symptoms of Acute Intoxication Hypotension, tachycardia, headache, nausea, dizziness, weakness syncope, warm flushed skin and palpitations; lethargy and ataxia may occur in children

When to Transport to Hospital Transport any symptomatic patient

Overdosage/Treatment Hypotension usually responds to I.V. fluids, Trendelenburg positioning or vasoconstrictor; treatment is primarily supportive and symptomatic

Warnings/Precautions Use with caution in patients with pulmonary hypertension, significant renal failure, or congestive heart failure; use with caution in patients with coronary artery disease or recent myocardial infarction; renal failure or dialysis patients may require smaller doses; usually used with a beta-blocker (to treat minoxidil-induced tachycardia) and a diuretic (for treatment of water retention/edema); may take 1-6 months for hypertrichosis to totally reverse after minoxidil therapy is discontinued.

Adverse Reactions

>10%:

 Cardiovascular: EKG changes, tachycardia, congestive heart failure, edema
 Dermatologic: Hypertrichosis (commonly occurs within 1-2 months of therapy)

 1% to 10%: Endocrine & metabolic: Fluid and electrolyte imbalance

Drug Interactions Increased toxicity:

 Concurrent administration with guanethidine may cause profound orthostatic hypotensive effects

 Additive hypotensive effects with other hypotensive agents or diuretics

Dosage Forms

 Solution, topical: 2% = 20 mg/metered dose (60 mL)
 Tablet: 2.5 mg, 10 mg

Specific References

 Poff SW and Rose SR, "Minoxidil Overdose With ECG Changes: Case Report and Review," *J Emerg Med*, 1992, 10(1):53-7.

Minute-Gel® see Fluoride on page 251

Mirakelblomst see Four-O'Clock on page 260

Mirsol® see Zipeprol on page 620

Mirtazapine (mir TAZ a peen)

Synonyms 6-Azamianserin

U.S. Brand Names Remeron®

Therapeutic Category Antidepressant

Impairment Potential Yes

Use Psychotic depression; presurgical insomnia

 Investigational: Endogenous depression, anxiolytic effects, presurgical insomnia

Usual Dosage Oral:

 Depression: Starting dose 15 mg/day; usual effective dose: 15-60 mg/day; maximum daily dose: 45 mg

 Presurgical:

 Insomnia: 15-30 mg night before surgery
 Anxiety: 15 mg

Mechanism of Action Strong alpha$_2$ antagonist with similar properties to mianserin; a tetracyclic piperazinoazepine that is a presynaptic alpha$_2$-adrenoreceptor antagonist as well as a 5-HT$_2$ and 5-HT$_3$ antagonist thus enhancing noradrenergic and serotonergic neurotransmission; does not inhibit serotonin reuptake

Pharmacodynamics/kinetics

 Protein binding: 85%

 (Continued)

Mirtazapine *(Continued)*

Metabolism: Hepatic demethylation and hydroxylation to less active metabolites

Half-life: 20-40 hours; mean: 21.5 hours

Signs and Symptoms of Acute Intoxication Sedation, coma, little or no cardiac complications, lethargy, disorientation, drowsiness

When to Transport to Hospital Transport any pediatric exposure, any ingestion over 45 mg, or any symptomatic patient

Warnings/Precautions Use with caution in elderly patients; use with caution in patients who are hypersensitive to other antidepressants, who exhibit seizures, mania, renal or liver impairment (33% reduction in hepatic clearance may occur), cardiovascular, gastrointestinal disorders, narrow-angle glaucoma, prostatic hypertrophy or urinary retention

Adverse Reactions

>10%:

Central nervous system: Somnolence

Endocrine & metabolic: Increased cholesterol

Gastrointestinal: Constipation, xerostomia, increased appetite, weight gain

1% to 10%:

Cardiovascular: Hypertension, vasodilatation, peripheral edema, edema

Central nervous system: Dizziness, abnormal dreams, abnormal thoughts, confusion, malaise

Endocrine & metabolic: Increased triglycerides

Gastrointestinal: Vomiting, anorexia, eructation, glossitis, cholecystitis

Genitourinary: Polyuria

Neuromuscular & skeletal: Myalgia, back pain, arthralgia, tremor, weakness

Respiratory: Dyspnea

Miscellaneous: Flu-like symptoms, thirst

Reference Range Following a 20 mg oral dose, peak serum levels: ~100 ng/mL

Drug Interactions Increased psychomotor impairment with diazepam or ethanol

Dosage Forms Tablet: 15 mg, 30 mg

Specific References

Stimmel GL, Dopheide JA, and Stahl SM, "Mirtazapine: An Antidepressant With Noradrenergic and Specific Serotonergic Effects," *Pharmacotherapy*, 1997, 17(1):10-21.

Mitac® *see* Amitraz *on page 39*

Mitidin® *see* Nitrazepam *on page 435*

Mitran® *see* Chlordiazepoxide *on page 124*

Mixtard® *see* Insulin Preparations *on page 314*

MK-421 *see* Enalapril *on page 217*

Moban® *see* Molindone *on next page*

Mobil Oil Cooling System Cleaner *see* Kerosene *on page 325*

Moclobemide *(moe KLOE be mide)*

Synonyms Ro 11-1163

U.S. Brand Names Aurorix®; Manerix®

Therapeutic Category Antidepressant

Use Investigational: Depression; smoking cessation

Usual Dosage Oral:

Depression: Initial: 100 mg 3 times/day immediately following a meal; maximum dose/day: 600 mg; reduce dosage by 30% to 50% in patients with hepatic disease

Smoking cessation: 400 mg/day for 2 months, then, 200 mg/day for 1 month

Mechanism of Action Selective and reversible monoamine oxidase (type A) inhibitor

Pharmacodynamics/kinetics
Peak levels: 1-2 hours
Duration: 16 hours
Protein binding: 50%
Metabolism: Hepatic to several metabolites
Half-life: ~2 hours; 3.2 hours in overdose

Signs and Symptoms of Acute Intoxication Tachycardia, tachypnea, disorientation

When to Transport to Hospital Transport any pediatric patient, any symptomatic patient, or any adult ingestion over 400 mg

Warnings/Precautions Reduce dose in liver disease; use with caution in hypertensive patients; avoid tyramine-rich foods (although this drug does not appear to potentiate pressor effects of tyramine)

Adverse Reactions
>10%:
  Gastrointestinal: Dry mouth
  Miscellaneous: Diaphoresis
<10%:
  Cardiovascular: Hypertension, tachycardia, sinus tachycardia, vasoconstriction
  Central nervous system: Agitation, dizziness, headache, hypomania, insomnia, anxiety
  Dermatologic: Rash, pruritus
  Gastrointestinal: Constipation, nausea, stomach pain
  Hepatic: Cholestasis
  Neuromuscular & skeletal: Tremor
  Ocular: Blurred vision

Reference Range Therapeutic serum range: 0.5-1.5 mg/L; plasma moclobemide levels as high as 62.5 mg/L associated with drowsiness

Drug Interactions Concomitant use with cimetidine can result in elevated moclobemide levels by decreasing moclobemide clearance; moclobemide may potentiate metoprolol-induced orthostatic hypotension; serotonin syndrome with concomitant fluoxetine; moclobemide potentiates effect of ephedrine

Dosage Forms Tablet: 100 mg, 150 mg

Specific References
Iwersen S and Schmold A, "Three Suicide Attempts With Moclobemide," *J Toxicol Clin Toxicol*, 1996, 34:223-5.

Moditen® *see* Fluphenazine *on page 255*

Mogadan® *see* Nitrazepam *on page 435*

Mogas *see* Gasoline *on page 264*

Mole Bean *see* Castor Bean *on page 117*

Molindone (moe LIN done)

U.S. Brand Names Lidone®; Moban®
Therapeutic Category Antipsychotic Agent
Use Management of psychotic disorder
Usual Dosage Oral:
Children:
  3-5 years: 1-2.5 mg/day divided into 4 doses
  5-12 years: 0.5-1 mg/kg/day in 4 divided doses
Adults: 50-75 mg/day increase at 3- to 4-day intervals up to 225 mg/day
Mechanism of Action Mechanism of action mimics that of chlorpromazine; however, it produces more extrapyramidal effects and less sedation than chlorpromazine
(Continued)

Molindone *(Continued)*

Pharmacodynamics/kinetics
Duration of action: 24-36 hours
Absorption: Rapid from gastrointestinal tract
Metabolism: In the liver
Half-life: 90 minutes
Time to peak serum concentration: Within 90 minutes

Signs and Symptoms of Acute Intoxication Deep sleep, extrapyramidal reaction, priapism, gynecomastia, galactorrhea, Parkinson's-like symptoms, leukocytosis, neuroleptic malignant syndrome, rhabdomyolysis; cardiac arrhythmias, myoglobinuria with oliguria renal failure, leukopenia; neutropenia; agranulocytosis; granulocytopenia

When to Transport to Hospital Transport any pediatric (<3 years of age) exposure or any symptomatic patient

Overdosage/Treatment Following initiation of essential overdose management, toxic symptom treatment and supportive treatment should be initiated. Hypotension usually responds to I.V. fluids or Trendelenburg positioning. If unresponsive to these measures, the use of a parenteral inotrope may be required (eg, norepinephrine 0.1-0.2 mcg/kg/minute titrated to response). Seizures commonly respond to lorazepam or diazepam (I.V. 5-10 mg bolus in adults every 15 minutes if needed up to a total of 30 mg; I.V. 0.25-0.4 mg/kg/ dose up to a total of 10 mg in children) or to phenytoin or phenobarbital. Also critical cardiac arrhythmias often respond to I.V. phenytoin (15 mg/kg up to 1 gram), while other antiarrhythmics can be used. Neuroleptics often cause extrapyramidal reaction (eg, dystonic reactions) requiring management with diphenhydramine 1-2 mg/kg (adults) up to a maximum of 50 mg I.M. or I.V. slow push followed by a maintenance dose for 48-72 hours. When these reactions are unresponsive to diphenhydramine, benztropine mesylate I.V. 1-2 mg (adults) may be effective. These agents are generally effective within 2-5 minutes.

Warnings/Precautions Avoid alcoholic beverages; use with caution in patients with cardiovascular disease or seizures

Adverse Reactions
>10%:
Cardiovascular: Orthostatic hypotension
Central nervous system: Akathisia, extrapyramidal effects, persistent tardive dyskinesia
Gastrointestinal: Constipation, xerostomia
Ocular: Blurred vision
Miscellaneous: Diaphoresis (decreased)
1% to 10%:
Central nervous system: Mental depression, altered central temperature regulation
Endocrine & metabolic: Change in menstrual periods, edema of the breasts

Test Interactions May give false-positive result for the EMIT® system for tricyclics antidepressants

Reference Range Antipsychotic range: 27-69 ng/mL; level of 152 ng/mL seen with rhabdomyolysis

Drug Interactions CNS depressants, antihypertensives, anticonvulsants; severe bradykinesia and tremor with paroxetine

Dosage Forms
Concentrate, oral: 20 mg/mL (120 mL)
Tablet: 5 mg, 10 mg, 25 mg, 50 mg, 100 mg

Specific References
Katz SE, "Tardive Dyskinesia Associated With Molindone Treatment," *Am J Psychiatry*, 1990, 147(1):124-5, (letter).

Molipaxin® *see* Trazodone *on page 590*

Mol-Iron® *see* Iron *on page 318*

Monacolin K *see* Lovastatin *on page 354*

Monafed® *see* Guaifenesin *on page 269*

Monafed® DM *see* Guaifenesin and Dextromethorphan *on page 271*

Monobromomethane *see* Methyl Bromide *on page 393*

Monochlorobenzene *see* Chlorobenzene *on page 128*

Monochloromethane *see* Chloromethane *on page 130*

Monocor® *see* Bisoprolol *on page 78*

Monoethylene Glycol *see* Ethylene Glycol *on page 237*

Monohydroxybenzene *see* Phenol *on page 476*

Monosodium Glutamate Food Poisoning

Synonyms Chinese Restaurant Syndrome; Chinese Seasoning; L-Sodium Glutamate; MSG; Sodium Glutamate

Commonly Found In Chinese food, sausage, canned soup, Accent®

Signs and Symptoms of Acute Intoxication Flushing, wheezing, chest pain, angina, burning sensation, tremor, angioedema, headache, paresthesia, syncope; occurs within 30 minutes postingestion and may last for 1-3 hours; minimal gastrointestinal symptoms

When to Transport to Hospital Transport any patient with difficulty breathing

Overdosage/Treatment Supportive therapy: Diphenhydramine may be useful, symptoms are usually self-limited

Additional Information Salty or sweet to taste; soluble in water; used as a flavor enhancer. Intravenous doses can cause hypokalemia or alkalosis; absorption is most rapid in a fasting state. Patients with severe, poorly controlled asthma are predisposed to an adverse reaction. The symptom complex can occur in healthy individuals within 1 hour after ingestion of 3 g of monosodium glutamate on an empty stomach. A typical serving of glutamate-treated food contains <0.5 mg of monosodium glutamate.

Specific References

Allen DH and Baker GJ, "Chinese Restaurant Asthma," *N Engl J Med*, 1981, 305(19):1154-5.

Mopatil® *see* Methyldopa *on page 393*

Morbicid *see* Formaldehyde *on page 259*

Mormon Tea (*Ephedra nevadensis*) *see* Ephedra *on page 219*

Morning Glory

Synonyms Blue Star; Flying Saucers; Heavenly Blue; *Ololiuqui*; Pearly Gates

Scientific Name *Ipomoea purpurea*
Rivea corymbosa

Abuse Potential Yes

Impairment Potential Yes

Usual Dosage 300 seeds contain the equivalent of 200-300 mcg of LSD

Mechanism of Toxic Action Source of lysergic acid amide which is ~10% as potent as lysergic acid diethylamide (LSD)

Signs and Symptoms of Acute Intoxication Diarrhea, anxiety, drowsiness, mydriasis, flushing, depersonalization, hypotension, tachycardia, depression

When to Transport to Hospital Transport any agitated patient or any patient with decreased mental status or psychosis

Adverse Reactions

Cardiovascular: Shock, sinus tachycardia

Central nervous system: CNS depression, memory loss, psychosis, delirium, dysphoria, memory disturbance

(Continued)

Morning Glory *(Continued)*

Ocular: Vision color changes (increased color perception)
Miscellaneous: Synesthesia
Additional Information Often a contaminant in soy bean crops
Specific References
Schultes RE, "Hallucinogens of Plant Origin," *Science*, 1969, 163(864):245-54.

Morphine Sulfate *(MOR feen SUL fate)*

Related Information
Controlled Substances - Uses and Effects *on page 741*
Synonyms MS
U.S. Brand Names Astramorph™ PF; Duramorph®; Epimorph Dolcontin®; MS Contin®; MSIR®; MST®; OMS®; Oramorph SR®; RMS®; Roxanol™; Roxanol SR™; Sevredol®; Statex®
Canadian Brand Names M-Eslon®; MST-Continus®; Epimorph®; Morphine-HP®; MS-IR®; Statex®
Therapeutic Category Analgesic, Narcotic
Abuse Potential Yes
Impairment Potential Yes
Use Relief of moderate to severe acute and chronic pain; pain of myocardial infarction; relieves dyspnea of acute left ventricular failure and pulmonary edema; preanesthetic medication
Usual Dosage Doses should be titrated to appropriate effect; when changing routes of administration in chronically treated patients, please note that oral doses are approximately one-half as effective as parenteral dose

Infants and Children:
  Oral: Tablet and solution (prompt release): 0.2-0.5 mg/kg/dose every 4-6 hours as needed; tablet (controlled release): 0.3-0.6 mg/kg/dose every 12 hours
  I.M., I.V., S.C.: 0.1-0.2 mg/kg/dose every 2-4 hours as needed; usual maximum: 15 mg/dose; may initiate at 0.05 mg/kg/dose
  I.V., S.C. continuous infusion: Sickle cell or cancer pain: 0.025-2 mg/kg/hour; postoperative pain: 0.01-0.04 mg/kg/hour
  Sedation/analgesia for procedures: I.V.: 0.05-0.1 mg/kg 5 minutes before the procedure

Adolescents >12 years: Sedation/analgesia for procedures: I.V.: 3-4 mg and repeat in 5 minutes if necessary

Adults:
  Oral: Prompt release: 10-30 mg every 4 hours as needed; controlled release: 15-30 mg every 8-12 hours
  I.M., I.V., S.C.: 2.5-20 mg/dose every 2-6 hours as needed; usual: 10 mg/dose every 4 hours as needed
  I.V., S.C. continuous infusion: 0.8-10 mg/hour; may increase depending on pain relief/adverse effects; usual range up to 80 mg/hour
  Rectal: 10-20 mg every 4 hours
Mechanism of Action Binds to opiate receptors in the CNS, causing inhibition of ascending pain pathways, altering the perception of and response to pain; produces generalized CNS depression
Pharmacodynamics/kinetics
Absorption: Oral: Variable
Metabolism: In the liver
Half-life:
  Neonates: Prolonged 6% to 10%
  Adults: 1.5-2 hours
See table.

410

Morphine Sulfate

Dosage Form/Route	Analgesia	
	Peak	Duration
Tablets	1 h	4-5 h
Oral solution	1 h	4-5 h
Extended release tablets	1 h	8-12 h
Suppository	20-60 min	3-7 h
Subcutaneous injection	50-90 min	4-5 h
I.M. injection	30-60 min	4-5 h
I.V. injection	20 min	4-5 h

Toxicodynamics/kinetics
Peak effect of analgesia: 50-90 minutes after S.C. administration; 20 minutes after I.V. injection
Half-life: 2.5-3 hours
Elimination: 90% found in urine after 24 hours, either free, or the majority in the flucuronide conjugated form

Signs and Symptoms of Acute Intoxication Apnea, encephalopathy, respiratory depression, hyponatremia, dry mouth, impotence, hypothermia, dysuria, constipation, myocardial depression, thirst, rhabdomyolysis, hypotension, seizures (in neonates), myoglobinuria, coma, miosis, pulmonary edema, hallucinations

When to Transport to Hospital Transport any patient with decreased mental status

Overdosage/Treatment Supportive therapy: Naloxone hydrochloride (0.4-2 mg I.V., S.C., or through an endotracheal tube); a continuous infusion (at 2/3 the response dose/hour) may be required

Warnings/Precautions Some preparations contain sulfites which may cause allergic reactions; infants <3 months of age are more susceptible to respiratory depression, use with caution and generally in reduced doses in this age group; use with caution in patients with impaired respiratory function or severe hepatic dysfunction and in patients with hypersensitivity reactions to other phenanthrene derivative opioid agonists (codeine, hydrocodone, hydromorphone, levorphanol, oxycodone, oxymorphone). Can cause hypertension in patients with pheochromocytoma. Use with caution in myasthenia gravis.

Adverse Reactions
Cardiovascular: Flushing
Central nervous system: CNS depression, drowsiness, sedation, increased intracranial pressure
Endocrine & metabolic: Antidiuretic hormone release
Miscellaneous: Physical and psychological dependence, diaphoresis

>10%:
Cardiovascular: Palpitations, hypotension, bradycardia
Central nervous system: Dizziness
Gastrointestinal: Nausea, vomiting, constipation, xerostomia
Local: Pain at injection site
Neuromuscular & skeletal: Weakness
Miscellaneous: Histamine release

1% to 10%:
Central nervous system: Restlessness, headache, false feeling of well being, confusion
Gastrointestinal: Anorexia, GI irritation, paralytic ileus
Genitourinary: Decreased urination
Neuromuscular & skeletal: Trembling

(Continued)

Morphine Sulfate *(Continued)*

Ocular: Vision problems
Respiratory: Respiratory depression, shortness of breath

Reference Range
Therapeutic: Surgical anesthesia: 65-80 ng/mL (SI: 227-280 nmol/L)
Toxic: 200-5000 ng/mL (SI: 700-17,500 nmol/L)

Drug Interactions Increased toxicity with CNS depressants, cimetidine, MAO inhibitors, phenothiazines, tricyclic antidepressants, ethanol, thiopental, and hydroxyzine; plasma morphine concentrations rise when co-administered with cisapride

Dosage Forms
Injection: 0.5 mg/mL (10 mL); 1 mg/mL (10 mL, 30 mL, 60 mL); 2 mg/mL (1 mL, 2 mL, 60 mL); 3 mg/mL (50 mL); 4 mg/mL (1 mL, 2 mL); 5 mg/mL (1 mL, 30 mL); 8 mg/mL (1 mL, 2 mL); 10 mg/mL (1 mL, 2 mL, 10 mL); 15 mg/mL (1 mL, 2 mL, 20 mL)
Injection:
Preservative free: 0.5 mg/mL (2 mL, 10 mL); 1 mg/mL (2 mL, 10 mL)
I.V. via PCA pump: 1 mg/mL (10 mL, 30 mL, 60 mL); 5 mg/mL (30 mL)
I.V. infusion preparation: 25 mg/mL (4 mL, 10 mL, 20 mL)
Solution, oral: 10 mg/5 mL (5 mL, 10 mL, 100 mL, 120 mL, 500 mL); 20 mg/5 mL (5 mL, 100 mL, 120 mL, 500 mL); 20 mg/mL (30 mL)
Suppository, rectal: 5 mg, 10 mg, 20 mg, 30 mg
Tablet: 15 mg, 30 mg
Tablet:
Controlled release: 15 mg, 30 mg, 60 mg, 100 mg
Soluble: 10 mg, 15 mg, 30 mg
Sustained release: 30 mg, 60 mg, 100 mg

Additional Information Poppy seed use can be essentially ruled out as a cause for a urinary morphine screen when codeine levels exceed 300 ng/mL; morphine to codeine ratio is <2 and high levels of morphine (>1000 ng/mL) are detected without codeine being present

Morphine, the major phenanthrene alkaloid of powdered opium, is used for relief of moderate to severe acute and chronic pain after non-narcotic analgesics have failed. It is also used as preanesthetic medication to relieve the pain of myocardial infarction and to relieve the dyspnea of acute left ventricular failure and pulmonary edema.

Specific References
Henry J and Volans G, "ABC of Poisoning. Analgesics: Opioids," *Br Med J (Clin Res)*, 1984, 289(6450):990-3.
Pelders M and Ros J, "Poppy Seeds: Differences in Morphine and Codeine Content and Variation in Inter- and Intra-Individual Excretion," *J Forensic Sci*, 1996, 41:209-12.

Mosco® Liquid [OTC] *see* Salicylic Acid *on page 530*

Mosegor® *see* Pizotyline *on page 490*

Motor Fuel *see* Gasoline *on page 264*

Motor Spirit *see* Gasoline *on page 264*

Motrin® *see* Ibuprofen *on page 308*

Motrin® IB [OTC] *see* Ibuprofen *on page 308*

Motrin® IB Sinus [OTC] *see* Pseudoephedrine and Ibuprofen *on page 517*

Mouse-Rid® *see* Strychnine *on page 549*

Mouse-Tox® *see* Strychnine *on page 549*

Movergan® *see* Selegiline *on page 536*

MS *see* Morphine Sulfate *on page 410*

MS Contin® *see* Morphine Sulfate *on page 410*

MSG *see* Monosodium Glutamate Food Poisoning *on page 409*

MSIR® *see* Morphine Sulfate *on page 410*

MST® *see* Morphine Sulfate *on page 410*

M-Toluamide *see* Diethyltoluamide *on page 197*

M-Toluic Acid Diethylamide *see* Diethyltoluamide *on page 197*

Muco-Fen-DM® *see* Guaifenesin and Dextromethorphan *on page 271*

Muco-Fen-LA® *see* Guaifenesin *on page 269*

Mugwort *see* Wormwood *on page 617*

Multipax® *see* Hydroxyzine *on page 303*

Murine® Plus [OTC] *see* Tetrahydrozoline *on page 569*

Murocoll-2® Ophthalmic *see* Phenylephrine and Scopolamine *on page 481*

Muro's Opcon® *see* Naphazoline *on page 422*

Mushrooms, Toxic Psychedelic

Related Information

Controlled Substances - Uses and Effects *on page 741*

Scientific Name *Conocybe cyanopus*

Conocybe smithii (Bog *Conocybe*)

Gymnopilus aeruginosa

Gymnopilus luteus

Gymnopilus spectabilis (Big Laughing Gym)

Gymnopilus validipes

Paneolus campanatuus

Paneolus foenisecii

Paneolus sphinctrinus

Paneolus subbalteatus (Girdled *Panaeolus*)

Pluteus salicinus

Psilocybe baeocystis (Potent *Psilocybe*)

Psilocybe caerulescens

Psilocybe caerulipes

Psilocybe cubensis (Common Large *Psilocybe*)

Psilocybe cyanescens (Bluing *Psilocybe*)

Psilocybe pelliculosa (Conifer *Psilocybe*)

Psilocybe semilanceolata

Psilocybe strictipes

Psilocybe stuntzii (Stuntz's Blue Legs)

Stropharia semiglobata (Round *Stropharia*)

Abuse Potential Yes

Impairment Potential Yes

Usual Dosage Roughly 5-6 dried mushroom caps may produce hallucinations, perceptual changes at 6-12 mg psilocybin, true hallucinations at >12 mg psilocibin

Mechanism of Toxic Action Contains psilocybin and psilocin which are indole alkaloids similar to LSD, possible serotonin antagonists

Toxicodynamics/kinetics

Onset of action: Within 20 minutes

Duration: 6-15 hours

Absorption: Oral: 50%

Metabolism: Hepatic

Elimination: Renal

Signs and Symptoms of Acute Intoxication Tachycardia, flushing, hypertension, sinus tachycardia, ataxia, chills, headache, synesthesia, asthenia, dizziness, fever, seizures, hallucinations (colored patterns, impaired distanced perception), psychosis, vomiting, urinary incontinence, methemoglobinemia, myalgias, paresthesias, hyperkinesis, rigors, mydriasis

(Continued)

413

Mushrooms, Toxic Psychedelic *(Continued)*

When to Transport to Hospital Transport any agitated, psychotic, or lethargic patient

Overdosage/Treatment Diazepam for panic attacks; chlorpromazine may be useful for treatment of hallucinations; flashback may occur 4 months later

Additional Information The base of the stem of most of these species turn blue to blue-green when handled; many of these species are small and brown to dark colored and as such are easy to confuse with other species including the deadly toxic Group I species *Conocybe filaris* (Deadly *Conocybe*); most species in these genera are not hallucinogenic.

Specific References

Schwartz RH and Smith BM, "Hallucinogenic Mushrooms," *Clin Pediatr (Phila)*, 1988, 27(2):70-3.

Muskel Trancopal® *see* Chlormezanone *on page 126*

Mustard Gas

Synonyms Bis(2-Chloroethyl) Sulfide; Distilled Mustard; HD; MG; S-Mustard; Yperite

Use Primarily of historical use during World War I as a vesicant chemical warfare agent; most recently used for this purpose during the Iran-Iraq War in the 1980s; derivative of this chemical has been used as an antineoplastic agent (an alkylating agent - nitrogen mustard)

Mechanism of Toxic Action Dermal, ocular, and respiratory corrosive agent; this agent combines with DNA thus preventing cell replication

Toxicodynamics/kinetics

Absorption: Lungs or skin

Metabolism: Hepatic

When to Transport to Hospital Transport any exposed patient

Overdosage/Treatment Decontamination:

Dermal: Remove all contaminated clothing; towels soaked in 0.2% chloramine-T in water (Dakin solution) placed over wounds for first 2 hours may be helpful; wash with soap and water (not hot); if no water is available, dry decontamination with Fuller's earth can be utilized; treat wounds as burns with use of 1% silver sulfadiazine (twice daily)

Ocular: Copious irrigation with saline

Adverse Reactions

Dermatologic: Erythema and pruritus; may be delayed for up to 8 hours, then dermal burns and blisters can result

Gastrointestinal: Vomiting

Hematologic: Bone marrow depression

Ocular: Lacrimation, photophobia, blepharospasm, ocular irritation

Respiratory: Dyspnea, cough

Reference Range Urinary thiodiglycol levels >30 ng/mL 12 days postexposure associated with severe ocular and skin lesions

Additional Information

Toxic dermal dose: 0.1% solution; fair skinned individuals are more at risk for adverse dermal effects than dark skinned individuals

Higher wind speeds, higher temperature and humidity increase the atmospheric vaporization rate; may persist in soil for weeks

Combat zones atmospheric concentration of mustard gas during WWI was estimated to be from 3-5 ppm; case fatality rate: 2% to 4%; since mustard gas binds rapidly and avidly to tissue proteins, decontamination must begin immediately and increasing elimination of absorbed chemical is difficult

Total white blood cell count under 200 is a harbinger for fatality; no mustard can be isolated in blister fluid

Specific References

Bismuth C, Blanchet-Bardon, and Baud FJ, "Delayed Admission of Five Soldiers Intoxicated With Mustard Gas," *Ann Emerg Med*, 1995, 26(6):715.

Myambutol® *see* Ethambutol *on page 230*

Mycinettes® [OTC] *see* Benzocaine *on page 70*

Mydfrin® Ophthalmic Solution *see* Phenylephrine *on page 479*

Myminic® Expectorant [OTC] *see* Guaifenesin and Phenylpropanolamine *on page 272*

Myphetane® DC *see* Brompheniramine, Phenylpropanolamine, and Codeine *on page 86*

Mysoline® *see* Primidone *on page 500*

Mytussin® [OTC] *see* Guaifenesin *on page 269*

Mytussin® AC *see* Guaifenesin and Codeine *on page 271*

Mytussin® DAC *see* Guaifenesin, Pseudoephedrine, and Codeine *on page 275*

Mytussin® DM [OTC] *see* Guaifenesin and Dextromethorphan *on page 271*

N-(1-Ethoxycarbonyl-3-Phenylpropyl)-I-Anal-I-Proline Hydrogen Maleate *see* Enalapril *on page 217*

Nabilone (NA bi lone)

U.S. Brand Names Cesamet®

Therapeutic Category Antiemetic

Abuse Potential Yes

Impairment Potential Yes

Use Treatment of nausea and vomiting associated with cancer chemotherapy

Usual Dosage Oral:

Children >4 years:

<18 kg: 0.5 mg twice daily

18-30 kg: 1 mg twice daily

>30 kg: 1 mg 3 times/day

Adults: 1-2 mg twice daily beginning 1-3 hours before chemotherapy is administered and continuing around-the-clock until 1 dose after chemotherapy is completed; maximum daily dose: 6 mg divided in 3 doses

Mechanism of Action Nabilone is a synthetic cannabinoid utilized as an antiemetic drug in the control of nausea and vomiting in patients receiving cancer chemotherapy; like delta-9-tetrahydrocannabinol (the active principal of marijuana), nabilone is a dibenzo(b,d)pyrans; has central CNS antiemetic action thorough the dopaminergic pathway

Pharmacodynamics/kinetics

Absorption: Oral: Rapid (96%)

Distribution: Rapid and extensive to body tissues

Metabolism: Undergoes rapid metabolism to one or more active metabolites

Bioavailability: 95.8%

Half-life: 35 hours (with metabolites); 2 hours (parent compound)

Elimination: Feces (65%) and urine (20%)

When to Transport to Hospital Transport any pediatric (<4 years of age) exposure, any symptomatic patient, or doses exceeding 6 mg in adults

Overdosage/Treatment Decontamination: Ingestion: Lavage (within 1 hour)/activated charcoal

Warnings/Precautions Use with caution in the elderly, those with pre-existing CNS depression, or a history of mental illness

Adverse Reactions

>10%:

Central nervous system: Dizziness, drowsiness, headache

Gastrointestinal: Dry mouth

(Continued)

415

Nabilone *(Continued)*

<10%:
  Cardiovascular: Hypotension, hypertension, tachycardia, sinus tachycardia
  Central nervous system: Changes of mood, confusion, hallucinations, CNS depression, headache
  Gastrointestinal: Loss of appetite or appetite (increased)
  Ocular: Blurred vision
  Respiratory: Breathing (difficulty in)
Reference Range Peak serum levels after a 2 mg dose: 10 ng/mL
Drug Interactions CNS depression is potentiated with ethanol
Dosage Forms Capsule: 1 mg
Specific References
  Ward A and Holmes B, "Nabilone: A Preliminary Review of Its Pharmacological Properties and Therapeutic Use," *Drugs*, 1985, 30(2):127-44.

Nabumetone *(na BYOO me tone)*
U.S. Brand Names Relafen®
Therapeutic Category Analgesic, Non-narcotic; Nonsteroidal Anti-Inflammatory Agent (NSAID)
Use Management of osteoarthritis and rheumatoid arthritis
  Unlabeled use: Sunburn, mild to moderate pain
Usual Dosage Adults: Oral: 1000 mg/day; an additional 500-1000 mg may be needed in some patients to obtain more symptomatic relief; may be administered once or twice daily
Mechanism of Action Nabumetone is a nonacidic, nonsteroidal anti-inflammatory drug that is rapidly metabolized after absorption to a major active metabolite, 6-methoxy-2-naphthylacetic acid. As found with previous nonsteroidal anti-inflammatory drugs, nabumetone's active metabolite inhibits the cyclooxygenase enzyme which is indirectly responsible for the production of inflammation and pain during arthritis by way of enhancing the production of endoperoxides and prostaglandins E_2 and I_2 (prostacyclin). The active metabolite of nabumetone is felt to be the compound primarily responsible for therapeutic effect.

Pharmacodynamics/kinetics
  Metabolism: A prodrug being rapidly metabolized to an active metabolite (6-methoxy-2-naphthylacetic acid)
  Half-life, elimination: Major metabolite: 24 hours
  Time to peak serum concentration: Metabolite: Oral: Within 3-6 hours
When to Transport to Hospital Transport any pediatric exposure, any symptomatic patient, or any ingestion over 1 g
Warnings/Precautions Elderly patients may sometimes require lower doses; patients with impaired renal function may need a dose reduction; use with caution in patients with severe hepatic impairment
Adverse Reactions
  >10%:
    Central nervous system: Dizziness
    Dermatologic: Rash
    Gastrointestinal: Abdominal cramps, heartburn, indigestion, nausea
  1% to 10%:
    Central nervous system: Headache, nervousness
    Dermatologic: Itching
    Endocrine & metabolic: Fluid retention
    Gastrointestinal: Vomiting
    Otic: Tinnitus
Dosage Forms Tablet: 500 mg, 750 mg

Specific References

Bernhard GC, "Worldwide Safety Experience With Nabumetone," *J Rheumatol*, 1992, 19(Suppl 36):48-57.

N-Acetyl-5-methoxytryptamine *see* Melatonin *on page 366*

N-Acetyl-P-Aminophenol *see* Acetaminophen *on page 20*

Nadolol (nay DOE lole)

U.S. Brand Names Apo-Nadol®; Corgard®; Solgol®

Canadian Brand Names Apo-Nadol®; Syn-Nadolol®

Therapeutic Category Beta-Adrenergic Blocker

Use Treatment of hypertension and angina pectoris; prevention of myocardial infarction; prophylaxis of migraine headaches

Investigational: Prevent esophageal variceal bleeding

Usual Dosage Adults: Oral: Initial: 40 mg once daily; increase by 40-80 mg increments gradually at 3- to 7-day intervals; usual dosage: 40-80 mg/day; may need up to 240-320 mg/day; doses as high as 640 mg/day have been used

Mechanism of Action Competitively blocks response to beta-adrenergic stimulation; hydrophilic

Pharmacodynamics/kinetics

Duration of effect: 24 hours

Absorption: Oral: 30% to 40%

Distribution: V_d: 2.1 L/kg; concentration in human breast milk is 4.6 times higher than serum

Protein binding: 25% to 28%

Half-life: Adults: 10-12 hours; increased half-life with decreased renal function

Time to peak serum concentration: Within 2-4 hours, persisting for 17-24 hours

Elimination: Renal 72%, feces 18%; clearance: 0.92 mL/min/kg; ~21% of the drug is normally excreted in 4 hours in a normal patient

Signs and Symptoms of Acute Intoxication Hyperglycemia, ataxia, hyperkalemia, impotence

When to Transport to Hospital Transport any pediatric exposure or any symptomatic patient

Warnings/Precautions Increase dosing interval in patients with renal dysfunction; abrupt withdrawal of beta-blockers may result in an exaggerated cardiac beta-adrenergic responsiveness; symptomatology has included reports of tachycardia, hypertension, ischemia, angina, myocardial infarction, and sudden death; it is recommended that patients be tapered gradually off of beta-blockers over a period of 1-2 weeks rather than via abrupt discontinuation; use with caution in patients with bronchial asthma, wheezings, CHF, or diabetes mellitus

Adverse Reactions

>10%: Cardiovascular: Bradycardia

1% to 10%:

Cardiovascular: Reduced peripheral circulation

Central nervous system: Mental depression, dizziness

Endocrine & metabolic: Decreased sexual ability

Gastrointestinal: Constipation

Neuromuscular & skeletal: Weakness

Respiratory: Dyspnea, wheezing

Reference Range Peak serum nadolol concentration of 5 ng/mL after a 2 mg dose; peak steady-state nadolol level after a 55 mg daily dose: 62 ng/mL

Drug Interactions Increased effect with diuretics, other antihypertensives, verapamil

Dosage Forms Tablet: 20 mg, 40 mg, 80 mg, 120 mg, 160 mg

(Continued)

Nadolol *(Continued)*

Specific References
Hitzenberger G, "Initial Experience With a New Long-Acting Beta-Blocker, Nadolol, In Hypertensive Patients," *J Int Med Res*, 1979, 7(1):33-8.

Nafazair® see Naphazoline on page 422

Nalbuphine *(NAL byoo feen)*
U.S. Brand Names Nubain®
Therapeutic Category Analgesic, Narcotic
Abuse Potential Yes
Impairment Potential Yes
Use Relief of moderate to severe pain
Usual Dosage I.M., I.V., S.C.:
Children 10 months to 14 years: Premedication: 0.2 mg/kg; maximum: 20 mg/dose
Adults: 10 mg/70 kg every 3-6 hours; maximum single dose: 20 mg; maximum daily dose: 160 mg
Mechanism of Action Binds to opiate receptors in the CNS, causing inhibition of ascending pain pathways, altering the perception of and response to pain; produces generalized CNS depression. A 14-hydroxymorphine derivative. A kappa-receptor opioid agonist but a μg-receptor antagonist.

Pharmacodynamics/kinetics
Peak effect:
I.M.: 30 minutes
I.V.: 1-3 minutes
Metabolism: In the liver, no active metabolites
Bioavailability: Oral: 12%
Half-life:
Children: 1 hour
Adults: 2 hours
Elderly: 2.3 hours
Time to peak serum concentration:
I.M.: 30 minutes
I.V.: 1-3 minutes
Signs and Symptoms of Acute Intoxication Coma, drowsiness, dysphoria, dyspepsia, depression, night terrors, insomnia, hypotension, miosis, clammy skin
When to Transport to Hospital Transport any symptomatic patient
Overdosage/Treatment Supportive therapy: Naloxone hydrochloride (0.4-2 mg I.V., S.C., or through an endotracheal tube); a continuous infusion (at ⅔ the response dose/hour) may be required
Warnings/Precautions Use with caution in patients with recent myocardial infarction, biliary tract surgery, or sulfite sensitivity; may produce apnea; use with caution in women delivering premature infants; use with caution in patients with a history of drug dependence, head trauma or increased intracranial pressure, decreased hepatic or renal function, or pregnancy; some products may contain sulfites

Adverse Reactions
>10%:
Central nervous system: Drowsiness, CNS depression, narcotic withdrawal
Miscellaneous: Histamine release
1% to 10%:
Cardiovascular: Hypotension, flushing
Central nervous system: Dizziness, headache
Dermatologic: Urticaria, rash

Gastrointestinal: Nausea, vomiting, anorexia, xerostomia
Local: Pain at injection site
Neuromuscular & skeletal: Weakness
Respiratory: Pulmonary edema

Drug Interactions Increased toxicity: Barbiturate anesthetics causes increased CNS depression

Dosage Forms Injection: 10 mg/mL (1 mL, 10 mL); 20 mg/mL (1 mL, 10 mL)

Additional Information Little abuse potential

Specific References

Yoo Y, Chung H, Kim I, et al, "Determination of Nalbuphine in Drug Abusers' Urine," *J Anal Toxicol*, 1995, 19:120-3.

Naldecol® *see* Carbinoxamine *on page 106*

Naldecon® *see* Chlorpheniramine, Phenyltoloxamine, Phenylpropanolamine, and Phenylephrine *on page 137*

Naldecon® DX Adult Liquid [OTC] *see* Guaifenesin, Phenylpropanolamine, and Dextromethorphan *on page 274*

Naldecon-EX® Children's Syrup [OTC] *see* Guaifenesin and Phenylpropanolamine *on page 272*

Naldecon® Senior DX [OTC] *see* Guaifenesin and Dextromethorphan *on page 271*

Naldecon® Senior EX [OTC] *see* Guaifenesin *on page 269*

Naldelate® *see* Chlorpheniramine, Phenyltoloxamine, Phenylpropanolamine, and Phenylephrine *on page 137*

Nalfon® *see* Fenoprofen *on page 245*

Nalgest® *see* Chlorpheniramine, Phenyltoloxamine, Phenylpropanolamine, and Phenylephrine *on page 137*

Nalmefene (NAL me feen)

Synonyms Nalmetrene

U.S. Brand Names Revex®

Therapeutic Category Antidote

Use Investigational in U.S.: Reversal of adverse opiate effects; may be useful for pruritus

Usual Dosage

Opiate overdose: Adults: I.V. bolus: 0.5-1 mg every 2 minutes as clinically needed up to a total dose of 2 mg; may be given I.M. or S.C.

Pruritus: Oral: 10-20 mg

Reversal of postoperative opioid depression: I.V.: 0.1-0.5 mcg/kg; may repeat up to a total dose of 1 mcg/kg

Mechanism of Action Derivative of naltrexone with opioid antagonist effects; does not produce opiate agonist effects

Pharmacodynamics/kinetics

Onset of action: 2 minutes

Metabolism: In the liver

Half-life:

Oral: 11 hours

I.V.: 8-9 hours

When to Transport to Hospital Transport any symptomatic patient

Warnings/Precautions In patients with renal or hepatic failure, administer doses over a 1-minute time period; renal or hepatic failure reduces clearance by 28%

Adverse Reactions

>10%: Gastrointestinal: Nausea

1% to 10%:

Cardiovascular: Tachycardia, hypertension

(Continued)

419

Nalmefene *(Continued)*

Central nervous system: Fever, dizziness
Gastrointestinal: Vomiting
Miscellaneous: Postoperative pain
Reference Range Therapeutic plasma level: 0.5 ng/mL
Dosage Forms I.V. ampuls at concentrations of 1 mL of 100 mcg/mL and 2 mL of 1 mg/mL
Specific References
Gaeta TJ, Capodano RJ, Spevack TA, et al, "Potential Danger of Nalmefene Use in the Emergency Department," *Ann Emerg Med*, 1997, 29(1):193-4.

Nalmetrene *see* Nalmefene *on previous page*

Nalorex® *see* Naltrexone *on this page*

Nalspan® *see* Chlorpheniramine, Phenyltoloxamine, Phenylpropanolamine, and Phenylephrine *on page 137*

Naltrexone *(nal TREKS one)*

U.S. Brand Names Antaxone®; Celupan®; Nalorex®; ReVia®; Trexan™
Therapeutic Category Antidote
Use Adjunct to the maintenance of an opioid-free state in detoxified individual; approved for use in the treatment of ethanol abuse; used in alternative medicine to treat HIV infection (T-cell count >500)
Usual Dosage Do not give until patient is opioid-free for 7-10 days as required by urine analysis

Adults: Oral: 25 mg; if no withdrawal signs within 1 hour give another 25 mg; maintenance regimen is flexible, variable, and individualized (50 mg/day to 100-150 mg 3 times/week)
Alcoholism: 50 mg once daily

Mechanism of Action Naltrexone is a cyclopropyl derivative of oxymorphone similar in structure to naloxone and nalorphine (a morphine derivative); it acts as a competitive antagonist at opioid receptor sites

Pharmacodynamics/kinetics
Duration of action:
50 mg: 24 hours
100 mg: 48 hours
150 mg: 72 hours
Absorption: Oral: Almost completely
Metabolism: Undergoes extensive metabolism
Half-life: 4 hours
Time to peak serum concentration: Within 60 minutes

Signs and Symptoms of Acute Intoxication Hepatocellular damage, dysphoria, insomnia, leukopenia, neutropenia, agranulocytosis, granulocytopenia
When to Transport to Hospital Transport any symptomatic patient
Warnings/Precautions Dose-related hepatocellular injury is possible; the margin of separation between the apparent safe and hepatotoxic doses appear to be only fivefold or less

Adverse Reactions
>10%:
Central nervous system: Insomnia, nervousness, headache
Gastrointestinal: Abdominal cramping, nausea, vomiting
Neuromuscular & skeletal: Arthralgia
1% to 10%:
Central nervous system: Dizziness
Dermatologic: Rash
Endocrine & metabolic: Polydipsia

Gastrointestinal: Anorexia
Respiratory: Sneezing

Test Interactions Elevates gonadotropin, serum cortisol

Reference Range Peak plasma naltrexone level after a 100 mg oral dose: 44 µg/L

Dosage Forms Tablet: 50 mg

Additional Information Up to 800 mg/day has been tolerated in adults without an adverse effect

Specific References

Volpicelli JR, "Naltrexone in Alcohol Dependence," *Lancet*, 1995, 346(8973):456.

Nandrolone (NAN droe lone)

Synonyms Nandrolone Decanoate; Nandrolone Phenpropionate

U.S. Brand Names Anabolin® Injection; Androlone®-D Injection; Androlone® Injection; Deca-Durabolin® Injection; Hybolin™ Decanoate Injection; Hybolin™ Improved Injection; Neo-Durabolic Injection

Therapeutic Category Androgen

Use Control of metastatic breast cancer; management of anemia of renal insufficiency

Adverse Reactions

Male:

Postpubertal:

>10%:

Dermatologic: Acne

Endocrine & metabolic: Gynecomastia

Genitourinary: Bladder irritability, priapism

1% to 10%:

Central nervous system: Insomnia, chills

Endocrine & metabolic: Decreased libido, hepatic dysfunction,

Gastrointestinal: Nausea, diarrhea

Genitourinary: Prostatic hypertrophy (elderly)

Hematologic: Iron deficiency anemia, suppression of clotting factors

Prepubertal:

>10%:

Dermatologic: Acne

Endocrine & metabolic: Virilism

1% to 10%:

Central nervous system: Chills, insomnia, factors

Dermatologic: Hyperpigmentation

Gastrointestinal: Diarrhea, nausea

Hematologic: Iron deficiency anemia, suppression of clotting

Miscellaneous: Necrosis

Female:

>10%: Endocrine & metabolic: Virilism

1% to 10%:

Central nervous system: Chills, insomnia

Endocrine & metabolic: Hypercalcemia

Gastrointestinal: Nausea, diarrhea

Hematologic: Iron deficiency anemia, suppression of clotting factors

Hepatic: Hepatic dysfunction

Dosage Forms

Injection, as phenpropionate, in oil: 25 mg/mL (5 mL); 50 mg/mL (2 mL)

Injection, as decanoate, in oil: 50 mg/mL (1 mL, 2 mL); 100 mg/mL (1 mL, 2 mL); 200 mg/mL (1 mL)

(Continued)

Nandrolone *(Continued)*

Injection, repository, as decanoate: 50 mg/mL (2 mL); 100 mg/mL (2 mL); 200 mg/mL (2 mL)

Nandrolone Decanoate *see Nandrolone on previous page*

Nandrolone Phenpropionate *see Nandrolone on previous page*

Nanslus® *see Clorazepate on page 156*

Naphazoline *(naf AZ oh leen)*

U.S. Brand Names AK-Con®; Albalon® Liquifilm®; Allerest® Eye Drops [OTC]; Clear Eyes® [OTC]; Comfort® [OTC]; Degest® 2 [OTC]; Estivin® II [OTC]; I-Naphline®; Muro's Opcon®; Nafazair®; Naphcon Forte®; Naphcon® [OTC]; Opcon®; Privine®; VasoClear® [OTC]; Vasocon Regular®

Therapeutic Category Adrenergic Agonist Agent

Use Topical ocular vasoconstrictor; will temporarily relieve congestion, itching, and minor irritation, and to control hyperemia in patients with superficial corneal vascularity; also has been used to treat myopathic ptosis

Usual Dosage

Nasal:

Children:

<6 years: Intranasal: Not recommended (especially infants) due to CNS depression

6-12 years: 1 spray of 0.05% into each nostril every 6 hours if necessary; therapy should not exceed 3-5 days

Children >12 years and Adults: 0.05%, instill 1-2 drops or sprays every 6 hours if needed; therapy should not exceed 3-5 days

Ophthalmic:

Children <6 years: Not recommended for use due to CNS depression (especially in infants)

Children >6 years and Adults: Instill 1-2 drops into conjunctival sac of affected eye(s) every 3-4 hours; therapy generally should not exceed 3-4 days

Mechanism of Action Stimulates alpha-adrenergic receptors in the arterioles of the conjunctiva and the nasal mucosa to produce vasoconstriction

Pharmacodynamics/kinetics

Onset of decongestant action: Topical: Within 10 minutes

Duration: 8 hours

Elimination: Not well defined

Signs and Symptoms of Acute Intoxication CNS depression, hypothermia, bradycardia, cardiovascular collapse, apnea, coma

When to Transport to Hospital Transport any pediatric (<6 years of age) exposure or any symptomatic patient

Warnings/Precautions Rebound congestion may occur with extended use; use with caution in the presence of hypertension, diabetes, hyperthyroidism, heart disease, coronary artery disease, cerebral arteriosclerosis, or long-standing bronchial asthma; should not use while wearing contact lenses

Adverse Reactions 1% to 10%:

Cardiovascular: Systemic cardiovascular stimulation

Central nervous system: Dizziness, headache, nervousness

Gastrointestinal: Nausea

Local: Transient stinging, nasal mucosa irritation, dryness, rebound congestion

Ocular: Mydriasis, increased intraocular pressure, blurring of vision

Respiratory: Sneezing

Drug Interactions Increased toxicity: Anesthetics (discontinue mydriatic prior to use of anesthetics that sensitize the myocardium to sympathomimetics, ie, cyclopropane, halothane), MAO inhibitors, tricyclic antidepressants → hypertensive reactions

Dosage Forms

Solution:

Drops, nasal: 0.05% (25 mL)

Ophthalmic: 0.012% (7.5 mL, 15 mL, 30 mL); 0.02% (15 mL); 0.03% (15 mL); 0.1% (15 mL)

Spray: 0.05% (20 mL, 473 mL)

Additional Information Recovery from overdose usually occurs within 36 hours

Specific References

Higgins GL III, Campbell B, Wallace K, et al, "Pediatric Poisoning From Over-The-Counter Imidazoline-Containing Products," *Ann Emerg Med*, 1991, 20(6):655-8.

Naphcon® [OTC] *see* Naphazoline *on previous page*

Naphcon Forte® *see* Naphazoline *on previous page*

Naprosyn® *see* Naproxen *on this page*

Naproxen (na PROKS en)

U.S. Brand Names Aleve® [OTC]; Anaprox®; Naprosyn®

Canadian Brand Names Apo-Naproxen®; Naxen®; Novo-Naprox®; Nu-Naprox®

Therapeutic Category Analgesic, Non-narcotic; Antipyretic; Nonsteroidal Anti-Inflammatory Agent (NSAID)

Use Management of inflammatory disease and rheumatoid disorders (including juvenile rheumatoid arthritis); acute gout; mild to moderate pain; dysmenorrhea; fever; menorrhagia

Usual Dosage Oral (as naproxen):

Children >2 years:

Fever: 2.5-10 mg/kg/dose; maximum: 10 mg/kg/day

Juvenile arthritis: 10 mg/kg/day in 2 divided doses

Adults:

EC-Naproxen: 375 mg or 500 mg twice daily

Rheumatoid arthritis, osteoarthritis, and ankylosing spondylitis: 500-1000 mg/day in 2 divided doses; may increase to 1.5 g/day of naproxen base for limited time period

Mild to moderate pain or dysmenorrhea: Initial: 500 mg, then 250 mg every 6-8 hours; maximum: 1250 mg/day naproxen base

Mechanism of Action Inhibits prostaglandin synthesis by decreasing the activity of the enzyme, cyclo-oxygenase, which results in decreased formation of prostaglandin precursors

Pharmacodynamics/kinetics

Onset of action: 1 hour

Duration: Up to 7 hours

Absorption: ~100% from gastrointestinal tract

Metabolism: Hepatic

Half-life: 9-20 hours

Time to peak serum concentration: Within 1-2 hours

Signs and Symptoms of Acute Intoxication Nausea, vomiting, wheezing, purpura, photosensitivity, nephrotic syndrome, night terrors, depression, impotence, gastrointestinal bleeding, stomatitis, intraocular pressure (increased), lightheadedness, gastritis, colitis, meningitis, cognitive dysfunction, gout, lichenoid eruptions, ejaculatory disturbances, ototoxicity, coagulopathy, tinnitus, drowsiness; severe poisoning can manifest with coma, seizures, renal and or hepatic failure, hypotension, respiratory depression, metabolic acidosis
(Continued)

Naproxen *(Continued)*

When to Transport to Hospital Transport any ingestion over 10 mg/kg or any symptomatic patient

Warnings/Precautions Use with caution in patients with gastrointestinal disease, cardiac disease, renal or hepatic impairment, and patients receiving anticoagulants

Adverse Reactions

>10%:

Central nervous system: Dizziness

Dermatologic: Pruritus, rash

Gastrointestinal: Abdominal discomfort, nausea, heartburn, constipation, GI bleeding, ulcers, perforation, indigestion

1% to 10%:

Central nervous system: Headache, nervousness

Dermatologic: Itching

Endocrine & metabolic: Fluid retention

Gastrointestinal: Vomiting

Otic: Tinnitus

Reference Range Trough concentrations of >50 µg/L (217 µmol/L) are therapeutic in patients with rheumatoid arthritis; serum naproxen level of 414 mg/L associated with oral ingestion of 25 g and mild toxicity

Drug Interactions Aspirin decreases serum concentrations probably by protein-binding displacement; there is an increased bleeding potential with concomitant warfarin therapy; may increase lithium and methotrexate concentrations by decreasing renal clearance; may decrease diuretic and hypotensive effects of thiazides, loop diuretics, ACE inhibitors, and beta-blockers; may increase nephrotoxicity of cyclosporine

Dosage Forms

Suspension, oral (Naprosyn®): 125 mg/5 mL (480 mL)

Tablet:

Aleve® [OTC]: 200 mg

Naprosyn®: 250 mg, 375 mg, 500 mg

Tablet, as sodium (Anaprox®): 275 mg (250 mg base); 550 mg (500 mg base)

Additional Information Naproxen: Naprosyn® naproxen sodium: Anaprox®; 275 mg of Anaprox® equivalent to 250 mg of Naprosyn®; Aleve® [OTC] available in 1994

Specific References

Martinez R, Smith DW, and Frankel LR, "Severe Metabolic Acidosis After Acute Naproxen Sodium Ingestion," *Ann Emerg Med*, 1989, 18(10):1102-4.

Narcotics *see* Opiates, Qualitative, Urine *on page 445*

Narcotics Drug Screen, Urine *see* Toxicology Drug Screen, Urine *on page 588*

Narcozep® *see* Flunitrazepam *on page 250*

Nardelzine® *see* Phenelzine *on page 471*

Nardil® *see* Phenelzine *on page 471*

Nasabid™ *see* Guaifenesin and Pseudoephedrine *on page 273*

Nasahist B® *see* Brompheniramine *on page 84*

Natil® *see* Oxitriptan *on page 451*

Natural Gas (85% Methane) *see* Methane *on page 385*

Natural Gasoline *see* Gasoline *on page 264*

Navane® *see* Thiothixene *on page 580*

ND-Stat® *see* Brompheniramine *on page 84*

Nebril® *see* Desipramine *on page 180*

Nedeltran® *see* Trimeprazine *on page 598*

Nefazodone (nef AY zoe done)

U.S. Brand Names Serzone®

Therapeutic Category Antidepressant

Impairment Potential Yes

Use Antidepressant; treatment of major depression in adults

Usual Dosage Adults: 200 mg/day in 2 divided doses; can increase in increments of 100-200 mg/day at intervals no less than one week; usual effective daily dose: 300-600 mg; maximum daily dose: 600 mg; starting dose for elderly patients: 100 mg/day

Mechanism of Action Chemically related to trazodone, $5-HT_2$ receptor antagonist; also alpha$_1$-adrenergic antagonist; acts to inhibit neuronal uptake of serotonin and norepinephrine

Pharmacodynamics/kinetics

Absorption: Rapid and complete

Metabolism: Undergoes extensive metabolism

Half-life: 2-4 hours

Peak plasma concentrations: Occur in 1 hour

Signs and Symptoms of Acute Intoxication Nausea, vomiting, lethargy, diaphoresis

When to Transport to Hospital Transport any pediatric exposure, any adult ingestion over 600 mg, or any symptomatic patient

Warnings/Precautions Coadministration with MAO inhibitors, alprazolam, triazolam (or other triazolobenzodiazepines); history of seizure disorders or cardiovascular disease; use with caution in patients bipolar affective disorder

Adverse Reactions

>10%:

Central nervous system: Headache, drowsiness, insomnia, agitation, dizziness, confusion

Gastrointestinal: Xerostomia, nausea

Neuromuscular & skeletal: Tremor

1% to 10%:

Cardiovascular: Postural hypotension

Gastrointestinal: Constipation, vomiting

Neuromuscular & skeletal: Weakness

Ocular: Blurred vision, amblyopia

Reference Range After a 150 mg oral dose, peak plasma nefazodone, HO-NEF, and meta-chlorophenylpiperazine levels were 1200 ng/mL, 400 ng/mL, and 25 ng/mL respectively

TLC detection limit: 1 µg/mL

HPLC detection limit: 1-10 ng/mL

Drug Interactions Can result in serotonin syndrome with concomitant serotonin reuptake inhibitors, monoamine oxidase inhibitors; may inhibit metabolism of terfenadine or astemizole leading to Q-T prolongation and torsade de pointes; inhibits metabolism of benzodiazepines, especially alprazolam and triazolam; can increase absorption of haloperidol (by 36%); can cause an increase (about double) of the half-life of digoxin; use with nonsteroidal anti-inflammatory agents may cause an increase in dry mouth and somnolence; concomitant nefazodone and cyclosporine administration may increase cyclosporine levels by 70%; myositis and rhabdomyolysis can occur with concurrent use of simvastatin and nefazodone

Dosage Forms Tablet: 100 mg, 150 mg, 200 mg, 250 mg

Additional Information May cause an increase in plasma prolactin levels; food delays absorption; inhibitor of cytochrome P-450 III4A and IID6; women and elderly receiving single doses attain significant higher peak concentrations than male volunteers

(Continued)

Nefazodone *(Continued)*
Specific References
Robinson DS, Roberts DL, Smith JM, et al, "The Safety Profile of Nefazodone," *J Clin Psychiatry*, 1996, 57(Suppl 2):31-8.

Nembutal® *see* Pentobarbital *on page 464*

Neo-Durabolic Injection *see* Nandrolone *on page 421*

Neofed® [OTC] *see* Pseudoephedrine *on page 516*

Neoloid® [OTC] *see* Castor Oil *on page 118*

Neopap® [OTC] *see* Acetaminophen *on page 20*

Neoquess® *see* Hyoscyamine *on page 305*

Neoquess® Injection *see* Dicyclomine *on page 194*

Neo-Synephrine® Nasal Solution [OTC] *see* Phenylephrine *on page 479*

Neo-Synephrine® Ophthalmic Solution *see* Phenylephrine *on page 479*

Nephro-Fer™ *see* Iron *on page 318*

Nerve Gases
Synonyms Sarin; Soman; Tabun; VX

Use Chemical warfare weapon

Mechanism of Toxic Action Similar to organophosphate agent; inhibits the enzyme acetylcholinesterase thus resulting in acetylcholine excess at the neuronal synapse; may penetrate blood brain barrier and thus affect GABA transmission

Toxicodynamics/kinetics
Onset of action:
Inhalation (except for V_x): Within 5 minutes
Dermal: 1 hour
Half-time:
Aging of sarin-acetylcholine complex: 5 hours
Aging of soman-acetylcholine complex: 2 minutes

When to Transport to Hospital Transport any exposed patient

Overdosage/Treatment
Decontamination:
Dermal: Remove all contaminated clothing; wash with 5% hypochlorite solution (household bleach) followed by copious water irrigation; if bleach is not available, a gentle blotting with an alkaline soap can be used
Inhalation: Administer 100% humidified oxygen
Ocular: Irrigate with saline
Supportive therapy: Atropine is the mainstay of treatment with doses from 10-20 mg cumulatively over the first 2-3 hours usually required; this should be titrated to bronchial secretions and not to ocular signs; pralidoxime (1-2 g I.V. over 10 minutes, repeat in 1 hour if weakness occurs, then every 4-12 hours as needed) should be administered; pralidoxime should be used within 3 hours post-sarin exposure; may not be useful for soman; homatropine can be utilized to treat miosis which may last for weeks postexposure; diazepam or midazolam has been effective anticonvulsant in primate models; since aging is longer for tabun or VX, pralidoxime may be particularly useful; administer oxygen. Seizures often respond to atropine or pralidoxime; for refractory seizures, diazepam can be used; in fact, 5-10 mg of diazepam is often given as pretreatment in severely affected patients. Hemodialysis/hemoperfusion has been noted to increase cholinesterase levels and improve clinical symptomatology in one patient; asoxime chloride may be useful when used with atropine; total dose for atropine: ~20 mg

Adverse Reactions
Cardiovascular: Sinus bradycardia

Central nervous system: Insomnia, fatigue, memory loss, seizures, ataxia, coma, headache

Gastrointestinal: Diarrhea, nausea

Ocular: Lacrimation, miosis

Respiratory: Rhinorrhea; death is usually due to respiratory failure, cough

Miscellaneous: Excess muscarinic activity (bronchial secretion, salivation, sweating, miosis, bronchospasm, bradycardia) and nicotinic activity (muscle twitching, weakness, paralysis)

Reference Range Cholinesterase activity <10% of normal is consistent with severe poisoning

Additional Information Sarin has been implicated in the Tokyo subway terrorist incident occurring in March, 1995. It has been estimated that 800 kg of sarin will cause heavy casualties over 1 square mile area. Sarin is 4000 times more potent than parathion. Lethal inhaled dose of tabun, sarin, and soman is ~1 mg; VX has highest lethality in dermal applications (as an oily liquid) rather than through inhalation; while sarin and tabun may cause a delayed neuropathy, VX is not known to cause a delayed neuropathy. Emergency medical ambulances in New York City now stock up to 52 mg of atropine; this is up from 4 mg which was a typical ambulance stock of atropine before the March, 1995 Tokyo subway sarin attack.

See table for maximum control limits:

Maximum Agent Control Limits

	Workplace (8 h in mg/m^3)	General Population (72 h TWA mg/m^3)
Sarin and tabun	1×10^{-5}	3×10^{-3}
VX	1×10^{-4}	3×10^{-6}

Rescuers should wear protective masks (ie, charcoal filter of self-contained breathing apparatus) with heavy rubber gloves

Pretreatment with pyridostigmine bromide (30 mg orally every 8 hours) may be effective (especially for soman)

Lethal dermal dose (70 kg adult):

Sarin: 1.7 g

Tabun: 1 g

Soman: 100 mg

VX: 6 mg

These agents are 4-6 times denser than air and thus remain close to the ground; they are soluble in water, but hydrolyze in alkaline solutions (see Treatment); contaminated vegetation with VX can cause toxic effects upon ingestion

Butyrylcholinesterase can sequester tabun, soman, VX, and sarin within 5 seconds in a rodent model. Human data is lacking.

In the sarin subway attack in Tokyo (March 20, 1995), of the 5510 cases there were 12 deaths and 17 patients requiring ventilatory support.

Specific References

Okumura T, Takasu N, Ishimatsu S, et al, "Report on 640 Victims of the Tokyo Subway Sarin Attack," *Ann Emerg Med*, 1996, 28:129-35.

Nervocaine® see Lidocaine on page 345

Network® Rodeo® see Glyphosate on page 269

Neucalm® see Hydroxyzine on page 303

Neulente see Insulin Preparations on page 314

Neuramate® see Meprobamate on page 371

Neuroclam® see Tryptophan on page 602

Neurontin® see Gabapentin on page 261

Neuroremed® see Tryptophan on page 602

Neurotoxic Shellfish Poisoning
Synonyms NSP; Red Tide Poisoning
Commonly Found In Mussels, shellfish (bivalves)
Mechanism of Toxic Action Shellfish ingestion of the toxic dinoflagellate *ptychodiscus brevis*, produces the neurotoxin brevetoxin; additionally, the dinoflagellate *ptychodiscus veneficum* can cause this illness. Brevetoxins is a muscarinic agonist.
Signs and Symptoms of Acute Intoxication Paresthesia, myalgia, ataxia, dizziness, reversal of hot/cold temperature, mydriasis, abdominal pain, headache, diarrhea, hyporeflexia, tremor, dysphagia, rhinorrhea, sneezing, lacrimation, bradycardia (lasting up to 12 hours), seizures, coma, confusion, pruritus; bronchospasm and cough can occur from aerosolized *P. brevis* particles
When to Transport to Hospital Transport any symptomatic patient
Overdosage/Treatment Decontamination: Dermal: Wash with soap and water; lavage (within 1 hour)/activated charcoal (avoid magnesium cathartics)
Additional Information
   Incubation period: ~3 hours (range: 15 minutes to 18 hours)
   Duration of illness: ~17 hours (range: 1-72 hours)
   Heat stable, lipid soluble toxin; may be a cause of red tides. Usually found off of Florida in the Gulf of Mexico.
Specific References
   Morris PD, Campbell DS, Taylor TJ, et al, "Clinical and Epidemiological Features of Neurotoxic Shellfish Poisoning in North Carolina," *Am J Public Health*, 1991, 81(4):471-4.

New Decongestant® see Chlorpheniramine, Phenyltoloxamine, Phenylpropanolamine, and Phenylephrine on page 137

Niac® [OTC] see Niacin on this page

Niacels™ [OTC] see Niacin on this page

Niacin (NYE a sin)
Synonyms Acidum Nicotinicum; Bionic; Nicotinic Acid; Vitamin B_3
U.S. Brand Names Niac® [OTC]; Niacels™ [OTC]; Nicobid® [OTC]; Nicolar® [OTC]; Nicotinex [OTC]; Slo-Niacin® [OTC]
Therapeutic Category Vitamin, Water Soluble
Use Treatment of hyperlipidemias and hypercholesterolemia; treatment of pellagra; dietary supplement; treatment of hypoalphalipoproteinemia
Usual Dosage Give I.M., I.V., or S.C. only if oral route is unavailable and use only for vitamin deficiencies (not for hyperlipidemia)

   Recommended daily allowances:
      0-1 year: 6-8 mg/day
      2-6 years: 9-11 mg/day
      7-10 years: 16 mg/day
      >10 years: 15-18 mg/day

   Children: Pellagra: Oral: 50-100 mg/dose 3 times/day
   Adults: Oral:
      Hyperlipidemia: 1.5-6 g/day in 3 divided doses with or after meals
      Pellagra: 50-100 mg/dose 3-4 times/day; maximum: 500 mg/day
      Niacin deficiency: 10-20 mg/day, maximum: 100 mg/day
Mechanism of Action Component of two coenzymes which is necessary for metabolism; inhibits the synthesis of very low density lipoproteins while increasing high density cholesterol; water soluble vitamin B complex
Pharmacodynamics/kinetics
   Peak serum concentrations: Oral: Within 45 minutes

Metabolism: Depending upon the dose, niacin converts to niacinamide; following this conversion, niacinamide is 30% metabolized in the liver

Half-life: 45 minutes

Signs and Symptoms of Acute Intoxication Delirium, nausea, thrombocytopenia, diarrhea, hepatitis, cholelithiasis, hyperuricemia, hyperglycemia, anorexia, arrhythmias, coagulopathy

When to Transport to Hospital Transport any symptomatic patient

Warnings/Precautions Monitor liver function tests, blood glucose; may elevate uric acid levels; use with caution in patients predisposed to gout; large doses should be administered with caution to patients with gallbladder disease, jaundice, liver disease, or diabetes; some products may contain tartrazine

Adverse Reactions 1% to 10%:

Cardiovascular: Generalized flushing

Central nervous system: Headache

Gastrointestinal: Bloating, flatulence, nausea

Hepatic: Abnormalities of hepatic function tests, jaundice

Neuromuscular & skeletal: Paresthesia in extremities

Miscellaneous: Increased sebaceous gland activity, sensation of warmth

Drug Interactions

Decreased effect of oral hypoglycemics

Decreased toxicity (flush) with aspirin

Increased toxicity with lovastatin (myopathy) and possibly with other HMG-CoA reductase inhibitors

Dosage Forms

Capsule, timed release: 125 mg, 250 mg, 300 mg, 400 mg, 500 mg

Elixir: 50 mg/5 mL (473 mL, 4000 mL)

Injection: 100 mg/mL (30 mL)

Tablet: 25 mg, 50 mg, 100 mg, 250 mg, 500 mg

Tablet, timed release: 150 mg, 250 mg, 500 mg, 750 mg

Additional Information Pretreatment with 325 mg of aspirin prevents niacin-induced flushing; >61 mg/day may result in slower progression of HIV illness (RR=0.52)

Specific References

Lasagna L, "Over-the-Counter Niacin," *JAMA*, 1994, 271(9):709-10.

Niagestin® see Megestrol Acetate on page 365

Nicardipine (nye KAR de peen)

U.S. Brand Names Cardene®; Cardene® SR

Canadian Brand Names Ridene®

Therapeutic Category Calcium Channel Blocker

Use Chronic stable angina; management of essential hypertension, migraine prophylaxis

Unlabeled use: Congestive heart failure

Usual Dosage

Children: Hypertension: 1-3 mcg/kg/minute

Adults:

Oral: 40 mg 3 times/day (allow 3 days between dose increases)

Oral, sustained release: Initial: 30 mg twice daily, titrate up to 60 mg twice daily

Mechanism of Action Inhibits calcium ion from entering the "slow channels" or select voltage-sensitive areas of vascular smooth muscle and myocardium during depolarization, producing a relaxation of coronary vascular smooth muscle and coronary vasodilation; increases myocardial oxygen delivery in patients with vasospastic angina

(Continued)

Nicardipine (Continued)

Pharmacodynamics/kinetics

Absorption:

Oral: Well absorbed, ~100%

Food reduces nicardipine absorption by 20% to 45%

Protein binding: 95% to 97%

Metabolism: Extensive metabolism; only metabolized in the liver

Half-life: 2-4 hours

Time to peak: Peak serum levels occur within 20-120 minutes and onset of hypotension: Within 20 minutes

Signs and Symptoms of Acute Intoxication
The primary cardiac symptoms of calcium blocker overdose includes hypotension and bradycardia. The hypotension is caused by peripheral vasodilation, myocardial depression, and bradycardia. Bradycardia results from sinus bradycardia, second- or third-degree atrioventricular block, or sinus arrest with junctional rhythm. The noncardiac symptoms include confusion, stupor, nausea, vomiting, metabolic acidosis and hyperglycemia.

When to Transport to Hospital
Transport any pediatric ingestion of any amount or any symptomatic patient

Warnings/Precautions
Use with caution in titrating dosages for impaired renal or hepatic function patients; may increase frequency, severity, and duration of angina during initiation of therapy; do not abruptly withdraw (chest pain); elderly may have a greater hypotensive effect

Adverse Reactions
1% to 10%:

Cardiovascular: Flushing, palpitations, tachycardia, pedal edema

Central nervous system: Headache, dizziness, nausea, somnolence

Neuromuscular & skeletal: Weakness

Reference Range
Therapeutic blood nicardipine levels: 24-50 ng/mL

Drug Interactions
Increased toxicity/effect/levels:

H_2-blockers cause increased bioavailability of nicardipine

Beta-blockers cause increased cardiac depressant effects on A-V conduction

Carbamazepine causes increased carbamazepine levels

Cimetidine increases nicardipine levels

Cyclosporine causes increased cyclosporine levels

Fentanyl causes increased hypotension

Quinidine causes increased quinidine levels (hypotension, bradycardia, and arrhythmias)

Theophylline causes increased pharmacologic actions of theophylline

Dosage Forms
Capsule: 20 mg, 30 mg

Capsule, sustained release: 30 mg, 45 mg, 60 mg

Injection: 2.5 mg/mL (10 mL)

Specific References

Aya AG, Bruelle P, Lefrant JY, et al, "Accidental Nicardipine Overdosage Without Serious Maternal or Neonatal Consequence," *Anaesth Intensive Care*, 1996, 24:99-101.

N'ice® Vitamin C Drops [OTC] see Ascorbic Acid on page 53

Nicobid® [OTC] see Niacin on page 428

Nicoderm® Patch see Nicotine on next page

Nicolar® [OTC] see Niacin on page 428

Niconyl® see Isoniazid on page 322

Nicorette® DS Gum [OTC] see Nicotine on next page

Nicorette® Gum [OTC] see Nicotine on next page

Nicotine (nik oh TEEN)

Related Information
Tobacco *on page 585*

UN Number 1654; 3144; 1655; 1656; 1657; 1658; 1659

Commonly Found In Nicotine gum (2-4 mg); cigars (15-40 mg); nicotine patch (8.3-114 mg); chewing tobacco (6-8 mg); cigarettes (13-19 mg); cigarette butt (5-7 mg)

U.S. Brand Names Habitrol™ Patch; Nicoderm® Patch; Nicorette® DS Gum [OTC]; Nicorette® Gum [OTC]; Nicotrol® NS; Nicotrol® Patch; ProStep® Patch

Canadian Brand Names Nicorette®; Nicorette® Plus

Therapeutic Category Smoking Deterrent

Use Insecticide, found in tobacco leaf (1% to 6% nicotine by weight) products

Usual Dosage

Gum: Chew 1 piece of gum when urge to smoke, up to 30 pieces/day; most patients require 10-12 pieces of gum/day

Transdermal patches: Apply new patch every 24 hours to nonhairy, clean, dry skin on the upper body or upper outer arm; each patch should be applied to a different site; start with the 21 mg/day or 22 mg/day patch, except those patients with stable coronary artery disease should start with 14 mg/day; most patients the dosage can be reduced after 6-8 weeks; progressively lower doses are used every 2 weeks, with complete nicotine elimination achieved after 10 weeks

Nasal spray: One dose is 1 mg of nicotine (2 sprays, 1 in each nostril); start at 1 or 2 doses/hour up to a maximum recommended dose of 40 mg or 80 sprays (<.5 bottle) per day

Mechanism of Action Direct stimulant to nicotinic acetylcholine receptor causing either sympathetic or parasympathetic effects

Pharmacodynamics/kinetics

Absorption: Through skin and oral mucosa, gastrointestinal tract (except in stomach), respiratory tract; increased gastrointestinal, buccal, and dermal absorption in alkali medium

Metabolism: Hepatic (cytochrome P-450) to cotinine and nicotine-N-oxide

Half-life:

Smokers: 0.8 hours

Nonsmokers: 1.3 hours

Cotinine: 15-20 hours

Gum/cigarette: 1-2 hours

Transdermal systems: 3-6 hours or higher

Signs and Symptoms of Acute Intoxication Nausea, cyanosis, hiccups, dry mouth, insomnia, dyspepsia, hyponatremia, blurred vision, hyperventilation, myalgia, hyperthermia, dementia, vomiting, hyperglycemia, lacrimation, A-V block, dysosmia, abdominal pain, mental confusion, diarrhea, apnea, salivation, lightheadedness, myoclonus, bronchial secretions (increased), muscle fasciculations/paralysis, paresthesia, respiratory depression, myasthenia gravis (exacerbation or precipitation of), mydriasis, tachycardia, hypertension then bradycardia, hypotension, diarrhea (may be delayed up to 24 hours in pediatric ingestion), seizures, methemoglobinemia, ototoxicity; tinnitus, hypotonia, hyperreflexia

When to Transport to Hospital Transport pediatric ingestions of any amount or any symptomatic patient

Overdosage/Treatment For dermal exposures, wash area well with cool water and dry; soap (especially alkaline soaps) may increase absorption; remove any remaining transdermal systems; nicotine will continue to be absorbed several hours after removal due to depot in skin

Warnings/Precautions Nicotine is known to be one of the most toxic of all poisons; while the gum is being used to help the patient overcome a health (Continued)

Nicotine *(Continued)*

hazard, it also must be considered a hazardous drug vehicle; use with caution in oropharyngeal inflammation and in patients with history of esophagitis or peptic ulcer

Adverse Reactions

Chewing gum:

>10%:

Cardiovascular: Tachycardia

Central nervous system: Headache (mild)

Gastrointestinal: Nausea, vomiting, indigestion, excessive salivation, belching, increased appetite, mouth or throat soreness

Neuromuscular & skeletal: Jaw muscle ache

Miscellaneous: Hiccups

1% to 10%:

Central nervous system: Insomnia, dizziness, nervousness

Endocrine & metabolic: Dysmenorrhea

Gastrointestinal: GI distress, eructation

Neuromuscular & skeletal: Myalgia

Respiratory: Hoarseness

Miscellaneous: Hiccups

Transdermal systems:

>10%:

Cardiovascular: Tachycardia

Central nervous system: Headache (mild)

Dermatologic: Pruritus, erythema

Gastrointestinal: Increased appetite

1% to 10%:

Central nervous system: Insomnia, nervousness

Endocrine & metabolic: Dysmenorrhea

Neuromuscular & skeletal: Myalgia

Reference Range A serum level of >50 ng/mL associated with toxicity; plasma nicotine level of 13,600 ng/mL associated with fatality; mean plasma level after smoking one cigarette: 5-30 ng/mL; plasma levels of cotinine averaged 0.001 mg/L in children from nonsmoking homes and 0.004 mg/L in children from homes with smoking cohabitants; arterial levels are ~6-8 times that of venous levels thus leading to rapidly elevated brain levels; cotinine serum levels as high as 800 ng/mL are associated with nausea, vomiting, and severe symptomatology; steady state plasma nicotine level from transdermal patches: 0.12-0.17 µg/mL

Dosage Forms

Patch, transdermal:

Habitrol™: 21 mg/day; 14 mg/day; 7 mg/day (30 systems/box)

Nicoderm®: 21 mg/day; 14 mg/day; 7 mg/day (14 systems/box)

ProStep®: 22 mg/day; 11 mg/day (7 systems/box)

Pieces, chewing gum, as polacrilex:

Nicorette® [OTC]: 2 mg/square (96 pieces/box)

Nicorette® DS [OTC]: 4 mg/square (96 pieces/box)

Nasal spray: Aqueous solution of nicotine: 10 mg/mL, 10 mL vial

Additional Information Symptoms usually do not occur in pediatric ingestions <1 mg/kg; not useful as maintenance therapy for ulcerative colitis

Lethal adult dose: 40 mg

Nicotine withdrawal is characterized by psychological distress, difficulty concentrating, tobacco craving, and hunger; average weight gain during smoking cessation is ~4 kg; 3% annual quit rate from smoking; contact the National Capital Poison Center (1-800-498-8666) with all cases of misuse, overdose or abuse of nicotine nasal spray; each actuation of Nicotrol® NS delivers a metered 50 µL spray containing 0.5 mg of nicotine

Specific References

McGee D, Brabson T, McCarthy J, et al, "Four-Year Review of Cigarette Ingestions in Children," *Pediatr Emerg Care*, 1995, 11(1):13-6.

Nicotinex [OTC] *see* Niacin *on page 428*

Nicotinic Acid *see* Niacin *on page 428*

Nicotrol® NS *see* Nicotine *on page 431*

Nicotrol® Patch *see* Nicotine *on page 431*

Nico-Vert® *see* Dimenhydrinate *on page 203*

Nidryl® Oral [OTC] *see* Diphenhydramine *on page 205*

Nifedipine (nye FED i peen)

Synonyms Nifedipinum

U.S. Brand Names Adalat®; Duradalat®; Duranifin®; Fenamon®; Procardia®; Procardia XL®

Canadian Brand Names Adalat PA®; Apo-Nifed®; Gen-Nifedipine®; Novo-Nifedin®; Nu-Nifedin®

Therapeutic Category Calcium Channel Blocker

Use Angina, hypertrophic cardiomyopathy, hypertension (sustained release only)

Usual Dosage

Children: Oral, S.L.:

Hypertensive emergencies: 0.25-0.5 mg/kg/dose

Hypertrophic cardiomyopathy: 0.6-0.9 mg/kg/24 hours in 3-4 divided doses

Adults: Oral: Initial: 10 mg 3 times/day as capsules or 30-60 mg once daily as sustained release tablet; maintenance: 10-30 mg 3-4 times/day (capsules); maximum: 180 mg/24 hours (capsules) or 120 mg/day (sustained release)

Mechanism of Action Inhibits calcium ion from entering the "slow channels" or select voltage-sensitive areas of vascular smooth muscle and myocardium during depolarization, producing a relaxation of coronary vascular smooth muscle and coronary vasodilation; increases myocardial oxygen delivery in patients with vasospastic angina

Pharmacodynamics/kinetics

Onset of action:

Oral: Within 20 minutes

S.L.: Within 1-5 minutes

Duration: Capsules, tablets: 4-8 hours

Absorption: Rapid from gastrointestinal tract (60% to 75%)

Metabolism: In the liver to inactive metabolites capsules

Half-life:

Normal adults: 2-5 hours

Cirrhosis: 7 hours

Overdose: 7.5 hours

Time to peak serum concentration:

Capsule: ~30-60 minutes

Tablet: 1-2 hours

Signs and Symptoms of Acute Intoxication Hypotension, exfoliative dermatitis, wheezing, Q-T prolongation, gingival hyperplasia, memory loss, lightheadedness, depression, enuresis, bradycardia, gynecomastia, Raynaud's (exacerbation of), heart block, congestive heart failure, extrapyramidal reaction, peripheral vasodilation, nocturia, chest pain, reflex tachycardia, hyperthermia, constipation, pulmonary edema, hypokalemia, hyperglycemia, hyperkalemia, A-V block, leukopenia; neutropenia; agranulocytosis; granulocytopenia

(Continued)

Nifedipine *(Continued)*

When to Transport to Hospital Transport pediatric ingestions of any amount or any symptomatic adult patient

Warnings/Precautions Increased angina may be seen upon starting or increasing doses; may increase frequency, duration, and severity of angina during initiation of therapy; use with caution in patients with congestive heart failure or aortic stenosis (especially with concomitant beta-adrenergic blocker)

Adverse Reactions

>10%:
Cardiovascular: Flushing
Central nervous system: Dizziness, lightheadedness, giddiness, headache
Gastrointestinal: Nausea, heartburn
Neuromuscular & skeletal: Weakness
Miscellaneous: Heat sensation

1% to 10%:
Cardiovascular: Peripheral edema, palpitations, hypotension
Central nervous system: Nervousness, mood changes
Gastrointestinal: Sore throat
Neuromuscular & skeletal: Muscle cramps, tremor
Respiratory: Dyspnea, cough, nasal congestion

Reference Range Therapeutic: 25-100 ng/mL; although levels >28 ng/mL correlate with negative inotropic effect after I.V. use; serum nifedipine level of 1290 ng/mL associated with fatality (postmortem urine nifedipine level was 130 ng/mL)

Drug Interactions Colonic bezoars have been reported with the combination of extended release formulations of nifedipine and procainamide. The following interactions occur with concomitant use

Atenolol: Additive hypotensive effects in normal volunteers
Captopril: Improved efficacy
Cimetidine: Impaired nifedipine elimination
Clonidine: Additive effect
Cyclosporin: Decrease nifedipine metabolism
Digoxin: Possible increase in serum digoxin level
Diltiazem: Decreased nifedipine metabolism
Famotidine: May reverse nifedipine's positive inotropic effect
Fentanyl: Hypotension
Grapefruit juice: Increased bioavailability by 34%
Magnesium sulfate: Potentiates neuromuscular toxicity of magnesium
Nortriptyline: Inhibition of nortriptyline's antidepressant actions
Omeprazole: Possible increase in nifedipine absorption
Prazosin: Hypotension
Propranolol: Increased propranolol absorption
Quinidine: Increased in nifedipine levels with an increase in heart rate
Rifampin: 50% decrease in level of nifedipine
Theophylline: Inconclusive/possible increase in serum theophylline levels
Vincristine: Increased vincristine neurotoxicity

Dosage Forms

Capsule, liquid-filled (Adalat®, Procardia®): 10 mg, 20 mg
Tablet, extended release (Adalat® CC): 30 mg, 60 mg, 90 mg
Tablet, sustained release (Procardia XL®): 30 mg, 60 mg, 90 mg

Additional Information Capsule may be punctured and drug solution administered sublingually to reduce blood pressure in recumbent patient; tasteless; response to atropine may not be observed until after I.V. calcium administration

Specific References

Whitebloom D and Fitzharris J, "Nifedipine Overdose," *Clin Cardiol*, 1988, 11(7):505-6.

Nifedipinum *see Nifedipine on page 433*

Niotal® *see Zolpidem on page 621*

Nistenal® *see Phenmetrazine on page 473*

Nitrados® *see Nitrazepam on this page*

Nitrazepam (nye TRA ze pam)

Related Information
Clonazepam *on page 153*
Flunitrazepam *on page 250*

Synonyms Nitrozepamum

U.S. Brand Names Alodorm®; Apodorm®; Arem®; Dormigen®; Insoma®; Ipersed®; Mitidin®; Mogadan®; Nitrados®; Nitrazepan®; Novanov®; Pelson®; Somnite®; Surem®; Tri®; Unisomnia®

Therapeutic Category Benzodiazepine

Abuse Potential Yes

Impairment Potential Yes; Brief or extended period (up to 1 year) of use is consistent with driving impairment in the elderly. The impairment is greatest in the first 7 days of use.

Use Investigational: Short-term management of insomnia; treatment of infantile spasm and seizures

Usual Dosage Oral:
Insomnia:
Children:
1-6 years: 2.5 mg
≥7 years: 5 mg
Adults: 5-10 mg at night
Epilepsy: Children and Adults: 1-6 mg/day; dosage should be decreased in elderly, hypothyroid patients, and cirrhosis

Mechanism of Action Facilitates gamma-aminobutyric acid neurotransmission; a 7-nitrobenzodiazepine derivative

Pharmacodynamics/kinetics
Peak serum levels: 1.4 hours
Duration of effect: 4-8 hours
Metabolism: Hepatic
Half-life: 24-29 hours
Elimination: Renal (80%), feces (20%)

Signs and Symptoms of Acute Intoxication Apnea, aspiration, slurred speech, ataxia, unsteady gait, gaze nystagmus, impairment in attention or memory, stupor, coma

When to Transport to Hospital Transport pediatric ingestions over 5 mg or any symptomatic adult patient

Warnings/Precautions Use with caution in patients with hypothyroidism, cirrhosis, elderly, pregnancy, and breast feeding

Adverse Reactions
Central nervous system: Lethargy, disorientation, night terrors, opisthotonos, ataxia, headache, hypothermia
Endocrine & metabolic: Gout
Gastrointestinal: Salivation, dysphagia, anorexia
Hematologic: Porphyria
Ocular: Intraocular pressure (increased)

Test Interactions Nitrazepam can cause a false elevation (about 15%) of clozapine serum levels

Reference Range Steady state plasma levels with a 5 mg/day oral dose: ~57 (±17) ng/mL; fatalities associated with postmortem blood levels of 1.2-9 mg/L
(Continued)

Nitrazepam (Continued)

Drug Interactions Birth control pills, probenecid, and cimetidine can result in decreased nitrazepam clearance; rifampin can result in increased clearance of nitrazepam; hallucinations with concomitant erythromycin

Additional Information Hangover can occur at 20 mg oral doses; hallucinations from withdrawal can be treated with chlorpromazine

Specific References
Murphy JV, Sawasky F, Marquardt KM, et al, "Deaths in Young Children Receiving Nitrazepam," *J Pediatr*, 1987, 111(1):145-7.

Nitrazepan® see Nitrazepam *on previous page*

Nitric Oxide (NYE trik OK side)

Synonyms NO

UN Number 1660

Therapeutic Category Antihypertensive

Use Orphan drug status for treatment of primary pulmonary hypertension in the newborn; may be useful for septic shock, ARDS, or treatment of pulmonary effects of paraquat; has been used to treat high altitude pulmonary edema (HAPE)

Usual Dosage High altitude pulmonary edema: 40 ppm of nitric oxide with room air

Mechanism of Action Produces selective pulmonary vasodilatation without systemic vasodilatation through direct effect on smooth muscle of pulmonary vasculature

Pharmacodynamics/kinetics

Metabolism: Reacts with hemoglobin (at an affinity of 1400 times that of oxygen) to cause a nitrosyl-hemoglobin which is oxidized to methemoglobin and then into nitrate

Half-life: 5-50 seconds

When to Transport to Hospital Transport any symptomatic patient

Adverse Reactions

Cardiovascular: Vasodilation

Hematologic: Methemoglobinemia

Respiratory: Pulmonary fibrosis, rebound pulmonary hypertension from nitric oxide withdrawal

Reference Range Normal plasma nitrate level: 24 μmol/L (range: 19-39 μmol/L); patients with congestive heart failure 56 μmol/L (range: 41-72 μmol/L)

Additional Information Flammable, can inactivate surfactant; colorless gas; paralysis (motor neuropathy) may develop in alcoholics

TLV-TWA: 25 ppm

IDLH: 100 ppm

Specific References
Heal CA and Spencer SA, "Methaemoglobinaemia With High-Dose Nitric Oxide Administration," *Acta Paediatr*, 1995, 84(11):1318-9.

Nitrites

Synonyms Poppers; Snappers; Thrust

UN Number 2627

Commonly Found In Inhalation abuse of volatile nitrates

Abuse Potential Yes

Impairment Potential Yes

Use In cyanide antidote kits; used in the manufacture of dyes, fabrics, and linen; photography; corrosive inhibition

Mechanism of Toxic Action Peripheral vasodilation; produces methemoglobin; is an oxidizing agent

Toxicodynamics/kinetics Metabolism: 60% metabolized - most to ammonia

Signs and Symptoms of Acute Intoxication Blurred vision, dyspnea, light headedness (postural), nausea, vomiting, flushing, seizures, cyanosis, headache, diarrhea, abdominal pain, skin irritation, tachycardia, hypotension, gaze nystagmus

When to Transport to Hospital Transport any symptomatic patient

Overdosage/Treatment Decontamination: Basic poison management

Adverse Reactions

Cardiovascular: Paradoxical bradycardia, hypotension, sinus bradycardia, vasodilation

Hematologic: Methemoglobinemia followed by hemolysis

Ocular: Visual disturbances

Respiratory: Tachypnea

Miscellaneous: Infants, pregnant women, and patients with malignancy may be especially sensitive

Reference Range Fatal nitrite serum range: 0.5-350 mg/L

Additional Information Ingestion of 10 mL of isobutyl or amyl nitrate may be toxic; oral ingestion produces more rapid methemoglobin than inhalation
May be toxic at >0.4 mg/kg

Specific References

Laaban JP, Bodenan P, and Rochemaure J, "Amyl Nitrite Poppers and Methemoglobinemia," *Ann Intern Med*, 1985, 103(5):804-5.

Nitro-Bid® *see* Nitroglycerin *on this page*

Nitrocap® TD *see* Nitroglycerin *on this page*

Nitrocine® *see* Nitroglycerin *on this page*

Nitrocontin® *see* Nitroglycerin *on this page*

Nitroderm® *see* Nitroglycerin *on this page*

Nitrodisc® *see* Nitroglycerin *on this page*

Nitro-Dur® *see* Nitroglycerin *on this page*

Nitrogard® *see* Nitroglycerin *on this page*

Nitrogen Monoxide *see* Nitrous Oxide *on page 439*

Nitroglicerina® *see* Nitroglycerin *on this page*

Nitroglycerin (nye troe GLI ser in)

Synonyms Glonoin; Glyceryl Trinitrate; Nitroglycerol; NTG; 1,2,3-Propanetriol Trinitrate; Trinitrin

U.S. Brand Names Deponit®; Minitran®; Nitro-Bid®; Nitrocap® TD; Nitrocine®; Nitrocontin®; Nitroderm®; Nitrodisc®; Nitro-Dur®; Nitrogard®; Nitroglicerina®; Nitroglyn®; Nitrol®; Nitrolan®; Nitrolingual®; Nitrong®; Nitrospan®; Nitrostat®; Sustachron®; Transdermal-NTG®; Transderm-Nitro®; Tridil®

Therapeutic Category Vasodilator

Use Angina pectoris; I.V. for congestive heart failure (especially when associated with acute myocardial infarction); hypertension due to ergotism; pulmonary hypertension; hypertensive emergencies occurring perioperatively (especially during cardiovascular surgery); industrial uses: dynamite, cordite; not FDA approved; topical use for relief of pain of anal fissures or ulcers

Usual Dosage Note: Hemodynamic and antianginal tolerance often develop within 24-48 hours of continuous nitrate administration

Children: Pulmonary hypertension: Continuous infusion: Start 0.25-0.5 mcg/kg/minute and titrate by 1 mcg/kg/minute at 20- to 60-minute intervals to desired effect; usual dose: 1-3 mcg/kg/minute; maximum: 5 mcg/kg/minute

Adults:

Buccal: Initial: 1 mg every 3-5 hours while awake (3 times/day); titrate dosage upward if angina occurs with tablet in place

Oral: 2.5-9 mg 2-4 times/day (up to 26 mg 4 times/day)

(Continued)

Nitroglycerin (Continued)

I.V.: 5 mcg/minute, increase by 5 mcg/minute every 3-5 minutes to 20 mcg/minute; if no response at 20 mcg/minute increase by 10 mcg/minute every 3-5 minutes, up to 200 mcg/minute

Ointment: 1" to 2" every 8 hours up to 4" to 5" every 4 hours

Patch, transdermal: Initial: 0.2-0.4 mg/hour, titrate to doses of 0.4-0.8 mg/hour; tolerance is minimized by using a patch-on period of 12-14 hours and patch-off period of 10-12 hours

Sublingual: 0.2-0.6 mg every 5 minutes for maximum of 3 doses in 15 minutes; may also use prophylactically 5-10 minutes prior to activities which may provoke an attack

Translingual: 1-2 sprays into mouth under tongue every 3-5 minutes for maximum of 3 doses in 15 minutes, may also be used 5-10 minutes prior to activities which may provoke an attack prophylactically

Anal fissure/ulcer pain: 200 mg applied topically to anal canal 4 times daily and after each bowel movement

May need to use nitrate-free interval (10-12 hours/day) to avoid tolerance development; tolerance may possibly be reversed with acetylcysteine; gradually decrease dose in patients receiving NTG for prolonged period to avoid withdrawal reaction

Mechanism of Action Reduces cardiac oxygen demand by decreasing left ventricular pressure and systemic vascular resistance; dilates coronary arteries and improves collateral flow to ischemic regions

Pharmacodynamics/kinetics Onset and duration of action is dependent upon dosage form administered; see table.

Nitroglycerin

Dosage Form	Onset of Effect	Peak Effect	Duration
Sublingual tablet	1-3 min	4-8 min	30-60 min
Lingual spray	2 min	4-10 min	30-60 min
Buccal tablet	2-5 min	4-10 min	2 h
Sustained release	20-45 min	45-120 min	4-8 h
Topical	15-60 min	30-120 min	2-12 h
Transdermal	40-60 min	60-180 min	8-24 h

Signs and Symptoms of Acute Intoxication Hypotension, throbbing headache, palpitations, bloody diarrhea, bradycardia, cyanosis, tissue hypoxia, metabolic acidosis, clonic seizures, circulatory collapse, methemoglobinemia

When to Transport to Hospital Transport any symptomatic patient

Warnings/Precautions Do not chew or swallow sublingual dosage form; do not use extended release preparations in patients with gastrointestinal hypermotility or malabsorptive syndrome; use with caution in patients with hypovolemia, constrictive pericarditis, hypertension, and hypotension; use with caution in patients with increased intracranial pressure

Adverse Reactions

>10%:

Cardiovascular: Postural hypotension, flushing

Central nervous system: Headache, lightheadedness, dizziness

Neuromuscular & skeletal: Weakness

1% to 10%: Dermatologic: Drug rash, exfoliative dermatitis

Test Interactions Increases catecholamines (U)

Reference Range Concentrations of 1.2-11.0 ng/mL produce 25% decrease in capillary wedge pressure

Drug Interactions I.V. nitroglycerin may antagonize the anticoagulant effect of heparin, monitor closely, may need to decrease heparin dosage when nitroglycerin is discontinued; alcohol, beta-blockers, calcium channel blockers may enhance nitroglycerin's hypotensive effect

Dosage Forms

Capsule, sustained release: 2.5 mg, 6.5 mg, 9 mg

Injection: 0.5 mg/mL (10 mL); 0.8 mg/mL (10 mL); 5 mg/mL (1 mL, 5 mL, 10 mL, 20 mL); 10 mg/mL (5 mL, 10 mL)

Ointment, topical (Nitrol®): 2% [20 mg/g] (30 g, 60 g)

Patch, transdermal, topical: Systems designed to deliver 2.5, 5, 7.5, 10, or 15 mg NTG over 24 hours

Spray, translingual: 0.4 mg/metered spray (13.8 g)

Tablet:

Buccal, controlled release: 1 mg, 2 mg, 3 mg

Sublingual (Nitrostat®): 0.15 mg, 0.3 mg, 0.4 mg, 0.6 mg

Sustained release: 2.6 mg, 6.5 mg, 9 mg

Additional Information I.V. preparations contain alcohol and/or propylene glycol; may need to use nitrate-free internal (10-12 hours/day) to avoid tolerance development; tolerance may possibly be reversed with acetylcysteine; gradually decrease dose in patients receiving NTG for prolonged period to avoid withdrawal reaction; monitor for ethanol toxicity due to diluent TLV-TWA 0.05 ppm; sweet, burning taste; tablets are not explosive.

Specific References

Ehrenpreis ED, Young MA, and Leikin JB, "Symptomatic Nitroglycerin Toxicity From Erroneous Use of Topical Nitroglycerin," *Vet Hum Toxicol*, 1990, 32(2):138-9.

Nitroglycerol see Nitroglycerin on page 437

Nitroglyn® see Nitroglycerin on page 437

Nitrol® see Nitroglycerin on page 437

Nitrolan® see Nitroglycerin on page 437

Nitrolingual® see Nitroglycerin on page 437

Nitrong® see Nitroglycerin on page 437

Nitrospan® see Nitroglycerin on page 437

Nitrostat® see Nitroglycerin on page 437

Nitrous Oxide

Synonyms Factitious Air; Laughing Gas; Nitrogen Monoxide; Whippet

UN Number 1020

Abuse Potential Yes

Impairment Potential Yes

Use Anesthetic, foaming agent, and rocket fuel

Mechanism of Toxic Action Asphyxiant; partial agonist of opioid receptors

Toxicodynamics/kinetics

Absorption: Readily through the lungs

Elimination: Through the lungs

Signs and Symptoms of Acute Intoxication Dyspnea, neuritis, headache, dizziness, euphoria, nausea and vomiting (rarely), mood disorder, leukopenia, agranulocytosis; can cause a pneumothorax by barotrauma

When to Transport to Hospital Transport any symptomatic patient

Overdosage/Treatment Supportive therapy: Give 100% humidified oxygen

Adverse Reactions

Cardiovascular: Hypotension, arrhythmias, A-V dissociation, cerebral edema

Central nervous system: CNS depression, ataxia

Hematologic: Bone marrow depression, methemoglobin formation, aplastic anemia (chronic use)

(Continued)

Nitrous Oxide (Continued)

Neuromuscular & skeletal: Neuropathy (peripheral), myeloneuropathies

Miscellaneous: Potential carcinogen

Reference Range Arterial blood nitrous oxide concentrations associated with surgical anesthesia range from 170-220 mL/L

Additional Information Colorless, sweet odor; chronic inhalation may result in pancytopenia including anemia (megaloblastic); nitrous oxide cylinders are painted blue; anemia (megaloblastic) (vitamin B_{12} deficiency)

TLV-TWA: 50 ppm

Minimal toxic dose by inhalation: 24 mg/kg over 2 hours

Specific References

Kunkel DB, "Nitrous Oxide: Not a Laughing Matter Anymore," *J Emerg Med*, 1987, 19:79-84.

Nitrozepamum *see* Nitrazepam *on page 435*

N-Methyl-Cathinone *see* Methcathinone *on page 389*

N,N-Diethyl-3-Methyl-Diethyl-M-Toluamide *see* Diethyltoluamide *on page 197*

N,N-Diethyl-M-Toluamide *see* Diethyltoluamide *on page 197*

N,N-Diethyl-M-Toluic Acid *see* Diethyltoluamide *on page 197*

NO *see* Nitric Oxide *on page 436*

Nobesine® *see* Diethylpropion *on page 196*

Noctec® *see* Chloral Hydrate *on page 122*

Nolafren® *see* Clobazam *on page 151*

Nolex® LA *see* Guaifenesin and Phenylpropanolamine *on page 272*

Noludar® *see* Methyprylon *on page 399*

11-Nor-9-Carboxy-Delta-9-Tetrahydrocannabinol *see* Cannabinoids, Qualitative *on page 100*

Nordryl® Injection *see* Diphenhydramine *on page 205*

Nordryl® Oral *see* Diphenhydramine *on page 205*

Norflex® *see* Orphenadrine *on page 448*

Norgesic™ *see* Orphenadrine, Aspirin, and Caffeine *on page 449*

Norgesic™ Forte *see* Orphenadrine, Aspirin, and Caffeine *on page 449*

Noriel® *see* Flunitrazepam *on page 250*

Normi-Nox® *see* Methaqualone Hydrochloride *on page 388*

Normison® *see* Temazepam *on page 559*

Normodyne® *see* Labetalol *on page 331*

Normoglic® *see* Chlorpropamide *on page 140*

Norocaine® *see* Lidocaine *on page 345*

Norpramin® *see* Desipramine *on page 180*

Nor-tet® Oral *see* Tetracycline *on page 568*

Nortimil® *see* Desipramine *on page 180*

Nortrilen® *see* Nortriptyline *on this page*

Nortriptyline (nor TRIP ti leen)

U.S. Brand Names Allegron®; Aventyl® Hydrochloride; Nortrilen®; Norval®; Pamelor®

Therapeutic Category Antidepressant

Impairment Potential Yes

Use Treatment of various forms of depression, often in conjunction with psychotherapy

Usual Dosage Oral:

Nocturnal enuresis: Children:

6-7 years (20-25 kg): 10 mg/day

8-11 years (25-35 kg): 10-20 mg/day
>11 years (35-54 kg): 25-35 mg/day
Depression: Adults: 25 mg 3-4 times/day up to 150 mg/day
Elderly and Adolescents: 30-50 mg/day in divided doses

Mechanism of Action Increases the synaptic concentration of serotonin and/ or norepinephrine in the central nervous system by inhibition of their reuptake by the presynaptic neuronal membrane

Pharmacodynamics/kinetics

Peak effect: Maximal antidepressant effects may not occur for 2 weeks or more after therapy is begun
Absorption: Oral: Rapidly and well after administration
Metabolism: Primarily detoxified in the liver
Half-life: 28-31 hours
Time to peak serum concentration: Within 7-8½ hours

Signs and Symptoms of Acute Intoxication Agitation, dental erosion, photosensitivity, insomnia, impotence, dysphagia, bone marrow depression, mania, intraocular pressure (increased), ejaculatory disturbances, memory loss, A-V block, dementia, depression, delirium, thrombocytopenia, night terrors, hypoglycemia, confusion, heart block, hyponatremia, visual hallucinations, hyperthermia, respiratory depression, pulmonary edema, urinary retention, coma, hypothermia, hypotension, tachycardia, P-R prolongation, QRS prolongation, Q-T prolongation, measurement of QRS interval >0.10 seconds, may indicate significant toxicity; seizures within 3 hours of ingestion, leukopenia; neutropenia; agranulocytosis; granulocytopenia

When to Transport to Hospital Transport any pediatric or adult overdose

Warnings/Precautions Safe use of tricyclic antidepressants in children <12 years of age has not been established; nortriptyline should not be abruptly discontinued in patients receiving high doses for prolonged periods; do not drink alcoholic beverages; use with caution in patients with cardiac conduction disturbances, history of hyperthyroid; generic formulations may result in higher plasma levels

Adverse Reactions

>10%:
Central nervous system: Dizziness, drowsiness, headache
Gastrointestinal: Xerostomia, constipation, increased appetite, nausea, unpleasant taste, weight gain
Neuromuscular & skeletal: Weakness
1% to 10%:
Cardiovascular: Postural hypotension, arrhythmias, tachycardia, sudden death
Central nervous system: Confusion, delirium, hallucinations, nervousness, restlessness, parkinsonian syndrome, insomnia
Endocrine & metabolic: Sexual dysfunction
Gastrointestinal: Diarrhea, heartburn, constipation
Genitourinary: Dysuria, urinary retention
Ocular: Blurred vision, eye pain, increased intraocular pressure
Neuromuscular & skeletal: Fine muscle tremors
Miscellaneous: Diaphoresis (excessive)

Reference Range

Therapeutic: 50-150 ng/mL (SI: 190-570 nmol/L)
Toxic: >500 ng/mL (SI: >1900 nmol/L)

Drug Interactions

Nortriptyline blocks the uptake of guanethidine and thus prevents the hypotensive effect of guanethidine; nortriptyline may be additive with or may potentiate the action of other CNS depressants such as sedatives or hypnotics; nortriptyline potentiates the pressor and cardiac effects of sympathomimetic agents such as isoproterenol, epinephrine, etc
(Continued)

Nortriptyline *(Continued)*

With MAO inhibitors, fever, hypertension, tachycardia, confusion, seizures, and death have been reported
Additive anticholinergic effects seen with other anticholinergic agents
Cimetidine reduces hepatic metabolism of nortriptyline
Nortriptyline may increase the prothrombin time in patients stabilized on warfarin
Lower serum tricyclic antidepressant levels may be noted in cigarette smokers due to increased hepatic metabolism

Dosage Forms
Nortriptyline hydrochloride:
Capsule: 10 mg, 25 mg, 50 mg, 75 mg
Solution: 10 mg/5 mL (473 mL)

Additional Information Maximum antidepressant effect may not be seen for 2 or more weeks after initiation of therapy

Specific References
Frommer DA, Kulig KW, Marx JA, et al, "Tricyclic Antidepressant Overdose," *JAMA*, 1987, 257(4):521-6.

Norval® *see* Nortriptyline *on page 440*
Nostril® Nasal Solution [OTC] *see* Phenylephrine *on page 479*
Novafed® *see* Pseudoephedrine *on page 516*
Novanov® *see* Nitrazepam *on page 435*
Novodorm® *see* Triazolam *on page 592*
Novoflurazine® *see* Trifluoperazine *on page 596*
Novolin® *see* Insulin Preparations *on page 314*
Novomedopa® *see* Methyldopa *on page 393*
Novoridazine® *see* Thioridazine *on page 578*
Novostrep® *see* Streptomycin *on page 548*
Novoxapin® *see* Doxepin *on page 211*
Noxaben® *see* Lorazepam *on page 351*
NPH *see* Insulin Preparations *on page 314*
NPH Iletin® I *see* Insulin Preparations *on page 314*
N-(Phosphonomethyl) glycine: GlySH *see* Glyphosate *on page 269*
n-Propyl Alcohol *see* 1-Propanol *on page 508*
NSP *see* Neurotoxic Shellfish Poisoning *on page 428*
NTG *see* Nitroglycerin *on page 437*
Nubain® *see* Nalbuphine *on page 418*
Nucofed® *see* Guaifenesin, Pseudoephedrine, and Codeine *on page 275*
Nucofed® Pediatric Expectorant *see* Guaifenesin, Pseudoephedrine, and Codeine *on page 275*
Nucotuss® *see* Guaifenesin, Pseudoephedrine, and Codeine *on page 275*
Nuctalon® *see* Estazolam *on page 228*
Numorphan® *see* Oxymorphone *on page 455*
Numzitdent® [OTC] *see* Benzocaine *on page 70*
Numzit Teething® [OTC] *see* Benzocaine *on page 70*
Nuprin® [OTC] *see* Ibuprofen *on page 308*
Nuran® *see* Cyproheptadine *on page 175*

Nutmeg

Scientific Name *Myristica fragrans*
Abuse Potential Yes
Impairment Potential Yes

Use In folk medicine for delayed menses

Toxic Dose It is estimated that 2 tablespoons of ground nutmeg will produce toxicity; however, amounts may vary depending on the content of volitile oil
Toxic dose: 1-3 nutmegs can cause toxic symptoms

Mechanism of Toxic Action One theory for nutmeg's pharmacologic properties is that myristicin and elemicin are metabolized to psychoactive amphetamine derivatives, MMDA (3-methoxy-4,5 dimethylenedioxyamphetamine) and TMA (3,4,5-trimethoxyamphetamine); geraniol is a potent emetic

Signs and Symptoms of Acute Intoxication The most prominent effects of significant ingestions appear to be hallucinations, nausea, and profound vomiting; tachycardia, mydriasis, hypothermia, dry skin, hypotension, and a feeling of impending doom may also be seen; symptoms may be delayed up to 8 hours after ingestion

When to Transport to Hospital Transport any symptomatic patient

Overdosage/Treatment Symptomatic and supportive treatment as needed

Adverse Reactions Cardiovascular: Sinus tachycardia

Drug Interactions
Decreased effect of antihypertensives
Increased toxicity with disulfiram (possible seizures, delirium), fluoxetine (and other serotonin active agents), TCAs (cardiovascular instability), meperidine (cardiovascular instability), phenothiazine (hyperpyretic crisis), levodopa, sympathomimetics (hyperpyretic crisis), barbiturates, rauwolfia alkaloids (eg, reserpine), dextroamphetamine (psychoses), foods containing tyramine (hypertension, headache, seizures); theophylline/caffeine (hyperthermia), cyclobenzaprine (fever/seizures)
Potentiation of hypoglycemia with oral hypoglycemic agents
Serotonin syndrome (shivering, muscle rigidity, salivation, agitation, and hyperthermia) can occur with concomitant administration of venlafaxine and tranylcypromine

Additional Information Nutmeg is the seed of *Myristica fragrans*; the spice mace is from the seed coat of *Myristica fragrans*
Family: Myristicaceae
Toxin: Myristicin, elemicin, geraniol
Range: Grows in India, Ceylon, and Granada
Toxic parts: Volitile oil in seed and seed coat appears to be responsible for pharmacologic effects

Specific References
Abernethy MK and Becker LB, "Acute Nutmeg Intoxication," *Am J Emerg Med*, 1992, 10(5):429-30.

Nutracort® see Hydrocortisone *on page 297*
Nydrazid® see Isoniazid *on page 322*
Nytol® Oral [OTC] see Diphenhydramine *on page 205*
Obermine® see Phentermine *on page 478*
Obesin® see Propylhexedrine *on page 513*
Occlusal-HP Liquid see Salicylic Acid *on page 530*
Octocaine® see Lidocaine *on page 345*
Ocu-Drop® [OTC] see Tetrahydrozoline *on page 569*
Ocupress® see Carteolol *on page 115*
OFF® see Diethyltoluamide *on page 197*
Off-Ezy® Wart Remover [OTC] see Salicylic Acid *on page 530*
Oil of Vitrial see Sulfuric Acid *on page 554*

Olanzapine (oh LAN za peen)
Related Information
Clozapine *on page 159*
(Continued)

Olanzapine *(Continued)*

Synonyms LY170053

U.S. Brand Names Zyprexa®

Therapeutic Category Antipsychotic Agent

Impairment Potential Yes

Use Antipsychotic; treatment of manifestations of psychotic disorders

Usual Dosage Adults: Oral: Initial: 5-10 mg once daily with a target dose of 10 mg/day within several days; maximum daily dose: 20 mg; increase or decrease dosages by no more than 5 mg once daily at 1-week intervals

Mechanism of Action A thienobenzodiazepine with properties similar to clozapine; exact mechanism of action is unknown; olanzapine acts primarily as a dopamine (D_1, D_2, D_4 and D_6) and $5HT_2$ antagonist; also inhibits serotonin type 3 and 6, muscarinic M_{1-5}, H_1, and adrenergic alpha$_1$-receptors

Pharmacodynamics/kinetics

Absorption: Well absorbed; not affected by food

Protein binding, plasma: 93% bound to albumin and alpha$_1$-glycoprotein

Metabolism: Highly metabolized

Peak concentrations: ~6 hours

Half-life: 21-31 hours; approximately 1.5 times greater in elderly

Signs and Symptoms of Acute Intoxication Slurred speech, drowsiness; although not described, hypotension is a possibility; rhinitis (10%)

When to Transport to Hospital Transport any adult ingestion over 20 mg

Warnings/Precautions Use with caution in patients exhibiting renal/hepatic impairment, central nervous system depression, clozapine hypersensitivity, tremors, cardiovascular disease, pregnancy and constipation; neuroleptic malignant syndrome (NMS), tardive dyskinesia, orthostatic hypotension, seizures, hyperprolactinemia, transaminase elevations

Adverse Reactions

>10%: Central nervous system: Headache, somnolence, insomnia, agitation, nervousness, hostility, dizziness

1% to 10%:

Central nervous system: Dystonic reactions, Parkinsonian events, akathisia, anxiety, personality changes, fever

Gastrointestinal: Xerostomia, constipation, abdominal pain, weight gain

Neuromuscular & skeletal: Arthralgia

Ocular: Amblyopia

Respiratory: Rhinitis, cough, pharyngitis

Drug Interactions

Increased clearance of olanzapine (~50%): Carbamazepine, inducers of CYP1A2 (eg, omeprazole, rifampin)

Decreased clearance of olanzapine: Inhibitors of CYP1A2 (eg, ciprofloxacin, fluvoxamine)

Olanzapine may antagonize the effects of levodopa and dopamine agonists

Dosage Forms Tablet: 5 mg, 7.5 mg, 10 mg

Additional Information Antipsychotic efficacy was established in short-term (6 weeks) controlled trials of psychotic disorders; effectiveness in long-term use (>6 weeks) has not been systematically evaluated in controlled trial, therefore, the physician who uses olanzapine for extended periods should periodically re-evaluate the long-term usefulness of the drug for the individual patient; less extrapyramidal effects and adverse hematological effects as compared with clozapine

Specific References

Silberman H, "Olanzapine," *Clin Toxicol Rev*, 1997, 19(6):1-2.

Oleum Ricini *see* Castor Oil *on page 118*

Ololiuqui *see* Morning Glory *on page 409*

Omnipen® see Ampicillin *on page 48*

Omnipen®-N see Ampicillin *on page 48*

Omnopon® see Opium Alkaloids (Hydrochlorides) *on this page*

OMS® see Morphine Sulfate *on page 410*

O,O-Diethyl O-2-Isopropyl-4-Methyl-6-Pyrimidinyl Thiophosphate see Diazinon *on page 192*

O,O-Diethyl-O-(3,5,6-Trichloro-2-Pyridyl) Phosphorothioate see Chlorpyrifos *on page 143*

Opcon® see Naphazoline *on page 422*

Opialum see Opium Alkaloids (Hydrochlorides) *on this page*

Opiates, Qualitative, Urine

Related Information

Codeine, Urine *on page 165*

Applies to Heroin; Narcotics; Poppy Seeds

Use Evaluate drug abuse; assess toxicity

Reference Range Negative (less than cutoff)

Additional Information A qualitative urine screen for opiates is performed in suspected overdose cases or as part of a drugs-of-abuse program. The test is most sensitive for morphine and codeine, but other drugs will cross react in an immunoassay and give positive results (eg, hydrocodone, hydromorphone). All presumptive positive assays should be confirmed, preferably by GC/MS. Morphine is a prescribed drug for pain relief, a metabolite of heroin, a metabolite of codeine, and a constituent of poppy seeds. Its presence in urine, even after confirmation, must be interpreted very carefully.

Opiates in general are a group of drugs (commonly referred to as narcotics) which are used medically to relieve pain, but which also have a high potential for abuse. Some opiates come from a resin taken from the seed pod of the Asian poppy. This group of drugs includes opium, morphine, and codeine. Other opiates are synthesized or manufactured (eg, heroin). Opium appears as dark brown chunks or as a powder, and is usually smoked or eaten. Heroin can be a white or brownish powder which is usually dissolved in water and injected.

Opiates tend to relax the user. When the opiates are injected, the user feels an immediate "rush." Other initial and unpleasant effects include restlessness, nausea, and vomiting. The user may go "on the nod," going back and forth from feeling alert to drowsy. With very large doses, the user cannot be awakened, pupils become smaller, and the skin becomes cold, moist, and bluish in color. Furthermore, breathing slows down and death may occur. Clearance may be slower in geriatric patients.

Specific References

Pettit BC Jr, Dyszel SM, and Hood LV, "Opiates in Poppy Seed: Effect on Urinalysis Results After Consumption of Poppy Seed Cake-Filling," *Clin Chem*, 1987, 33(7):1251-2.

Opiran® see Pimozide *on page 487*

Opium Alkaloids (Hydrochlorides) (OH pee um AL ka loyds)

Related Information

Controlled Substances - Uses and Effects *on page 741*

Synonyms Opialum; Papaveretum

U.S. Brand Names Escopon®; Omnopon®; Pantopon®

Therapeutic Category Analgesic, Narcotic

Abuse Potential Yes

Impairment Potential Yes

Use Relief of severe pain

Usual Dosage Adults: I.M., S.C.: 5-20 mg every 4-5 hours

(Continued)

445

Opium Alkaloids (Hydrochlorides) *(Continued)*

Pharmacodynamics/kinetics
Absorption: Oral: Variable, more slowly absorbed than morphine
Metabolism: In the liver via glucuronide conjugation
Half-life: Adults: 2-4 hours
Elimination: Excreted unchanged in urine

Signs and Symptoms of Acute Intoxication
Apnea, delirium, dysphoria, respiratory depression, rhabdomyolysis, hypotension, ptosis, seizures (in neonates), myoglobinuria, coma, miosis, pulmonary edema

When to Transport to Hospital
Transport any patient with change in mental status

Overdosage/Treatment
Supportive therapy: Naloxone hydrochloride (0.4-2 mg I.V., S.C., or through an endotracheal tube); a continuous infusion (at ²/₃ the response dose/hour) may be required

Adverse Reactions
>10%:
  Cardiovascular: Hypotension
  Gastrointestinal: Nausea, vomiting
<10%:
  Cardiovascular: Palpitations, bradycardia, peripheral vasodilation, sinus bradycardia
  Central nervous system: CNS depression, agitation, intracranial pressure (increased), cognitive dysfunction, paranoia
  Dermatologic: Pruritus
  Endocrine & metabolic: Syndrome of inappropriate antidiuretic hormone (SIADH)
  Gastrointestinal: Constipation (more constipating than morphine), biliary tract spasm
  Genitourinary: Urinary tract spasm
  Ocular: Miosis
  Respiratory: Apnea, respiratory depression
  Miscellaneous: Physical and psychological dependence, histamine release

Dosage Forms
Injection: 20 mg/mL (1 mL)

Specific References
Robinson LQ and Stephenson TP, "Self Injection Treatment for Impotence," *BMJ*, 1989, 299(6715):1568.

Opium and Belladonna *see Belladonna and Opium on page 66*

Opium Tincture *(OH pee um TING chur)*

Synonyms Deodorized Opium Tincture; DTO; Laudanum
Therapeutic Category Analgesic, Narcotic
Abuse Potential Yes
Impairment Potential Yes
Use Treatment of diarrhea or relief of pain
Usual Dosage Oral:
Children:
  Diarrhea: 0.005-0.01 mL/kg/dose every 3-4 hours for a maximum of 6 doses/ 24 hours
  Analgesia: 0.01-0.02 mL/kg/dose every 3-4 hours
Adults:
  Diarrhea: 0.3-1 mL/dose every 2-6 hours to maximum of 6 mL/24 hours
  Analgesia: 0.6-1.5 mL/dose every 3-4 hours
Mechanism of Action Contains many narcotic alkaloids including morphine; its mechanism for gastric motility inhibition is primarily due to this morphine

content; it results in a decrease in digestive secretions, an increase in gastrointestinal muscle tone, and therefore a reduction in gastrointestinal propulsion

Pharmacodynamics/kinetics
Duration of effect: 4-5 hours
Absorption: Variable from gastrointestinal tract
Metabolism: In the liver

Signs and Symptoms of Acute Intoxication Apnea, respiratory depression, myasthenia gravis (exacerbation or precipitation of), ptosis, rhabdomyolysis, hypotension, seizures (in neonates), myoglobinuria, coma, miosis, pulmonary edema

When to Transport to Hospital Transport any patient with change in mental status

Overdosage/Treatment Supportive therapy: Naloxone hydrochloride (0.4-2 mg I.V., S.C., or through an endotracheal tube); a continuous infusion (at 2/3 the response dose/hour) may be required

Warnings/Precautions Opium shares the toxic potential of opiate agonists, and usual precautions of opiate agonist therapy should be observed; some preparations contain sulfites which may cause allergic reactions; infants <3 months of age are more susceptible to respiratory depression, use with caution and generally in reduced doses in this age group; this is **not** paregoric, dose accordingly

Adverse Reactions
>10%:
    Cardiovascular: Palpitations, hypotension, bradycardia
    Central nervous system: Drowsiness, dizziness
    Neuromuscular & skeletal: Weakness
1% to 10%:
    Central nervous system: Restlessness, headache, malaise
    Genitourinary: Decreased urination
    Miscellaneous: Histamine release

Drug Interactions
Increased effect with CNS depressants, cimetidine, MAO inhibitors, tricyclic antidepressants, ethanol, thiopental, and hydroxyzine
Phenothiazines may antagonize the analgesic effect of morphine and other opiate agonists
Dextroamphetamine may enhance the analgesic effect of morphine and other opiate agonists
Plasma morphine concentrations rise when co-administered with cisapride

Dosage Forms Liquid: 10% [0.6 mL equivalent to morphine 6 mg]

Optal *see* 1-Propanol *on page 508*

Optigene® [OTC] *see* Tetrahydrozoline *on page 569*

Optimax® WV *see* Tryptophan *on page 602*

Optimine® *see* Azatadine *on page 62*

Orabase®-B [OTC] *see* Benzocaine *on page 70*

Orabase® HCA *see* Hydrocortisone *on page 297*

Orabase®-O [OTC] *see* Benzocaine *on page 70*

Orajel® Brace-Aid Oral Anesthetic [OTC] *see* Benzocaine *on page 70*

Orajel® Maximum Strength [OTC] *see* Benzocaine *on page 70*

Orajel® Mouth-Aid [OTC] *see* Benzocaine *on page 70*

Oramide® *see* Tolbutamide *on page 585*

Oraminic® II *see* Brompheniramine *on page 84*

Oramorph SR® *see* Morphine Sulfate *on page 410*

Orap™ *see* Pimozide *on page 487*

Orasept® [OTC] *see* Benzocaine *on page 70*

Orasol® [OTC] *see Benzocaine on page 70*

Orasone® *see Prednisone on page 497*

Oratect® [OTC] *see Benzocaine on page 70*

Orbinamon® *see Thiothixene on page 580*

Orciprenaline Sulfate *see Metaproterenol on page 376*

Ordrine AT® Extended Release Capsule *see Caramiphen and Phenylpropanolamine on page 103*

Oretic® *see Hydrochlorothiazide on page 291*

Oreton® Methyl *see Methyltestosterone on page 398*

Organidin® NR *see Guaifenesin on page 269*

Orinase® *see Tolbutamide on page 585*

ORLAAM® *see Levomethadyl Acetate Hydrochloride on page 341*

Ormazine® *see Chlorpromazine on page 138*

Ornade® Spansule® *see Chlorpheniramine and Phenylpropanolamine on page 134*

Ornex® No Drowsiness [OTC] *see Acetaminophen and Pseudoephedrine on page 22*

Orphenadrine (or FEN a dreen)

Synonyms Orphenadrine Citrate

U.S. Brand Names Norflex®

Therapeutic Category Skeletal Muscle Relaxant

Impairment Potential Yes

Use Treatment of muscle spasm associated with acute painful musculoskeletal conditions; supportive therapy in tetanus

Usual Dosage Adults:
Oral: 100 mg twice daily
I.M., I.V.: 60 mg every 12 hours

Mechanism of Action Indirect skeletal muscle relaxant thought to work by central atropine-like effects; has some ephorogenic and analgesic properties

Pharmacodynamics/kinetics
Onset of action:
Oral: Within 1 hour
I.M.: 5 minutes
I.V.: Immediate
Duration: 12 hours
Peak effect: Within 2-4 hours
Absorption: Oral: Readily after administration from gastrointestinal tract; may be variable in overdose due to anticholinergic effects
Distribution: Widely distributed throughout the body
Protein binding: 20%
Metabolism: Hepatic
Half-life: 14-16 hours
Time to peak serum concentration:
Oral: 6-8 hours
I.M.: 0.5 hours
I.V.: Immediate
Elimination: Primarily (60%) in urine (8% as unchanged drug)

Signs and Symptoms of Acute Intoxication Blurred vision, tachycardia, rhabdomyolysis, confusion, seizures, respiratory arrest, arrhythmias, hypertension, vasodilation, anticholinergic symptoms, dystonic reactions, paralysis, psychosis, myoglobinuria

When to Transport to Hospital Transport any pediatric ingestion over 1 mg/kg or any patient with change in mental status

448

Adverse Reactions
>10%:
Central nervous system: Drowsiness, dizziness
Ocular: Blurred vision
1% to 10%:
Cardiovascular: Flushing of face, tachycardia, syncope
Dermatologic: Rash
Gastrointestinal: Nausea, vomiting, constipation
Genitourinary: Decreased urination
Neuromuscular & skeletal: Weakness
Ocular: Gaze nystagmus, increased intraocular pressure
Respiratory: Nasal congestion

Reference Range
Toxic: 2-3 mg/mL
Fatal: 4-8 mg/L

Dosage Forms
Injection: 30 mg/mL (2 mL, 10 mL)
Tablet: 100 mg
Tablet, sustained release: 100 mg

Additional Information Aplastic anemia has occurred rarely

Specific References
Clarke B, Mair J, and Rudolf M, "Acute Poisoning With Orphenadrine," *Lancet*, 1985, 1(8442):1386.

Orphenadrine, Aspirin, and Caffeine
(or FEN a dreen, AS pir in, & KAF een)
U.S. Brand Names Norgesic™; Norgesic™ Forte
Therapeutic Category Analgesic, Non-narcotic; Skeletal Muscle Relaxant
Impairment Potential Yes
Dosage Forms
Tablet: Orphenadrine citrate 25 mg, aspirin 385 mg, and caffeine 30 mg
Tablet (Norgesic® Forte): Orphenadrine citrate 50 mg, aspirin 770 mg, and caffeine 60 mg

Orphenadrine Citrate see Orphenadrine on previous page

Orthoboric Acid see Boric Acid on page 80

Ortho-Chlorobenzylidene Malonitrile see Chlorobenzylidene Malonitrile on page 128

Or-Tyl® see Dicyclomine on page 194

Orudis® see Ketoprofen on page 328

Orudis® KT see Ketoprofen on page 328

Orulop® see Loperamide on page 349

Ospolot® see Sulthiame on page 555

Ospronim® see Pentazocine on page 463

Ovaban® see Megestrol Acetate on page 365

Oxandrin® see Oxandrolone on this page

Oxandrolone (oks AN droe lone)
U.S. Brand Names Oxandrin®
Therapeutic Category Androgen
Use Treatment of catabolic or tissue-depleting processes
Adverse Reactions
Male:
Postpubertal:
>10%: Bladder irritability, priapism, gynecomastia, acne
(Continued)

Oxandrolone *(Continued)*

1% to 10%: Decreased libido, hepatic dysfunction, chills, nausea, diarrhea, insomnia, iron deficiency anemia, suppression of clotting factors, prostatic hypertrophy (geriatric)

Prepubertal: Virilism

>10%: Acne, virilism

1% to 10%: Hyperpigmentation, chills, diarrhea, nausea, insomnia, iron deficiency anemia, suppression of clotting factors

Female:

>10%: Virilism

1% to 10%: Hypercalcemia, hepatic dysfunction, nausea, chills, diarrhea, insomnia, iron deficiency anemia, suppression of clotting factors

Dosage Forms Tablet: 2.5 mg

Oxazepam *(oks A ze pam)*

Related Information

Controlled Substances - Uses and Effects *on page 741*

U.S. Brand Names Adumbran®; Serax®; Serenid® Forte

Canadian Brand Names Apo-Oxazepam®; Novo-Oxazepam®; Oxpam®; PMS-Oxazepam®; Zapex®

Therapeutic Category Anticonvulsant; Benzodiazepine

Abuse Potential Yes

Impairment Potential Yes; Blood oxazepam levels exceeding 0.2 mg/L associated with impaired driving. Brief or extended periods of exposure are less likely to cause driving impairment in the elderly as compared with the longer half-life benzodiazepines.

Baselt RC and Cravey RH, *Disposition of Toxic Drugs and Chemicals in Man*, 4th ed, Foster City, CA: Chemical Toxicology Institute, 1995, 569.

Use Treatment of anxiety and management of alcohol withdrawal; may also be used as an anticonvulsant in management of simple partial seizures

Usual Dosage Oral:

Children: 1 mg/kg/day has been administered

Adults:

Anxiety: 10-30 mg 3-4 times/day

Alcohol withdrawal: 15-30 mg 3-4 times/day

Hypnotic: 15-30 mg

Mechanism of Action Benzodiazepine anxiolytic sedative that produces CNS depression at the subcortical level, except at high doses, whereby it works at the cortical level

Pharmacodynamics/kinetics Studies have shown that the elderly are more sensitive to the effects of benzodiazepine as compared to younger adults.

Absorption: Oral: Almost completely through gastrointestinal tract

Metabolism: In the liver to inactive compounds (primarily as glucuronides)

Half-life: 5-15 hours

Time to peak serum concentration: Within 2-3 hours

Signs and Symptoms of Acute Intoxication Confusion, coma, hypoactive reflexes, hyporeflexia, dyspnea, gaze nystagmus, slurred speech, unsteady gait, hyponatremia, hypochloremia, hyperglycemia (spurious)

When to Transport to Hospital Transport any patient with change in mental status or ingestions over 1 mg/kg

Warnings/Precautions Avoid using in patients with pre-existing CNS depression, severe uncontrolled pain, or narrow-angle glaucoma; use with caution in patients using other CNS depressants and in the elderly

Adverse Reactions
>10%:
Cardiovascular: Tachycardia, chest pain
Central nervous system: Drowsiness, fatigue, ataxia, lightheadedness, memory impairment, insomnia, anxiety, depression, headache
Dermatologic: Rash
Endocrine & metabolic: Decreased libido
Gastrointestinal: Xerostomia, constipation, diarrhea, decreased salivation, nausea, vomiting, increased or decreased appetite
Neuromuscular & skeletal: Dysarthria
Ocular: Blurred vision
Miscellaneous: Diaphoresis
1% to 10%:
Cardiovascular: Syncope, hypotension
Central nervous system: Confusion, nervousness, dizziness, akathisia
Dermatologic: Dermatitis
Gastrointestinal: Increased salivation, weight gain or loss
Neuromuscular & skeletal: Rigidity, tremor, muscle cramps
Ocular: Blurred vision
Otic: Tinnitus
Respiratory: Nasal congestion, hyperventilation
Reference Range Therapeutic: 0.2-1.4 µg/mL (SI: 0.7-4.9 µmol/L)
Drug Interactions Ethanol delays absorption; antiepileptics increase clearance
Dosage Forms
Capsule: 10 mg, 15 mg, 30 mg
Tablet: 15 mg
Specific References
Moshkowitz M, Pines A, Finkelstein A, et al, "Skin Blisters as a Manifestation of Oxazepam Toxicity," *J Toxicol Clin Toxicol*, 1990, 28(3):383-6.

Oxilapine Succinate see Loxapine on page 354

Oxitriptan
Related Information
Tryptophan on page 602
Synonyms 5-HTP; L-5-Hydroxytryptophan
U.S. Brand Names Cincofarm®; Dromia®; Levothym®; Le Votonine®; Natil®; Oxyfan®; Pretonin®; Quietim®; Telesol®; Trimeg®; Triptene®; Tript-OH®; Triptum®
Therapeutic Category Antidepressant
Use Approved in U.S. as an orphan drug for use in postanoxic intention myoclonus
Investigational: Antidepressant, also used for sleep disorders, migraine headaches; epilepsy, Parkinson, psychostimulant
Usual Dosage
Postanoxic myoclonus: Initial: 25 mg 4 times/day; can increase dose by 100 mg every 3-5 days
Depression: Initial: 10 mg/day; maximum daily dose: 600 mg
I.V.: 1-2 mg/kg
Mechanism of Action A precursor of serotonin which is a neurotransmitter
Pharmacodynamics/kinetics
Absorption: 1-2 hours
Protein binding: 19%
Metabolism: Hepatic and peripheral decarboxylation to serotonin and 5-hydroxyindoleacetic acid
Bioavailability: 47% to 84%
Half-life: 4.3 hours
(Continued)

Oxitriptan *(Continued)*

Elimination: Renal

When to Transport to Hospital Transport any pediatric ingestion of any amount or any patient with change in mental status

Warnings/Precautions Do not administer with MAO inhibitors, reserpine, tricyclic antidepressants, fenfluramine, or selective serotonin reuptake inhibitors; discontinue above drugs for 2 weeks prior to initiation of oxitriptan therapy

Adverse Reactions

Cardiovascular: Transient hypotension

Central nervous system: Hypomania, agitation, anxiety, insomnia, akinesia

Dermatologic: Scleroderma

Gastrointestinal: Nausea, anorexia, diarrhea, vomiting

Respiratory: Dyspnea

Drug Interactions With concomitant use with MAO inhibitor agents or selective serotonin reuptake inhibitors; a serotonin-like reaction can develop; tryptophan can reduce blood levels of levodopa; carbidopa inhibits peripheral decarboxylation of oxitriptan to serotonin

Dosage Forms Capsule: 25 mg, 50 mg, 100 mg, 200 mg

Additional Information An orphan drug for postanoxic intention myoclonus, available through Circa pharmaceuticals (516-842-8383), or in combination with carbidopa through Du Pont pharmaceuticals (1-800-474-2762). Has been used to treat LSD-induced psychosis

Specific References

Byerley WF, Judd LL, Reimherr FW, et al, "5-Hydroxytryptophan: A Review of Its Antidepressant Efficacy and Adverse Effects," *J Clin Psychopharmacol*, 1987, 7(3):127-37.

2-Oxobutane see Methyl Ethyl Ketone *on page 396*

Oxtriphylline see Theophylline Salts *on page 571*

Oxycodone *(oks i KOE done)*

Related Information

Controlled Substances - Uses and Effects *on page 741*

Oxycodone and Acetaminophen *on next page*

Oxycodone and Aspirin *on page 454*

Synonyms Dihydrohydroxycodeinone; Oxycodone and Acetaminophen; Oxycodone and Aspirin

U.S. Brand Names Endone®; Eukodal®; Roxicodone™; Supeudol®

Canadian Brand Names Supeudol®

Therapeutic Category Analgesic, Narcotic

Abuse Potential Yes

Impairment Potential Yes

Use Management of moderate to severe pain, normally used in combination with non-narcotic analgesics

Usual Dosage Oral:

Children:

6-12 years: 1.25 mg every 6 hours as needed

>12 years: 2.5 mg every 6 hours as needed

Adults: 5 mg every 6 hours as needed

Mechanism of Action Binds to opiate receptors in the CNS, causing inhibition of ascending pain pathways, altering the perception of and response to pain; produces generalized CNS depression

Pharmacodynamics/kinetics

Onset of pain relief: Oral: Within 15-30 minutes

Peak effect: 60 minutes

Duration: 3-6 hours

Metabolism: In the liver to noroxycodone by demethylation

Half-life: 2-5 hours

Elimination: Excreted in urine

Signs and Symptoms of Acute Intoxication CNS depression, lightheadedness, respiratory depression, miosis, noncardiogenic pulmonary edema, coma

When to Transport to Hospital Transport pediatric (<6 years of age) ingestions of any amount or any patient with change in mental status

Overdosage/Treatment Supportive therapy: Naloxone hydrochloride (0.4-2 mg I.V., S.C., or through an endotracheal tube); a continuous infusion (at $^2/_3$ the response dose/hour) may be required

Warnings/Precautions Use with caution in patients with hypersensitivity reactions to other phenanthrene derivative opioid agonists (morphine, hydrocodone, hydromorphone, levorphanol, oxycodone, oxymorphone); respiratory diseases including asthma, emphysema, COPD, or severe liver or renal insufficiency; some preparations contain sulfites which may cause allergic reactions; may be habit-forming; dextromethorphan has equivalent antitussive activity but has much lower toxicity in accidental overdose

Adverse Reactions

>10%:

Cardiovascular: Hypotension

Central nervous system: Fatigue, drowsiness, dizziness

Gastrointestinal: Nausea, vomiting

Neuromuscular & skeletal: Weakness

1% to 10%:

Central nervous system: Nervousness, headache, restlessness, malaise, confusion

Gastrointestinal: Anorexia, stomach cramps, xerostomia, constipation, biliary spasm

Genitourinary: Ureteral spasms, decreased urination

Local: Pain at injection site

Respiratory: Dyspnea, shortness of breath

Reference Range Blood level of 5 mg/L associated with fatality

Drug Interactions MAO inhibitors → ↑ adverse symptoms

Dosage Forms

Liquid, oral: 5 mg/5 mL (500 mL)

Solution, oral concentrate: 20 mg/mL (30 mL)

Tablet: 5 mg

Specific References

Turturro MA and O'Toole KS, "Oxycodone-Induced Pulmonary Edema," *Am J Emerg Med*, 1991, 9(2):201-3.

Oxycodone and Acetaminophen

(oks i KOE done & a seet a MIN oh fen)

Synonyms Acetaminophen and Oxycodone

U.S. Brand Names Percocet®; Roxicet® 5/500; Roxilox®; Tylox®

Canadian Brand Names Endocet®; Oxycocet®; Percocet-Demi®

Therapeutic Category Analgesic, Narcotic

Dosage Forms

Caplet: Oxycodone hydrochloride 5 mg and acetaminophen 500 mg

Capsule: Oxycodone hydrochloride 5 mg and acetaminophen 500 mg

Solution, oral: Oxycodone hydrochloride 5 mg and acetaminophen 325 mg per 5 mL (5 mL, 500 mL)

Tablet: Oxycodone hydrochloride 5 mg and acetaminophen 325 mg

Oxycodone and Acetaminophen *see* Oxycodone *on previous page*

Oxycodone and Aspirin (oks i KOE done & AS pir in)
U.S. Brand Names Codoxy®; Percodan®; Percodan®-Demi; Roxiprin®
Canadian Brand Names Endodan®; Oxycodan®
Therapeutic Category Analgesic, Narcotic
Dosage Forms Tablet:
Percodan®: Oxycodone hydrochloride 4.5 mg, oxycodone terephthalate 0.38 mg, and aspirin 325 mg
Percodan®-Demi: Oxycodone hydrochloride 2.25 mg, oxycodone terephthalate 0.19 mg, and aspirin 325 mg

Oxycodone and Aspirin see Oxycodone on page 452

Oxyfan® see Oxitriptan on page 451

Oxymetholone (oks i METH oh lone)
Related Information
Controlled Substances - Uses and Effects on page 741
U.S. Brand Names Anadrol®
Canadian Brand Names Anapolon®
Therapeutic Category Anabolic Steroid
Use Anemias caused by the administration of myelotoxic drugs
Usual Dosage Adults: Erythropoietic effects: Oral: 1-5 mg/kg/day in 1 daily dose; maximum: 100 mg/day; give for a minimum trial of 3-6 months because response may be delayed
Mechanism of Action Stimulates receptors in organs and tissues to promote growth and development of male sex organs and maintains secondary sex characteristics in androgen-deficient males
Pharmacodynamics/kinetics
Half-life: 9 hours
Elimination: Primarily in urine
Signs and Symptoms of Acute Intoxication Abnormal liver function test, confusion
When to Transport to Hospital Transport any pediatric exposure or any patient who demonstrates any change in mental status
Warnings/Precautions Anabolic steroids may cause peliosis hepatis, liver cell tumors, and blood lipid changes with increased risk of arteriosclerosis; monitor diabetic patients carefully; use with caution in elderly patients, they may be at greater risk for prostatic hypertrophy; use with caution in patients with cardiac, renal, or hepatic disease or epilepsy
Adverse Reactions
Male:
Postpubertal:
>10%:
Dermatologic: Acne
Endocrine & metabolic: Gynecomastia
Genitourinary: Bladder irritability, priapism
1% to 10%:
Central nervous system: Insomnia, chills
Endocrine & metabolic: Decreased libido
Gastrointestinal: Nausea, diarrhea
Genitourinary: Prostatic hypertrophy (elderly)
Hematologic: Iron deficiency anemia, suppression of clotting factors
Hepatic: Hepatic dysfunction
Prepubertal:
>10%:
Dermatologic: Acne
Endocrine & metabolic: Virilism

1% to 10%:
    Central nervous system: Chills, insomnia
    Dermatologic: Hyperpigmentation
    Gastrointestinal: Diarrhea, nausea
    Hematologic: Iron deficiency anemia, suppression of clotting factors

Female:
  >10%: Endocrine & metabolic: Virilism
  1% to 10%:
    Central nervous system: Chills, insomnia
    Endocrine & metabolic: Hypercalcemia
    Gastrointestinal: Nausea, diarrhea
    Hematologic: Iron deficiency anemia, suppression of clotting factors
    Hepatic: Hepatic dysfunction

Drug Interactions Increased toxicity: Increased oral anticoagulants, insulin requirements may be decreased

Dosage Forms Tablet: 50 mg

Additional Information May increase glucagon levels

Specific References
  Ginsburg AD, "Oxymethalone and Hematologic Disease," *Ann Intern Med*, 1973, 79:914.

Oxymorphone (oks i MOR fone)

U.S. Brand Names Numorphan®

Therapeutic Category Analgesic, Narcotic

Abuse Potential Yes

Impairment Potential Yes

Use Management of moderate to severe pain and preoperatively as a sedative and a supplement to anesthesia

Usual Dosage Adults:
  I.M., S.C.: 0.5 mg initially, 1-1.5 mg every 4-6 hours as needed
  I.V.: 0.5 mg initially
  Rectal: 5 mg every 4-6 hours

Mechanism of Action Oxymorphone hydrochloride (Numorphan®) is a potent narcotic analgesic with uses similar to those of morphine. The drug is a semi-synthetic derivative of morphine (phenanthrene derivative) and is closely related to hydromorphone chemically (Dilaudid®).

Pharmacodynamics/kinetics
  Onset of analgesia:
    I.M., I.V., S.C.: Within 5-10 minutes
    Rectal: Within 15-30 minutes
  Metabolism: Conjugated with glucuronic acid
  Peak effect: 30-60 minutes

Signs and Symptoms of Acute Intoxication Miosis, bradycardia, hypotension, sedation, drowsiness, ptosis, fatigue, vomiting, slow and raspy speech

When to Transport to Hospital Transport any pediatric exposure, any patient with mental status changes, or any ingestion over 2 mg

Warnings/Precautions Some preparations contain sulfites which may cause allergic reactions; infants <3 months of age are more susceptible to respiratory depression, use with caution and generally in reduced doses in this age group; use with caution in patients with impaired respiratory function or severe hepatic dysfunction and in patients with hypersensitivity reactions to other phenanthrene derivative opioid agonists (codeine, hydrocodone, hydromorphone, levorphanol, oxycodone, oxymorphone)

Adverse Reactions
  >10%:
    Cardiovascular: Hypotension

(Continued)

Oxymorphone *(Continued)*

Central nervous system: Fatigue, drowsiness, dizziness
Gastrointestinal: Nausea, vomiting, constipation
Neuromuscular & skeletal: Weakness
Miscellaneous: Histamine release
1% to 10%:
Central nervous system: Nervousness, headache, restlessness, malaise, confusion
Gastrointestinal: Anorexia, stomach cramps, xerostomia, biliary spasm
Genitourinary: Decreased urination, ureteral spasms
Local: Pain at injection site
Respiratory: Dyspnea, shortness of breath

Drug Interactions
Decreased effect with phenothiazines
Increased effect/toxicity with CNS depressants, tricyclic antidepressants, dextroamphetamine

Dosage Forms
Injection: 1 mg (1 mL); 1.5 mg/mL (1 mL, 10 mL)
Suppository, rectal: 5 mg

Specific References
Sinatra RS and Harrison DM, "Oxymorphone in Patient-Controlled Analgesia," *Clin Pharm*, 1989, 8(8):541, 544.

Ozothine® *see* Turpentine Oil *on page 603*
P-071 *see* Cetirizine *on page 120*
Pacitron® *see* Tryptophan *on page 602*
Painters' Naphtha *see* Petroleum Distillates - Naphtha *on page 469*
Pallidan® *see* Methaqualone Hydrochloride *on page 388*
Palmil® *see* Castor Oil *on page 118*
Pamelor® *see* Nortriptyline *on page 440*
Pamine® *see* Scopolamine *on page 532*
Pamprin IB® [OTC] *see* Ibuprofen *on page 308*
Panadol® [OTC] *see* Acetaminophen *on page 20*
Panasal® 5/500 *see* Hydrocodone and Aspirin *on page 294*
Panectyl® *see* Trimeprazine *on page 598*
Panmycin® Oral *see* Tetracycline *on page 568*
Panscol® [OTC] *see* Salicylic Acid *on page 530*
Pantopon® *see* Opium Alkaloids (Hydrochlorides) *on page 445*
Papaveretum *see* Opium Alkaloids (Hydrochlorides) *on page 445*
Parabromdylamine *see* Brompheniramine *on page 84*
Paracetaldehyde *see* Paraldehyde *on this page*
Paracetamol *see* Acetaminophen *on page 20*
Paradione® *see* Paramethadione *on page 458*
Paraflex® *see* Chlorzoxazone *on page 145*
Paraform *see* Formaldehyde *on page 259*
Paraguay Tea *see* Maté *on page 360*
Para-Hist AT® *see* Promethazine, Phenylephrine, and Codeine *on page 507*
Paral® *see* Paraldehyde *on this page*

Paraldehyde *(par AL de hyde)*
Synonyms Elaldehyde; Paracetaldehyde
UN Number 1264
U.S. Brand Names Paral®
Therapeutic Category Anticonvulsant

Abuse Potential Yes
Impairment Potential Yes
Use Cyclic acetaldehyde trimer which is utilized as a treatment of status epilepticus and tetanus-induced seizures; has been used as a sedative/hypnotic, no longer used in the treatment of alcohol withdrawal symptoms
Usual Dosage
  Oral: Sedation:
    Children: 0.15-0.3 mL/kg
    Adults: 4-8 mL
  I.M., I.V.: I.V. use is rare and should be diluted (4% to 5% solution): 0.1-0.3 mL/kg
  Rectal:
    Children: 0.3 mL/kg to a maximum dose of 5 mL
    Adults: 4-8 mL diluted with sodium chloride

  Minimal lethal dose:
    Oral: 25 mL
    I.V.: 35 mL
    Rectal: 12 mL
Mechanism of Action Unknown mechanism of action; causes depression of CNS, including the ascending reticular activating system to provide sedation/hypnosis and anticonvulsant activity
Pharmacodynamics/kinetics
  Onset of hypnosis:
    Oral: Within 10-15 minutes
    I.M.: Within 2-3 minutes
  Duration: 6-8 hours
  Absorption:
    Oral: 95%
    Rectal: 75%
  Metabolism: ~70% to 80% of a dose metabolized in the liver probably to acetaldehyde and then to acetic acid whereupon it is further metabolized via the Kreb's cycle to carbon dioxide and water
  Bioavailability: 95%
  Half-life:
    Neonates: 10 hours
    Adults: 6-7.4 hours
Signs and Symptoms of Acute Intoxication Mild hypotension, dyspnea, confusion, hyperventilation, tachypnea, coma, respiratory depression, metabolic acidosis, pulmonary edema, pulmonary hemorrhage, mental confusion, acetone breath, stomatitis, myasthenia gravis (exacerbation or precipitation of), hemorrhagic gastritis, feces discoloration (black), renal failure; death has occurred with as little as 12-25 mL usually due to pulmonary edema
When to Transport to Hospital Transport any patient with change in mental status
Warnings/Precautions Use with caution in patients with asthma or other bronchopulmonary disease
Adverse Reactions
  >10%
    Central nervous system: Drowsiness
    Dermatologic: Skin rash
    Gastrointestinal: Strong and unpleasant breath, nausea, vomiting, stomach pain, irritation of mucous membrane
    Respiratory: Coughing
  <10%:
    Cardiovascular: Cardiovascular collapse, tachycardia, sinus bradycardia, sinus tachycardia
(Continued)

457

Paraldehyde *(Continued)*

Central nervous system: Clumsiness, dizziness, "hangover effect"
Endocrine & metabolic: Metabolic acidosis
Gastrointestinal: Abdominal pain
Hematologic: Leukocytosis, porphyrinogenic
Hepatic: Hepatitis
Local: Thrombophlebitis
Renal: Acidosis (renal tubular), albuminuria, acute tubular necrosis
Respiratory: Respiratory depression, pulmonary edema, laryngeal spasm
Miscellaneous: Psychological and physical dependence with prolonged use

Test Interactions Ketonuria may be present

Reference Range Antiseizure therapeutic blood level: 100-200 mg/L; blood levels approaching 1000 mg/L associated with fatality

Drug Interactions Barbiturates and alcohol may enhance CNS depression; "disulfiram reaction" with disulfiram

Dosage Forms
Injection: 100% paraldehyde (5 mL ampul)
Liquid, oral or rectal: 1 g/mL (30 mL)

Additional Information Do not abruptly discontinue in patients receiving chronic therapy; decomposes to acetic aid in air; 4-8 mL of paraldehyde is equivalent to 30 mg of phenobarbital; was used for the treatment of delirium, tremors, but its use has been supplanted by benzodiazepines; odor of acetic acid indicates that decomposition has occurred; may be irritating to mucosa

Specific References
Bostrum B, "Paraldehyde Toxicity During Treatment of Status Epilepticus," *Am J Dis Child*, 1982, 136:414-5.

Paralyzer *see* Chlorobenzylidene Malonitrile *on page 128*
Paramethad *see* Paramethadione *on this page*

Paramethadione *(par a meth a DYE one)*

Synonyms Isoethadione; Paramethad
U.S. Brand Names Paradione®
Therapeutic Category Anticonvulsant
Use Control absence (petit mal) seizures refractory to other drugs
Usual Dosage Oral:
Children: 300-900 mg/day in 3-4 equally divided doses
Adults: Initial: 900 mg/day in 3-4 equally divided doses, increase by 300 mg at weekly intervals to maximum of 2.4 g/day

Mechanism of Action Elevates the cortical and basal seizure thresholds, and reduces the synaptic response to low frequency impulses; similar properties to troxidone

Pharmacodynamics/kinetics
Absorption: Rapid from gastrointestinal tract
Metabolism: Hepatic metabolism via microsomal enzymes
Half-life: 12-24 hours

Signs and Symptoms of Acute Intoxication Nausea, ataxia, visual disturbances, vision color changes (white tinge), leukopenia; neutropenia; agranulocytosis; granulocytopenia

When to Transport to Hospital Transport any patient with change in mental status

Warnings/Precautions Because of the potential for fetal malformations, paramethadione should only be used when less toxic agents are ineffective; use with caution in patients with hepatic or renal impairment, systemic lupus erythematosus, retina or optic nerve disease, blood dyscrasias, or porphyria; some products may contain tartrazines

Adverse Reactions
>10%:
Central nervous system: Drowsiness
Ocular: Photophobia
<10%:
Dermatologic: Exfoliative dermatitis, rash, photosensitivity
Gastrointestinal: Feces discoloration (black)
Hematologic: Agranulocytosis, aplastic anemia, thrombocytopenia, exacerbation of porphyria
Hepatic: Hepatitis
Neuromuscular & skeletal: Myasthenia gravis (exacerbation)
Ocular: Blurred vision
Renal: Nephrosis, proteinuria
Miscellaneous: Systemic lupus erythematosus (SLE)

Dosage Forms Capsule: 150 mg, 300 mg

Additional Information Only supplied graduated dropper should be used to measure oral solution; clean, colorless liquid with aromatic odor

Specific References
Fabro S and Brown NA, "Teratogenic Potential of Anticonvulsants," *N Engl J Med*, 1979, 300(22):1280-1.

Par Decon® see Chlorpheniramine, Phenyltoloxamine, Phenylpropanolamine, and Phenylephrine on page 137

Paredrine® see Hydroxyamphetamine on page 303

Paregoric (par e GOR ik)

Synonyms Camphorated Tincture of Opium

Therapeutic Category Analgesic, Narcotic

Abuse Potential Yes

Impairment Potential Yes

Use Treatment of diarrhea or relief of pain; neonatal opiate withdrawal (heroin or methadone-induced withdrawal seizures)

Usual Dosage Oral:
Neonatal opiate withdrawal: 3-6 drops every 3-6 hours as needed, or initially 0.2 mL every 3 hours; increase dosage by approximately 0.05 mL every 3 hours until withdrawal symptoms are controlled; it is rare to exceed 0.7 mL/dose. Stabilize withdrawal symptoms for 3-5 days, then gradually decrease dosage over a 2- to 4-week period.
Children: 0.25-0.5 mL/kg 1-4 times/day
Adults: 5-10 mL 1-4 times/day

Mechanism of Action Increases smooth muscle tone in gastrointestinal tract, decreases motility and peristalsis, diminishes digestive secretions

Pharmacodynamics/kinetics In terms of opium
Duration of action: 4-5 hours
Metabolism: In the liver

Signs and Symptoms of Acute Intoxication Miosis, bradycardia, hypotension, sedation, drowsiness, ptosis, fatigue, vomiting, slow and raspy speech

When to Transport to Hospital Transport any patient with change of mental status

Overdosage/Treatment Supportive therapy: Naloxone hydrochloride (0.4-2 mg I.V., S.C., or through an endotracheal tube); a continuous infusion (at ²/₃ the response dose/hour) may be required

Warnings/Precautions Use with caution in patients with respiratory, hepatic or renal dysfunction, severe prostatic hypertrophy, or history of narcotic abuse; opium shares the toxic potential of opiate agonists, and usual precautions of opiate agonist therapy should be observed; some preparations contain sulfites
(Continued)

Paregoric *(Continued)*

which may cause allergic reactions; infants <3 months of age are more suscep-tible to respiratory depression, use with caution and generally in reduced doses in this age group

Adverse Reactions
>10%:
Cardiovascular: Hypotension
Central nervous system: Drowsiness, dizziness
Gastrointestinal: Constipation
Neuromuscular & skeletal: Weakness
1% to 10%:
Central nervous system: Restlessness, headache, malaise
Genitourinary: Ureteral spasms, decreased urination
Miscellaneous: Histamine release

Drug Interactions Increased effect/toxicity with CNS depressants (eg, alcohol, narcotics, benzodiazepines, tricyclic antidepressants, MAO inhibitors, pheno-thiazine)

Dosage Forms Liquid: 2 mg morphine equivalent/5 mL [equivalent to 20 mg opium powder] (5 mL, 60 mL, 473 mL, 4000 mL)

Additional Information Contains morphine 0.4 mg/mL and alcohol 45%

Specific References
Calabrese JR and Gulledge AD, "The Neonatal Narcotic Abstinence Syndrome: A Brief Review," *Can J Psychiatry*, 1985, 30(8):623-6.

Parlodel® see Bromocriptine *on page 83*
Parnate® see Tranylcypromine *on page 590*
Paronfon® Forte ESC see Chlorzoxazone *on page 145*

Paroxetine *(pa ROKS e teen)*

U.S. Brand Names Paxil™; Seroxat®
Therapeutic Category Antidepressant
Impairment Potential Yes
Use Treatment of depression; treatment of panic disorder
Investigational: Obsessive-compulsive disorder
Usual Dosage Adults: Oral: 20 mg once daily (maximum: 50 mg/day), prefer-ably in the morning; tapering should be gradual at daily doses >20 mg; in elderly, debilitated, or patients with hepatic or renal impairment, start with 10 mg/day (maximum: 40 mg/day); adjust doses at 7-day intervals
Panic disorder: 40 mg/day
Mechanism of Action Paroxetine is a selective serotonin reuptake inhibitor (similar to fluvoxamine maleate), chemically unrelated to tricyclic, tetracyclic, or other antidepressants; presumably, the inhibition of serotonin reuptake from brain synapse stimulated serotonin activity in the brain; a phenylpiperidine derivative

Pharmacodynamics/kinetics
Metabolism: Extensive by cytochrome P-450 enzymes to catechol and other inactive metabolites
Half-life: 21 hours; prolonged to 30-40 hours in elderly

Signs and Symptoms of Acute Intoxication Anxiety, confusion, dyspepsia, priapism, tachycardia, insomnia, hyponatremia, diarrhea, urinary frequency, fatigue, ejaculatory disturbances, extrapyramidal reaction, hypotension
When to Transport to Hospital Transport any pediatric exposure, any patient with a change in mental status or anxiety, or any adult ingestion over 100 mg
Warnings/Precautions Use cautiously in patients with a history of seizures, mania, renal disease, cardiac disease, suicidal patients, children, or during

breast-feeding in lactating women; avoid ECT; may unmask the adverse effects of pheochromocytoma (such as hypertension)

Adverse Reactions

>10%:

Central nervous system: Headache, somnolence, dizziness, insomnia

Gastrointestinal: Nausea, xerostomia, constipation, diarrhea

Genitourinary: Ejaculatory disturbances

Neuromuscular & skeletal: Weakness

Miscellaneous: Diaphoresis

1% to 10%:

Cardiovascular: Palpitations, vasodilation, postural hypotension

Central nervous system: Nervousness, anxiety

Endocrine & metabolic: Decreased libido

Gastrointestinal: Anorexia, flatulence, vomiting

Neuromuscular & skeletal: Tremor, paresthesia

Test Interactions ↑ LFTs, hyponatremia (especially in elderly)

Reference Range Oral doses of 40 mg produced a peak serum level of 26.6 ng/mL

Drug Interactions

Decreased effect with phenobarbital, phenytoin

Increased effect/toxicity with alcohol, cimetidine, methohexital (seizures), MAO inhibitors (hyperpyrexic crisis); increased effect/toxicity of tricyclic antidepressants, fluoxetine, sertraline, phenothiazines, class 1C antiarrhythmics, warfarin (need to monitor for bleeding)

Increased toxicity (serotonin syndrome) when administered with over-the-counter cold medications (dextromethorphan); sertraline or paroxetine can incite occurrence of LSD flashback episodes (primarily visual); severe bradykinesia and tremor with molindone; paroxetine can increase serum trimipramine levels

Due to mild inhibition of monoamine oxidase by isoniazid, a potential reaction with selective serotonin-reuptake inhibitors may occur

Paranoid delusions with psychosis can develop after administration of cyproheptadine and paroxetine

Delirium can be induced by an interaction of paroxetine with zolpidem; inappropriate antidiuretic hormone secretion (SIADH) can occur with coadministration of paroxetine with fluoxetine

Fluoxetine, paroxetine and sertraline increased serum concentrations of clozapine and its major metabolite, norclozapine

Dosage Forms Tablet: 20 mg, 30 mg

Additional Information Similar properties to fluvoxamine maleate; buspirone (15-60 mg/day) may be useful in treatment of sexual dysfunction during treatment with a selective serotonin reuptake inhibitor

Specific References

Nemeroff CB, "The Clinical Pharmacology and Use of Paroxetine, A New Selective Serotonin Reuptake Inhibitor," *Pharmacotherapy*, 1994, 14(2):127-38.

Parson Parsley *see* Poison Hemlock *on page 491*

Partuss® LA *see* Guaifenesin and Phenylpropanolamine *on page 272*

Paveral *see* Codeine *on page 164*

Paxil™ *see* Paroxetine *on previous page*

Paxipam® *see* Halazepam *on page 279*

PBX *see* RDX *on page 522*

PBZ® *see* Tripelennamine *on page 601*

PBZ-SR® *see* Tripelennamine *on page 601*

PCE *see* Tetrachloroethylene *on page 567*

PCE® Oral *see* Erythromycin *on page 226*
Pearly Gates *see* Morning Glory *on page 409*
PediaCare® Oral *see* Pseudoephedrine *on page 516*
Pediacof® *see* Chlorpheniramine, Phenylephrine, and Codeine *on page 135*
Pediaflor® *see* Fluoride *on page 251*
Pediapred® *see* Prednisolone *on page 495*
PediaProfen™ *see* Ibuprofen *on page 308*
Pediatric Triban® *see* Trimethobenzamide *on page 599*
Pediazole® *see* Erythromycin and Sulfisoxazole *on page 228*
Pedituss® *see* Chlorpheniramine, Phenylephrine, and Codeine *on page 135*
Pelin *see* Wormwood *on page 617*
Pelson® *see* Nitrazepam *on page 435*

Pemoline (PEM oh leen)

Synonyms Phenoxazole; Phenylisohydantoin; Phenylpseudohydantoin
U.S. Brand Names Cylert®; Dynalert®; Tradon®; Volital®
Therapeutic Category Central Nervous System Stimulant, Nonamphetamine
Abuse Potential Yes
Impairment Potential Yes
Use Controlling undirected hyperkinetic behavior; treat narcolepsy and antihistamine-induced drowsiness
Usual Dosage Oral: Initial: 37.5 mg increasing by 18.75 mg weekly; usual dose: 56.25-75 mg/day; maximum: 112.5 mg
Mechanism of Action Sympathetic amine similar in action to amphetamines; central nervous system stimulant
Pharmacodynamics/kinetics
Metabolism: Hepatic
Half-life:
Children: 7 hours
Adults: 12 hours
Signs and Symptoms of Acute Intoxication Choreoathetosis, rhabdomyolysis, hyperthermia, leukocytosis, mydriasis, vomiting, neutropenia, stuttering, dyskinesias, exacerbates Tourette's syndrome, anorexia, elevated liver function tests (1% to 2%), mania, insomnia, visual, tactile, and auditory hallucinations
When to Transport to Hospital Transport any patient with hallucinations, mydriasis, agitation, muscle pain, or change in mental status
Warnings/Precautions Can produce dependence, can decrease seizure threshold; use with caution in patients with hepatic or renal dysfunction
Adverse Reactions
>10%:
Central nervous system: Insomnia
Gastrointestinal: Anorexia, weight loss
1% to 10%:
Central nervous system: Dizziness, drowsiness, mental depression
Dermatologic: Rash
Gastrointestinal: Stomach pain, nausea
Test Interactions May produce false elevations of acid phosphatase
Reference Range Therapeutic plasma range: 1-7 µg/mL
Drug Interactions Do not use with MAO inhibitors in that hypertensive crisis can occur; magnesium hydroxide may increase absorption of pemoline
Dosage Forms
Tablet: 18.75 mg, 37.5 mg, 75 mg
Tablet, chewable: 37.5 mg

Additional Information Choreiform movements can occur in children at doses as low as 2 mg/kg; similar to dexamphetamine sulfate

Specific References

Polchert SE and Morse RM, "Pemoline Abuse," *JAMA*, 1985, 254(7):946-7.

Penecort® *see* Hydrocortisone *on page 297*

Pentafen® *see* Pentazocine *on this page*

Pentalgina® *see* Pentazocine *on this page*

Pentazocine (pen TAZ oh seen)

Related Information

Controlled Substances - Uses and Effects *on page 741*

U.S. Brand Names Algopent®; Fortal®; Fortral®; Fortulgesic®; Fortwin®; Liticon®; Ospronim®; Pentafen®; Pentalgina®; Sosegon®; Sosenol®; Talwin®; Talwin® NX

Therapeutic Category Analgesic, Narcotic

Abuse Potential Yes

Impairment Potential Yes

Use Relief of moderate to severe pain; has also been used as a sedative prior to surgery and as a supplement to surgical anesthesia

Usual Dosage

Children: I.M., S.C.:

5-8 years: 15 mg

8-14 years: 30 mg

Children >12 years and Adults: Oral: 50 mg every 3-4 hours; may increase to 100 mg/dose if needed, but should not exceed 600 mg/day

Adults:

I.M., S.C.: 30-60 mg every 3-4 hours, not to exceed total daily dose of 360 mg

I.V.: 30 mg every 3-4 hours

Mechanism of Action Binds to opiate receptors in the CNS, causing inhibition of ascending pain pathways, altering the perception of and response to pain; produces generalized CNS depression; partial opiate agonist-antagonist

Pharmacodynamics/kinetics

Onset of action:

Oral, I.M., S.C.: Within 15-30 minutes

I.V.: Within 2-3 minutes

Duration:

Oral: 4-5 hours

Parenteral: 2-3 hours

Metabolism: In liver

Bioavailability, oral: ~20%; increased to 60% to 70% in patients with cirrhosis

Half-life: 2-3 hours; increased with decreased hepatic function

Signs and Symptoms of Acute Intoxication Hypertension, diarrhea, asterixis, toxic epidermal necrolysis, dry mouth, diplopia, myalgia, hyperthermia, erythema multiforme, tachycardia, seizures, respiratory depression, nephrotic syndrome, miosis, seizures

When to Transport to Hospital Transport any patient with decreased mental status

Warnings/Precautions Use with caution in seizure-prone patients, acute myocardial infarction, patients undergoing biliary tract surgery, patients with renal and hepatic dysfunction, head trauma, increased intracranial pressure, and patients with a history of prior opioid dependence or abuse; pentazocine may precipitate opiate withdrawal symptoms in patients who have been receiving opiates regularly; injection contains sulfites which may cause allergic reaction

(Continued)

Pentazocine *(Continued)*

Adverse Reactions

>10%:
  Central nervous system: Euphoria, drowsiness
  Gastrointestinal: Nausea, vomiting
  Neuromuscular & skeletal: Weakness

1% to 10%:
  Cardiovascular: Hypotension
  Central nervous system: Malaise, headache, restlessness, nightmares
  Dermatologic: Rash
  Gastrointestinal: Xerostomia
  Genitourinary: Ureteral spasm
  Ocular: Blurred vision
  Respiratory: Dyspnea

Reference Range

Therapeutic: 0.05-0.2 mg/L
Fatal: >1.0 mg/L

Drug Interactions May potentiate or reduce analgesic effect of opiate agonist, (eg, morphine) depending on patients tolerance to opiates can precipitate withdrawal in narcotic addicts

Decreased analgesic effect in smokers; smokers may require a 40% to 50% increase in dosage for the same analgesic effect as nonsmokers

Increased effect/toxicity with tripelennamine (can be lethal), CNS depressants (phenothiazines, tranquilizers, anxiolytics, sedatives, hypnotics, or alcohol)

Dosage Forms

Injection, as lactate: 30 mg/mL (1 mL, 1.5 mL, 2 mL, 10 mL)
Tablet: Pentazocine hydrochloride 50 mg and naloxone hydrochloride 0.5 mg

Additional Information Pentazocine hydrochloride: Talwin® NX tablet (with naloxone); naloxone is used to prevent abuse by dissolving tablets in water and using as injection; may be combined with tripelennamine (Ts and blues)

Specific References

Challoner KR, McCarron MM, and Newton EJ, "Pentazocine (Talwin®) Intoxication: Report of 57 Cases," *J Emerg Med*, 1990, 8(1):67-74.

Pentobarbital *(pen toe BAR bi tal)*

Related Information

Controlled Substances - Uses and Effects *on page 741*

U.S. Brand Names Lethobard®; Nembutal®; Pentosol®; Repocal®; Sopental®

Therapeutic Category Barbiturate

Abuse Potential Yes

Impairment Potential Yes

Use Short-term treatment of insomnia; preoperative sedation; high-dose barbiturate coma for treatment of increased intracranial pressure or status epilepticus unresponsive to other therapy

Usual Dosage

Children:
  Sedative: Oral: 2-6 mg/kg/day divided in 3 doses; maximum: 100 mg/day
  Hypnotic: I.M.: 2-6 mg/kg; maximum: 100 mg/dose
  Rectal:
    2 months to 1 year (10-20 lb): 30 mg
    1-4 years (20-40 lb): 30-60 mg
    5-12 years (40-80 lb): 60 mg
    12-14 years (80-110 lb): 60-120 mg **or**
    <4 years: 3-6 mg/kg/dose
    >4 years: 1.5-3 mg/kg/dose

Preoperative/preprocedure sedation: ≥6 months:
Oral, I.M., rectal: 2-6 mg/kg; maximum: 100 mg/dose
I.V.: 1-3 mg/kg to a maximum of 100 mg until asleep
Children 5-12 years: Conscious sedation prior to a procedure: I.V.: 2 mg/kg
5-10 minutes before procedures, may repeat one time

Adolescents: Conscious sedation: Oral, I.V.: 100 mg prior to a procedure

Adults:
Hypnotic:
Oral: 100-200 mg at bedtime or 20 mg 3-4 times/day for daytime sedation
I.M.: 150-200 mg
I.V.: Initial: 100 mg, may repeat every 1-3 minutes up to 200-500 mg total dose
Rectal: 120-200 mg at bedtime
Preoperative sedation: I.M.: 150-200 mg

Children and Adults: Barbiturate coma in head injury patients: I.V.:
Loading dose: 5-10 mg/kg given slowly over 1-2 hours; monitor blood pressure and respiratory rate
Maintenance infusion: Initial: 1 mg/kg/hour; may increase to 2-3 mg/kg/hour; maintain burst suppression on EEG

Mechanism of Action Short-acting barbiturate with sedative, hypnotic, and anticonvulsant properties

Pharmacodynamics/kinetics
Onset of action:
Oral or rectal: 15-60 minutes
I.M.: Within 10-15 minutes
I.V.: Within 1 minute
Duration:
Oral or rectal: 1-4 hours
I.V.: 15 minutes
Absorption: Oral, rectal: Rapid
Metabolism: Extensive in the liver via hydroxylation and oxidation pathways
Half-life: Terminal:
Children: 25 hours
Adults, normal: 22 hours
Range: 35-50 hours

Signs and Symptoms of Acute Intoxication Unsteady gait, slurred speech, rhabdomyolysis, confusion, bullous skin lesions, jaundice, ptosis, vision color changes (green tinge), vision color changes (yellow tinge); hypothermia, fever, hypotension, renal failure, myoglobinuria, hypoglycemia, gaze nystagmus

When to Transport to Hospital Transport any patient with decreased mental status or adult ingestion over 200 mg

Warnings/Precautions Use with caution in patients with hypovolemic shock, congestive heart failure, and hepatic impairment

Adverse Reactions
Renal: Oliguria
>10%:
Cardiovascular: Cardiac arrhythmias, bradycardia, hypotension, arterial spasm,
Central nervous system: Drowsiness, lethargy, CNS excitation or depression, impaired judgment, "hangover" effect
Local: Pain at injection site, thrombophlebitis with I.V. use
Miscellaneous: Gangrene with inadvertent intra-arterial injection
1% to 10%:
Central nervous system: Confusion, mental depression, unusual excitement, nervousness, faint feeling, headache, insomnia, nightmares
Gastrointestinal: Nausea, vomiting, constipation
(Continued)

Pentobarbital (Continued)

Reference Range
Hypnotic: 1-5 µg/mL (SI: 4-22 µmol/L)
Drowsy: 6-10 µg/mL (SI: 44 µmol/L)
Stuporous: 11-17 µg/mL (SI: 46-76 µmol/L)
Coma: 20-50 µg/mL (SI: 88-221 µmol/L)

Drug Interactions Chloramphenicol, cimetidine, CNS depressants, doxycycline; can reduce effectiveness of beta-blockers

Dosage Forms
Pentobarbital sodium:
   Capsule: 50 mg, 100 mg
   Elixir: 18.2 mg/5 mL (473 mL, 4000 mL)
   Injection: 50 mg/mL (1 mL, 2 mL, 20 mL, 50 mL)
   Suppository, rectal: 30 mg, 60 mg, 120 mg, 200 mg

Specific References
McCarron MM, Schulze BW, Walberg CB, et al, "Short-Acting Barbiturate Overdosage. Correlation of Intoxication Score With Serum Barbiturate Concentration," *JAMA*, 1982, 248(1):55-61.

Pentogen (clove oil) see Clove on page 158

Pentosol® see Pentobarbital on page 464

Pentothal® Sodium see Thiopental on page 577

Pepcid® see Famotidine on page 242

Pepcidine® see Famotidine on page 242

Pepdul® see Famotidine on page 242

Pepdulmite® see Famotidine on page 242

Peptard® see Hyoscyamine on page 305

Pepto® Diarrhea Control [OTC] see Loperamide on page 349

Peratasico® see Potassium Permanganate on page 491

Perchlor see Tetrachloroethylene on page 567

Perchlormethane see Carbon Tetrachloride on page 113

Perclene see Tetrachloroethylene on page 567

Percocet® see Oxycodone and Acetaminophen on page 453

Percodan® see Oxycodone and Aspirin on page 454

Percodan®-Demi see Oxycodone and Aspirin on page 454

Percogesic® [OTC] see Acetaminophen and Phenyltoloxamine on page 22

Pergolide (PER go lide)

U.S. Brand Names Celance®; Permax®

Therapeutic Category Anti-Parkinson's Agent; Dopaminergic Agent (Antiparkinson's); Ergot Alkaloid

Use Adjunctive treatment to levodopa/carbidopa in the management of Parkinson's disease
Investigational: Acromegaly and hyperprolactinemia

Usual Dosage When adding pergolide to levodopa/carbidopa, the dose of the latter can usually and should be decreased. Patients no longer responsive to bromocriptine may benefit by being switched to pergolide.

Adults: Oral: Start with 0.05 mg/day for 2 days, then increase dosage by 0.1 or 0.15 mg/day every 3 days over next 12 days, increase dose by 0.25 mg/day every 3 days until optimal therapeutic dose is achieved, up to 5 mg/day maximum; usual dosage range: 2-3 mg/day in 3 divided doses
Acromegaly: 0.1-0.35 mg once daily
Hyperprolactinemia: 0.025-1 mg once daily

Mechanism of Action Pergolide is a semisynthetic ergot alkaloid similar to bromocriptine but stated to be more potent and longer-acting; it is a centrally-active dopamine agonist stimulating both D_1 and D_2 receptors

Pharmacodynamics/kinetics

Absorption: Oral: Well absorbed

Metabolism: Extensive in the liver

Half-life: 27 hours

When to Transport to Hospital Transport any pediatric exposure, any ingestion over 5 mg, or any patient with change in mental status

Warnings/Precautions Symptomatic hypotension occurs in 10% of patients; use with caution in patients with a history of cardiac arrhythmias, hallucinations, or mental illness; may need to reduce levodopa dosage by 44%

Adverse Reactions

>10%:

Central nervous system: Dizziness, somnolence, insomnia, confusion, hallucinations, anxiety, dystonia

Gastrointestinal: Nausea, constipation

Neuromuscular & skeletal: Dyskinesia

Respiratory: Rhinitis

1% to 10%:

Cardiovascular: Myocardial infarction, postural hypotension, syncope, arrhythmias, peripheral edema, vasodilation, palpitations, chest pain

Central nervous system: Chills

Gastrointestinal: Diarrhea, abdominal pain, vomiting, xerostomia, anorexia, weight gain

Neuromuscular & skeletal: Weakness

Ocular: Abnormal vision

Respiratory: Dyspnea

Miscellaneous: Flu syndrome

Drug Interactions

Decreased effect: Dopamine antagonists, metoclopramide

Increased toxicity: Highly plasma protein bound drugs

Hypotensive episodes can occur with associated administration of lisinopril

Dosage Forms Tablet: 0.05 mg, 0.25 mg, 1 mg

Specific References

Collier DS, Berg MJ, and Fincham RW, "Parkinsonism Treatment: Part III - Update," *Ann Pharmacother*, 1992, 26(2):227-33.

Periactin® see Cyproheptadine on page 175

Periactinol® see Cyproheptadine on page 175

Permax® see Pergolide on previous page

Permitabs® see Potassium Permanganate on page 491

Permitil® see Fluphenazine on page 255

Perphenazine (per FEN a zeen)

U.S. Brand Names Decentan®; Fentazin®; Trilafon®

Canadian Brand Names Apo-Perphenazine®; PMS-Perphenazine®

Therapeutic Category Antipsychotic Agent; Phenothiazine Derivative

Impairment Potential Yes

Use Symptomatic management of psychotic disorders, as well as severe nausea and vomiting

Usual Dosage

Children:

Psychoses: Oral:

1-6 years: 4-6 mg/day in divided doses

6-12 years: 6 mg/day in divided doses

>12 years: 4-16 mg 2-4 times/day

(Continued)

Perphenazine *(Continued)*

      I.M.: 5 mg every 6 hours
    Nausea/vomiting: I.M.: 5 mg every 6 hours
  Adults:
    Psychoses:
      Oral: 4-16 mg 2-4 times/day not to exceed 64 mg/day
      I.M.: 5 mg every 6 hours up to 15 mg/day in ambulatory patients and 30 mg/day in hospitalized patients
    Nausea/vomiting:
      Oral: 8-16 mg/day in divided doses up to 24 mg/day
      I.M.: 5-10 mg every 6 hours as necessary up to 15 mg/day in ambulatory patients and 30 mg/day in hospitalized patients
      I.V. (severe): 1 mg at 1- to 2-minute intervals up to a total of 5 mg

Mechanism of Action Blocks postsynaptic mesolimbic dopaminergic receptors in the brain; exhibits a strong alpha-adrenergic blocking effect and depresses the release of hypothalamic and hypophyseal hormones

Pharmacodynamics/kinetics
  Onset of action: 30 minutes to 1 hour
  Absorption: Oral: Well absorbed
  Metabolism: In the liver
  Half-life: 9 hours
  Time to peak serum concentration:
    Oral: Within 4-8 hours
    Decanoate injection: Within 7-8 days

Signs and Symptoms of Acute Intoxication Deep sleep, dystonic reactions, galactorrhea, Parkinson's-like symptoms, agitation, coma, jaundice, neuroleptic malignant syndrome, gynecomastia, impotence, extrapyramidal reaction, thrombocytopenia, seizures, abnormal involuntary muscle movements, vision color changes (brown tinge), vision color changes (yellow tinge); urine discoloration (pink), urine discoloration (red), urine discoloration (red-brown), leukopenia; neutropenia; agranulocytosis; granulocytopenia

When to Transport to Hospital Transport any patient exhibiting change in mental status or ingestions over 30 mg

Warnings/Precautions Avoid alcoholic beverages; safety in children <12 years of age has not been established; use with caution in patients with cardiovascular disease or seizures; use with caution in patients with a history of seizures and in those receiving anticonvulsant agents

Adverse Reactions
  >10%:
    Cardiovascular: Hypotension, orthostatic hypotension
    Central nervous system: Pseudoparkinsonism, akathisia, dystonias, tardive dyskinesia (persistent), dizziness
    Gastrointestinal: Constipation
    Ocular: Pigmentary retinopathy
    Respiratory: Nasal congestion
    Miscellaneous: Diaphoresis (decreased)
  1% to 10%:
    Dermatologic: Increased sensitivity to sun, rash
    Endocrine & metabolic: Changes in menstrual cycle, changes in libido, breast pain
    Gastrointestinal: Weight gain, vomiting, stomach pain, nausea
    Genitourinary: Dysuria, ejaculatory disturbances
    Neuromuscular & skeletal: Trembling of fingers

Reference Range 0.004-0.064 mg/L

Drug Interactions Other CNS depressants, anticonvulsants, disulfiram can enhance biotransformation of orally administered perphenazine, due to first-pass effect

Dosage Forms
Concentrate, oral: 16 mg/5 mL (118 mL)
Injection: 5 mg/mL (1 mL)
Tablet: 2 mg, 4 mg, 8 mg, 16 mg

Specific References
Harper G, Dawes M, Azlin C, et al, "Small Bowel Obstruction in a Child on an Antipsychotic," *J Child Adolesc Psychopharmacol*, 1995, 5:81-4.

Perphenazine and Amitriptyline see Amitriptyline and Perphenazine on page 42

Pertofrane® see Desipramine on page 180

Pertofrin® see Desipramine on page 180

Pertussin® CS [OTC] see Dextromethorphan on page 187

Pertussin® ES [OTC] see Dextromethorphan on page 187

Pesos® see Fenfluramine on page 244

Pethidine Hydrochloride see Meperidine on page 367

Petrol see Gasoline on page 264

Petroleum Distillates - Naphtha

Synonyms Benzin; Painters' Naphtha; Petroleum Spirit; White Spirit
UN Number 2553
Commonly Found In Coal tar, solvent for oils, lacquers, paints, rubber cement
Abuse Potential Yes
Impairment Potential Yes
Mechanism of Toxic Action Aspiration pneumonia related to low viscosity agents
Toxicodynamics/kinetics Absorption: Not well absorbed in the gastrointestinal tract
Signs and Symptoms of Acute Intoxication Headache, dizziness, nausea, hematuria, dyspnea, dermatitis, coughing (persistent), fever, hemoptysis, erythema, unlikely to produce systemic signs
When to Transport to Hospital Transport any ingestion of any amount or patients with cough or any other respiratory symptoms

Adverse Reactions
Central nervous system: CNS depression
Gastrointestinal: Irritant of mucous membranes
Hematologic: Methemoglobinemia
Respiratory: Aspiration pneumonitis
Miscellaneous: Intravenous administration produces fever and local tissue damage

Additional Information
IDLH: 10,000 ppm
PEL-TWA: 500 ppm

Specific References
Case ME, Poklis A, and Mackell MA, "Homicide by Intravenous Injection of Naphtha," *J Forensic Sci*, 1985, 30(1):208-12.

Petroleum Spirit see Petroleum Distillates - Naphtha on this page

Peyote

Related Information
Controlled Substances - Uses and Effects on page 741
Mescaline on page 374

Synonyms Peyotyl
(Continued)

469

Peyote *(Continued)*

Scientific Name *Lophophora williamsii*

Abuse Potential Yes

Impairment Potential Yes

Mechanism of Toxic Action Mescaline - structurally similar to amphetamines producing CNS and sympathetic stimulation and hallucinations

Pharmacodynamics/kinetics Urine, blood levels not correlated with clinical effects

Signs and Symptoms of Acute Intoxication Hypertension, pulse, fever, respiratory rate, salivation, mydriasis, blurred vision, headache, dizziness, ataxia, drowsiness, tremor, asthenia, nausea/vomiting preceding hallucinations, hunger, polyuria, flushing, visual hallucinations, auditory hallucinations, anxiety, suicide, flashbacks, paranoia

When to Transport to Hospital Transport any patient with decreased mental status, paranoia, or fever

Overdosage/Treatment Symptoms may need to be treated with benzodiazepines and/or haloperidol/chlorpromazine; flashbacks may be worsened by phenothiazines; no deaths reported from overdosage of mescaline/peyote

Additional Information May be contaminated; consider coingestants; "microdots" may also contain LSD

Specific References

Kapadia GJ and Fayez BN, "Peyote Constituents: Chemistry, Biogenesis, and Biological Effects," *J Pharm Sci*, 1970, 59:1699-727.

Peyotyl *see* Peyote *on previous page*

PFl-Lith® *see* Lithium *on page 347*

PG 12 *see* Propylene Glycol *on page 513*

Phanatuss® Cough Syrup [OTC] *see* Guaifenesin and Dextromethorphan *on page 271*

Pharmaflur® *see* Fluoride *on page 251*

Phasal® *see* Lithium *on page 347*

Phenacyl Chloride *see* Chloroacetophenone *on page 127*

Phenadex® Senior [OTC] *see* Guaifenesin and Dextromethorphan *on page 271*

Phenadone, Serum *see* Methadone, Quantitative, Serum *on page 381*

Phenahist-TR® *see* Chlorpheniramine, Phenylephrine, Phenylpropanolamine, and Belladonna Alkaloids *on page 136*

Phenameth® DM *see* Promethazine and Dextromethorphan *on page 506*

Phenantoin *see* Mephenytoin *on page 369*

Phenaphen® With Codeine *see* Acetaminophen and Codeine *on page 21*

Phenazine® *see* Promethazine *on page 505*

Phencen® *see* Promethazine *on page 505*

Phenchlor® S.H.A. *see* Chlorpheniramine, Phenylephrine, Phenylpropanolamine, and Belladonna Alkaloids *on page 136*

Phencyclidine Hydrochloride

(fen SYE kli deen hye droe KLOR ide)

Related Information

Controlled Substances - Uses and Effects *on page 741*

Therapeutic Category General Anesthetic

Abuse Potential Yes

Impairment Potential Yes; Blood phencyclidine levels >0.007 mg/L associated with driving impairment

Baselt RC and Cravey RH, *Disposition of Toxic Drugs and Chemicals in Man*, 4th ed, Foster City, CA: Chemical Toxicology Institute, 1995, 602.

Toxic Dose Joints are 100-400 mg PCP by weight; tablets are ~5 mg

Mechanism of Toxic Action Related to ketamine, PCP is an arylcyclohexylamine which stimulates alpha-adrenergic receptors

Toxicodynamics/kinetics

Metabolism: Hepatic by oxidative hydroxylation

Half-life: 1 hour (in overdose: 17.6 hours)

Elimination: Renal (33 mL/minute)

Signs and Symptoms of Acute Intoxication Myoglobinuria, fear, hyperuricemia, mania, delirium, hyperacusis, lacrimation, insomnia, ptosis, hypoglycemia, myopathy, impotence, fasciculations, depression, encephalopathy, hyperthermia, headache, rhabdomyolysis, fever, coma, sweating, respiratory depression, hypothermia, seizures, hypertension, tachycardia, myoclonus, gaze nystagmus

When to Transport to Hospital Transport any psychotic patient with agitation, delirium, headache, fever, muscle pain, or decreased mental status

Adverse Reactions

Cardiovascular: Tachycardia, pericardial effusion/pericarditis

Central nervous system: Violent behavior, psychosis, paranoia, hallucinations, ataxia, synesthesia, dysphoria

Endocrine & metabolic: Hypoglycemia

Gastrointestinal: Vomiting

Ocular: Gaze nystagmus, lacrimation

Reference Range

Catatonia and excitation: 20-30 ng/mL

Myoclonus and coma: 30-100 ng/mL

Hypotension, seizures, fatalities: >100 ng/mL

Urinary levels do not correlate with clinical symptoms

Additional Information Phencyclidine is most often called "angel dust;" it was first developed as an anesthetic in the 1950s, and was taken off the market for human use because it sometimes caused hallucinations. PCP is available in a number of forms. It can be a pure white crystal-like powder, a tablet or capsule, and it can be swallowed, smoked (alone or with marijuana), sniffed, or injected. Although PCP is illegal, it is easily manufactured.

Effects depend on how much of the drug is taken, the way it is used, and the individual. Small amounts act as a stimulant, speeding up body functions. For many users, PCP changes how they see their own bodies and things around them. Speech, muscle coordination, and vision are affected; sense of touch and pain are dulled; and body movements are slowed. Time seems to "space out." Taking large amounts of PCP can cause death from repeated convulsions, heart and lung failure, or ruptured blood vessels in the brain. PCP can be detected for 7 days after administration; 2-4 weeks in chronic users.

Specific References

McCarron MM, Schulze BW, Thompson GA, et al, "Acute Phencyclidine Intoxication: Clinical Patterns, Complications, and Treatment," *Ann Emerg Med*, 1981, 10(6):290-7.

Phendry® Oral [OTC] *see Diphenhydramine on page 205*

Phene *see Benzene on page 69*

Phenelzine (FEN el zeen)

Synonyms Phenethylhydrazine Hydrogen Sulfate

U.S. Brand Names Nardelzine®; Nardil®

Therapeutic Category Antidepressant

Use Symptomatic treatment of atypical, nonendogenous or neurotic depression

(Continued)

Phenelzine *(Continued)*

Usual Dosage Adults: Oral: 15 mg 3 times/day; may increase to 60-90 mg/day during early phase of treatment, then reduce to dose for maintenance therapy slowly after maximum benefit is obtained; takes 2-4 weeks for a significant response to occur

Mechanism of Action Thought to act by increasing endogenous concentrations of epinephrine, norepinephrine, dopamine and serotonin through inhibition of the enzyme (monoamine oxidase) responsible for the breakdown of these neurotransmitters

Pharmacodynamics/kinetics

Onset of action: As early as 7-10 days in some patients but may take up to 4-8 weeks

Duration: At least 10 days for MAO activity to be recovered because of irreversible binding

Absorption: Oral: Well absorbed from gastrointestinal tract

Metabolism: Hepatic

Time to peak serum concentration: Oral: 2-4 hours

Signs and Symptoms of Acute Intoxication Sinus tachycardia, photosensitivity, exfoliative dermatitis, dry mouth, delirium, ejaculatory disturbances, rhabdomyolysis, myoglobinuria, palpitations, ptosis, mania, muscle myoclonus, impotence, extrapyramidal reaction, seizures, insomnia, neuroleptic malignant syndrome, restlessness, methemoglobinemia, transient hypertension, hypotension, drowsiness, fever, coma, muscle rigidity, hyperthermia, sweating, metabolic acidosis, flushing, tachypnea, mydriasis, hallucinations

When to Transport to Hospital Transport any pediatric exposure, any patient with fever, diaphoresis, or change in mental status, or any ingestion over 100 mg

Warnings/Precautions Avoid tyramine-containing foods: red wine, cheese (except cottage, ricotta, and cream), smoked or pickled fish, beef or chicken liver, dried sausage, fava or broad bean pods, yeast vitamin supplements; safety in children <16 years of age has not been established; use with caution in patients with a history of seizures

Adverse Reactions

>10%:

Cardiovascular: Orthostatic hypotension

Central nervous system: Drowsiness

Endocrine & metabolic: Decreased sexual ability

Neuromuscular & skeletal: Trembling, weakness

Ocular: Blurred vision

1% to 10%:

Cardiovascular: Tachycardia, peripheral edema

Central nervous system: Nervousness, chills

Gastrointestinal: Diarrhea, anorexia, xerostomia, constipation

Drug Interactions Hypertensive crisis with foods containing tyramine (cheese, beer, wine); sympathomimetic drugs, meperidine, tricyclic antidepressants, phenothiazines, antihypertensives, disulfiram; serotonin syndrome can develop after concomitant administration of venlafaxine and phenelzine

Dosage Forms Tablet: 15 mg

Specific References

Breheny FX, Dobb GJ, and Clarke GM, "Phenelzine Poisoning," *Anaesthesia*, 1986, 41(1):53-6.

Phenerbel-S® *see* Belladonna, Phenobarbital, and Ergotamine Tartrate *on page 66*

Phenergan® *see* Promethazine *on page 505*

Phenergan® VC Syrup *see* Promethazine and Phenylephrine *on page 507*

Phenergan® VC With Codeine *see* Promethazine, Phenylephrine, and Codeine *on page 507*

Phenergan® With Codeine *see* Promethazine and Codeine *on page 506*

Phenergan® with Dextromethorphan *see* Promethazine and Dextromethorphan *on page 506*

Phenethylhydrazine Hydrogen Sulfate *see* Phenelzine *on page 471*

Phenetron® *see* Chlorpheniramine *on page 132*

Phenhist® Expectorant *see* Guaifenesin, Pseudoephedrine, and Codeine *on page 275*

Pheniramine, Phenylpropanolamine, and Pyrilamine
(fen EER a meen, fen il proe pa NOLE a meen, & peer IL a meen)
U.S. Brand Names Triaminic® Oral Infant Drops
Therapeutic Category Antihistamine/Decongestant Combination
Abuse Potential Yes
Impairment Potential Yes
Dosage Forms Drops: Pheniramine maleate 10 mg, phenylpropanolamine hydrochloride 20 mg, and pyrilamine maleate 10 mg per mL (15 mL)

Phenmetrazine
Related Information
Controlled Substances - Uses and Effects *on page 741*
Dextroamphetamine *on page 186*
U.S. Brand Names Nistenal®; Preludin®
Therapeutic Category Anorexiant
Abuse Potential Yes
Impairment Potential Yes
Use Anorectic agent
Usual Dosage Oral: 12.5-75 mg/day
Mechanism of Action A central nervous system stimulant similar to dexamphetamine; a methylchloroformate derivative
Pharmacodynamics/kinetics
Metabolism: Hepatic
Half-life: 8 hours
Signs and Symptoms of Acute Intoxication Dizziness, anxiety, tremor, headache, tachycardia, hypertension, confusion, tachypnea, hallucinations, seizures, shock, coma, dysrhythmias, noncardiogenic pulmonary edema, retinal vein occlusion, mydriasis
When to Transport to Hospital Transport any pediatric exposure, any patient who exhibits a change in mental status, or any ingestion over 100 mg
Adverse Reactions
>10%: Central nervous system: Insomnia, nervousness
<10%:
  Cardiovascular: Hypertension, tachycardia (ventricular), tachycardia, palpitations, cardiac arrhythmias, vasculitis, pulmonary hypertension
  Central nervous system: Headache, dizziness, seizures, mania, may precipitate Tourette's syndrome, CNS depression, dysphonia, irritability, agitation, euphoria, hallucination, extrapyramidal reaction, movement disorders, paranoia
  Endocrine & metabolic: Growth suppression, respiratory alkalosis, increased serum thyroxine (hyperthyroidism)
  Gastrointestinal: Anorexia, nausea, vomiting, diarrhea, abdominal cramps, metallic taste, dry mouth
  Genitourinary: Impotence
  Hematologic: Porphyria
(Continued)

473

Phenmetrazine *(Continued)*

Neuromuscular & skeletal: Tremors, choreoathetoid movements, fasciculations

Ocular: Cataracts

Renal: Myoglobinuria

Respiratory: Tachypnea

Reference Range Therapeutic serum level: 60-130 ng/mL

Dosage Forms Tablet: 25 mg, 75 mg

Additional Information Primarily found in Europe

Specific References

Norheim G, "A Fatal Case of Phenmetrazine Poisoning," *J Forensic Sci Soc*, 1973, 13:287-9.

Phenobarbital *(fee noe BAR bi tal)*

Related Information

Controlled Substances - Uses and Effects *on page 741*

Synonyms Phenobarbitone; Phenylethylmalonylurea

U.S. Brand Names Barbita®; Comizial®; Fenilcal®; Gardenale®; Luminal®; Solfoton®

Canadian Brand Names Barbilixir®

Therapeutic Category Anticonvulsant; Barbiturate

Abuse Potential Yes

Impairment Potential Yes

Use Management of generalized tonic-clonic (grand mal) and partial seizures; prevention of febrile seizures in infants and young children; sedation

Usual Dosage

Children:

Sedation: Oral: 2 mg/kg 3 times/day

Hypnotic: I.M., I.V., S.C.: 3-5 mg/kg at bedtime

Anticonvulsant: Status epilepticus: **Loading dose:** I.V.:

Neonates: 15-20 mg/kg in a single or divided dose

Infants and Children: 10-20 mg/kg in a single or divided dose; in select patients may give additional 5 mg/kg/dose every 15-30 minutes until seizure is controlled or a total dose of 40 mg/kg is reached

Adults: 300-800 mg initially followed by 120-240 mg/dose at 20-minute intervals until seizures are controlled or a total dose of 1-2 g

Anticonvulsant maintenance dose: Oral, I.V.:

Neonates: 2-4 mg/kg/day in 1-2 divided doses; assess serum concentrations; increase to 5 mg/kg/day if needed (usually by second week of therapy)

Infants: 5-8 mg/kg/day in 1-2 divided doses

Children:

1-5 years: 6-8 mg/kg/day in 1-2 divided doses

5-12 years: 4-6 mg/kg/day in 1-2 divided doses

Children >12 years and Adults: 1-3 mg/kg/day in divided doses or 50-100 mg 2-3 times/day

Adults:

Sedation: Oral, I.M.: 30-120 mg/day in 2-3 divided doses

Hypnotic: Oral, I.M., I.V., S.C.: 100-320 mg at bedtime

Mechanism of Action Interferes with transmission of impulses from the thalamus to the cortex of the brain resulting in an imbalance in central inhibitory and facilitatory mechanisms

Pharmacodynamics/kinetics

Onset of action:

Oral: Within 20-60 minutes

I.V.: Within 5 minutes with peak effect within 30 minutes

Duration:
  Oral: 6-10 hours
  I.V.: 4-10 hours
Absorption: Oral: 70% to 90%
Metabolism: In the liver via hydroxylation (60% to 75%) and glucuronide conjugation
Half-life:
  Neonates: 45-500 hours
  Infants: 20-133 hours
  Children: 37-73 hours
  Adults: 53-140 hours
  Overdose: 96-168 hours
Time to peak serum concentration: Within 1-6 hours

Signs and Symptoms of Acute Intoxication Unsteady gait, toxic epidermal necrolysis, asterixis, dysarthria, hyporeflexia, gingival hyperplasia, ataxia, myocardial depression, anemia (megaloblastic), hypothyroidism, ptosis, miosis, extrapyramidal reaction, cognitive dysfunction, pemphigus, rhabdomyolysis, hyperactivity, slurred speech, myoglobinuria, confusion, jaundice, hypothermia, fever, hypotension, bullous lesions, focal neurological signs, vision color changes (green tinge), pulmonary edema, methemoglobinemia, porphyria, gaze nystagmus

When to Transport to Hospital Transport any pediatric (<6 years of age) ingestion over 8 mg/kg or any patient with change in mental status or low body temperature

Warnings/Precautions Use with caution in patients with renal or hepatic impairment; abrupt withdrawal in patients with epilepsy may precipitate status epilepticus

Adverse Reactions
>10%:
  Cardiovascular: Hypotension, cardiac arrhythmias, bradycardia, arterial spasm
  Central nervous system: Dizziness, lightheadedness, "hangover" effect, drowsiness, lethargy, CNS excitation or depression, impaired judgment
  Local: Pain at injection site, thrombophlebitis with I.V. use
  Miscellaneous: Gangrene with inadvertent intra-arterial injection
1% to 10%:
  Central nervous system: Confusion, mental depression, unusual excitement, nervousness, faint feeling, headache, insomnia, nightmares
  Gastrointestinal: Nausea, vomiting, constipation

Test Interactions Increases alkaline phosphatase (S), ammonia (B); decreases bilirubin (S), calcium (S)

Reference Range
Therapeutic:
  Infants and children: 15-30 µg/mL (SI: 65-129 µmol/L)
  Adults: 20-40 µg/mL (SI: 86-172 µmol/L)
Toxic: >40 µg/mL (SI: >172 µmol/L); levels >80 µg/mL (SI: 344 µmol/L) are associated with coma
Fatal: 50-130 µg/mL (SI: 215-559 µmol/L)

Drug Interactions Phenobarbital may decrease the serum concentration or effect of ethosuximide, warfarin, oral contraceptives, phenylbutazone, chloramphenicol, griseofulvin, doxycycline, beta-blockers, theophylline, corticosteroids, tricyclic antidepressants, cyclosporine, quinidine, haloperidol, and phenothiazines; valproic acid, methylphenidate, chloramphenicol, propoxyphene, furosemide may inhibit the metabolism of phenobarbital with resultant increase in phenobarbital serum concentration; phenobarbital and benzodiazepines or other CNS depressants may cause an increase of CNS and respiratory depression (especially with I.V. loading doses of phenobarbital). Pyridoxine may
(Continued)

Phenobarbital *(Continued)*

reduce serum phenobarbital levels. Felbamate can cause a 24% increase in peak phenobarbital levels.

Dosage Forms

Capsule: 16 mg

Elixir: 15 mg/5 mL (5 mL, 10 mL, 20 mL); 20 mg/5 mL (3.75 mL, 5 mL, 7.5 mL, 120 mL, 473 mL, 946 mL, 4000 mL)

Injection, as sodium: 30 mg/mL (1 mL); 60 mg/mL (1 mL); 65 mg/mL (1 mL); 130 mg/mL (1 mL)

Powder for injection: 120 mg

Tablet: 8 mg, 15 mg, 16 mg, 30 mg, 32 mg, 60 mg, 65 mg, 100 mg

Specific References

Kintz P, Tracqui A, Jamey C, et al, "Detection of Codeine and Phenobarbital in Sweat Collected With a Sweat Patch," *J Anal Toxicol*, 1996, 20:197-201.

Phenobarbitone *see* Phenobarbital *on page 474*

Phenol *(FEE nol)*

Synonyms Carbolic Acid; Monohydroxybenzene; Phenol Hydrate; Phenylic Acid

Commonly Found In Production of resin; industrial coatings, adhesives, dyes, perfumes, textiles, lubricating oils, antiseptic agents

U.S. Brand Names Baker's P&S [OTC]; Cepastat® [OTC]; Chloraseptic® [OTC]

Therapeutic Category Pharmaceutical Aid

Use Relief of sore throat pain, mouth, gum, and throat irritations, neurologic pain, rectal prolapse, hemorrhoids, hydrocele

Usual Dosage Allow to dissolve slowly in mouth; may be repeated every 2 hours as needed

Pharmacodynamics/kinetics

Absorption: Readily absorbed across mucous membranes, skin, or via inhalation

Metabolism: In liver

Half-life:

Conjugated phenol: 1 hour

Elimination: 1-4.5 hours

Signs and Symptoms of Acute Intoxication Urine discoloration (dark), urine discoloration (brown), urine discoloration (green), dermal burns, wheezing, hypothermia, nephritis, hematuria, cyanosis, seizures

When to Transport to Hospital Transport any patient with change in mental status, dermal burns, wheezing, or seizures

Overdosage/Treatment Decontamination:

Dermal: Remove clothing, wash exposed skin with isopropyl alcohol, polyethylene glycol, or industrial methylated spirits

Ocular: Flush eyes with copious amounts of water (if exposed); low or high (3500 mw) molecular weight polyethylene glycol can be useful for dermal irrigation of affected areas

Inhalation: Remove from source and provide oxygen

Adverse Reactions

Cardiovascular: Hypotension, cardiovascular collapse, tachycardia, arrhythmias (atrial and ventricular), sinus tachycardia

Central nervous system: CNS depression, slurred speech, coma, agitation, confusion, seizures, panic attacks (with inhalation)

Dermatologic: Skin irritation, burns; white, red, or brown skin discoloration

Gastrointestinal: Nausea, vomiting, hemorrhage, GI ulceration, GI bleeding

Genitourinary: Urine discoloration (green)

Renal: Nephritis

Respiratory: Pulmonary edema, wheezing, coughing, dyspnea, pneumonia
Miscellaneous: Oral burns

Reference Range

Normal total phenol level: 0.15-7.96 mg/100 mL
Lowest reported toxic serum level of phenol: 27 µg/mL
Toxic: >75 mg/L
Fatal: 1 g ingestion may be fatal
Dinitrophenol or hydroquinone may produce methemoglobin BEI (urine) is 250 mg/g creatinine; serum levels <20 mg/L not associated with acute toxicity

Dosage Forms

Liquid, surface cleaning/disinfecting (nonmedicinal) agent: Creolina®: 26% phenol with xylene
Liquid, topical (Baker's P&S): 1% with sodium chloride, liquid paraffin oil and water (120 mL, 240 mL)
Lozenge:
Cēpastat®: 1.45% with menthol and eucalyptus oil
Cēpastat® Cherry: 0.72% with menthol and eucalyptus oil
Chloraseptic®: 32.5 mg total phenol, sugar, corn syrup
Mouthwash (Chloraseptic®): 1.4% with thymol, sodium borate, menthol, and glycerin (180 mL)
Solution (Liquified Phenol): 88% [880 mg/mL]

Additional Information Colorless or white crystals, acrid odor

Specific References

Soares ER and Tift JP, "Phenol Poisoning: Three Fatal Cases," *J Forensic Sci*, 1982, 27(3):729-31.

Phenol Hydrate see Phenol on previous page

Phenoxazole see Pemoline on page 462

Phensuximide (fen SUKS i mide)

U.S. Brand Names Milontin®

Therapeutic Category Anticonvulsant

Use Control of absence (petit mal) seizures

Usual Dosage Children and Adults: Oral: 0.5-1 g 2-3 times/day

Mechanism of Action Increases the seizure threshold and suppresses paroxysmal spike-and-wave pattern in absence seizures; depresses nerve transmission in the motor cortex

Pharmacodynamics/kinetics

Absorption: Oral: Well absorbed
Metabolism: In the liver to norphensuximide (30%)
Half-life: 5-12 hours (8 hours for metabolite)
Time to peak serum concentration: Within 1-4 hours

Signs and Symptoms of Acute Intoxication Acute overdosage can cause CNS depression, blood dyscrasias, ataxia, stupor, coma, urinary frequency, photophobia, hypotension, night terrors, chronic overdose can cause skin rash, confusion, ataxia, albuminuria, hepatic dysfunction, hematuria

When to Transport to Hospital Transport any patient with change in mental status

Warnings/Precautions Use with caution in patients with hepatic or renal disease; abrupt withdrawal of the drug may precipitate absence status

Adverse Reactions

>10%:
Central nervous system: Dizziness, drowsiness, headache, ataxia
Gastrointestinal: Anorexia, nausea, vomiting, weight loss
Miscellaneous: Hiccups
(Continued)

Phensuximide (Continued)

<10%:

Central nervous system: Aggressiveness, CNS depression, night terrors, tiredness, paranoid psychosis, psychosis, asthenia

Dermatologic: Rash, exfoliative dermatitis

Genitourinary: Urine discoloration (pink/red to red/brown)

Hematologic: Agranulocytosis, leukopenia, aplastic anemia, thrombocytopenia, pancytopenia

Ocular: Photophobia

Miscellaneous: Systemic lupus erythematosus (SLE)

Test Interactions ↑ alkaline phosphatase (S); positive Coombs' [direct]; ↓ calcium (S)

Reference Range Therapeutic: 10-20 µg/mL (SI: 57-114 µmol/L)

Dosage Forms Capsule: 500 mg

Specific References

Porter RJ, Penry JK, Lacy JR, et al, "Plasma Concentrations of Phensuximide, Methsuximide, and Their Metabolites in Relation to Clinical Efficacy," *Neurology*, 1979, 29:1509-13.

Phentanyl see Fentanyl on page 247

Phentermine (FEN ter meen)

Synonyms Alpha Alpha-Dimethyl Phenethylamine

U.S. Brand Names Adipex-P®; Fastin®; Ionamin®; Obermine®; Termine®; Zantryl®

Therapeutic Category Anorexiant

Abuse Potential Yes

Impairment Potential Yes

Use Short-term adjunct in exogenous obesity

Usual Dosage Oral:

Children 3-15 years: 5-15 mg/day for 4 weeks

Adults: 8 mg 3 times/day 30 minutes before meals or food or 15-37.5 mg/day before breakfast or 10-14 hours before retiring

Mechanism of Action Phentermine is structurally similar to dextroamphetamine and is comparable to dextroamphetamine as an appetite suppressant, but is generally associated with a lower incidence and severity of CNS side effects. Phentermine, like other anorexiants, stimulates the hypothalamus to result in decreased appetite; anorexiant effects are most likely mediated via norepinephrine and dopamine metabolism. However, other CNS effects or metabolic effects may be involved.

Pharmacodynamics/kinetics

Absorption: Well absorbed; resin absorbed slower and produces more prolonged clinical effects

Half-life: 20 hours

Signs and Symptoms of Acute Intoxication Hyperactivity, agitation, hyperthermia, insomnia, hypertension, seizures

When to Transport to Hospital Transport any pediatric (<3 years of age) exposure or any agitated or febrile patient

Warnings/Precautions Do not use in children <12 years of age; use with caution in patients with diabetes mellitus, cardiovascular disease, nephritis, angina pectoris, hypertension, glaucoma, patients with a history of drug abuse

Adverse Reactions

>10%:

Cardiovascular: Hypertension

Central nervous system: Euphoria, nervousness, insomnia

1% to 10%:
   Central nervous system: Confusion, mental depression, restlessness
   Gastrointestinal: Nausea, vomiting, constipation
   Endocrine & metabolic: Changes in libido
   Hematologic: Blood dyscrasias
   Neuromuscular & skeletal: Tremor
   Ocular: Blurred vision

Reference Range Therapeutic plasma level: 30-90 ng/mL

Drug Interactions

Decreased effect of guanethidine; decreased effect with CNS depressants

Increased effect/toxicity with MAO inhibitors (hypertensive crisis), sympathomimetics, CNS stimulants

Sympathetic hyperstimulation can occur with concomitant fluoxetine and phentermine

Dosage Forms

Capsule: 15 mg, 18.75 mg, 30 mg, 37.5 mg
Capsule, resin complex: 15 mg, 30 mg
Tablet: 8 mg, 37.5 mg

Specific References

Levine B, Caplan YH, and Dixon AM, "A Fatality Involving Phentermine," *J Forensic Sci*, 1984, 29(4):1242-5.

Phentermine see Methamphetamines, Urine *on page 384*

Phenylephrine (fen il EF rin)

U.S. Brand Names AK-Dilate® Ophthalmic Solution; AK-Nefrin® Ophthalmic Solution; Alconefrin® Nasal Solution [OTC]; Doktors® Nasal Solution [OTC]; I-Phrine® Ophthalmic Solution; Isopto® Frin Ophthalmic Solution; Mydfrin® Ophthalmic Solution; Neo-Synephrine® Nasal Solution [OTC]; Neo-Synephrine® Ophthalmic Solution; Nostril® Nasal Solution [OTC]; Prefrin™ Ophthalmic Solution; Relief® Ophthalmic Solution; Rhinall® Nasal Solution [OTC]; Sinarest® Nasal Solution [OTC]; St. Joseph® Measured Dose Nasal Solution [OTC]; Vicks® Sinex® Nasal Solution [OTC]

Canadian Brand Names Dionephrine®; Novahistine® Decongestant; Prefrin™ Liquifilm®

Therapeutic Category Adrenergic Agonist Agent

Use Treatment of hypotension, vascular failure in shock; as a vasoconstrictor in regional analgesia; symptomatic relief of nasal and nasopharyngeal mucosal congestion; as a mydriatic in ophthalmic procedures and treatment of wide-angle glaucoma; supraventricular tachycardia

Usual Dosage

Ophthalmic procedures:
   Infants <1 year: Instill 1 drop of 2.5% 15-30 minutes before procedures
   Children and Adults: Instill 1 drop of 2.5% or 10% solution, may repeat in 10-60 minutes as needed

Nasal decongestant: (therapy should not exceed 5 continuous days)
   Children:
      2-6 years: Instill 1 drop every 2-4 hours of 0.125% solution as needed
      6-12 years: Instill 1-2 sprays or instill 1-2 drops every 4 hours of 0.25% solution as needed
   Children >12 years and Adults: Instill 1-2 sprays or instill 1-2 drops every 4 hours of 0.25% to 0.5% solution as needed; 1% solution may be used in adult in cases of extreme nasal congestion; do not use nasal solutions more than 3 days

Mechanism of Action Potent, direct-acting alpha-adrenergic stimulator with weak beta-adrenergic activity; causes vasoconstriction of the arterioles of the
(Continued)

Phenylephrine (Continued)

nasal mucosa and conjunctiva; activates the dilator muscle of the pupil to cause contraction; produces vasoconstriction of arterioles in the body

Pharmacodynamics/kinetics

Onset of effect: Topical mydriasis: 45-90 minutes

Duration:

Nasal decongestion: 3-6 hours

Topical mydriasis:

2.5% concentration: 5.5-7 hours

10% concentration: >7 hours

Metabolism: To phenolic conjugates; metabolized in liver and intestine by monoamine oxidase

Bioavailability: Oral: 38%

Half-life: 2.5 hours

When to Transport to Hospital Transport any agitated, febrile patient or any patient with any changes in mental status

Warnings/Precautions Injection may contain sulfites which may cause allergic reaction in some patients; do not use if solution turns brown or contains a precipitate; use with extreme caution in elderly patients, patients with hyperthyroidism, bradycardia, partial heart block, myocardial disease, or severe arteriosclerosis; infuse into large veins to help prevent extravasation which may cause severe necrosis; the 10% ophthalmic solution has caused increased blood pressure in elderly patients and its use should, therefore, be avoided

Adverse Reactions

Nasal:

>10%: Burning, rebound congestion, sneezing

1% to 10%: Stinging, dryness

Ophthalmic:

>10%: Transient stinging

1% to 10%:

Central nervous system: Headache, browache

Ocular: Blurred vision, photophobia, lacrimation

Systemic:

>10%: Neuromuscular & skeletal: Tremor

1% to 10%:

Cardiovascular: Peripheral vasoconstriction hypertension, angina, reflex bradycardia, arrhythmias

Central nervous system: Restlessness, excitability

Reference Range Peak plasma phenylephrine concentration after an oral dose of 9 mg: ~0.03 mg/L

Drug Interactions

Decreased effect: With alpha- and beta-adrenergic blocking agents

Increased effect: With oxytocic drugs

Increased toxicity: With sympathomimetics, tachycardia or arrhythmias may occur; with MAO inhibitors, actions may be potentiated

Hypertensive reactions can occur with simultaneous administration of debrisoquine, reserpine or guanethidine

Dosage Forms

Jelly, nasal: 0.5% [5 mg/mL] (18.75 g)

Injection: 1% [10 mg/mL] (1 mL)

Solution:

Nasal:

Drops: 0.125% (15 mL, 30 mL); 0.16% (30 mL); 0.2% (30 mL); 0.25% (15 mL, 30 mL, 473 mL)

Spray: 0.25% (15 mL, 30 mL); 0.5% (15 mL, 30 mL); 1% (15 mL)

Ophthalmic: 0.12% (15 mL); 2.5% (2 mL, 3 mL, 5 mL, 15 mL); 10% (1 mL, 2 mL, 5 mL)

Additional Information Do not administer if patient is exposed to chloroform, cyclopropane, halothane, trichloroethylene or other organic solvents in that ventricular arrhythmia may occur; pKa is ~8.8

Specific References

Moreno-Ancillo A, Muñoz-Robles ML, Cabañas R, et al, "Allergic Contact Reactions Due to Phenylephrine Hydrochloride in Eyedrops," *Ann Allergy Asthma Immunol*, 1997, 78(6):569-72.

Phenylephrine and Chlorpheniramine see Chlorpheniramine and Phenylephrine on page 134

Phenylephrine and Cyclopentolate see Cyclopentolate and Phenylephrine on page 174

Phenylephrine and Scopolamine (fen il EF rin & skoe POL a meen)

Synonyms Scopolamine and Phenylephrine

U.S. Brand Names Murocoll-2® Ophthalmic

Therapeutic Category Anticholinergic/Adrenergic Agonist

Abuse Potential Yes

Impairment Potential Yes

Dosage Forms Solution, ophthalmic: Phenylephrine hydrochloride 10% and scopolamine hydrobromide 0.3% (7.5 mL)

Phenylephrine and Zinc Sulfate (fen il EF rin & zingk SUL fate)

U.S. Brand Names Zincfrin® Ophthalmic [OTC]

Therapeutic Category Adrenergic Agonist Agent

Dosage Forms Solution, ophthalmic: Phenylephrine hydrochloride 0.12% and zinc sulfate 0.25% (15 mL)

Phenylethane see Ethylbenzene on page 236

Phenylethylene see Styrene on page 551

Phenylethylmalonylurea see Phenobarbital on page 474

Phenylfenesin® L.A. see Guaifenesin and Phenylpropanolamine on page 272

Phenyl Hydride see Benzene on page 69

Phenylic Acid see Phenol on page 476

Phenylisohydantoin see Pemoline on page 462

Phenylpropanolamine (fen il proe pa NOLE a meen)

Synonyms dl-Norephedrine Hydrochloride; PPA

U.S. Brand Names Acutrim® [OTC]; Control® [OTC]; Dex-A-Diet® [OTC]; Dexatrim® [OTC]; Maigret-50; Prolamine® [OTC]; Propadrine; Propagest® [OTC]; Rhindecon®; Stay Trim® Diet Gum [OTC]; Westrim® LA [OTC]

Therapeutic Category Adrenergic Agonist Agent

Abuse Potential Yes

Impairment Potential Yes

Use Anorexiant and nasal decongestant

Usual Dosage Oral:

Children: Decongestant:

2-6 years: 6.25 mg every 4 hours

6-12 years: 12.5 mg every 4 hours not to exceed 75 mg/day

Adults:

Decongestant: 25 mg every 4 hours or 50 mg every 8 hours, not to exceed 150 mg/day

(Continued)

Phenylpropanolamine *(Continued)*

Anorexic: 25 mg 3 times/day 30 minutes before meals or 75 mg (timed release) once daily in the morning
Precision release: 75 mg after breakfast

Mechanism of Action Releases tissue stores of epinephrine and thereby produces an alpha- and beta-adrenergic stimulation; this causes vasoconstriction and nasal mucosa blanching; also appears to depress central appetite centers

Pharmacodynamics/kinetics
Onset of action: Nasal decongestion: 15-30 minutes
Duration:
Tablet: 3 hours
Extended release: 12-16 hours
Absorption: Oral: Well absorbed
Metabolism: In the liver to norephedrine
Bioavailability: ~100%
Half-life: 4.6-6.5 hours

Signs and Symptoms of Acute Intoxication Vomiting, hypertension, extrapyramidal reaction, seizures, cognitive dysfunction, hyperthermia, palpitations, paresthesia, tachycardia, anorexia, reflex bradycardia, renal failure

When to Transport to Hospital Transport any pediatric ingestion (<6 years of age) over 8 mg/kg or any ingestion exhibiting agitation, heart symptoms, tremors, fever, or change in mental status

Warnings/Precautions Use with caution in patients with high blood pressure, may cause excitement, acute narrow-angle glaucoma

Adverse Reactions
>10%: Cardiovascular: Hypertension, palpitations
1% to 10%:
Central nervous system: Insomnia, restlessness, dizziness
Gastrointestinal: Xerostomia, nausea

Reference Range Peak serum phenylpropanolamine: ~0.28 mg/L 6 hours after oral ingestion of 150 mg sustained release dose

Dosage Forms
Capsule: 37.5 mg
Capsule, timed release: 25 mg, 75 mg
Tablet: 25 mg
Tablet:
Precision release: 75 mg
Timed release: 75 mg

Specific References
Puder KS and Morgan JP, "Persuading by Citation: An Analysis of the References of Fifty-Three Published Reports of Phenylpropanolamine's Clinical Toxicity," *Clin Pharmacol Ther*, 1987, 42(1):1-9.

Phenylpropanolamine *see* Methamphetamines, Urine *on page 384*

Phenylpropanolamine and Brompheniramine *see* Brompheniramine and Phenylpropanolamine *on page 85*

Phenylpropanolamine and Caramiphen *see* Caramiphen and Phenylpropanolamine *on page 103*

Phenylpropanolamine and Chlorpheniramine *see* Chlorpheniramine and Phenylpropanolamine *on page 134*

Phenylpropanolamine and Guaifenesin *see* Guaifenesin and Phenylpropanolamine *on page 272*

Phenylpropanolamine and Hydrocodone *see* Hydrocodone and Phenylpropanolamine *on page 296*

Phenylpseudohydantoin *see* Pemoline *on page 462*

Phenyltoloxamine, Phenylpropanolamine, and Acetaminophen

(fen il tol OKS a meen, fen il proe pa NOLE a meen, & a seet a MIN oh fen)

Therapeutic Category Antihistamine/Decongestant/Analgesic

Abuse Potential Yes

Impairment Potential Yes

Dosage Forms Tablet: Phenyltoloxamine citrate 22 mg, phenylpropanolamine hydrochloride 25 mg, and acetaminophen 325 mg

Phenyltoloxamine, Phenylpropanolamine, Pyrilamine, and Pheniramine

(fen il tol OKS a meen, fen il proe pa NOLE a meen, peer IL a meen, & fen IR a meen)

U.S. Brand Names Poly-Histine-D® Capsule

Therapeutic Category Cold Preparation

Abuse Potential Yes

Impairment Potential Yes

Dosage Forms Capsule: Phenyltoloxamine citrate 16 mg, phenylpropanolamine hydrochloride 50 mg, pyrilamine maleate 16 mg, and pheniramine maleate 16 mg

Phenytoin (FEN i toyn)

Synonyms Diphenylhydantoin; DPH; Fenitoina

U.S. Brand Names Antisacer®; Dilantin®; Dintoina®; Diphenylan Sodium®; Ditan®; Epanutin®; Epinat®; Fenytoin®

Canadian Brand Names Tremytoine®

Therapeutic Category Anticonvulsant

Abuse Potential Yes

Impairment Potential Yes

Use Management of generalized tonic-clonic (grand mal), simple partial and complex partial seizures; prevention of seizures following head trauma/neurosurgery; ventricular arrhythmias, including those associated with digitalis intoxication; beneficial effects in the treatment of migraine or trigeminal neuralgia in some patients

Investigational: Treatment of cocaine abuse

Usual Dosage

Status epilepticus: I.V.:

Neonates: Loading dose: 15-20 mg/kg in a single or divided dose; maintenance dose: Initial: 5 mg/kg/day in 2 divided doses; usual: 5-8 mg/kg/day in 2 divided doses; some patients may require dosing every 8 hours

Infants and Children: Loading dose: 15-20 mg/kg in a single or divided dose; maintenance dose: Initial: 5 mg/kg/day in 2 divided doses, usual doses:

6 months to 3 years: 8-10 mg/kg/day

4-6 years: 7.5-9 mg/kg/day

7-9 years: 7-8 mg/kg/day

10-16 years: 6-7 mg/kg/day, some patients may require every 8 hours dosing

Children with acute neurotrauma:

0.5-9 years: 8-10 mg/kg/day

10-16 years: 6-8 mg/kg/day

Adults: Loading dose: 15-20 mg/kg in a single or divided dose, followed by 100-150 mg/dose at 30-minute intervals up to a maximum of 1500 mg/24 hours; maintenance dose: 300 mg/day or 5-6 mg/kg/day in 3 divided doses

Cocaine abuse treatment: 300 mg/day
(Continued)

Phenytoin (Continued)

Anticonvulsant: Children and Adults: Oral:
  Loading dose: 15-20 mg/kg; based on phenytoin serum concentrations and recent dosing history; administer oral loading dose in 3 divided doses given every 2-4 hours to decrease gastrointestinal adverse effects and to ensure complete oral absorption; maintenance dose: 300 mg/day or 5-6 mg/kg/day in 3 divided doses

Mechanism of Action Stabilizes neuronal membranes and decreases seizure activity by increasing efflux or decreasing influx of sodium ions across cell membranes in the motor cortex during generation of nerve impulses; prolongs effective refractory period and suppresses ventricular pacemaker automaticity, shortens action potential in the heart

Pharmacodynamics/kinetics

Absorption: Oral: Slow

Metabolism: In the liver

Half-life: Changes with dose and serum concentrations; 8-60 hours after initiation of therapy with oral administration

Time to peak serum concentration: Dependent upon formulation administered
  Extended release capsule: Within 4-12 hours
  Immediate release preparation: Within 2-3 hours

Signs and Symptoms of Acute Intoxication Unsteady gait, toxic epidermal necrolysis, nephrotic syndrome, pseudotumor cerebri, acrodynia, hypocalcemia, enuresis, dementia, hypothyroidism, hyperprolactinemia, hyperglycemia, leukemoid reaction, gynecomastia, dysarthria, chorea (extrapyramidal), myasthenia gravis (exacerbation or precipitation of), extrapyramidal reaction, gingival hyperplasia, encephalopathy, delirium, vision color changes (white tinge), dysosmia, periarteritis nodosa, hirsutism, hypertrichosis, headache, cognitive dysfunction, tremors, Parkinson's-like symptoms, myoglobinuria, rhabdomyolysis, slurred speech, gaze nystagmus, myoclonus, confusion, hyperthermia, drowsiness, eosinophilia, nausea, hypothermia, fever, hypotension, respiratory depression, leukopenia, neutropenia, agranulocytosis, granulocytopenia, hyperreflexia, coma, erythema multiforme, ophthalmoplegia, hypoglycemia, myocarditis; see table. While toxicity from oral ingestion is relatively low, cardiac toxicity due to I.V. administration is primarily due to propylene glycol moiety.

Manifestations of Phenytoin Toxicity

Levels	Manifestation
20 mcg/mL (79 μmol/L)	Nystagmus
30 mcg/mL (118.9 μmol/L)	Ataxia
40 mcg/mL (159 μmol/L)	Decreased mental status
50 mcg/mL (200 μmol/L)	Coma
95 mcg/mL (377 μmol/L)	Fatal

When to Transport to Hospital Transport any pediatric (<6 years of age) ingestion over 20 mg/kg or any patient with ataxia or changes in mental status

Warnings/Precautions Use with caution in patients with hepatic dysfunction; avoid abrupt discontinuation; dosing should be slowly reduced to avoid precipitation of seizures; increased toxicity with nephrotic syndrome patient; may increase frequency of petit mal seizures; I.V. form may cause hypotension, skin necrosis at I.V. site; avoid I.V. administration in small veins; use with caution in patients with porphyria; discontinue if rash or lymphadenopathy occurs

Adverse Reactions I.V. effects: Hypotension, bradycardia, cardiac arrhythmias, cardiovascular collapse (especially with rapid I.V. use), venous irritation and pain, thrombophlebitis

Effects not related to plasma phenytoin concentrations: Hypertrichosis, gingival hypertrophy, thickening of facial features, carbohydrate intolerance, folic acid deficiency, peripheral neuropathy, vitamin D deficiency, osteomalacia, systemic lupus erythematosus

Dose-related effects: Gaze nystagmus, blurred vision, diplopia, ataxia, slurred speech, dizziness, drowsiness, lethargy, coma, rash, fever, nausea, vomiting, gum tenderness, confusion, mood changes, folic acid depletion, osteomalacia, hyperglycemia

Related to elevated concentrations:
>20 mcg/mL: Far lateral nystagmus
>30 mcg/mL: 45° lateral gaze nystagmus and ataxia
>40 mcg/mL: Decreased mentation
>100 mcg/mL: Death

>10%:
Central nervous system: Psychiatric changes, slurred speech, dizziness, drowsiness
Gastrointestinal: Constipation, nausea, vomiting, gingival hyperplasia
Neuromuscular & skeletal: Trembling
1% to 10%:
Central nervous system: Headache, insomnia
Dermatologic: Rash
Gastrointestinal: Anorexia, weight loss
Hematologic: Leukopenia
Hepatic: Hepatitis
Renal: Increase in serum creatinine

Test Interactions Increases glucose, alkaline phosphatase (S); decreases thyroxine (S), calcium (S); serum sodium increases in overdose setting

Reference Range
Therapeutic: 10-20 µg/mL (SI: 40-79 µmol/L); toxicity is measured clinically, and some patients require levels outside the suggested therapeutic range
Toxic: 30-50 µg/mL (SI: 120-200 µmol/L)
Lethal: >100 µg/mL (SI: >400 µmol/L)

Manifestations of toxicity:
Nystagmus: 20 µg/mL (SI: 79 µmol/L)
Ataxia: 30 µg/mL (SI: 118.9 µmol/L)
Decreased mental status: 40 µg/mL (SI: 159 µmol/L)
Coma: 50 µg/mL (SI: 200 µmol/L)

Dosage Forms
Phenytoin sodium:
Capsule, extended: 30 mg, 100 mg
Capsule, prompt: 30 mg, 100 mg
Injection: 50 mg/mL (2 mL, 5 mL)
Suspension, oral: 30 mg/5 mL (5 mL, 240 mL); 125 mg/5 mL (5 mL, 240 mL)
Tablet, chewable: 50 mg

Specific References
Battino D, Estienne M, and Avanzini G, "Clinical Pharmacokinetics of Antiepileptic Drugs in Paediatric Patients. Part II. Phenytoin, Carbamazepine, Sulthiame, Lamotrigine, Vigabatrin, Oxcarbazepine and Felbamate," *Clin Pharmacokinet*, 1995, 29(5):341-69.

Pherazine® VC w/ Codeine *see* Promethazine, Phenylephrine, and Codeine *on page 507*

Pherazine® w/DM *see* Promethazine and Dextromethorphan *on page 506*

Pherazine® With Codeine *see* Promethazine and Codeine *on page 506*

Phos-Flur® *see* Fluoride *on page 251*

Phosphorothioic Acid *see* Chlorpyrifos *on page 143*

Phosphorus Tetramen *see White Phosphorus on page 615*

Phrenilin® *see Butalbital Compound on page 93*

Phrenilin® Forte *see Butalbital Compound on page 93*

Phu *see Valerian on page 606*

***p*-Hydroxyampicillin** *see Amoxicillin on page 45*

Physeptone® *see Methadone on page 379*

Pied Piper Mouse Seed® *see Strychnine on page 549*

P.I.L. *see Pilocarpine on this page*

Pilocarpine (pye loe KAR peen)

Synonyms P.I.L.

U.S. Brand Names Isopto® Carpine; Pilopt®; Pilostat®; P.V. Carpine®

Canadian Brand Names Minims® Pilocarpine

Therapeutic Category Cholinergic Agent

Use For treatment of glaucoma (open-angle); oral form has been used for xerostomia

Usual Dosage

Glaucoma: 1% to 2% solution: 1 drop every 6-8 hours; can be given as frequently as every 2-3 hours

Xerostomia: Oral: 5 mg 3 times/day up to 30 mg/day

Minimal lethal oral dose: 60 mg

Toxic ophthalmic dose: Systemic anticholinergic symptoms will occur after intraocular dose >30 drops (2% solution) or 60 drops (3% solution)

Mechanism of Action Stimulates parasympathetic receptors causing pupillary constriction and ciliary muscle contraction

Pharmacodynamics/kinetics

Onset of miosis: 10-30 minutes

Duration of miosis: 4-8 hours

Duration of intra-ocular pressure reduction: 1-14 hours

Half-life, oral: 0.8-1.5 hours

Signs and Symptoms of Acute Intoxication Nausea, vomiting, abdominal cramps, bronchorrhea, third degree A-V block (15%), dizziness, photophobia

When to Transport to Hospital Transport any patient with tremor, dizziness, cardiac, or gastrointestinal symptoms

Overdosage/Treatment Decontamination: Ocular: Irrigate copiously with saline

Warnings/Precautions Use with extreme caution in patients with a history of retinal detachment or young patients with myopia; following its use, patients should use caution when driving or operating machinery; use with caution in patients with underlying psychiatric disturbances or biliary tract disease

Adverse Reactions

>10%: Ocular: Blurred vision, miosis

1% to 10%:

Central nervous system: Headache

Genitourinary: Polyuria

Local: Stinging, burning

Ocular: Ciliary spasm, retinal detachment, browache, photophobia, acute iritis, lacrimation, conjunctival and ciliary congestion early in therapy

Miscellaneous: Hypersensitivity reactions

Reference Range After 2 days of oral dosage of 10 mg 3 times/day, maximum serum concentrations are ~41 ng/mL

Drug Interactions Impaired vision can occur when pilocarpine is used with tropicamide; due to the possibility of precipitation, do not instill pilocarpine with sodium sulfacetamide ophthalmic solutions within 20 minutes

Dosage Forms
Solution, ophthalmic: Up to 8 concentration
Tablet: 5 mg, 10 mg

Additional Information May exacerbate dementia of Alzheimer's disease; can reverse the mydriasis caused by sympathomimetic agents (phenylephrine, hydroxyamphetamine) but is not effective in reversing mydriasis due to antimuscarinic agents (ie, homatropine); no corneal effects due to pilocarpine use

Specific References
Pfliegler GP and Palatka K, "Attempted Suicide With Pilocarpine Eyedrops," *Am J Ophthalmol*, 1995, 120(3):399-400.

Pilopt® see Pilocarpine *on previous page*

Pilostat® see Pilocarpine *on previous page*

Pimozide (PI moe zide)

U.S. Brand Names Opiran®; Orap™

Therapeutic Category Neuroleptic Agent

Use Suppression of severe motor and phonic tics in patients with Tourette's disorder

Usual Dosage Children >12 years and Adults: Oral: Initial: 1-2 mg/day, then increase dosage as needed every other day; range is usually 7-16 mg/day, maximum dose: 20 mg/day or 0.3 mg/kg/day should not be exceeded

Mechanism of Action A potent centrally-acting dopamine receptor antagonist resulting in its characteristic neuroleptic effects

Pharmacodynamics/kinetics
Absorption: Oral: 50%; poor from gastrointestinal tract
Metabolism: In the liver to two inactive metabolites
Bioavailability: 50%
Half-life: 50 hours
Time to peak serum concentration: Within 6-8 hours

Signs and Symptoms of Acute Intoxication Hypotension, enuresis, galactorrhea, impotence, respiratory depression, Parkinson's-like symptoms, EKG abnormalities, numbness, extrapyramidal reaction, drowsiness, seizures, Q-T interval prolongation, torsade de pointes

When to Transport to Hospital Transport any pediatric (<12 years of age) exposure, any symptomatic patient, or ingestions over 0.5 mg/kg

Adverse Reactions
>10%:
Cardiovascular: Tachycardia, orthostatic hypotension
Central nervous system: Akathisia, akinesia, extrapyramidal effects, drowsiness
Dermatologic: Rash
Endocrine & metabolic: Edema of the breasts
Gastrointestinal: Constipation, xerostomia
1% to 10%:
Cardiovascular: Facial edema
Central nervous system: Tardive dyskinesia, mental depression
Gastrointestinal: Diarrhea, anorexia

Reference Range 3 mg dose produces a plasma level of 3.3 ng/mL

Drug Interactions Use of pimozide with macrolide antibiotics can result in sudden death due to increased pimozide plasma levels and resultant cardiac arrhythmia

Dosage Forms Tablet: 2 mg

Additional Information Less sedation but more likely to cause extrapyramidal signs than chlorpromazine
(Continued)

Pimozide *(Continued)*

Specific References
Larkin C, "Epileptogenic Potential of Pimozide," *Am J Psychiatry*, 1983, 140(3):372-3.

Pinbetol® *see* Pindolol *on this page*

Pindolol *(PIN doe lole)*

U.S. Brand Names Barblac®; Betadren®; Durapindol®; Pinbetol®; Viskaldix®; Visken®

Canadian Brand Names Apo-Pindol®; Gen-Pindolol®; Novo-Pindol®; Nu-Pindol®; Syn-Pindol®

Therapeutic Category Beta-Adrenergic Blocker

Impairment Potential Yes

Use Management of hypertension

Usual Dosage Adults: Oral: Initial: 5 mg twice daily, increase by 10 mg/day at 3- to 4-week intervals to a maximum of 60 mg/day

Mechanism of Action Blocks both beta$_1$- and beta$_2$-receptors and has mild intrinsic sympathomimetic activity; pindolol has negative inotropic and chronotropic effects and can significantly slow A-V nodal conduction

Pharmacodynamics/kinetics
Onset of action: 3 hours

Duration: 24 hours; beta blockade lasted longer in elderly patients as compared to younger patients

Absorption: 50% to 95% of a dose is rapidly absorbed from gastrointestinal tract

Metabolism: In the liver (60% to 65%) to conjugates

Half-life: 2.5-4 hours (increased with renal insufficiency, age, and cirrhosis)

Time to peak serum concentration: Within 1-2 hours

Signs and Symptoms of Acute Intoxication Severe hypotension, dry mouth, ataxia, insomnia, heart block, confusion, colitis, cold extremities, A-V block, myasthenia gravis (exacerbation or precipitation of), hypoglycemia, depression, bradycardia, impotence, heart failure and wheezing; hypertension and tachycardia also associated; coma

When to Transport to Hospital Transport any pediatric exposure or any symptomatic patient

Adverse Reactions
>10%:
  Central nervous system: Anxiety, dizziness, insomnia, fatigue
  Endocrine & metabolic: Decreased sexual ability
  Neuromuscular & skeletal: Arthralgia, weakness, back pain

1% to 10%:
  Cardiovascular: Congestive heart failure, arrhythmia, reduced peripheral circulation
  Central nervous system: Hallucinations, nightmares, vivid dreams
  Dermatologic: Rash, itching
  Gastrointestinal: Diarrhea, nausea, vomiting, stomach discomfort
  Neuromuscular & skeletal: Numbness of extremities
  Respiratory: Dyspnea

Reference Range Therapeutic: 0.02-0.04 µg/mL; 250 mg ingestion was associated with a serum level of 0.66 µg/mL; 500 mg ingestion produced a serum level of 1.5 µg/mL

Drug Interactions Nonsteroidal anti-inflammatory agents, salicylates, sympathomimetics, thyroid hormones, insulins, lidocaine, calcium channel blockers, nifedipine, catecholamine-depleting drugs, clonidine, disopyramide, prazosin, theophylline

Dosage Forms Tablet: 5 mg, 10 mg
Specific References
Meier J, "Pharmacokinetic Comparison of Pindolol With Other Beta-Adrenoceptor-Blocking Agents," *Am Heart J*, 1982, 104(2 Pt 2):364-73.

Piroxicam (peer OKS i kam)

U.S. Brand Names Feldene®

Canadian Brand Names Apo-Piroxicam®; Novo-Piroxicam®; Nu-Pirox®; Pro-Piroxicam®

Therapeutic Category Analgesic, Non-narcotic; Nonsteroidal Anti-Inflammatory Agent (NSAID)

Use Management of inflammatory disorders; symptomatic treatment of acute and chronic rheumatoid arthritis, osteoarthritis, and ankylosing spondylitis

Usual Dosage Oral:
Children: 0.2-0.3 mg/kg/day once daily; maximum dose: 15 mg/day
Adults: 10-20 mg/day once daily; although associated with increase in gastrointestinal adverse effects, doses >20 mg/day have been used (ie, 30-40 mg/day)

Mechanism of Action Inhibits prostaglandin synthesis by decreasing the activity of the enzyme, cyclo-oxygenase, which results in decreased formation of prostaglandin precursors

Pharmacodynamics/kinetics
Onset of action: Within 1 hour
Duration: 24 hours
Absorption: Oral: Well absorbed from gastrointestinal tract; food delays absorption
Metabolism: In the liver
Half-life: 30-86 hours
Time to peak serum concentration:
Oral: 3-5 hours
Rectal: 10 hours

Signs and Symptoms of Acute Intoxication Nausea, cognitive dysfunction, wheezing, toxic epidermal necrolysis, photosensitivity, pemphigus, nephrotic syndrome, hyponatremia, stomatitis, gastrointestinal bleeding, vomiting, gastritis; syndrome of inappropriate antidiuretic hormone (SIADH), coagulopathy, ototoxicity; tinnitus, drowsiness; severe poisoning can manifest with coma, seizures, renal and or hepatic failure, hypotension, respiratory depression, blurred vision, tremors

When to Transport to Hospital Transport any symptomatic patient or any ingestion over 0.5 mg/kg

Warnings/Precautions Use with caution in patients with impaired cardiac function, hypertension, impaired renal function, gastrointestinal disease and patients receiving anticoagulants, porphyria

Adverse Reactions
>10%:
Central nervous system: Dizziness
Dermatologic: Rash
Gastrointestinal: Abdominal cramps, heartburn, indigestion, nausea
1% to 10%:
Central nervous system: Headache, nervousness
Dermatologic: Itching
Endocrine & metabolic: Fluid retention
Gastrointestinal: Vomiting
Otic: Tinnitus

Dosage Forms Capsule: 10 mg, 20 mg
(Continued)

Piroxicam *(Continued)*

Specific References
Gerber D, "Adverse Reactions of Piroxicam," *Drug Intell Clin Pharm*, 1987, 21(9):707-10.

p-Isobutylhydratropic Acid *see* Ibuprofen *on page 308*

Pizotifen Malate *see* Pizotyline *on this page*

Pizotyline (pi ZOE ti leen)

Synonyms Pizotifen Malate

U.S. Brand Names Mosegor®; Sandomigran®; Sandomigrin®; Sanmigran®; Sanomigran®

Therapeutic Category Antimigraine Agent

Impairment Potential Yes

Use Migraine prophylaxis; also used for cyclical vomiting

Usual Dosage
Migraine prophylaxis:
  Children: Up to 1.5 mg/day in divided doses
  Adult: Initial: 0.5 mg; usual adult daily dose: ~1.5 mg; maximum daily dose: 4.5 mg
Cyclical vomiting: Children: 1.5 mg nightly

Mechanism of Action A serotonin, histamine (H_1 receptor) and tryptamine antagonist; also has weak antimuscarinic actions

Pharmacodynamics/kinetics
Peak serum levels: 5 hours
Metabolism: Hepatic
Half-life: 23 hours

When to Transport to Hospital Transport any lethargic patient or ingestion over 5 mg

Warnings/Precautions Use with caution in patients intolerant to tricyclic antidepressants, phenothiazines or cyproheptadine; obese patients; liver or renal insufficiency or cardiovascular diseases

Adverse Reactions
>10%: Central nervous system: Drowsiness (up to 30%)
<10%:
  Cardiovascular: Tachycardia, edema
  Central nervous system: Dizziness, headache
  Gastrointestinal: Weight gain (1-3 kg), nausea, dry mouth, appetite (increased)
  Hepatic: Cholestatic jaundice
  Ocular: Blurred vision
  Neuromuscular & skeletal: Muscle cramps

Drug Interactions May decrease the effectiveness of cisapride

Dosage Forms Tablet: 0.5 mg, 1 mg

Additional Information May prevent gastrointestinal adverse effects of calcitonin injections (at a dose of 0.5 mg 3 times/day)

Specific References
Peet KM, "Use of Pizotifen in Severe Migraine: A Long-Term Study," *Curr Med Res Opin*, 1977, 5:192-9.

Placidyl® *see* Ethchlorvynol *on page 231*

Plurimen® *see* Selegiline *on page 536*

Pneumomist® *see* Guaifenesin *on page 269*

Point-Two® *see* Fluoride *on page 251*

Poison Hemlock

Synonyms Deadly Hemlock; Hemlock; Parson Parsley; Spotted Hemlock; Winter Fern

Scientific Name *Conium maculatum*

Mechanism of Toxic Action Coniine toxicity resembles that of nicotine; there is initial stimulation of autonomic ganglia, followed by depression

Signs and Symptoms of Acute Intoxication Nausea, ataxia, vomiting, and burn sensation in the throat; tachycardia, followed by bradycardia, seizures, slurred speech, paralysis of skeletal muscles, myoglobinuria, rhabdomyolysis, apnea, renal failure, respiratory paralysis, miosis, disconjugate gaze, coma

When to Transport to Hospital Transport any suspected exposure

Adverse Reactions Cardiovascular: Sinus bradycardia, sinus tachycardia

Additional Information Reportedly used by the Greeks to execute Socrates; human toxicity has been reported from eating birds that feed on poison hemlock

Family: Umbelliferae

Range: Found in the Eastern U.S., the West coast, and the Rocky Mountains

Toxin: Coniine

Toxic parts: Whole plant

Specific References

Frank BS, Michelson WB, Panter KE, et al, "Ingestion of Poison Hemlock (*Conium maculatum*)," *West J Med*, 1995, 163(6):573-4.

Poisonous Nightshade see Deadly Nightshade *on page 178*

Polistine® see Carbinoxamine *on page 106*

Polycillin® see Ampicillin *on page 48*

Polycillin-N® see Ampicillin *on page 48*

Poly-Histine® CS see Brompheniramine, Phenylpropanolamine, and Codeine *on page 86*

Poly-Histine-D® Capsule see Phenyltoloxamine, Phenylpropanolamine, Pyrilamine, and Pheniramine *on page 483*

Polymox® see Amoxicillin *on page 45*

Polystream® see Benzene *on page 69*

Ponderax® see Fenfluramine *on page 244*

Pondimin® see Fenfluramine *on page 244*

Ponflural® see Fenfluramine *on page 244*

Ponstel® see Mefenamic Acid *on page 364*

Poppers see Nitrites *on page 436*

Poppy Seeds see Opiates, Qualitative, Urine *on page 445*

Porfanil® see Tiapride *on page 581*

Pork NPH Iletin® II see Insulin Preparations *on page 314*

Pork Regular Iletin® II see Insulin Preparations *on page 314*

Pot see Cannabinoids, Qualitative *on page 100*

Potassium Metabisulfite see Sulfite Food Poisoning *on page 553*

Potassium Permanganate

Synonyms Chameleon Mineral; Condy't Crustals

UN Number 1490

U.S. Brand Names Peratasico®; Permitabs®

Use Bleaching agent, dying wood, chemistry reagent, photography, purifying water; also used in illegal fireworks production; used as a topical bactericidal agent at concentrations of 0.01% (1 in 10,000 solution)

Toxic Dose Fatal oral dose: 10 g

(Continued)

Potassium Permanganate *(Continued)*

Mechanism of Action Solutions >1:5000 concentration are irritating; an oxidizing agent with alkaline caustic effects

Pharmacodynamics/kinetics Absorption: Poor

When to Transport to Hospital Transport any ingestion or topical exposure with >1:5000 concentration

Overdosage/Treatment Ocular: Irrigate with saline or 5% to 10% ascorbic acid solution to dissolve manganese oxide deposits (dissolve 500 mg tablet of ascorbic acid in 25 mL of 0.9% sodium chloride and irrigate the eyes)

Potensan® *see Yohimbine on page 618*

PPA *see Phenylpropanolamine on page 481*

Prava® *see Pravastatin on this page*

Pravachol® *see Pravastatin on this page*

Pravastatin *(PRA va stat in)*

Synonyms Eptastatin

U.S. Brand Names Lipostat®; Prava®; Pravachol®; Selektine®; Selipram®

Therapeutic Category HMG-CoA Reductase Inhibitor

Use Adjunct to diet for the reduction of elevated total and LDL-cholesterol levels in patients with hypercholesterolemia (Type IIa, IIb, and IIc)

Usual Dosage Adults: Oral: 10-20 mg once daily at bedtime, may increase to 40 mg/day at bedtime

Mechanism of Action Pravastatin is a competitive inhibitor of 3-hydroxy-3-methylglutaryl coenzyme A (HMG-CoA) reductase, which is the rate-limiting enzyme involved in *de novo* cholesterol synthesis.

Pharmacodynamics/kinetics

Absorption: Poor

Metabolism: In the liver to at least two metabolites

Half-life, elimination: ~2-3 hours

Time to peak serum concentration: 1-1.5 hours

When to Transport to Hospital Transport any ingestion over 1 mg/kg

Warnings/Precautions May elevate aminotransferases; LFTs should be performed before and every 4-6 weeks during the first 12-15 months of therapy and periodically thereafter; can also cause myalgia and rhabdomyolysis; use with caution in patients who consume large quantities of alcohol or who have a history of liver disease

Adverse Reactions 1% to 10%:

Central nervous system: Headache, dizziness

Dermatologic: Rash

Endocrine & metabolic: Elevated creatine phosphokinase (CPK)

Gastrointestinal: Flatulence, abdominal cramps, diarrhea, constipation, nausea, dyspepsia, heartburn

Neuromuscular & skeletal: Myalgia

Reference Range Peak plasma levels following a 19.2 mg oral dose: ~27 ng/mL

Drug Interactions

Increased effect/toxicity of oral anticoagulants

Increased toxicity with gemfibrozil, clofibrate, cyclosporine

Dosage Forms Tablet: 10 mg, 20 mg, 40 mg

Specific References

Halkin A, Lossos IS, and Mevorach D, "HMG-CoA Reductase Inhibitor-Induced Impotence," *Ann Pharmacother*, 1996, 30:192.

Prazepam (PRA ze pam)

Related Information

Controlled Substances - Uses and Effects *on page 741*

U.S. Brand Names Centrax®; Demetrin®; Lysanxia®; Trepidan®

Therapeutic Category Antianxiety Agent; Anticonvulsant; Benzodiazepine

Abuse Potential Yes

Impairment Potential Yes

Use Treatment of anxiety and management of alcohol withdrawal; may also be used as an anticonvulsant in management of simple partial seizures

Usual Dosage Adults: Oral: 30 mg/day in divided doses, may increase gradually to a maximum of 60 mg/day

Mechanism of Action Benzodiazepine anxiolytic sedative that produces CNS depression at the subcortical level, except at high doses, whereby it works at the cortical level

Pharmacodynamics/kinetics Studies have shown that the elderly are more sensitive to the effects of benzodiazepines as compared to younger adults

Onset of action: Peak actions occur within 6 hours

Duration: 48 hours

Absorption: Readily from gastrointestinal tract

Distribution: V_d: 9.3-19.5 L/kg; distributed widely distributed throughout body

Protein binding: 85% to 97%

Metabolism: First-pass hepatic metabolism, primarily desmethyldiazepam (active)

Half-life:

Parent: 78 minutes

Desmethyldiazepam: 30-100 hours

Half-life of desmethyldiazepam is significantly prolonged in elderly men (127.8 hours) as compared to young men (61.8 hours) and older women (75.4 hours); V_d is increased in the elderly

Time to peak serum concentration: Oral single dose: 2.5-6 hours

Elimination: Renal and feces (71%)

Signs and Symptoms of Acute Intoxication Confusion, hypoactive reflexes, hyporeflexia, dry mouth, rhabdomyolysis, acute myoglobinuria, light-headedness, visual and auditory hallucinations, dyspnea, labored breathing, "alpha" coma (alpha frequency rhythm on EEG), ataxia, gaze nystagmus

When to Transport to Hospital Transport any patient exhibiting any signs or symptoms of acute overdose or asymptomatic ingestions over 1 mg/kg

Warnings/Precautions May cause drug dependency; avoid abrupt discontinuance in patients with prolonged therapy or seizure disorders; not considered a drug of choice in the elderly; safety and efficacy in children <18 years of age have not been established

Adverse Reactions

>10%:

Central nervous system: Drowsiness, anxiety, ataxia

Ocular: Blurred vision

<10%:

Cardiovascular: Cardiac arrest, hypotension, bradycardia, cardiovascular collapse, sinus bradycardia

Central nervous system: Confusion, dizziness, amnesia, slurred speech, paradoxical excitation or rage, delirium, persecutory delusions

Local: Phlebitis, pain with injection

Neuromuscular & skeletal: Orofacial dyskinesia

Ocular: Diplopia

Respiratory: Respiratory rate (decreased), apnea, laryngospasm

Miscellaneous: Physical and psychological dependence with prolonged use

Reference Range Therapeutic: 50-240 ng/mL (SI: 156-746 nmol/L)

(Continued)

493

Prazepam *(Continued)*

Drug Interactions CNS depressants, disulfiram, cimetidine, levodopa, anticonvulsants, digoxin

Dosage Forms
Capsule: 5 mg, 10 mg, 20 mg
Tablet: 5 mg, 10 mg

Additional Information Prazepam offers no significant advantage over other benzodiazepines

Specific References
Skielboe M, Anderson PM, Weber M, et al, "Reversal of Benzodiazepine Intoxication by Flumazenil," *Resuscitation*, 1991, 22:245-52.

Prazosin *(PRA zoe sin)*

Synonyms Furazosin

U.S. Brand Names Hypovase®; Minipress®

Canadian Brand Names Apo-Prazo®; Novo-Prazin®; Nu-Prazo®

Therapeutic Category Alpha-Adrenergic Blocking Agent

Use Hypertension, severe congestive heart failure (in conjunction with diuretics and cardiac glycosides)

Usual Dosage Oral:
Children: Initial: 5 mcg/kg/dose (to assess hypotensive effects); usual dosing interval: every 6 hours; increase dosage gradually up to maximum of 25 mcg/kg/dose every 6 hours
Adults: Initial: 1 mg/dose 2-3 times/day; usual maintenance dose: 3-15 mg/day in divided doses 2-4 times/day; maximum daily dose: 20 mg

Mechanism of Action Competitively inhibits postsynaptic alpha-adrenergic receptors which results in vasodilation of veins and arterioles and a decrease in total peripheral resistance and blood pressure; effective for ergotism-induced hypertension

Pharmacodynamics/kinetics
Onset of action: Hypotensive effect: Within 2 hours; Maximum decrease: 2-4 hours
Duration: 10-24 hours
Absorption: Well from gastrointestinal tract
Metabolism: Extensive in the liver
Bioavailability: Oral: 43% to 82%
Half-life: 2-4 hours; increased half-life with congestive heart failure
Time to peak serum concentration: 1-3 hours

Signs and Symptoms of Acute Intoxication Hypotension, drowsiness, bone marrow depression, enuresis, night terrors, impotence, syncope, ptosis, hypothermia, conjunctivitis, respiratory depression

When to Transport to Hospital Transport any patient exhibiting hypotension or decreased mental status

Warnings/Precautions Can cause marked hypotension and syncope with sudden loss of consciousness with the first few doses. Anticipate a similar effect if therapy is interrupted for a few days, if dosage is increased rapidly, or if another antihypertensive drug is introduced.

Adverse Reactions
>10%:
Cardiovascular: Orthostatic hypotension
Central nervous system: Dizziness, lightheadedness, drowsiness, headache, malaise
1% to 10%:
Cardiovascular: Edema, palpitations
Central nervous system: Fatigue, nervousness
Gastrointestinal: Xerostomia

Genitourinary: Urinary incontinence

Reference Range Plasma level of 47.6 ng/mL was noted in an overdose setting 11 hours after a 120 mg ingestion

Drug Interactions Diuretics and antihypertensive medications (especially beta-blockers) may increase prazosin's hypotensive effect

Dosage Forms Capsule: 1 mg, 2 mg, 5 mg

Specific References

Lenz K, Druml W, Kleinberger G, et al, "Acute Intoxication With Prazosin: Case Report," *Hum Toxicol*, 1985, 4(1):53-6.

Predair® see Prednisolone *on this page*

Predaject® see Prednisolone *on this page*

Predalone T.B.A.® see Prednisolone *on this page*

Predcor® see Prednisolone *on this page*

Predcor-TBA® see Prednisolone *on this page*

Pred Forte® see Prednisolone *on this page*

Pred Mild® see Prednisolone *on this page*

Prednicen-M® see Prednisone *on page 497*

Prednisolone (pred NIS oh lone)

Synonyms Deltahydrocortisone; Metacortandralone

U.S. Brand Names AK-Pred®; Articulose-50®; Delta-Cortef®; Econopred®; Econopred® Plus; Hydeltrasol®; Hydeltra-T.B.A.®; Inflamase®; Inflamase® Mild; Key-Pred®; Key-Pred-SP®; Metreton®; Pediapred®; Predair®; Predaject®; Predalone T.B.A.®; Predcor®; Predcor-TBA®; Pred Forte®; Pred Mild®; Prelone®

Canadian Brand Names Novo-Prednisolone®

Therapeutic Category Adrenal Corticosteroid

Use Treatment of palpebral and bulbar conjunctivitis; corneal injury from chemical, radiation, thermal burns, or foreign body penetration; endocrine disorders, rheumatic disorders, collagen diseases, dermatologic diseases, allergic states, ophthalmic diseases, respiratory diseases, hematologic disorders, neoplastic diseases, edematous states, and gastrointestinal diseases; useful in patients with inability to activate prednisone (liver disease)

Usual Dosage Dose depends upon condition being treated and response of patient; dosage for infants and children should be based on severity of the disease and response of the patient rather than on strict adherence to dosage indicated by age, weight, or body surface area. Consider alternate day therapy for long-term therapy. Discontinuation of long-term therapy requires gradual withdrawal by tapering the dose.

Children:

Acute asthma: Oral: 1-2 mg/kg/day in divided doses 1-2 times/day for 3-5 days

Anti-inflammatory or immunosuppressive dose: Oral, I.V., I.M. (sodium phosphate salt): 0.1-2 mg/kg/day in divided doses 1-4 times/day

Nephrotic syndrome: Oral:

Initial: 2 mg/kg/day (maximum: 80 mg/day) in divided doses 3-4 times/day until urine is protein free for 5 days (maximum: 28 days); if proteinuria persists, use 4 mg/kg/dose every other day for an additional 28 days

Maintenance: 2 mg/kg/dose (maximum: 80 mg/dose) every other morning for 28 days, then taper by 10 mg/dose at intervals of 2-3 weeks to 30 mg/dose, then by 5 mg/dose at intervals of 2-3 weeks until discontinued

Adults:

Oral, I.V., I.M. (sodium phosphate salt): 5-60 mg/day

I.M. (acetate salt): 4-60 mg/day

Rheumatoid arthritis: Oral: Initial: 5-7.5 mg/day, adjust dose as necessary

(Continued)

Prednisolone *(Continued)*

Multiple sclerosis (sodium phosphate): Oral: 200 mg/day for 1 week followed by 80 mg every other day for 1 month

Multiple sclerosis (acetate salt): I.M.: 200 mg/day for 1 week followed by 80 mg every other day for 1 month

Elderly: Use lowest effective adult dose

Slightly dialyzable (5% to 20%)

Intra-articular, intralesional, soft-tissue administration:
Tebutate salt: 4-40 mg/dose
Acetate salt: 4-100 mg/dose
Sodium phosphate salt: 2-30 mg/dose

Ophthalmic suspension/solution: Instill 1-2 drops into conjunctival sac every hour during day, every 2 hours at night until favorable response is obtained, then use 1 drop every 4 hours

Mechanism of Action Decreases inflammation by suppression of migration of polymorphonuclear leukocytes and reversal of increased capillary permeability; suppresses the immune system by reducing activity and volume of the lymphatic system

Pharmacodynamics/kinetics

Distribution: V_d: 0.31 L/kg (after conversion)

Protein binding: 65% to 91% (concentration dependent)

Metabolism: Primarily in the liver, but also metabolized in most tissues, to inactive compounds

Half-life: 3.6 hours
Biological: 18-36 hours
End stage renal disease: 3-5 hours

Elimination: In urine principally as glucuronides, sulfates, and unconjugated metabolites; clearance: ~0.1 L/hour/kg

Signs and Symptoms of Acute Intoxication When consumed in excessive quantities for prolonged periods, systemic hypercorticism and adrenal suppression may occur, in those cases discontinuation and withdrawal of the corticosteroid should be done judiciously.

When to Transport to Hospital Transport any psychotic patient

Warnings/Precautions Use with caution in patients with hyperthyroidism, cirrhosis, nonspecific ulcerative colitis, hypertension, osteoporosis, thromboembolic tendencies, CHF, convulsive disorders, myasthenia gravis, thrombophlebitis, peptic ulcer, diabetes; acute adrenal insufficiency may occur with abrupt withdrawal after long-term therapy or with stress; young pediatric patients may be more susceptible to adrenal axis suppression from topical therapy. Because of the risk of adverse effects, systemic corticosteroids should be used cautiously in the elderly, in the smallest possible dose, and for the shortest possible time.

Adverse Reactions

>10%:
Central nervous system: Insomnia, nervousness
Gastrointestinal: Increased appetite, indigestion

1% to 10%:
Dermatologic: Hirsutism
Endocrine & metabolic: Diabetes mellitus
Neuromuscular & skeletal: Arthralgia
Ocular: Cataracts, glaucoma
Respiratory: Epistaxis

Test Interactions Response to skin tests

Drug Interactions Decreased effect with barbiturates, phenytoin, rifampin; decreased effect of salicylates, vaccines, toxoids

Dosage Forms
Prednisolone acetate:
Injection (for I.M., intralesional, intra-articular, or soft tissue administration only): 25 mg/mL (10 mL, 30 mL); 50 mg/mL (30 mL)

Suspension, ophthalmic: 0.12% (5 mL, 10 mL); 0.125% (5 mL, 10 mL, 15 mL); 1% (1 mL, 5 mL, 10 mL, 15 mL)

Prednisolone sodium phosphate:
Injection (for I.M., I.V., intra-articular, intralesional, or soft tissue administration): 20 mg/mL (2 mL, 5 mL, 10 mL)

Liquid, oral: 5 mg/5 mL (120 mL)

Solution, ophthalmic: 0.125% (5 mL, 10 mL, 15 mL); 1% (5 mL, 10 mL, 15 mL)

Injection, **as tebutate** (for intra-articular, intralesional, soft tissue administration only): 20 mg/mL (1 mL, 5 mL, 10 mL)

Syrup: 15 mg/5 mL (240 mL)

Tablet: 5 mg

Additional Information
Sodium phosphate injection: For I.V., I.M., intra-articular, intralesional, or soft tissue administration

Tebutate injection: For intra-articular, intralesional, or soft tissue administration only

Specific References
Johnson I, "Steroid-Induced Prepartum Psychosis," *Br J Psychiatry*, 1996, 169:522.

Prednisone (PRED ni sone)
Synonyms Deltacortisone; Deltadehydrocortisone

U.S. Brand Names Deltasone®; Liquid Pred®; Meticorten®; Orasone®; Prednicen-M®; Sterapred®

Canadian Brand Names Apo-Prednisone®; Jaa-Prednisone®; Novo-Prednisone®; Wimpred®

Therapeutic Category Adrenal Corticosteroid

Use Treatment of a variety of diseases including adrenocortical insufficiency, hypercalcemia, rheumatic, and collagen disorders; dermatologic, ocular, respiratory, gastrointestinal, and neoplastic diseases; organ transplantation and a variety of diseases including those of hematologic, allergic, inflammatory, and autoimmune in origin; not available in injectable form, prednisolone must be used

Investigational: Prevention of postherpetic neuralgia and relief of acute pain in the early stages

Usual Dosage Oral:
Dose depends upon condition being treated and response of patient; dosage for infants and children should be based on severity of the disease and response of the patient rather than on strict adherence to dosage indicated by age, weight, or body surface area. Consider alternate day therapy for long-term therapy. Discontinuation of long-term therapy requires gradual withdrawal by tapering the dose.

Children:
Anti-inflammatory or immunosuppressive dose: 0.05-2 mg/kg/day divided 1-4 times/day

Acute asthma: 1-2 mg/kg/day in divided doses 1-2 times/day for 3-5 days
Alternatively (for 3- to 5-day "burst"):
<1 year: 10 mg every 12 hours
1-4 years: 20 mg every 12 hours
5-13 years: 30 mg every 12 hours
>13 years: 40 mg every 12 hours

(Continued)

Prednisone *(Continued)*

Asthma long-term therapy (alternative dosing by age):
  <1 year: 10 mg every other day
  1-4 years: 20 mg every other day
  5-13 years: 30 mg every other day
  >13 years: 40 mg every other day
Nephrotic syndrome: Initial (first 3 episodes): 2 mg/kg/day **OR** 60 mg/m^2/day (maximum: of 80 mg/day) in divided doses 3-4 times/day until urine is protein free for 3 consecutive days (maximum: 28 days); followed by 1-1.5 mg/kg/dose **OR** 40 mg/m^2/dose given every other day for 4 weeks
Maintenance dose (long-term maintenance dose for frequent relapses): 0.5-1 mg/kg/dose given every other day for 3-6 months

Children and Adults: Physiologic replacement: 4-5 mg/m^2/day

Adults: 5-60 mg/day in divided doses 1-4 times/day

Elderly: Use the lowest effective dose

Mechanism of Action Decreases inflammation by suppression of migration of polymorphonuclear leukocytes and reversal of increased capillary permeability; suppresses the immune system by reducing activity and volume of the lymphatic system; suppresses adrenal function at high doses. Antitumor effects may be related to inhibition of glucose transport, phosphorylation, or induction of cell death in immature lymphocytes. Antiemetic effects are thought to occur due to blockade of cerebral innervation of the emetic center via inhibition of prostaglandin synthesis.

Pharmacodynamics/kinetics

Metabolism: Converted rapidly to prednisolone (active)
  Prednisone is inactive and must be metabolized to prednisolone which may be impaired in patients with impaired liver function
Half-life: Normal renal function: 2.5-3.5 hours

Signs and Symptoms of Acute Intoxication When consumed in excessive quantities for prolonged periods, systemic hypercorticism and adrenal suppression may occur

When to Transport to Hospital Transport any psychotic patient

Overdosage/Treatment In cases of systemic hypercorticism and adrenal suppression, discontinuation and withdrawal of the corticosteroid should be done judiciously

Warnings/Precautions Withdraw therapy with gradual tapering of dose, may retard bone growth; use with caution in patients with hypothyroidism, cirrhosis, hypertension, congestive heart failure, ulcerative colitis, thromboembolic disorders, and patients at increased risk for peptic ulcer disease. Because of the risk of adverse effects, systemic corticosteroids should be used cautiously in the elderly, in the smallest possible dose, and for the shortest possible time.

Adverse Reactions

>10%:
  Central nervous system: Insomnia, nervousness
  Gastrointestinal: Increased appetite, indigestion
1% to 10%:
  Dermatologic: Hirsutism
  Endocrine & metabolic: Diabetes mellitus
  Ocular: Cataracts, glaucoma
  Neuromuscular & skeletal: Arthralgia
  Respiratory: Epistaxis

Test Interactions Response to skin tests

Drug Interactions
Inducer of cytochrome P-450 enzymes
Cytochrome P-450 3A enzyme substrate

Decreased effect:
   Barbiturates, phenytoin, rifampin decrease corticosteroid effectiveness
   Decreases salicylates
   Decreases vaccines
   Decreases toxoids effectiveness

Dosage Forms
   Solution, oral: Concentrate (30% alcohol): 5 mg/mL (30 mL); Nonconcentrate
   (5% alcohol): 5 mg/5 mL (5 mL, 500 mL)
   Syrup: 5 mg/5 mL (120 mL, 240 mL)
   Tablet: 1 mg, 2.5 mg, 5 mg, 10 mg, 20 mg, 50 mg

Specific References
   Wolkowitz OM, "Long-Lasting Behavioral Changes Following Prednisone Withdrawal," *JAMA*, 1989, 261(12):1731-2.

Prefrin™ Ophthalmic Solution *see* Phenylephrine *on page 479*

Pregnancy Test

Synonyms Beta-Subunit Human Chorionic Gonadotropin, Urine or Serum;
hCG, Slide Test, Stat; hCG, Urine; Human Chorionic Gonadotropin, Urine; β-
Subunit of hCG

Use Diagnose pregnancy; screen for women at risk of being pregnant prior to
performance of x-ray, sterilization, menstrual regulation, and curettage procedures and/or prior to the initiation of gestation/embryo/fetal potentially injurious
medication; detect and/or evaluate incomplete/complete abortions; detect
ectopic gestation; screen for gestational trophoblastic neoplasia or ectopic
hCG producing tumor. (A sensitive and quantitative test for the presence of
hCG is preferable for these applications.)

Reference Range Normal males and nonpregnant females: negative; normal
pregnant females: positive. Sensitivity and specificity of β-subunit two point RIA
or EIA tests may allow early diagnosis of pregnancy, within 6 days after
conception.

Additional Information Pregnancy testing is usually performed on urine. It is
based on the the detection of human chorionic gonadotropin (hCG). Levels of
hCG in the urine approach those seen in serum. In normal pregnancy, hCG
levels rise at implantation and peak at 8-12 weeks. Although newer urine
pregnancy tests are quite sensitive, false-negatives can occur early in gestation. In such cases, if ectopic pregnancy is suspected, serum hCG assays may
be of value.

Early in the first trimester of pregnancy (1-2 weeks) serum hCG levels are from
50-500 mIU/mL (SI: 50-500 IU/L). Current generation sensitive tests can detect
pregnancy shortly (2-3 days) after implantation of the ovum. By 3-4 weeks of
gestation, hCG is at the 500-10,000 mIU/mL level (SI: 500-10,000 IU/L). Serum
hCG levels peaks during the second to third month of gestation (30,000-100,000
mIU/mL) (SI: 30,000-100,000 IU/L). Use of serum for pregnancy testing may
provide greater sensitivity, of special value in cases of early pregnancy, and is
of greater value in serial testing for follow-up of an abnormal gestation (eg,
ectopic pregnancy or a gestational trophoblastic neoplasm). If serum (or urine)
hCG levels do not appear to correlate with the anticipated clinical situation,
periodic repeat hCG determinations may be helpful. If there is demise of the
developing embryo/fetus (eg, ectopic pregnancy), hCG levels will fall. Because
of slow clearance from the serum, hCG may be detected in serum/urine for as
long as 4 weeks following abortion.

Currently, the tests most commonly used to screen for pregnancy are two-point
EIA "concentration" methods. A variety of different forms are commercially
available. An antibody (frequently monoclonal) is immobilized on a membrane
or other solid phase and the sample hCG is "concentrated" in a small central
(Continued)

Pregnancy Test *(Continued)*

area of the surface (a membrane, bead, paddle, tube, or dipstick). Color development occurs within minutes of addition of enzyme tagged monoclonal anti-β-hCG. These tests are sensitive, specific, and fast. They have largely supplanted slide/tube screening procedures.

A study of specificity (six commercially available ELISA urine pregnancy tests) utilizing specimens from men and postmenopausal females found variable performance by the different methods, not explained by review of the medical records. Test systems with provision for a negative reference area gave fewer false-positive results (had greater specificity). Correlation was found between mucous content of the postmenopausal female group's urine samples and the incidence of false-positive hCG results.

One year of routine use of Tandem® ICON® system for urine pregnancy testing (University of Texas) did not result in a report of known false-positive results. Stability of color development after addition of color reagents and presence or absence of a built in positive control could influence choice of a test system for routine use.

Serum progesterone levels used with beta-hCG levels may assist in differentiating normal intrauterine from abnormal intrauterine or ectopic pregnancy (cutoff point 15 ng/mL) (SI: 48 nmol/L). Beta-hCG and progesterone levels are lower in abnormal pregnancies. Less overlap occurs, however, between progesterone (as compared to beta-hCG) values in normal versus ectopic and abnormal pregnancies. When a positive pregnancy test is obtained, differential considerations should include the possibility of simultaneous intrauterine and extrauterine gestations (albeit unlikely) and the possibility of passively acquired hCG as in an individual recently transfused with fresh frozen plasma prepared from pregnant donors.

A number of commercially successful home pregnancy tests have been introduced. They have been found to vary widely in performance (optimal accuracy, sensitivity, specificity, human factor useability). A study of the use of such home pregnancy test kits has resulted in the suggestion that pharmacists have an opportunity in taking a more active role in promoting the appropriate use of such self-testing products.

Specific References
Fields SA and Toffler WL, "Pregnancy Testing - Home and Office," *West J Med,* 1991, 154(3):327-8.

Prelis® *see* Metoprolol *on page 400*

Prelone® *see* Prednisolone *on page 495*

Preludin® *see* Phenmetrazine *on page 473*

Premarin® With Methyltestosterone *see* Estrogens and Methyltestosterone *on page 230*

Premphase™ *see* Estrogens and Medroxyprogesterone *on page 229*

Prempro™ *see* Estrogens and Medroxyprogesterone *on page 229*

Pres® *see* Enalapril *on page 217*

Presamine® *see* Imipramine *on page 309*

Pretonin® *see* Oxitriptan *on page 451*

Prevident® *see* Fluoride *on page 251*

Pridonal® *see* Tiapride *on page 581*

Primaclone *see* Primidone *on this page*

Primidone *(PRI mi done)*
Synonyms Desoxyphenobarbital; Hexamidinum; Primaclone
U.S. Brand Names Mysoline®

Canadian Brand Names Apo-Primidone®; Sertan®

Therapeutic Category Anticonvulsant; Barbiturate

Abuse Potential Yes

Impairment Potential Yes

Use Prophylactic management of partial seizures with complex symptomatology (psychomotor seizures), generalized tonic-clonic, and akinetic seizure

Usual Dosage Oral:

Children <8 years: Initial: 50-125 mg/day given at bedtime; increase by 50-125 mg/day increments every 3-7 days; usual dose: 10-25 mg/kg/day in divided doses 3-4 times/day

Children >8 years and Adults: Initial: 125-250 mg/day at bedtime; increase by 125-250 mg/day every 3-7 days; usual dose: 750-1500 mg/day in divided doses 3-4 times/day with maximum dosage of 2 g/day

Mechanism of Action Decreases neuron excitability, raises seizure threshold similar to phenobarbital

Pharmacodynamics/kinetics

Absorption: Rapid; usually complete with wide individual variation

Metabolism: In the liver to phenobarbital (active) and phenylethylmalonamide (PEMA)

Bioavailability: 90% to 100%

Half-life:

Primidone: 3-24 hours

PEMA: 24-48 hours

Phenobarbital: 72-144 hours (age-dependent)

Time to peak serum concentration: Within 4 hours

Signs and Symptoms of Acute Intoxication Unsteady gait, slurred speech, confusion, severe flapping tremors, loss of deep tendon reflexes, hypothyroidism, dementia, jaundice, hypothermia, fever, hypotension, ptosis, crystalluria (white, hexagonal crystals), ankle clonus, gaze nystagmus, leukopenia; neutropenia; vision color changes (green tinge); agranulocytosis; granulocytopenia

When to Transport to Hospital Transport any symptomatic patient

Warnings/Precautions Avoid abrupt discontinuation; dosage should be slowly decreased to avoid precipitation of seizures or status epilepticus; use with caution in patients with renal or hepatic impairment, pulmonary insufficiency

Adverse Reactions

>10%: Central nervous system: Drowsiness, vertigo, ataxia, lethargy, behavior change, sedation, headache

1% to 10%:

Gastrointestinal: Nausea, vomiting, anorexia

Genitourinary: Impotence

Reference Range

Therapeutic:

Children <5 years: 7-10 µg/mL (SI: 32-46 µmol/L)

Adults: 5-12 µg/mL (SI: 23-55 µmol/L); toxic effects rarely present with levels <10 µg/mL (SI: <46 µmol/L) if phenobarbital concentrations are low

Dosage of primidone is adjusted with reference mostly to the phenobarbital level

Toxic: >15 µg/mL (SI: >69 µmol/L) associated with ataxia and/or drowsiness

Dosage Forms

Suspension, oral: 250 mg/5 mL (240 mL)

Tablet: 50 mg, 250 mg

Specific References

Schwankhaus JD, Kattah JC, Lux WE, et al, "Primidone/Phenobarbital-Induced Periodic Alternating Nystagmus," *Ann Ophthalmol*, 1989, 21(6):230-2.

Principen® *see* Ampicillin *on page 48*

Prinzide® *see Lisinopril and Hydrochlorothiazide on page 347*

Privine® *see Naphazoline on page 422*

Procardia® *see Nifedipine on page 433*

Procardia XL® *see Nifedipine on page 433*

Prochlorperazine (proe klor PER a zeen)

U.S. Brand Names Compazine®

Canadian Brand Names Stemetil®; Nu-Prochlor®; PMS-Prochlorperazine®; Prorazin®

Therapeutic Category Antipsychotic Agent; Phenothiazine Derivative

Impairment Potential Yes

Use Management of nausea and vomiting; acute and chronic psychosis

Usual Dosage

Children >10 kg:

Oral, rectal: 0.4 mg/kg/24 hours in 3-4 divided doses; **or**

9-14 kg: 2.5 mg every 12-24 hours as needed; maximum: 7.5 mg/day

14-18 kg: 2.5 mg every 8-12 hours as needed; maximum: 10 mg/day

18-39 kg: 2.5 mg every 8 hours or 5 mg every 12 hours as needed; maximum: 15 mg/day

I.M.: 0.1-0.15 mg/kg/dose; usual: 0.13 mg/kg/dose; change to oral as soon as possible

I.V.: Not recommended in children <10 kg or <2 years

Adults:

Oral: 5-10 mg 3-4 times/day or sustained release twice daily; usual maximum: 40 mg/day; doses up to 150 mg/day may be required in some patients for treatment of severe psychotic disturbances

I.M.: 5-10 mg every 3-4 hours; usual maximum: 40 mg/day; doses up to 10-20 mg every 4-6 hours may be required in some patients for treatment of severe psychotic disturbances

I.V.: 2.5-10 mg; maximum 10 mg/dose or 40 mg/day; may repeat dose every 3-4 hours as needed

Rectal: 25 mg twice daily

Mechanism of Action Blocks postsynaptic mesolimbic dopaminergic receptors in the brain, including the medullary chemoreceptor trigger zone; exhibits a strong alpha-adrenergic blocking effect and depresses the release of hypothalamic and hypophyseal hormones

Pharmacodynamics/kinetics

Onset of action:

Oral: Within 30-40 minutes

I.M.: Within 10-20 minutes

Rectal: Within 60 minutes

Duration:

Oral (immediate release), rectal doses: 3-4 hours

Oral (extended release), I.M. doses: 12 hours

Metabolism: Primarily eliminated by hepatic metabolism

Half-life: 23 hours

Signs and Symptoms of Acute Intoxication Deep sleep, coma, photosensitivity, extrapyramidal reaction, impotence, Parkinson's-like symptoms, neuroleptic malignant syndrome, vision color changes (brown tinge); urine discoloration (pink), urine discoloration (red), urine discoloration (red-brown), muscle spasm, akathisia

When to Transport to Hospital Transport any pediatric (<2 years of age) exposure or any symptomatic patient

Warnings/Precautions High incidence of extrapyramidal reactions occurs especially in children; hypotension with parenteral use; due to high incidence of extrapyramidal effects, injection contains sulfite which may cause allergic reactions in some patients; safety and efficacy have not been established in children <9 kg or <2 years of age; avoid in patients with Reye's syndrome

Adverse Reactions Incidence of extrapyramidal reactions are higher with prochlorperazine than chlorpromazine

Central nervous system: Sedation, drowsiness, restlessness, anxiety, extrapyramidal reactions, parkinsonian signs and symptoms, seizures, altered central temperature regulation

Dermatologic: Photosensitivity, hyperpigmentation, pruritus, rash

Endocrine & metabolic: Amenorrhea, galactorrhea, gynecomastia

Gastrointestinal: Weight gain, GI upset

Miscellaneous: Anaphylactoid reactions

>10%:

Cardiovascular: Hypotension (especially with I.V. use), orthostatic hypotension, tachycardia, arrhythmias

Central nervous system: Pseudoparkinsonism, akathisia, tardive dyskinesia (persistent), dizziness, dystonias

Gastrointestinal: Xerostomia, constipation

Genitourinary: Urinary retention

Ocular: Pigmentary retinopathy, blurred vision

Respiratory: Nasal congestion

Miscellaneous: Diaphoresis (decreased)

1% to 10%:

Dermatologic: Increased sensitivity to sun, rash

Endocrine & metabolic: Changes in menstrual cycle, breast pain, changes in libido

Gastrointestinal: Nausea, vomiting, stomach pain

Genitourinary: Dysuria, ejaculatory disturbances

Neuromuscular & skeletal: Trembling of fingers

Reference Range Blood level >1 µg/mL associated with toxicity

Drug Interactions Additive effects with other CNS depressants

Dosage Forms

Prochlorperazine edisylate:

Injection: 5 mg/mL (2 mL, 10 mL)

Syrup: 5 mg/5 mL (120 mL)

Prochlorperazine maleate:

Capsule, sustained action: 10 mg, 15 mg, 30 mg

Tablet: 5 mg, 10 mg, 25 mg

Suppository, rectal: 2.5 mg, 5 mg, 25 mg

Specific References

Dukoff R, Horak ID, Hassan R, et al, "Akathisia Associated With Prochlorperazine as an Antiemetic: A Case Report," *Ann Oncol*, 1996, 7:103.

Promazine (PROE ma zeen)

U.S. Brand Names Calmotal®; Prozine-50®; Sparine®

Therapeutic Category Antipsychotic Agent; Phenothiazine Derivative

Use Treatment of psychoses

Usual Dosage Oral, I.M.:

Children >12 years: Antipsychotic: 10-25 mg every 4-6 hours

Adults:

Psychosis: 10-200 mg every 4-6 hours not to exceed 1000 mg/day

Antiemetic: 25-50 mg every 4-6 hours as needed

Mechanism of Action Excess dopamine in the mesolimbic and mesocortical areas of the brain has been postulated to produce psychoses. Antipsychotics such as promazine act by blocking postsynaptic dopamine receptors, thus ameliorating psychotic symptoms. Promazine, an aliphatic phenothiazine, shares similar properties with chlorpromazine and thus produces a higher frequency of sedation and cardiovascular effects while producing only a moderate frequency of extrapyramidal reactions. Promazine has very weak antipsychotic activity.

Pharmacodynamics/kinetics Specific pharmacokinetics are poorly established but probably resemble those of other phenothiazines.

Absorption: Phenothiazines are only partially absorbed; great variability in plasma levels resulting from a given dose

Metabolism: Extensive in the liver

Half-life: Most phenothiazines have long half-lives in the range of 24 hours or more

Signs and Symptoms of Acute Intoxication Deep sleep, coma, Parkinson's-like symptoms, impotence, hypoglycemia, galactorrhea, neuroleptic malignant syndrome, gynecomastia, dermatitis, extrapyramidal reaction, abnormal involuntary muscle movements, hypotension, seizures, respiratory depression, vision color changes (brown tinge); urine discoloration (pink), urine discoloration (red), urine discoloration (red-brown), leukopenia; neutropenia; agranulocytosis; granulocytopenia

When to Transport to Hospital Transport any pediatric (<12 years of age) exposure or any symptomatic patient

Warnings/Precautions Promazine shares the toxic potentials of other phenothiazines, and the usual precautions of phenothiazine therapy should be observed

Adverse Reactions

>10%:

Cardiovascular: Hypotension, orthostatic hypotension

Central nervous system: Pseudoparkinsonism, akathisia, dystonias, tardive dyskinesia (persistent), dizziness

Gastrointestinal: Constipation

Ocular: Pigmentary retinopathy

Respiratory: Nasal congestion

Miscellaneous: Diaphoresis (decreased)

1% to 10%:

Dermatologic: Increased sensitivity to sun, rash

Endocrine & metabolic: Changes in menstrual cycle, changes in libido, breast pain

Gastrointestinal: Weight gain, nausea, vomiting, stomach pain

Genitourinary: Dysuria, ejaculatory disturbances

Neuromuscular & skeletal: Trembling of fingers

Drug Interactions Antihypertensives, anticonvulsants, CNS depressants, MAO inhibitors, progesterone, oral contraceptives, and ethanol may accentuate toxicity

Dosage Forms
  Injection: 25 mg/mL (10 mL); 50 mg/mL (1 mL, 2 mL, 10 mL)
  Tablet: 25 mg, 50 mg, 100 mg
Additional Information More likely to cause seizures than other phenothiazines and has smaller amount protein bound than other phenothiazines
Specific References
  Gold N, "Attempted Suicide With Chlorpromazine," *Med J Aust*, 1966, 1(12):492-4.

Prometa® *see* Metaproterenol *on page 376* ·

Prometh® *see* Promethazine *on this page*

Promethazine (proe METH a zeen)
Synonyms Diprazinum
U.S. Brand Names Anergan®; Fargan; Phenazine®; Phencen®; Phenergan®; Progan®; Promahist®; Prometh®; Prorex®; V-Gan®
Therapeutic Category Antiemetic; Antipsychotic Agent; Phenothiazine Derivative
Impairment Potential Yes
Use Symptomatic treatment of various allergic conditions, antiemetic, motion sickness, and as a sedative
Usual Dosage
  Children:
    Antihistamine: Oral, rectal: 0.1 mg/kg/dose every 6 hours during the day and 0.5 mg/kg/dose at bedtime as needed
    Antiemetic: Oral, I.M., I.V., rectal: 0.25-1 mg/kg 4-6 times/day as needed
    Motion sickness: Oral, rectal: 0.5 mg/kg/dose 30 minutes to 1 hour before departure, then every 12 hours as needed
    Sedation: Oral, I.M., I.V., rectal: 0.5-1 mg/kg/dose every 6 hours as needed
  Adults:
    Antihistamine (including allergic reactions to blood or plasma):
      Oral, rectal: 12.5 mg 3 times/day and 25 mg at bedtime
      I.M., I.V.: 25 mg, may repeat in 2 hours when necessary; switch to oral route as soon as feasible
    Antiemetic: Oral, I.M., I.V., rectal: 12.5-25 mg every 4 hours as needed
    Motion sickness: Oral, rectal: 25 mg 30-60 minutes before departure, then every 12 hours as needed
    Sedation: Oral, I.M., I.V., rectal: 25-50 mg/dose
Mechanism of Action Blocks postsynaptic mesolimbic dopaminergic receptors in the brain; exhibits a strong alpha-adrenergic blocking effect and depresses the release of hypothalamic and hypophyseal hormones; competes with histamine for the H_1-receptor; reduces stimuli to the brainstem reticular system; blocks acetylcholine
Pharmacodynamics/kinetics
  Duration: 4-6 hours
  Protein binding: 76% to 93%
  Metabolism: In the liver
  Time to peak plasma concentration: 3.4 hours
Signs and Symptoms of Acute Intoxication CNS depression, mydriasis, anticholinergic hallucinations, seizures, fever, tachycardia, leukemoid reaction, hyperthermia, eclampsia, coma, anticholinergic toxidrome, dry mouth, vision color changes (brown tinge); hyperreflexia, myoclonus, impotence, flushing, urine discoloration (pink), urine discoloration (red), urine discoloration (red-brown), leukopenia, neutropenia, agranulocytosis, granulocytopenia
When to Transport to Hospital Transport any symptomatic patient or oral ingestions over 1 mg/kg
(Continued)

Promethazine *(Continued)*

Warnings/Precautions Use with caution in patients with cardiovascular disease, impaired liver function, asthma, sleep apnea, seizures; do not give S.C. or intra-arterially, necrotic lesions may occur; injection may contain sulfites which may cause allergic reactions in some patients

Adverse Reactions

Hematologic: Thrombocytopenia

Hepatic: Jaundice

>10%:

Central nervous system: Slight to moderate drowsiness

Respiratory: Thickening of bronchial secretions

1% to 10%:

Central nervous system: Headache, fatigue, nervousness, dizziness

Gastrointestinal: Xerostomia, abdominal pain, nausea, diarrhea, increased appetite, weight gain

Neuromuscular & skeletal: Arthralgia

Respiratory: Pharyngitis

Reference Range

Therapeutic: 11-23 ng/mL

Toxic: >48 ng/mL

Fatal: 156 ng/mL (postmortem)

Drug Interactions Increased toxicity with epinephrine, CNS depressants; increased sedation when used with meperidine

Dosage Forms

Injection: 25 mg/mL (1 mL, 10 mL); 50 mg/mL (1 mL, 10 mL)

Suppository, rectal: 12.5 mg, 25 mg, 50 mg

Syrup: 6.25 mg/5 mL (5 mL, 120 mL, 240 mL, 480 mL, 4000 mL); 25 mg/5mL (120 mL, 480 mL, 4000 mL)

Tablet: 12.5 mg, 25 mg, 50 mg

Specific References

Dollberg S, Hurvitz H, Kerem E, et al, "Hallucinations and Hyperthermia After Promethazine Ingestion," *Acta Paediatr Scand*, 1989, 78(1):131-2.

Promethazine and Codeine (proe METH a zeen & KOE deen)

U.S. Brand Names Phenergan® With Codeine; Pherazine® With Codeine; Prothazine-DC®

Therapeutic Category Antihistamine/Antitussive

Impairment Potential Yes

Dosage Forms Syrup: Promethazine hydrochloride 6.25 mg and codeine phosphate 10 mg per 5 mL (120 mL, 180 mL, 473 mL)

Promethazine and Dextromethorphan

(proe METH a zeen & deks troe meth OR fan)

U.S. Brand Names Phenameth® DM; Phenergan® with Dextromethorphan; Pherazine® w/DM

Therapeutic Category Antihistamine/Antitussive

Abuse Potential Yes

Impairment Potential Yes

Dosage Forms Syrup: Promethazine hydrochloride 6.25 mg and dextromethorphan hydrobromide 15 mg per 5 mL with alcohol 7% (120 mL, 480 mL, 4000 mL)

Promethazine and Phenylephrine
(proe METH a zeen & fen il EF rin)
U.S. Brand Names Phenergan® VC Syrup; Promethazine VC Plain Syrup; Promethazine VC Syrup; Prometh VC Plain Liquid
Therapeutic Category Antihistamine/Decongestant Combination
Impairment Potential Yes
Dosage Forms Liquid: Promethazine hydrochloride 6.25 mg and phenylephrine hydrochloride 5 mg per 5 mL

Promethazine, Phenylephrine, and Codeine
(proe METH a zeen, fen il EF rin, & KOE deen)
U.S. Brand Names Para-Hist AT®; Phenergan® VC With Codeine; Pherazine® VC w/ Codeine; Promethist® with Codeine; Prometh® VC with Codeine
Therapeutic Category Antihistamine/Decongestant/Antitussive
Impairment Potential Yes
Dosage Forms Liquid: Promethazine hydrochloride 6.25 mg, phenylephrine hydrochloride 5 mg, and codeine phosphate 10 mg per 5 mL with alcohol 7% (120 mL, 240 mL, 480 mL, 4000 mL)

Promethazine VC Plain Syrup *see* Promethazine and Phenylephrine *on this page*

Promethazine VC Syrup *see* Promethazine and Phenylephrine *on this page*

Promethist® with Codeine *see* Promethazine, Phenylephrine, and Codeine *on this page*

Prometh VC Plain Liquid *see* Promethazine and Phenylephrine *on this page*

Prometh® VC with Codeine *see* Promethazine, Phenylephrine, and Codeine *on this page*

Propacet® *see* Propoxyphene and Acetaminophen *on page 510*

Propadrine *see* Phenylpropanolamine *on page 481*

Propagest® [OTC] *see* Phenylpropanolamine *on page 481*

Propane
Synonyms Dimethylmethane; Propyl Hydride
UN Number 1978
Commonly Found In Component in fuels, solvent
Abuse Potential Yes
Impairment Potential Yes
Use In the manufacture of ethylene
Mechanism of Toxic Action Displaces oxygen resulting in hypoxia
Signs and Symptoms of Acute Intoxication Chest pain, dyspnea, cyanosis, headache, dizziness, seizures
When to Transport to Hospital Transport any symptomatic patient
Overdosage/Treatment Supportive therapy: Oxygen therapy - 100% humidified oxygen
Adverse Reactions
Cardiovascular: Tachycardia, myocardial ischemia, angina, sinus tachycardia
Central nervous system: Coma
Neuromuscular & skeletal: Rhabdomyolysis
Ocular: Visual acuity (decreased)
Respiratory: Tachypnea
Additional Information Colorless gas; petroleum-like odor; heavier than air; may form a vapor cloud as a result from refrigeration effect of liquified propane
IDLH: 20,000 ppm
Specific References
Siegel E and Wason S, "Sudden Death Caused by Inhalation of Butane and Propane," *N Engl J Med*, 1990, 323(23):1638.

Propane-1,2-Diol *see* Propylene Glycol *on page 513*

1,2,3-Propanetriol Trinitrate *see* Nitroglycerin *on page 437*

Propanol *see* 1-Propanol *on this page*

1-Propanol

Synonyms n-Propyl Alcohol; Optal; Propanol; Propyl Alcohol; Propylic Alcohol

UN Number 1274

Use In lacquers, cosmetics, cleaners, polishes, and antiseptic agents

Mechanism of Toxic Action Central nervous system depression

Toxicodynamics/kinetics Absorption: Quick from gastrointestinal tract; can be absorbed dermally

Signs and Symptoms of Acute Intoxication Cutaneous erythema, porphyria, hypotension, nausea, vomiting, diarrhea, gastrointestinal irritation, feces discoloration (black); seizures and coma may develop

When to Transport to Hospital Transport any patient with any oral exposure

Adverse Reactions

Central nervous system: Delirium, coma, personality changes

Dermatologic: Dermal irritation

Gastrointestinal: Nausea, vomiting, mucous membrane irritation

Ocular: Eye irritation

Additional Information More toxic than isopropyl alcohol; 20 mL of 1-propanol with water can cause hypotension

Specific References

Wallgren H, "Relative Intoxicating Effects on Rats of Ethyl, Propyl, and Butyl Alcohols," *Acta Pharmacol Toxicol*, 1960, 16:217-22.

2-Propanone *see* Acetone *on page 25*

2-Propenenitrile *see* Acrylonitrile *on page 27*

Propheptatriene *see* Cyclobenzaprine *on page 173*

Propol *see* Isopropyl Alcohol *on page 323*

Propoxyphene (proe POKS i feen)

Related Information

Controlled Substances - Uses and Effects *on page 741*

Synonyms Dextropropoxyphene

U.S. Brand Names Darvon®; Darvon-N®; Dolene®

Canadian Brand Names 624® Tablets; Novo-Propoxyn®

Therapeutic Category Analgesic, Narcotic

Abuse Potential Yes

Impairment Potential Yes

Use Management of mild to moderate pain

Usual Dosage Adults: Oral:

Hydrochloride: 65 mg every 3-4 hours as needed for pain; maximum: 390 mg/day

Napsylate: 100 mg every 4 hours as needed for pain; maximum: 600 mg/day

Mechanism of Action Binds to opiate receptors in the CNS, causing inhibition of ascending pain pathways, altering the perception of and response to pain; produces generalized CNS depression

Pharmacodynamics/kinetics

Onset of effect: Oral: Within 30-60 minutes

Duration: 4-6 hours

Metabolism: Metabolized in the liver to an active metabolite (norpropoxyphene) and inactive metabolites

Bioavailability: Oral: 30% to 70%

Half-life:
Adults:
Parent drug: 8-24 hours (mean: ~15 hours)
Norpropoxyphene: 34 hours
Elderly:
Parent drug: 37 hours
Norpropoxyphene: 42 hours

Signs and Symptoms of Acute Intoxication Vomiting, pulmonary edema, insomnia, impotence, hyperreflexia, disorientation, deafness, jaundice, hyperthermia, hypernatremia, dementia, thrombocytopenia, ptosis, neutropenia, seizures, rhabdomyolysis, diabetes insipidus, myoglobinuria, hypothermia, cyanosis, miosis, cardiac arrhythmia (ventricular), tremors, primary atrioventricular block, nodal tachycardia; dizziness, coma, death can occur within 1 hour

When to Transport to Hospital Transport any pediatric (<6 years of age) ingestion over 10 mg/kg or any symptomatic patient

Warnings/Precautions Give with caution in patients dependent on opiates, substitution may result in acute opiate withdrawal symptoms, use with caution in patients with severe renal or hepatic dysfunction; when given in excessive doses, either alone or in combination with other CNS depressants or propoxyphene products, propoxyphene is a major cause of drug-related deaths; do not exceed recommended dosage

Adverse Reactions

Hepatic: Increased liver enzymes

>10%:
Cardiovascular: Hypotension
Central nervous system: Dizziness, lightheadedness, sedation, paradoxical excitement and insomnia, fatigue, drowsiness
Gastrointestinal: Nausea, vomiting, constipation
Neuromuscular & skeletal: Weakness
Miscellaneous: Histamine release

1% to 10%:
Central nervous system: Nervousness, headache, restlessness, malaise, confusion
Gastrointestinal: Anorexia, stomach cramps, xerostomia, biliary spasm
Genitourinary: Decreased urination, ureteral spasms
Respiratory: Dyspnea, shortness of breath

Reference Range

Therapeutic: 0.2 µg/mL, ranges published vary between laboratories and may not correlate with clinical effect
Toxic: >0.5 µg/mL (SI: >1.5 µmol/L)

Drug Interactions

Decreased effect with charcoal, cigarette smoking
Increased toxicity with CNS depressants; increased toxicity/effect of carbamazepine, phenobarbital, tricyclic antidepressants, warfarin, MAO inhibitors, ethanol

Dosage Forms

Capsule, as hydrochloride: 32 mg, 65 mg
Propoxyphene napsylate:
Suspension, oral: 50 mg/5 mL (480 mL)
Tablet: 100 mg

Specific References

Lawson AA and Northridge DB, "Dextropropoxyphene Overdose. Epidemiology, Clinical Presentation, and Management," *Adv Drug Exp Med Toxicol*, 1987, 2(6):430-44.

Propoxyphene and Acetaminophen
(proe POKS i feen & a seet a MIN oh fen)

Synonyms Propoxyphene Hydrochloride and Acetaminophen; Propoxyphene Napsylate and Acetaminophen

U.S. Brand Names Darvocet-N®; Darvocet-N® 100; Propacet®; Wygesic®

Therapeutic Category Analgesic, Narcotic

Abuse Potential Yes

Impairment Potential Yes

Adverse Reactions 1% to 10%:
Central nervous system: Dizziness, lightheadedness, headache, sedation, paradoxical excitement and insomnia, tolerance, psychologic and physical dependence
Dermatologic: Rashes
Gastrointestinal: GI upset
Neuromuscular & skeletal: Weakness

Dosage Forms Tablet:
Darvocet-N®: Propoxyphene napsylate 50 mg and acetaminophen 325 mg
Darvocet-N® 100: Propoxyphene napsylate 100 mg and acetaminophen 650 mg
Genagesic®, Wygesic®: Propoxyphene hydrochloride 65 mg and acetaminophen 650 mg

Propoxyphene and Aspirin (proe POKS i feen & AS pir in)

Synonyms Propoxyphene Hydrochloride and Aspirin; Propoxyphene Napsylate and Aspirin

U.S. Brand Names Bexophene®; Darvon® Compound-65 Pulvules®

Canadian Brand Names Darvon-N® With ASA; Novo-Propoxyn Compound (contains caffeine); Darvon-N® Compound (contains caffeine)

Therapeutic Category Analgesic, Narcotic

Abuse Potential Yes

Impairment Potential Yes

Adverse Reactions 1% to 10%:
Central nervous system: Dizziness, lightheadedness, weakness, sedation, paradoxical excitement and insomnia, headache, psychologic and physical dependence with prolonged use
Dermatologic: Rashes
Gastrointestinal: GI upset, nausea, vomiting, constipation
Hepatic: Increased liver enzymes

Dosage Forms
Capsule: Propoxyphene hydrochloride 65 mg and aspirin 389 mg with caffeine 32.4 mg
Tablet (Darvon-N® with A.S.A.): Propoxyphene napsylate 100 mg and aspirin 325 mg

Propoxyphene Hydrochloride and Acetaminophen see Propoxyphene and Acetaminophen on this page

Propoxyphene Hydrochloride and Aspirin see Propoxyphene and Aspirin on this page

Propoxyphene Napsylate and Acetaminophen see Propoxyphene and Acetaminophen on this page

Propoxyphene Napsylate and Aspirin see Propoxyphene and Aspirin on this page

Propranolol (proe PRAN oh lole)
U.S. Brand Names Angilol®; Apsolol®; Beaden®; Bedranol®; Berkolol®; Deralin®; Inderal®; Inderal® LA

Canadian Brand Names Apo-Propranolol®; Detensol®; Nu-Propranolol®

Therapeutic Category Antiarrhythmic Agent, Class II; Beta-Adrenergic Blocker

Impairment Potential Yes

Use Management of hypertension, angina pectoris, pheochromocytoma, essential tremor, tetralogy of Fallot cyanotic spells, and arrhythmias (such as fibrillation (atrial) and flutter, A-V nodal re-entrant tachycardias, and catecholamine-induced arrhythmias); prevention of myocardial infarction, migraine headache; symptomatic treatment of hypertrophic subaortic stenosis; termination of thyrotoxic periodic paralysis

Usual Dosage

Tachyarrhythmias: Oral:

Children: Initial: 0.5-1 mg/kg/day in divided doses every 6-8 hours; titrate dosage upward every 3-7 days; usual dose: 2-4 mg/kg/day; higher doses may be needed; do not exceed 16 mg/kg/day or 60 mg/day

Adults: 10-80 mg/dose every 6-8 hours

Hypertension: Oral:

Children: Initial: 0.5-1 mg/kg/day in divided doses every 6-12 hours; increase gradually every 3-7 days; maximum: 2 mg/kg/24 hours

Adults: Initial: 40 mg twice daily or 60-80 mg once daily as sustained release capsules; increase dosage every 3-7 days; usual dose: ≤320 mg divided in 2-3 doses/day or once daily as sustained release; maximum daily dose: 640 mg

Migraine headache prophylaxis: Oral:

Children: 0.6-1.5 mg/kg/day or

≤35 kg: 10-20 mg 3 times/day

>35 kg: 20-40 mg 3 times/day

Adults: Initial: 80 mg/day divided every 6-8 hours; increase by 20-40 mg/dose every 3-4 weeks to a maximum of 160-240 mg/day given in divided doses every 6-8 hours; if satisfactory response not achieved within 6 weeks of starting therapy, drug should be withdrawn gradually over several weeks

Tetralogy spells: Children: Oral: 1-2 mg/kg/day every 6 hours as needed, may increase by 1 mg/kg/day to a maximum of 5 mg/kg/day, or if refractory may increase slowly to a maximum of 10-15 mg/kg/day

Thyrotoxicosis:

Neonates: Oral: 2 mg/kg/day in divided doses every 6-12 hours; occasionally higher doses may be required

Adolescents and Adults: Oral: 10-40 mg/dose every 6 hours

Adults: Oral:

Angina: 80-320 mg/day in doses divided 2-4 times/day or 80-160 mg of sustained release once daily

Pheochromocytoma: 30-60 mg/day in divided doses

Myocardial infarction prophylaxis: 180-240 mg/day in 3-4 divided doses

Hypertrophic subaortic stenosis: 20-40 mg 3-4 times/day

Essential tremor: 40 mg twice daily initially; maintenance doses: usually 120-320 mg/day

Mechanism of Action Competitively blocks response to beta$_1$- and beta$_2$-adrenergic stimulation; no intrinsic sympathomimetic or alpha-receptor antagonist activity; propranolol cardiotoxicity may be mediated through calcium dyshomeostasis

Pharmacodynamics/kinetics

Onset of action: Oral: Within 1-2 hours

Duration: Oral: 6 hours

Absorption: Almost completely from gastrointestinal tract (90%)

Metabolism: In the liver to active and inactive compounds

Bioavailability: 30% to 40%; oral bioavailability may be increased in Down syndrome children

(Continued)

511

Propranolol (Continued)

Half-life:

Children: 3.9-6.4 hours; possible increased half-life in neonates and infants, and overdose setting

Adults: 4-6 hours

Time to peak serum concentration: 1-1.5 hours

Signs and Symptoms of Acute Intoxication Severe hypotension, dyspnea, ataxia, impotence, hypoglycemia, hyperthyroidism, hyperreflexia, shock, retroperitoneal fibrosis, pemphigus, paranoia, hypothyroidism, urticaria, sexual dysfunction; A-V block, rhinorrhea, dementia, purpura, depression, hyperglycemia, cognitive dysfunction, sinus bradycardia, heart/respiratory failure and wheezing; myasthenia gravis (exacerbation or precipitation of), Graves' disease, pulmonary edema, mesenteric ischemia, cardiovascular collapse, alopecia, leukopenia; neutropenia; agranulocytosis; granulocytopenia; seizures (>1.5 g ingestion in adults)

When to Transport to Hospital Transport any symptomatic patient

Warnings/Precautions In patients with angina pectoris, exacerbation of angina and, in some cases, myocardial infarction, occurred following abrupt discontinuance of therapy; use with caution in patients with renal or hepatic impairment

Adverse Reactions

>10%:

Cardiovascular: Bradycardia

Central nervous system: Mental depression

Endocrine & metabolic: Decreased sexual ability

1% to 10%:

Cardiovascular: Congestive heart failure, reduced peripheral circulation

Central nervous system: Confusion, hallucinations, dizziness, insomnia, fatigue

Dermatologic: Rash

Gastrointestinal: Diarrhea, nausea, vomiting, stomach discomfort

Neuromuscular & skeletal: Weakness

Respiratory: Wheezing

Reference Range

Therapeutic: 50-100 ng/mL (SI: 190-390 nmol/L) at end of dose interval

Fatal: Levels >2000 ng/mL (SI: >7702 nmol/L)

Drug Interactions Phenobarbital, rifampin may increase propranolol clearance and may decrease its activity; cimetidine may reduce propranolol clearance and may increase its effects; aluminum-containing antacid may reduce gastrointestinal absorption of propranolol; use of ipecac may precipitate cardiovascular collapse due to increased vagal tone; may enhance cardiac effects of digitalis; hypertension may occur with epinephrine; cigarette smoking may reduce the effectiveness of propranolol

Dosage Forms

Capsule, sustained action: 60 mg, 80 mg, 120 mg, 160 mg

Injection: 1 mg/mL (1 mL)

Solution, oral (strawberry-mint flavor): 4 mg/mL (5 mL, 500 mL); 8 mg/mL (5 mL, 500 mL)

Solution, oral, concentrate: 80 mg/mL (30 mL)

Tablet: 10 mg, 20 mg, 40 mg, 60 mg, 80 mg, 90 mg

Specific References

Love JN and Handler JA, "Toxic Psychosis: An Unusual Presentation of Propranolol Intoxication," *Am J Emerg Med*, 1995, 13(5):536-7.

Propranolol and Hydrochlorothiazide
(proe PRAN oh lole & hye droe klor oh THYE a zide)
U.S. Brand Names Inderide®
Therapeutic Category Antihypertensive, Combination
Impairment Potential Yes
Dosage Forms

Capsule, long acting (Inderide® LA):
80/50 Propranolol hydrochloride 80 mg and hydrochlorothiazide 50 mg
120/50 Propranolol hydrochloride 120 mg and hydrochlorothiazide 50 mg
160/50 Propranolol hydrochloride 160 mg and hydrochlorothiazide 50 mg
Tablet (Inderide®):
40/25 Propranolol hydrochloride 40 mg and hydrochlorothiazide 25 mg
80/25 Propranolol hydrochloride 80 mg and hydrochlorothiazide 25 mg

Propyl Alcohol see 1-Propanol on page 508

Propylcarbinol see Butyl Alcohol on page 97

Propylene Aldehyde see Acrolein on page 27

Propylene Glycol
Synonyms Methyl Glycol; PG 12; Propane-1,2-Diol; Trimethyl Glycol
Impairment Potential Yes
Use In cosmetics and as a solvent in pharmaceuticals; also used as a deicer
Mechanism of Toxic Action Metabolized to lactic acid, pyruvic acid, acetic acid, and propionaldehyde
Toxicodynamics/kinetics

Metabolism: To lactic acid and pyruvic acid
Half-life: Adults: 2-5 hours
Peak serum concentration: 1 hour postingestion

Signs and Symptoms of Acute Intoxication Stupor, seizures, porphyria, feces discoloration (black), lacrimation, hypotension, central nervous system depression
When to Transport to Hospital Transport any symptomatic patient
Adverse Reactions

Cardiovascular: Bradycardia, arrhythmias (ventricular), arrhythmias, shock, sinus bradycardia
Endocrine & metabolic: Hypoglycemia, lactic acidosis, hyperosmolality, acidosis
Hematologic: Hemolysis, anemia
Renal: Renal failure

Reference Range Propylene glycol level (mg/dL): 84.6 + (7.8 x osmolar gap in mOsm/kg); serum levels of 6-1000 mg/L have been noted following intravenous administration; serum propylene glycol levels >177 mg/L can result in an anion gap lactic acidosis
Additional Information 60 mL of propylene glycol can cause stupor in infants; clear, colorless, and odorless; found in intravenous preparations of diazepam and phenytoin; added to foods at concentrations up to 15% to food seasoning; ~1/3 as intoxicating as ethanol; emergency information can be obtained by Dow Chemical Company (Midland, Michigan) (517) 636-4400
Specific References

Glover ML and Reed MD, "Propylene Glycol: The Safe Diluent That Continues to Cause Harm," *Pharmacotherapy*, 1996, 16(4):690-3.

Propylhexedrine (proe pil HEKS e dreen)
Synonyms Hexahydrodesoxyephedrine
U.S. Brand Names Benzedrex® [OTC]; Eventin®; Obesin®
Therapeutic Category Adrenergic Agonist Agent
(Continued)

Propylhexedrine *(Continued)*

Abuse Potential Yes

Impairment Potential Yes

Use Topical nasal decongestant; inhalant for nasal congestion; short-term management of obesity

Usual Dosage Inhalation: Inhale through each nostril while blocking the other; 2 inhalations (0.5 g) into each nostril every 1-2 hours

Oral (obesity): 50-150 mg/day in divided doses

Toxic single dose: 250 mg

Mechanism of Action Related to amphetamine, propylhexedrine causes vasoconstriction of dilated arterioles (potent alpha-adrenergic agonist)

Pharmacodynamics/kinetics

Onset of action: Intranasal: 10 minutes

Duration: Intranasal: 1-2 hours

Elimination: Renal

Signs and Symptoms of Acute Intoxication Chronic abuse has caused cardiomyopathy, pulmonary hypertension, foreign body granulation, dyspnea and sudden death

When to Transport to Hospital Transport any patient with dyspnea, chest pain, or oral adult ingestion over 250 mg

Warnings/Precautions Avoid excessive use

Adverse Reactions I.V. administration can cause vasoconstriction

Cardiovascular: Pulmonary hypertension, hypertension, cardiomegaly, acrocyanosis, cor pulmonale, vasoconstriction

Central nervous system: Headache, psychosis, hyperthermia, paranoia, schizophrenia

Gastrointestinal: Nausea

Hematologic: Thrombocytopenia

Ocular: Diplopia, ophthalmoloplegia

Respiratory: Epistaxis, chronic rhinitis, pulmonary fibrosis

Miscellaneous: Stimulation

Reference Range Blood propylhexedrine levels with normal therapeutic use range around 0.01 mg/L; serum and urine level of 30 mg/L and 60 mg/L respectively associated with fatality

Dosage Forms Inhaler: 250 mg propylhexedrine in 12.5 mg of menthol

Additional Information Drug has been extracted from inhaler and injected I.V. as an amphetamine substitute; often utilized as a drug of abuse (similar to amphetamines) in which sudden death can occur due to heart failure or cardiac arrhythmia; PKA of solution: ~10.4; has been ingested by soaking fibrous interior of inhaler in hot water; exhibits ~10% of effect of CNS stimulation as amphetamine

Specific References

Ligget SB, "Propylhexedrine Intoxication: Clinical Presentation and Pharmacology," *South Med J*, 1982, 75:250-1.

Propyl Hydride *see* Propane *on page 507*

Propylic Alcohol *see* 1-Propanol *on page 508*

Propylmethanol *see* Butyl Alcohol *on page 97*

2-Propylpentanoic Acid *see* Valproic Acid and Derivatives *on page 607*

2-Propylvaleric Acid *see* Valproic Acid and Derivatives *on page 607*

Prorex® *see* Promethazine *on page 505*

ProSom™ *see* Estazolam *on page 228*

ProStep® Patch *see* Nicotine *on page 431*

Prothazine-DC® *see* Promethazine and Codeine *on page 506*

Protriptyline (proe TRIP ti leen)

U.S. Brand Names Concordin®; Triptil®; Vivactil®

Canadian Brand Names Triptil®

Therapeutic Category Antidepressant

Impairment Potential Yes

Use Treatment of various forms of depression, often in conjunction with psychotherapy

Usual Dosage Oral:

Adolescents: 15-20 mg/day in 3 divided doses

Adults: 15-60 mg in 3-4 divided doses

Elderly: 15-20 mg/day

Maximum dose: 60 mg/day

Mechanism of Action Increases the synaptic concentration of serotonin and/or norepinephrine in the central nervous system by inhibition of their reuptake by the presynaptic neuronal membrane

Pharmacodynamics/kinetics

Maximum antidepressant effect: 2 weeks of continuous therapy is commonly required

Metabolism: Extensively metabolized in the liver by N-oxidation

Half-life: 54-92 hours, averaging 74 hours

Time to peak serum concentration: Oral: Within 24-30 hours

When to Transport to Hospital Transport any pediatric (<12 years of age) exposure, any ingestion over 60 mg, or any patient exhibiting cardiac or central nervous system effects

Warnings/Precautions Use with caution in patients with cardiac conduction disturbances, history of hyperthyroid, seizure disorders, or decreased renal function; safe use of tricyclic antidepressants in children <12 years of age has not been established; protriptyline should not be abruptly discontinued in patients receiving high doses for prolonged periods

Adverse Reactions

>10%:

Central nervous system: Dizziness, drowsiness, headache

Gastrointestinal: Xerostomia, constipation, unpleasant taste, weight gain, increased appetite, nausea

Neuromuscular & skeletal: Weakness

1% to 10%:

Cardiovascular: Arrhythmias, hypotension

Central nervous system: Confusion, delirium, hallucinations, nervousness, restlessness, parkinsonian syndrome, insomnia

Gastrointestinal: Diarrhea, heartburn

Genitourinary: Dysuria, sexual dysfunction

Neuromuscular & skeletal: Fine muscle tremors

Ocular: Blurred vision, eye pain

Miscellaneous: Diaphoresis (excessive)

Reference Range Therapeutic: 70-250 ng/mL (SI: 266-950 nmol/L); Toxic: >500 ng/mL (SI: >1900 nmol/L); levels >1000 ng/mL (SI: >3800 nmol/L) associated with cardiotoxic effects

Dosage Forms Tablet: 5 mg, 10 mg

Specific References

Biggs JT and Ziegler VE, "Protriptyline Plasma Levels and Antidepressant Response," *Clin Pharmacol Ther*, 1977, 22:269-73.

Conner CS, "Sleep Apnea," *Drug Intell Clin Pharm*, 1983, 17:736-7.

Protylol® *see* Dicyclomine *on page 194*

Proventil® *see* Albuterol *on page 31*

Proventil® HFA *see* Albuterol *on page 31*

Prozac® *see* Fluoxetine *on page 253*

Prozil® *see* Chlorpromazine *on page 138*

Prozine-50® *see* Promazine *on page 504*

Pseudo-Car® DM *see* Carbinoxamine, Pseudoephedrine, and Dextromethorphan *on page 107*

Pseudoephedrine (soo doe e FED rin)

Synonyms *d*-Isoephedrine Hydrochloride

U.S. Brand Names Afrinol® [OTC]; Cenafed® [OTC]; Decofed® Syrup [OTC]; Neofed® [OTC]; Novafed®; PediaCare® Oral; Sudafed® [OTC]; Sudafed® 12 Hour [OTC]; Sufedrin® [OTC]

Canadian Brand Names Balminil® Decongestant; Eltor®; PMS-Pseudoephedrine®; Robidrine®

Therapeutic Category Adrenergic Agonist Agent

Abuse Potential Yes

Impairment Potential Yes

Use Temporary symptomatic relief of nasal congestion due to common cold, upper respiratory allergies, and sinusitis; also promotes nasal or sinus drainage

Usual Dosage Oral:

Children (do not give sustained release tablets):
<2 years: 4 mg/kg/day in divided doses every 6 hours
2-5 years: 15 mg every 6 hours; maximum: 60 mg/24 hours
6-12 years: 30 mg every 6 hours; maximum: 120 mg/24 hours
Adults: 30-60 mg every 4-6 hours, sustained release: 120 mg every 12 hours; maximum: 480 mg/24 hours

Mechanism of Action Directly stimulates alpha-adrenergic receptors of respiratory mucosa causing vasoconstriction; directly stimulates beta-adrenergic receptors causing bronchial relaxation, increased heart rate and contractility

Pharmacodynamics/kinetics

Onset of action: Within 15-30 minutes

Duration: 4-6 hours (up to 12 hours with extended release formulation administration)

Metabolism: Partially in liver

Half-life: 9-16 hours

Signs and Symptoms of Acute Intoxication Convulsions, nausea, depression, mydriasis, vomiting, insomnia, arrhythmias

When to Transport to Hospital Transport any pediatric (<6 years of age) ingestion over 11 mg/kg or any symptomatic patient

Overdosage/Treatment There is no specific antidote for pseudoephedrine intoxication and the bulk of the treatment is supportive. Hyperactivity and agitation usually respond to reduced sensory input; however, with extreme agitation, haloperidol (2-5 mg I.M. for adults) may be required. Hyperthermia is best treated with external cooling measures, or when severe or unresponsive, muscle paralysis with pancuronium may be needed. Hypertension is usually transient and generally does not require treatment unless severe. For diastolic blood pressures >110 mm Hg, a nitroprusside infusion should be initiated. Seizures usually respond to lorazepam or diazepam I.V. and/or phenytoin maintenance regimens.

Warnings/Precautions Use with caution in patients with hyperthyroidism, diabetes mellitus, prostatic hypertrophy, ischemic, heart disease; use with caution in patients >60 years of age

Adverse Reactions

>10%:
Cardiovascular: Tachycardia, palpitations, arrhythmias

Central nervous system: Nervousness, transient stimulation, insomnia, excitability, dizziness, drowsiness, headache
Neuromuscular & skeletal: Tremor
1% to 10%:
Central nervous system: Headache
Neuromuscular & skeletal: Weakness
Miscellaneous: Diaphoresis
Reference Range Following an oral dose of 180 mg, peak plasma pseudoephedrine levels range from 0.5-0.9 µg/mL
Drug Interactions MAO inhibitors, beta-adrenergic blocking agents; sympathomimetic agents
Dosage Forms
Pseudoephedrine hydrochloride:
Capsule: 60 mg
Capsule, timed release: 120 mg
Drops, oral: 7.5 mg/0.8 mL (15 mL)
Liquid: 15 mg/5 mL (120 mL); 30 mg/5 mL (120 mL, 240 mL, 473 mL)
Tablet: 30 mg, 60 mg
Tablet, timed release: 120 mg
Tablet, extended release, as sulfate: 120 mg, 240 mg
Specific References
Pentel P, "Toxicity of Over-the-Counter Stimulants," *JAMA*, 1984, 252(14):1898-903.

Pseudoephedrine and Dextromethorphan
(soo doe e FED rin & deks troe meth OR fan)
U.S. Brand Names Drixoral® Cough & Congestion Liquid Caps [OTC]; Vicks® 44D Cough & Head Congestion; Vicks® 44 Non-Drowsy Cold & Cough Liqui-Caps [OTC]
Therapeutic Category Antitussive/Decongestant
Abuse Potential Yes
Impairment Potential Yes
Dosage Forms
Capsule: Pseudoephedrine hydrochloride 60 mg and dextromethorphan hydrobromide 30 mg
Liquid: Pseudoephedrine hydrochloride 20 mg and dextromethorphan hydrobromide 10 mg per 5 mL

Pseudoephedrine and Ibuprofen
(soo doe e FED rin & eye byoo PROE fen)
U.S. Brand Names Advil® Cold & Sinus Caplets [OTC]; Dimetapp® Sinus Caplets [OTC]; Dristan® Sinus Caplets [OTC]; Motrin® IB Sinus [OTC]; Sine-Aid® IB [OTC]
Therapeutic Category Decongestant/Analgesic
Abuse Potential Yes
Impairment Potential Yes
Dosage Forms Caplet: Pseudoephedrine hydrochloride 30 mg and ibuprofen 200 mg

Pseudoephedrine see Methamphetamines, Urine *on page 384*
Pseudoephedrine and Acrivastine see Acrivastine and Pseudoephedrine *on page 27*
Pseudoephedrine and Chlorpheniramine see Chlorpheniramine and Pseudoephedrine *on page 134*
Pseudoephedrine and Dexbrompheniramine see Dexbrompheniramine and Pseudoephedrine *on page 184*

Pseudoephedrine and Guaifenesin see Guaifenesin and Pseudoephedrine on page 273

Pseudo-Gest Plus® Tablet [OTC] see Chlorpheniramine and Pseudoephedrine on page 134

Psor-a-set® Soap [OTC] see Salicylic Acid on page 530

P&S® Shampoo [OTC] see Salicylic Acid on page 530

Psyquil® see Triflupromazine on page 597

"Puke Weed" see Indian Tobacco on page 312

Punktyl® see Lorazepam on page 351

Purge® [OTC] see Castor Oil on page 118

Purgoxin® see Digoxin on page 199

P.V. Carpine® see Pilocarpine on page 486

P-V-Tussin® see Hydrocodone, Phenylephrine, Pyrilamine, Phenindamine, Chlorpheniramine, and Ammonium Chloride on page 296

Pyran Aldehyde see Acrolein on page 27

Pyribenzamine® see Tripelennamine on page 601

Pyridine
Synonyms Azabenzine; Azine
UN Number 1282
Use Primarily in production of pesticides, herbicides, antihistamines, steroids, sulfa antibiotics, water repellents, dyes, paint, and rubber; flavoring agent and as an agent to denature alcohol
Mechanism of Toxic Action Lipid peroxidation of the brain can occur
Toxicodynamics/kinetics
  Absorption: With oral ingestion
  Metabolism: Hepatic to N-methylpyridinium
When to Transport to Hospital Transport any patient with any oral ingestion
Overdosage/Treatment Decontamination:
  Dermal: Wash with soap and water
  Ocular: Irrigate with saline
Adverse Reactions
  Cardiovascular: Tachycardia, sinus tachycardia
  Central nervous system: Lethargy, headaches, slurred speech, insomnia, fatigue
  Dermatologic: Dermatitis
  Gastrointestinal: Nausea, vomiting
  Hematologic: Methemoglobinemia
  Hepatic: Cirrhosis
  Respiratory: Tachypnea
Additional Information Central nervous symptoms can occur with exposures of 6-12 ppm; inhibits metabolism of benzene; not usually detected in ambient air
Specific References
  U.S. Department of Health and Human Services, "Toxicological Profile for Pyridine TP-91/24," Agency for Toxic Substances and Diseases Registry, September 1992.

Pyrinex® see Chlorpyrifos on page 143

Qinghaosu extract see Wormwood on page 617

Quaalude® see Methaqualone Hydrochloride on page 388

Quazepam (KWAY ze pam)
U.S. Brand Names Doral®; Dormalin®; Temodal®
Therapeutic Category Benzodiazepine
Abuse Potential Yes

Impairment Potential Yes

Use Short-term treatment of insomnia

Usual Dosage Adults: Oral: Initial: 15 mg at bedtime, in some patients the dose may be reduced to 7.5 mg after a few nights

Mechanism of Action Depresses all levels of the CNS, including the limbic and reticular formation, probably through the increased action of gamma-aminobutyric acid (GABA), which is a major inhibitory neurotransmitter in the brain

Pharmacodynamics/kinetics Studies have shown that the elderly are more sensitive to the effects of benzodiazepines as compared to younger adults
Absorption: Rapid through gastrointestinal tract
Metabolism: In the liver to two active compounds (2-oxoquazepam and N-desalkyl-2-oxoquazepam)
Half-life:
Parent: 25-41 hours
Active metabolite: 40-114 hours
In the elderly:
Parent: 53 hours
Active metabolite: 39-73 hours
Time to peak serum concentration: 2 hours

Signs and Symptoms of Acute Intoxication Somnolence, confusion, coma, hyporeflexia, hypoactive reflexes, dyspnea, hypotension, slurred speech, ataxia, gaze nystagmus

When to Transport to Hospital Transport any pediatric exposure, any symptomatic patient, or any ingestion over 30 mg

Warnings/Precautions Abrupt discontinuance may precipitate withdrawal or rebound insomnia; has potential for drug dependence and abuse

Adverse Reactions
>10%:
Cardiovascular: Tachycardia, chest pain
Central nervous system: Drowsiness, fatigue, ataxia, lightheadedness, memory impairment, insomnia, anxiety, depression, headache
Dermatologic: Rash
Endocrine & metabolic: Decreased libido
Gastrointestinal: Xerostomia, constipation, diarrhea, decreased salivation, nausea, vomiting, increased or decreased appetite
Neuromuscular & skeletal: Dysarthria
Ocular: Blurred vision
Miscellaneous: Diaphoresis
1% to 10%:
Cardiovascular: Syncope, hypotension
Central nervous system: Confusion, nervousness, dizziness, akathisia
Dermatologic: Dermatitis
Gastrointestinal: Increased salivation, weight gain or loss
Neuromuscular & skeletal: Rigidity, tremor, muscle cramps
Otic: Tinnitus
Respiratory: Nasal congestion, hyperventilation

Reference Range Mean plasma level of 148 ng/mL 1.5 hours after ingestion of 25 mg

Drug Interactions CNS depressants may increase CNS adverse effects; cimetidine may decrease and enzyme inducers may increase the metabolism of quazepam

Dosage Forms Tablet: 7.5 mg, 15 mg

Additional Information More likely than triazolam to cause daytime sedation and fatigue; is classified as a long-acting benzodiazepine hypnotic (like flurazepam - Dalmane®), this long duration of action may prevent withdrawal symptoms when therapy is discontinued. There is little experience with this drug in
(Continued)

519

Quazepam *(Continued)*

the elderly; but because of its long duration of action, it is probably not a drug of choice.

Specific References

Chung M, Hilbert JM, Gural RP, et al, "Multiple Dose Quazepam Kinetics," *Clin Pharmacol Ther*, 1984, 35(4):520-4.

Quibron® *see* Theophylline and Guaifenesin *on page 571*

Quibron®-T *see* Theophylline Salts *on page 571*

Quibron®-T/SR *see* Theophylline Salts *on page 571*

Quiess® *see* Hydroxyzine *on page 303*

Quietim® *see* Oxitriptan *on page 451*

Quinalbarbitone Sodium *see* Secobarbital *on page 534*

R40 *see* Chloromethane *on page 130*

R-64766 *see* Risperidone *on page 527*

Racemic Amphetamine Sulfate *see* Amphetamine *on page 47*

Radix Valerinae *see* Valerian *on page 606*

Range Oil *see* Kerosene *on page 325*

Ranitidine (ra NI ti deen)

U.S. Brand Names Zantac®; Zantac® 75 [OTC]

Canadian Brand Names Apo-Ranitidine®; Novo-Ranidine®; Nu-Ranit®

Therapeutic Category Histamine H_2 Antagonist

Use Short-term treatment of active duodenal ulcers and benign gastric ulcers; long-term prophylaxis of duodenal ulcer and gastric hypersecretory states, gastroesophageal reflux, recurrent postoperative ulcer, upper GI bleeding, prevention of acid-aspiration pneumonitis during surgery, and prevention of stress-induced ulcers; causes fewer interactions than cimetidine

Usual Dosage Giving oral dose at 6 PM may be better than 10 PM bedtime, the highest acid production usually starts at approximately 7 PM, thus giving at 6 PM controls acid secretion better

Children: Oral: 1.25-2.5 mg/kg/dose every 12 hours; maximum: 300 mg/day

Adults:

Short-term treatment of ulceration: 150 mg/dose twice daily or 300 mg at bedtime

Prophylaxis of recurrent duodenal ulcer: Oral: 150 mg at bedtime

Gastric hypersecretory conditions: Oral: 150 mg twice daily, up to 6 g/day

Mechanism of Action Competitive inhibition of histamine at H_2-receptors of the gastric parietal cells, which inhibits gastric acid secretion, gastric volume and hydrogen ion concentration reduced

Pharmacodynamics/kinetics

Absorption: Oral: 50% to 60%

Metabolism: In the liver (<10%)

Half-life:

Children 3.5-16 years: 1.8-2 hours

Adults: 2-2.5 hours

End stage renal disease: 6-9 hours

Time to peak serum concentration: Oral: Within 1-3 hours and persisting for 8 hours

Signs and Symptoms of Acute Intoxication Muscular tremors, vomiting, rapid respiration, renal failure, CNS depression

When to Transport to Hospital Transport any symptomatic patient

Overdosage/Treatment Treatment is primarily symptomatic and supportive

Warnings/Precautions Use with caution in children <12 years of age; use with caution in patients with liver and renal impairment; dosage modification required in patients with renal impairment; long-term therapy may cause vitamin B_{12} deficiency

Adverse Reactions

Endocrine & metabolic: Gynecomastia

Hepatic: Hepatitis

Neuromuscular & skeletal: Arthralgia

1% to 10%:

Central nervous system: Dizziness, sedation, malaise, headache, drowsiness

Dermatologic: Rash

Gastrointestinal: Constipation, nausea, vomiting, diarrhea

Dosage Forms

Ranitidine hydrochloride:

Capsule (GELdose™): 150 mg, 300 mg

Granules, effervescent (EFFERdose™): 150 mg

Infusion, preservative free, in NaCl 0.45%: 1 mg/mL (50 mL)

Injection: 25 mg/mL (2 mL, 10 mL, 40 mL)

Syrup (peppermint flavor): 15 mg/mL (473 mL)

Tablet: 75 mg [OTC]; 150 mg, 300 mg

Tablet, effervescent (EFFERdose™): 150 mg

Specific References

Maack DK and Spiller HA, "Rare Dystonic Reaction From Accidental Overdose of Ranitidine in a 3 Month Old," *Vet Hum Toxicol*, 1993, 35:343.

Ranitidine *see* Methamphetamines, Urine *on page 384*

Rapidal® *see* Terfenadine *on page 563*

Raudixin® *see* Rauwolfia Serpentina *on this page*

Rauverid® *see* Rauwolfia Serpentina *on this page*

Rauwolfia Serpentina (rah WOOL fee a ser pen TEEN ah)

Synonyms Whole Root Rauwolfia

U.S. Brand Names Hypercal®; Lesten®; Raudixin®; Rauverid®; Wolfina®

Therapeutic Category Rauwolfia Alkaloid

Impairment Potential Yes

Use Mild essential hypertension; relief of agitated psychotic states

Usual Dosage Adults: Oral: 200-400 mg/day in 2 divided doses

Signs and Symptoms of Acute Intoxication Hypotension, bradycardia, Parkinson's-like symptoms, galactorrhea, gynecomastia, CNS depression, hypothermia, vomiting, miosis, tremors, coma, extensor plantar response, facial flushing

When to Transport to Hospital Transport any pediatric exposure or any symptomatic patient

Warnings/Precautions Electroshock therapy: Discontinue reserpine 7 days before electroshock therapy; may increase gastrointestinal motility and secretions; acute hypersensitivity reactions may occur; tartrazine sensitivity; use cautiously in patients with renal insufficiency

Adverse Reactions

Cardiovascular: Hypotension, tachycardia, flushing, sinus bradycardia, sinus tachycardia

Central nervous system: Drowsiness, fatigue, CNS depression, coma, parkinsonism, hypothermia

Endocrine & metabolic: Sodium and water retention, gynecomastia, galactorrhea

Gastrointestinal: Abdominal cramps, nausea, vomiting, gastric acid secretion (increased), dry mouth, diarrhea

Ocular: Miosis, conjunctival flushing

(Continued)

Rauwolfia Serpentina *(Continued)*

Respiratory: Nasal congestion

Drug Interactions Use lower doses with diuretic treatment or other antihypertensive use

Dosage Forms Tablet: 50 mg, 100 mg

Specific References

Walker WR and Mathis JL, "Rauwolfia Serpentia Revisited," *N C Med J*, 1981, 42(6):401-2.

RDX

Synonyms Cyclonite; Hexogen; Hexolite; PBX

Applies to Composition C-4

Use Class A explosive; nitrate compound used in plastic explosives, fireworks, and as a detonator; rodenticide

Mechanism of Toxic Action Causes fatty degeneration of liver; seizure mechanism of action is unknown

Toxicodynamics/kinetics

Absorption: Oral (slowly) and inhalation; not readily absorbed by dermal route

Half-life: 15 hours

When to Transport to Hospital Transport any patient with any ingestion

Overdosage/Treatment Decontamination:

Dermal: Wash hands with soap and water

Ocular: Irrigate with saline

Adverse Reactions

Cardiovascular: Tachycardia, sinus tachycardia

Central nervous system: Seizures, irritability, amnesia, confusion, hyperthermia

Dermatologic: Dermal irritant

Gastrointestinal: Nausea, vomiting

Hematologic: Anemia

Hepatic: Hepatic steatosis

Neuromuscular & skeletal: Muscle twitching, myoclonus

Renal: Hematuria

Miscellaneous: Liver tumors (adenomas and carcinomas) produced in rodent models

Reference Range Serum RDX level of 10.7 mg/L associated with seizures

Additional Information Oral dose of 85 mg/kg has caused seizures in a child; symptoms can occur with ingested daily dose of 0.1 mg/kg; can produce a "high" similar to ethanol

Specific References

Harrell-Bruder B and Hutchins KL, "Seizures Caused by Ingestion of Composition C-4," *Ann Emerg Med*, 1995, 26(6):746-8.

Reactine® *see* Cetirizine *on page 120*

Recormon® *see* Epoetin Alfa *on page 222*

Rectules® *see* Chloral Hydrate *on page 122*

Red Phosphorus *see* White Phosphorus *on page 615*

Red Tide Poisoning *see* Neurotoxic Shellfish Poisoning *on page 428*

Redutemp® [OTC] *see* Acetaminophen *on page 20*

Redux® *see* Dexfenfluramine *on page 185*

Regenon® *see* Diethylpropion *on page 196*

Regular Iletin® I *see* Insulin Preparations *on page 314*

Regular [Concentrated] Iletin® II U-500 *see* Insulin Preparations *on page 314*

Regular Strength Bayer® Enteric 500 Aspirin [OTC] *see* Aspirin *on page 56*

Reishi Mushroom

Synonyms Holy Mushroom

Scientific Name *Ganoderma lucidum*

Use Antineoplastic/immune stimulant agent in herbal medicine

Mechanism of Toxic Action Contains ganoderan B which can induce hepatic enzymes and increase plasma insulin levels

When to Transport to Hospital Transport any patient exhibiting any adverse reactions

Overdosage/Treatment Oral antihistamines can be used to treat pruritus

Adverse Reactions
Central nervous system: Dizziness
Dermatologic: Dermatitis, pruritus
Gastrointestinal: Diarrhea
Neuromuscular & skeletal: Bone pain

Additional Information Contraindications with hemophilia (due to high adenosine content); an edible brown mushroom found on California hardwoods

Rela® *see* Carisoprodol *on page 114*

Relafen® *see* Nabumetone *on page 416*

Relax Llano® *see* Methocarbamol *on page 390*

Relief® Ophthalmic Solution *see* Phenylephrine *on page 479*

Remeron® *see* Mirtazapine *on page 405*

Reniten® *see* Enalapril *on page 217*

Rentamine® *see* Chlorpheniramine, Ephedrine, Phenylephrine, and Carbetapentane *on page 135*

Repan® *see* Butalbital Compound *on page 93*

Repazine® *see* Chlorpromazine *on page 138*

Repocal® *see* Pentobarbital *on page 464*

Resaid® *see* Chlorpheniramine and Phenylpropanolamine *on page 134*

Rescaps-D® S.R. Capsule *see* Caramiphen and Phenylpropanolamine *on page 103*

Rescon Liquid [OTC] *see* Chlorpheniramine and Phenylpropanolamine *on page 134*

Reserpine (re SER peen)

Synonyms Reserpinum

U.S. Brand Names Abicol®; Lemiserp®; Seominal®; Serpalin®; Serpasil®; SK-Reserpine®

Canadian Brand Names Novo-Reserpine®

Therapeutic Category Rauwolfia Alkaloid

Impairment Potential Yes

Use Management of mild to moderate hypertension; possible use for tardive dyskinesia

Usual Dosage Oral (full antihypertensive effects may take as long as 3 weeks):
Children: 0.01-0.02 mg/kg/24 hours divided every 12 hours; maximum dose: 0.25 mg/day
Adults: 0.1-0.5 mg/day in 1-2 doses

Mechanism of Action Reduces blood pressure via depletion of sympathetic biogenic amines (norepinephrine and dopamine); this also commonly results in sedative effects

Pharmacodynamics/kinetics
Onset of action: Within 3-6 days
Duration: 2-6 weeks
Absorption: Oral: ~40%
Metabolism: Extensive in the liver (>90%)

(Continued)

Reserpine *(Continued)*

Half-life: 50-100 hours

Time to peak plasma concentration: 1-3 hours

Signs and Symptoms of Acute Intoxication Hypotension, galactorrhea, bradycardia, impotence, hyperglycemia, gynecomastia, Parkinson's-like symptoms, hypertension, depression, wheezing, CNS depression, hypothermia, syncope, sexual dysfunction, ptosis, vomiting, miosis, mydriasis, tremors, coma, extensor plantar response, flushing

When to Transport to Hospital Transport any symptomatic patient

Warnings/Precautions Electroshock therapy: Discontinue reserpine 7 days before electroshock therapy; may increase gastrointestinal motility and secretions; acute hypersensitivity reactions may occur; tartrazine sensitivity; use cautiously in patients with renal insufficiency

Adverse Reactions

>10%:

Central nervous system: Dizziness

Gastrointestinal: Anorexia, diarrhea, xerostomia, nausea, vomiting

Respiratory: Nasal congestion

1% to 10%:

Cardiovascular: Peripheral edema, arrhythmias, bradycardia, chest pain

Central nervous system: Headache

Gastrointestinal: Black stools

Genitourinary: Impotence

Miscellaneous: Bloody vomit

Test Interactions Increases catecholamines (U) 1 or 2 days postingestion; elevates prolactin levels

Dosage Forms Tablet: 0.1 mg, 0.25 mg, 1 mg

Additional Information Full antihypertensive effects may take as long as 3 weeks; at high doses, mental depression is possible and might lead to suicide

Specific References

Fraser HS, "Reserpine: A Tragic Victim of Myths, Marketing, and Fashionable Prescribing," *Clin Pharmacol Ther*, 1996, 60:368-73.

Reserpine and Chlorothiazide *see* Chlorothiazide and Reserpine *on page 132*

Reserpine and Hydrochlorothiazide *see* Hydrochlorothiazide and Reserpine *on page 292*

Reserpinum *see* Reserpine *on previous page*

Respa-1st® *see* Guaifenesin and Pseudoephedrine *on page 273*

Respa-DM® *see* Guaifenesin and Dextromethorphan *on page 271*

Respa-GF® *see* Guaifenesin *on page 269*

Respaire®-60 SR *see* Guaifenesin and Pseudoephedrine *on page 273*

Respaire®-120 SR *see* Guaifenesin and Pseudoephedrine *on page 273*

Respbid® *see* Theophylline Salts *on page 571*

Respilene® *see* Zipeprol *on page 620*

Respirase® *see* Zipeprol *on page 620*

Respirex® *see* Zipeprol *on page 620*

Resposan-10® *see* Chlordiazepoxide *on page 124*

Restandol® *see* Testosterone *on page 564*

Restoril® *see* Temazepam *on page 559*

Retard® *see* Biperiden *on page 77*

Revex® *see* Nalmefene *on page 419*

ReVia® *see* Naltrexone *on page 420*

Rexitene® *see* Guanabenz *on page 276*

Rezine® see Hydroxyzine on page 303

Rhinall® Nasal Solution [OTC] see Phenylephrine on page 479

Rhinatate® Tablet see Chlorpheniramine, Pyrilamine, and Phenylephrine on page 138

Rhindecon® see Phenylpropanolamine on page 481

Rhinosyn-DMX® [OTC] see Guaifenesin and Dextromethorphan on page 271

Rhinosyn® Liquid [OTC] see Chlorpheniramine and Pseudoephedrine on page 134

Rhinosyn-PD® Liquid [OTC] see Chlorpheniramine and Pseudoephedrine on page 134

Rhinosyn-X® Liquid [OTC] see Guaifenesin, Pseudoephedrine, and Dextromethorphan on page 275

rHuEPO-α see Epoetin Alfa on page 222

Rhulicaine® [OTC] see Benzocaine on page 70

Ricifruit® see Castor Oil on page 118

Ricinus Oil see Castor Oil on page 118

Rid-A-Pain® [OTC] see Benzocaine on page 70

Ridazine® see Thioridazine on page 578

Ridenol® [OTC] see Acetaminophen on page 20

Rifadin® see Rifampin on this page

Rifampicin see Rifampin on this page

Rifampin (RIF am pin)

Synonyms Rifampicin

U.S. Brand Names Rifadin®; Rimactane®

Canadian Brand Names Rifadin®; Rimactane®; Rofact®

Therapeutic Category Antibiotic, Miscellaneous

Use Management of active tuberculosis; eliminate meningococci from asymptomatic carriers; prophylaxis of *Haemophilus influenzae* type b infection

Usual Dosage I.V. infusion dose is the same as for the oral route

Tuberculosis:

Children: 10-20 mg/kg/day in divided doses every 12-24 hours

Adults: 10 mg/kg/day; maximum: 600 mg/day

Treatment for 9 months with isoniazid or 6 months with isoniazid/pyrazinamide

American Thoracic Society and CDC recommendations should be consulted for current guidelines

Children: 10-20 mg/kg/dose (up to 600 mg) twice weekly under supervision to ensure compliance

Adults: 10 mg/kg (up to 600 mg) twice weekly

H. influenza prophylaxis:

Infants and Children: 20 mg/kg/day every 24 hours for 4 days

Adults: 600 mg every 24 hours for 4 days

Meningococcal prophylaxis:

<1 month: 10 mg/kg/day in divided doses every 12 hours

Infants and Children: 20 mg/kg/day in divided doses every 12 hours for 2 days

Adults: 600 mg every 12 hours for 2 days

Nasal carriers of *Staphylococcus aureus*: Adults: 600 mg/day for 5-10 days in combination with other antibiotics

Synergy for *Staphylococcus aureus* infections: Adults: 300-600 mg twice daily with other antibiotics

(Continued)

Rifampin *(Continued)*

Mechanism of Action Inhibits bacterial RNA synthesis by binding to the beta subunit of DNA-dependent RNA polymerase, blocking RNA transcription

Pharmacodynamics/kinetics

Absorption: Oral: Well absorbed from gastrointestinal tract (90%); food may delay or slightly reduce peak serum level

Metabolism: In the liver; undergoes enterohepatic recycling

Half-life: 3-4 hours, prolonged with hepatic impairment; increased in overdose

Time to peak serum concentration: Within 2-4 hours

Signs and Symptoms of Acute Intoxication Nausea, vomiting, wheezing, dyspnea, pemphigus, colitis, hepatitis, Red man syndrome, myopathy, erythema multiforme, facial edema, toxic epidermal necrolysis, stomatitis, nephritis, scleral discoloration after 6-10 hours, pulmonary edema, abdominal pain, cholelithiasis, renal failure (acute), thrombocytopenia, skin discoloration, pruritus, hypersensitivity, hyperglycemia, urine discoloration (brown), urine discoloration (orange), urine discoloration (orange-red), urine discoloration (orange-yellow), urine discoloration (red), feces discoloration (orange-red), feces discoloration (red-brown), leukopenia, coma

When to Transport to Hospital Transport any patient with dyspnea, lethargy, or ingestions exceeding 20 mg/kg

Warnings/Precautions Use with caution in patients with liver impairment; modification of dosage should be considered in patients with severe liver impairment

Adverse Reactions 1% to 10%:

Gastrointestinal: Diarrhea, stomach cramps, fecal discoloration, discoloration of saliva (reddish orange)

Genitourinary: Discoloration of urine

Miscellaneous: Discoloration of sputum, sweat, and tears (reddish orange); fungal overgrowth

Drug Interactions Rifampin induces liver enzymes which may decrease the plasma concentration of the following drugs: verapamil, methadone, digoxin, cyclosporine, corticosteroids, oral anticoagulants, theophylline, barbiturates, chloramphenicol, ketoconazole, oral contraceptives, quinidine; halothane; benzodiazepines; isoniazid; beta-adrenergic blockers

Rifampin may markedly decrease calcium channel blocker levels

Increased tacrolimus levels can occur with concomitant administration of erythromycin or rifampin

Rifampin reduces the plasma concentration of oral midazolam by >90%

Reduced plasma levels of haloperidol when given with rifampin

Reduced therapeutic efficacy of concomitant warfarin

Dosage Forms

Capsule: 150 mg, 300 mg

Injection: 600 mg

Specific References

Herrera Trevilla P, Oritz Jimenez E, and Tena T, "Presence of Rifampicin in Urine Causes Cross-Reactivity With Opiates Using the KIMS Method," *J Anal Toxicol*, 1995, 19(3):200.

Rimactane® *see* Rifampin *on previous page*

Rimantadine *(ri MAN ta deen)*

Synonyms EXP-126; Rimantadinum

U.S. Brand Names Flumadine®; Roflual®

Therapeutic Category Antiviral Agent

Use Prophylaxis (adults and children) and treatment (adults) of influenza A viral infection

Usual Dosage Oral:
Prophylaxis:
    Children <10 years: 5 mg/kg give once daily
    Children >10 years and Adults: 100 mg twice/day
Treatment: Adults: 100 mg twice/day
Mechanism of Action Similar to amantadine; inhibits viral RNA and protein synthesis
Pharmacodynamics/kinetics
Absorption: Oral: 92%
Metabolism: Liver
Half-life: 24-36 hours; renal failure: 48-72 hours
Elimination: Renal (75%)
Signs and Symptoms of Acute Intoxication Convulsions (especially in the elderly), sedation
When to Transport to Hospital Transport any sedated or seizing patient or ingestions over 10 mg/kg
Warnings/Precautions Use with caution in patients with liver disease, a history of recurrent and eczematoid dermatitis, uncontrolled psychosis or severe psychoneurosis, seizures in those receiving CNS stimulant drugs
Adverse Reactions 1% to 10%:
Cardiovascular: Orthostatic hypotension, edema
Central nervous system: Dizziness, confusion, headache, insomnia, difficulty in concentrating, anxiety, restlessness, irritability, hallucinations; incidence of CNS side effects may be less than that associated with amantadine
Gastrointestinal: Nausea, vomiting, xerostomia, abdominal pain, anorexia
Genitourinary: Urinary retention
Reference Range Peak serum levels: 240-320 ng/mL after a 200 mg dose
Dosage Forms
Syrup: 50 mg/5 mL (60 mL, 240 mL, 480 mL)
Tablet: 100 mg
Specific References
Bentley DW, Karki SD, and Betts RF, "Rimantadine and Seizures," *Ann Intern Med*, 1989, 110(4):323-4.

Rimantadinum see Rimantadine *on previous page*
Risperdal® see Risperidone *on this page*

Risperidone (ris PER i done)
Synonyms R-64766
U.S. Brand Names Risperdal®
Therapeutic Category Antipsychotic Agent
Impairment Potential Yes
Use Management of psychotic disorders (eg, schizophrenia)
Usual Dosage Oral: Recommended starting dose: 1 mg twice daily; slowly increase to the optimum range of 4-8 mg/day; daily dosages >10 mg do not appear to confer any additional benefit, and the incidence of extrapyramidal reactions is higher than with lower doses
Mechanism of Action Risperidone is a benzisoxazole derivative, mixed serotonin-dopamine antagonist; binds to 5-HT$_2$ receptors in the CNS and in the periphery with a very high affinity; binds to dopamine-D$_2$ receptors with less affinity. The binding affinity to the dopamine-D$_2$ receptor is 20 times lower than the 5-HT$_2$ affinity. The addition of serotonin antagonism to dopamine antagonism (classic neuroleptic mechanism) is thought to improve negative symptoms of psychoses and reduce the incidence of extrapyramidal side effects.
Pharmacodynamics/kinetics
Absorption: Oral: Rapid (not affected by food)
Metabolism: Extensive to 9-hydroxyrisperidone (active metabolite)
(Continued)

Risperidone *(Continued)*

Half-life: 24 hours (risperidone and its active metabolite)

Time to peak: Peak plasma concentrations within 1 hour

Signs and Symptoms of Acute Intoxication Hypotension, ejaculatory disturbances, neuroleptic malignant syndrome, mania, hallucinations, enuresis, palpitations, prolonged Q-T interval

When to Transport to Hospital Transport any symptomatic patient or ingestions over 10 mg

Adverse Reactions 1% to 10%:

Cardiovascular: Hypotension (especially orthostatic), tachycardia, arrhythmias, abnormal T waves with prolonged ventricular repolarization; EKG changes, syncope

Central nervous system: Sedation (occurs at daily doses ≥20 mg/day), headache, dizziness, restlessness, anxiety, extrapyramidal reactions, dystonic reactions, pseudoparkinsonian signs and symptoms, tardive dyskinesia, neuroleptic malignant syndrome, altered central temperature regulation

Dermatologic: Photosensitivity (rare)

Endocrine & metabolic: Amenorrhea, galactorrhea, gynecomastia sexual dysfunction (up to 60%)

Gastrointestinal: Constipation, adynamic ileus, GI upset, xerostomia (problem for denture user), nausea and anorexia, weight gain

Genitourinary: Urinary retention, overflow incontinence, priapism

Hematologic: Agranulocytosis, leukopenia (usually in patients with large doses for prolonged periods)

Hepatic: Cholestatic jaundice

Ocular: Blurred vision, retinal pigmentation, decreased visual acuity (may be irreversible)

Reference Range Within 2 hours of a 1 mg oral dose, peak plasma level: 3-8 µg/L; postmortem blood and urinary risperidone levels following a suicidal ingestion: 1.8 mg/L and 14.4 mg/L respectively

Dosage Forms Tablet: 1 mg, 2 mg, 3 mg, 4 mg

Specific References

Lo Vecchio F, Hamilton RJ, and Hoffman RJ, "Risperidone Overdose," *Am J Emerg Med*, 1996, 14:95-6.

Robitussin®-DAC *see* Guaifenesin, Pseudoephedrine, and Codeine *on page 275*

Robitussin®-DM [OTC] *see* Guaifenesin and Dextromethorphan *on page 271*

Robitussin-PE® [OTC] *see* Guaifenesin and Pseudoephedrine *on page 273*

Robitussin® Pediatric [OTC] *see* Dextromethorphan *on page 187*

Robitussin® Severe Congestion Liqui-Gels [OTC] *see* Guaifenesin and Pseudo-ephedrine *on page 273*

Robomol *see* Methocarbamol *on page 390*

Ro-Dex® *see* Strychnine *on page 549*

Roflual® *see* Rimantadine *on page 526*

Rogaine® for Men [OTC] *see* Minoxidil *on page 404*

Rogaine® for Women [OTC] *see* Minoxidil *on page 404*

Rohipnol® *see* Flunitrazepam *on page 250*

Rohypnol® *see* Flunitrazepam *on page 250*

Rolpnol® *see* Flunitrazepam *on page 250*

Rolatuss® Plain Liquid *see* Chlorpheniramine and Phenylephrine *on page 134*

Rondamine-DM® Drops *see* Carbinoxamine, Pseudoephedrine, and Dextromethor-phan *on page 107*

Rondec® *see* Carbinoxamine *on page 106*

Rondec®-DM *see* Carbinoxamine, Pseudoephedrine, and Dextromethorphan *on page 107*

Rondec® Drops *see* Carbinoxamine and Pseudoephedrine *on page 107*

Rondec® Filmtab *see* Carbinoxamine and Pseudoephedrine *on page 107*

Rondec® Syrup *see* Carbinoxamine and Pseudoephedrine *on page 107*

Rondec-TR® *see* Carbinoxamine and Pseudoephedrine *on page 107*

Rotet® *see* Tetracycline *on page 568*

Roundup® *see* Glyphosate *on page 269*

Roxanol™ *see* Morphine Sulfate *on page 410*

Roxanol SR™ *see* Morphine Sulfate *on page 410*

Roxicet® 5/500 *see* Oxycodone and Acetaminophen *on page 453*

Roxicodone™ *see* Oxycodone *on page 452*

Roxilox® *see* Oxycodone and Acetaminophen *on page 453*

Roxiprin® *see* Oxycodone and Aspirin *on page 454*

RP10248 *see* Sulthiame *on page 555*

R-Tannamine® Tablet *see* Chlorpheniramine, Pyrilamine, and Phenylephrine *on page 138*

R-Tannate® Tablet *see* Chlorpheniramine, Pyrilamine, and Phenylephrine *on page 138*

Rubifen *see* Methylphenidate *on page 397*

Rufen *see* Ibuprofen *on page 308*

Ru-Tuss® *see* Chlorpheniramine, Phenylephrine, Phenylpropanolamine, and Bella-donna Alkaloids *on page 136*

Ru-Tuss® DE *see* Guaifenesin and Pseudoephedrine *on page 273*

Ru-Tuss® Expectorant [OTC] *see* Guaifenesin, Pseudoephedrine, and Dextro-methorphan *on page 275*

Ru-Tuss® Liquid *see* Chlorpheniramine and Phenylephrine *on page 134*

Ru-Vert-M® *see* Meclizine *on page 361*

Rymed® *see* Guaifenesin and Pseudoephedrine *on page 273*

Rymed-TR® *see* Guaifenesin and Phenylpropanolamine *on page 272*

Ryna-C® Liquid *see* Chlorpheniramine, Pseudoephedrine, and Codeine *on page 138*

Ryna-CX® *see* Guaifenesin, Pseudoephedrine, and Codeine *on page 275*

Ryna® Liquid [OTC] see Chlorpheniramine and Pseudoephedrine on page 134

Rynatan® Pediatric Suspension see Chlorpheniramine, Pyrilamine, and Phenylephrine on page 138

Rynatan® Tablet see Chlorpheniramine, Pyrilamine, and Phenylephrine on page 138

Rynatuss® Pediatric Suspension see Chlorpheniramine, Ephedrine, Phenylephrine, and Carbetapentane on page 135

S5614 see Dexfenfluramine on page 185

Sabril® see Vigabatrin on page 612

Sabrilex® see Vigabatrin on page 612

Safe Tussin® 30 [OTC] see Guaifenesin and Dextromethorphan on page 271

Sal-Acid® Plaster [OTC] see Salicylic Acid on this page

Salactic® Film [OTC] see Salicylic Acid on this page

Salbutamol see Albuterol on page 31

Saleto-200® [OTC] see Ibuprofen on page 308

Saleto-400® see Ibuprofen on page 308

Salicylic Acid (sal i SIL ik AS id)

U.S. Brand Names Clear Away® Disc [OTC]; Compound W® [OTC]; Dr Scholl's® Disk [OTC]; Dr Scholl's® Wart Remover [OTC]; DuoFilm® [OTC]; DuoPlant® Gel [OTC]; Freezone® Solution [OTC]; Gordofilm® Liquid; Mediplast® Plaster [OTC]; Mosco® Liquid [OTC]; Occlusal-HP Liquid; Off-Ezy® Wart Remover [OTC]; Panscol® [OTC]; Psor-a-set® Soap [OTC]; P&S® Shampoo [OTC]; Sal-Acid® Plaster [OTC]; Salactic® Film [OTC]; Sal-Plant® Gel [OTC]; Trans-Ver-Sal® AdultPatch [OTC]; Trans-Ver-Sal® PediaPatch [OTC]; Trans-Ver-Sal® PlantarPatch [OTC]; Wart-Off® [OTC]

Therapeutic Category Keratolytic Agent

Use Topically for its keratolytic effect in controlling seborrheic dermatitis or psoriasis of body and scalp, dandruff, and other scaling dermatoses; also used to remove warts, corns, and calluses

Usual Dosage
Lotion, cream, gel: Apply a thin layer to affected area once or twice daily
Plaster: Cut to size that covers the corn or callus, apply and leave in place for 48 hours; do not exceed 5 applications over a 14-day period
Solution: Apply a thin layer directly to wart using brush applicator once daily as directed for 1 week or until wart is removed

Mechanism of Action Produces desquamation of hyperkeratotic epithelium via dissolution of the intercellular cement which causes the cornified tissue to swell, soften, macerate, and desquamate. Salicylic acid is keratolytic at concentrations of 3% to 6%; it becomes destructive to tissue at concentrations >6%. Concentrations of 6% to 60% are used to remove corns and warts and in the treatment of psoriasis and other hyperkeratotic disorders.

Pharmacodynamics/kinetics
Absorption: Absorbed percutaneously, but systemic toxicity is unlikely with normal use
Time to peak serum concentration: Topical: Within 5 hours of application with occlusion

Signs and Symptoms of Acute Intoxication Nausea, vomiting, dizziness, tinnitus, loss of hearing, lethargy, diarrhea, psychic disturbances

When to Transport to Hospital Transport any symptomatic patient

Warnings/Precautions Should not be used systemically, severe irritating effect on GI mucosa; use with caution in areas of ischemia; prolonged use over large areas, especially in children, may result in salicylate toxicity; do not apply on irritated, reddened, or infected skin; for external use only; avoid contact with eyes, face, and other mucous membranes

Adverse Reactions
>10%: Local: Burning and irritation at site of exposure on normal tissue
1% to 10%:
  Central nervous system: Dizziness, mental confusion, headache
  Otic: Tinnitus
  Respiratory: Hyperventilation

Dosage Forms
Cream: 2% (30 g)
Disk: 40%
Gel: 5% (60 g); 6% (30 g); 17% (7.5 g)
Liquid: 13.6% (9.3 mL); 17% (9.3 mL, 13.5 mL, 15 mL); 16.7% (15 mL)
Lotion: 3% (120 mL)
Ointment: 3% (90 g)
Patch, transdermal: 15% (20 mm); 40% (20 mm)
Plaster: 40%
Soap: 2% (97.5 g)
Strip: 40%

Salmeterol *see* Salmeterol *on this page*

Salmeterol (sal ME te role)

Synonyms Salmeterol
U.S. Brand Names Serevent®
Therapeutic Category Adrenergic Agonist Agent
Use Maintenance therapy for chronic asthma; prevention of exercise-induced asthma or nocturnal asthma
Usual Dosage Inhalation: Two inhalations (25 mcg) twice daily from a metered dose inhaler; maximum dose: 100 mcg twice daily
Mechanism of Action Relaxes bronchial smooth muscle by action on beta$_2$-receptors with little effect on heart rate; longer-acting than albuterol
Pharmacodynamics/kinetics
Onset of action: 30-60 minutes
Peak effect: 2 hours
Duration: 12 hours
Protein binding: 94% to 99%
Half-life: 3-4 hours
Elimination: Fecal

When to Transport to Hospital Transport any pediatric (<12 years of age) exposure or any patient exhibiting any cardipulmonary effects, tremor, or dizziness
Warnings/Precautions Do not initiate in patients with significantly worsening or acutely deteriorating bronchospasm (acute asthmatic attacks); may cause paradoxical bronchospasm; use with caution in patients with cardiovascular disease, hypertension, hyperthyroidism, diabetes mellitus; avoid concomitant use of tricyclic antidepressants or MAO inhibitors

Adverse Reactions
>10%:
  Central nervous system: Headache
  Respiratory: Pharyngitis
1% to 10%:
  Cardiovascular: Tachycardia, palpitations, elevation or depression of blood pressure, cardiac arrhythmias
  Central nervous system: Nervousness, CNS stimulation, hyperactivity, insomnia, malaise, dizziness
  Gastrointestinal: GI upset, diarrhea, nausea
  Neuromuscular & skeletal: Tremors (may be more common in the elderly), myalgias, back pain, arthralgia
(Continued)

531

Salmeterol *(Continued)*

Respiratory: Upper respiratory infection, cough, bronchitis

Dosage Forms Inhaler: 21 mcg/metered inhalation (60 & 120 doses)

Additional Information Tachyphylaxis usually does not occur

Specific References

Bone RC, "Another Word of Caution Regarding a new Long-Acting Bronchodilator," *JAMA*, 1995, 273(12):967-8.

Sal-Plant® Gel [OTC] *see* Salicylic Acid *on page 530*

Sandomigran® *see* Pizotyline *on page 490*

Sandomigrin® *see* Pizotyline *on page 490*

Sanmigran® *see* Pizotyline *on page 490*

Sanoma® *see* Carisoprodol *on page 114*

Sanomigran® *see* Pizotyline *on page 490*

Sanorex® *see* Mazindol *on page 360*

Sansert® *see* Methysergide *on page 400*

Sarin *see* Nerve Gases *on page 426*

Sassolite® *see* Boric Acid *on page 80*

Scalpicin® *see* Hydrocortisone *on page 297*

Scarlet Berry *see* Deadly Nightshade *on page 178*

SCH-29851 *see* Loratadine *on page 350*

Scombroid Food Poisoning

Synonyms Mahi Mahi Flush

Commonly Found In Skipjack, mackerel, bluefish, Mahi Mahi, salmon, Japanese saury, kingfish, tuna (usually poorly refrigerated)

Mechanism of Toxic Action Histidine found in fish musculature causes clinical syndrome; onset develops within 1 hour (often with 10 minutes); resolves within 36 hours

Signs and Symptoms of Acute Intoxication Erythematous flushing, pruritus, slurred speech, watery diarrhea (explosive), nausea, vomiting, facial edema, palpitations, wheezing, and headache

When to Transport to Hospital Transport any symptomatic patient

Additional Information Heat stable; refrigeration prevents scombroid poisoning; fish may have a peppery taste; can cause elevated blood and urine histamine levels; cultures are not useful; isoniazid may exacerbate symptoms

Specific References

McInerney J, Sahgal P, Vogel M, et al, "Scombroid Poisoning," *Ann Emerg Med*, 1996, 28:235-8.

Scop *see* Scopolamine *on this page*

Scopex® *see* Scopolamine *on this page*

Scopine Tropate *see* Scopolamine *on this page*

Scopoderm® *see* Scopolamine *on this page*

Scopolamine *(skoe POL a meen)*

Synonyms Hyoscine; Scop; Scopine Tropate

U.S. Brand Names Buscapina®; Isopto® Hyoscine; Kwells®; Pamine®; Scopex®; Scopoderm®; Transderm Scop®; Vorigeno®

Therapeutic Category Anticholinergic Agent

Abuse Potential Yes

Impairment Potential Yes

Use Preoperative medication to produce amnesia and decrease salivation and respiratory secretions to produce cycloplegia and mydriasis; treatment of iridocyclitis, prevention of nausea and vomiting by motion; produces more CNS depression, mydriasis, and cycloplegia but less effective in preventing reflex bradycardia and effecting the intestines than atropine

Usual Dosage
Preoperatively:
Children: I.M., S.C.: 6 mcg/kg/dose (maximum: 0.3 mg/dose) or 0.2 mg/m² may be repeated every 6-8 hours **or** alternatively:
4-7 months: 0.1 mg
7 months to 3 years: 0.15 mg
3-8 years: 0.2 mg
8-12 years: 0.3 mg
Adults: I.M., I.V., S.C.: 0.3-0.65 mg; may be repeated every 4-6 hours

Motion sickness: Transdermal: Children >12 years and Adults: Apply 1 disc behind the ear at least 4 hours prior to exposure and every 3 days as needed; effective if applied as soon as 2-3 hours before anticipated need, best if 12 hours before

Ophthalmic:
Refraction:
Children: Instill 1 drop of 0.25% to eye(s) twice daily for 2 days before procedure
Adults: Instill 1-2 drops of 0.25% to eye(s) 1 hour before procedure
Iridocyclitis:
Children: Instill 1 drop of 0.25% to eye(s) up to 3 times/day
Adults: Instill 1-2 drops of 0.25% to eye(s) up to 4 times/day

Mechanism of Action Blocks the action of acetylcholine at parasympathetic sites in smooth muscle, secretory glands and the CNS; increases cardiac output, dries secretions, antagonizes histamine and serotonin; a tropane alkaloid

Pharmacodynamics/kinetics
Absorption: Well absorbed by all routes of administration
Metabolism: Hepatic

Signs and Symptoms of Acute Intoxication Mydriasis, confusion, bronchospasm, photophobia, dysuria, delirium, tachycardia, memory loss, intraocular pressure (increased), dementia, hypertension, seizures, coma, bradycardia, hyperthermia, visual hallucinations

When to Transport to Hospital Transport any symptomatic patient or ingestions over 1 mg

Warnings/Precautions Use with caution with hepatic or renal impairment since adverse CNS effects occur more often in these patients; use with caution in infants and children since they may be more susceptible to adverse effects of scopolamine; use with caution in patients with gastrointestinal obstruction

Adverse Reactions
Ophthalmic:
>10%: Ocular: Blurred vision, photophobia
1% to 10%:
Ocular: Local irritation, increased intraocular pressure
Respiratory: Congestion
Systemic:
>10%:
Dermatologic: Dry skin
Gastrointestinal: Constipation, xerostomia, dry throat
Local: Irritation at injection site
Respiratory: Dry nose
Miscellaneous: Diaphoresis (decreased)
1% to 10%:
Dermatologic: Increased sensitivity to light
Endocrine & metabolic: Decreased flow of breast milk
(Continued)

Scopolamine *(Continued)*

Gastrointestinal: Dysphagia

Note: Systemic adverse effects have been reported following ophthalmic administration

Reference Range Serum level of 890 pg/mL (SI: 7.93 nmol/L) correlated with psychosis

Dosage Forms

Disc, transdermal: 1.5 mg/disc (4s)

Injection, as hydrobromide: 0.3 mg/mL (1 mL); 0.4 mg/mL (0.5 mL, 1 mL); 0.86 mg/mL (0.5 mL); 1 mg/mL (1 mL)

Solution, ophthalmic, as hydrobromide: 0.25% (5 mL, 15 mL)

Specific References

CDC, "Scopolamine Poisoning Among Heroin Users - New York City, Newark, Philadelphia, and Baltimore 1995 and 1996," *MMWR Morb Mortal Wkly Rep*, 1996, 45:457-60.

Scopolamine and Phenylephrine *see* Phenylephrine and Scopolamine *on page 481*

Scot-Tussin® [OTC] *see* Guaifenesin *on page 269*

Scot-Tussin DM® Cough Chasers [OTC] *see* Dextromethorphan *on page 187*

Scot-Tussin® Senior Clear [OTC] *see* Guaifenesin and Dextromethorphan *on page 271*

Secobarbital (see koe BAR bi tal)

Related Information

Controlled Substances - Uses and Effects *on page 741*

Synonyms Meballymal; Quinalbarbitone Sodium

U.S. Brand Names Immenoctal®; Seconal™; Sedonal®; Seral®

Canadian Brand Names Seconal®; Novo-Secobarb®

Therapeutic Category Barbiturate

Abuse Potential Yes

Impairment Potential Yes; 200 mg dose results in driving impairment

O'Hanlon JF, "Driving Performance Under the Influence of Drugs: Rationale for, and Application of, a New Test," *Br J Clin Pharmacol*, 1984, 18(Suppl 1): 121S-9S.

Use Short-term treatment of insomnia and as preanesthetic agent

Usual Dosage

Children:

Hypnotic: I.M.: 3-5 mg/kg/dose; maximum: 100 mg/dose

Preoperative sedation:

Oral: 50-100 mg 1-2 hours before procedure

Rectal: 5 mg/kg **or** <6 months: 30-60 mg; 6 months to 3 years: 60 mg; >3 years: 60-120 mg

Sedation: Oral: 6 mg/kg/day divided every 8 hours

Adults:

Hypnotic:

Oral, I.M.: 100-200 mg/dose

I.V.: 50-250 mg/dose

Preoperative sedation: Oral: 100-300 mg 1-2 hours before procedure

Sedation: Oral: 20-40 mg/dose 2-3 times/day

Fatal dose: 2-3 g

Mechanism of Action Interferes with transmission of impulses from the thalamus to the cortex of the brain resulting in an imbalance in central inhibitory and facilitatory mechanisms

Pharmacodynamics/kinetics

Onset of action: I.V.: Hypnosis occurs within 15-30 minutes

Duration: ~15 minutes

Absorption: Oral: Well absorbed (90%) from gastrointestinal tract; can also be absorbed through inhalation

Metabolism: In the liver

Half-life: 25 hours

Time to peak serum concentration: Within 2-4 hours

Signs and Symptoms of Acute Intoxication Unsteady gait, slurred speech, myasthenia gravis (exacerbation or precipitation of), ptosis, vision color changes (green tinge); confusion, jaundice, hypothermia, gaze nystagmus, fever, hypotension, CNS depression; can cause bezoars

When to Transport to Hospital Transport any symptomatic patient or any ingestion over 6 mg/kg

Warnings/Precautions Use with caution in patients with CHS, hepatic or renal insufficiency, marked liver impairment or latent porphyria; avoid alcoholic beverages; potential for drug dependency exists

Adverse Reactions

>10%:

Central nervous system: Dizziness, lightheadedness, drowsiness, "hang-over" effect

Local: Pain at injection site

1% to 10%:

Central nervous system: Confusion, mental depression, unusual excitement, nervousness, faint feeling, headache, insomnia, nightmares

Gastrointestinal: Constipation, nausea, vomiting

Reference Range

Therapeutic: 3-5 µg/mL (SI: 12.6-21.0 µmol/L)

Toxic: >5 µg/mL (SI: >21.0 µmol/L)

Drug Interactions CNS depressants

Dosage Forms

Secobarbital sodium:

Capsule: 100 mg

Injection: 50 mg/mL (2 mL)

Injection, rectal: 50 mg/mL (20 mL)

Tablet: 100 mg

Specific References

Tracqui A, Kintz P, Mangin P, et al, "A Fatality Involving Secobarbital, Nitrazepam, and Codeine," *Am J Forensic Med Pathol*, 1989, 10(2):130-3.

Secobarbital and Amobarbital see Amobarbital and Secobarbital on page 43

Seconal™ see Secobarbital on previous page

Sectral® see Acebutolol on page 18

Securon® see Verapamil on page 609

Sedanoct® see Tryptophan on page 602

Sedantoinal® see Mephenytoin on page 369

Sedapap-10® see Butalbital Compound on page 93

Sederlona® see Clobazam on page 151

Sedonal® see Secobarbital on previous page

Segontin® see Diltiazem on page 201

Seldane® see Terfenadine on page 563

Seldane-D® see Terfenadine and Pseudoephedrine on page 564

Selegiline (seh LEDGE ah leen)

Synonyms Deprenyl; L-Deprenyl

U.S. Brand Names Eldepryl®; Jumex®; Jumexal®; Movergan®; Plurimen®

Canadian Brand Names Novo-Selegiline®

Therapeutic Category Anti-Parkinson's Agent; Dopaminergic Agent (Antiparkinson's)

Use Adjunct in the management of parkinsonian patients in which levodopa/carbidopa therapy is deteriorating

Unlabeled use: Early Parkinson's disease

Investigational use: Alzheimer's disease

Selegiline is also being studied in Alzheimer's disease. Small studies have shown some improvement in behavioral and cognitive performance in patients, however, further study is needed.

Usual Dosage Oral:

Adults: 5 mg twice daily with breakfast and lunch or 10 mg in the morning

Elderly: Initial: 5 mg in the morning, may increase to a total of 10 mg/day

Mechanism of Action Potent monoamine oxidase (MAO) type-B inhibitor; MAO-B plays a major role in the metabolism of dopamine; selegiline may also increase dopaminergic activity by interfering with dopamine reuptake at the synapse

Pharmacodynamics/kinetics

Onset of therapeutic effects: Within 1 hour

Duration: 24-72 hours

Half-life:

Parent compound: 9 minutes

N-desmethyldeprenyl: 2 hours

Amphetamine: 17.7 hours

Methamphetamine: 20.5 hours

Metabolism: In the liver to amphetamine (L-isomer), methamphetamine (L-isomer), and N-desmethyldeprenyl

When to Transport to Hospital Transport any pediatric exposure, any patient with change in mental status, or any ingestion over 20 mg

Warnings/Precautions Increased risk of nonselective MAO inhibition occurs with doses >10 mg/day; is a monoamine oxidase inhibitor type "B", there should **not** be a problem with tyramine-containing products as long as the typical doses are employed; use with caution in elderly

Adverse Reactions

>10%:

Central nervous system: Mood changes, dizziness

Gastrointestinal: Nausea, vomiting, xerostomia, abdominal pain

Neuromuscular & skeletal: Dyskinesias

1% to 10%:

Cardiovascular: Orthostatic hypotension, arrhythmias, hypertension

Central nervous system: Hallucinations, confusion, depression, insomnia, agitation, loss of balance

Neuromuscular & skeletal: Increased involuntary movements, bradykinesia, muscle twitches

Miscellaneous: Bruxism

Drug Interactions Increased toxicity:

Meperidine, in combination with selegiline, has caused agitation, delirium, and death; it may be prudent to avoid other opioids as well

Fluoxetine increases pressor effect

May exacerbate involuntary movements when used with maximum doses of levodopa; reduce doses of levodopa by 30%

Dosage Forms Tablet: 5 mg

Specific References
Tolbert SR and Fuller MA, "Selegiline in Treatment of Behavioral and Cognitive Symptoms of Alzheimer Disease," *Ann Pharmacother*, 1996, 30:1122-9.

Selektine® *see Pravastatin on page 492*

Selenious Acid
Synonyms Selenous Acid, Monohydrated Selenium Dioxide
Commonly Found In Component of compound for gun blueing agent, reagent for alkaloids
Mechanism of Toxic Action Inhibition of sulfhydryl-containing enzymes
Toxicodynamics/kinetics
Absorption:
Inhalation: 97%
Ingestion: 87%
Dermal
Half-life: 1.2 days
Elimination: 50% excreted renally
Signs and Symptoms of Acute Intoxication Hypersalivation, vomiting, diarrhea, seizures, muscle spasms, dermal irritant, garlic odor
When to Transport to Hospital Transport any symptomatic patient
Adverse Reactions
Cardiovascular: Hypertension, tachycardia, cardiomyopathy, sinus tachycardia
Central nervous system: Convulsions
Dermatologic: Alopecia
Gastrointestinal: Pharyngeal edema, intestinal distention, hypersalivation, garlic odor, vomiting, watery diarrhea, burns to the esophagus, pharyngeal, and gastrointestinal tract
Neuromuscular & skeletal: Myopathy
Reference Range
Normal range:
Urine: 7.0-160.0 µg/L
Blood: 100.0-340.0 µg/L
Serum: 86.0-125.0 µg/L
Toxic range:
Urine: >400.0 µg/L
Postmortem serum level of 18.4 mg/L and urine level of 2.11 mg/L described in one case report
Specific References
Nantel AJ, Brown M, Dery P, et al, "Acute Poisoning by Selenious Acid," *Vet Hum Toxicol*, 1985, 27(6):531-3.

Selenium Dioxide
Synonyms Selenium Oxide
UN Number 2811
Commonly Found In Gun-blueing solution
Use Catalyst in production of organic compounds
Mechanism of Toxic Action Inhibition of sulfhydryl-containing enzymes; selenium is a component of glutathione peroxidase enzyme
Toxicodynamics/kinetics Absorption: Inhalation: Well absorbed
Signs and Symptoms of Acute Intoxication Cough, dyspnea, transient loss of consciousness, tachypnea, fever, throat irritation, sternal pain, dermal burns, gagging, headache, dizziness
When to Transport to Hospital Transport any symptomatic patient
Overdosage/Treatment
Decontamination: Oxygenation; 10% ointment of sodium thiosulfate may be useful; British Anti-Lewisite (BAL) is contraindicated
(Continued)

Selenium Dioxide *(Continued)*

Dermal: Remove contaminated clothing; wash with soap and water
Ocular: Irrigate with saline

Adverse Reactions
Central nervous system: Coma
Neuromuscular & skeletal: Rhabdomyolysis
Respiratory: Wheezing
Miscellaneous: Fingernails, teeth, and hair may stain red

Reference Range Normal range:
Serum: 95-165 ng/mL
Urine: 15-150 µg/L

Specific References
Clark RF, Strukle E, Williams SR, et al, "Selenium Poisoning From a Nutritional Supplement," *JAMA*, 1996, 275(14):1087-8.
Koppel C, Baudisch H, and Beyer KH, "Fatal Poisoning With Selenium Dioxide," *J Toxicol Clin Toxicol*, 1986, 24(1):21-35.

Selenium Oxide *see* Selenium Dioxide *on previous page*

Selenous Acid, Monohydrated Selenium Dioxide *see* Selenious Acid *on previous page*

Selipram® *see* Pravastatin *on page 492*

Selokeen® *see* Metoprolol *on page 400*

Selo-Zok® *see* Metoprolol *on page 400*

Semilente® *see* Insulin Preparations *on page 314*

Semilente® Iletin® I *see* Insulin Preparations *on page 314*

Semprex-D® *see* Acrivastine and Pseudoephedrine *on page 27*

Seominal® *see* Reserpine *on page 523*

Septra® *see* Co-Trimoxazole *on page 168*

Septra® DS *see* Co-Trimoxazole *on page 168*

Seral® *see* Secobarbital *on page 534*

Ser-Ap-Es® *see* Hydralazine, Hydrochlorothiazide, and Reserpine *on page 291*

Serax® *see* Oxazepam *on page 450*

Serenace® *see* Haloperidol *on page 280*

Serenid® Forte *see* Oxazepam *on page 450*

Serentil® *see* Mesoridazine *on page 375*

Sereprile *see* Tiapride *on page 581*

Serevent® *see* Salmeterol *on page 531*

Seromycin® Pulvules® *see* Cycloserine *on page 174*

Seroxat® *see* Paroxetine *on page 460*

Serpalin® *see* Reserpine *on page 523*

Serpasil® *see* Reserpine *on page 523*

Sertofren® *see* Desipramine *on page 180*

Sertraline *(SER tra leen)*

U.S. Brand Names Zoloft™

Therapeutic Category Antidepressant

Impairment Potential Yes

Use Treatment of major depression; also being studied for use in obesity and obsessive-compulsive disorder

Usual Dosage Oral:
Adults: Start with 50 mg/day in the morning and increase by 50 mg/day increments every 2-3 days if tolerated to 100 mg/day; additional increases may be necessary; maximum dose: 200 mg/day. If somnolence is noted, administer at bedtime.

Elderly: Start treatment with 25 mg/day in the morning and increase by 25 mg/day increments every 2-3 days if tolerated to 75-100 mg/day; additional increases may be necessary; maximum dose: 200 mg/day

Mechanism of Action Antidepressant with selective inhibitory effects on presynaptic serotonin (5-HT) reuptake

Pharmacodynamics/kinetics

Absorption: Slow

Protein binding: High

Metabolism: Extensive

Half-life:

Parent: 24 hours

Metabolites: 66 hours

Elimination: In both urine and feces

Signs and Symptoms of Acute Intoxication Serious toxicity has not yet been reported, monitor cardiovascular, gastrointestinal, and hepatic functions

When to Transport to Hospital Transport any pediatric exposure, any symptomatic patient, or any ingestion over 300 mg

Warnings/Precautions Do not use in combination with monoamine oxidase inhibitor or within 14 days of discontinuing treatment or initiating treatment with a monoamine oxidase inhibitor due to the risk of serotonin syndrome; use with caution in patients with pre-existing seizure disorders, patients in whom weight loss is undesirable, patients with recent myocardial infarction, unstable heart disease, hepatic or renal impairment, patients taking other psychotropic medications, agitated or hyperactive patients as drug may produce or activate mania or hypomania; because the risk of suicide is inherent in depression, patient should be closely monitored until depressive symptoms remit and prescriptions should be written for minimum quantities to reduce the risk of overdose

Adverse Reactions

1% to 10%: In clinical trials, dizziness and nausea were two most frequent side effects that led to discontinuation of therapy

Cardiovascular: Palpitations

Central nervous system: Insomnia, agitation, dizziness, headache, somnolence, nervousness, fatigue, pain

Dermatologic: Dermatological reactions

Endocrine & metabolic: Sexual dysfunction in men

Gastrointestinal: Xerostomia, diarrhea or loose stools, nausea, constipation

Genitourinary: Urinary disorders

Neuromuscular & skeletal: Tremors

Ocular: Visual difficulty

Otic: Tinnitus

Miscellaneous: Diaphoresis

Drug Interactions

All serotonin reuptake inhibitors are capable of inhibiting cytochrome P-450 IID6 isoenzyme enzyme system. The drugs metabolized by this system include desipramine, dextromethorphan, encainide, haloperidol, imipramine, metoprolol, perphenazine, propafenone, and thioridazine

Increased toxicity:

MAO inhibitors and possibly with lithium or tricyclic antidepressants → **serotonin syndrome** serotonergic hyperstimulation with the following clinical features: mental status changes, restlessness, myoclonus, hyperreflexia, diaphoresis, diarrhea, shivering, and tremor

May decrease metabolism/plasma clearance of some drugs (diazepam, tolbutamide) to result in increased duration and pharmacological effects

May displace highly plasma protein bound drugs from binding sites (eg, warfarin) to result in increased effect

Dosage Forms Tablet, as hydrochloride: 25 mg, 50 mg, 100 mg

(Continued)

Sertraline *(Continued)*

Specific References
Doogan DP and Caillard V, "Sertraline: A New Antidepressant," *J Clin Psychiatry*, 1988, 49(Suppl):46-51.

Serzone® *see* Nefazodone *on page 425*

Sevredol® *see* Morphine Sulfate *on page 410*

Siladryl® Oral [OTC] *see* Diphenhydramine *on page 205*

Silaminic® Cold Syrup [OTC] *see* Chlorpheniramine and Phenylpropanolamine *on page 134*

Silaminic® Expectorant [OTC] *see* Guaifenesin and Phenylpropanolamine *on page 272*

Sildicon-E® [OTC] *see* Guaifenesin and Phenylpropanolamine *on page 272*

Silphen® Cough [OTC] *see* Diphenhydramine *on page 205*

Silphen DM® [OTC] *see* Dextromethorphan *on page 187*

Siltussin® [OTC] *see* Guaifenesin *on page 269*

Siltussin-CF® [OTC] *see* Guaifenesin, Phenylpropanolamine, and Dextromethorphan *on page 274*

Siltussin DM® [OTC] *see* Guaifenesin and Dextromethorphan *on page 271*

Simron® *see* Iron *on page 318*

Sinarest® Nasal Solution [OTC] *see* Phenylephrine *on page 479*

Sinarest®, No Drowsiness [OTC] *see* Acetaminophen and Pseudoephedrine *on page 22*

Sine-Aid® IB [OTC] *see* Pseudoephedrine and Ibuprofen *on page 517*

Sine-Aid®, Maximum Strength [OTC] *see* Acetaminophen and Pseudoephedrine *on page 22*

Sinemet® *see* Levodopa and Carbidopa *on page 339*

Sine-Off® Maximum Strength No Drowsiness Formula [OTC] *see* Acetaminophen and Pseudoephedrine *on page 22*

Sinequan® *see* Doxepin *on page 211*

Sinufed® Timecelles® *see* Guaifenesin and Pseudoephedrine *on page 273*

Sinumist®-SR Capsulets® *see* Guaifenesin *on page 269*

Sinupan® *see* Guaifenesin and Phenylephrine *on page 272*

Sinus Excedrin® Extra Strength [OTC] *see* Acetaminophen and Pseudoephedrine *on page 22*

Sinusol-B® *see* Brompheniramine *on page 84*

Sinus-Relief® [OTC] *see* Acetaminophen and Pseudoephedrine *on page 22*

Sinutab® Tablets [OTC] *see* Acetaminophen, Chlorpheniramine, and Pseudoephedrine *on page 23*

Sinutab® Without Drowsiness [OTC] *see* Acetaminophen and Pseudoephedrine *on page 22*

Siquil® *see* Triflupromazine *on page 597*

Sirdalud® *see* Tizanidine *on page 584*

Sirdulud® *see* Tizanidine *on page 584*

SK-Choral® Hydrate *see* Chloral Hydrate *on page 122*

Skellysolve B *see* Hexane *on page 286*

SK-Lygen® *see* Chlordiazepoxide *on page 124*

SK-Pramine® *see* Imipramine *on page 309*

SK-Reserpine® *see* Reserpine *on page 523*

Sleep-eze 3® Oral [OTC] *see* Diphenhydramine *on page 205*

Sleepinal® [OTC] *see* Diphenhydramine *on page 205*

Sleepwell 2-nite® [OTC] *see* Diphenhydramine *on page 205*

Slim-Mint® [OTC] *see* Benzocaine *on page 70*

Slo-bid™ Slo-Phyllin® *see* Theophylline Salts *on page 571*

Slo-Niacin® [OTC] *see* Niacin *on page 428*

Slo-Phyllin GG® *see* Theophylline and Guaifenesin *on page 571*

Slow FE® *see* Iron *on page 318*

Smail® *see* Chlordiazepoxide *on page 124*

SMFA *see* Sodium Monofluoroacetate *on next page*

S-Mustard *see* Mustard Gas *on page 414*

SMZ-TMP *see* Co-Trimoxazole *on page 168*

Snaplets-EX® [OTC] *see* Guaifenesin and Phenylpropanolamine *on page 272*

Snappers *see* Nitrites *on page 436*

Snow *see* Cocaine (Cocaine Metabolite), Qualitative *on page 163*

Sodium Azide

Synonyms Azium; Azomide

UN Number 1687

Use Shell detonators in explosive industry; found as principle agent (350-600 g) for providing nitrogen for the rapid expansion (in 0.05 seconds) of automobile air bags; preservative for laboratory reagents (concentration ~1 mg/mL); nematocide; herbicide

Mechanism of Toxic Action Mucosal irritant; may inhibit oxidative phosphorylation; can cause vasodilitation

Toxicodynamics/kinetics

Absorption: Inhalation, dermal or ingestion

Metabolism: Converted to nitric oxide

When to Transport to Hospital Transport any symptomatic patient

Overdosage/Treatment Decontamination:

Dermal: Flush with water

Inhalation: Administer 100% humidified oxygen

Ocular: Copious irrigation with saline or water

Adverse Reactions

Cardiovascular: Asystole, hypotension, initial bradycardia followed by tachycardia, chest pain, arrhythmias (atrial/ventricular), myocardial depression, congestive heart failure, vasodilation

Central nervous system: Hypothermia, hyperthermia, headache, agitation, seizures, coma

Dermatologic: Dermal burns

Endocrine & metabolic: Polydipsia, metabolic acidosis

Gastrointestinal: Diarrhea, nausea

Hematologic: Leukocytosis

Neuromuscular & skeletal: Weakness, hyporeflexia, paresthesia

Ocular: Photophobia, lacrimation, keratitis, corneal burn, mydriasis

Respiratory: Hyperventilation, tachypnea, dyspnea, pulmonary edema

Miscellaneous: Diaphoresis

Reference Range Postmortem blood levels (following ingestion of sodium azide): 8-262 mg/L

Specific References

Abrams J, El-Mallakh RS, and Meyer R, "Suicidal Sodium Azide Ingestion," *Ann Emerg Med*, 1987, 16(12):1378-80.

Sodium Biborate *see* Borates *on page 80*

Sodium Bisulfite *see* Sulfite Food Poisoning *on page 553*

Sodium Borate *see* Borates *on page 80*

Sodium Fluoacetate *see* Sodium Monofluoroacetate *on next page*

Sodium Fluoride *see* Fluoride *on page 251*

Sodium Glutamate *see* Monosodium Glutamate Food Poisoning *on page 409*

Sodium Hydrofluoride *see* Fluoride *on page 251*
Sodium Metabisulfite *see* Sulfite Food Poisoning *on page 553*
Sodium Metaborate *see* Borates *on page 80*

Sodium Monofluoroacetate

Synonyms Fluoroacetic Acid (Sodium Salt); SMFA; Sodium Fluoacetate
UN Number 2629
U.S. Brand Names Compound 1080®
Use Rodenticide
Mechanism of Toxic Action Metabolized to fluorocitrate which then blocks
   Kreb cycle metabolism by inhibiting the mitochondrial enzyme aconitase
Toxicodynamics/kinetics Absorption: Orally and in lungs; dermal absorption
   does not appear to occur if skin is intact
Signs and Symptoms of Acute Intoxication Hallucinations, paresthesia,
   myoglobinuria, muscle spasms, stupor, seizures, coma, mydriasis, sinus tachy-
   cardia, hypotension; late findings include renal and/or hepatic necrosis; typi-
   cally begin 30-90 minutes after exposure
When to Transport to Hospital Transport any suspected exposure
Overdosage/Treatment
   Decontamination: Dermal: Remove contaminated clothing and irrigate skin with
      soap and water with dermal contact
Adverse Reactions
   Cardiovascular: Prolonged Q-T intervals on EKG, fibrillation (ventricular), hypo-
      tension, arrhythmias (ventricular)
   Central nervous system: Auditory hallucinations, seizures, tetany, coma, ataxia
   Endocrine & metabolic: Hypocalcemia
   Gastrointestinal: Vomiting, salivation
   Hepatic: Hepatic necrosis
   Neuromuscular & skeletal: Paresthesia, hypertonicity, carpopedal spasms
   Renal: Renal failure (acute)
   Respiratory: Hemorrhagic pulmonary edema, hyperventilation
Reference Range Autopsy urinary levels of 368 mg/L associated with lethality
   17 hours after exposure to 465 mg of sodium fluoroacetate
Additional Information Odorless, tasteless, water soluble; initially developed
   for chemical warfare; available only for commercially licensed rodenticide use;
   when heated, toxic sodium oxide and fluoride fumes are emitted; a white
   odorless powder usually associated with a blue dye; approximately 5 mg/kg is
   fatal; fluoroacetamide less toxic; trifluoroacetic acid used in high performance
   liquid chromatography is an irritant and can be dermally absorbed, but is not as
   toxic; ethanol treatment may aggravate hypokalemia
Specific References
   Chi CH, Chen KW, Chan SH, et al, "Clinical Presentation and Prognostic
      Factors in Sodium Monofluoroacetate Intoxication," *Clin Toxicol*, 1996,
      34(6):707-12.

Sodium Oxybate *see* Gamma Hydroxybutyric Acid *on page 262*
Sodium Perborate *see* Borates *on page 80*
Sodium Pyroborate *see* Borates *on page 80*
Sodium Sulfite *see* Sulfite Food Poisoning *on page 553*
Sodium Tetraborate *see* Borates *on page 80*
Sodium Valproate *see* Valproic Acid and Derivatives *on page 607*
Sodol® *see* Carisoprodol *on page 114*
Solarcaine® [OTC] *see* Benzocaine *on page 70*
Solaxin® *see* Chlorzoxazone *on page 145*
Solazine® *see* Trifluoperazine *on page 596*
Solfoton® *see* Phenobarbital *on page 474*

Solgol® *see Nadolol on page 417*

Solis® *see Diazepam on page 189*

Solium® *see Chlordiazepoxide on page 124*

Solu-Cortef® *see Hydrocortisone on page 297*

Solurex® *see Dexamethasone on page 182*

Solurex L.A.® *see Dexamethasone on page 182*

Solustrep® *see Streptomycin on page 548*

Soma® *see Carisoprodol on page 114*

Soma® Compound *see Carisoprodol and Aspirin on page 115*

Soma® Compound w/Codeine *see Carisoprodol, Aspirin, and Codeine on page 115*

Somadril® *see Carisoprodol on page 114*

Soman *see Nerve Gases on page 426*

Somatomax PM® *see Gamma Hydroxybutyric Acid on page 262*

Somaz® *see Temazepam on page 559*

Sominex® Oral [OTC] *see Diphenhydramine on page 205*

Somnite® *see Nitrazepam on page 435*

Somnomed® *see Methaqualone Hydrochloride on page 388*

Somsanit® *see Gamma Hydroxybutyric Acid on page 262*

Songar® *see Triazolam on page 592*

Soothe® [OTC] *see Tetrahydrozoline on page 569*

Sopental® *see Pentobarbital on page 464*

Soprodol® *see Carisoprodol on page 114*

Soprol® *see Bisoprolol on page 78*

Soridol® *see Carisoprodol on page 114*

Sosegon® *see Pentazocine on page 463*

Sosenol® *see Pentazocine on page 463*

Sotalol (SOE ta lole)

U.S. Brand Names Betapace®

Canadian Brand Names Sotacor®

Therapeutic Category Antiarrhythmic Agent, Class II; Antiarrhythmic Agent, Class III

Use Treatment of ventricular arrhythmias, prevention of life-threatening arrhythmias, and sudden death postmyocardial infarction

Usual Dosage Adults:

Oral: Initial: 80 mg twice daily; may be increased to 240-320 mg/day and up to 480-640 mg/day in patients with life-threatening refractory ventricular arrhythmias; adjust dose every 2-3 days

I.V.: Termination of supraventricular tachycardia: 1-1.5 mg/kg

Mechanism of Action Has both B- and B_2-receptor blocking activity; also passes some type III antiarrhythmic activity

Pharmacodynamics/kinetics

Onset of action: Rapid, 1-2 hours

Peak effect: 3-4 hours

Absorption: ~70% which is decreased 20% to 30% by meals (especially milk products)

Bioavailability: 90% to 100%

Half-life: 7-15 hours

Signs and Symptoms of Acute Intoxication Leukopenia or neutropenia (agranulocytosis, granulocytopenia); Q-T prolongation; lightheadedness, depression, LDL (increased), eosinophilia, thrombocytopenia, myasthenia gravis (exacerbation or precipitation of), heart block, insomnia, impotence, hypoglycemia, bleeding

(Continued)

Sotalol *(Continued)*

When to Transport to Hospital Transport any pediatric exposure or any symptomatic patient

Warnings/Precautions Use with caution in patients with congestive heart failure, peripheral vascular disease, hypokalemia, hypomagnesemia, renal dysfunction, sick sinus syndrome; abrupt withdrawal may result in return of life-threatening arrhythmias; sotalol can provoke new or worsening ventricular arrhythmias

Adverse Reactions

>10%:

Cardiovascular: Bradycardia

Central nervous system: Mental depression

Endocrine & metabolic: Decreased sexual ability

1% to 10%:

Cardiovascular: Congestive heart failure, reduced peripheral circulation

Central nervous system: Mental confusion, hallucinations, anxiety, dizziness, drowsiness, nightmares, insomnia, fatigue

Dermatologic: Itching

Gastrointestinal: Constipation, diarrhea, nausea, vomiting, stomach discomfort

Neuromuscular & skeletal: Weakness

Respiratory: Dyspnea

Reference Range Peak serum level: ~1.7 mg/L after 160 mg oral dose

Drug Interactions Decreased effect/levels with coadministration of aluminum- and/or magnesium-containing antacids

Dosage Forms Tablet: 80 mg, 160 mg, 240 mg

Specific References

Pill MW and McCloskey WW, "Sotalol: What the Emergency Nurse Needs to Know," *J Emerg Nurs*, 1995, 21(3):229-31.

Sung RJ, Tan HL, Karagounis L, et al, "Intravenous Sotalol for the

South American Holly see Maté on page 360

Span-FF® see Iron on page 318

Sparine® see Promazine on page 504

Spasmobam® see Dicyclomine on page 194

Spasmoject® see Dicyclomine on page 194

Spasmolin® see Hyoscyamine, Atropine, Scopolamine, and Phenobarbital on page 306

Specimen Chain-of-Custody Protocol see Chain-of-Custody Protocol on page 121

Spec-T® [OTC] see Benzocaine on page 70

Spectracide® see Diazinon on page 192

Spirit of Hartshorn see Ammonia on page 42

Spirits see Ethyl Alcohol on page 233

Spirits of Turpentine see Turpentine Oil on page 603

Spirolone® see Spironolactone on this page

Spironolactone (speer on oh LAK tone)

U.S. Brand Names Aldace®; Aldactone®; Aldopur®; Laractone®; Spirolone®; Spironone®; Spirotone®; Tensin®; Uractone®

Canadian Brand Names Novo-Spiroton®

Therapeutic Category Diuretic

Use Management of edema associated with excessive aldosterone excretion; hypertension; primary hyperaldosteronism; treatment of hirsutism; acidosis

Investigational: Congestive heart failure

Usual Dosage Oral (to reduce delay in onset of effect, a loading dose of 2 or 3 times the daily dose may be administered on the first day of therapy):

Children: 1-3.3 mg/kg/day in divided doses every 6-24 hours up to a maximum of 200 mg/day

Adults:

Edema, hypertension, hypokalemia: 25-200 mg/day in 1-2 divided doses
Diagnosis of primary aldosteronism: 100-400 mg/day in 1-2 divided doses

Mechanism of Action Competes with aldosterone for receptor sites in the distal renal tubules, increasing sodium chloride and water excretion while conserving potassium and hydrogen ions; may block the effect of aldosterone on arteriolar smooth muscle as well

Pharmacodynamics/kinetics

Metabolism: In the liver to multiple metabolites, including canrenone (active)
Half-life: 1.4 hours (canrenone: 13-24 hours)
Time to peak serum concentration: Within 1-3 hours (primarily as the active metabolite)

When to Transport to Hospital Transport any symptomatic patient

Warnings/Precautions Use with caution in patients with dehydration, hepatic disease, hyponatremia, renal sufficiency, patients receiving other potassium-sparing diuretics, ACE inhibitors, or potassium supplements; it is recommended the drug may be discontinued several days prior to adrenal vein catheterization

Adverse Reactions 1% to 10%:

Cardiovascular: Arrhythmia
Central nervous system: Confusion, nervousness, dizziness, drowsiness, lack of energy, unusual fatigue, headache, fever, chills
Endocrine & metabolic: Hyperkalemia, breast tenderness in females, deepening of voice in females, enlargement of breast in males, inability to achieve or maintain an erection, increased hair growth in females, decreased sexual ability
Gastrointestinal: Diarrhea, nausea, vomiting, stomach cramps, dryness of mouth
Neuromuscular & skeletal: Weakness, numbness or paresthesia in hands, feet, or lips
Respiratory: Shortness of breath, dyspnea
Miscellaneous: Increased thirst

Reference Range Steady-state of canrenone levels (of spironolactone dosing 50 mg twice daily) are 50-70 ng/mL (trough) and 146-250 ng/mL (peak)

Drug Interactions Increased serum potassium levels with potassium, potassium-sparing diuretics, indomethacin, angiotensin-converting enzymes inhibitors; reduces activity of warfarin; salicylates block spironolactone's diuretic effects; hyperkalemia can result with concomitant ACE inhibitor administration; cholestyramine and spironolactone can cause a hyperchloremic metabolic acidosis

Dosage Forms Tablet: 25 mg, 50 mg, 100 mg

Specific References

Al-Zaki T and Talbot-Stern J, "A Body-Builder With Diuretic Abuse Presenting With Symptomatic Hypotension and Hyperkalemia," *Am J Emerg Med*, 1996, 14:96-8.

Spironone® see Spironolactone *on previous page*

Spirotone® see Spironolactone *on previous page*

Spotted Hemlock see Poison Hemlock *on page 491*

Spotting Naphtha see Stoddard Solvent *on page 547*

Squaw Tea see Ephedra *on page 219*

SRC® Expectorant see Hydrocodone, Pseudoephedrine, and Guaifenesin on page 297

Stadol® see Butorphanol on page 95

Stadol® NS see Butorphanol on page 95

Stagesic® see Hydrocodone and Acetaminophen on page 293

Stahist® see Chlorpheniramine, Phenylephrine, Phenylpropanolamine, and Belladonna Alkaloids on page 136

Stannous Fluoride see Fluoride on page 251

Stanozolol (stan OH zoe lole)

U.S. Brand Names Winstrol®

Therapeutic Category Anabolic Steroid

Abuse Potential Yes

Use Prophylactic use against hereditary angioedema

Usual Dosage

Children: Acute attacks:

<6 years: 1 mg/day

6-12 years: 2 mg/day

Adults: Oral: Initial: 2 mg 3 times/day, may then reduce to a maintenance dose of 2 mg/day or 2 mg every other day after 1-3 months

Mechanism of Action Synthetic testosterone derivative with similar androgenic and anabolic actions

Pharmacodynamics/kinetics

Metabolism: In an analogous fashion to testosterone

Elimination: In an analogous fashion to testosterone

When to Transport to Hospital Transport any patient with ingestion over 10 mg

Warnings/Precautions May stunt bone growth in children; anabolic steroids may cause peliosis hepatis, liver cell tumors, and blood lipid changes with increased risk of arteriosclerosis; monitor diabetic patients carefully; use with caution in elderly patients, they may be at greater risk for prostatic hypertrophy; use with caution in patients with cardiac, renal, or hepatic disease or epilepsy

Adverse Reactions

Male:

Postpubertal:

>10%:

Dermatologic: Acne

Endocrine & metabolic: Gynecomastia

Genitourinary: Bladder irritability, priapism

1% to 10%:

Central nervous system: Insomnia, chills

Endocrine & metabolic: Decreased libido, hepatic dysfunction,

Gastrointestinal: Nausea, diarrhea

Genitourinary: Prostatic hypertrophy (elderly)

Hematologic: Iron deficiency anemia, suppression of clotting factors

Prepubertal:

>10%:

Dermatologic: Acne

Endocrine & metabolic: Virilism

1% to 10%:

Central nervous system: Chills, insomnia, factors

Dermatologic: Hyperpigmentation

Gastrointestinal: Diarrhea, nausea

Hematologic: Iron deficiency anemia, suppression of clotting

Female:

>10%: Endocrine & metabolic: Virilism

1% to 10%:
Central nervous system: Chills, insomnia
Endocrine & metabolic: Hypercalcemia
Gastrointestinal: Nausea, diarrhea
Hematologic: Iron deficiency anemia, suppression of clotting factors
Hepatic: Hepatic dysfunction

Dosage Forms Tablet: 2 mg

Specific References

Höld KM, Wilkins DG, Crouch DJ, et al, "Detection of Stanozolol in Hair by Negative Ion Chemical Ionization Mass Spectrometry," *J Anal Toxicol*, 1996, 20:345-9.

Staten® see Zopiclone on page 621

Statex® see Morphine Sulfate on page 410

Staurodorm® see Flurazepam on page 256

Stay Trim® Diet Gum [OTC] see Phenylpropanolamine on page 481

St. Bartholomew's Tea see Maté on page 360

S-T Cort® see Hydrocortisone on page 297

Steclin® see Tetracycline on page 568

Stelazine® see Trifluoperazine on page 596

Sterapred® see Prednisone on page 497

Stesolid® see Diazepam on page 189

Stilnox® see Zolpidem on page 621

St Joseph® Adult Chewable Aspirin [OTC] see Aspirin on page 56

St. Joseph® Cough Suppressant [OTC] see Dextromethorphan on page 187

St. Joseph® Measured Dose Nasal Solution [OTC] see Phenylephrine on page 479

Stoddard Solvent

Related Information

Jet Fuel-4 on page 325

Synonyms Dry Cleaning Safety Solvent; Spotting Naphtha; White Spirits

UN Number 1271; 1255; 1256; 2553

U.S. Brand Names Texsolve S®; Varsol 1®

Impairment Potential Yes

Use Petroleum solvent which is used as a paint thinner, printing ink, adhesive, in liquid photocopier toners, degreaser used in dry cleaning plants

Mechanism of Toxic Action Mixture of hydrocarbons (alkanes, cycloalkanes, and aromatics), this solvent can cause central nervous system depression and cerebral atrophy and axonal prenodal swellings

Toxicodynamics/kinetics

Absorption: From lungs, orally, and dermally
Metabolism: Hepatic to dimethylbenzoic acid

When to Transport to Hospital Transport any suspected ingestion

Overdosage/Treatment Decontamination:
Dermal: Wash with soap and water
Ocular: Irrigate with saline
Oral: Dilute with water

Adverse Reactions

Central nervous system: Dizziness, headache, ataxia, memory disturbance
Gastrointestinal: Nausea
Hematologic: Methemoglobinemia
Hepatic: Liver function tests (elevated)
Ocular: Eye irritation
Renal: Glomerulonephritis, nephritis
(Continued)

Stoddard Solvent *(Continued)*

Reference Range Mean blood level after an exposure (airborne) of 600 mg/m³ for 5 days (6 hours/day): ~2-2.5 mg/L
Specific References
U.S. Department of Health and Human Services, "Toxicological Profile of Stoddard Solvent," Agency for Toxic Substances and Diseases Registry, May 1993.

Stop® [OTC] *see* Fluoride *on page 251*
Straight Run Kerosene *see* Kerosene *on page 325*
Streptocol® *see* Streptomycin *on this page*

Streptomycin *(strep toe MYE sin)*

U.S. Brand Names Cidan Est®; Novostrep®; Solustrep®; Streptocol®
Therapeutic Category Antibiotic, Aminoglycoside; Antitubercular Agent
Use Combination therapy of active tuberculosis; used in combination with other agents for treatment of streptococcal or enterococcal endocarditis, mycobacterial infections, plague, tularemia, and brucellosis. Streptomycin is indicated for persons from endemic areas of drug-resistant *Mycobacterium tuberculosis* or who are HIV infected.
Usual Dosage Intramuscular (may also be given intravenous piggyback):
Tuberculosis therapy: **Note:** A four-drug regimen (isoniazid, rifampin, pyrazinamide and either streptomycin or ethambutol) is preferred for the initial, empiric treatment of TB. When the drug susceptibility results are available, the regimen should be altered as appropriate.
Patients with TB and without HIV infection:
OPTION 1:
Isoniazid resistance rate <4%: Administer daily isoniazid, rifampin, and pyrazinamide for 8 weeks followed by isoniazid and rifampin daily or directly observed therapy (DOT) 2-3 times/week for 16 weeks
If isoniazid resistance rate is not documented, ethambutol or streptomycin should also be administered until susceptibility to isoniazid or rifampin is demonstrated. Continue treatment for at least 6 months or 3 months beyond culture conversion.
OPTION 2: Administer daily isoniazid, rifampin, pyrazinamide, and either streptomycin or ethambutol for 2 weeks followed by DOT 2 times/week administration of the same drugs for 6 weeks, and subsequently, with isoniazid and rifampin DOT 2 times/week administration for 16 weeks
OPTION 3: Administer isoniazid, rifampin, pyrazinamide, and either ethambutol or streptomycin by DOT 3 times/week for 6 months

Patients with TB and with HIV infection: Administer any of the above OPTIONS 1, 2 or 3, however, treatment should be continued for a total of 9 months and at least 6 months beyond culture conversion

Note: Some experts recommend that the duration of therapy should be extended to 9 months for patients with disseminated disease, miliary disease, disease involving the bones or joints, or tuberculosis lymphadenitis

Children:
Daily therapy: 20-30 mg/kg/day (maximum: 1 g/day)
Directly observed therapy (DOT): Twice weekly: 25-30 mg/kg (maximum: 1.5 g)
DOT: 3 times/week: 25-30 mg/kg (maximum: 1 g)
Adults:
Daily therapy: 15 mg/kg/day (maximum: 1 g)
Directly observed therapy (DOT): Twice weekly: 25-30 mg/kg (maximum: 1.5 g)
DOT: 3 times/week: 25-30 mg/kg (maximum: 1 g)

Enterococcal endocarditis: 1 g every 12 hours for 2 weeks, 500 mg every 12 hours for 4 weeks in combination with penicillin

Streptococcal endocarditis: 1 g every 12 hours for 1 week, 500 mg every 12 hours for 1 week

Tularemia: 1-2 g/day in divided doses for 7-10 days or until patient is afebrile for 5-7 days

Plague: 2-4 g/day in divided doses until the patient is afebrile for at least 3 days

Elderly: 10 mg/kg/day, not to exceed 750 mg/day; dosing interval should be adjusted for renal function; some authors suggest not to give more than 5 days/week or give as 20-25 mg/kg/dose twice weekly

Mechanism of Action Inhibits bacterial protein synthesis by binding directly to the 30S ribosomal subunits causing faulty peptide sequence to form in the protein chain

Pharmacodynamics/kinetics

Absorption: Oral: Absorbed poorly; usually given parenterally

Time to peak serum concentration: Within 1 hour

Metabolism: None

Half-life:

Newborns: 4-10 hours

Adults: 2-4.7 hours, prolonged with renal impairment

When to Transport to Hospital Transport any symptomatic patient

Warnings/Precautions Use with caution in patients with pre-existing vertigo, tinnitus, hearing loss, neuromuscular disorders, or renal impairment; modify dosage in patients with renal impairment; aminoglycosides are associated with nephrotoxicity or ototoxicity; the ototoxicity may be proportional to the amount of drug given and the duration of treatment; tinnitus or vertigo are indications of vestibular injury and impending hearing damage; renal damage is usually reversible

Adverse Reactions

1% to 10%:

Neuromuscular & skeletal: Neuromuscular blockade

Otic: Ototoxicity (auditory), ototoxicity (vestibular)

Renal: Nephrotoxicity

Reference Range

Peak serum streptomycin level after a 15 mg/kg I.M. dose: ~40 µg/mL

Therapeutic: Peak: 15-40 µg/mL; Trough: <5 µg/mL

Toxic: Peak: >50 µg/mL; Trough: >10 µg/mL

Drug Interactions

Increased/prolonged effect: Depolarizing and nondepolarizing neuromuscular blocking agents

Increased toxicity: Concurrent use of amphotericin, loop diuretics may increase nephrotoxicity

Dosage Forms Injection: 400 mg/mL (2.5 mL)

Additional Information Withdrawn from market in 1991; access and questions of this drug may be directed to: Pfizer Streptomycin Program, Pfizer Incorporated, 235 East 42nd Street, New York, NY 10017, (800) 254-4445

Specific References

Bass JB Jr, Farer LS, Hopewell PC, et al, "Treatment of Tuberculosis and Tuberculosis Infection in Adults and Children," *Am J Respir Crit Care Med*, 1994, 149(5):1359-74.

Strobane see Trichloroethane on page 594

Strychnine

Synonyms *Strychnos ignatii; Strychnos nux-vomica; Strychnos tiente*

UN Number 1692

(Continued)

Strychnine *(Continued)*

U.S. Brand Names Certox®; Dolco Mouse Cereal®; Kwik-kil®; Mouse-Rid®; Mouse-Tox®; Pied Piper Mouse Seed®; Ro-Dex®

Use Rodenticide; also used as an adulterant in production of illicit cocaine, heroin, and amphetamine; an antiquated antidote historically used in analeptic treatment for barbiturate overdose; unapproved use for nonketotic hyperglycinemia and sleep apnea (100 mcg/kg)

Mechanism of Toxic Action Strychnine competitively antagonizes the inhibitory action of glycine at the postsynaptic receptors in the spinal cord; this loss of postsynaptic inhibition results in excessive motor neuron activity; binding within the CNS may also be responsible for exaggerated responses to visual, auditory, and tactile stimulation

Toxicodynamics/kinetics

Onset of symptoms:

Oral: 15-30 minutes

Intranasal, parenteral: <5 minutes

Absorption: Complete and rapid absorption following oral or parenteral exposure; readily absorbed through intact skin and mucosal surfaces

Distribution: V_d: 13 L/kg; rapid tissue distribution

Metabolism: Hepatic microsomal oxidation

Half-life: 10 hours; half-life in overdose: 10-16 hours

Signs and Symptoms of Acute Intoxication Prodromal syndrome of muscular cramps and pain; neck and back stiffness; limb rigidity; agitation and anxiety, followed by excessive muscular activity and hypertonicity; seizures during which the patients remain awake and lucid; opisthotonos; trismus; tachycardia, metabolic acidosis; hypertension, hypomagnesemia, tachypnea and hyperthermia accompanying muscular activity; risus sardonicus (sardonic grinning); respiratory paralysis, fasciculations, apnea and cyanosis; acidosis; rhabdomyolysis and myoglobinuria; leukocytosis; death from respiratory and cardiac arrest

When to Transport to Hospital Transport patients with any suspected exposure

Overdosage/Treatment Decontamination:

Dermal exposure: Prompt thorough scrubbing of all affected areas with soap and water

Ocular exposure: Irrigation with copious tepid water or saline

Warnings/Precautions Any external visual, auditory, or tactile stimuli may precipitate muscle hyperactivity and seizures; minimize any external stimuli

Adverse Reactions

Cardiovascular: Sinus tachycardia

Central nervous system: Anxiety and seizures without loss of consciousness, dysesthesia

Gastrointestinal: Dysphagia

Neuromuscular & skeletal: Rigidity, muscle cramps, hypertonicity, trismus

Respiratory: Tachypnea, apnea, respiratory paralysis

Miscellaneous: Hypersensitivity to external stimuli

Additional Information Any exposure to strychnine should be considered potentially life-threatening; intensive care unit admission criteria include seizures, acidosis, and hypoxia; observation care unit admission criteria include evidence of hyperreflexia or neuromuscular irritability, hypertension or tachycardia, that persists longer than 4 hours for onset; patients who remain asymptomatic for at least 6 hours, or who become asymptomatic and remain so for at least 6 hours, may be considered for medical clearance; has a bitter taste

Lethal dose: 5-10 mg

How supplied: Powder/tablets (veterinary)

Specific References
Heiser JM, Daya MR, Magnussen AR, et al, "Massive Strychnine Intoxication: Serial Blood Levels in a Fatal Case," *J Toxicol Clin Toxicol*, 1992, 30(2):269-83.

Strychnos ignatii see Strychnine *on page 549*
Strychnos nux-vomica see Strychnine *on page 549*
Strychnos tiente see Strychnine *on page 549*

Styrene

Synonyms Cinnamene; Ethenylbenzene; Phenylethylene; Vinylbenzene
UN Number 2055
Impairment Potential Yes; Air levels of 100 ppm or blood styrene levels over 2.4 mg/L are likely to result in central nervous system effects or impairment

Pierce CH, Becker CE, Tozer TN, et al, "Modeling the Acute Neurotoxicity of Styrene," *JOEM*, 1998, 40(3):230-40.

Use Production of polystyrene plastics for use in insulation or fiberglass materials
Mechanism of Toxic Action Essentially unknown; may cause increase in brain serotonin and noradrenaline levels; can cause central nervous system depression
Toxicodynamics/kinetics
Absorption:
Inhalation: 63%
Oral/dermal: LImited with absorption rate being 1 mcg/cm^2/minute or ~0.1% to 2% of inhalation absorption amount
Metabolism: Hepatic to hippuric acid, mandelic acid (MA) and phenylglyoxilic acid (PGA)
Half-life: 2-4 days
When to Transport to Hospital Transport any suspected ingestion or any symptomatic patient
Overdosage/Treatment
Decontamination:
Dermal: Remove contaminated clothing; wash with soap and water
Ocular: Irrigate with saline
Oral: Dilute with water; **do not** induce emesis; activated charcoal may be effective
Adverse Reactions
Central nervous system: Air styrene levels >30 ppm can cause changes in EEG and psychomotor changes, cognitive dysfunction
Gastrointestinal: Nausea (at 376 ppm after 1 hour), metallic taste, stomatitis, sore throat
Neuromuscular & skeletal: Neuropathy (peripheral)
Ocular: Eye irritation (at 376 ppm after 1 hour exposure), rotatory nystagmus, neuritis (retrobulbar), optic neuropathy
Respiratory: Rhinorrhea, bronchospasm, cough, aspiration
Reference Range
Workers exposed to TWA levels of inhalation of styrene (biological exposure indices or BEI):
Before shift: 0.02 mg/L
End shift: 1 mg/L
Urinary levels of MA (1 g/L) and PGA (250 mcg/L); urine level of AA of 0.8 g/L has been associated with some central nervous system depression
An exposure of 80 ppm of styrene has been associated with a blood styrene level of ~1 mcg/mL; general population blood styrene level: 0.4 mcg/L
Fat levels range from 8-350 ng/g
(Continued)

Styrene *(Continued)*

Specific References

U.S. Department of Health and Human Services, "Toxicological Profile for Styrene TP-91/25," Agency for Toxic Substances and Diseases Registry, September 1992.

Sublimaze® *see* Fentanyl *on page 247*

β-Subunit of hCG *see* Pregnancy Test *on page 499*

Sucrets® Cough Calmers [OTC] *see* Dextromethorphan *on page 187*

Sudafed® [OTC] *see* Pseudoephedrine *on page 516*

Sudafed® 12 Hour [OTC] *see* Pseudoephedrine *on page 516*

Sudafed® Cold & Cough Liquid Caps [OTC] *see* Guaifenesin, Pseudoephedrine, and Dextromethorphan *on page 275*

Sudafed Plus® Liquid [OTC] *see* Chlorpheniramine and Pseudoephedrine *on page 134*

Sudafed Plus® Tablet [OTC] *see* Chlorpheniramine and Pseudoephedrine *on page 134*

Sudafed® Severe Cold [OTC] *see* Acetaminophen, Dextromethorphan, and Pseudoephedrine *on page 23*

Sufedrin® [OTC] *see* Pseudoephedrine *on page 516*

Sufenta® *see* Sufentanil *on this page*

Sufentanil *(soo FEN ta nil)*

Related Information

Controlled Substances - Uses and Effects *on page 741*

U.S. Brand Names Sufenta®

Therapeutic Category Analgesic, Narcotic; General Anesthetic

Abuse Potential Yes

Impairment Potential Yes

Use Analgesic supplement in maintenance of balanced general anesthesia

Usual Dosage

Children <12 years: 10-25 mcg/kg with 100% O_2, maintenance: 25-50 mcg as needed

Adults: Dose should be based on body weight; **Note:** In obese patients (ie, >20% above ideal body weight), use lean body weight to determine dosage

1-2 mcg/kg with N_2O/O_2 for endotracheal intubation; maintenance: 10-25 mcg as needed

2-8 mcg/kg with N_2O/O_2 more complicated major surgical procedures; maintenance: 10-50 mcg as needed

8-30 mcg/kg with 100% O_2 and muscle relaxant produces sleep; at doses of ≥8 mcg/kg maintains a deep level of anesthesia; maintenance: 10-50 mcg as needed

Mechanism of Action Binds with stereospecific receptors at many sites within the CNS, increases pain threshold, alters pain reception, inhibits ascending pain pathways; ultra short-acting narcotic; not a partial opiate antagonist

Pharmacodynamics/kinetics

Onset of action: 1-3 minutes

Duration: Dose dependent; usually 30-60 minutes, may be up to 3.5 hours

Metabolism: Primarily by the liver

Half-life: 158 minutes

Patients with cardiac surgery: 595 minutes

Patients with abdominal aortic surgery: 12 hours

Patients hyperventilating: 232 minutes

Obese patients: Increased half-life

Signs and Symptoms of Acute Intoxication Convulsions, myoclonus, biliary tract spasm, coma, miosis

When to Transport to Hospital Transport patients with any exposure

Warnings/Precautions Sufentanil can cause severely compromised apnea; use with caution in patients with head injuries, hepatic or renal impairment or with pulmonary disease; sufentanil shares the toxic potential of opiate agonists, precaution of opiate agonist therapy should be observed; rapid I.V. infusion may result in skeletal muscle and chest wall rigidity → impaired ventilation → respiratory distress/arrest; inject slowly over 3-5 minutes; nondepolarizing skeletal muscle relaxant may be required

Adverse Reactions

>10%:
Cardiovascular: Bradycardia, hypotension
Central nervous system: Drowsiness
Gastrointestinal: Nausea, vomiting
Respiratory: Respiratory depression

1% to 10%:
Cardiovascular: Cardiac arrhythmias, orthostatic hypotension
Central nervous system: Confusion, CNS depression
Gastrointestinal: Biliary tract spasm
Ocular: Blurred vision

Reference Range Peak serum sufentanil levels are about 11 μg/L 10 minutes after I.V. administration of 1.5 μg/kg of the drug

Dosage Forms Injection: 50 mcg/mL (1 mL, 2 mL, 5 mL)

Specific References

Scholz J, Steinfath M, and Schulz M, "Clinical Pharmacokinetics of Alfentanil, Fentanyl and Sufentanil," *Clin Pharmacokinet*, 1996, 31(4):275-92.

Sulfamethoprim® see Co-Trimoxazole on page 168

Sulfamethoxazole and Trimethoprim see Co-Trimoxazole on page 168

Sulfatrim® see Co-Trimoxazole on page 168

Sulfatrim® DS see Co-Trimoxazole on page 168

Sulfisoxazole and Erythromycin see Erythromycin and Sulfisoxazole on page 228

Sulfite see Sulfite Food Poisoning on this page

Sulfite Food Poisoning

Synonyms Ammonium Sulfite; Calcium Sulfite; Metabisulfites; Potassium Metabisulfite; Sodium Bisulfite; Sodium Metabisulfite; Sodium Sulfite; Sulfite; Sulfur Dioxide

Commonly Found In Sausages, fruits, vegetables, wine, beer, soft drinks, bronchodilator aerosols, injectable preparation of metoclopramide, epinephrine, aminophylline, photography, metal lubricants, lidocaine, dexamethasone, phenylephrine, isoproterenol, dopamine

Mechanism of Toxic Action Preservative in food as an antioxidant; can cause type I hypersensitivity reaction due to a cholinergic reflex mechanism. Onset of symptoms: Within 1 hour

Signs and Symptoms of Acute Intoxication Nausea, watery diarrhea, abdominal cramps, hypotension, wheezing, flushing, sweating, tachycardia, seizures, vomiting, rash, hand eczema

When to Transport to Hospital Transport any symptomatic patient

Overdosage/Treatment Decontamination: Dilute with 4-8 oz of milk or water

Adverse Reactions Cardiovascular: Sinus tachycardia

Additional Information Primary route of exposure is by ingestion, inhalation, or intravenous; minimum dose for CNS toxicity is 6 mg/kg

Specific References

Dalton-Bunnow MF, "Sulfite Content of Drug Products," *Am J Hosp Pharm*, 1985, 42(10):2196-201.

Sulfur Acid see Sulfuric Acid *on this page*
Sulfur Dioxide see Sulfite Food Poisoning *on previous page*

Sulfuric Acid

Synonyms Battery Acid; Oil of Vitrial; Sulfur Acid; Vitriol Brown Oil

UN Number 1832

Commonly Found In Automotive batteries; used in fur and leather industries; component in smog; major component in acid rain; formed from sulfur trioxide and water

Use In the manufacture of acetic acid, hydrochloric acid, hydrolysis of cellulose; used for metal cleaning

Mechanism of Toxic Action Acid oxidizer; corrosive to the skin, eyes, mucous membranes, gastrointestinal and respiratory tract; chars tissue by removing water

Toxicodynamics/kinetics

Absorption: Can be absorbed

Metabolism: Dissociates into hydronium and sulfate

Signs and Symptoms of Acute Intoxication Dyspnea, discoloration of teeth, corneal or dermal burns, cough, choking, hemoptysis/hematemesis; esophageal/gastric burns are rare

When to Transport to Hospital Transport patients with any exposure

Overdosage/Treatment Decontamination: **Do not** induce emesis. Treat inhalation injuries with supplemental oxygen; activated charcoal is not effective. Dilute with cold milk, cornstarch, or large amounts of cold water. Endoscopy for severe mouth burns.

Adverse Reactions

Cardiovascular: Shock, vascular collapse, chest pain, angina

Gastrointestinal: Gastritis, throat irritation

Renal: Renal failure

Respiratory: Tachypnea, bronchoconstriction, ARDS, laryngeal edema

Additional Information Clear, colorless gas; odorless except when heating (choking odor)

Specific References

Penner GE, "Acid Ingestion: Toxicology and Treatment," *Ann Emerg Med*, 1980, 9(7):374-9.

Sulindac (sul IN dak)

U.S. Brand Names Clinoril®

Canadian Brand Names Apo-Sulin®; Novo-Sundac®

Therapeutic Category Analgesic, Non-narcotic; Nonsteroidal Anti-Inflammatory Agent (NSAID)

Use Management of inflammatory disease, rheumatoid disorders; acute gouty arthritis; structurally similar to indomethacin but acts like aspirin; safest NSAID for use in mild renal impairment

Usual Dosage Maximum therapeutic response may not be realized for up to 3 weeks. Oral:

Children: Dose not established

Adults: 150-200 mg twice daily or 300-400 mg once daily; not to exceed 400 mg/day

Mechanism of Action Inhibits prostaglandin synthesis by decreasing the activity of the enzyme, cyclo-oxygenase, which results in decreased formation of prostaglandin precursors

Pharmacodynamics/kinetics

Absorption: Oral: 90% from gastrointestinal tract

Metabolism: Prodrug requiring metabolic activation; hepatic metabolism to sulfide metabolite (active) for therapeutic effects; also metabolized in the liver to sulfone metabolites (inactive)

Half-life:
Parent: 7 hours
Active metabolite: 18 hours

Time to peak serum concentration:
Fasting: Within 2 hours
With food: 3-4 hours

Signs and Symptoms of Acute Intoxication Nausea, chills, azotemia, purpura, wheezing, nephrotic syndrome, nephritis, gastrointestinal bleeding, gastritis; leukemoid reaction, leukocytosis, photosensitivity, cognitive dysfunction, toxic epidermal necrolysis, thrombocytopenia, coagulopathy, vomiting, insomnia, hyperthermia, ototoxicity; tinnitus, drowsiness; severe poisoning can manifest with coma, seizures, renal and or hepatic failure, hypotension, respiratory depression, alopecia

When to Transport to Hospital Transport any symptomatic patient or ingestions over 1 g

Warnings/Precautions Use with caution in patients with peptic ulcer disease, gastrointestinal bleeding, bleeding abnormalities, impaired renal or hepatic function, congestive heart failure, hypertension, and patients receiving anticoagulants

Adverse Reactions
>10%:
Central nervous system: Dizziness
Dermatologic: Rash
Gastrointestinal: Abdominal cramps, heartburn, indigestion, nausea
1% to 10%:
Central nervous system: Headache, nervousness
Dermatologic: Itching
Endocrine & metabolic: Fluid retention
Gastrointestinal: Vomiting
Otic: Tinnitus

Reference Range Peak plasma levels after a 200 mg oral dose: ~4 mg/L (parent compound); 3 mg/L (sulfide metabolite); and 2 mg/L (sulfone metabolite)

Drug Interactions Aspirin decreases serum concentrations probably by protein-binding displacement; there is an increased bleeding potential with concomitant warfarin therapy; may increase lithium and methotrexate concentrations by decreasing renal clearance; may decrease diuretic and hypotensive effects of thiazides, loop diuretics, ACE inhibitors, and beta-blockers; may increase nephrotoxicity of cyclosporine

Dosage Forms Tablet: 150 mg, 200 mg

Additional Information Structurally similar to indomethacin but acts like aspirin; associated with the highest incidence of upper gastrointestinal bleeds among NSAIDs; safest NSAID for use in mild renal impairment; maximum therapeutic response may not be realized for up to 3 weeks

Specific References
Hoppmann RA, Peden JG, and Ober SK, "Central Nervous System Side Effects of Nonsteroidal Anti-inflammatory Drugs. Aseptic Meningitis, Psychosis, and Cognitive Dysfunction," *Arch Intern Med*, 1991, 151(7):1309-13.

Sulthiame (sul THYE ame)

Synonyms RP10248; Sultiame; Tetrahydro-2-para-sulfamoylphenyl-1,2-thiazine 1,1 dioxide

U.S. Brand Names Elisal®; Ospolot®
(Continued)

Sulthiame *(Continued)*

Therapeutic Category Anticonvulsant
Impairment Potential Yes
Use Anticonvulsant agent used for generalized seizures temporal lobe seizures, myoclonic or focal seizures; not useful for absence seizures
Usual Dosage Oral:
 Children: Initial: 3-5 mg/kg/day; can increase daily dose: 10-15 mg/kg; maximum daily dose: 1.2 g
 Adults: Initial: 100 mg 2 times/day; can be increased to 200 mg 3 times/day
Mechanism of Action Antiepileptic agent and a weak carbonic anhydrase inhibitor; a synthetic sulfonamide
Pharmacodynamics/kinetics
 Protein binding: 29%
 Half-life: 30 hours
 Elimination: Renal
Signs and Symptoms of Acute Intoxication Drowsiness, catatonia, hyperreflexia, hypotension, prolonged extensor plantar reflexes, vomiting, crystalluria (in acidic urine)
When to Transport to Hospital Transport any symptomatic patient
Warnings/Precautions Use with caution in patients with renal impairment
Adverse Reactions
 Central nervous system: Headache, lethargy, ataxia, vertigo
 Genitourinary: Crystalluria
 Neuromuscular & skeletal: Paresthesia
 Ocular: Ptosis
 Respiratory: Hyperpnea, dyspnea
Reference Range Therapeutic plasma level is up to 12 µg/mL; severe toxicity is associated with plasma levels over 30 µg/mL
Drug Interactions By inhibiting its metabolism, sulthiamine can raise phenytoin serum levels
Dosage Forms
 Suspension: 50 mg/5 mL
 Tablet: 50 mg, 200 mg
Specific References
 Rockley G, "Attempted Suicide With Sulthiamine," *Br Med J*, 1975, 2:632.

Sultiame see Sulthiame *on previous page*

Sumatriptan Succinate *(SOO ma trip tan SUKS i nate)*

U.S. Brand Names Imigran®; Imitrex®
Therapeutic Category Antimigraine Agent
Impairment Potential Yes
Use May be useful to treat cyclic vomiting; acute treatment of migraine with or without aura
 Unlabeled use: Cluster headaches
Usual Dosage Adults:
 S.C.: 6 mg; a second injection may be administered at least 1 hour after the initial dose, but not more than 2 injections in a 24-hour period
 Oral: Recommended dose: 25 mg; maximum single dose: 100 mg; maximum 24-hour dose: 300 mg
 Cyclic vomiting: S.C.: 6 mg
Mechanism of Action Selective agonist for serotonin (5HT, ID subtype receptor) in cranial arteries to cause vasoconstriction and reduces sterile inflammation associated with antidromic neuronal transmission correlating with relief of migraine

Pharmacodynamics/kinetics After S.C. administration:
Metabolism: Hepatic (80%)
Half-life:
Distribution: 15 minutes
Terminal: 115 minutes
Time to peak serum concentration: 5-20 minutes

Signs and Symptoms of Acute Intoxication Chest pain/angina, numbness, hypertension; fatalities due to myocardial infarction usually occur 3 or more hours after treatment

When to Transport to Hospital Transport any patient exhibiting any cardio-pulmonary symptoms

Warnings/Precautions Use with caution in elderly, patients with hepatic or renal impairment; may cause mild, transient elevation of blood pressure; may cause coronary vasospasm

Adverse Reactions
>10%:
Central nervous system: Dizziness
Endocrine & metabolic: Hot flashes
Local: Injection site reaction
Neuromuscular & skeletal: Paresthesia
1% to 10%:
Cardiovascular: Tightness in chest
Central nervous system: Drowsiness, headache
Dermatologic: Burning sensation
Gastrointestinal: Abdominal discomfort, mouth discomfort
Neuromuscular & skeletal: Myalgia, numbness, weakness, neck pain, jaw discomfort
Miscellaneous: Diaphoresis

Reference Range Therapeutic range: 18-60 ng/mL

Drug Interactions Increased toxicity: Ergot-containing drugs; avoid concomitant use with lithium and irreversible monoamine oxidase inhibitors; use with caution with concomitant serotonin reuptake inhibitor therapy

Dosage Forms
Injection: 12 mg/mL (0.5 mL, 2 mL)
Tablet: 25 mg, 50 mg

Additional Information May increase growth hormone level; oral dose of 100 mg is investigational; oral sumatriptan (100 mg) may prevent headache recurrence; may exacerbate depression

Specific References
Visser WH, Jaspers NM, de Vriend RH, et al, "Chest Symptoms After Sumatriptan: A Two-Year Clinical Practice Review in 735 Consecutive Migraine Patients," *Cephalalgia*, 1996, 16:554-9.

Sumycin® Oral see Tetracycline *on page 568*
Super Blue see Tripelennamine *on page 601*
Super Nail Glue Off® see Acetonitrile *on page 26*
Super Nail Off® see Acetonitrile *on page 26*
Supeudol® see Oxycodone *on page 452*
Suppress® [OTC] see Dextromethorphan *on page 187*
Surem® see Nitrazepam *on page 435*
Surmontil® see Trimipramine *on page 599*
Sustachron® see Nitroglycerin *on page 437*
Sustaire® see Theophylline Salts *on page 571*
Swim-Ear® [OTC] see Boric Acid *on page 80*
Symmetrel® see Amantadine *on page 37*
Symoron® see Methadone *on page 379*

Synacol® CF [OTC] *see* Guaifenesin and Dextromethorphan *on page 271*

Synacort® *see* Hydrocortisone *on page 297*

Syracol-CF® [OTC] *see* Guaifenesin and Dextromethorphan *on page 271*

Tabernathe Iboga Baill

Related Information

Controlled Substances - Uses and Effects *on page 741*

Abuse Potential Yes

Impairment Potential Yes

Mechanism of Toxic Action African shrub which contains ibogaine (or igobine) which is an indole alkaloid that acts as an interrupter of psychostimulant or opiate addiction; decreases extracellular dopamine levels

Pharmacodynamics/kinetics

Distribution (in primate model): 7 L/kg;

Metabolism: To noribogaine in liver by, demethylation

Bioavailability (in primate model): 8%

When to Transport to Hospital Transport any symptomatic patient

Adverse Reactions Central nervous system: Chewing roots can cause excitement, confusion, hallucinations

Additional Information Can potentiate analgesic effect of morphine; after a 25 mg/kg dose, peak serum ibogaine concentration is almost 200 ng/mL (peak noribogaine level: 600 ng/mL); brand name of ibogaine: Endabuse® (NIH - 10567)

Specific References

Hearn WL, Pablo J, Hime GW, et al, "Identification and Quantitation of Ibogaine and an O-Demethylated Metabolite in Brain and Biological Fluids Using Gas Chromatography-Mass Spectrometry," *J Anal Toxicol*, 1995, 19:427-34.

Tabun *see* Nerve Gases *on page 426*

Tagamet® *see* Cimetidine *on page 147*

Taktic® *see* Amitraz *on page 39*

Talbutal *see* Barbiturates, Quantitative, Blood *on page 64*

Talwin® *see* Pentazocine *on page 463*

Talwin® NX *see* Pentazocine *on page 463*

Tamine® [OTC] *see* Brompheniramine and Phenylpropanolamine *on page 85*

Tanac® [OTC] *see* Benzocaine *on page 70*

Tanoral® Tablet *see* Chlorpheniramine, Pyrilamine, and Phenylephrine *on page 138*

Tanyl® *see* Fentanyl *on page 247*

Taractan® *see* Chlorprothixene *on page 141*

Tarasan® *see* Chlorprothixene *on page 141*

Tavegil® *see* Clemastine *on page 149*

Tavist® *see* Clemastine *on page 149*

Tavist®-1 [OTC] *see* Clemastine *on page 149*

Tavist-D® *see* Clemastine and Phenylpropanolamine *on page 150*

3TC *see* Lamivudine *on page 333*

TCA *see* Trichloroethane *on page 594*

TCE *see* Trichloroethane *on page 594*

T'Chai from the Sea *see* Kombucha *on page 330*

TCM *see* Chloroform *on page 129*

TCN *see* Tetracycline *on page 568*

Teamsters' Tea *see* Ephedra *on page 219*

Tebamide® *see* Trimethobenzamide *on page 599*

Teekwass *see* Kombucha *on page 330*

Tega-Cert® [OTC] see Dimenhydrinate on page 203

Tegretol® see Carbamazepine on page 103

Tegrin®-HC see Hydrocortisone on page 297

Telachlor® see Chlorpheniramine on page 132

Teldane® see Terfenadine on page 563

Teldanex® see Terfenadine on page 563

Teldrin® [OTC] see Chlorpheniramine on page 132

Telesol® see Oxitriptan on page 451

Teline® Oral see Tetracycline on page 568

Tema³® see Temazepam on this page

Temaril® see Trimeprazine on page 598

Temaz® see Temazepam on this page

Temazepam (te MAZ e pam)

Related Information
Controlled Substances - Uses and Effects on page 741

Synonyms 3-hydroxydiazepam

U.S. Brand Names Euphypnos®; Levanxol®; Normison®; Restoril®; Somaz®; Tema³®; Temaz®; Tenso®

Therapeutic Category Benzodiazepine

Abuse Potential Yes

Impairment Potential Yes; A single oral 20 mg dose at bedtime may cause driving impairment the next morning. Brief or extended periods of exposure are less likely to cause driving impairment in the elderly as compared with the longer half-life benzodiazepines.

Betts TA and Birtle J, "Effect of Two Hypnotic Drugs on Actual Driving Performances Next Morning," Br Med J, 1982, 285(6345):852.

Use Treatment of anxiety and as an adjunct in the treatment of depression; also may be used in the management of panic attacks; transient insomnia and sleep latency

Usual Dosage Adults: Oral: 15-30 mg at bedtime; 15 mg in elderly or debilitated patients

Mechanism of Action Benzodiazepine anxiolytic sedative that produces CNS depression at the subcortical level, except at high doses, whereby it works at the cortical level

Pharmacodynamics/kinetics
Onset of hypnotic effect: 30-60 minutes

Absorption: Nearly complete through gastrointestinal tract; slower through rectal route

Metabolism: In the liver to oxazepam

Half-life: 10-15 hours

Time to peak serum concentration: Within 2-3 hours

Signs and Symptoms of Acute Intoxication Somnolence, diarrhea, confusion, night terrors, hyporeflexia, cognitive dysfunction, coma, hypoactive reflexes, dyspnea, hypotension, slurred speech, ataxia, hypothermia, gaze nystagmus

When to Transport to Hospital Transport any pediatric exposure, any symptomatic patient, or any ingestion over 60 mg

Adverse Reactions
>10%:

Cardiovascular: Tachycardia, chest pain

Central nervous system: Drowsiness, fatigue, ataxia, lightheadedness, memory impairment, insomnia, anxiety, depression, headache

Dermatologic: Rash

Endocrine & metabolic: Decreased libido

(Continued)

Temazepam (Continued)

Gastrointestinal: Xerostomia, constipation, diarrhea, decreased salivation, nausea, vomiting, increased or decreased appetite

Neuromuscular & skeletal: Dysarthria

Ocular: Blurred vision

Miscellaneous: Diaphoresis

1% to 10%:

Cardiovascular: Syncope, hypotension

Central nervous system: Confusion, nervousness, dizziness, akathisia

Dermatologic: Dermatitis

Gastrointestinal: Increased salivation, weight gain or loss

Neuromuscular & skeletal: Rigidity, tremor, muscle cramps

Otic: Tinnitus

Respiratory: Nasal congestion, hyperventilation

Reference Range Therapeutic: 26 ng/mL after 24 hours; can be quantified by high performance liquid chromatography; postmortem levels >88.5 ng/mL have been correlated with fatalities

Drug Interactions CNS depressants, alcohol, tricyclic antidepressants, unlike other benzodiazepines, there is minimal interaction with cimetidine, ranitidine, or oral contraceptives

Dosage Forms Capsule: 15 mg, 30 mg

Specific References

Betts TA and Birtle J, "Effect of Two Hypnotic Drugs on Actual Driving Performances Next Morning," *Br Med J*, 1982, 285(6345):852.

Grahame-Smith DG, "Misuse of Temazepam," *Br Med J (Clin Res)*, 1991, 302(6786):1210.

Wesnes K and Warburton DM, "A Comparison of Temazepam and Flurazepam in Terms of Sleep Quality and Residual Changes in Performance," *Neuropsychobiology*, 1984, 34(11):1601-4.

Temazin® Cold Syrup [OTC] see Chlorpheniramine and Phenylpropanolamine on page 134

Temodal® see Quazepam on page 518

Tempra® [OTC] see Acetaminophen on page 20

Tenavoid® see Meprobamate on page 371

Tenormin® see Atenolol on page 60

Tensin® see Spironolactone on page 544

Tensium® see Diazepam on page 189

Tenso® see Temazepam on previous page

Tenuate® see Diethylpropion on page 196

Tenuate® Dospan® see Diethylpropion on page 196

Teoptic® see Carteolol on page 115

Tepanil® see Diethylpropion on page 196

Terabol® see Methyl Bromide on page 393

Terazosin (ter AY zoe sin)

U.S. Brand Names Heitrin®; Hytrin®; Hytrinex®; Vasocard®

Therapeutic Category Alpha-Adrenergic Blocking Agent

Impairment Potential Yes

Use Management of mild to moderate hypertension; benign prostate hypertrophy

Usual Dosage Adults: Oral: 1 mg; slowly increase dose to achieve desired blood pressure or to desired urinary flow rates (BPH), up to 20 mg/day maximum

Mechanism of Action An alpha$_1$-specific blocking agent with minimal alpha$_2$ effects; this allows peripheral postsynaptic blockade, with the resultant decrease in arterial tone, while preserving the negative feedback loop which is mediated by the peripheral presynaptic alpha$_2$-receptors (similar in action to prazosin but longer duration of action)

Pharmacodynamics/kinetics

Onset of action: 15 minutes

Duration: 24 hours

Absorption: Oral: Rapidly absorbed

Metabolism: Extensive in the liver to yield piperazine

Bioavailability: ~90%

Half-life: 9.2-12 hours

Time to peak serum concentration: Within 60 minutes

Signs and Symptoms of Acute Intoxication Hypotension, dyspnea, drowsiness, syncope, night terrors, impotence, hypothermia, shock

When to Transport to Hospital Transport any pediatric exposure or any symptomatic patient

Warnings/Precautions Syncope and hypotension (orthostatic) frequently occur with the first dose; use with caution in patients with confirmed or suspected coronary artery disease

Adverse Reactions

>10%:

Cardiovascular: Orthostatic hypotension

Central nervous system: Dizziness, lightheadedness, drowsiness, headache, malaise

1% to 10%:

Cardiovascular: Edema, palpitations

Central nervous system: Fatigue, nervousness

Gastrointestinal: Xerostomia

Genitourinary: Urinary incontinence

Reference Range Single dose of 5 mg produces a peak concentration of 45 µg/L at 2 hours

Drug Interactions Ibuprofen

Dosage Forms Tablet: 1 mg, 2 mg, 5 mg, 10 mg

Specific References

Sonders RC, "Pharmacokinetics of Terazosin," *Am J Med*, 1986, 80(Suppl 5B):20-4.

Terbutaline (ter BYOO ta leen)

U.S. Brand Names Brethaire®; Brethine®; Bricanyl®

Therapeutic Category Adrenergic Agonist Agent

Use Bronchodilator in reversible airway obstruction and bronchial asthma; management of preterm labor

Usual Dosage

Children <12 years:

Oral: Initial: 0.05 mg/kg/dose 3 times/day, increased gradually as required; maximum: 0.15 mg/kg/dose 3-4 times/day or a total of 5 mg/24 hours

S.C.: 0.005-0.01 mg/kg/dose to a maximum of 0.3 mg/dose every 15-20 minutes for 3 doses

Nebulization: 0.1-0.3 mg/kg/dose up to a maximum of 10 mg/dose every 4-6 hours

Inhalation: 1-2 inhalations every 4-6 hours

Children >12 years and Adults:

Oral:

12-15 years: 2.5 mg every 6 hours 3 times/day; not to exceed 7.5 mg in 24 hours

(Continued)

Terbutaline *(Continued)*

>15 years: 5 mg/dose every 6 hours 3 times/day; if side effects occur, reduce dose to 2.5 mg every 6 hours; not to exceed 15 mg in 24 hours

S.C.: 0.25 mg/dose repeated in 15-30 minutes for one time only; a total dose of 0.5 mg should not be exceeded within a 4-hour period

Nebulization: 0.1-0.3 mg/kg/dose every 4-6 hours

Inhalation: 2 inhalations every 4-6 hours; wait 1 minute between inhalations

Mechanism of Action Relaxes bronchial smooth muscle by action on beta$_2$-receptors with less effect on heart rate

Pharmacodynamics/kinetics S.C. doses are more bioavailable and of quicker onset than oral doses

Onset of action:

Inhalation: 5-30 minutes

Oral: Within 60-120 minutes

Parenteral: Within 15 minutes

S.C.: 6-15 minutes

Duration:

Inhalation: 3-6 hours

Oral: 4-8 hours

Parenteral: 1.5-4 hours

Absorption: 33% to 50% through gastrointestinal tract

Metabolism: In the liver to inactive sulfate conjugates

Half-life: 11-16 hours

Signs and Symptoms of Acute Intoxication Convulsions, nausea, hypokalemia, myoglobinuria, hepatitis, insomnia, hypocalcemia, rhabdomyolysis, vomiting, arrhythmias, hyperglycemia, chest pain

When to Transport to Hospital Transport any symptomatic patient

Warnings/Precautions Paradoxical bronchoconstriction may occur with excessive use, if it occurs, discontinue terbutaline immediately; use with caution in patients with diabetes mellitus, hypertension, hyperthyroidism, history of seizures, or cardiac disease

Adverse Reactions

>10%:

Central nervous system: Nervousness, restlessness

Neuromuscular & skeletal: Trembling

1% to 10%:

Cardiovascular: Tachycardia, hypertension

Central nervous system: Dizziness, drowsiness, headache, insomnia

Gastrointestinal: Xerostomia, nausea, vomiting, bad taste in mouth

Neuromuscular & skeletal: Muscle cramps, weakness

Miscellaneous: Diaphoresis

Reference Range Peak plasma level after a 0.75 mg S.C. dose: ~10 µg/L 30 minutes after injection

Drug Interactions MAO inhibitors, tricyclic antidepressants, beta-receptor blocking agents

Dosage Forms

Aerosol, oral: 0.2 mg/actuation (10.5 g)

Injection: 1 mg/mL (1 mL)

Tablet: 2.5 mg, 5 mg

Additional Information Used unofficially to delay delivery in preterm labor; has short-lived clinical effectiveness with development of tolerance with chronic use

Specific References

Lee DC, "Terbutaline Sulfate Overdose," *Ann Emerg Med*, 1995, 26(1):107-8.

Terfenadine (ter FEN a deen)

U.S. Brand Names Alergist®; Allerplus®; Cyater®; Rapidal®; Seldane®; Teldane®; Teldanex®; Ternadin®; Triludan®

Therapeutic Category Antihistamine

Impairment Potential Yes; Doses over 240 mg can impair driving ability (brake reaction time)

Bhatti JZ and Hindmarch I, "The Effects of Terfenadine With and Without Alcohol on an Aspect of Car Driving Performance," *Clin Exp Allergy*, 1989, 19(6):609-11.

Use Perennial and seasonal allergic rhinitis and other allergic symptoms including rash; has drying effect in patients with asthma

Usual Dosage Oral:

Children:

3-6 years: 15 mg twice daily

6-12 years: 30 mg twice daily

Children >12 years and Adults: 60 mg twice daily

Maximum daily dose: 120 mg, doses >1 g can produce arrhythmias

Mechanism of Action Competes with histamine for H_1-receptor sites on effector cells in the gastrointestinal tract, blood vessels, and respiratory tract; binds to lung receptors significantly greater than it binds to cerebellar receptors, resulting in a reduced sedative potential; lacks anticholinergic activity

Pharmacodynamics/kinetics

Duration of antihistaminic effect: Up to 12 hours

Protein binding: 97%

Metabolism: Extensive first-pass metabolism; metabolized in the liver to an active carboxylic acid metabolite and an inactive piperidine-carbinol metabolite

Half-life: 16-22 hours

Time to peak serum concentration: Within 1-2 hours

Elimination: Primarily excreted in feces (60%) and secondarily in urine (40%)

Signs and Symptoms of Acute Intoxication Nausea, confusion, sedation, insomnia, prolonged Q-T interval, torsade de pointes, seizures

When to Transport to Hospital Transport any pediatric (<3 years of age) exposure, any symptomatic patient, or any ingestion over 120 mg

Warnings/Precautions Safety and efficacy in children <12 years of age have not been established; use with caution in patients with a history of cardiac conduction disturbances or cardiac arrhythmias, or those receiving antiarrhythmic medication

Adverse Reactions 1% to 10%:

Central nervous system: Headache, fatigue, nervousness, dizziness

Gastrointestinal: Appetite increase, weight gain, nausea, diarrhea, abdominal pain, xerostomia

Neuromuscular & skeletal: Arthralgia

Respiratory: Pharyngitis

Reference Range Terfenadine levels >10 ng/mL consistent with toxicity; carboxylic acid metabolite level between 250-300 ng/mL associated with steady-state dosing (60 mg twice daily)

Drug Interactions

Serious cardiac events have occurred with elevated terfenadine levels, which may occur with the use of ketoconazole, itraconazole, fluconazole, metronidazole, miconazole, erythromycin, troleandomycin, clarithromycin, fluoxetine, sotalol, troleandomycin, azithromycin, cimetidine, fluoxetine, bepridil, sotalol; odds ratio for Q-T_c prolongation with concomitant erythromycin and terfenadine use is 2.33

(Continued)

Terfenadine *(Continued)*

Increased levels/toxicity of carbamazepine; increased toxicity of carbamazepine with displacement of carbamazepine from protein-binding sites by terfenadine

Prolonged Q-T interval can occur with concomitant terfenadine/fluoxetine therapy

Dosage Forms Tablet: 60 mg

Additional Information Causes less drowsiness than other antihistamines; patients on medications that prolong the Q-T interval should be on a cardiac monitor when starting this drug; concomitant administration with grapefruit juice can result in an increase in bioavailability of terfenadine and thus a prolonged Q-T interval on EKG

Specific References

Burns M and Moskowitz H, "Prescription Drugs and Risk for the Road User: Three Studies of Antihistamines," *The Vulnerable Road User,* New Delhi: MacMillan India, 1991, 69-72.

Moskowitz H and Burns M, "Effects of Terfenadine, Diphenhydramine, and Placebo on Skills Performance," *Cutis* 1988, 42(4A):14-8.

Terfenadine and Pseudoephedrine

(ter FEN a deen & soo doe e FED rin)

U.S. Brand Names Seldane-D®

Therapeutic Category Antihistamine/Decongestant Combination

Abuse Potential Yes

Impairment Potential Yes; Terfenadine doses over 240 mg can impair driving ability (brake reaction time)

Bhatti JZ and Hindmarch I, "The Effects of Terfenadine With and Without Alcohol on an Aspect of Car Driving Performance," *Clin Exp Allergy,* 1989, 19(6):609-11.

Dosage Forms Tablet: Terfenadine 60 mg and pseudoephedrine hydrochloride 120 mg

Terfluzin® *see* Trifluoperazine *on page 596*

Termine® *see* Phentermine *on page 478*

Ternadin® *see* Terfenadine *on previous page*

Téronac® *see* Mazindol *on page 360*

Terpin Hydrate and Codeine (TER pin HYE drate & KOE deen)

Synonyms ETH and C

Therapeutic Category Antitussive/Expectorant

Abuse Potential Yes

Impairment Potential Yes

Dosage Forms Elixir: Terpin hydrate 85 mg and codeine 10 mg per 5 mL with alcohol 42.5%

Testo-Enant® *see* Testosterone *on this page*

Testosterone (tes TOS ter one)

Related Information

Controlled Substances - Uses and Effects *on page 741*

Synonyms Aqueous Testosterone; Trans-Testosterone

U.S. Brand Names Andriol®; Andro-Cyp® Injection; Andro® Injection; Andro-L.A.® Injection; Andronate® Injection; Andropository® Injection; Delatest® Injection; Delatestryl®; Depotest® Injection; Depo®-Testosterone Injection;

Duratest® Injection; Durathate® Injection; Everone® Injection; Histerone® Injection; Lontanyl®; Malogex®; Restandol®; Testo-Enant®; Testoviron®; Testovis®; Undestor®; Virilon®; Virormone®

Therapeutic Category Androgen

Abuse Potential Yes

Use Androgen replacement therapy in the treatment of delayed male puberty; postpartum breast pain and engorgement; inoperable breast cancer; male hypogonadism

Usual Dosage I.M.:

Delayed puberty: Children: 40-50 mg/m²/dose (cypionate or enanthate) monthly for 6 months

Male hypogonadism: 50-400 mg every 2-4 weeks
Initiation of pubertal growth: 40-50 mg/m²/dose (cypionate or enanthate) monthly until the growth rate falls to prepubertal levels (~5 cm/year)
During terminal growth phase: 100 mg/m²/dose (cypionate or enanthate) monthly until growth ceases
Maintenance virilizing dose: 100 mg/m²/dose (cypionate or enanthate) twice monthly or 50-400 mg/dose every 2-4 weeks

Inoperable breast cancer: Adults: 200-400 mg every 2-4 weeks

Hypogonadism: Adults:
Testosterone or testosterone propionate: 10-25 mg 2-3 times/week
Testosterone cypionate or enanthate: 50-400 mg every 2-4 weeks
Postpubertal cryptorchism: Testosterone or testosterone propionate: 10-25 mg 2-3 times/week

Mechanism of Action Principal endogenous androgen responsible for promoting the growth and development of the male sex organs and maintaining secondary sex characteristics in androgen-deficient males

Pharmacodynamics/kinetics

Absorption: From skin, gastrointestinal tract, oral mucosa
Duration of effect: Based upon the route of administration and which testosterone ester is used; the cypionate and enanthate esters have the longest duration, up to 2-4 weeks after I.M. administration
Metabolism: In the liver to androsterone and etiocholanolone; methylation or alkylation at the 17-position of testosterone reduces hepatic metabolism
Half-life: 10-100 minutes

Signs and Symptoms of Acute Intoxication Leukopenia or neutropenia (agranulocytosis, granulocytopenia); hirsutism, gynecomastia, hypertrichosis, oligospermia, jaundice, hypertension, depression, hypercalcemia, impotence, cholestatic jaundice

When to Transport to Hospital Transport any patient with change in mental status

Warnings/Precautions Perform radiographic examination of the hand and wrist every 6 months to determine the rate of bone maturation; may accelerate bone maturation without producing compensating gain in linear growth; has both androgenic and anabolic activity, the anabolic action may enhance hypoglycemia

Adverse Reactions

>10%:
Dermatologic: Acne
Endocrine & metabolic: Menstrual problems (amenorrhea), virilism, breast soreness
Genitourinary: Epididymitis, priapism, bladder irritability

1% to 10%:
Cardiovascular: Flushing, edema
(Continued)

Testosterone *(Continued)*

Central nervous system: Excitation, aggressive behavior, sleeplessness, anxiety, mental depression, headache

Dermatologic: Hirsutism (increase in pubic hair growth)

Gastrointestinal: Nausea, vomiting, GI irritation

Genitourinary: Prostatic hypertrophy, prostatic carcinoma, impotence, testicular atrophy

Hepatic: Hepatic dysfunction

Reference Range

Testosterone, urine:

Male: 100-1500 ng/24 hours

Female: 100-500 ng/24 hours

Normal serum ranges (male): 12.1-35.7 nmol/L

Normal ratio of testosterone to epitestosterone: <6

Injected agents can be detectable in urine for 2 months while oral agents can be detectable for 2 weeks

Dosage Forms

Injection:

Aqueous suspension: 25 mg/mL (10 mL, 30 mL); 50 mg/mL (10 mL, 30 mL); 100 mg/mL (10 mL, 30 mL)

In oil, as cypionate: 100 mg/mL (1 mL, 10 mL); 200 mg/mL (1 mL, 10 mL)

In oil, as enanthate: 100 mg/mL (5 mL, 10 mL); 200 mg/mL (5 mL, 10 mL)

In oil, as propionate: 50 mg/mL (10 mL, 30 mL); 100 mg/mL (10 mL, 30 mL)

Specific References

Scott DM, Wagner JC, and Barlow TW, "Anabolic Steroid Use Among Adolescents in Nebraska Schools," *Am J Health Syst Pharm*, 1996, 53:2068-72.

Testosterone and Estradiol *see* Estradiol and Testosterone *on page 229*

Testoviron® *see* Testosterone *on page 564*

Testovis® *see* Testosterone *on page 564*

Testred® *see* Methyltestosterone *on page 398*

Tetra *see* Tetrachloroethylene *on next page*

Tetracap® Oral *see* Tetracycline *on page 568*

Tetrachloroethane

Synonyms Acetylene Tetrachloride; 1,1,2,2-Tetrachloroethane

UN Number 1702

U.S. Brand Names Bonoform®; Cellon®; Westron®

Abuse Potential Yes

Impairment Potential Yes

Use Primarily as a solvent in metal cleaning procedures, paint removers, varnishes, photographic films, and oil or fat extractant; production of trichloroethylene, tetrachloroethylene, and 1,2-dichloroethylene

Mechanism of Toxic Action Central nervous system depression; direct effect on neuronal membrane and hepatotoxic effects can occur through lipid peroxidation

Toxicodynamics/kinetics

Absorption: Through inhalation (97%), oral, and dermal routes

Metabolism: Hepatic to glyoxylic acid and oxyalic acid, tetrachloroethylene is also a metabolite

Elimination: Through lungs, feces, and urine

When to Transport to Hospital Transport any oral ingestion or any symptomatic patient

Overdosage/Treatment Decontamination:

Dermal: Remove contaminated clothing; wash with soap and water

Ocular: Irrigate with saline

Oral: Dilute with milk or water

Adverse Reactions

Cardiovascular: Hypotension

Central nervous system: Confusion, delirium, coma

Gastrointestinal: Nausea, vomiting, anorexia (gastrointestinal effects seen with exposure levels of 116 ppm for 10-30 minutes), diarrhea

Hematologic: Leukocytosis

Hepatic: Fatty degeneration of liver, centrilobular hepatic necrosis

Ocular: Lacrimation, eye irritation

Miscellaneous: Multiple chemical sensitivity syndrome

Reference Range Toxic effects are predicted to occur at blood tetrachloroethane levels >1.1 ng/mL (1.1 ppt)

Specific References

U.S. Department of Health and Human Services, "Toxicological Profile of 1,1,2,2-Tetrachloroethane," Agency for Toxic Substances and Diseases Registry, August 1994.

1,1,2,2-Tetrachloroethane see Tetrachloroethane on previous page

Tetrachloroethylene

Synonyms PCE; Perchlor; Perclene; Tetra; 1,1,2,2-Tetrachloroethylene

UN Number 1897

Impairment Potential Yes

Use In textile industry for dry cleaning fabric; degreasing; used in the manufacture of freons, antihelminth for animals

Mechanism of Toxic Action CNS depressant, irritant; probable human carcinogen

Toxicodynamics/kinetics

Absorption: Well absorbed in the lungs and gastrointestinal tract; not well absorbed dermally; highly lipid soluble

Half-life:

Oral: 144 hours

Inhalation: 33-72 hours

In adipose tissues: 72 hours

Metabolism: In the liver to trichloroacetic acid and trichloroethanol

Elimination: 80% excreted through the lungs, metabolites excreted renally

Signs and Symptoms of Acute Intoxication Headache, irritability, conjunctival injection, epistaxis, dermatitis, short-term memory deficiency, hepatomegaly, euphoria, ataxia, nausea, cough, sweating

When to Transport to Hospital Transport any oral ingestion or any symptomatic patient

Overdosage/Treatment Decontamination:

Inhalation: Give 100% humidified oxygen

Ocular: Irrigate with saline

Dermal: Remove contaminated clothing; wash with soap and water

Adverse Reactions

Central nervous system: CNS depression

Ocular: Eye irritation at air levels >1000 ppm

Respiratory: Irritation, respiratory depression

Reference Range Tetrachloroethylene serum level of 100 µg/dL and trichloroacetic acid levels in urine of 7 mg/L correlate with weekly exposure of 50 ppm; BEI of 1 mg/L; an oral ingestion of 12-16g in a 6-year-old boy resulted in a blood tetrachloroethylene level of 21 µg/dL 1-hour postingestion; mean blood concentration of tetrachloroethylene following 50 ppm exposure 8 hours daily, 5 days weekly: Estimated to range from 1.6-2.3 mg/L; urinary levels would be ~19 mg/L

Additional Information Clear, colorless; fruity odor of chloroform

(Continued)

Tetrachloroethylene *(Continued)*

Odor threshold: 5-50 ppm

TLV-TWA: 50 ppm; radiopaque. Symptoms occur at 75 ppm.

See table for duration and effect of inhaling vapors.

Dose-Response Relationship for Humans Inhaling Tetrachlorothylene Vapors

Levels in Air	Duration of Exposure	Effect on Nervous System
50 ppm		Odor threshold
100 ppm	7 h	Headache, drowsiness
200 ppm	2 h	Dizziness, uncoordination
600 ppm	10 min	Dizziness, loss of inhibitions
1000 ppm	1-2 min	Marked dizziness, intolerable eye and respiratory tract irritation
1500 ppm	30 min	Coma

U.S. Department of Health and Human Services, 'Hospital Emergency Departments: A Planning Guide for the Management of Contaminated Patients,' *Managing Hazardous Materials Incidents,* Agency for Toxic Substances and Disease Registry, 1995, 2:796.

Specific References

Garnier R, Bédouin J, Pépin G, et al, "Coin-Operated Dry Cleaning Machines May Be Responsible for Acute Tetrachloroethylene Poisoning: Report of 26 Cases Including One Death," *J Toxicol Clin Toxicol*, 1996, 34(2):191-7.

1,1,2,2-Tetrachloroethylene *see* Tetrachloroethylene *on previous page*

Tetrachloromethane *see* Carbon Tetrachloride *on page 113*

Tetraclear® [OTC] *see* Tetrahydrozoline *on next page*

Tetracycline (tet ra SYE kleen)

Synonyms TCN; Tetradecin; Tetraverine

U.S. Brand Names Achromycin®; Achromycin® V Oral; Ala-Tet® Oral; Econo-mycin®; Hexacycline®; Hortetracin®; Imex®; Latycin®; Nor-tet® Oral; Panmycin® Oral; Robitet® Oral; Rotet®; Steclin®; Sumycin® Oral; Teline® Oral; Tetracap® Oral; Tetralan® Oral; Tetralen®; Tetram® Oral; Topicycline® Topical; Tripha-cycline®

Canadian Brand Names Apo-Tetra®; Novo-Tetra®; Nu-Tetra®

Therapeutic Category Antibiotic, Ophthalmic; Antibiotic, Topical; Tetracy-cline Derivative

Use Treatment of susceptible bacterial infections of both gram-positive and gram-negative organisms; also some unusual organisms including *Mycoplasma, Chlamydia,* and *Rickettsia;* may also be used for acne, exacerbations of chronic bronchitis, treatment of "seal finger", *Helicobacter pylori,* and treatment of gonorrhea and syphilis in patients that are allergic to penicillin

Usual Dosage

Children >8 years:

Oral: 25-50 mg/kg/day in divided doses every 6 hours; not to exceed 3 g/day

Ophthalmic:

Suspension: Instill 1-2 drops 2-4 times/day or more often as needed

Ointment: Instill every 2-12 hours

Adults:

Oral: 250-500 mg/dose every 6 hours

Ophthalmic:
  Suspension: Instill 1-2 drops 2-4 times/day or more often as needed
  Ointment: Instill every 2-12 hours
Topical: Apply to affected areas 1-4 times/day

Mechanism of Action Inhibits bacterial protein synthesis by binding with the 30S and possibly the 50S ribosomal subunit(s) of susceptible bacteria; may also cause alterations in the cytoplasmic membrane

Pharmacodynamics/kinetics
  Absorption: Oral: 75%
  Half-life: Normal renal function: 8-11 hours
  Time to peak serum concentration: Within 2-4 hours

Signs and Symptoms of Acute Intoxication Nausea, diplopia; vomiting, tongue discoloration, coagulopathy, colitis, azotemia, metallic taste, lichenoid eruptions, toxic epidermal necrolysis, dysphagia, hypoglycemia, hypothermia, thrombocytopenia, Fanconi syndrome, myasthenia gravis (exacerbation or precipitation of)

When to Transport to Hospital Transport any symptomatic patient or any ingestion over 1 g

Warnings/Precautions Use of tetracyclines during tooth development may cause permanent discoloration of the teeth and enamel, hypoplasia, and retardation of skeletal development and bone growth; use with caution in patients with renal or hepatic impairment and in pregnancy; pseudomotor cerebri has been reported with tetracycline use

Adverse Reactions
  >10%: Discoloration of teeth and enamel hypoplasia (infants)
  1% to 10%:
    Dermatologic: Photosensitivity
    Gastrointestinal: Nausea, diarrhea

Reference Range
  Therapeutic: Not established
  Toxic: >16 µg/mL

Dosage Forms
  Tetracycline hydrochloride:
    Capsule: 100 mg, 250 mg, 500 mg
    Ointment:
      Ophthalmic: 1% [10 mg/mL] (3.5 g)
      Topical: 3% [30 mg/mL] (14.2 g, 30 g)
    Solution, topical: 2.2 mg/mL (70 mL)
    Suspension:
      Ophthalmic: 1% [10 mg/mL] (0.5 mL, 1 mL, 4 mL)
      Oral: 125 mg/5 mL (60 mL, 480 mL)
    Tablet: 250 mg, 500 mg

Specific References
  Fox SA, Berenyi MR, and Straus B, "Tetracycline Toxicity Presenting as a Multisystem Disease," *Mt Sinai J Med*, 1976, 43(2):129-35.

Tetradecin *see* Tetracycline *on previous page*

Tetraform® *see* Carbon Tetrachloride *on page 113*

Tetrahydro-2-para-sulfamoylphenyl-1,2-thiazine 1,1 dioxide *see* Sulthiame *on page 555*

Tetrahydrocannabinol *see* Dronabinol *on page 213*

Tetrahydrozoline (tet ra hye DROZ a leen)
  Synonyms Tetryzoline
  U.S. Brand Names Collyrium Fresh® [OTC]; Eye-Zine® [OTC]; Murine® Plus [OTC]; Ocu-Drop® [OTC]; Optigene® [OTC]; Soothe® [OTC]; Tetraclear® [OTC]; Tetra-Ide® [OTC]; Tyzine®; Visine® [OTC]; Visine A.C.® [OTC]
  (Continued)

Tetrahydrozoline *(Continued)*

Therapeutic Category Adrenergic Agonist Agent

Use Symptomatic relief of nasal congestion and conjunctival congestion

Usual Dosage

Nasal congestion: Intranasal:

Children 2-6 years: Instill 2-3 drops of 0.05% solution every 4-6 hours as needed, no more frequent than every 3 hours

Children >6 years and Adults: Instill 2-4 drops or 3-4 sprays of 0.1% solution every 3-4 hours as needed, no more frequent than every 3 hours

Conjunctival congestion: Ophthalmic: Adults: Instill 1-2 drops in each eye 2-4 times/day

Mechanism of Action Stimulates alpha-adrenergic receptors in the arterioles of the conjunctiva and the nasal mucosa to produce vasoconstriction

Pharmacodynamics/kinetics

Onset of decongestant effect: Intranasal: Within 4-8 hours

Duration: Ophthalmic vasoconstriction: 2-3 hours

Absorption: Topical: Systemic absorption sometimes occurs

Signs and Symptoms of Acute Intoxication CNS depression, hypothermia, bradycardia, cardiovascular collapse, coma

When to Transport to Hospital Transport any symptomatic patient

Warnings/Precautions Do not use in children <2 years of age; excessive use may cause rebound congestion or chemical rhinitis; use with caution in patients with hypertension, diabetes, cardiovascular or coronary artery disease; discontinue use prior to the use of anesthetics which sensitize the myocardium to the systemic effects of sympathomimetics

Adverse Reactions

>10%:

Local: Transient stinging

Respiratory: Sneezing

1% to 10%:

Cardiovascular: Tachycardia, palpitations, increased blood pressure, increased heart rate

Central nervous system: Headache

Neuromuscular & skeletal: Tremor

Ocular: Blurred vision

Drug Interactions Increased toxicity: MAO inhibitors can cause an exaggerated adrenergic response if taken concurrently or within 21 days of discontinuing MAO inhibitor; beta-blockers can cause hypertensive episodes and increased risk of intracranial hemorrhage; anesthetics

Dosage Forms

Solution:

Nasal: 0.05% (15 mL), 0.1% (15 mL spray, 30 mL drops)

Ophthalmic: 0.05% (15 mL, 22.5 mL, 30 mL)

Specific References

Higgins GL III, Campbell B, Wallace K, et al, "Pediatric Poisoning From Over-The-Counter Imidazoline-Containing Products," *Ann Emerg Med*, 1991, 20(6):655-8.

Tetra-Ide® [OTC] *see* Tetrahydrozoline *on previous page*

Tetralan® Oral *see* Tetracycline *on page 568*

Tetralen® *see* Tetracycline *on page 568*

Tetram® Oral *see* Tetracycline *on page 568*

Tetrasol *see* Carbon Tetrachloride *on page 113*

Tetraverine *see* Tetracycline *on page 568*

Tetryzoline *see* Tetrahydrozoline *on previous page*

Texacort™ *see* Hydrocortisone *on page 297*

Texsolve S® see Stoddard Solvent on page 547

T-Gen® see Trimethobenzamide on page 599

T-Gesic® see Hydrocodone and Acetaminophen on page 293

Thalitone® see Chlorthalidone on page 144

THC see Dronabinol on page 213

THC (Delta-9-Tetrahydrocannabinol) see Cannabinoids, Qualitative on page 100

Theo-24® see Theophylline Salts on this page

Theobid® see Theophylline Salts on this page

Theochron® Theoclear® L.A. see Theophylline Salts on this page

Theo-Dur® see Theophylline Salts on this page

Theodur-Sprinkle® see Theophylline Salts on this page

Theolair™ Theon® see Theophylline Salts on this page

Theophylline and Guaifenesin (thee OF i lin & gwye FEN e sin)
U.S. Brand Names Bronchial®; Glycerol-T®; Quibron®; Slo-Phyllin GG®
Therapeutic Category Theophylline Derivative
Dosage Forms
Capsule: Theophylline 150 mg and guaifenesin 90 mg; theophylline 300 mg and guaifenesin 180 mg
Elixir: Theophylline 150 mg and guaifenesin 90 mg per 15 mL (480 mL)

Theophylline, Ephedrine, and Hydroxyzine
(thee OF i lin, e FED rin, & hye DROKS i zeen)
U.S. Brand Names Hydrophed®; Marax®
Therapeutic Category Theophylline Derivative
Abuse Potential Yes
Impairment Potential Yes
Dosage Forms
Syrup, dye free: Theophylline 32.5 mg, ephedrine 6.25 mg, and hydroxyzine 2.5 mg per 5 mL
Tablet: Theophylline 130 mg, ephedrine 25 mg, and hydroxyzine 10 mg

Theophylline, Ephedrine, and Phenobarbital
(thee OF i lin, e FED rin, & fee noe BAR bi tal)
Therapeutic Category Theophylline Derivative
Abuse Potential Yes
Impairment Potential Yes
Dosage Forms
Suspension: Theophylline 65 mg, ephedrine sulfate 12 mg, and phenobarbital 4 mg per 5 mL
Tablet: Theophylline 118 mg, ephedrine sulfate 25 mg, and phenobarbital 11 mg; theophylline 130 mg, ephedrine sulfate 24 mg, and phenobarbital 8 mg

Theophylline Salts (thee OFF i lin salts)
Synonyms Aminophylline; Choline Theophyllinate; Ethylenediamine; Oxtriphylline
U.S. Brand Names Aerolate®; Aerolate III®; Aerolate JR®; Aerolate SR®; Aminophyllin™; Aquaphyllin®; Asmalix®; Bronkodyl®; Choledyl® Constant-T®; Duraphyl™; Elixophyllin®; Elixophyllin® SR; LaBID® Phyllocontin®; Quibron®-T; Quibron®-T/SR; Respbid®; Slo-bid™ Slo-Phyllin®; Sustaire®; Theo-24®; Theobid®; Theochron® Theoclear® L.A.; Theo-Dur®; Theodur-Sprinkle®; Theolair™ Theon®; Theospan®-SR; Theovent®; Truphylline®
Therapeutic Category Bronchodilator; Theophylline Derivative
(Continued)

Theophylline Salts *(Continued)*

Use Bronchodilator in reversible airway obstruction due to asthma, chronic bronchitis, and emphysema; for neonatal apnea/bradycardia

Usual Dosage Use ideal body weight for obese patients

Neonates:

Apnea of prematurity: Oral, I.V.: Loading dose: 4 mg/kg (theophylline); 5 mg/kg (aminophylline)

There appears to be a delay in theophylline elimination in infants <1 year of age, especially neonates; both the initial dose and maintenance dosage should be conservative

I.V.: Initial: Maintenance infusion rates:

Neonates:

≤24 days: 0.08 mg/kg/hour theophylline

>24 days: 0.12 mg/kg/hour theophylline

Infants 6-52 weeks: 0.008 (age in weeks) + 0.21 mg/kg/hour theophylline

Children:

6 weeks to 6 months: 0.5 mg/kg/hour

6 months to 1 year: 0.6-0.7 mg/kg/hour

Children >1 year and Adults:

Treatment of acute bronchospasm: I.V.: Loading dose (in patients not currently receiving aminophylline or theophylline): 6 mg/kg (based on aminophylline) given I.V. over 20-30 minutes; administration rate should not exceed 25 mg/minute (aminophylline). See table.

Approximate I.V. maintenance dosages are based upon continuous infusions; bolus dosing (often used in children <6 months of age) may be determined by multiplying the hourly infusion rate by 24 hours and dividing by the desired number of doses/day; see table.

Maintenance Dose for Acute Symptoms

Population Group	Oral Theophylline (mg/kg/day)	I.V. Aminophylline
Premature infant or newborn - 6 wk (for apnea/bradycardia)	4	5 mg/kg/day
6 wk - 6 mo	10	12 mg/kg/day or continuous I.V. infusion*
Infants 6 mo - 1 y	12-18	15 mg/kg/day or continuous I.V. infusion*
Children 1-9 y	20-24	1 mg/kg/h
Children 9-12 y, and adolescent daily smokers of cigarettes or marijuana, and otherwise healthy adult smokers <50 y	16	0.9 mg/kg/h
Adolescents 12-16 y (nonsmokers)	13	0.7 mg/kg/h
Otherwise healthy nonsmoking adults (including elderly patients)	10 (not to exceed 900 mg/day)	0.5 mg/kg/h
Cardiac decompensation, cor pulmonale and/or liver dysfunction	5 (not to exceed 400 mg/day)	0.25 mg/kg/h

*For continuous I.V. infusion divide total daily dose by 24 = mg/kg/h.

Approximate I.V. Theophylline Dosage for Treatment of Acute Bronchospasm

Group	Dosage for Next 12 h*	Dosage After 12 h*
Infants 6 wk - 6 mo	0.5 mg/kg/h	
Children 6 mo - 1 y	0.6-0.7 mg/kg/h	
Children 1-9 y	0.95 mg/kg/h (1.2 mg/kg/h)	0.79 mg/kg/h (1 mg/kg/h)
Children 9-16 y and young adult smokers	0.79 mg/kg/h (1 mg/kg/h)	0.63 mg/kg/h (0.8 mg/kg/h)
Healthy, nonsmoking adults	0.55 mg/kg/h (0.7 mg/kg/h)	0.39 mg/kg/h (0.5 mg/kg/h)
Older patients and patients with cor pulmonale	0.47 mg/kg/h (0.6 mg/kg/h)	0.24 mg/kg/h (0.3 mg/kg/h)
Patients with congestive heart failure or liver failure	0.39 mg/kg/h (0.5 mg/kg/h)	0.08-0.16 mg/kg/h (0.1-0.2 mg/kg/h)

*Equivalent hydrous aminophylline dosage indicated in parentheses.

Dosage should be adjusted according to serum level measurements during the first 12- to 24-hour period; see table.

Dosage Adjustment After Serum Theophylline Measurement

Serum Theophylline		Guidelines
Within normal limits	10-20 mcg/mL	Maintain dosage if tolerated. Recheck serum theophylline concentration at 6- to 12-month intervals.*
Too high	20-25 mcg/mL	Decrease doses by about 10%. Recheck serum theophylline concentration after 3 days and then at 6- to 12-month intervals.*
	25-30 mcg/mL	Skip next dose and decrease subsequent doses by about 25%. Recheck serum theophylline.
	>30 mcg/mL	Skip next 2 doses and decrease subsequent doses by 50%. Recheck serum theophylline.
Too low	7.5-10 mcg/mL	Increase dose by about 25%.† Recheck serum theophylline concentration after 3 days and then at 6- to 12-month intervals.*
	5-7.5 mcg/mL	Increase dose by about 25% to the nearest dose increment† and recheck serum theophylline for guidance in further dosage adjustment (another increase will probably be needed, but this provides a safety check).

*Finer adjustments in dosage may be needed for some patients.

†Dividing the daily dose into 3 doses administered at 8-hour intervals may be indicated if symptoms occur repeatedly at the end of a dosing interval.

From Weinberger M and Hendeles L, "Practical Guide to Using Theophylline," *J Resp Dis*, 1981,2:12-27.

(Continued)

Theophylline Salts *(Continued)*

Oral theophylline: Initial dosage recommendation: Loading dose (to achieve a serum level of about 10 mcg/mL; loading doses should be given using a rapidly absorbed oral product **not** a sustained release product):

If no theophylline has been administered in the previous 24 hours: 4-6 mg/kg theophylline

If theophylline has been administered in the previous 24 hours: administer ½ loading dose or 2-3 mg/kg theophylline can be given in emergencies when serum levels are not available

On the average, for every 1 mg/kg theophylline given, blood levels will rise 2 mcg/mL

Ideally, defer the loading dose if a serum theophylline concentration can be obtained rapidly. However, if this is not possible, exercise clinical judgment. If the patient is not experiencing theophylline toxicity, this is unlikely to result in dangerous adverse effects.

See table.

Oral Theophylline Dosage for Bronchial Asthma*

Age	Initial 3 Days	Second 3 Days	Steady-State Maintenance
<1 y	0.2 x (age in weeks) + 5		0.3 x (age in weeks) + 8
1-9 y	16 up to a maximum of 400 mg/24 h	20	22
9-12 y	16 up to a maximum of 400 mg/24 h	16 up to a maximum of 600 mg/24 h	20 up to a maximum of 800 mg/24 h
12-16 y	16 up to a maximum of 400 mg/24 h	16 up to a maximum of 600 mg/24 h	18 up to a maximum of 900 mg/24 h
Adults	400 mg/24 h	600 mg/24 h	900 mg/24 h

*Dose in mg/kg/24 hours of theophylline.

Increasing dose: The dosage may be increased in approximately 25% increments at 2- to 3-day intervals so long as the drug is tolerated or until the maximum dose is reached

Maintenance dose: In newborns and infants, a fast-release oral product can be used. The total daily dose can be divided every 12 hours in newborns and every 6-8 hours in infants. In children and healthy adults, a slow-release product can be used. The total daily dose can be divided every 8-12 hours.

These recommendations, based on mean clearance rates for age or risk factors, were calculated to achieve a serum level of 10 mcg/mL (5 mcg/mL for newborns with apnea/bradycardia)

Dosage should be adjusted according to serum level

Oral oxtriphylline:

Children 1-9 years: 6.2 mg/kg/dose every 6 hours

Children 9-16 years and Adult smokers: 4.7 mg/kg/dose every 6 hours

Adult nonsmokers: 4.7 mg/kg/dose every 8 hours

Dose should be further adjusted based on serum levels

Mechanism of Action Causes bronchodilatation, diuresis, CNS and cardiac stimulation, and gastric acid secretion by blocking phosphodiesterase which increases tissue concentrations of cyclic adenine monophosphate (cAMP) which in turn promotes catecholamine stimulation of lipolysis, glycogenolysis, and gluconeogenesis and induces release of epinephrine from adrenal medulla cells

When to Transport to Hospital Transport any pediatric (<6 years of age) exposure exceeding 10 mg/kg (**not** time- or sustained-release preparation) or any symptomatic patient

Adverse Reactions 1% to 10%:

Cardiovascular: Tachycardia

Central nervous system: Nervousness, restlessness

Gastrointestinal: Nausea, vomiting

Test Interactions May elevate uric acid levels

Reference Range

Sample size: 0.5-1 mL serum (red top tube)

Saliva levels are approximately equal to 60% of plasma levels

Therapeutic levels: 10-20 µg/mL

Neonatal apnea 6-13 µg/mL

Pregnancy: 3-12 µg/mL

Toxic concentration: >20 µg/mL

Timing of serum samples: If toxicity is suspected, draw a level any time during a continuous I.V. infusion, or 2 hours after an oral dose; if lack of therapeutic is effected, draw a trough immediately before the next oral dose; see table.

Drug Interactions Cytochrome P-450 1A2 enzyme substrate and cytochrome P-450 2E enzyme substrate (minor)

Decreased effect/increased toxicity: Changes in diet may affect the elimination of theophylline; charcoal-broiled foods may increase elimination, reducing half-life by 50%; see table for factors affecting serum levels.

Factors Reported to Affect Theophylline Serum Levels

Decreased Theophylline Level	Increased Theophylline Level
Aminoglutethimide	Allopurinol (>600 mg/d)
Barbiturates	Beta-blockers
Carbamazepine	Calcium channel blockers
Charcoal	Carbamazepine
High protein/low carbohydrate diet	CHF
Hydantoins	Cimetidine
Isoniazid	Ciprofloxacin
I.V. isoproterenol	Cor pulmonale
Ketoconazole	Corticosteroids
Loop diuretics	Disulfiram
Phenobarbital	Ephedrine
Phenytoin	Erythromycin
Rifampin	Fever/viral illness
Smoking (cigarettes, marijuana)	Hepatic cirrhosis
Sulfinpyrazone	Influenza virus vaccine
Sympathomimetics	Interferon
	Isoniazid
	Loop diuretics
	Macrolides
	Mexiletine
	Oral contraceptives
	Propranolol
	Quinolones
	Thiabendazole
	Thyroid hormones
	Troleandomycin

(Continued)

Theophylline Salts *(Continued)*

Guidelines for Drawing Theophylline Serum Levels

Dosage Form	Time to Draw Level
I.V. bolus	30 min after end of 30 min infusion
I.V. continuous infusion	12-24 h after initiation of infusion
P.O. liquid, fast-release tab	Peak: 1 h postdose after at least 1 day of therapy Trough: Just before a dose after at least one day of therapy
P.O. slow-release product	Peak: 4 h postdose after at least 1 day of therapy Trough: Just before a dose after at least one day of therapy

Dosage Forms

Aminophylline (79% theophylline):

Injection: 25 mg/mL (10 mL, 20 mL); 250 mg (equivalent to 187 mg theophylline) per 10 mL; 500 mg (equivalent to 394 mg theophylline) per 20 mL

Liquid, oral: 105 mg (equivalent to 90 mg theophylline) per 5 mL (240 mL, 500 mL)

Suppository, rectal: 250 mg (equivalent to 198 mg theophylline); 500 mg (equivalent to 395 mg theophylline)

Tablet: 100 mg (equivalent to 79 mg theophylline); 200 mg (equivalent to 158 mg theophylline)

Tablet, controlled release: 225 mg (equivalent to 178 mg theophylline)

Oxtriphylline (64% theophylline):

Elixir: 100 mg (equivalent to 64 mg theophylline)/5 mL (5 mL, 10 mL, 473 mL)

Syrup: 50 mg (equivalent to 32 mg theophylline)/5 mL (473 mL)

Tablet: 100 mg (equivalent to 64 mg theophylline); 200 mg (equivalent to 127 mg theophylline)

Tablet, sustained release: 400 mg (equivalent to 254 mg theophylline); 600 mg (equivalent to 382 mg theophylline)

Theophylline:

Capsule:

Immediate release: 100 mg, 200 mg

Sustained release (8-12 hours): 50 mg, 60 mg, 65 mg, 75 mg, 100 mg, 125 mg, 130 mg, 200 mg, 250 mg, 260 mg, 300 mg

Timed release (12 hours): 50 mg, 75 mg, 125 mg, 130 mg, 200 mg, 250 mg, 260 mg

Timed release (24 hours): 100 mg, 200 mg, 300 mg

Injection: Theophylline in 5% dextrose: 200 mg/container (50 mL, 100 mL); 400 mg/container (100 mL, 250 mL, 500 mL, 1000 mL); 800 mg/container (250 mL, 500 mL, 1000 mL)

Elixir, oral: 80 mg/15 mL (15 mL, 30 mL, 500 mL, 4000 mL)

Solution, oral: 80 mg/15 mL (15 mL, 18.75 mL, 30 mL, 120 mL, 500 mL, 4000 mL); 150 mg/15 mL (480 mL)

Syrup, oral: 80 mg/15 mL (5 mL, 15 mL, 30 mL, 120 mL, 500 mL, 4000 mL); 150 mg/15 mL (480 mL)

Tablet:

Immediate release: 100 mg, 125 mg, 200 mg, 250 mg, 300 mg

Timed release (8-12 hours): 100 mg, 200 mg, 250 mg, 300 mg, 500 mg

Timed release (8-24 hours): 100 mg, 200 mg, 300 mg, 450 mg

Timed release (12-24 hours): 100 mg, 200 mg, 300 mg

Timed release (24 hours): 400 mg

Theospan®-SR *see* Theophylline Salts *on page 571*

Theovent® *see* Theophylline Salts *on page 571*

Theraflu® Non-Drowsy Formula Maximum Strength [OTC] *see* Acetaminophen, Dextromethorphan, and Pseudoephedrine *on page 23*

Thera-Hist® Syrup [OTC] *see* Chlorpheniramine and Phenylpropanolamine *on page 134*

Theralene® *see* Trimeprazine *on page 598*

Theramin® Expectorant [OTC] *see* Guaifenesin and Phenylpropanolamine *on page 272*

3-Thiacytidine *see* Lamivudine *on page 333*

Thiopental (thye oh PEN tal)

U.S. Brand Names Pentothal® Sodium

Therapeutic Category Barbiturate

Abuse Potential Yes

Impairment Potential Yes

Use Induction of anesthesia; adjunct for intubation in head injury patients; control of convulsive states; treatment of elevated intracranial pressure

Usual Dosage I.V.:

Induction anesthesia:
Infants: 5-8 mg/kg
Children 1-12 years: 5-6 mg/kg
Adults: 3-5 mg/kg

Maintenance anesthesia:
Children: 1 mg/kg as needed
Adults: 25-100 mg as needed

Increased intracranial pressure: Children and Adults: 1.5-5 mg/kg/dose; repeat as needed to control intracranial pressure

Seizures:
Children: 2-3 mg/kg/dose, repeat as needed
Adults: 75-250 mg/dose, repeat as needed

Rectal administration: (Patient should be NPO for no less than 3 hours prior to administration)

Suggested initial doses of thiopental rectal suspension are:
<3 months: 15 mg/kg/dose
>3 months: 25 mg/kg/dose

Note: The age of a premature infant should be adjusted to reflect the age that the infant would have been if full-term (eg, an infant, now age 4 months, who was 2 months premature should be considered to be a 2-month old infant).

Doses should be rounded downward to the nearest 50 mg increment to allow for accurate measurement of the dose

Inactive or debilitated patients and patients recently medicated with other sedatives, (eg, chloral hydrate, meperidine, chlorpromazine, and promethazine), may require smaller doses than usual

If the patient is not sedated within 15-20 minutes, a single repeat dose of thiopental can be given. The single repeat doses are:
<3 months: <7.5 mg/kg/dose
>3 months: 15 mg/kg/dose

Adults weighing >90 kg should not receive >3 g as a total dose (initial plus repeat doses)

Children weighing >34 kg should not receive >1 g as a total dose (initial plus repeat doses)

Neither adults nor children should receive more than one course of thiopental rectal suspension (initial dose plus repeat dose) per 24-hour period

(Continued)

Thiopental *(Continued)*

Note: Accumulation may occur with chronic dosing due to lipid solubility; prolonged recovery may result from redistribution of thiopental from fat stores

Mechanism of Action Interferes with transmission of impulses from the thalamus to the cortex of the brain resulting in an imbalance in central inhibitory and facilitatory mechanisms

Pharmacodynamics/kinetics

Onset of action: I.V.: Anesthesia occurs in 30-60 seconds

Duration: 5-30 minutes

Distribution: V_d: 1.4 L/kg

Protein binding: 72% to 86%

Metabolism: In the liver primarily to inactive metabolites but pentobarbital is also formed

Half-life: 3-11.5 hours, decreased in children vs adults

Signs and Symptoms of Acute Intoxication Respiratory depression, hypotension, shock

When to Transport to Hospital Transport patients with any exposure

Warnings/Precautions Use with caution in patients with asthma, unstable aneurysms, severe cardiovascular disease, hepatic or renal disease, laryngospasm or bronchospasms which can occur; hypotension; extravasation or intra-arterial injection causes necrosis due to pH of 10.6, ensure patient has intravenous access

Adverse Reactions

>10%: Local: Pain on I.M. injection

1% to 10%: Gastrointestinal: Cramping, diarrhea, rectal bleeding

Reference Range Therapeutic: Hypnotic: 1-5 µg/mL (SI: 4.1-20.7 µmol/L); Coma: 30-100 µg/mL (SI: 124-413 µmol/L); Anesthesia: 7-130 µg/mL (SI: 29-536 µmol/L); Toxic: >10 µg/mL (SI: >41 µmol/L)

Drug Interactions Increased toxicity with CNS depressants (especially narcotic analgesics and phenothiazines), salicylates, sulfisoxazole

Dosage Forms

Thiopental sodium:

Injection: 250 mg, 400 mg, 500 mg, 1 g, 2.5 g, 5 g

Suspension, rectal: 400 mg/g (2 g)

Thioridazine *(thye oh RID a zeen)*

U.S. Brand Names Mallorol®; Meleretten®; Mellaril®; Mellaril-S®; Novoridazine®; Ridazine®

Canadian Brand Names Apo-Thioridazine®; Novo-Ridazine®; PMS-Thioridazine®

Therapeutic Category Antipsychotic Agent; Phenothiazine Derivative

Use Management of manifestations of psychotic disorders; depressive neurosis; alcohol withdrawal; dementia in elderly; behavioral problems in children

Usual Dosage Oral:

Children >2 years: Range: 0.5-3 mg/kg/day in 2-3 divided doses; usual: 1 mg/kg/day; maximum: 3 mg/kg/day

Behavior problems: Initial: 10 mg 2-3 times/day, increase gradually

Severe psychoses: Initial: 25 mg 2-3 times/day, increase gradually

Adults:

Psychoses: Initial: 50-100 mg 3 times/day with gradual increments as needed and tolerated; maximum: 800 mg/day in 2-4 divided doses; if >65 years, initial dose: 10 mg 3 times/day

Depressive disorders, dementia: Initial: 25 mg 3 times/day; maintenance dose: 20-200 mg/day

Mechanism of Action Blocks postsynaptic mesolimbic dopaminergic receptors in the brain; exhibits a strong alpha-adrenergic blocking effect and depresses the release of hypothalamic and hypophyseal hormones

Pharmacodynamics/kinetics

Onset of action: 30-60 minutes

Duration: 4-6 hours

Absorption: Absorbed well from gastrointestinal tract

Metabolism: Hepatic

Half-life: 26-36 hours

Time to peak serum concentration: Within 1 hour

Signs and Symptoms of Acute Intoxication Deep sleep, coma, impotence, tachycardia (ventricular), Q-T prolongation, hypertonia, hyponatremia, neuroleptic malignant syndrome, hepatic failure, hyperprolactinemia, ejaculatory disturbances, galactorrhea, gynecomastia, extrapyramidal reaction, dysphagia, abnormal involuntary muscle movements, hypotension or hypertension, hypothermia or hyperthermia, hirsutism, hyperreflexia, myoclonus, QRS prolongation, first degree A-V block, vision color changes (brown tinge); priapism, urine discoloration (pink), urine discoloration (red), urine discoloration (red-brown)

When to Transport to Hospital Transport any pediatric (<6 years of age) ingestion exceeding 3 mg/kg, any symptomatic patient, or any ingestion over 5 mg/kg

Warnings/Precautions Use with caution in patients with severe cardiovascular disorder or seizures

Adverse Reactions

>10%:

Central nervous system: Pseudoparkinsonism, akathisia, dystonias, tardive dyskinesia (persistent), dizziness

Cardiovascular: Hypotension, orthostatic hypotension

Gastrointestinal: Constipation

Ocular: Pigmentary retinopathy

Respiratory: Nasal congestion

Miscellaneous: Diaphoresis (decreased)

1% to 10%:

Dermatologic: Increased sensitivity to sun, rash

Endocrine & metabolic: Changes in menstrual cycle, changes in libido, breast pain

Gastrointestinal: Weight gain, nausea, vomiting, stomach pain

Genitourinary: Dysuria, ejaculatory disturbances

Neuromuscular & skeletal: Trembling of fingers

Reference Range

Therapeutic: 1.0-1.5 µg/mL (SI: 2.7-4.1 µmol/L)

Toxic: >10.0 µg/mL (SI: >27.0 µmol/L); no relationship between serum levels and cardiac toxicity

Drug Interactions Additive effects with other CNS depressants; concurrent use with lithium has rarely caused acute encephalopathy-like syndrome; increased cardiac arrhythmias with tricyclic antidepressants; epinephrine may cause hypotension; beta-blockers may cause increased plasma levels of thioridazine

Dosage Forms

Concentrate, oral: 30 mg/mL (120 mL); 100 mg/mL (3.4 mL, 120 mL)

Suspension, oral: 25 mg/5 mL (480 mL); 100 mg/5 mL (480 mL)

Tablet: 10 mg, 15 mg, 25 mg, 50 mg, 100 mg, 150 mg, 200 mg

Specific References

Oshika T, "Ocular Adverse Effects of Neuropsychiatric Agents. Incidence and Management," *Drug Saf*, 1995, 12(4):256-63.

Thiothixene (thye oh THIKS een)

Synonyms Tiotixene

U.S. Brand Names Navane®; Orbinamon®

Therapeutic Category Antipsychotic Agent

Impairment Potential Yes

Use Management of psychotic disorders

Usual Dosage

Children <12 years: Oral: 0.25 mg/kg/24 hours in divided doses (dose not well established)

Children >12 years and Adults: Mild to moderate psychosis:

Oral: 2 mg 3 times/day, up to 20-30 mg/day; more severe psychosis: Initial: 5 mg 2 times/day, may increase gradually, if necessary; maximum: 60 mg/day

I.M.: 4 mg 2-4 times/day, increase dose gradually; usual: 16-20 mg/day; maximum: 30 mg/day; change to oral dose as soon as able

Mechanism of Action Elicits antipsychotic activity by postsynaptic blockade of CNS dopamine receptors resulting in inhibition of dopamine-mediated effects; also has alpha-adrenergic blocking activity

Pharmacodynamics/kinetics

Duration: Up to 12 hours

Absorption: Rapid

Metabolism: Extensive liver metabolism

Half-life: >24 hours with chronic use

Time to peak serum concentration: 1-3 hours

Signs and Symptoms of Acute Intoxication Muscle myoclonus, priapism, eosinophilia, impotence, hyponatremia, gynecomastia, neuroleptic malignant syndrome, ejaculatory disturbances, extrapyramidal reaction, leukocytosis, drowsiness, rigidity, tremors, hypotension, urine discoloration (pink), urine discoloration (red), urine discoloration (red-brown), leukopenia; neutropenia; agranulocytosis; granulocytopenia

When to Transport to Hospital Transport any symptomatic patient or any ingestion over 1 mg/kg

Warnings/Precautions Watch for hypotension when administering I.M. or I.V.; safety in children <6 months of age has not been established; use with caution in patients with narrow-angle glaucoma, bone marrow depression, severe liver or cardiac disease, seizures

Adverse Reactions

>10%:

Cardiovascular: Hypotension, orthostatic hypotension

Central nervous system: Pseudoparkinsonism, akathisia, dystonias, tardive dyskinesia (persistent), dizziness

Gastrointestinal: Constipation

Respiratory: Nasal congestion

Miscellaneous: Diaphoresis (decreased)

1% to 10%:

Dermatologic: Increased sensitivity to sun, rash

Endocrine & metabolic: Changes in menstrual cycle, changes in libido, breast pain

Gastrointestinal: Weight gain, nausea, vomiting, stomach pain

Genitourinary: Dysuria, ejaculatory disturbances

Neuromuscular & skeletal: Trembling of fingers

Ocular: Pigmentary retinopathy

Reference Range At 2.5 hours after dosing of 15-60 mg/day, serum levels ranged from 10.0-22.5 ng/mL; therapeutic: 10-40 ng/mL

Drug Interactions May potentiate the action of other CNS depressants, anticholinergics, or hypotensive agents; ethanol has an additive effect

Dosage Forms
Capsule: 1 mg, 2 mg, 5 mg, 10 mg, 20 mg
Thiothixene hydrochloride:
Concentrate, oral: 5 mg/mL (30 mL, 120 mL)
Injection: 2 mg/mL (2 mL)
Powder for injection: 5 mg/mL (2 mL)

Specific References
Schneider SM, "Neuroleptic Malignant Syndrome: Controversies in Treatment," *Am J Emerg Med*, 1991, 9(4):360-2.

Thorazine® see Chlorpromazine on page 138
Thrombran® see Trazodone on page 590
Thrust see Nitrites on page 436
Tiapridal® see Tiapride on this page

Tiapride (TYE a pride)

U.S. Brand Names Delpral®; Equilium®; Italprid®; Luxoben®; Porfanil®; Pridonal®; Sereprile®; Tiapridal®; Tiapridex®; Tiaprizal®
Therapeutic Category Dopamine Antagonist
Impairment Potential Yes
Use Management of behavioral disorders and dyskinesias; also used for alcohol withdrawal

Usual Dosage
Alcohol detoxification: 100 mg 3 times/day
Extrapyramidal symptomatology: 100-300 mg/day (reduce dosage in renal insufficiency)

Mechanism of Action A dopamine (D_2 receptor) antagonist (a substituted benzamide)

Pharmacodynamics/kinetics
Absorption: 1.4 hours
Metabolism: Hepatic to N-monodesethyl tiapride
Bioavailability: 75%
Half-life: 3-4 hours

When to Transport to Hospital Transport any pediatric exposure, any patient exhibiting lethargy, dystonia, fever, or any ingestion over 500 mg

Warnings/Precautions Use with caution in patients with epilepsy, renal dysfunction, pregnancy or lactation

Adverse Reactions
Cardiovascular: Orthostatic hypotension
Central nervous system: Drowsiness, tardive dyskinesia (in the elderly), malignant neuroleptic syndrome, dystonia
Dermatologic: Erythema
Endocrine & metabolic: Hyperprolactinemia

Reference Range Following 100 mg oral dose, peak plasma tiapride level is ~1.47 mcg/mL

Dosage Forms
Injection: 100 mg/2 mL
Tablet: 100 mg

Specific References
Peters DH and Faulds D, "Tiapride: A Review of Its Pharmacology and Therapeutic Potential in the Management of Alcohol Dependence Syndrome," *Drugs*, 1994, 47:1010-32.

Tiapridex® see Tiapride on this page
Tiaprizal® see Tiapride on this page

Ticon® *see* Trimethobenzamide *on page 599*
Tigan® *see* Trimethobenzamide *on page 599*
Tildiem® *see* Diltiazem *on page 201*
Tildate *see* Tilidine *on this page*
Tilidin *see* Tilidine *on this page*

Tilidine (TIL i deen)
Synonyms Tildate; Tilidin
U.S. Brand Names Tilitrate®; Valoron®
Therapeutic Category Analgesic, Non-narcotic
Abuse Potential Yes
Impairment Potential Yes
Use Treat moderate to severe pain
Usual Dosage
Oral:
Children >2 years: 5 mg plus 2.5 mg per year of age, not to exceed 1 mg/kg
Adults: 50-100 mg up to 4 times/day; maximum daily dose: 400 mg
Parenteral: Up to 400 mg
Rectal: 75 mg 4 times/day
Mechanism of Action Binds to opiate receptors in the CNS, causing inhibition of ascending pain pathways, altering the perception of and response to pain; produces generalized CNS depression; a cogenor of atropine
Pharmacodynamics/kinetics
Onset of action: Oral: 15-30 minutes
Duration of action: 4-6 hours
Distribution: V_d: 3.71 L/kg
Metabolism: Hepatic to nortilidine (active metabolite) and bis-nortilidine
Half-life: 5 hours
When to Transport to Hospital Transport any pediatric ingestion over 1 mg/kg or any patient with neurologic symptoms
Overdosage/Treatment Supportive therapy: Naloxone hydrochloride (0.4-2 mg I.V., S.C., or through an endotracheal tube); a continuous infusion (at $2/3$ the response dose/hour) may be required
Warnings/Precautions Use with caution in patients with myasthenia gravis; may cause dependency
Adverse Reactions
Central nervous system: Hallucinations, dizziness, confusion
Dermatologic: Pruritus
Gastrointestinal: Nausea, vomiting, salivation
Hematologic: Porphyrinogenic
Neuromuscular & skeletal: Tremors, hyperreflexia, hyperactive deep tendon reflexes, clonus, myoclonus
Ocular: Miosis
Respiratory: Apnea, respiratory depression
Reference Range Maximum tilidine plasma concentration of 907 ng/mL achieved after 50 mg dose (I.V.); nortilidine peak plasma level after a 50 mg dose: 69 ng/mL
Drug Interactions Increased sedation with alcohol or other sedative agents
Additional Information Often combined orally with naloxone (ie, Valoron N®)
Specific References
Levenstein JH, "An Evaluation of Tilidine Hydrochloride in the Treatment of Pain Requiring Immediate Analgesia," *S Afr Med J*, 1975, 49:143-6.

Tilitrate® *see* Tilidine *on this page*

Timolol (TYE moe lole)

U.S. Brand Names Betimol® Ophthalmic; Blocadren® Oral; Timoptic® Ophthalmic; Timoptic-XE® Ophthalmic

Canadian Brand Names Apo-Timol®; Apo-Timop®; Gen-Timolol®; Novo-Timol®; Nu-Timolol®

Therapeutic Category Beta-Adrenergic Blocker

Use Ophthalmic dosage form used to treat elevated intraocular pressure such as glaucoma or ocular hypertension; orally for treatment of hypertension and angina and reduce mortality following myocardial infarction and prophylaxis of migraine

Usual Dosage

Children and Adults: Ophthalmic: Initial: 0.25% solution, instill 1 drop twice daily; increase to 0.5% solution if response not adequate; decrease to 1 drop/day if controlled; do not exceed 1 drop twice daily of 0.5% solution

Adults: Oral:

Hypertension: Initial: 10 mg twice daily, increase gradually every 7 days, usual dosage: 20-40 mg/day in 2 divided doses; maximum: 60 mg/day

Prevention of myocardial infarction: 10 mg twice daily initiated within 1-4 weeks after infarction

Migraine headache: Initial: 10 mg twice daily, increase to maximum of 30 mg/day

Mechanism of Action Blocks both beta$_1$- and beta$_2$-adrenergic receptors, reduces intraocular pressure by reducing aqueous humor production or possibly outflow; reduces blood pressure by blocking adrenergic receptors and decreasing sympathetic outflow, produces a negative chronotropic and inotropic activity through an unknown mechanism

Pharmacodynamics/kinetics

Onset of hypotensive effect: Oral: Within 15-45 minutes

Peak effect: Within 0.5-2.5 hours

Duration of action: ~4 hours; intraocular effects persist for 24 hours after ophthalmic instillation

Metabolism: Extensively metabolized in the liver

Half-life: 2-2.7 hours; prolonged with reduced renal function

Signs and Symptoms of Acute Intoxication Cardiac disturbances, CNS toxicity, bronchospasm, hypoglycemia and hyperkalemia. The most common cardiac symptoms include hypotension and bradycardia; atrioventricular block, intraventricular conduction disturbances, cardiogenic shock, and systole may occur with severe overdose, especially with membrane-depressant drugs (eg, propranolol); CNS effects include convulsions, coma, and respiratory arrest is commonly seen with propranolol and other membrane-depressant and lipid-soluble drugs.

When to Transport to Hospital Transport any symptomatic patient

Warnings/Precautions Some products contain sulfites which can cause allergic reactions; tachyphylaxis may develop; use with a miotic in angle-closure glaucoma; use with caution in patients with decreased renal or hepatic function (dosage adjustment required); severe CNS, cardiovascular and respiratory adverse effects have been seen following ophthalmic use; patients with a history of asthma, congestive heart failure, or bradycardia appear to be at a higher risk

Adverse Reactions

Ophthalmic:

1% to 10%:

Dermatologic: Alopecia

Ocular: Burning, stinging of eyes

Oral:

>10%: Endocrine & metabolic: Decreased sexual ability

(Continued)

Timolol *(Continued)*

1% to 10%:
Cardiovascular: Bradycardia, arrhythmia, reduced peripheral circulation
Central nervous system: Dizziness, fatigue
Dermatologic: Itching
Neuromuscular & skeletal: Weakness
Ocular: Burning eyes, stinging of eyes
Respiratory: Dyspnea

Dosage Forms

Solution, as hemihydrate, ophthalmic (Betimol®): 0.25% (2.5 mL, 5 mL, 10 mL, 15 mL); 0.5% (2.5 mL, 5 mL, 10 mL, 15 mL)
Timolol maleate:
Gel, ophthalmic (Timoptic-XE®): 0.25% (2.5 mL, 5 mL); 0.5% (2.5 mL, 5 mL)
Solution, ophthalmic (Timoptic®): 0.25% (2.5 mL, 5 mL, 10 mL, 15 mL); 0.5% (2.5 mL, 5 mL, 10 mL, 15 mL)
Solution, ophthalmic, preservative free, single use (Timoptic® OcuDose®): 0.25%, 0.5%
Tablet (Blocadren®): 5 mg, 10 mg, 20 mg

Specific References

Botet C, Grau J, Benito P, et al, "Timolol Ophthalmic Solution and Respiratory Arrest," *Ann Intern Med*, 1986, 105(2):306-7.

Timoptic® Ophthalmic *see* Timolol *on previous page*

Timoptic-XE® Ophthalmic *see* Timolol *on previous page*

Tiotixene *see* Thiothixene *on page 580*

Titus® *see* Lorazepam *on page 351*

Tizanidine *(tye ZAN i deen)*

U.S. Brand Names Dirdalud®; Sirdalud®; Sirdulud®; Zanaflex®
Therapeutic Category Alpha$_2$-Adrenergic Agonist Agent
Impairment Potential Yes
Use Skeletal muscle relaxant used for treatment of muscle spasticity, tension headaches

Usual Dosage

Muscle spasm: Initial: Oral: 2-4 mg 3 times/day; maximum daily dose: 36 mg
Tension headache: Initial: 2 mg 3 times/day; can titrate after 2 week intervals to a maximum daily dose: 18 mg

Mechanism of Action An alpha$_2$-adrenergic agonist agent which decreases excitatory input to alpha motor neurons; an imidazole derivative which acts as a centrally acting muscle relaxant with alpha$_2$-adrenergic agonist properties; acts on the level of the spinal cord

Pharmacodynamics/kinetics

Metabolism: Hepatic
Bioavailability: 98%
Half-life: 2-8 hours (immediate release); 13-18 hours (sustained release)

Signs and Symptoms of Acute Intoxication Dry mouth, bradycardia, hypotension

When to Transport to Hospital Transport any pediatric exposure, any symptomatic patient, or any ingestion over 20 mg

Warnings/Precautions Reduce dose in patients with liver or renal disease; use with caution in patients with hypotension or cardiac disease

Adverse Reactions

>10%:
Gastrointestinal: Dry mouth
Neuromuscular & skeletal: Muscle weakness

<10%:
  Cardiovascular: Hypotension, bradycardia, palpitations, sinus bradycardia
  Central nervous system: Insomnia, fatigue, headache, dizziness, drowsiness
  Dermatologic: Pruritus
  Gastrointestinal: Nausea, vomiting
  Neuromuscular & skeletal: Tremor
Reference Range Peak serum level after a 12 mg oral dose: ~12 ng/mL
Drug Interactions Use of alcohol or other central nervous system depressants can have an additive effect; additional hypotensive effects when used with diuretic agents; can cause an increase in serum phenytoin levels
Dosage Forms Tablet: 2 mg, 4 mg, 6 mg
Additional Information 20 mg/day of tizanidine is similar in efficacy to 50 mg/day of baclofen in treating spasticity due to cerebrovascular lesions
Specific References
  Coward DM, "Tizanidine: Neuropharmacology and Mechanism of Action," *Neurology*, 1994, 44(11 Suppl 9):S6-S10; discussion S10-1.

TMP-SMZ *see* Co-Trimoxazole *on page 168*

Tobacco
Synonyms Cultivated Tobacco
Scientific Name *Nicotiana tabacum*
Usual Dosage Human fatalities have been seen at 0.8 mg/kg of nicotine, but depend largely on the extent of spontaneous vomiting
Mechanism of Toxic Action All parts of the plant contain the toxin nicotine which stimulates motor endplates, ganglionic sites, and smooth muscles by a direct acetylcholine-like action
Pharmacodynamics/kinetics
  Onset of action: 15-60 minutes
  Duration: 3-12 hours
  Absorption: Well absorbed by all routes
  Half-life: 0.8-2.2 hours
Signs and Symptoms of Acute Intoxication Low doses can cause nausea, vomiting, oral irritation, headache, thirst, sweating, and asthenia; higher doses can cause hallucinations, confusion; CNS stimulation followed by depression, seizures, hyperthermia, hypertension, and tachycardia followed by hypotension, bradycardia, and an irregular pulse
When to Transport to Hospital Transport any symptomatic patient
Adverse Reactions Cardiovascular: Sinus bradycardia, sinus tachycardia
Additional Information Toxin: Nicotine

Tofranil® *see* Imipramine *on page 309*
Tofranil-PM® *see* Imipramine *on page 309*

Tolbutamide (tole BYOO ta mide)
U.S. Brand Names Oramide®; Orinase®
Canadian Brand Names Apo-Tolbutamide®; Mobenol®; Novo-Butamide®
Therapeutic Category Antidiabetic Agent (Oral)
Use Adjunct to diet for the management of mild to moderately severe, stable, noninsulin-dependent (type II) diabetes mellitus
Usual Dosage Divided doses may increase side effects
  Adults: Oral: Initial: 500-1000 mg 1-3 times/day; usual dose should not be more than 2 g/day
  Elderly: Oral: Initial: 250 mg 1-3 times/day; usual: 500-2000 mg; maximum: 2 g/day
Mechanism of Action A sulfonylurea hypoglycemic agent; its ability to lower elevated blood glucose levels in patients with functional pancreatic beta cells is
(Continued)

Tolbutamide *(Continued)*

similar to the other sulfonylurea agents; stimulates synthesis and release of endogenous insulin from pancreatic islet tissue. The hypoglycemic effect is attributed to an increased sensitivity of insulin receptors and improved peripheral utilization of insulin. Suppression of glucagon secretion may also contribute to the hypoglycemic effects of tolbutamide.

Pharmacodynamics/kinetics

Peak hypoglycemic action: Oral: 1-3 hours

Duration: Oral: 6-12 hours

Time to peak serum concentration: 2-5 hours

Absorption: Oral: Rapid

Distribution: V_d: 0.1-0.15 L/kg

Metabolism: Hepatic metabolism to hydroxymethyltolbutamide (mildly active) and carboxytolbutamide (inactive); metabolism does not appear to be affected by age

Half-life, plasma: 4-6 hours

Signs and Symptoms of Acute Intoxication Leukopenia or neutropenia (agranulocytosis, granulocytopenia); hypothyroidism, eczema, photophobia, photosensitivity, hypoglycemia

When to Transport to Hospital Transport any symptomatic patient, any pediatric ingestion, or any adult ingestion over 2 g

Warnings/Precautions False-positive response has been reported in patients with liver disease, idiopathic hypoglycemia of infancy, severe malnutrition, acute pancreatitis. Because of its low potency and short duration, it is a useful agent in the elderly if drug interactions can be avoided. How "tightly" an elderly patient's blood glucose should be controlled is controversial; however, a fasting blood sugar of <150 mg/dL is now an acceptable end point. Such a decision should be based on the patient's functional and cognitive status, how well they recognize hypoglycemic or hyperglycemic symptoms, and how to respond to them and their other disease states.

Adverse Reactions

>10%:

Central nervous system: Headache, dizziness

Gastrointestinal: Constipation, diarrhea, heartburn, anorexia, epigastric fullness

1% to 10%: Dermatologic: Rash, urticaria, photosensitivity

Reference Range Fasting blood glucose: Adults: 80-140 mg/dL; Elderly: 100-180 mg/dL

Dosage Forms

Injection, diagnostic, as sodium: 1 g (20 mL)

Tablet: 250 mg, 500 mg

Specific References

Seger D, "Toxic Emergencies of Endocrine and Metabolic Therapeutic Agents," *J Emerg Med*, 1988, 6(6):527-37.

Toluene

Synonyms Methyl Benzene; Tolu-Sol

UN Number 1294

Commonly Found In Glues, paint removers, pesticides, degreasers

Abuse Potential Yes

Impairment Potential Yes; Blood toluene levels over 1 mg/L associated with intoxication along with the breath odor of toluene

Baselt RC and Cravey RH, *Disposition of Toxic Drugs and Chemicals in Man*, 4th ed, Foster City, CA: Chemical Toxicology Institute, 1995, 742.

Mechanism of Toxic Action Three mechanisms proposed:
Alters lipid structure of cell membranes
Alters membrane-bound enzyme or receptor-site specificity
Toxic metabolite modifies function of cell microsomal proteins and RNA

Toxicodynamics/kinetics
Absorption: Readily by inhalation (within 30 minutes) or ingestion (within 2 hours); slowly by dermal route (14-23 mg/cm^2/hour); accumulates in adipose tissue
Metabolism: Hepatic to hippuric acid (60% to 70%), benzoyl glucuronide (10% to 20%), and ortho or para cresol (<1%)
Half-life: 3 days
Elimination: Hippuric acid excreted in urine, 20% excreted through the lungs, unchanged

Signs and Symptoms of Acute Intoxication Eye irritation, asthenia, dementia, chorea (extrapyramidal), skin irritation, myoglobinuria, metabolic acidosis, hypokalemia, ototoxicity, tinnitus, euphoria, memory loss, fatigue, irritability, vomiting, mydriasis, burns, nonoliguric renal failure, gaze nystagmus

When to Transport to Hospital Transport patients with any exposure

Overdosage/Treatment Decontamination:
Dermal: Wash with soap and water
Inhalation: Administer 100% humidified oxygen
Ocular: Irrigate with saline

Adverse Reactions
Cardiovascular: Angina, cardiomyopathy, cardiomegaly
Central nervous system: CNS depression following early CNS stimulation, panic attacks, memory disturbance
Hepatic: Transient liver injury
Neuromuscular & skeletal: Rhabdomyolysis
Renal: Acidosis (renal tubular) Type IV, renal tubular acidosis type I
Respiratory: Bronchitis/wheezing, pulmonary edema
Miscellaneous: Multiple chemical sensitivity syndrome

Reference Range Determined by measurement of urine hippuric acid. Blood toluene levels of 1.0-2.5 mg/L are associated with intoxication. Coma and death occur at levels of 2.5-10.0 mg/L. Blood toluene BEI is 1.0 mg/L. S-benzyl-N-acetyl-L-cysteine can be measured by HPLC and GC/MS at a lower urinary detection limit of 0.01 mg/L.

Additional Information Colorless liquid, sweet odor

Specific References
Meadows R and Verghese A, "Medical Complications of Glue Sniffing," *South Med J*, 1996, 89(5):455-61.

Tolu-Sed® DM [OTC] see Guaifenesin and Dextromethorphan *on page 271*
Tolu-Sol see Toluene *on previous page*
Topicycline® Topical see Tetracycline *on page 568*
Toprol XL® see Metoprolol *on page 400*
Toradol® see Ketorolac Tromethamine *on page 329*
Toscal® see Carbinoxamine *on page 106*
Totacillin® see Ampicillin *on page 48*
Totacillin®-N see Ampicillin *on page 48*
Touro Ex® see Guaifenesin *on page 269*
Touro LA® see Guaifenesin and Pseudoephedrine *on page 273*

Toxicology Drug Screen, Blood
Related Information
Toxicology Drug Screen, Urine *on next page*
Synonyms Drug Screen, Comprehensive Panel or Analysis
(Continued)

Toxicology Drug Screen, Blood *(Continued)*

Applies to Comatose Profile

Use Monitor toxic/overdose situations; most desirable to analyze in conjunction with urine toxicology testing; used to quantitate drug identified qualitatively in urine

Additional Information If only documentation of exposure to toxic drugs or drugs of abuse is desired, a urine drug screen is the most economical approach. See listing for Toxicology Drug Screen, Urine. When Toxicology Drug Screen, Blood is ordered, the individual drugs are quantitated in serum. When Toxicology Drug Screen, Urine is ordered, qualitative identification is carried out.

Specific References

Hepler B, Sutheimer C, and Sunshine I, "Role of the Toxicology Laboratory in Suspected Ingestions," *Pediatr Clin North Am*, 1986, 33(2):245-60.

Toxicology Drug Screen, Urine

Related Information

Toxicology Drug Screen, Blood *on previous page*

Synonyms Drug Screen, Comprehensive Panel or Analysis, Urine

Applies to Narcotics Drug Screen, Urine

Use Screen for drug abuse, drug toxicity alone or in conjunction with serum/plasma testing

Reference Range None detected or negative (less than cutoff for drugs of abuse)

Additional Information Some toxins (eg, metals, volatiles, gaseous compounds) may require specific methodology (eg, atomic absorption spectrophotometry, gas chromatography). Also see Toxicology Drug Screen, Blood test listing.

Specific References

Caplan YH, "Drug Testing in Urine," *J Forensic Sci*, 1989, 34:1417-21.

Toxicology, Hypnotics and Tranquilizers, Serum

Synonyms Hypnotics and Tranquilizers, Toxicology, Blood

Use Detect drug abuse; evaluate toxicity; most desirable to analyze in conjunction with urine toxicology testing to quantitate drug identified qualitatively in urine

Reference Range Therapeutic:

- amobarbital: 7-15 µg/mL
- butabarbital: mildly sedated 3-25 µg/mL
- chlordiazepoxide: 0.1-3.0 µg/mL
- diazepam: 105-1540 ng/mL
- ethchlorvynol: 0.5-6.5 µg/mL
- glutethimide: 4-12 µg/mL
- meprobamate: 10-20 µg/mL
- methaqualone 0.9-8.0 µg/mL
- pentobarbital: 4-6 µg/mL
- phenobarbital: 15-40 µg/mL
- secobarbital: 3-5 µg/mL

Additional Information If only documentation of exposure to toxic drugs or drugs of abuse is desired, a urine drug screen is the most economical approach.

Tradon® *see Pemoline on page 462*

Tramadol (TRA ma dole)

U.S. Brand Names Crispin®; Tramal®; Trodon®; Ultram®

Therapeutic Category Analgesic, Non-narcotic

Abuse Potential Yes

Impairment Potential Yes

Use Relief of moderate to moderately severe pain

Usual Dosage

Oral:

Children >1 year: 1-2 mg/kg

Adults: 50-100 mg every 4-6 hours; maximum daily dose: 400 mg (healthy patients), 300 mg in elderly (>75 years)

Patients with cirrhosis: 50 mg every 12 hours

Rectal: 100 mg

Mechanism of Action Centrally acting analgesic with selective (mu) opioid receptor agonist and norepinephrine and serotonin reuptake inhibition; ~1.5-3 times less potent than morphine but more antitussive effect than codeine

Pharmacodynamics/kinetics

Duration of action: 9 hours

Peak serum levels: 2 hours

Absorption: Rapid and complete

Metabolism: Extensive in the liver via demethylation, glucuronidation, and sulfation; has pharmacologically active metabolite

Half-life, elimination:

Tramadol: 6 hours

Active metabolite: 7 hours

Half-life prolonged in the elderly and/or hepatic/renal dysfunction

Bioavailability: 75%

Signs and Symptoms of Acute Intoxication Sleepiness, coma, seizures (at oral doses exceeding 700 mg or I.V. doses exceeding 300 mg), miosis, respiratory depression

When to Transport to Hospital Transport any pediatric (<1 year of age) exposure, any other pediatric exposure over 10 mg/kg (<6 years of age), any symptomatic patient, or adult oral ingestions over 500 mg

Warnings/Precautions Concomitant CNS depressants, MAO inhibitors may predispose to additive toxicities

Adverse Reactions >1%:

Central nervous system: Dizziness, headache, somnolence, stimulation, restlessness

Gastrointestinal: Nausea, diarrhea, constipation, vomiting, dyspepsia

Neuromuscular & skeletal: Weakness

Miscellaneous: Diaphoresis

Reference Range Serum tramadol levels ranging from 100-300 ng/mL can be considered therapeutic

Drug Interactions Carbamazepine induces tramadol metabolism; with its discontinuation, tramadol toxicity may occur; MAO inhibitors in combination with tramadol may result in serotonin syndrome

Dosage Forms Tablet: 50 mg

Specific References

Levien TL and Baker DE, "Reviews of Tramadol and Tretinoin," *Hosp Pharm*, 1996, 31(1):54, 59-64, 67-8, 71-3.

Tramal® *see Tramadol on this page*

Trancopal® *see Chlormezanone on page 126*

Trandate® *see Labetalol on page 331*

Tranilcipromina *see Tranylcypromine on next page*

Tranquilizers (Valium®, Librium®, etc) *see* Benzodiazepines, Qualitative, Urine *on page 71*

Transamine *see* Tranylcypromine *on this page*

Transdermal-NTG® *see* Nitroglycerin *on page 437*

Transderm-Nitro® *see* Nitroglycerin *on page 437*

Transderm Scop® *see* Scopolamine *on page 532*

Transene® *see* Clorazepate *on page 156*

Trans-Testosterone *see* Testosterone *on page 564*

Trans-Ver-Sal® AdultPatch [OTC] *see* Salicylic Acid *on page 530*

Trans-Ver-Sal® PediaPatch [OTC] *see* Salicylic Acid *on page 530*

Trans-Ver-Sal® PlantarPatch [OTC] *see* Salicylic Acid *on page 530*

Tranxene® *see* Clorazepate *on page 156*

Tranxilium® *see* Clorazepate *on page 156*

Tranylcypromine (tran il SIP roe meen)

Synonyms Tranilcipromina; Transamine

U.S. Brand Names Parnate®

Therapeutic Category Antidepressant

Impairment Potential Yes

Use Symptomatic treatment of atypical, nonendogenous or neurotic depression

Usual Dosage Adults: Oral: 10 mg twice daily, increase by 10 mg increments at 1- to 3-week intervals; maximum: 60 mg/day

Minimum lethal dose: 170 mg

Mechanism of Action Thought to act by increasing endogenous concentrations of epinephrine, norepinephrine, dopamine and serotonin through inhibition of the enzyme (monoamine oxidase) responsible for the breakdown of these neurotransmitters

Pharmacodynamics/kinetics Half-life: 1.5-2.5 hours (longer in overdose)

Signs and Symptoms of Acute Intoxication Fever, impotence, numbness, extrapyramidal reaction, insomnia, neutropenia, ptosis, hypertension, agranulocytosis, granulocytopenia, delirium, thrombocytopenia

When to Transport to Hospital Transport any symptomatic patient or any ingestion over 80 mg

Warnings/Precautions Avoid tyramine-containing foods: red wine, cheese (except cottage, ricotta, and cream), smoked or pickled fish, beef or chicken liver, dried sausage, fava or broad bean pods, yeast vitamin supplements; avoid use with patients <16 or >60 years of age

Adverse Reactions 1% to 10%: Cardiovascular: Orthostatic hypotension

Reference Range Therapeutic blood level: 0.1 mg/L; serum level of 1 mg/L has been associated with coma

Dosage Forms Tablet: 10 mg

Specific References

Boniface PJ, "Two Cases of Fatal Intoxication Due to Tranylcypromine Overdose," *J Anal Toxicol*, 1991, 15(1):38-40.

Traumacut® *see* Methocarbamol *on page 390*

Trazodone (TRAZ oh done)

U.S. Brand Names Deprax®; Desyrel®; Molipaxin®; Thrombran®; Trittico®

Therapeutic Category Antidepressant

Abuse Potential Yes

Impairment Potential Yes

Use Treatment of depression

Usual Dosage Therapeutic effects may take up to 4 weeks to occur; therapy is normally maintained for several months after optimum response is reached to prevent recurrence of depression

Oral:

Adolescents: Initial: 25-50 mg/day; increase to 100-150 mg/day in divided doses

Adults: Initial: 150 mg/day in 3 divided doses (may increase by 50 mg/day every 3-7 days); maximum: 600 mg/day

Maximum tolerated dose:

Children: 200 mg

Adults: 9 g

Mechanism of Action Inhibits reuptake of serotonin and norepinephrine; hypotension may be due to alpha-receptor blockade

Pharmacodynamics/kinetics

Onset of action: 7 days

Peak effect: Maximum antidepressant effect usually occurs within 2 weeks; roughly 25% of patients require up to 4 weeks of therapy to reach optimum response

Absorption: Absorbed well; when taken after ingestion of food, there may be an increase in the amount of drug absorbed

Metabolism: In the liver to an active metabolite (m-chlorophenylpiperazine)

Half-life: 4-7.5 hours

Time to peak serum concentration: Within 30-100 minutes, prolonged in the presence of food (up to 2½ hours)

Elimination: Primarily in urine and secondarily in feces

Signs and Symptoms of Acute Intoxication Drowsiness, delirium, photosensitivity; erythema multiforme, insomnia, dry mouth, myoclonus, hepatic failure, vomiting, ejaculatory disturbances, clitoral hypertrophy, extrapyramidal reaction, hypotension, drowsiness, heart block, ataxia, ototoxicity; tinnitus, incontinence, bradycardia, coma, priapism, seizures (rarely), bradycardia, first degree A-V block, respiratory depression, muscle asthenia, torsade de pointes

When to Transport to Hospital Transport any pediatric (<12 years of age) exposure, any symptomatic patient, or any ingestion over 200 mg

Warnings/Precautions Monitor closely and use with extreme caution in patients with cardiac disease, arrhythmias, epilepsy, or penile erection disorders; safety and efficacy in children <18 years of age have not been established

Adverse Reactions

>10%:

Central nervous system: Dizziness, headache, confusion

Gastrointestinal: Nausea, bad taste in mouth, xerostomia

Neuromuscular & skeletal: Muscle tremors

1% to 10%:

Gastrointestinal: Diarrhea, constipation

Neuromuscular & skeletal: Weakness

Ocular: Blurred vision

Reference Range Therapeutic: 0.5-2.5 µg/mL (SI: 1-6 µmol/L); overdoses of 4-5 g are associated with levels of 15-19 µg/mL

Dosage Forms Tablet: 50 mg, 100 mg, 150 mg, 300 mg

Additional Information Therapeutic effects may take up to 4 weeks to occur; therapy is normally maintained for several months after optimum response is reached to prevent recurrence of depression

Specific References

Burns M, Moskowitz H, and Jaffe J, "A Comparison of the Effects of Trazodone and Amitriptyline on Skills Performance by Geriatric Subjects," *J Clin Psychiatry*, 1986, 47(5):252-4.

(Continued)

Trazodone *(Continued)*

Taylor DP, Hyslop DK, and Riblet LA, "Trazodone. A New Nontricyclic Antidepressant Without Anticholinergic Activity," *Biochem Pharmacol*, 1980, 29(15):2149-50.

Zmitek A, "Trazodone-Induced Mania," *Br J Psychiatry*, 1987, 151:274-5.

Trendar® [OTC] *see* Ibuprofen *on page 308*

Trepidan® *see* Prazepam *on page 493*

Tresortil® *see* Methocarbamol *on page 390*

Trexan™ *see* Naltrexone *on page 420*

Tri® *see* Nitrazepam *on page 435*

TRI *see* Trichloroethylene *on page 594*

Triacin-C® *see* Triprolidine, Pseudoephedrine, and Codeine *on page 602*

Triadapin® *see* Doxepin *on page 211*

Triaminic® Allergy Tablet [OTC] *see* Chlorpheniramine and Phenylpropanolamine *on page 134*

Triaminic® Cold Tablet [OTC] *see* Chlorpheniramine and Phenylpropanolamine *on page 134*

Triaminic® Expectorant [OTC] *see* Guaifenesin and Phenylpropanolamine *on page 272*

Triaminicol® Multi-Symptom Cold Syrup [OTC] *see* Chlorpheniramine, Phenylpropanolamine, and Dextromethorphan *on page 137*

Triaminic® Oral Infant Drops *see* Pheniramine, Phenylpropanolamine, and Pyrilamine *on page 473*

Triaminic® Syrup [OTC] *see* Chlorpheniramine and Phenylpropanolamine *on page 134*

Triapin® *see* Butalbital Compound *on page 93*

Triatox® *see* Amitraz *on page 39*

Triavil® *see* Amitriptyline and Perphenazine *on page 42*

Triazid *see* Amitraz *on page 39*

Triazolam *(trye AY zoe lam)*

Related Information

Controlled Substances - Uses and Effects *on page 741*

Synonyms Cloxazolam

U.S. Brand Names Halcion®; Novodorm®; Songar®

Canadian Brand Names Apo-Triazo®; Gen-Triazolam®; Novo-Triolam®; Nu-Triazo®

Therapeutic Category Benzodiazepine

Abuse Potential Yes

Impairment Potential Yes; Blood triazolam concentration averaging 23 µg/L (range 4-40 µg/L) associated with driving impairment. Brief or extended periods of exposure are less likely to cause driving impairment in the elderly as compared with the longer half-life benzodiazepines.

Joynt BP, "Triazolam Blood Concentrations in Forensic Cases in Canada," *J Anal Toxicol*, 1993, 17(3):171-7.

Use Short-term treatment of insomnia

Usual Dosage Onset of action is rapid, patient should be in bed when taking medication. Oral:

Children <18 years: Dosage not established
Adults: 0.125-0.25 mg at bedtime

Mechanism of Action Depresses all levels of the CNS, including the limbic and reticular formation, probably through the increased action of gamma-aminobutyric acid (GABA), which is a major inhibitory neurotransmitter in the brain

Pharmacodynamics/kinetics Studies have shown that the elderly are more sensitive to the effects of benzodiazepines as compared to younger adults

Onset of action: Hypnotic effects occur within 15-30 minutes

Duration: 6-7 hours

Absorption: Readily from gastrointestinal tract

Metabolism: Extensive in the liver

Half-life: 1.7-5 hours

Time to peak plasma concentration: 42 minutes

Signs and Symptoms of Acute Intoxication Somnolence, confusion, night terrors, cognitive dysfunction, hypothermia, cholestatic jaundice, mania, coma, rhabdomyolysis, ataxia, myoglobinuria, slurred speech, diminished reflexes, respiratory depression, hypotension, visual or auditory hallucinations, gaze nystagmus

When to Transport to Hospital Transport any pediatric exposure, any symptomatic patient, or any ingestion over 0.5 mg

Warnings/Precautions Anterograde amnesia has occurred with triazolam, generally it occurred with doses of 0.5 mg but it has also been reported with lower doses; prolonged clearance noted in obese patients; abrupt discontinuance of the drug should be avoided since manifestations of withdrawal can be precipitated or rebound insomnia can result

Adverse Reactions

>10%:

Cardiovascular: Tachycardia, chest pain

Central nervous system: Drowsiness, fatigue, ataxia, lightheadedness, memory impairment, insomnia, anxiety, depression, headache

Dermatologic: Rash

Endocrine & metabolic: Decreased libido

Gastrointestinal: Xerostomia, decreased salivation, constipation, nausea, vomiting, diarrhea, increased or decreased appetite

Neuromuscular & skeletal: Dysarthria

Ocular: Blurred vision

Miscellaneous: Diaphoresis

1% to 10%:

Cardiovascular: Syncope, hypotension

Central nervous system: Confusion, nervousness, dizziness, akathisia

Dermatologic: Dermatitis

Gastrointestinal: Weight gain or loss, increased salivation, muscle cramps

Neuromuscular & skeletal: Rigidity, tremor

Otic: Tinnitus

Respiratory: Nasal congestion, hyperventilation

Reference Range Fatalities associated with postmortem levels >47 nmol/L

Dosage Forms Tablet: 0.125 mg, 0.25 mg

Additional Information Onset of action is rapid, patient should be in bed when taking medication; grapefruit juice can increase the bioavailability and thus serum level of triazolam

Specific References

Olson KR, Yin L, Osterloh J, et al, "Coma Caused by Trivial Triazolam Overdose," *Am J Emerg Med*, 1985, 3(3):210-1.

Triban® *see* Trimethobenzamide *on page 599*

Trichloren *see* Trichloroethylene *on next page*

Trichloroacetaldehyde Monohydrate *see* Chloral Hydrate *on page 122*

Trichloroethane

Synonyms CF 2; Methyl Chloroform; Strobane; TCA; TCE

UN Number 2831

Commonly Found In Cleaning solvent lubricant, ink, typewriter correction fluid; also is frequently used in an abused setting ("bagging")

Abuse Potential Yes

Impairment Potential Yes; Due to its central nervous system depression effects, impaired performance is likely to occur at air concentrations over 175 ppm

Gamberale F and Hultengren M, "Methyl-Chloroform Exposure. II. Psychophysiological Function," *Work Environ Health*, 1973, 10:82-92.

Mackay CJ, Campbell L, Samuel AM, et al, "Behavioral Changes During Exposure to 1,1,1-Trichloroethane: Time-Course and Relationship to Blood Solvent Levels," *Am J Ind Med*, 1987, 11:223-40.

Mechanism of Toxic Action CNS depression, rapid anesthetic action

Toxicodynamics/kinetics

Absorption: Rapid dermally, through inhalation, or through ingestion

Metabolism: Hepatic (<10%) to trichloroacetic acid

Half-life: 53 hours

Elimination: Primarily by the lungs (91%)

Signs and Symptoms of Acute Intoxication Diplopia, dizziness, acetone breath, coma, ataxia, agitation, drowsiness, hallucinations, nausea, vomiting, diarrhea, erythema, seizures, gaze nystagmus

When to Transport to Hospital Transport any exposed patient

Overdosage/Treatment Decontamination:

Dermal: Wash with soap and water; isopropyl alcohol can be used

Inhalation: Administer 100% humidified oxygen

Ocular: Irrigate with saline

Oral: Emesis is contraindicated; dilute with milk

Adverse Reactions

Cardiovascular: Hypotension, cardiovascular collapse, fibrillation (ventricular), shock, arrhythmias (ventricular)

Central nervous system: Anesthesia, axonopathy (peripheral)

Hematologic: Methemoglobinemia

Neuromuscular & skeletal: Neuropathy (peripheral), paresthesias

Ocular: Eye irritation

Respiratory: Pulmonary edema, respiratory depression

Miscellaneous: Multiple chemical sensitivity syndrome

Reference Range Fatal serum levels range from 1.7-42.0 mg/L of trichloroethane concentration; blood level of 1.4 mg/L consistent with exposure of 250 ppm

Additional Information Pleasant odor; door spray lubricants, VCR cleaners, typewriter correction fluid, and nonacid drain cleaners have highest amount of 1,1,1-trichloroethane

Specific References

King GS, Smialek JE, and Troutman WG, "Sudden Death in Adolescents Resulting From the Inhalation of Typewriter Correction Fluid," *JAMA*, 1985, 253(111):1604-6.

Trichloroethylene

Synonyms Acetylene Trichloride; TRI; Trichloren; Trilene

UN Number 1710

Abuse Potential Yes

Impairment Potential Yes; Psychomotor and reaction time decrements probably occur at air concentration of ≥200 ppm for approximately 1- to 2-hour period

Bleecker ML and Hansen JA, *Occupational Neurology and Clinical Neurotoxicology*, Baltimore, MD: Williams & Wilkins, 1994, 223.

Use Industrial degreaser, fire retardant, lacquer/adhesive, house cleaning solvent, typewriter correction fluid

Mechanism of Toxic Action CNS depressant; may induce peroxisome proliferation

Toxicodynamics/kinetics

Absorption: Rapid by ingestion and inhalation; minimal dermal exposure

Metabolism: In the liver; fat soluble

Half-life: 30-38 hours

Excretion: Excreted in urine, feces, and lung (16%)

Signs and Symptoms of Acute Intoxication Mydriasis, salivation, slurred speech, loss of taste, cyanosis, dyspnea, ataxia, gaze nystagmus, dizziness, dementia, cranial nerve palsies, fatigue, resting tremor, headache, vomiting, impotence, seizures, bradycardia

When to Transport to Hospital Transport any exposed patient

Overdosage/Treatment Decontamination:

Dermal: Wash with soap and water

Ocular: Irrigate with saline

Oral: **Do not** induce emesis; activated charcoal with cathartic may be used

Adverse Reactions

Cardiovascular: Fibrillation (ventricular), bradycardia, Raynaud's phenomenon, sinus bradycardia, arrhythmias (ventricular)

Central nervous system: CNS depression

Hepatic: Hepatitis, centrilobular hepatic necrosis

Ocular: Diplopia, blurred vision progressing to blindness, optic neuropathy

Renal: Tubular necrosis (acute)

Respiratory: Pulmonary edema, respiratory depression

Reference Range Blood concentrations of 5.0-10.0 mg/dL related to anesthetic action; levels of 0.3-11.0 mg/dL are associated with fatalities; blood level of 0.1 mg/dL is consistent with exposure of 100 ppm

Additional Information Chloroform odor; degreaser's flush occurs in workers who ingest ethanol following exposure to trichloroethylene

Trichloroethylene Subregistry
Jo Anne Burg PhD
Agency for Toxic Substances and Disease Registry
1600 Clifton Road, NE
Mailstop E 31
Atlanta, GA 30333
(404) 639-6202

Specific References

Barceloux DG and Rosenberg J, "Trichloroethylene Toxicity," *J Toxicol Clin Toxicol*, 1990, 28:479-504.

Trichloroform *see* Chloroform *on page 129*

Trichloromethane *see* Chloroform *on page 129*

Trichlorpyriphos (Discontinued) *see* Chlorpyrifos *on page 143*

Tri-Clear® Expectorant [OTC] *see* Guaifenesin and Phenylpropanolamine *on page 272*

Tricodein *see* Codeine *on page 164*

Tricosal® *see* Choline Magnesium Trisalicylate *on page 146*

Tridil® *see* Nitroglycerin *on page 437*

Trifed-C® *see* Triprolidine, Pseudoephedrine, and Codeine *on page 602*

Trifluoperazine (trye floo oh PER a zeen)

U.S. Brand Names Calmazine®; Eskazina®; Novoflurazine®; Solazine®; Stelazine®; Terfluzin®

Therapeutic Category Antipsychotic Agent; Phenothiazine Derivative

Impairment Potential Yes

Use Treatment of psychoses and management of anxiety

Usual Dosage

Children 6-12 years: Psychoses:

Oral: Hospitalized or well supervised patients: Initial: 1 mg 1-2 times/day, gradually increase until symptoms are controlled or adverse effects become troublesome; maximum: 15 mg/day

I.M.: 1 mg twice daily

Adults:

Psychoses:

Outpatients: Oral: 1-2 mg twice daily

Hospitalized or well supervised patients: Initial: 2-5 mg twice daily with optimum response in the 15-20 mg/day range; do not exceed 40 mg/day

I.M.: 1-2 mg every 4-6 hours as needed up to 10 mg/24 hours maximum

Nonpsychotic anxiety: Oral: 1-2 mg twice daily; maximum: 6 mg/day; therapy for anxiety should not exceed 12 weeks; do not exceed 6 mg/day for longer than 12 weeks when treating anxiety; agitation, jitteriness, or insomnia may be confused with original neurotic or psychotic symptoms

Mechanism of Action Blocks postsynaptic mesolimbic dopaminergic receptors in the brain; exhibits a strong alpha-adrenergic blocking effect and depresses the release of hypothalamic and hypophyseal hormones

Pharmacodynamics/kinetics

Onset of action: Rapid

Duration: ≥12 hours

Metabolism: Extensive liver metabolism

Half-life: >24 hours with chronic use; 7-18 hours with one dose

Time to peak plasma concentration: 1.5-4.5 hours

Elimination: Primarily excreted renally; biliary

Signs and Symptoms of Acute Intoxication Deep sleep, coma, impotence, Parkinson's-like symptoms, gynecomastia, galactorrhea, dysphagia, extrapyramidal reaction, abnormal involuntary muscle movements, neuroleptic malignant syndrome, hyperthermia, hepatic failure, hypotension or hypertension; generalized rigidity, torticollis, facial grimacing, slurred speech, stridor trismus, urine discoloration (pink), urine discoloration (red), urine discoloration (red-brown), vision color changes (brown tinge); leukopenia; neutropenia; agranulocytosis; granulocytopenia

When to Transport to Hospital Transport any pediatric (<6 years of age) exposure or any symptomatic patient

Warnings/Precautions Watch for hypotension when administering I.M. or I.V.; safety in children <6 months of age has not been established; use with caution in patients with cardiovascular disease or seizures

Adverse Reactions

>10%:

Cardiovascular: Hypotension, orthostatic hypotension

Central nervous system: Pseudoparkinsonism, akathisia, dystonias, tardive dyskinesia (persistent), dizziness

Gastrointestinal: Constipation

Ocular: Pigmentary retinopathy

Respiratory: Nasal congestion

Miscellaneous: Diaphoresis (decreased)

1% to 10%:

Genitourinary: Dysuria, ejaculatory disturbances

Dermatologic: Increased sensitivity to sun, rash
Endocrine & metabolic: Changes in menstrual cycle, changes in libido, breast pain
Gastrointestinal: Weight gain, nausea, vomiting, stomach pain
Neuromuscular & skeletal: Trembling of fingers

Drug Interactions Other CNS depressants, anticonvulsants, lithium, metrizamide

Dosage Forms
Concentrate, oral: 10 mg/mL (60 mL)
Injection: 2 mg/mL (10 mL)
Tablet: 1 mg, 2 mg, 5 mg, 10 mg

Additional Information Do not exceed 6 mg/day for longer than 12 weeks when treating anxiety; agitation, jitteriness or insomnia may be confused with original neurotic or psychotic symptoms; radiopaque

Specific References
FitzGerald MX and FitzGerald O, "Reaction to Trifluoperazine Abuse," *Lancet*, 1969, 1(605):1100.

Triflupromazine (trye floo PROE ma zeen)

Synonyms Fluopromazine
U.S. Brand Names Psyquil®; Siquil®; Vesprin®
Therapeutic Category Antipsychotic Agent; Phenothiazine Derivative
Impairment Potential Yes
Use Treatment of psychoses, nausea, vomiting, and intractable hiccups
Usual Dosage
Children: I.M.: 0.2-0.25 mg/kg
Adults:
I.M.: 5-15 mg every 4 hours
I.V.: 1 mg

Signs and Symptoms of Acute Intoxication Deep sleep, euphoria, ejaculatory disturbances, priapism, insomnia, hyperglycemia, leukopenia, neuroleptic malignant syndrome, coma, extrapyramidal reaction, depression, neutropenia, abnormal involuntary muscle movements, hypotension or hypertension; vision color changes (brown tinge); generalized rigidity, torticollis, facial grimacing, slurred speech, stridor trismus

When to Transport to Hospital Transport any symptomatic patient or any exposure over 0.3 mg/kg

Adverse Reactions
Cardiovascular: Hypotension, sinus tachycardia
Central nervous system: Neuroleptic malignant syndrome, extrapyramidal signs, sedation, psychosis
Endocrine & metabolic: Syndrome of inappropriate antidiuretic hormone
Miscellaneous: Systemic lupus erythematosus (SLE)

Reference Range Therapeutic: 0.002-0.0600 mg/L
Dosage Forms Injection: 20 mg/mL (1 mL)
Specific References
Bhugra DK and Low NC, "Neuroleptic Malignant Syndrome," *Br J Clin Pract*, 1986, 40(10):445-6.

Trimeprazine (trye MEP ra zeen)

Synonyms Alimemazine Tartrate

U.S. Brand Names Nedeltran®; Panectyl®; Temaril®; Theralene®; Vallergon®; Variargil®

Therapeutic Category Antihistamine; Antipsychotic Agent; Phenothiazine Derivative

Impairment Potential Yes

Use Cough suppressant; relief of pruritus; anesthesia induction; useful for plant-induced dermatitis; allergic rhinitis; sleep disorders

Usual Dosage Oral, (maximum daily dose): 100 mg

Children:
>3 years: 2.5 mg up to 3 times/day
>6 years: Sustained release (Spansule®) capsule: 5 mg/day
Night walking: 6 mg/kg up to 60 mg
Preoperative anesthesia (children >2 years): 2-5 mg/kg

Adults:
Pruritus: 2.5 mg 4 times/day
Sustained release (Spansule®) capsule: 5 mg every 12 hours; decrease dose in elderly

Mechanism of Action A phenothiazine derivation with antimuscarinic and antihistaminic (H$_1$- receptor) effects

Pharmacodynamics/kinetics
Metabolism: Hepatic to sulfoxide and glucuronide conjugates
Bioavailability: 70%
Half-life: 5-8 hours

Signs and Symptoms of Acute Intoxication Hypotension, CNS depression, coma, parkinsonism, akathisia

When to Transport to Hospital Transport any pediatric (<3 years of age) exposure or any patient with change in mental status

Warnings/Precautions Use with caution in patients with glaucoma, prostatic hypertrophy, pyloric stenosis, alcohol or other CNS depressant use, children with sleep apnea or family history of sudden infant death syndrome, cardiovascular disease, intestinal obstruction or hepatic dysfunction

Adverse Reactions
Cardiovascular: Hypotension (orthostatic), bradycardia, sinus tachycardia
Central nervous system: Nightmares, headache, CNS depression, sedation, malignant hyperthermia, dystonia, ataxia
Endocrine & metabolic: Gynecomastia
Gastrointestinal: Dry mouth, constipation
Hematologic: Leukopenia, pancytopenia
Neuromuscular & skeletal: Tremors
Ocular: Mydriasis, diplopia
Otic: Tinnitus
Respiratory: Respiratory depression

Reference Range Therapeutic plasma level: 0.05-4.0 µg/mL; postmortem blood level of 6.52 µg/mL associated with fatality due to overdose of trimeprazine (postmortem urine was 6.22 µg/mL)

Dosage Forms
Capsule: 5 mg
Syrup: 2.5 mg/5 mL
Tablet: 2.5 mg

Specific References
Kintz P, Berthault F, Tracqui A, et al, "A Fatal Case of Alimemazine Poisoning," *J Anal Toxicol*, 1995, 19(7):591-4.

Trimethobenzamide (trye meth oh BEN za mide)

U.S. Brand Names Arrestin®; Pediatric Triban®; Tebamide®; T-Gen®; Ticon®; Tigan®; Triban®; Trimazide®

Therapeutic Category Anticholinergic Agent; Antiemetic

Impairment Potential Yes

Use Control of nausea and vomiting (especially for long-term antiemetic therapy); less effective than phenothiazines but may be associated with fewer side effects

Usual Dosage Rectal use is contraindicated in neonates and premature infants
Children:
Rectal: <14 kg: 100 mg 3-4 times/day
Oral, rectal: 14-40 kg: 100-200 mg 3-4 times/day
Adults:
Oral: 250 mg 3-4 times/day
I.M., rectal: 200 mg 3-4 times/day

Mechanism of Action Acts centrally to inhibit the medullary chemoreceptor trigger zone

Pharmacodynamics/kinetics
Onset of antiemetic effect:
Oral: Within 10-40 minutes
I.M.: Within 15-35 minutes
Duration: 3-4 hours
Absorption: Rectal: ~60%

Signs and Symptoms of Acute Intoxication Hypotension, seizures, CNS depression, cardiac arrhythmias, disorientation, confusion

When to Transport to Hospital Transport any symptomatic patient

Warnings/Precautions May mask emesis due to Reye's syndrome or mimic CNS effects of Reye's syndrome in patients with emesis of other etiologies; use in patients with acute vomiting should be avoided

Adverse Reactions
>10%: Central nervous system: Drowsiness
1% to 10%:
Cardiovascular: Hypotension
Central nervous system: Dizziness, headache
Gastrointestinal: Diarrhea
Neuromuscular & skeletal: Muscle cramps

Dosage Forms
Trimethobenzamide hydrochloride:
Capsule: 100 mg, 250 mg
Injection: 100 mg/mL (2 mL, 20 mL)
Suppository, rectal: 100 mg, 200 mg

Specific References
Kaan SK and Eshelman FN, "The Antiemetic Effects of Trimethobenzamide During Chemotherapy: A Controlled Study," *Curr Ther Res*, 1979, 26:210-3.

Trimethoprim and Sulfamethoxazole *see* Co-Trimoxazole *on page 168*
Trimethyl Glycol *see* Propylene Glycol *on page 513*

Trimipramine (trye MI pra meen)

Synonyms Trimepramine

U.S. Brand Names Surmontil®

Canadian Brand Names Apo-Trimip®; Novo-Tripramine®; Nu-Trimipramine®; Rhotrimine®

Therapeutic Category Antidepressant

Impairment Potential Yes
(Continued)

Trimipramine *(Continued)*

Use Treatment of various forms of depression, often in conjunction with psychotherapy

Usual Dosage Adults: Oral: 50-150 mg/day as a single bedtime dose up to a maximum of 200 mg/day outpatient and 300 mg/day inpatient

Mechanism of Action Increases the synaptic concentration of serotonin and/or norepinephrine in the central nervous system by inhibition of their reuptake by the presynaptic neuronal membrane

Pharmacodynamics/kinetics

Absorption: Rapid from the gastrointestinal tract

Metabolism: In the liver to desmethyl trimipramine

Half-life: 20-26 hours

Time to peak serum concentration: Within 6 hours

Elimination: Urine

Signs and Symptoms of Acute Intoxication Agitation, confusion, hallucinations, urinary retention, hypothermia, hypotension, intraocular pressure (increased), dementia, neuroleptic malignant syndrome, tachycardia, seizures, coma, leukopenia; neutropenia; agranulocytosis; granulocytopenia

When to Transport to Hospital Transport any symptomatic patient or any ingestion over 300 mg

Warnings/Precautions Use with caution in patients with cardiovascular disease, conduction disturbances, seizure disorders, urinary retention, hyperthyroidism or those receiving thyroid replacement; avoid use during lactation; use with caution in pregnancy; do not discontinue abruptly in patients receiving chronic high-dose therapy

Adverse Reactions

>10%:

Central nervous system: Dizziness, drowsiness, headache

Gastrointestinal: Xerostomia, constipation, increased appetite, nausea, unpleasant taste, weight gain

Neuromuscular & skeletal: Weakness

1% to 10%:

Cardiovascular: Arrhythmias, hypotension

Central nervous system: Confusion, delirium, hallucinations, nervousness, restlessness, parkinsonian syndrome, insomnia

Endocrine & metabolic: Sexual dysfunction

Gastrointestinal: Diarrhea, heartburn

Genitourinary: Dysuria

Neuromuscular & skeletal: Fine muscle tremors

Ocular: Blurred vision, eye pain

Miscellaneous: Diaphoresis (excessive)

Reference Range An oral dose of 50 mg yields a peak serum level of 260 nmol/L

Dosage Forms Capsule: 25 mg, 50 mg, 100 mg

Specific References

Nebinger P and Koel M, "Specificity Data of the Tricyclic Antidepressants Assay by Fluorescent Polarization Immunoassay," *J Anal Toxicol*, 1990, 14(4):219-21.

Trimox® see Amoxicillin *on page 45*

Tri-Nefrin® Extra Strength Tablet [OTC] see Chlorpheniramine and Phenylpropanolamine *on page 134*

Triniad® see Isoniazid *on page 322*

Trinitrin see Nitroglycerin *on page 437*

Triotann® Tablet see Chlorpheniramine, Pyrilamine, and Phenylephrine *on page 138*

Trioxane *see* Formaldehyde *on page 259*

Tripelennamine (tri pel EN a meen)

Synonyms Pyribenzamine®; Super Blue

U.S. Brand Names PBZ®; PBZ-SR®

Therapeutic Category Antihistamine

Abuse Potential Yes

Impairment Potential Yes

Use Perennial and seasonal allergic rhinitis and other allergic symptoms including rash

Usual Dosage Oral:

  Infants and Children: 5 mg/kg/day in 4-6 divided doses, up to 300 mg/day maximum

  Adults: 25-50 mg every 4-6 hours, extended release tablets 100 mg morning and evening up to 100 mg every 8 hours

Mechanism of Action Competes with histamine for H_1-receptor sites on effector cells in the gastrointestinal tract, blood vessels, and respiratory tract

Pharmacodynamics/kinetics

  Onset of action: Within 15-30 minutes

  Duration: 4-6 hours (up to 8 hours with PBZ-SR®)

  Metabolism: Almost completely in the liver

  Elimination: Urine

Signs and Symptoms of Acute Intoxication CNS stimulation or CNS depression; mydriasis, ataxia, athetosis, flushing

When to Transport to Hospital Transport any symptomatic patient or any ingestion over 5 mg/kg

Adverse Reactions

  >10%:

    Central nervous system: Slight to moderate drowsiness

    Respiratory: Thickening of bronchial secretions

  1% to 10%:

    Central nervous system: Headache, fatigue, nervousness, dizziness

    Gastrointestinal: Appetite increase, weight gain, nausea, diarrhea, abdominal pain, xerostomia

    Neuromuscular & skeletal: Arthralgia

    Respiratory: Pharyngitis

Reference Range Peak serum concentration: 60-200 µg/L

Dosage Forms

  Elixir, as citrate: 37.5 mg/5 mL (473 mL)

  Tripelennamine hydrochloride:

    Tablet: 25 mg, 50 mg

    Tablet, extended release: 100 mg

Additional Information Do not crush extended release tablets; urinary hesitancy can be reduced if patient voids just prior to taking drug; occasionally associated with pentazocine abuse (Ts and blues)

Specific References

  Yeh SY, Todd GD, Johnson RE, et al, "The Pharmacokinetics of Pentazocine and Tripelennamine," *Clin Pharmacol Ther*, 1986, 39(6):669-76.

Triphacycline® *see* Tetracycline *on page 568*

Tri-Phen-Chlor® *see* Chlorpheniramine, Phenyltoloxamine, Phenylpropanolamine, and Phenylephrine *on page 137*

Triphenyl® Expectorant [OTC] *see* Guaifenesin and Phenylpropanolamine *on page 272*

Triphenyl® Syrup [OTC] *see* Chlorpheniramine and Phenylpropanolamine *on page 134*

Triprolidine, Pseudoephedrine, and Codeine
(trye PROE li deen, soo doe e FED rin, & KOE deen)

U.S. Brand Names Actagen-C®; Actifed® With Codeine; Allerfrin® w/Codeine; Aprodine® w/C; Triacin-C®; Trifed-C®

Therapeutic Category Antihistamine/Decongestant/Antitussive

Abuse Potential Yes

Impairment Potential Yes

Dosage Forms Syrup: Triprolidine hydrochloride 1.25 mg, pseudoephedrine hydrochloride 30 mg, and codeine phosphate 10 mg per 5 mL with alcohol 4.3%

Triptene® see Oxitriptan on page 451

Triptil® see Protriptyline on page 515

Tript-OH® see Oxitriptan on page 451

TripTone® Caplets® [OTC] see Dimenhydrinate on page 203

Triptum® see Oxitriptan on page 451

Tri-Tannate Plus® see Chlorpheniramine, Ephedrine, Phenylephrine, and Carbetapentane on page 135

Tri-Tannate® Tablet see Chlorpheniramine, Pyrilamine, and Phenylephrine on page 138

Trittico® see Trazodone on page 590

Trocal® [OTC] see Dextromethorphan on page 187

Trodon® see Tramadol on page 589

Trofan® see Tryptophan on this page

Trofan-DS® see Tryptophan on this page

Tropical Myrtle see Clove on page 158

Tropium® see Chlordiazepoxide on page 124

Truphylline® see Theophylline Salts on page 571

Truxal® see Chlorprothixene on page 141

Truxaletter® see Chlorprothixene on page 141

Tryptacin® see Tryptophan on this page

Tryptan® see Tryptophan on this page

Tryptophan (TRIP toe fan)
Related Information
Oxitriptan on page 451

Synonyms L-Tryptophan

U.S. Brand Names Ardeytropin®; Atrimon®; Biotonin®; Kalma®; Neuroclam®; Neuroremed®; Optimax® WV; Pacitron®; Sedanoct®; Trofan®; Trofan-DS®; Tryptacin®; Tryptan®; Tryto-Som®

Therapeutic Category Nutritional Supplement

Use Antidepressant, insomnia, dietary supplement, postanoxic myoclonus

Usual Dosage Insomnia: 1-2 g at bedtime; doses up to 6 g/day in divided doses have been used to treat depression

Mechanism of Action An essential amino acid which is a precursor to serotonin

Pharmacodynamics/kinetics
Protein binding: 65% to 78%
Metabolism: In the brain (to serotonin) and in the liver (via kynurenine pathway to quinolinic acid, tryptamine, niacin among other metabolites)
Half-life: 1-3 hours

Signs and Symptoms of Acute Intoxication Nausea (>5 g intake), hypoglycemia, dizziness, headache

When to Transport to Hospital Transport any symptomatic patient or any ingestion over 5 g

Adverse Reactions Eosinophilia-myalgia syndrome has been associated with L-tryptophan use manufactured by a single Japanese company (Showa-Denko). Thought to be related by presence of impurities (3-phenylaminoalanine) this syndrome is characterized by an early phase (0-2 months) which consists of myalgia, skin rash, edema, fever, arthralgia, and dyspnea. Tachycardia may also be present. Later manifestations may include weight loss, muscle weakness, progressing ascending axonal polyneuropathy, paresthesias, alopecia, scleroderma-like cutaneous induration, liver function abnormalities. Leukocytosis with eosinophilia (eosinophil counts ranging from 1000-36,000/mm^3) usually occur. Eosinophilic fasciitis may also occur. Doses associated with development of this syndrome involve 1.2-2.4 g/day for 2 weeks to 8 years.

Central nervous system: Headache, drowsiness, fever, euphoria
Endocrine & metabolic: Sexual dysfunction
Gastrointestinal: Nausea
Neuromuscular & skeletal: Dyskinesias
Respiratory: Pneumonitis

Drug Interactions With concomitant use with MAO inhibitor agents or selective serotonin reuptake inhibitors; a serotonin-like reaction can develop; tryptophan can reduce blood levels of levodopa

Dosage Forms
Capsule: 500 mg
Tablet: 200 mg, 500 mg, 667 mg, 1000 mg

Additional Information Usual daily dietary intake: 0.5-2 g; minimum daily requirement: ~3 mg/kg; may exacerbate Huntington's disease; 60 mg of L-tryptophan provide the equivalent of 1 mg of niacin; 1 glass of cow's milk contains ~100 mg tryptophan

Specific References
Varga J, Uitto J, and Jimenez SA, "The Cause and Pathogenesis of the Eosinophilia-Myalgia Syndrome," *Ann Intern Med*, 1992, 116(2):140-7.

Tryto-Som® *see* Tryptophan *on previous page*
Tuinal® *see* Amobarbital and Secobarbital *on page 43*

Turpentine Oil

Synonyms Gum Spirits; Spirits of Turpentine
UN Number 1299
Commonly Found In Oleoresin solvent, paint vehicle, deodorizer fragrance, rubefacient
U.S. Brand Names Ozothine®
Abuse Potential Yes
Impairment Potential Yes
Mechanism of Toxic Action CNS depressant, irritant to mucous membranes; high volatility with low viscosity
Toxicodynamics/kinetics
Absorption: Well absorbed through the gastrointestinal tract, by inhalation, and dermally; high fat solubility
Metabolism: In the liver
Elimination: Renally and through the lungs
Signs and Symptoms of Acute Intoxication Eye pain, vomiting, aspiration, fever, chills, cough, dyspnea, seizures, gaze nystagmus
When to Transport to Hospital Transport patients with any ingestion
Overdosage/Treatment Ocular: Irrigate copiously with saline
(Continued)

Turpentine Oil *(Continued)*

Adverse Reactions

Cardiovascular: Tachycardia, sinus tachycardia

Central nervous system: Ataxia, coma, fever, insomnia, dizziness, seizures (can occur after ingestions over 200 mL), headache (inhalation over 750 ppm for several hours)

Dermatologic: Contact dermatitis, erythema, blister, urticaria, nonimmunologic contact urticaria

Gastrointestinal: Hemorrhagic gastritis, diarrhea

Genitourinary: Hemorrhagic cystitis, dysuria

Ocular: Conjunctivitis, blepharospasm, mydriasis, eye irritation is perceptible at 175 ppm

Renal: Glomerulonephritis, hematuria, albuminuria

Respiratory: Pulmonary edema, aspiration pneumonitis, wheezing, coughing, dyspnea

Miscellaneous: Hypersensitivity reactions in 2.6% of population

Additional Information Pungent odor, although an odor of violets may be noted in overdose settings; combustible

Specific References

Mack RB, "Don Giovanni and Hellfire - Turpentine Poisoning," *Contemporary Pediatrics*, 1996, 13(7):67-79.

Valacyclovir (val ay SYE kloe veer)

Synonyms Valaciclovir

U.S. Brand Names Valtrex®

Therapeutic Category Antiviral Agent

Use Herpes simplex genital infections; may be effective in reducing postherpetic neuralgia in herpes zoster infections

Usual Dosage Herpes simplex: 1 g twice daily for 5 days

Mechanism of Action Inhibits DNA synthesis and viral replication by competing with deoxyguanosine triphosphate for viral DNA polymerase (thymidine kinase) and being incorporated into viral DNA

Pharmacodynamics/kinetics

Absorption: Oral: Rapid

Metabolism: Converted to acyclovir rapidly

Half-life: Valacyclovir: 30 minutes; acyclovir: 3 hours

Elimination: Renal

(Continued)

Valacyclovir (Continued)

When to Transport to Hospital Transport any symptomatic patient

Warnings/Precautions Use with caution in patients with pre-existing renal disease or in those receiving other nephrotoxic drugs concurrently; maintain adequate urine output during the first 2 hours after I.V. infusion; use with caution in patients with underlying neurologic abnormalities, serious hepatic or electrolyte abnormalities, or substantial hypoxia; appears to reduce the length and severity of chickenpox, but should not be used unless patient is immunosuppressed

Adverse Reactions

>10%: Gastrointestinal: Nausea

1% to 10%:

Central nervous system: Headache, dizziness

Gastrointestinal: Diarrhea, constipation, abdominal pain, anorexia

Neuromuscular & skeletal: Weakness

Reference Range After a 1 g oral dose, peak serum acyclovir levels were ~5.65 µg/mL

Specific References

Jacobson MA, "Valaciclovir (BW256U87): the L-Valyl Ester of Acyclovir," *J Med Virol*, 1993, Suppl 1:150-3.

Valerian

Synonyms Garden Heliotrope; Jacob's Ladder; Phu; Radix Valerinae

Scientific Name *Valerian officinalis*

Applies to Valerian Root

Use Herbal medicine use as a sleep-promoting agent and minor tranquilizer (similar to benzodiazepines)

Usual Dosage Up to 1 g at night

Mechanism of Toxic Action Most pharmacologic activity located in fresh root or dried rhizome; the plant contains essential oils (valerenic acid and valenol, valepotriates, and alkaloids <0.2% concentration) which may affect neurotransmitter levels (serotonin, GABA, and norepinephrine); also has antispasmodic properties

Signs and Symptoms of Acute Intoxication Headache, blurred vision, fine tremor, fatigue, mydriasis, abdominal cramping; intravenous exposure can cause hypotension, lethargy, hypophosphatemia, hypocalcemia, hypokalemia, and piloerection. Contact with the plant can cause contact dermatitis. Hepatotoxicity (probably due to an idiosyncratic hypersensitivity) has been noted.

When to Transport to Hospital Transport any symptomatic patient

Additional Information *Valeriana officinalis* is a perennial plant that can reach 5 feet in height with tiny white or pink flowers. It is found in Europe, Canada, and Northern U.S.

Specific References

Willey LB, Mady SP, Cobaugh DJ, et al, "Valerian Overdose: A Case Report," *Vet Hum Toxicol*, 1995, 37(4):364-5.

Valerian Root *see* Valerian *on this page*

Valertest No.1® Injection *see* Estradiol and Testosterone *on page 229*

Valium® *see* Diazepam *on page 189*

Valkote® *see* Valproic Acid and Derivatives *on next page*

Vallergon® *see* Trimeprazine *on page 598*

Valoron® *see* Tilidine *on page 582*

Valproic Acid and Derivatives
(val PROE ik AS id & dah RIV ah tives)

Synonyms Dipropylacetic Acid; Divalproex Sodium; DPA; 2-Propylpentanoic Acid; 2-Propylvaleric Acid; Sodium Valproate

U.S. Brand Names Depakene®; Depakote®; Epilim®; Ergenyl®; Leptilan®; Valkote®

Therapeutic Category Anticonvulsant

Use Management of simple and complex absence seizures; mixed seizure types; myoclonic and generalized tonic-clonic (grand mal) seizures; may be effective in partial seizures and infantile spasm; approved for migraine prophylaxis (after other traditional agents have failed); acute and maintenance therapy for bipolar disease

Usual Dosage Children and Adults:

Oral: Initial: 10-15 mg/kg/day in 1-3 divided doses; increase by 5-10 mg/kg/day at weekly intervals until therapeutic levels are achieved; maintenance: 30-60 mg/kg/day in 2-3 divided doses

Children receiving more than 1 anticonvulsant (ie, polytherapy) may require doses up to 100 mg/kg/day in 3-4 divided doses

Rectal: Dilute syrup 1:1 with water for use as a retention enema; loading dose: 17-20 mg/kg one time; maintenance: 10-15 mg/kg/dose every 8 hours

Status epilepticus: As a retention enema or suppository: 200-1200 mg every 6 hours in adult or 15-20 mg/kg in pediatric patients

Mechanism of Action Causes increased availability of gamma-aminobutyric acid (GABA), an inhibitory neurotransmitter, to brain neurons or may enhance the action of GABA or mimic its action at postsynaptic receptor sites

Pharmacodynamics/kinetics

Absorption: Rapid from gastrointestinal tract; slight delay when taken with food

Metabolism: Extensive in the liver to glucuronide salt

Half-life:

Children: 4-14 hours, increased half-life in neonates and patients with liver disease

Adults: 8-17 hours

In overdose: 19-20 hours

Time to peak serum concentration: Within 1-4 hours; 3-5 hours after divalproex (enteric coated)

Signs and Symptoms of Acute Intoxication Coma, cholestatic jaundice, jaundice, photophobia, hypothyroidism, hyporeflexia, hyperglycemia, nephritis, myoclonus, night terrors, mania, dementia, ileus, Fanconi syndrome, extrapyramidal reaction, pseudotumor cerebri, migraine headache (exacerbation of), enuresis, encephalopathy, coagulopathy, gaze nystagmus, tremors, irritability, hyperactivity, confusion, cerebral edema, optic nerve atrophy, metabolic acidosis, miosis, hyperthermia, hypothermia, leukopenia; neutropenia; agranulocytosis; granulocytopenia

When to Transport to Hospital Transport any pediatric (<6 years of age) ingestion over 20 mg/kg or any symptomatic patient

Warnings/Precautions Hepatic failure resulting in fatalities has occurred in patients; children <2 years of age especially those on polytherapy are at considerable risk; hepatitis has been reported after 3 days to 6 months of therapy; monitor patients closely for appearance of malaise, asthenia, facial edema, anorexia, jaundice, and vomiting; may cause severe thrombocytopenia, bleeding

Adverse Reactions 1% to 10%:

Endocrine & metabolic: Change in menstrual cycle

Gastrointestinal: Abdominal cramps, anorexia, diarrhea, nausea, vomiting, weight gain

(Continued)

Valproic Acid and Derivatives *(Continued)*

Reference Range
Therapeutic: 50-100 µg/mL (SI: 350-690 µmol/L); seizure control may improve at levels >100 µg/mL (SI: >690 µmol/L)

Toxic: Toxicity may occur at levels of 100-150 µg/mL (SI: 690-1040 µmol/L)

Dosage Forms
Valproic acid as divalproex sodium:
  Capsule, sprinkle (Depakote® Sprinkle): 125 mg
  Tablet, delayed release (Depakote®): 125 mg, 250 mg, 500 mg

Valproic acid as sodium valproate:
  Syrup (Depakene®): 250 mg/5 mL (5 mL, 50 mL, 480 mL)

Capsule, as valproic acid (Depakene®): 250 mg

Specific References
Holle LM, Gidal BE, and Collins DM, "Valproate in Status Epilepticus," *Ann Pharmacother*, 1995, 29:1042-4.

Valrelease® *see* Diazepam *on page 189*

Valsera® *see* Flunitrazepam *on page 250*

Valtrex® *see* Valacyclovir *on page 605*

Vamate® *see* Hydroxyzine *on page 303*

Variargil® *see* Trimeprazine *on page 598*

Varsol 1® *see* Stoddard Solvent *on page 547*

Vascor® *see* Bepridil *on page 74*

Vaseretic® 10-25 *see* Enalapril and Hydrochlorothiazide *on page 219*

Vasocard® *see* Terazosin *on page 560*

VasoClear® [OTC] *see* Naphazoline *on page 422*

Vasocon Regular® *see* Naphazoline *on page 422*

Vasotec® *see* Enalapril *on page 217*

Vatran® *see* Diazepam *on page 189*

V-Dec-M® *see* Guaifenesin and Pseudoephedrine *on page 273*

Velosulin® *see* Insulin Preparations *on page 314*

Velosulin® BR *see* Insulin Preparations *on page 314*

Veltane® *see* Brompheniramine *on page 84*

Venlafaxine *(VEN la faks een)*

U.S. Brand Names Effexor®

Therapeutic Category Antidepressant

Impairment Potential Yes

Use Treatment of depression in adults

Usual Dosage Adults: Oral: 75 mg/day, administered in 2 or 3 divided doses, taken with food; dose may be increased to 150 mg/day up to 225-375 mg/day; a daily maximum of 375 mg may be needed for severely depressed patients

Mechanism of Action Phenylethylamine antidepressant which inhibits norepinephrine, serotonin, and dopamine (weakly) reuptake in the central nervous system

Pharmacodynamics/kinetics
Metabolism: Hepatic to an active metabolite, O-desmethyl-venlafaxine (ODV)
Bioavailability: Oral: 92% to 100%
Half-life: 5 hours (venlafaxine); 11 hours (ODV); prolonged in renal impairment
Time to peak serum levels: Oral: 1-2 hours

Signs and Symptoms of Acute Intoxication Sedation, tachycardia (sinus); profound CNS depression can occur with concomitant ingestions of other CNS depressants; seizures (7%)

When to Transport to Hospital Transport any pediatric patient or any symptomatic patient

Warnings/Precautions Use with caution in patients with mania, high diastolic blood pressure, epilepsy, coronary heart disease, hyperlipidemia

Adverse Reactions

≥10%:

Central nervous system: Headache, somnolence, dizziness, insomnia, nervousness

Gastrointestinal: Nausea, xerostomia, constipation

Genitourinary: Abnormal ejaculation

Neuromuscular & skeletal: Weakness, neck pain

Miscellaneous: Diaphoresis

1% to 10%:

Cardiovascular: Palpitations, hypertension, sinus tachycardia

Central nervous system: Anxiety

Gastrointestinal: Weight loss, anorexia, vomiting, diarrhea, dysphagia

Genitourinary: Impotence

Neuromuscular & skeletal: Tremor

Ocular: Blurred vision

Reference Range Peak serum level of 163 ng/mL (325 ng/mL of ODV metabolite) obtained after a 150 mg oral dose; 4-hour postingestion serum level of 6100 ng/mL (1800 ng/mL of ODV metabolite) associated with coma; a venlafaxine plasma level of 7040 ng/mL (ODV of 1000 ng/mL) was associated with seizures

Drug Interactions Increased drug concentration with concomitant use of cimetidine; serotonin syndrome (shivering, muscle rigidity, salivation, agitation, and hyperthermia) can occur with concomitant administration of venlafaxine and tranylcypromine

Dosage Forms Tablet: 25 mg, 37.5 mg, 50 mg, 75 mg, 100 mg

Specific References

Parsons AT, Anthony RM and Meeker JE, "Two Fatal Cases of Venlafaxine Poisoning," *J Anal Toxicol*, 1996, 20:266-8.

Ventolin® *see Albuterol on page 31*

Ventolin® Rotocaps® *see Albuterol on page 31*

Veracur *see Formaldehyde on page 259*

Veramex® *see Verapamil on this page*

Verapamil (ver AP a mil)

Synonyms Iproveratril Hydrochloride

U.S. Brand Names Azupamil®; Calan®; Cordilox®; Ikacor®; Isoptin®; Securon®; Veramex®; Verelan®

Canadian Brand Names Apo-Verap®; Novo-Veramil®; Nu-Verap®

Therapeutic Category Antiarrhythmic Agent, Class IV; Calcium Channel Blocker

Use Angina, hypertension; I.V. for supraventricular tachyarrhythmias (PSVT, fibrillation (atrial), flutter); hypertrophic cardiomyopathy; has been used as prophylaxis of bipolar disorders in pregnant women, reduction of severity of tardive dyskinesia and Tourette's syndrome; may reverse cocaine-induced coronary artery vasoconstriction

Investigational: Persistent gastric antral spasm

Usual Dosage

Children: SVT: Oral (dose not well established):

1-5 years: 4-8 mg/kg/day in 3 divided doses or 40-80 mg every 8 hours

>5 years: 80 mg every 6-8 hours

(Continued)

Verapamil *(Continued)*

Adults:
   Angina: Oral: Initial dose: 80-120 mg 2 times/day (elderly or small stature: 40 mg 2 times/day); range: 240-480 mg/day in 3-4 divided doses
   Hypertension: Usual dose is 80 mg 3 times/day or 240 mg/day (sustained release); range 240-480 mg/day (no evidence of additional benefit in doses >360 mg/day)

Mechanism of Action Inhibits calcium ion from entering the "slow channels" or select voltage-sensitive areas of vascular smooth muscle and myocardium during depolarization; produces a relaxation of coronary vascular smooth muscle and coronary vasodilation; increases myocardial oxygen delivery in patients with vasospastic angina

Pharmacodynamics/kinetics

Onset of action: Oral: 1-2 hours

Duration: Oral: 6-8 hours

Peak effects: Oral (nonsustained tablets): 2 hours

Absorption: Rapid and complete from gastrointestinal tract (90%)

Metabolism: In the liver to norverapamil

Bioavailability: Oral: 20% to 35%

Half-life: (single dose):
   Infants: 4.4-6.9 hours
   Adults: 2-8 hours, increased up to 12 hours with multiple dosing; increased half-life with hepatic cirrhosis

Time to peak serum concentration: Oral:
   Extended-release tablets: 5-7 hours
   Tablets: 1-2 hours

Signs and Symptoms of Acute Intoxication Nausea, constipation, eosinophilia, gingival hyperplasia, flatulence, dyspnea, cholestatic jaundice, gynecomastia, extrapyramidal reaction, coma, coagulopathy, syncope, impotence, A-V block, asthenia, hypoglycemia, esophageal ulceration, rhabdomyolysis, myoglobinuria, drowsiness, confusion, acidosis, may result in bezoars with resultant bowel infarction, heart block, hypotension, asystole, cardiac arrhythmias, bundle-branch block, seizures, skin flushing, junctional bradycardia, hyperglycemia, colonic ischemia, colon perforation, hyperkalaemia

When to Transport to Hospital Transport any infant exposure, any symptomatic patient, or any ingestion over 10 mg/kg

Warnings/Precautions Avoid I.V. use in neonates and young infants due to severe apnea, bradycardia, or hypotensive reactions; monitor EKG and blood pressure closely in patients receiving I.V. therapy; sick sinus syndrome, severe left ventricular dysfunction, hepatic or renal impairment, hypertrophic cardiomyopathy (especially obstructive), concomitant therapy with beta-blockers or digoxin

Adverse Reactions

1% to 10%:
   Cardiovascular: Bradycardia; first, second, or third degree A-V block; congestive heart failure, hypotension, peripheral edema
   Central nervous system: Dizziness, lightheadedness, nausea, fatigue
   Dermatologic: Rash
   Gastrointestinal: Constipation
   Neuromuscular & skeletal: Weakness

Reference Range A ratio of verapamil/norverapamil >2.3 may be a predictor for fatal outcome

Therapeutic: 50-200 ng/mL (SI: 100-410 nmol/L) for parent; under normal conditions norverapamil concentration is the same as parent drug

Toxic: >845 ng/mL

Fatal: >2000 ng/mL

Drug Interactions Cardiogenic shock and complete heart block has occurred with concomitant use of verapamil and metoprolol (oral) in an elderly patient The following interactions occur with concomitant use

Adenosine: Prolonged bradycardia
Amiodarone: Slow sinus heart rate or worsen A-V block
Aspirin: Increased risk of bleeding
Atenolol: Increased atenolol levels
Caffeine: Increased caffeine levels by 25%
Carbamazepine: Neurotoxicity
Cimetidine: Inconclusive/possible increase in verapamil levels can occur
Clonidine: A-V block may occur
Cyclosporin: Decreased cyclosporin clearance
Dantrolene: Hyperkalemia
Digoxin: Increased serum digoxin levels
Disopyramide: Increase in adverse cardiac effects
Ethanol: Increases peak ethanol level by 17%
Glucagon: Exacerbates verapamil induced hyperglycemia
Imipramine: Decreases clearance by 25%
Lithium: Decrease serum lithium levels
Metoprolol: Increased metoprolol absorption
Midazolam: Increased midazolam levels and sedation
Moxonidine: Enhanced hypotensive effects
Nadolol: Hypotension, bradycardia
Phenytoin: Decreased verapamil levels
Pindolol: Hypotension, bradycardia
Prazosin: Increased prazosin concentration
Propranolol: Increased propranolol absorption with < heart rate reduction than either drug used alone
Quinidine: Decreased quinidine clearance
Rifampin: Decreased serum verapamil levels
Sulfinpyrazone: Increased verapamil clearance
Terazosin: Increased terazosin levels by 25%
Theophylline: Decreased theophylline clearance

Dosage Forms

Verapamil hydrochloride:
Capsule, sustained release: 120 mg, 180 mg, 240 mg
Injection: 2.5 mg/mL (2 mL, 4 mL)
Tablet: 40 mg, 80 mg, 120 mg
Tablet, sustained release: 120 mg, 180 mg, 240 mg

Specific References

Cobb MM, Johnson D, Gallo J, et al, "Large Scale Postmarketing Surveillance of Hypertensive Patients Treated With Verapamil," *Am J Therapeut*, 1995, 2:455-61.

Verelan® *see* Verapamil *on page 609*

Versacaps® *see* Guaifenesin and Pseudoephedrine *on page 273*

Versed® *see* Midazolam *on page 402*

Vesprin® *see* Triflupromazine *on page 597*

V-Gan® *see* Promethazine *on page 505*

Vicks® 44D Cough & Head Congestion *see* Pseudoephedrine and Dextromethorphan *on page 517*

Vicks® 44E [OTC] *see* Guaifenesin and Dextromethorphan *on page 271*

Vicks® 44 Non-Drowsy Cold & Cough Liqui-Caps [OTC] *see* Pseudoephedrine and Dextromethorphan *on page 517*

Vicks Children's Chloraseptic® [OTC] *see* Benzocaine *on page 70*

Vicks Chloraseptic® Sore Throat [OTC] *see* Benzocaine *on page 70*

Vicks® DayQuil® Allergy Relief 4 Hour Tablet [OTC] *see* Brompheniramine and Phenylpropanolamine *on page 85*

Vicks® DayQuil® Sinus Pressure & Congestion Relief [OTC] *see* Guaifenesin and Phenylpropanolamine *on page 272*

Vicks Formula 44® [OTC] *see* Dextromethorphan *on page 187*

Vicks Formula 44® Pediatric Formula [OTC] *see* Dextromethorphan *on page 187*

Vicks® Pediatric Formula 44E [OTC] *see* Guaifenesin and Dextromethorphan *on page 271*

Vicks® Sinex® Nasal Solution [OTC] *see* Phenylephrine *on page 479*

Vicks® Vaporub® *see* Camphor *on page 99*

Vicks® Vaposteam® *see* Camphor *on page 99*

Vicks Vatronol® *see* Ephedrine *on page 220*

Vicodin® *see* Hydrocodone and Acetaminophen *on page 293*

Vicodin® ES HP *see* Hydrocodone and Acetaminophen *on page 293*

Vicoprofen® *see* Hydrocodone and Ibuprofen *on page 296*

Vigabatrin (vye GA ba trin)

Synonyms GVG; MDL-71754

U.S. Brand Names Sabril®; Sabrilex®

Therapeutic Category Anticonvulsant

Impairment Potential Yes

Use Investigational: Partial/secondary generalized seizures; useful for spasticity or tardive dyskinesia

Usual Dosage
Initial dose: 1-2 g/day then titrate to maintenance dose of 2-4 g/day in 1-2 divided doses (lower initial doses in the elderly, patients with renal insufficiency, or patients with psychiatric illnesses)
Infantile spasm: 50-200 mg/kg/day
Spasticity: 2-3 g/day
Tardive dyskinesia: 2-8 g/day

Mechanism of Action Irreversible inhibitor of GABA transaminase - a structural analog of GABA

Pharmacodynamics/kinetics
Duration of effect: >24 hours
Absorption: 60% to 80%
Metabolism: Hepatic and renal
Half-life: 5-7 hours

When to Transport to Hospital Transport any patient exhibiting dry mouth or central nervous system abnormalities

Adverse Reactions
Central nervous system: Lethargy, mania, confusion, CNS depression, insomnia, fatigue, dizziness, sedation (at onset of therapy), psychosis (especially in patients with behavioral abnormalities, acute and reversible), headache, mania, paranoia
Dermatologic: Alopecia
Gastrointestinal: Dry mouth
Hepatic: Liver failure, hepatic necrosis
Neuromuscular & skeletal: Myoclonus
Ocular: Diplopia

Reference Range
Peak S+ enantiomer: 93 nmol/mL after 1.5 g dose
Peak R- enantiomer: 169 nmol/mL after 1.5 g dose

Drug Interactions Decreases phenytoin level by 20% to 30%

Dosage Forms Tablet: 500 mg

Specific References
   Davie MB, Cook MJ, and Ng C, "Vigabatrin Overdose," *Med J Aust*, 1996, 165:403.

Vikonon® *see* Yohimbine *on page 618*

Vinyl Acetate

Synonyms Acetic Acid; 1-Acetoxy-Ethylene; Ethanoic Acid; Ethenyl Ester; Vinyl Ethanoate
UN Number 1301
U.S. Brand Names VAC®; VYAC®; Zeset T®
Use Production of polyvinyl acetate (adhesives, wood gluing, paints) and polyvinyl alcohol (adhesives, textiles, automobile glass)
Mechanism of Toxic Action Primarily a respiratory irritant
Toxicodynamics/kinetics
   Absorption: Probably through inhalation, oral, and dermal routes
   Metabolism: Plasma and liver esterases hydrolyze vinyl acetate to acetaldehyde and acetic acid along with carbon dioxide
When to Transport to Hospital Transport any patient with cardiopulmonary symptoms
Overdosage/Treatment Decontamination:
   Dermal: Wash with soap and water
   Inhalation: Administer 100% humidified oxygen
   Ocular: Irrigate with saline
   Oral: Dilute with milk or water
Adverse Reactions
   Cardiovascular: Chest pain, angina
   Central nervous system: Insomnia, dizziness
   Dermatologic: Dermatitis, blisters
   Gastrointestinal: Throat irritation, mucous membrane irritation
   Hepatic: Liver function tests (elevated)
   Neuromuscular & skeletal: Neuropathy (peripheral)
   Ocular: Eye irritation
   Respiratory: Cough, hoarseness, bronchospasm
   Miscellaneous: Polyneuritis
Specific References
   U.S. Department of Health and Human Services, "Toxicological Profile for Vinyl Acetate TP-91/30," Agency for Toxic Substances and Diseases Registry, July 1992.

Vinylbenzene *see* Styrene *on page 551*

Vinyl Chloride

Synonyms Chloroethylene; Ethylene Monochloride
UN Number 1086
Commonly Found In Adhesives, propellants
Use As a refrigerant, used in production of methylchloroform and in manufacture of polyvinyl chloride (PVC)
Mechanism of Toxic Action Dermal exposure to escaping pressurized gas may cause injury or frostbite due to rapid evaporation; narcotic properties; metabolite (chloroethylene epoxide) is toxic; human carcinogen - angiosarcoma of the liver
Toxicodynamics/kinetics
   Absorption: Inhalation or dermal exposure; 42% retained in the lungs; concentrated in the liver and kidneys
   Metabolism: In the liver, thiodiglycolic acid is the major metabolite
Signs and Symptoms of Acute Intoxication Inhalation of high concentrations may result in narcotic-like CNS and apnea; chronic exposure may result
(Continued)

Vinyl Chloride *(Continued)*

in angiosarcoma, cancers of the brain, liver, and lung have also been documented; in addition, chronic exposure may result in "vinyl chloride disease" which consists of a scleroderma-like condition of the connective tissue of the fingers and a thickening of the dermas, acro-osteolysis and a Raynaud's-type phenomenon; thrombocytopenia may also occur; ocular irritation, dyspnea, headache, fatigue, seizures, euphoria, ataxia, fingernail clubbing, epigastric pain, hepatomegaly, loss of libido, arthralgia

When to Transport to Hospital Transport any symptomatic patient

Overdosage/Treatment

Decontamination:

Dermal: Remove and discard all contaminated clothing as hazardous waste; wash exposed areas twice with soap and water and rinse well; wash water should be contained and appropriately discarded

Ocular: Irrigate with saline

Supportive therapy: Symptomatic and supportive care are the mainstay of treatment; administer 100% humidified oxygen as needed; frostbite should be treated with rapid rewarming in a 42°C water bath

Adverse Reactions

Cardiovascular: Fibrillation (ventricular), Raynaud's phenomenon, arrhythmias (ventricular)

Central nervous system: CNS depression

Respiratory: Respiratory irritation, respiratory depression

Reference Range Urinary thiodiglycolic acid level of 0.3-4.0 mg/L may indicate recent exposure

Additional Information Colorless, pleasant sweet ether odor

Specific References

U.S. Department of Health and Human Services, "Toxicological Profile for Vinyl Chloride TP-92/20," Agency for Toxic Substances and Diseases Registry, April 1993.

Vinyl Cyanide *see* Acrylonitrile *on page 27*

Vinyl Ethanoate *see* Vinyl Acetate *on previous page*

Violet 3 *see* Xylene *on page 617*

Violet Bloom *see* Deadly Nightshade *on page 178*

Violin Brown Recluse Spider *see* Brown Recluse Spider *on page 87*

Virilon® *see* Methyltestosterone *on page 398*

Virilon® *see* Testosterone *on page 564*

Virlix® *see* Cetirizine *on page 120*

Virormone® *see* Testosterone *on page 564*

Visine® [OTC] *see* Tetrahydrozoline *on page 569*

Visine A.C.® [OTC] *see* Tetrahydrozoline *on page 569*

Viskaldix® *see* Pindolol *on page 488*

Visken® *see* Pindolol *on page 488*

Viskos® *see* Boric Acid *on page 80*

Vistacon-50® *see* Hydroxyzine *on page 303*

Vistaject-25® *see* Hydroxyzine *on page 303*

Vistaject-50® *see* Hydroxyzine *on page 303*

Vistaquel® *see* Hydroxyzine *on page 303*

Vistaril® *see* Hydroxyzine *on page 303*

Vistazine® *see* Hydroxyzine *on page 303*

Vita-C® [OTC] *see* Ascorbic Acid *on page 53*

Vitamin B_3 *see* Niacin *on page 428*

Vitamin C *see* Ascorbic Acid *on page 53*

Vitriol Brown Oil *see* Sulfuric Acid *on page 554*

Vivactil® *see* Protriptyline *on page 515*

Vivol® *see* Diazepam *on page 189*

Volital® *see* Pemoline *on page 462*

Volmax® *see* Albuterol *on page 31*

Volplan® *see* Megestrol Acetate *on page 365*

"Vomit Wort" *see* Indian Tobacco *on page 312*

Vorigeno® *see* Scopolamine *on page 532*

VX *see* Nerve Gases *on page 426*

VYAC® *see* Vinyl Acetate *on page 613*

Wart-Off® [OTC] *see* Salicylic Acid *on page 530*

Weed *see* Cannabinoids, Qualitative *on page 100*

Weedoff® *see* Glyphosate *on page 269*

Weedy Nightshade *see* Deadly Nightshade *on page 178*

Weeviltox® *see* Carbon Disulfide *on page 108*

Wehamine® *see* Dimenhydrinate *on page 203*

Wellbutrin® *see* Bupropion *on page 90*

Wellbutrin® SR *see* Bupropion *on page 90*

Westcort® *see* Hydrocortisone *on page 297*

Westrim® LA [OTC] *see* Phenylpropanolamine *on page 481*

Westron® *see* Tetrachloroethane *on page 566*

Whippet *see* Nitrous Oxide *on page 439*

White Phosphorus

Synonyms Phosphorus Tetramen; Red Phosphorus; Yellow Phosphorus

UN Number 1381 (Dry or in Water); 2447 (molten)

Commonly Found In Phosphorus sesquisulfide, phosphine gas

Use Fertilizers, roach poisons, rodenticides, water treatment; used in military as ammunition in motor/artillery shells

Mechanism of Toxic Action Damages endoplasmic reticulum; inhibits fatty acid oxidation

Toxicodynamics/kinetics

Absorption: By oral routes; yellow phosphorus well absorbed dermally and orally; phosphine gas absorbable in lungs; red phosphorus nonabsorbable

Metabolism: Oxidation and hydrolysis to hypophosphites

Elimination: Urine and feces

Signs and Symptoms of Acute Intoxication Gastrointestinal irritant, dermal burns, seizures, coma, breath odor, luminescent stool, flatulence, hypocalcemia, vomiting followed by asymptomatic phase of <12 to 3 days; subsequent signs/symptoms of hepatic or renal failure develop; chronic exposure (5+ years) results in osteoporosis and bone degeneration, commonly of jaw ("phossy jaw"), feces discoloration (black)

When to Transport to Hospital Transport any symptomatic patient

Overdosage/Treatment

Decontamination:

Dermal: Remove contaminated clothing; brush off phosphorus from skin and then continuously irrigate skin with water; apply saline soaked dressings to affected area; phosphorus will fluoresce under a Wood's lamp; 1% copper sulfate solution or silver nitrate has been advocated to aid in decontamination of dermal burns, although its use is controversial

Ocular: Irrigate with saline; following saline irrigation, several drops of 3% copper sulfate solution (applied within 15 minutes) can be given to help prevent ocular burns and then remove particles mechanically

Inhalation: Administer 100% humidified oxygen

(Continued)

White Phosphorus *(Continued)*

Oral: **Do not** induce emesis; lavage within 2-3 hours with 1:5000 to 1:10,000 potassium permanganate or water; activated charcoal may be used

Supportive therapy: Treat dermal burns in traditional method; monitor calcium; steroids are of no benefit in preventing liver injury

Adverse Reactions

Cardiovascular: Hypotension, tachycardia, fibrillation (atrial), flutter (atrial), sinus tachycardia

Central nervous system: Lethargy, irritability, coma, hyperthermia

Dermatologic: Dermal burns

Endocrine & metabolic: Hypoglycemia can occur on chronic exposure

Gastrointestinal: GI Irritant, vomiting, abdominal cramps

Hematologic: Anemia, leukopenia, hemolysis

Hepatic: Degeneration and hepatic necrosis

Neuromuscular & skeletal: Degeneration and osteoporosis, fasciculations, asterixis, hemiplegia

Renal: Tubular necrosis (acute) and cortical necrosis

Respiratory: Cough on inhalation, tachypnea, dyspnea

Miscellaneous: "Phossy jaw" (degeneration and necrosis of soft tissue and teeth in oral cavity resulting in life-threatening infections); fatty deposition of muscles and liver, decreases in serum calcium, potassium, and sodium; liver/renal toxicity along with cerebral edema may occur after 5-10 days

Reference Range Normal serum phosphate concentrations: 3.0-4.5 mg/100 mL

Additional Information Garlic breath odor and luminescent vomitus, flatus, or stool is pathognomonic although not frequent; phosphine gas has garlic odor; gas release occurs in industrial use or with moisture contamination of aluminum or zinc phosphide rodenticides; match phosphorus content essentially nontoxic; match toxicities are secondary to potassium chlorate content; vomiting can occur after oral ingestion of 2-23 mg/kg; red phosphorus is not soluble and essentially not absorbed through the gastrointestinal tract and is, therefore, considered nontoxic

Lethal oral dose: >1.5 g

Atmospheric half-life: 5 minutes

Specific References

U.S. Department of Health and Human Services, "Toxicological Profile for White Phosphorus," Agency for Toxic Substances and Diseases Registry, June 1994.

Wormwood

Synonyms Absinthium; Assenzio; Bitter Wormwood; Losna; Mugwort; Pelin; Qinghaosu extract; Wormseed

Scientific Name *Artemisia absinthium*

Use Homeopathic medicine, used as an anthelmintic, bitter tonic, hair tonic, sedative, flavoring agent (in vermouth)

Mechanism of Toxic Action Contains Thujone (a volatile oil of tenpene structure), which binds to the same neuronal receptors as tetrahydrocannabinol; can inhibit porphyrin synthesis; also contains absinthin (bittering agent) and santonica (anthelmintic for roundworms)

Toxicodynamics/kinetics Metabolism: (Thujone) Hepatic (oxidative metabolism)

Signs and Symptoms of Acute Intoxication Called "Absinthism": Headache, vertigo, thirst, vomiting, giddiness, paranoia, tremors, diarrhea, diaphoresis, color vision disturbance, psychosis, seizures (>15 g ingestion), visual hallucinations, euphoria, coma, respiratory depression, contact dermatitis (from flowers), dysphoria, delirium, mania, anorexia, memory impairment

When to Transport to Hospital Transport any symptomatic patient

Additional Information Taste threshold (Absinthin): 1 part in 70,000: A shrub with small green-yellow flowers from July through September. Grows naturally in Europe but found in Northeastern and North Central U.S. Wormwood extract has been used in absinth, an emerald green bitter liquor banned in Europe and U.S. absinth has been thought to cause Vincent van Gogh's psychosis. The tea uses dried leaves and flowering tops.

Specific References

Arnold WN, "Vincent van Gogh and the Thujone Connection," *JAMA*, 1988, 260(20):3042-4.

WY-8678 see Guanabenz on page 276

Wyamycin® S Oral see Erythromycin on page 226

Wygesic® see Propoxyphene and Acetaminophen on page 510

Wymox® see Amoxicillin on page 45

Wytensin® see Guanabenz on page 276

Xanax® see Alprazolam on page 36

Xanef® see Enalapril on page 217

Ximovan® see Zopiclone on page 621

Xylene

Related Information

Amitraz on page 39

Synonyms Dimethyl Benzene; Methyltoluene; Violet 3; Xylol

UN Number 1307

Impairment Potential Yes; Reaction time and balance is probably impaired at exposure levels >100 ppm

Bleecker ML and Hansen JA, *Occupational Neurology and Clinical Neurotoxicology*, Baltimore, MD: Williams & Wilkins, 1994, 224.

Use In histology laboratories (*M*-xylene), manufacture of polymers, glues, paints, and as a vehicle for pesticides

Mechanism of Toxic Action Anesthetic at high doses (>5000 ppm)

Toxicodynamics/kinetics
Absorption: By inhalation, dermally, or through the gastrointestinal tract
Protein binding: 90%
Metabolism: In the liver
Half-life: 20-30 hours
(Continued)

Xylene (Continued)

Elimination: 2,4-Xylenol and methyl hippuric acid are excreted renally; xylene is protein bound

Signs and Symptoms of Acute Intoxication Dizziness, headache, fatigue, dementia, nausea, ocular irritation, syncope, throat burning, gaze nystagmus, skin irritation, cough, CNS depression

When to Transport to Hospital Transport any ingestion or any symptomatic patient

Overdosage/Treatment Decontamination:

Dermal: Wash with soap and water

Ocular: Irrigate with saline

Oral: **Do not** induce emesis; dilute with milk or water

Adverse Reactions

Central nervous system: CNS depression

Dermatologic: Scleroderma

Endocrine & metabolic: Sexual dysfunction

Hepatic: Liver necrosis

Renal: Hematuria

Respiratory: Irritation to upper airway

Miscellaneous: Multiple chemical sensitivity syndrome

Reference Range BEI of methyl hippuric acid (urine) is 1.5 g/g creatinine; blood level of 1 mg/L is consistent with exposure of 100 ppm

Additional Information Patients may be more sensitive to ethanol; sweet odor

Specific References

U.S. Department of Health and Human Services, "Toxicological Profile for Xylenes," Agency for Toxic Substances and Diseases Registry, October 1993.

Xylocaine® see Lidocaine on page 345

Xylol see Xylene on previous page

Yanpon see Holly on page 287

Yellow Horse see Ephedra on page 219

Yellow Phosphorus see White Phosphorus on page 615

Yerba de Mate see Maté on page 360

Yerba Maté see Maté on page 360

Yobinol® see Yohimbine on this page

Yocon® see Yohimbine on this page

Yohimbine (yo HIM bine)

Synonyms Aphrodine Hydrochloride; Corynathe Yohimbe; Corynine Hydrochloride

U.S. Brand Names Afrodex®; Aphrodyne™; Dayto Himbin®; Potensan®; Vikonon®; Yobinol®; Yocon®; Yohimex™

Therapeutic Category Miscellaneous Product

Abuse Potential Yes

Impairment Potential Yes; Doses of 10-30 mg can products central nervous system stimulation including mydriasis. Dissociative state similar to phencyclidine can occur with excessive dosages (about 250 mg)

Linden CH, Vellman WP, and Rumack B, "Yohimbine: A New Street Drug," *Ann Emerg Med*, 1985, 14(10):1002-4.

Use No FDA sanctioned indications; has been used to treat male erectile impotence; allegedly has aphrodisiac properties; has been used in veterinary medicine as a reversal agent for xylazine

Usual Dosage Adults: Impotence: Oral: 5.4 mg 3 times/day

Mechanism of Action Derived from the bark of the yohimbe tree (Pausingstalia yohimbe), this indole alkaloid produces an alpha$_2$-adrenergic blockade; also is a weak MAO inhibitor; parasympathetic tone is also decreased

Pharmacodynamics/kinetics
Duration of action: Usually 3-4 hours, but may last 36 hours
Absorption: Oral: 33%
Half-life: 0.6 hour

When to Transport to Hospital Transport any patient exhibiting cardiopulmonary or central nervous system symptoms

Warnings/Precautions Do not use in pregnancy; do not use in children; not for use in geriatric, psychiatric, or cardio-renal patients with a history of gastric or duodenal ulcer; generally not for use in females

Adverse Reactions
Cardiovascular: Tachycardia, bradycardia, hypertension, hypotension (orthostatic), flushing, shock, sinus tachycardia, vasodilation, sinus bradycardia
Central nervous system: Anxiety, mania, hallucinations, irritability, dizziness, psychosis, insomnia, headache, panic attacks
Gastrointestinal: Nausea, vomiting, anorexia
Hematologic: Neutropenia, agranulocytosis
Neuromuscular & skeletal: Tremors, paresthesia
Ocular: Lacrimation, mydriasis
Respiratory: Bronchospasm, sinusitis
Miscellaneous: Antidiuretic action, salivation, sweating

Test Interactions Elevation of serum catecholamine levels can occur

Reference Range After a 10 mg oral dose, peak plasma yohimbine level achieved was ~75 µg/L after 45 minutes

Drug Interactions Antidepressants, other mood-modifying drugs

Dosage Forms Tablet: 5.4 mg

Additional Information Also a street drug of abuse that can be smoked; has a bitter taste; dissociative state may resemble phencyclidine intoxication

Yohimex™ see Yohimbine on previous page

Yperite see Mustard Gas on page 414

Yurelax® see Cyclobenzaprine on page 173

Zanaflex® see Tizanidine on page 584

Zantac® see Ranitidine on page 520

Zantac® 75 [OTC] see Ranitidine on page 520

Zantryl® see Phentermine on page 478

Zarontin® see Ethosuximide on page 232

Zebeta® see Bisoprolol on page 78

Zebrax® see Clidinium and Chlordiazepoxide on page 150

Zephrex® see Guaifenesin and Pseudoephedrine on page 273

Zephrex LA® see Guaifenesin and Pseudoephedrine on page 273

Zergamet® see Cimetidine on page 147

Zeset T® see Vinyl Acetate on page 613

Zestoretic® see Lisinopril and Hydrochlorothiazide on page 347

Zetran® see Diazepam on page 189

Zidovudine and Lamivudine
(zye DOE vyoo deen & la MI vyoo deen)
Synonyms AZT + 3TC
U.S. Brand Names Combivir®
Therapeutic Category Antiviral Agent

ZilaDent® [OTC] see Benzocaine on page 70

Zilden® see Diltiazem on page 201

Zimovane® *see* Zopiclone *on next page*
Zincfrin® Ophthalmic [OTC] *see* Phenylephrine and Zinc Sulfate *on page 481*

Zipeprol (ZI pa prole)

U.S. Brand Names Antituxil-Z®; Bechizolo®; Bronocozina®; Bronx®; Mirsol®; Respilene®; Respirase®; Respirex®; Zitoxil®

Therapeutic Category Antitussive

Abuse Potential Yes

Impairment Potential Yes

Use Cough suppressant; often used as a drug of abuse (not FDA approved in U.S.)

Usual Dosage
Children:
Oral: 3-5 mg/kg/day in divided doses
Rectal: 100-150 mg/day
Adults:
Oral: 150-300 mg/day in divided doses
Rectal: 150 mg 1-2 times/day
Abusers use 750 mg to 1 g for euphoric effect
Minimum lethal dose: 2 g

Mechanism of Action A substituted, non-opiate piperazine with centrally acting antitussive action and peripheral actions on bronchospasm; also has antihistaminic and antiserotonin properties

Pharmacodynamics/kinetics
Absorption: 15 minutes
Metabolism: Hepatic

Signs and Symptoms of Acute Intoxication Seizures, coma, respiratory depression, opisthotonic crises, restlessness, lethargy, ataxia, tremor, headache

When to Transport to Hospital Transport any ingestion over 8 mg/kg in children (<6 years of age) or 1 g in adults or any symptomatic patient

Warnings/Precautions Use with caution in patients with a seizure history, history of drug abuse, pregnancy

Adverse Reactions
Central nervous system: Drowsiness, dizziness, auditory and visual hallucinations, ataxia, retrograde amnesia (with doses exceeding 300 mg), CNS depression, pseudotumor cerebri, extrapyramidal reactions, amnesia, opisthotonos, cognitive dysfunction
Gastrointestinal: Nausea, constipation
Neuromuscular & skeletal: Chorea
Respiratory: Apnea
Miscellaneous: Abuse potential

Reference Range Postmortem blood zipeprol level after ~1.5 g ingestion ranges from 2 µg/mL to 20.5 µg/mL; liver to blood postmortem distribution ranges from 2.5-6.3

Dosage Forms Capsule: 75 mg

Additional Information Seizuregenic dose is 1.5 g in adults or 25 mg/kg in children; mechanism for seizures may be GABA Inhibition; cerebral edema can occur

Specific References
Crippa O, Polettini A, and Avato FM, "Lethal Poisoning by Zipeprol in Drug Addicts," *J Forensic Sci*, 1990, 35(4):992-9.

Ziriton® *see* Carbinoxamine *on page 106*

Zitoxil® *see Zipeprol on previous page*

Zoloft™ *see Sertraline on page 538*

Zolpidem (zole PI dem)

U.S. Brand Names Ambien™; Bikalm®; Niotal®; Stilnox®

Therapeutic Category Hypnotic, Nonbarbiturate

Abuse Potential Yes

Impairment Potential Yes; 10 mg ingestion (associated with a serum zolpidem level of 199 µg/L) associated with driving impairment

Baselt RC and Cravey RH, *Disposition of Toxic Drugs and Chemicals in Man*, 4th ed, Foster City, CA: Chemical Toxicology Institute, 1995, 788.

Use Hypnotic for short-term management of insomnia

Usual Dosage Adults: Oral: 10 mg immediately before bedtime; 5 mg in elderly patients or patients with renal/liver disease; maximum dose: 20 mg

Mechanism of Action Selective agonist of the omega-1 receptor at the CNS gamma amino butyric acid (GABA)/chloride channel complex; not a benzodiazepine, but an imidazopyridin

Pharmacodynamics/kinetics

Onset of action: 7-27 minutes

Peak oral plasma levels: 2 hours

Duration: 6-8 hours

Absorption: Rapid

Metabolism: Hepatic to inactive metabolites

Bioavailability: 70%

Half-life: 2 hours, (4 hours in renal failure, 10 hours in cirrhosis)

Signs and Symptoms of Acute Intoxication Coma, diplopia, esophageal ulceration, night terrors, respiratory depression, hypotension, gaze nystagmus

When to Transport to Hospital Transport any pediatric exposure, any symptomatic patient, or any ingestion over 20 mg

Warnings/Precautions Elderly, debilitated, depression, behavior changes, not recommended for use in children <18 years of age

Adverse Reactions

1% to 10%:

Central nervous system: Headache, drowsiness, dizziness

Gastrointestinal: Nausea, diarrhea

Neuromuscular & skeletal: Myalgia

Reference Range Therapeutic: 80-150 ng/mL; serum levels of 500 ng/mL associated with coma; autopsy blood zolpidem level of 4.1 µg/mL associated with fatality

Dosage Forms Tablet: 5 mg, 10 mg

Specific References

Berlin I, Warot D, Hergueta T, et al, "Comparison of the Effects of zolpidem and Triazolam on Memory Functions, Psychomotor Performances, and Postural Sway in Healthy Subjects," *J Clin Psychopharmacol*, 1993, 13(2):100-6.

Evans SM, Funderburk FR, and Griffiths RR, "Zolpidem and Triazolam in Humans: Behavioral and Subjective Effects and Abuse Liability," *J Pharmacol Exp Ther*, 1990, 255(3):1246-55.

Wilkinson CJ, "The Acute Effects of Zolpidem, Administered Alone and With Alcohol on Cognitive and Psychomotor Function," *J Clin Psychiatry*, 1995, 56(7):309-18.

Zopiclone (ZOE pi clone)

Related Information

Diazepam *on page 189*

(Continued)

Zopiclone *(Continued)*

U.S. Brand Names Amoban®; Cronus®; Datolan®; Foltran®; Imovan®; Imovane®; Inomnium® LF; Insomnium® NF; Limovan®; Staten®; Ximovan®; Zimovane®

Therapeutic Category Hypnotic, Nonbarbiturate

Impairment Potential Yes

Use Treatment of insomnia (to be used <28-day duration)

Investigational in U.S.: Insomnia (<1-month duration)

Usual Dosage Oral: 7.5 mg 30-60 minutes before bedtime

Mechanism of Action A nonbenzodiazepine sedative hypnotic agent which facilitates gamma aminobutyric acid function

Pharmacodynamics/kinetics

Absorption: Within 1.5 hours

Metabolism: Hepatic

Bioavailability: Oral: 80%

Half-life: 3.5-6.5 hours

Signs and Symptoms of Acute Intoxication CNS depression, respiratory depression, coma, hyperkalemia, hyperglycemia

When to Transport to Hospital Transport any pediatric exposure, any patient exhibiting central nervous system depression, or any ingestion over 30 mg

Warnings/Precautions Reduce dosage by 50% in elderly patients or patients with hepatic disease; use with caution in patients with psychiatric disorders, dependency/drug abuse patients, myasthenia gravis, or epilepsy

Adverse Reactions

>10%: Gastrointestinal: Bitter taste

<10%:

Cardiovascular: Palpitations

Central nervous system: Dizziness, headache, confusion, slurred speech, ataxia, nightmares, memory disturbance, psychosis, drowsiness, lethargy, insomnia

Gastrointestinal: Dry mouth, nausea, vomiting

Genitourinary: Urinary retention

Neuromuscular & skeletal: Dysarthria, tremor

Ocular: Blurred vision

Miscellaneous: Dependence

Reference Range After a 7.5 mg oral dose, peak serum levels are about 60-70 mcg/L at 1-1.5 hours and decline to 3 mcg/L at 24 hours; postmortem levels associated with fatal overdoses of zopiclone: 1.4-3.9 mg/L

Dosage Forms Tablet: 7.5 mg

Specific References

Boniface PJ and Russell SG, "Two Cases of Fatal Zopiclone Overdose," *J Anal Toxicol*, 1996, 20:131-3.

Zorkaptil® *see* Captopril *on page 101*

ZORprin® *see* Aspirin *on page 56*

Zovirax® *see* Acyclovir *on page 29*

Zyban® *see* Bupropion *on page 90*

Zydone® *see* Hydrocodone and Acetaminophen *on page 293*

Zyprexa® *see* Olanzapine *on page 443*

Zyrlex® *see* Cetirizine *on page 120*

Zyrtec® *see* Cetirizine *on page 120*

SPECIAL TOPICS/ISSUES FOR THE CRIMINAL JUSTICE PROFESSIONAL

TABLE OF CONTENTS

THE DRUG RECOGNITION EXPERT (DRE) PROGRAM

The DRE Response to the Drug Impaired Driver: An Overview of the DRE Program, Officer, and Procedures

by Thomas E. Page, MA, Sergeant, Officer-in-Charge
Drug Recognition Expert Unit, Los Angeles Police Department

THE EVOLUTION OF THE DRE OFFICER AND PROGRAM

The Dark Ages

In the 1970s, prior to the establishment of the Drug Recognition Expert (DRE) Program, the following scenario was regularly played out on the streets of American communities:

> While on routine patrol in city traffic in a marked police car, the watchful officer suddenly directs his attention to a specific car. Alerted perhaps by a traffic violation, such as speeding or an illegal left turn, or perhaps by erratic braking (not an actual breach of the law, but suspicious nonetheless), the officer activates the police car's emergency lights, and signals the car to stop. Both cars pull to the curb lane and stop.

> The officer radios in his location to the police station, and slowly, yet attentively, walks up to the apprehensive and still-seated driver. The officer says firmly but politely, "Good day, sir. May I see your driver's license and registration please." It's a demand, not a question.

> As the nervous driver reaches for the glove box the officer asks, "By the way, what year is this car?" The driver stops reaching and replies, "It's a 93, no, 94 Ford. What's this all about officer?" The officer says, "I'll get to that in a moment. Remember? Your license and registration please."

> The officer completes a mental checklist: bloodshot eyes, check, slurred words, check, forgetting about the driver's license, check, car smells like a brewery, check. "I think this guy might be deuce,[1]" the officer thinks.

> "Step out of the car, sir. I'd like you to do a few tests to see if you've had too much to drink."

During the "dark ages," roadside tests to determine if a person was under the influence of alcohol or drugs were not standardized. Through trial and error, each officer developed his or her own procedures in order to determine if the individual should be arrested for driving under the influence (DUI). Junior officers, modelling their superiors, would often add their own nuances to the procedures. These nonstandardized roadside sobriety tests frequently included variations of counting and alphabet-recitation exercises,[2] coin pick-up tests,[3] and assorted balance and coordination tests.

Young officers quickly learned that the intoxicated person had difficulty remembering instructions, particularly more than one at the same time. In the above example, the officer demanded the driver's license and registration. As the suspect began to reach for these items, the officer asked another question - the year of the car. The driver had to be reminded to produce the license and registration. Without being aware of it, the officer was assessing the person's ability to divide his attention, that is, to do more than one thing at the same time.

Based on the totality of the investigation, including the individual's driving, the officer's general observations of the person's speech, appearance, demeanor, and the person's performance on the nonstandardized roadside tests, the officer would make an arrest or release decision. If arrested, the driver would be taken to a police station, and would be advised of his rights and obligations under the implied consent law.[4] Typically, the driver (now an "arrestee") would be administered an alcohol breath test. If the arrestee's alcohol concentration, as measured in breath, reached a certain statutory level, such as 0.10% BAC (blood alcohol concentration),[5] the individual would be booked into the jail. The case would then be presented to the prosecuting attorney for review and prosecution.

During the 1960s and 1970s, many individuals were producing breath test results that were below the statutory level, even though they appeared to be inordinately intoxicated. Officers' options were both unsatisfactory and limited.

Releasing the person and requesting him or her not to drive was one option.[6] A psychiatric evaluation of the driver was another option. In essence, the officer would suspect that the individual's erratic driving, behavior, and appearance were related to a psychiatric disorder. A third option for handling the so-called "low blow" driver was to obtain an assessment for drug influence by medical personnel, such as doctors and nurses. (Los Angeles, as well as many other jurisdictions, has medical personnel on-duty throughout the day at larger jail facilities.) Unfortunately, then and now, many medical professionals receive limited formal training about the observable effects of abused drugs. And even if they have received formal training, actual experience in dealing with drug abusers in a nontraditional clinical setting may be limited.

More importantly, however, the medical professionals were assessing the arrestee at a different, sometimes significantly later, time. The person had been observed driving, was arrested, was taken to a police station and was given a breath test, all before being taken to an appropriate facility for a medical evaluation. The individual may no longer be under the influence of drugs at the time of the medical assessment. Simply, the drugs may have worn off.

Poly-drug (multiple drugs) use was another complicating factor. The polydrug user, at different times, may exhibit nearly opposite drug effects. For example, at the time of the officer's encounter with an individual, the person may exhibit the behavior associated with stimulant use, such as aggressiveness, agitation, and dilated pupils. At the time of the medical evaluation, however, the same person may be sedated, lethargic, and sleepy, consistent with a narcotic analgesic such as heroin. The stimulant, cocaine for example, has worn off; heroin now dominates.

For these reasons and more, a medical evaluation was not a viable solution to the problem of identifying the drug-impaired driver.

In some cases, a blood or urine sample disclosed the presence of drugs in a suspected impaired driver. It was still difficult, nevertheless, if not impossible, to obtain a filing of charges in court, much less a conviction. Prosecutors were hampered by officers' limited abilities in articulating the basis of the opinion that the person was under the influence of a drug. A procedure was needed that officers could utilize in order to be able to detect, apprehend, assess, document, and subsequently prove in a court of law that the individual was under the influence of drug(s). The Drug Recognition Expert (DRE) Program, procedures, and DRE-trained officer were the response to this recognized need.

THE DRUG RECOGNITION EXPERT (DRE) PROGRAM
(Continued)

OUT OF THE DARK

Little has changed over the years from the above arrest scenario. The typical driving under the influence arrest begins with the officer's observations of driving, followed by the officer's face-to-face contact with the person. The major difference between the 1970s and the present is that officers now have a standardized method of assessing alcohol and drug-impairment at roadside: the Standardized Field Sobriety Test (SFST).

In the United States and parts of Canada, most police officers are taught the three phases of Driving Under the Influence (DUI)[7] detection: (1) vehicle in motion, (2) personal contact, and (3) pre-arrest screening. Each of these phases requires decision making on the officer's part. In phase one, vehicle in motion, the officer's decision is whether or not to stop the vehicle. In phase two, the officer's primary decision is whether or not the driver should be instructed to exit the vehicle. The officer's primary decision in phase three is whether or not to arrest the person. The development, refinement, and validation of standardized procedures for phase three commenced at the same time that the need for procedures to detect the drug-impaired driver was growing. The resulting development of the SFST, which was largely through the efforts and research of Marcelline Burns, PhD, of the Southern California Research Institute (SCRI), was a critical step toward the development of DRE.[8]

Without repeating the extensive volumes of research conducted by Dr. Burns and her associates, the outcome was a standardized procedure that officers could use to determine at roadside if an individual was under the influence of alcohol. Dr. Burns evaluated the assortment of tests that officers, through trial and error, had developed throughout the United States and Europe. Three tests were found to be the most reliable predictor of a .10% BAC: the horizontal gaze nystagmus (HGN) test, a walk-and-turn test, and the one-leg stand test.[9] When these tests were administered by a trained officer as a battery of examinations, officers could reliably determine if an individual's BAC was at or above the most common legal level at the time — .10%.[10]

The SFST battery includes an assessment of an individual's ability to pay attention, follow simple instructions, and divide his or her attention.[11] For example, during the walk-and-turn test, the suspect is instructed to stand on a real or imaginary line with one foot in front of the other. While the suspect stands in this position, the administering officer gives verbal instructions while at the same time demonstrating how the test is to be performed. Often, a suspect who is under the influence, will "forget" to maintain the initial position, and will either begin to perform the walking portion of the test before being told to do so, or will step out of the initial (instructional) position. During the walking or performance phase, the individual who is unable to divide his or her attention will frequently forget part of the instructions, such as counting out loud or touching heel to toe. With the support of the United States Department of Transportation, the battery of tests, known as the SFST, became the curriculum to train American officers in DUI detection.

Concurrently with the development of the SFST, drug use continued its steady incline. There was also a growing awareness by police officers, traffic safety researchers, prosecutors, and the general public, that drug-impaired drivers were significantly contributing to traffic injuries and fatalities. Police officers, seeing first-hand the carnage on the roads caused by drug abusers, were frustrated. They could arrest the drug-impaired driver, but were unable to obtain a conviction.

Frustrated officers, problem-solvers by training and avocation, sought out solutions. In particular, traffic enforcement officers from the Los Angeles Police Department (LAPD) began to develop their own expertise on the effects of impairing drugs other than alcohol. These officers consulted and worked with officers from LAPD's Narcotics Division.[12] They consulted with doctors, psychologists, and drug abusers to educate themselves about the effects of drugs. In time, LAPD officers developed a step-by-step procedure that enabled them to determine drug influence.

These innovative LAPD officers did not "invent" new knowledge about the effects of drugs, as the effects of many drugs have been known for thousands of years. The writer Aldous Huxley has been quoted as saying that "Pharmacology antedated agriculture." Simply, this means that people were learning about the effects of drugs before they learned to plant and harvest crops. Probably, through the observation of animals, humans very early on learned of the pharmacologic, mood, and mind altering effects of certain drugs.

DRE DRUG CATEGORIZATION: PATTERNS OF SIGNS AND SYMPTOMS

Borrowing extensively from medicine, psychiatry, physiology, toxicology, and associated fields, a drug categorization system was developed that placed the primary drugs of abuse into seven categories. These categories are not based on shared chemical structures, nor on their legality, nor on the user's subjective experience. Rather, this categorization system is based on the premise that each drug within a category produces a pattern of effects, known as signs and symptoms. (A "sign" is detectable by an observer. Signs include bloodshot eyes, horizontal gaze nystagmus, pulse rate, impaired coordination, etc. A "symptom," on the other hand, is by nature subjective. It is experienced by the individual, and may be reported to the observer. For example, a feeling of nausea is a symptom. Hallucinations are symptoms, although they may elicit behavioral signs.) It is the **pattern** of effects, rather than a specific effect, that is unique to the category.

The LAPD officers borrowed extensively from existing bodies of knowledge to develop their drug categorization system. They also borrowed from the medical field to develop procedures to evaluate individuals for suspected drug influence. For example, it has been established for years that an individual's state of health, or intoxication for that matter, can be assessed by taking the person's vital signs (blood pressure, pulse, and temperature in the case of the DRE). Likewise, the eye examinations,[13] the balance and coordination tests, as well as the other parts of a DRE evaluation have an historically accepted role in medicine. As one court stated in its decision regarding the scientific acceptance of DRE procedures, DRE is simply a compilation of the "tried and true."

To summarize, the initial DREs used accepted medical techniques in order to detect the well-established effects of the drugs of abuse. What was new, however, was the development of a systematic and standardized step-by-step procedure that law enforcement officers could use to detect drug influence. This procedure began taking shape in the early 1980s.

A step-by-step checklist procedure is standard within law enforcement. Following a checklist ensures that nothing is left out, and aids in the presentation of evidence in court. Although the procedure was not nearly as standardized as it is today, these early DRE officers were increasingly called upon by prosecutors to testify about the effects of drugs on driving. Los Angeles judges began to routinely recognize the officers as experts, which meant that these officers could render opinions, unlike the non-expert who could only relate facts. Over a relatively short period of time, the rate of filing and subsequent conviction of drugged drivers equalled that of alcohol alone (approximately 95%).[14]

THE DRUG RECOGNITION EXPERT (DRE) PROGRAM
(Continued)

The testimony of DREs was usually not (and is still not) the only evidence that would be introduced into court in DUI - drug cases. Usually, the prosecutor has been/is able to present scientific evidence of use of drugs through urinalysis or blood analysis by toxicologists. **A greater portion of the burden of proof that the individual was under the influence, however, was placed upon the observer of impairment, the DRE.**

LABORATORY AND FIELD EVALUATION OF THE DRE PROGRAM

The Drug Recognition Expert Program was becoming institutionalized within the LAPD and within Los Angeles courts. The National Highway Traffic Safety Administration (NHTSA), an agency within the Department of Transportation, began to receive requests from various sources to study the validity and reliability of the DRE procedure. In response, NHTSA, in cooperation with the National Institute on Drug Abuse, undertook a laboratory evaluation of DRE procedures in 1984 at the Johns Hopkins University.[15] Four LAPD DREs travelled to Johns Hopkins University. An experimental protocol was designed to test the accuracy of the DREs. Each of the officers was isolated, and independently conducted an assessment of 80 volunteer drug users. In a double-blind format, each of the volunteers had received either marijuana (2 dose levels), diazepam (2 dose levels), amphetamine (2 dose levels), secobarbital (1 dose level), or a placebo. Upon completing a 15-minute assessment, each of the officers was required to determine if the volunteer was impaired, and if so, the type of drug that was causing the observed impairment. The results of this study were reported as extremely encouraging to the DRE Program. In this controlled study, DREs were over 90% accurate in determining impairment, and in correctly identifying the type of drug causing the impairment. The time had come to evaluate the DRE procedures in the law enforcement environment.

In 1985, NHTSA conducted a Field Validation Study of the LAPD DRE program. This study, which is also commonly known as the 173 Case Study, involved a much larger group of Los Angeles DREs, and involved individuals actually arrested for suspicion of driving under the influence of drugs. NHTSA contracted with a private toxicology laboratory to conduct blood analyses of samples obtained from the arrestees. The opinion of the DREs was then compared to the results of the laboratory's analyses for drugs. The results were very similar to the Johns Hopkins Study.[16] 94% of the time (162 suspects) a drug other than alcohol was found when the DREs said that the suspect was impaired by drugs. The drug determination was complicated by the fact that over 70% of the suspects yielded detectable levels of more than one drug. Overall the DREs were totally correct in their judgments on 49% of the suspects, ie, all the drugs were identified, and partially correct, ie, they identified at least one of the drugs in an additional 38% of the cases. They were wrong on only twenty-three subjects (13%) in that the correct drug category was not identified. Only in one case was no drug or alcohol found.

To summarize the findings as reported by NHTSA:[17]

1. When the DREs claimed drugs other than alcohol were present, they were almost always detected in the blood (94%);

2. Multiple drug use was common: 72% used two or more drugs including alcohol. 45% used three or more drugs including alcohol;

3. All of the drugs were identified in almost 50% of the subjects;

4. 87% of the time the DREs correctly identified at least one drug other than alcohol;

5. Only 3.7% of the suspects who had used drugs had BACs equal to or greater than .10%.

It is likely that most, if not all, of the remainder would have been released to possibly drive again if the drug symptoms had not been recognized by the DREs.

The overall conclusion of the two studies was:

- The LAPD drug recognition procedure provides the trained police officer with the ability to accurately recognize the symptoms of many types of drugs used by drivers.

- Subsequent studies of the DRE protocol and program in other jurisdictions, particularly Arizona,[18] supported the conclusions of the NHTSA studies.[19]

Curriculum Development and Institutionalization of the DRE Program

In the early to mid-1980s, the LAPD periodically conducted DRE training. There was no formal curriculum or course outline. Rather, the training included presentations by experienced police officers, narcotics detectives, physicians, and other technical experts. The training course, which varied in length between three and seven days, included a field certification stage. During this certification stage, candidate DREs were required to conduct DRE evaluations on actual suspects while under the supervision of an experienced DRE. Periodically, senior LAPD DREs would meet and decide as a group if the candidate was sufficiently proficient to be recognized as a DRE by the LAPD. Those that were recognized as proficient were deemed certified by the LAPD as a DRE. Out of need, standards for training and certification were slowly evolving.

In 1986, in recognition of the need to develop a formal curriculum, eighteen senior LAPD DREs were selected to develop and present the DRE curriculum.[20] A DRE school was conducted in May of 1986 in Los Angeles utilizing this initial cadre of instructors. NHTSA and other agencies monitored this school, with the goals of standardizing the curriculum, and developing a comprehensive curricula package for administrators, instructors, and students.[21] In 1987, NHTSA completed the development of these lesson plans. NHTSA also conducted an instructor development school in Los Angeles to prepare DREs to present the curriculum. A successful DRE school was then held in Los Angeles using this new standardized curriculum.[22]

The next step in the development and expansion of the DRE Program was the selection of four states to pilot the expansion of the Program outside of Los Angeles. The states of New York, Arizona, Colorado, and Virginia were selected. These states were selected because they had in place aggressive DUI enforcement programs, including the training of officers in the SFST battery. Initially, officers from these jurisdictions travelled to Los Angeles to receive the classroom portion of DRE training. Upon completing the classroom training, Los Angeles DREs travelled to these other states to supervise field application and certification of these student DREs. After these students had attained certification as DREs, instructor schools were held to develop some of these new DREs as instructors. Subsequent DRE schools, conducted primarily by these new instructors, were then held in these additional states. This basic format of DRE expansion through the development of an initial cadre of DREs, followed by an instructor school, has continued to this day.

In the late 1980s, it was becoming clear to U.S. law enforcement and traffic safety officials that the DRE Program was poised for tremendous growth. Undoubtedly, for the DRE Program to expand, it needed administrative support and oversight on a national level. The International Association of Chiefs of Police (IACP) had for years maintained an ongoing relationship with NHTSA. The IACP supported

THE DRUG RECOGNITION EXPERT (DRE) PROGRAM
(Continued)

NHTSA training programs for police officers, and advised NHTSA on research needs in traffic enforcement. The IACP was the logical organization to assume the oversight and administration of the growing DRE Program. In 1989, the IACP assumed this oversight, and became the certifying and regulating body for Drug Recognition Experts.[23]

In 1988, the United States government passed the Omnibus Drug Bill. This legislation funded a large scale expansion of DRE training. Due in large measure to this bill, law enforcement agencies in 33 states have adopted the DRE program. As of 1998, there are approximately 4000 DREs nationwide, including approximately 400 DRE instructors. In addition, DREs now serve in Canada, Australia, Sweden, and Norway. South Africa, through the auspices of its Council on Scientific and Industrial Research, is expected to adopt the DRE Program in the near future.

DRE training and certification records are now maintained by the IACP.[24] NHTSA has maintained its role in the DRE Program by sponsoring curriculum update conferences, coordinating DRE courses nationwide, developing and issuing training materials, and generally providing administrative support of the DRE Program. The DRE Program is now formally titled the Drug Evaluation and Classification Program (DECP).

NHTSA REPORT TO CONGRESS ON THE DRE PROGRAM

In 1996, NHTSA evaluated its support of the development of the DECP in its report to the U.S. Congress.[25] This report concluded:

"The Drug Evaluation and Classification Program has been remarkably successful in producing meaningful results... saving lives on our nation's roads... gaining court acceptance... and showing a steady return on investment. NHTSA's leadership role in development and implementation of the DECP produced scientific validation of the program, effective training and certification standards, and rapid expansion and institutionalization of the program. Taking into consideration the enormous cost to society of impaired driving injuries today, the economic impact of the DEC has more than compensated for the funds expended to implement and conduct the program. Added to this are the many lives that have been saved by DREs who identified medical crises in time to save the drivers. The Drug Evaluation and Classification Program has unquestionably produced profitable results which can be counted on for years to come."

DRUG CATEGORIES

SIGN AND SYMPTOM BASED

Drug Recognition Experts (DRE) classify the drugs of abuse into seven categories. This categorization system is based on the premise that each drug within a category produces a pattern of effects, known as signs and symptoms. This system is analogous to a handwritten signature, rather than a fingerprint. Each time a signature is written, it will be slightly different. The signature will still be recognizable as identifying a specific individual. Fingerprints, on the other hand, do not change.

Practically, this means that although there are numerous drugs within each of the seven categories, the overall pattern of effects within the category at hand is the same. The effects can and do vary from drug to drug, primarily in terms of intensity and duration of action.

The effects of any drug depend upon many factors. A major factor is amount, that is, the dose. Generally, the effects of a drug are dose-dependent. More of the drug, such as alcohol, will generally produce more pronounced effects. The effects also depend on the user's tolerance to the drug, how the drug was administered, the drug's purity, the user's expectations, coexisting illness, fatigue, and the presence of other drugs. Also, for many reasons, individuals vary in their response to the same drug. For example, people differ in metabolic rates. The effects of a drug also vary in the same individual. Indeed, rarely will a single individual experience or display all the effects associated with a drug.

Drug abusers use drugs for effects on the central nervous system (CNS), primarily the brain. If a drug does not affect the brain, then it will not be abused (although, of course, it may be misused).[26] The seven DRE drug categories are: CNS Depressants (including alcohol), Inhalants, Phencyclidine, Cannabis, CNS Stimulants, Hallucinogens, and Narcotic Analgesics.

THE DRUGS OF ABUSE: AN OVERVIEW

Central Nervous System Depressants

This category includes the most widely abused drug, alcohol. In addition, the category consists of barbiturates, nonbarbiturates that have barbiturate-like effects, antianxiety tranquilizers, antipsychotic tranquilizers, certain antidepressants, and certain pharmaceutical combinations that contain more than one type of CNS depressant. The benzodiazepines,[27] chloral hydrate, GHB,[28] methaqualone (Mandrax®), lithium, phenobarbital, the sedating antihistamines, and many other substances are included in this category. Commonly referred to as "downers," and also as sedative-hypnotics, the effects of these drugs at intoxicating doses mirror the effects of alcohol. Importantly, however, they are not detected by an alcohol breath test, and do not produce an odor of an alcoholic beverage. Unlike the case with alcohol, there are generally no consistent correlations between the levels of these drugs ingested and the degree of intoxication. These drugs produce relaxation, drowsiness, impaired balance and coordination, slurred speech, a lowering of inhibitions, and increased risk taking. They also produce horizontal gaze nystagmus, do not generally affect pupil size, and typically depress the vital signs. The nonalcohol CNS depressants are extremely dangerous when taken with alcohol. Pharmaceutical preparations of these drugs usually contain warnings advising the user not to drink alcohol at the same time, and to be aware that they may impair driving.

Inhalants

The drugs in this category are usually inhaled. Three subcategories comprise the inhalants: volatile solvents, aerosols, and anesthetic gases. The typical user of these drugs is young, and as a result, does not have ready access to more preferred drugs. Included are solvents, such as paint thinner, gasoline, toluene, turpentine, and paint. Nitrous oxide ("laughing gas"), freon, ether, and many other substances are also included. Common indicators of the use of these drugs are the presence of chemical odors on the user, and residue of the substance on the user's face, clothing, and hands. Intoxicated individuals may look and act similar to one under the influence of alcohol. They may display impaired gait, slurred speech, bloodshot eyes, and a blank stare. Since these substances displace oxygen, the heart generally will accelerate, resulting in an increased pulse rate. Depending on the specific substance, blood pressure can be elevated or depressed.[29] As with the CNS depressants, these drugs generally produce horizontal gaze nystagmus, but do not usually affect pupil size.

THE DRUG RECOGNITION EXPERT (DRE) PROGRAM
(Continued)

Phencyclidine (PCP)

This drug is usually known as PCP, which represents its longer chemical name of phenylcyclohexyl piperidine. It is also commonly called phencyclidine. Although frequently classified as a hallucinogen, and sometimes as a depressant, a stimulant, or an analgesic, PCP is appropriately termed a dissociative anesthetic. The drug ketamine,[30] which has uses in veterinary medicine, in pediatric surgery, and in other areas, is included in this category, as are chemical analogs of PCP.

The typical effects of PCP are elevated vital signs, accompanied by both horizontal and vertical gaze nystagmus. In addition, rigid skeletal muscles, a blank stare, an absence of pain, hallucinations, and many other effects may be evident. PCP users may become suddenly violent and pose an extreme danger to police officers. Many nonlethal control devices, such as "taser"[31] dart guns, have been developed in order to subdue the PCP user.

Cannabis

This category, which includes marijuana, hash, hash oil, and the synthetic drug dronabinol,[32] is the most widely abused illicit drug. Although it has a popular reputation as a relatively benign drug, it is extremely impairing, affecting judgment, depth perception, ability to maintain attention, as well as having effects on the cardiovascular system. Cannabis causes blood shot eyes, accelerated heart rate (tachycardia), muscle tremors, forgetfulness, and many other effects. Unlike the first three categories (CNS Depressants, Inhalants, and PCP), this category does not produce horizontal gaze nystagmus. Users of cannabis frequently also use alcohol, as well as the other drugs, at the same time.

Central Nervous System Stimulants

This category includes the ubiquitous cocaine in all its various forms, amphetamine, methamphetamine, ephedrine, Ritalin®, certain diet pills, and other related substances. Commonly known as the "uppers," the effects of these drugs mimic the body's "fight or flight" response, the autonomic nervous system's response to perceived danger.[33] Their effects include dilated pupils, elevated vital signs, hyperalertness, rapid and agitated body movements, extreme weight loss accompanied by deteriorating health and hygiene, and a diminished ability to "filter" environmental stimuli, such as noises and movement. CNS stimulants do not produce horizontal gaze nystagmus. The user may overreact to seemingly minor events, and may view minor inconveniences as elaborate plots. As the effects wear off, the user may physiologically "crash," and may appear nearly the opposite of when he or she was under the influence of the drug. The user may sleep for long periods, may wake voraciously hungry, and may be extremely dysphoric.

Hallucinogens

Hallucinogens are used for their distorted sensory perceptions known as hallucinations. In many respects, they are closely related to the CNS stimulants, as is evidenced by the fact that they also cause dilated pupils and elevated vital signs, and do not produce horizontal gaze nystagmus. The user may experience a mixing of the senses, called synesthesia, in which the user may "hear" visual stimuli, such as colors, and may "see" sounds, such as music. LSD, psilocybin, mescaline, peyote, bufotenine, morning glory seeds, jimson weed, nutmeg, and the psychedelic amphetamines are some of the drugs in this category. The psychedelic amphetamines include MDMA, or methylenedioxy methamphetamine, which is known in the vernacular as "Ecstasy," and many other related preparations. Very popular in the 1960s, these drugs have experienced a resurgence of use in the 1990s.

Narcotic Analgesics

This final category includes the opiates, such as morphine, codeine, heroin, meperidine, methadone, fentanyl, and numerous others.[34] These drugs relieve pain, but also produce sedation. The specific effects include constricted pupils, depressed vital signs, slow and deliberate movements, and forgetfulness. These drugs do not produce horizontal gaze nystagmus. Although these drugs are frequently injected, more users, because of the concern over the spread of infectious disease through the sharing of hypodermic needles, are insufflating (intranasal administration) and inhaling drugs such as heroin.[35] These drugs are known for their physically addictive qualities, as well as for the extremely unpleasant, though not life-threatening, withdrawal syndrome.

POLY-DRUG USE

Polydrug use is the norm for today's drug user. Polydrug use, also termed polypharmacy and multi-habituation, simply means that the drug user is using more than one category of drugs simultaneously or serially. Often, the drugs have nearly opposite effects. For example, an extremely common drug combination in many parts of the United States is the "speed ball." This slang term refers to combining a CNS stimulant, usually cocaine, with a narcotic analgesic, typically heroin. In many respects, these drugs have opposite effects. For example, cocaine dilates the pupils and elevates the vital signs, whereas heroin constricts the pupils and depresses the vitals. Contrary to what defense attorneys attempt to coax the DRE to say, neither drug "cures" the effects of the other. What typically occurs is that the user displays a mixture of signs and symptoms, such as dilated pupils with depressed vitals, that can best be explained by polydrug use.

DREs apply four concepts to interpret polydrug signs and symptoms: additive, antagonistic, overlapping, and null.

"Additive" means that each of the drugs used produce the same effect. Each of the drugs reinforces a specific effect of the other. For example, CNS stimulants and cannabis independently elevate pulse rate. Taken together, the user's pulse will be elevated, probably to a greater degree than either drug would separately. Each drug is reinforcing an effect of the other.

"Antagonistic" means that each of the drugs produces an opposite effect. Cocaine dilates the pupils, while heroin constricts them. When taken together, the user's pupils may be dilated, may be constricted, or may be within the normal range (3.0 mm to 6.5 mm diameter). The effects displayed are dependent on the dose of each of the drugs, the user's tolerance to each of the drugs, and importantly, the point in time that the user is evaluated by the DRE. Cocaine, a short-acting drug, may "wear off" quickly, and the effects of the heroin may then dominate.

An "overlapping" effect refers to the case in which one of the drugs produces the effect, but the other drug is neither additive nor antagonistic to it. For example, alcohol produces horizontal gaze nystagmus. If alcohol is taken with cocaine, a drug that does not cause horizontal gaze nystagmus, the user will display nystagmus - again, due to the alcohol.

"Null" effect refers to a combination of drugs in which neither of the drugs used produces the effect. For example, cocaine does not produce horizontal gaze nystagmus; neither does heroin. Taken together, the user will not have nystagmus since neither of the drugs produces nystagmus. To paraphrase an old rock 'n roll song, "Nothin' and nothin' means nothin'."

THE DRUG RECOGNITION EXPERT (DRE) PROGRAM
(Continued)

THE DRE PROCESS

THE THREE DETERMINATIONS OF A DRE

Although DREs may initiate their own arrests for DUI-drugs, the usual case is for a different officer, the arresting officer, to request the expertise and assistance of the DRE after making a DUI arrest. The DRE should be requested to conduct an evaluation for drug influence when the suspect's signs of impairment are not consistent with the arrestee's BAC. Simply, the arrestee may appear more impaired than the alcohol level alone would account for. Some agencies, such as the LAPD, mandate a drug influence evaluation by a DRE whenever an individual is arrested for DUI and produces a BAC below the statutory per se level (.08% in California). In addition, an evaluation is mandated whenever the arrestee's degree and/or type of impairment is not consistent with the arrestee's BAC.

A DRE is responsible for making three determinations: (1) That the arrestee's impairment is not consistent with the BAC; (2) That the individual is under the influence of drugs, and not suffering from a medical condition that requires immediate attention; and (3) That the individual is under the influence of a specific category (or categories) of drugs.

Determination two, the ruling in or out of medical conditions, is a critical determination. There are many medical conditions, such as stroke, epilepsy, multiple sclerosis, uncontrolled diabetes, and others that produce effects that mimic drug impairment. The DRE needs to be able to quickly and accurately assess the arrestee for the presence of these conditions. It is a frequent occurrence for DREs to determine that the arrestee, who was appropriately arrested, is actually in need of urgent medical care, and is not under the influence of drugs. Only after ruling out these medical conditions does a DRE proceed with an evaluation to determine what category of drug the person is under the influence of.

A SYSTEMATIC AND STANDARDIZED 12-STEP PROCESS

In order to reach an opinion that the individual is under the influence of a specific category (or categories) of drugs, DREs utilize a 12-step, systematic and standardized process. The DRE will not reach a final opinion until the entire evaluation has been completed. The process is standardized in that all DREs, regardless of agency, utilize the same procedure, in the same order, on all suspects. It is systematic in that it logically proceeds from a BAC, through an assessment of signs of impairment, to toxicological analysis for the presence of drugs. This procedure is rooted in standard medical procedures that are used to reach a diagnosis of illness or injury.[36]

The 12 steps are:

Step One: The Blood (or Breath) Alcohol Concentration
Step Two: Interview of the Arresting Officer
Step Three: Preliminary Examination (includes the first of three pulses)
Step Four: Eye Examinations
Step Five: Divided Attention Tests
Step Six: Vital Signs Examinations (includes the second of three pulses)
Step Seven: Darkroom examinations of pupil size (includes an examination of the nasal and oral cavities)
Step Eight: Muscle Tone
Step Nine: Examination of Injection Sites (includes the third pulse)
Step Ten: Statements, Interrogation
Step Eleven: Opinion
Step Twelve: Toxicology: Obtaining a specimen and subsequent analysis

Step One: BAC

This step usually precedes the involvement of the DRE. If the arresting officer has determined that the BAC is consistent with both the type and degree of impairment, no DRE is called. On the other hand, if the BAC is not consistent with the degree and/or type of impairment, a DRE should be requested.

Step Two: Interview of the Arresting Officer

Based on the results in Step One, the arresting officer requests the assistance of a DRE. The DRE will discuss the circumstances of the arrest, and will inquire as to the suspect's condition at the time of the arrest, whether the arrestee had been involved in a traffic collision, any statements the arrestee had made, whether or not the arrestee had drugs in his or her possession, and any other relevant matters. This step is analogous to the interview an emergency room physician conducts when an unconscious individual is brought by ambulance to the hospital. The physician will of course inquire of the ambulance attendants as to how long the person has been in that state, if the person has come in and out of consciousness, and so forth.

Step Three: Preliminary Examination

This step is commonly referred to as a "fork in the road." The purpose of this step is to determine if there is sufficient reason to suspect drug influence. As was mentioned earlier, there are often serious medical conditions that may mimic drug influence. Therefore, an extremely important part of this step is the determination that it is in fact a drug, rather than a medical condition, that is inducing the observed impairment. In order to make this critical determination, the DRE will make general observations of the arrestee's condition, inquire of the arrestee as to any health problems, and conduct a pupil size and eye tracking examination. Pupils of different size and/or differences in the tracking movements of the eyes often provide evidence of serious, life-threatening, medical conditions. In addition, the DRE takes the first of three pulses in this step.

Based on what the DRE detects in this phase, a number of outcomes are possible. The DRE may find no signs of drug influence, and may return the arrestee to the arresting officer for routine processing. The DRE may see evidence of a medical condition, and may obtain a medical assessment. Or the DRE may proceed with a full DRE evaluation. Even though the DRE may have decided to proceed with the drug evaluation, if the DRE at any time finds evidence of a serious medical condition, the DRE will cease the evaluation and obtain the medical assessment.

Step Four: Eye Examination

During this step, the DRE conducts three separate eye movement examinations. They are: horizontal gaze nystagmus, vertical gaze nystagmus, and an eye convergence examination.

The Standardized Field Sobriety Testing (SFST) research found that horizontal gaze nystagmus (HGN) was the best predictor of an individual's alcohol level. Although there are many different types of nystagmus, some of which are caused by pathology, the HGN examined for by DREs is rarely confused with nystagmus caused by other physiological conditions. Simply, nystagmus refers to an involuntary, but visible jerking of the eye balls. Horizontal gaze nystagmus refers to the visible jerking of the eyeballs as the eyes move side to side while gazing at an object. The DRE uses a pencil or pen held in front of the suspect's eyes, and moves the object horizontally in front of the individual, while the individual moves his or her eyes attempting to follow the object. In addition to alcohol, other central nervous system depressants, inhalants, and PCP induce this visible jerking.

During the vertical gaze nystagmus (VGN) examination, the suspect is directed to follow an object that is moved up and down. Importantly, any drug that induces HGN may also cause, if the dose is sufficient, VGN. There are no drugs, however, that

THE DRUG RECOGNITION EXPERT (DRE) PROGRAM
(Continued)

may cause VGN without first causing HGN. Certain medical conditions, such as brain stem damage, may however cause VGN but not HGN.

During the convergence examination, the DRE, again using a pencil or pen, directs the suspect to look at the object while the DRE places the object at the bridge of the arrestee's nose. The arrestee will attempt to "cross" his or her eyes while looking at the object. CNS depressants, inhalants, PCP, and cannabis impair the ability of the individual to converge (or cross) the eyes.

Step Five: Divided Attention Testing

To a degree, this step repeats some of the tests that were given to the suspect at the time of the arrest. The setting now, however, is a controlled environment, a police station, rather than at roadside.

The DRE administers the following tests in the following order: Romberg Balance Test, a Walk-and-Turn Test, the One-Leg Stand Test, and a Finger-to-Nose Test.[37] These tests are divided attention tests, in that they require the individual to not only balance and coordinate body movements, but to remember instructions, and to perform more than one task at once. Frequently, the individual's performance on these tests during the DRE evaluation will be markedly different from the suspect's performance in the field. There are many explanations for this variance: the drug(s) may have worn off during the intermittent time period; the individual may have used multiple drugs, and a different drug may now be dominant. The officer will document the performance of the suspect, and will then continue to Step Six.

Step Six: Vital Signs Examination

The DRE takes three vital signs: blood pressure, using a sphygmomanometer and stethoscope, body temperature utilizing an oral thermometer, and pulse. This is the second of three pulses, the first having been taken in the preliminary examination. Of course, if the arrestee's vital signs are dangerously high or low, the DRE will immediately obtain a medical assessment. DREs are trained to accurately take these vital signs, and to compare the results with medically-accepted normal ranges. Certain drugs elevate specific vital signs, other drugs depress the vitals, and other drugs may have no effect on certain vital signs.[38]

Step Seven: Darkroom Examination

The eyes have been called "the window to the soul." They are certainly a "window" to the inner body. The pupils enlarge in response to darkness, fear and excitement, as well as in response to certain drugs.[39] They also constrict in response to bright light, as well as in response to certain drugs. The DRE uses a pupillometer to estimate the arrestee's pupil sizes in four different light levels: room light, near total darkness, indirect artificial light, and direct light. The DRE also examines the individual's nasal and oral cavities for evidence of drug use.

Step Eight: Muscle Tone

Certain drugs cause the skeletal muscles to become rigid, whereas other types of drugs, such as alcohol, cause muscle flaccidity. The arrestee's muscle tone is evaluated throughout the examination, through observations of the arrestee's movements. During this step, however, the DRE gently moves the arrestee's arms to determine muscle tone.

Step Nine: Injection Sites Examinations

Many drug users inject drugs intravenously. Rarely, however, do medical procedures involve injecting drugs into an artery or vein. For example, insulin-dependent diabetics do not inject into blood vessels. During this step, the DRE examines the individual for injection sites. Although the drug user may inject anywhere on the body, the more frequently used areas are the arms, neck, and ankles. Importantly, the presence of injections, even recent ones, are indicators of use, rather than drug influence. Their presence, however, may provide evidence of frequency of use, and the type of drug used. A third pulse is also taken.

Step Ten: Statements, Interview

The DRE now conducts a structured interrogation of the suspect. In the United States, if the suspect has not been advised of his or her constitutional rights (Miranda warnings) previously, the DRE will do so at this point. The DRE will question the person about the use of specific drugs. Frequently, the arrestee will make self-serving denials of drug use, but may admit or even confess drug use and impairment by drugs while driving to the DRE. Arrestees often state that they were using a prescribed drug. The DRE may ask the arrestee about any warnings given to the arrestee by the prescribing physician or pharmacist regarding operating a motor vehicle while taking the drug.

Step Eleven: Opinion

The DRE now forms an opinion as to drug influence, and the category(s) of drug(s) causing the impairment. This opinion is not a guess nor is it a hunch. **Rather, it is an informed opinion that is based on the totality of the evaluation.** Although opinions by nature are subjective, the DRE opinion is based, in part, on objective criteria.

It is a primary dictum of DRE training that when in doubt, the DRE shall always find "in favor of freedom" of the suspect. As written, a typical DRE opinion is: "In my opinion, the arrestee is under the influence of a Central Nervous System Stimulant, and cannot safely operate a vehicle.[40]

Step Twelve: Toxicology: Specimen and Subsequent Analysis

The fact that this step is the twelfth or last should not be construed to mean that it is the least important part of the evaluation. In fact, toxicological corroboration of drug use is usually necessary for successful prosecution. During this step, the DRE obtains a urine and/or blood specimen from the suspect, which is later analyzed for the presence of certain drugs by a toxicological laboratory. Under the implied consent laws that DRE states have, an individual is required to provide blood or urine to the police when requested. This blood or urine sample is required even though the arrestee may have already provided a breath test.

Typically, a week or more will elapse until the laboratory reports their results. The decision to prosecute the individual will usually be delayed until these results have been obtained.

It is critical to understand the laboratory's role in a nonalcohol drug case. In a drug influence case, the laboratory's role is usually not to determine if the individual was impaired, but is to determine use of a specific substance. For example, the DRE has determined the arrestee is under the influence of a central nervous system stimulant. The laboratory analyzes for specific drugs, such as cocaine, amphetamines, and others. The laboratory report, assuming it corroborates the opinion of the DRE, will identify a specific stimulant the person used. In court, the consistency between the DRE's opinion and the laboratory analysis is critical in demonstrating the accuracy of the DRE.

THE TOOLS OF THE TRADE: DRE EQUIPMENT

A DRE utilizes the following equipment in conducting a drug influence evaluation:

- Pupillometer: A small, approximately 3 inch by 5 inch card (approximately 7 to 12 cm), that is usually plastic, that displays dark circles, ranging in half-millimeter gradations from 1.0 millimeters to 9.0 millimeters.

THE DRUG RECOGNITION EXPERT (DRE) PROGRAM
(Continued)

- Sphygmomanometer: A manual, aneroid blood pressure cuff, consisting of a pumping bulb, a screw valve, an analog gauge, and a bladder.

- Stethoscope: Single or double diaphragm, double tubed.

- Thermometer: Oral, digital, with disposable covers.

- Penlight: Low power, medical style.

- Magnifying light: Generally five to ten magnification power, similar to those used by stamp collectors and model builders.

- Pen or pencil: Used as a stylus to conduct eye movement examinations.

- Evidence containers: For blood or urine.

- Protective gloves, latex, and/or rubber.

In addition, DREs may utilize a specialized, short distance, instant camera to take photos of injection marks, nasal and oral cavities, and of other evidence. DREs may also utilize various types of breath testing equipment, including preliminary breath testers.

DRE TRAINING AND CERTIFICATION

Drug Recognition Expert (DRE) training is probably the most rigorous academic training that any law enforcement officer can undertake. Only selected experienced officers are allowed to enroll in the course. In order to attend DRE training, the candidate is typically nominated in writing by the officer's commanding officer. Some agencies, such as the Los Angeles Police Department, require the candidate to submit a formal application form, while other agencies may require the candidate to appear for an oral interview. The criteria for selection include a demonstrated aptitude and interest in DUI enforcement and/or narcotics enforcement.[41] Candidates must also have demonstrated an ability to conduct thorough crime scene investigations, and to testify clearly and convincingly in court.

The International Association of Chiefs of Police (IACP) is the regulating and certifying body for the Drug Recognition Expert program. The IACP establishes minimum standards for all phases of DRE training, including recertification.[42]

DRE training and eventual certification by the IACP consists of numerous criteria.

They are:

1. Standardized Field Sobriety Test (SFST) training
2. DRE preliminary training
3. DRE School
4. DRE School Classroom Examination
5. Minimum number of evaluations
6. Minimum number of drug categories observed
7. Toxicological corroboration
8. "Rolling" log reviewed
9. Resume reviewed
10. Certification final examination
11. Endorsement by an instructor
12. Endorsement by a second instructor
13. Certification by the International Association of Chiefs of Police

Criterion One: Standardized Field Sobriety Test (SFST) Training

Although there are a number of formats for this first phase of DRE training, the usual format consists of two days of training in the proper administration and interpretation of the standardized field sobriety test battery. This segment is primarily skill-oriented. Students practice administering the SFST on volunteers who consume alcohol. In order to complete this phase, students must successfully pass both a written examination and a proficiency test. SFST training is a "stand-alone" course, in that most officers who complete SFST training never continue into DRE training. This phase of the training may also include an introductory overview of the drugs that impair driving.

Criterion Two: DRE Preliminary Training

Following the SFST training, officers that will continue with DRE training must successfully complete a two day DRE preliminary training course. This course expands upon the officers' SFST skills, provides an overview of the DRE procedures, and provides an overview of the effects of the drugs of abuse. In this segment, officers are also taught to properly administer the vital signs examinations that are conducted in a DRE evaluation. Some agencies combine the SFST and DRE preliminary training into a unified four-day course. The LAPD also conducts an accelerated ten-day format that combines SFST training, DRE Preliminary Training, and the DRE course itself into one unified ten-day training event.

Criterion Three: DRE School

This segment of the training consists of seven classroom days of intensive training. There are 31 separate segments to the course. Some of the specific segments are: the physiology of the drugs of abuse, the development and effectiveness of the DRE procedures, vital signs examinations, eye examinations, courtroom testimony, and drug combinations. Each of the seven categories of drugs are covered in depth. Commonly used substances, methods of administration, and the duration of effects are extensively covered. Students view video-tapes of individuals under the influence of the various categories, and participate in many interpretative exercises. Students also practice the administration of the DRE procedure while under the direct supervision of DRE instructors. Students are tested throughout this phase. Under the guidelines established for DRE training by the International Association of Chiefs of Police, students cannot "test-out" of any of the segments of the course, and must make-up any missed classes.

Criterion Four: DRE School Examination

At the conclusion of the DRE school, students take a comprehensive written objective examination. 80% is the minimum passing score.

Criterion Five: Minimum number of evaluations

This stage begins the certification phase of DRE training. Much like an internship, the student must demonstrate his or her proficiency in properly conducting and interpreting DRE evaluations that are given to actual suspects. The minimum national standards require the DRE student to conduct 12 full drug evaluations. Many agencies, including the LAPD, require 15 evaluations. Some of the required evaluations may include medical rule-outs, and evaluations in which no drug influence was determined by the DRE student. All of the evaluations during this phase must be conducted under the direct supervision of a DRE instructor.

Criterion Six: Minimum number of drug categories observed

Student DREs must evaluate individuals who are under the influence of at least three of the seven categories of drugs. (The LAPD and many other agencies require four drug categories.) The student DRE must correctly conduct the evaluations, and must reach appropriate conclusions. All three drug categories must be supported by toxicology.

THE DRUG RECOGNITION EXPERT (DRE) PROGRAM
(Continued)

Criterion Seven: Toxicological corroboration

During certification, student DREs must submit a minimum of nine physical specimens, blood or urine, to a laboratory for analysis. The laboratory analysis is compared to the student DRE's opinion as to the type of drug influencing the individual. The student must achieve a 75% laboratory confirmation rate. This means that at least 75% of the samples submitted to the laboratory must result in the laboratory finding a drug belonging to the category the student DRE identified.[43] A 75% standard does not mean that the student can be wrong 25% of the time. A student's opinion must always be supported by the individual's presenting signs and symptoms. It does allow, however, for those instances in which the laboratory is not able to detect the type of drug the student DRE had identified.

Criterion Eight: "Rolling" log reviewed

All DREs must maintain a log of all the evaluations, including toxicological results, they have conducted. This log is then submitted to a DRE instructor for review. This log is critical in establishing the DRE's expertise in court, as in documenting DRE experience for recertification.

Criterion Nine: Resume reviewed

Each DRE must maintain an up-to-date resume. This resume should list the training the DRE has received, additional readings, court qualifications, formal education, publications, and other relevant experiences. As is the case with the "rolling" log, the primary purpose of the resume is to enhance the credibility and consistency of the DRE when testifying in court. This resume must be presented for review by a DRE instructor. A copy of the resume is maintained by an agency's DRE coordinator.

Criterion Ten: Certification Final Examination

This comprehensive written examination is given when the student DRE is approaching the conclusion of certification training. This examination, which typically takes from between three and six hours, requires the student DRE to articulate the signs and symptoms of the various drugs, including numerous drug combinations. The examination is scored on a pass-fail basis by a DRE instructor. This examination is similar in concept to examinations given in graduate school that require the student to demonstrate knowledge of all aspects of drug effects.

Criterion Eleven: Endorsement by an instructor

The student DRE is required to secure in writing the recommendation of a DRE instructor stating that the student should be awarded certification. Only DRE instructors that have actually supervised the student DRE may endorse the student.

Criterion Twelve: Endorsement by a second instructor

This step requires the written endorsement of a second DRE instructor.

Criterion Thirteen: Certification by the International Association of Chiefs of Police.

Once criteria one through twelve have been completed, the student DRE submits all the required documentation to the agency's DRE coordinator. After reviewing the completed package, the agency coordinator approves and submits certification documents to the International Association of Chiefs of Police (IACP) through a state coordinator. A tracking number is assigned to the DRE, and certificates are issued to the new DRE by the IACP. Certification is for a two-year period.

RECERTIFICATION AND CONTINUING EDUCATION

In order to maintain certification, the DRE must attend a minimum of eight hours of continuing education training each two years. Many agencies require a minimum of eight hours of continuing education annually. Typically, the continuing education includes reviewing and practicing the DRE procedures, case law, toxicological issues, and an update on new drugs and drug use trends. The DRE must also have conducted a minimum of four drug influence evaluations during this period, one of which is directly supervised by a DRE instructor.

The IACP has also adopted continuing education requirements for DRE instructors.

CONCLUSION

The Drug Recognition Expert Program grew out of the need that law enforcement recognized: a need to better identify, apprehend, and prosecute the drug-impaired driver. From its humble beginnings in Los Angeles, law enforcement agencies in 33 American states have adopted the DRE Program. As the new millennia approaches, traffic enforcement officers from other countries are increasingly recognizing that the DRE approach may be a solution in part to the drug problem in their communities.

In 1995, the Royal Canadian Mounted Police hosted the first DRE training to be held outside of the United States. Canadian officers from British Columbia are now applying DRE to the Canadian drugged-driver problem. A successful Canadian DRE program will undoubtedly increase world-wide interest in the DRE approach, a user-accountable response to drugged-driving.

Footnotes

1. "Deuce" is a slang term, primarily used in California, for a person who drives under the influence of alcohol. "Deuce" is derived from 502, a former California penal code for DUI.
2. A "counting" test may require the person to count backwards out loud from 38-11. In an "alphabet-recitation" test the individual may be instructed to recite the alphabet beginning with the letter G through X.
3. In one type of "coin pick-up" test, the officer would place three coins of varying denominations on the road. The suspect would be instructed to pick up the coins in an order determined by the officer. For examples, the officer might say: "Pick up the coins the following order: quarter first, then the nickel, then the dime."
4. Under the laws of most of the United States, an individual is considered to have given his or her consent to submit to a breath, blood, or urine test subsequent to an arrest for driving under the influence. Driving is considered to be a privilege, and not a right. This is frequently termed "implied consent."
5. In most of the United States, proscribed alcohol levels are defined as a weight of alcohol to volume of blood ratio. A .10% BAC is equivalent to 100 milligrams of alcohol per 100 milliliters of blood, or 100 milligrams of alcohol per 210 liters of breath.
6. In many of the release and request dispositions, the individual had, in fact, ingested a relatively small amount of alcohol. Since the person was more impaired than would normally be expected, the officer would suspect that the person was simply an infrequent and intolerant drinker.
7. Driving While Impaired (DWI), Driving While Abilities Impaired (DWAI), Operating Under the Influence (OUI), and DUI are for the most part synonymous terms. Terms vary according to jurisdiction.
8. The National Highway Traffic Safety Administration sponsored two important studies that directly led to the development of the SFST battery, including specific procedures. Both studies were conducted by the Southern California Research Institute. They are: "Psychophysical Tests for DWI Arrest" (Final report, June, 1977), and "Development and Field Test of Psychophysical Tests for DWI Arrest" (Final report, March, 1981). A subsequent field evaluation of the SFST battery was conducted. This field evaluation, as reported in "Field Evaluation of a Behavioral Test Battery for DWI Report" (released September, 1983), by Anderson et al., supported the effectiveness of the SFST battery.
9. Horizontal gaze nystagmus (HGN) refers to an involuntary side to side jerking of the eyes as they fixate and follow an object, such as a pen or pencil, that is moved horizontally in front of the person.
10. In 1995, the Colorado Department of Transportation sponsored a field validation study of the SFST battery. This study documented the effectiveness of the battery at a .05 BAC. ("1995 Colorado SFST Field Validation Study" by Burns and Anderson).
11. This important concept, termed divided attention, has direct association with the multiple tasks involved in operating a motor vehicle, during which many tasks are being done simultaneously.
12. Los Angeles Police Department officers Sergeant Richard Studdard (retired) and Detective Len Leeds (deceased) were largely responsible for the early development of DRE procedures.
13. Horizontal gaze nystagmus, pupil size estimates, pupillary light reaction, and additional eye examinations are included in the DRE procedure.

THE DRUG RECOGNITION EXPERT (DRE) PROGRAM
(Continued)

14. The People of the State of New York v. Mary Quinn, Defendant, Docket No. 3130122, District Court, Suffolk County, October 24, 1991, 580 N.Y. S. 2d 818, 153 Misc. 2d 139 (N.Y.D.C. 1991). Los Angeles City Attorneys Office, Hill Street Branch.

15. The four LAPD officers who participated in this study as evaluators were: Sergeant Richard Studdard, Sergeant Jerry Powell, Officer Patricia Berry, and Officer Doug Laird. All have since retired from the LAPD.

16. Identifying Types of Drug Intoxication: Laboratory Evaluation of a Subject Examination Procedure, May 1984 Final Report. George E. Bigelow, PhD, et al. Behavioral Pharmacology Research Unit, Department of Psychiatry and Behavioral Sciences. Funded by the U.S. Department of Transportation's NHTSA and the National Institute of Drug Abuse. (Commonly called the Johns Hopkins Study), NHTSA, Pub. No. DOT HS 806 753 (1985).

17. Field Evaluation of the Los Angeles Police Department Drug Detection Procedure. February, 1986, DOT HS 807 012, A NHTSA Technical Report, National Highway Traffic Safety Administration. Richard P. Compton. (Commonly referred to as the 173 Case Study).

18. Drug Recognition Expert (DRE) Validation Study, Final Report to Governor's Office of Highway Safety, State of Arizona, June 4, 1994. Eugene V. Adler, Arizona Department of Public Safety and Marcelline Burns, Southern California Research Institute.

19. Preusser, Ulmer and Preusser studied the impact of DRE training on alcohol-impaired driver arrests, finding that DRE-trained officers are more likely to arrest drivers with lower alcohol levels. Evaluation of the Impact of the Drug Evaluation and Classification Program on Enforcement and Adjudication, December, 1992. D.F. Preusser, R.G. Ulmer and C.W. Preusser.

20. Report no. DOT HSA 808 058. (The DRE Program is also known as the Drug Evaluation and Classification Program (DECP)).

21. The following Los Angeles Police Department officers were responsible for the development and presentation of the DRE curriculum: Patricia (Russell) Berry, James Brown, Milt Dodge, Ian Hall, Arthur Haversat, Clark John, Baron Laetzsch, Gary Lynch, Ron Moen, Michael Murray, Thomas Page, Craig Peters, Jerry Powell, Scott Sherman, Richard Studdard, Larry Voelker, Michael Widder, and Nicholas Zingo.

22. John "Jack" Oates, William Nash, and Bill Tower (on loan to NHTSA from the Maryland State Police), represented NHTSA at this course.

23. At this time, the Los Angeles Police Department was the certifying agency for DREs.

24. The IACP also supports a DRE Section which serves as a resource and responds to the needs of DREs, program coordinators, and other traffic safety professionals. For information on membership requirements, the reader should contact the IACP at 1-800-THEIACP.

25. A Study of Working Partnerships: A Report to Congress on the Drug Evaluation and Classification Program. National Highway Traffic Safety Administration, April 1, 1996.

26. Misuse refers to an inappropriate use of a drug. For example, taking an antibiotic for a viral infection is misuse. Abuse refers to the use of a substance for psychoactive (mind altering) effects.

27. Benzodiazepines are anti-anxiety tranquilizers that share a similar chemical structure. Examples include: Valium® (diazepam), Librium®, Xanax®, Halcion®, flunitrazepam ("roofies" or Rohypnol®), Klonopin® (clonazepam) and many others.

28. Gammahydroxy butyrate

29. The anesthetic gases cause blood vessels to enlarge or dilate. This may cause a drop in blood pressure.

30. Ketamine is used legitimately only in an injectable form. The Physician's Desk Reference (PDR) includes Ketamine. Its effects are basically identical to that of PCP.

31. "Taser" is an acronym for Thomas A. Swift Electronic Rifle.

32. Dronabinol's brand name is Marinol®. Listed in the Physician's Desk Reference, it is a U.S. Drug Enforcement Administration Schedule II drug. Its uses include combatting nausea induced by cancer chemotherapy. Dronabinol is synthetic tetrahydrocannabinol, the psychoactive component of marijuana.

33. These drugs are sometimes called sympathomimetics and adrenomimetics. This means that they mimic the naturally occurring and appropriate response of the body to danger.

34. The term "opioid" is often applied to this category. This means that the effects are similar to opium, although the substance may not contain any actual opium.

35. The National Institute of Drug Abuse and the National Institutes of Health sponsored the Heroin Use and Addiction: A National Conference on Prevention, Treatment, and Research, in Washington, D.C. in September of 1997. Researchers reported that the potency of street heroin has increased substantially, thus making insufflating (snorting) heroin more attractive and effective.

36. A "history and physical" is the common term applied to the making of a medical diagnosis.

37. Although the Romberg Balance and the Finger-to-Nose tests are not part of the Standardized Field Sobriety Test battery, experience has shown these tests to provide valuable clues of drug impairment.

38. DREs are taught the following normal ranges for the vital signs. Pulse rate: 60 to 90 pulsations per minute; Blood Pressure: 120 mm Hg to 140 systolic over 70 to 90 diastolic; Temperature: 98.6 degrees Fahrenheit, plus or minus one degree.

39. DREs are taught that the normal pupil size range in all levels of light is 3.0 to 6.5 mm.

40. The legal definitions of driving under the influence and drugs vary according to jurisdiction. For example, some jurisdictions specify "motor vehicle," while others simply use the word "vehicle."

41. In California, it is illegal to be under the influence of several specified controlled substances (heroin, cocaine, PCP, methamphetamine and others). This law (11550 Health and Safety Code) empowers officers to arrest individuals anywhere when they are under the influence

42. The IACP relies upon a Technical Advisory Panel (TAP) in matters pertaining to DRE training, curricula, and certification. TAP includes representatives from the fields of prosecution, toxicology, law enforcement, and medicine. of the proscribed drugs. Driving is not an element of this offense.

43. This standard was originally recommended by a nationwide panel of toxicologists that was selected by the National Highway Traffic Safety Administration (NHTSA).

AMERICAN PROSECUTORS RESEARCH INSTITUTE
NATIONAL TRAFFIC LAW CENTER
Drug Recognition Evaluation Case Law

(The following cases may be obtained by
contacting the National Traffic Law Center)

ARIZONA

State of Arizona v. Johnson, Nos. 90-56865, 90-35883 Tucson Mun. Ct. (Ariz. Mun. Ct. Nov. 2, 1990) (unpublished opinion)

Although Arizona has adopted URE/FRE Rules, the trial court ruled that the DRE protocol satisfies the Frye standard and is therefore admissible.

"Virtually all the witnesses agreed that the scientific procedures utilized by trained drug recognition experts are reliable and are generally accepted in the scientific community. The methodology in place, used by trained law enforcement personnel in the field, has been shown to produce reasonably reliable and uniform results that will contribute materially to the ascertainment of the truth."

The Arizona Supreme Court later rejected the application of *Frye* to the DRE testimony during oral argument in Johnson and declined jurisdiction to reconsider the lower court opinion. The *Frye* standard does not apply to DRE testimony because, as Chief Justice Stanley Feldman observed, "the component examination procedures had been established for fifty years," thus they were not new or novel. Instead, DRE testimony was admissible as simple observations of physical signs and symptoms of drug influence. (Information taken from the May/June/July 1992 issue of *The DRE*.)

ARKANSAS

Mace v. State of Arkansas, 328 Ark. 536, 944 S.W.2d 830 (1997)

The Arkansas Supreme Court held that a police officer trained in DRE qualifies as an expert under Rule 702 of the Arkansas Rules of Evidence. The circuit court did not err in qualifying the police officer as an expert under Rule 702 because the officer had specialized knowledge of the cause of defendant's impairment. The trial court did not conduct a separate hearing to address the issue of the reliability of the DRE protocol.

"The circuit court specifically stated that it was qualifying [the police officer] as an expert for a narrow purpose — whether [the defendant] was impaired because of some kind of intoxicant. We agree that [the police officer's] specialized training and knowledge aided the circuit court in determining this fact in issue."

COLORADO

State of Colorado v. Hernandez, No. 92-M181 Boulder County (Colo. Aug. 14, 1992) (unpublished opinion)

Although Colorado has adopted URE/FRE Rules it continues to follow *Frye* in reference to novel scientific evidence. The County Court in *Hernandez* found no novelty in the DRE procedures and therefore used Rule 702 to determine the admissibility of DRE testimony. DRE evidence held admissible.

"The DRE methods are accepted within the scientific community because they have been found to be reliable. The court finds that the expert does have sufficient

specialized knowledge to assist the jurors in better deciding whether the defendant drove his car when under the influence of a specific drug. The DRE testimony can be used at trial provided a sufficient foundation is laid."

See also *State of Colorado v. Turner*, Case No. 92T413 Kit Carson County (Colo. County Ct. Nov. 29, 1993) (unpublished opinion).

FLORIDA

State of Florida v. Beam et al, 2 Fla. L. Weekly Supp. 444 (Dade County Ct. August 22, 1994)

> Florida granted the state's motion to admit DRE testimony. Florida follows the *Frye* rule for admitting expert testimony, but the court in this case found that *Frye* does not apply because DRE, while relevant in determining whether the defendant was driving under the influence of drugs, is not new or novel. The court also held that even if *Frye* did apply, DRE evidence is generally accepted in the scientific community.

In holding that DRE is not new or novel, the court stated that "law enforcement officers have administered DRE or DRE-type tests, and its predecessor, since the late 1970s... [A] scientific principle does not become 'new' or 'novel' simply because the person employing it is someone other than one who traditionally applied it."

The court also found that "[t]he DRE protocol belongs to the fields of traffic law enforcement, forensic toxicology, behavioral and research psychology, and, to a lesser extent, the medical profession. Even a cursory review of the scientific literature and caselaw conclusively demonstrates that the DRE protocol generally is accepted in these fields."

State of Florida v. Williams, Case No. 245998, 9-I (January 1995) (unpublished opinion) (case currently under appeal)

> Although Florida has adopted the URE/FRE, it continues to follow *Frye*. The court held that *Frye* is inapplicable to the DRE protocol because neither the protocol or any of its subsets (excluding HGN, VGN and lack of convergence) are "scientific" within the meaning of *Frye*. Although HGN, VGN and LOC are scientific, they are not new or novel and therefore the *Frye* standard does not apply to them either. The court also held that HGN test results may be used to establish: (1) the defendant was impaired, and/or (2) the defendant was over the legal limit, and/or (3) the defendant's specific breath or blood alcohol level at the time s/he performed the test. According to the court, DRE testimony and evidence is admissible because it is reasonably accurate, reliable and relevant.

"Drug recognition training is not designed to qualify police as scientists, but to train them as observers. The training is intended to refine and enhance the skill of acute observation... and to focus that power... in a particular situation."

The court followed the Klawitter (Minnesota) decision, that it requires the state to "lay a proper predicate before referring to a DRE as anything other than a DRE or Drug Recognition Evaluator or Examiner."

"The real issue is not the admissibility of the evidence, but the weight it should receive. That is a matter for the jury to decide."

IOWA

State of Iowa v. Sanders, No. OWCR041844, Johnson County District Court (Iowa October 31, 1997) (ruling denying defendant's motion to exclude evidence).

AMERICAN PROSECUTORS RESEARCH INSTITUTE
NATIONAL TRAFFIC LAW CENTER *(Continued)*

The court held DRE testimony is governed by Iowa Rule 702, but not by *Daubert* because a DRE's testimony is not "scientific in nature." Even under a *Daubert* analysis, the court concluded the DRE witness can testify because the *Daubert* factors have been met.

"This Court concludes that a DRE witness should be permitted to testify based upon the DRE's other specialized knowledge gained from training and experience. The DRE will be permitted to testify to the observations made during the DRE evaluation and to the conclusions drawn therefrom, including the opinion of the officer that the subject was behaviorally [sic] impaired and that the observed impairment was caused by a drug or drugs, other than alcohol. The DRE may be permitted to testify as to conclusions or opinions concerning the drug and/or drug class upon proper foundation as further discussed herein."

"This Court does maintain some reservations about the testimony of DREs. First, the very designation selected, Drug Recognition Expert, may convey a status which could unfairly give a higher degree of reliability... This Court will require the DRE to be referred to as a 'Drug Recognition Officer...' or... 'Evaluator'."

MARYLAND

State of Maryland v. Squire, Case No. 892099008, Baltimore City (Md. Cir. Ct. Oct. 13, 1992) (order denying State's motion to reconsider).

In an earlier oral opinion, the trial court denied the admissibility of DRE testimony. In denying the State's motion to reconsider that ruling, the trial court stated its belief that a DRE is an expert and that it was not established that DRE is a technique that "has been 'sufficiently established to have gained general acceptance in the particular field in which it belongs.'" Had the court found the DRE to be a lay witness, the testimony would be admissible as lay opinion testimony provided the witness "has had the opportunity to observe the facts upon which he bases his opinion."

MINNESOTA

State of Minnesota v. Klawitter, 518 N.W.2d 577 (Minn. 1994)

Minnesota is yet another state that has adopted URE/FRE but continues to follow *Frye*. The Minnesota Supreme Court affirmed the lower court's ruling that horizontal gaze nystagmus satisfies the *Frye* standard and expressly refused to address the issue of whether Minnesota should abandon *Frye* in favor of applying the standard articulated in *Daubert v. Merrell Dow Pharmaceutical*, Inc., 113 S. Ct. 2786 (1993). *Klawitter* held that the drug recognition evaluation is not a novel scientific discovery or technique and that DRE evidence is admissible. The Court further stated, however, that an officer may not be referred to in the courtroom as a "Drug Recognition **Expert**" because the use of the term "expert" suggests unwarranted scientific expertise. The Court indicated that the term "Drug Recognition Officer" would be acceptable.

"Given proper foundation and subject to other qualifications, opinion testimony by experienced police officer trained in use of so-called drug recognition protocol is generally admissible in evidence in a trial of a defendant for driving while under the influence of a controlled substance."

The trial court stated, "...there is nothing scientifically new, novel, or controversial about any component of the DRE protocol itself. The symptomatology matrix used by DREs to reach their conclusions is not new and is generally accepted in the medical community as an accurate compilation of signs and symptoms of impairment by the various drug categories."

State of Minnesota v. Cammack, 1997 Minn. App. LEXIS 278 (1997)

The Court of Appeals of Minnesota held that a DRE officer need not complete the entire twelve step evaluation for the officer's opinion to be admissible as long as there is sufficient admissible evidence that supports the DRE's opinion.

"Klawitter does not require... that all 12 steps [of the DRE protocol] be complete before a court may find sufficient foundation for an officer's opinion on impairment."

NEW YORK

People of New York v. Quinn, 580 N.Y.S.2d 818 (Dist. Ct. 1991)

New York Courts apply the *Frye* standard in assessing admissibility of scientific evidence. The District Court held that the DRE protocol meets the *Frye* test. On appeal the case was reversed due to failure of the record to contain a written jury waiver. See *People v. Quinn*, 607 N.Y.S.2d 534, 158 Misc.2d 1015 (NY Supreme Ct. 1993). On appeal, the court did not address the trial court's finding as to the reliability of HGN and the DRE protocol. Nevertheless, since the case has been overturned, it is of limited use as precedent.

OREGON

State of Oregon v. Wallace, No. 96020425 Linn County Circuit/District Court (Oregon July 15, 1996) (unpublished opinion)

The court held that DRE evidence was admissible under the seven factors espoused in the Oregon case of *State v. Brown*. The seven factors include (1) the technique's general acceptance in the field, (2) the expert's qualifications and stature, (3) what use has been made of the technique, (4) the potential rate of error, (5) the existence of specialized literature, (6) novelty of the technique and (7) the extent to which the technique relies on the subjective interpretation of the expert. DRE technology "does well in regard to almost all [of these factors]." Furthermore, the court held that the Oregon State troopers qualified as experts.

"[T]he Court finds that the two Oregon State troopers in this case are both qualified as experts based on the testimony given as to their training, experience and expertise in administering Drug Recognition tests. Of course, the foundation for qualification as expert witnesses will need to be repeated for the trier of fact at trial."

The court found that *"[i]n the evidence submitted by the State in this case, it appears that highly qualified medical experts did participate in developing the technology and that there is acceptance in the scientific community of law enforcement as argued by the State."* It also found that *"reliability and validity are very high [with DRE] because results can be verified."*

Finally, although *"DRE testing is fairly recent compared to other law enforcement techniques... the human body's reaction to the presence of certain types of drugs is as old as the practice of medicine itself. It is not novel to attempt to measure these reactions and draw conclusions from them."*

State of Oregon v. Buford, Case No. 97CR0207MI Douglas County Circuit/District Court (Oregon July 8, 1997) (unpublished opinion)

The court found that the DRE protocol is scientific evidence and must satisfy *Daubert*. The court held that the DRE protocol does in fact satisfy *Daubert*, the DRE evidence is relevant, the evidence will assist the trier of fact to reach a

AMERICAN PROSECUTORS RESEARCH INSTITUTE
NATIONAL TRAFFIC LAW CENTER *(Continued)*

conclusion and that its probative value outweighs the prejudicial effect to the defendant. The court also held that the DRE protocol meets the seven criteria of *State v. Brown.*

"The [DRE protocol] is not novel. It simply relies upon a specific series of tests used for other purposes and relies upon the trained observer to interpret the behavior demonstrated by the subject. The subjective interpretation of the expert is qualified through training and the expert's conclusions are measured against the toxicological analysis of the subject's urine."

WASHINGTON

City of Seattle v. Mandell, No. 2886205 Municipal Court of the City of Seattle (Washington June 11, 1997)

The trial court admitted testimony concerning the drug recognition evaluation. Although the court stated that *Frye* applied to only some of the steps of the evaluation, and that almost all of those steps were not novel, it appears that the entire protocol satisfies the *Frye* standard. The court concluded that DRE evidence is admissible "where there is evidence of drug use contemporaneous or near-contemporaneous with driving..."

"Lay witnesses in Washington may testify to an opinion of alcohol intoxication... Courts in other jurisdictions have held that lay witnesses may testify to drug intoxication even absent independent evidence of drug use... as long as a sufficient foundation is laid by the witness, establishing that the effects of drugs are sufficiently known to the witness... The [state] has established that a police officer trained in drug recognition protocol is more than a lay witness, i.e., has greater expertise in recognizing the physiological effects of certain controlled substances than the average citizen."

FEDERAL COURT

United States v. Everett, 732 F.Supp.1313 (D. Nev. 1997)

A magistrate judge in the United States District Court of Nevada admitted DRE testimony. The magistrate found that *Daubert* did not apply to the DRE protocol because the protocol was made up of nothing more than physical observations. The magistrate states that multiple physical observations "used in concert, to reach a conclusion, does not necessarily elevate the result from the technical to the scientific. The pertinent components of the DRE protocol have long been established and used in the medical community as part of physical examinations..."

"...[U]pon the appropriate foundation being laid, the Drug Recognition Evaluation protocol conducted by Ranger Bates, together with his conclusions drawn therefrom, shall be admitted into evidence to the extent that the DRE can testify to the probabilities, based upon his or her observations and clinical findings, but cannot testify, by way of scientific opinion, that the conclusion is an established fact by any reasonable scientific standard. In other words, the otherwise qualified DRE cannot testify as to scientific knowledge, but can as to specialized knowledge which will assist the trier of fact to understand the evidence."

UNITED STATES SUPREME COURT

Daubert v. Merrell Dow Pharmaceutical, Inc., 509 U.S. 1993 (1993)

The United States Supreme Court settled the legal controversy within the federal system over which standard should be used to determine the admissibility of scientific evidence, i.e. *Frye* versus the Federal Rules. The Court held that the legislatively enacted FRE superseded *Frye* because there is no mention of the "general acceptance" standard in Rule 702 and this standard is incompatible with the liberal thrust of the FRE. In addition, Rules 401 and 402 pertaining to relevancy of evidence are applicable to the admission of scientific evidence.

PENDING DECISIONS

Hawaii: In August, 1996, a trial court in Hawaii held that DRE testimony was admissible. There is no written opinion.

Idaho: Also in 1996, an Idaho trial court was asked to consider the admissibility of DRE evidence. The formal written opinion has not been issued.

Updated: 2/2/98

For future updates, please contact the National Traffic Law Center, 99 Canal Center Plaza, Suite 510, Alexandria, Virginia, 22314, Phone: (703) 549-4253, Fax: 703-836-3195

CROSS EXAMINATION OF THE DRUG RECOGNITION EXPERT: WHAT TO EXPECT

by Sgt. Thomas Page, LAPD and DDA Linda Condron,
Santa Clara (California) County

March 1, 1996; Revised February, 1998.

Following the direct examination by the prosecuting attorney, the defense counsel will typically challenge the Drug Recognition Expert's (DRE) opinion, and its basis, by posing the following types of questions to the DRE. These questions are in addition to challenges to the officer's motivation, bias, completeness of reports, and so on.

The Defendant is identified as Miss Alicia Ann Ace.

• Missing Signs or Symptoms

This line of questioning attempts to elicit the fact that the defendant did not have all of the expected signs or symptoms of the drug(s) in question.

Officer, you were taught that bruxism or grinding of the teeth is a sign of CNS stimulant influence, isn't it?

Miss Ace didn't have that sign, did she?

NOTE: It is rare indeed for an individual to display all of the classic effects of a drug. The DRE's opinion is based on the totality of the observed signs and symptoms as elicited by the DRE evaluation.

• Point Out What's Normal

The defense may also focus on those signs or symptoms that were normal, and were, therefore, not consistent with the drug in question.

Officer, you learned the normal range of temperature in DRE training, didn't you?

And that range is 98.6 Fahrenheit plus or minus one degree, isn't it?

You recorded Miss Ace's temperature as 98 degrees, didn't you?

98 is within normal ranges, isn't it?

Miss Ace's temperature was, therefore, normal, wasn't it?

Stimulants cause elevated temperature, don't they?

Miss Ace's was not elevated, was it?

• Alternative Explanations

The defense elicits alternative explanations for the signs and symptoms of the drug(s) in question. These alternative explanations usually deal with medical conditions, stress, a traffic collision, etc.

Officer, an elevated pulse rate can be caused by things other than drugs, can't it?

Excitement may cause it?

Stress may cause it?

Being involved in a traffic accident is stressful, isn't it?

And being involved in a traffic accident may cause elevated pulse, right?

Being interviewed in the early morning by three police officers is stressful?

And that may also cause the pulse to be elevated, can't it?

NOTE: Certainly, any single sign or symptom can be caused by something other than drugs. The DRE, much like a medical doctor, focuses on the totality of the signs and symptoms.

• **Defendant's Normals**

The defense attempts to emphasize the fact that not everyone is so-called normal, that normal is subjective.

Officer, you were taught the normal range for pulse in DRE training, weren't you?

And you agree that not all people fall in that normal range, don't you?

That there are people with pulse rates above normal that aren't on drugs, right?

And that there are people with a pulse rate below normal that aren't on any drugs, right?

A person's pulse changes over time, doesn't it?

You don't know what Miss Ace's normal pulse is, do you?

It could be in the normal range, right?

But her normal pulse, normal for her, could be above or could be below the so-called normal range, isn't that true?

• **Doctor Cop**

This line of questioning challenges the credibility of the officer's teachers - that they are police officers, rather than medical professionals.

Officer, the teachers in this DRE school weren't doctors, were they?

They weren't nurses, either?

Toxicologists?

Pharmacologists?

Paramedics?

They were police officers, right?

NOTE: At a minimum, the instructors in a DRE course are certified (by the International Association of Chiefs of Police) DREs who have completed an additional course of instruction to become a certified instructor.

• **Just a Cop**

This line of questioning challenges the DRE's credentials - that he or she is "just a cop." This infers that the DRE evaluation is an ersatz medical evaluation that should be undertaken only by a medical professional.

Officer, you're not a doctor, are you?

A toxicologist?

A pharmacologist?

A nurse?

A physiologist?

You don't have a degree in chemistry, do you?

You're a police officer, right?

NOTE: Nobody is everything! Even if the officer was also a medical doctor, the defense would probably point out that DRE belongs to the speciality of neurology!

CROSS EXAMINATION OF THE DRUG RECOGNITION EXPERT:
WHAT TO EXPECT *(Continued)*

The DRE has what few other professionals have — experience in encountering the drug-impaired person.

• The Unknown

By causing the officer to state that he or she doesn't know how a sign or symptom is caused, the defense attacks the officer's credibility. This line of questioning challenges the officer's expertise, by implying that a real expert would know these things.

Officer, you don't know how stimulants dilate the pupil, do you?

You don't know how alcohol supposedly causes nystagmus, do you?

You don't know how stimulants supposedly elevate the heart rate, do you?

NOTE: This line of questioning implies that "somebody" knows how the drugs produce all of their effects. In fact, many drugs in the Physician's Desk Reference contain the statement: "The exact mechanism of action of this drug remains unknown."

• Guessing Game

This tactic attacks the DRE opinion as a subjective guess, a belief, rather than an objective finding. And guesses can be wrong.

Officer, your opinion in a DRE case is subjective, isn't it?

It's really a belief on your part?

You've made these beliefs in DRE cases in the past, haven't you?

And sometimes toxicology didn't find the drug you predicted, isn't that so?

And, in fact, sometimes, toxicology didn't find any drug, isn't that so?

And so, sometimes your opinion is not correct, right?

Sometimes, you guess wrong.

NOTE: Opinions, by nature, are subjective. A psychiatric diagnosis, which is an opinion, for example, is based almost totally upon subjective criteria, as there is no urine test for schizophrenia. A DRE's opinion, which is based upon both subjective and objective criteria, such as pulse rate, blood pressure, and the eye signs, is an opinion which is "to a reasonable degree of certainty." This is not a guess. Never state that the DRE opinion is a guess.

THE TOXICOLOGICAL ASPECTS OF DRUG RECOGNITION EXPERT INVESTIGATIONS

by Eugene V. Adler, BS, DABFT

THE SCIENCE OF FORENSIC TOXICOLOGY

PREFACE

In most impaired driving cases, the toxicological analysis of chemical substances in body fluids provides the single most reliable and objective piece of evidence. In any given case, it is important for criminal justice system professionals to understand what the toxicology findings mean. For example, an arresting officer wants to know if the lab results support the pending charges. The prosecutor must understand both the Drug Recognition Expert (DRE) evaluation and the toxicology findings, in order to present a coherent theory of the case to the trier of fact. If the prosecutor doesn't understand what the evidence means, neither will the jury.

Officers, prosecutors, and scientists all have important roles to play in this multidisciplinary program, but their roles are inherently different. Real understanding requires recognizing the limitations of one's knowledge. Still, the prosecutor or officer who understands a few scientific concepts will become dramatically more effective in DUI Drug cases. Science is on your side. Use it.

DEFINITION AND OVERVIEW

Toxicology means the "science of poisons," of which forensic toxicology is one branch.

Forensic toxicology is defined by the American Board of Forensic Toxicology as "the study and application of toxicology to the purpose of the law." It is also helpful to define it in terms of the two objectives most apparent to prosecuting attorneys and law enforcement officers: the chemical analysis of drugs and metabolites in biological specimens, and; the interpretation of what the analytical findings mean, in terms of effects on behavior, determination of cause of death, and exposure to the drug or poison (route of administration, dosage, time of administration). The chemical analysis is factual information, because the accuracy and reliability of chemical tests, when properly conducted by qualified persons, approaches complete certainty. The interpretation is opinion information; more than one interpretation may be possible by different experts.

TOXICOLOGY AND THE DRE PROGRAM

(Note: The use of the unmodified term "toxicology" will hereafter refer to forensic toxicology.)

Decreased mental and physical abilities (impairment) can be caused by chemicals, medical conditions, or fatigue. The primary role of toxicology in a DRE case is corroborative, that is, to corroborate the opinion of the DRE that one or more drug categories caused impairment. Secondarily, toxicology may be applied further towards "an understanding of the incident", as will be discussed.

That toxicology is primarily corroborative in a DRE case does not diminish its importance. The most objective, scientific evidence in a typical DUI case is the chemical analysis.

THE TOXICOLOGICAL ASPECTS OF DRUG RECOGNITION EXPERT INVESTIGATIONS *(Continued)*

The arrest is based upon the opinion of the arresting officer, which is formed prior to toxicological testing and not based upon toxicological results. When the toxicology results are available, often days or weeks after the incident, the case may be reevaluated in the light of the toxicological findings. "Putting together" the DRE opinion and the toxicology findings is of paramount importance. The lab findings may completely corroborate the DRE's opinion, may partially support the DRE opinion, or may provide no support whatsoever for the DRE opinion.

In the context of the DRE program, toxicologists confront numerous decisions... about specimen choice, analytical methods, instrument purchases, and the best utilization of laboratory resources. Which drugs should be tested for? Which cutoffs are appropriate? Should the screening panel be the same for all cases? Which screening positives should be confirmed? When should quantitative analysis be performed? How should the toxicology laboratory provide scientific support in DUI-drug cases?

It is imperative to find reasonable and effective answers to these questions in order to integrate toxicological support with the DRE program in a manner which significantly advances the overall goal of detecting drug-impaired drivers. Although there are no "best" answers at present, there are good answers. What is most important is that each DRE program find an effective, sound, and affordable way to weld together the DRE program and toxicology.

TOXICOLOGICAL ANALYSIS: AN INTRODUCTION FOR PROSECUTORS

DRUGS AND METABOLITES IN BODY FLUIDS

It would appear from the difficulty that attends the detection of certain poisons after death, that they probably undergo some chemical alterations in the living body.

J. J. Reese
A Manual of Toxicology, 1874

The toxicological analysis is focused on **psychoactive drugs** (those affecting the central nervous system, ie, the brain) and their **metabolites**. Metabolites are substances produced within the body by its action upon the drug.

Metabolites are generally more water soluble and more readily excreted in the urine, than the parent drug. Metabolites are sometimes psychoactive, but are often inactive. Drug metabolism can be generally viewed as a process which the body gets rid of drugs.

Drug metabolism may be influenced by the dosage, route of administration, use of other drugs, individual tolerance, age, etc. Although drug metabolism is a labyrinthine subject, our interest is limited to a few frequently encountered drugs, so let's consider some important examples.

Cocaine is readily metabolized in the body, and even subject to chemical decomposition during specimen storage. Therefore, analytical methods are primarily designed to target the important metabolite and decomposition product, **BE** (which stands for **benzoylecgonine**, pronounced ben'-zoyle-eck'-ugh-nine). The presence of BE in blood or urine is evidence of previous cocaine use. Cocaine itself may be detectable when cocaine use was very recent to the collection of specimen, and the specimen is stored in a certain way (to minimize decomposition). However, the absence of cocaine itself in the specimen does not necessarily rule out recent use, and is not a problem from the prosecutor's perspective.

The **benzodiazepines** (Valium®, Xanax®, Ativan®) are the "minor tranquilizers," the sedatives related closely to Valium® (diazepam). Their metabolism is complex and a comprehensive survey could fill an entire book. In the urine unchanged diazepam will usually be undetectable, but two metabolites, desmethydiazepam and oxazepam will generally be found; a third metabolite, temazepam, may also be found. All of these metabolite substances are also available as prescription drugs in their own right. If all three of these substances appear in urine, this pattern suggests that diazepam* was used, resulting in this predictable metabolic profile. It is unlikely that someone actually took all three drugs, and they certainly would not have been prescribed three such similar drugs. (*The use of clorazepate, a very close relative of diazepam, could also result in a similar metabolic profile.)

The metabolism of the psychoactive ingredient of **marijuana, THC (tetrahydrocannabinol),** is also complex. An important urinary metabolite is called **carboxy-THC** (the full name is 9-carboxy-11-nor-delta-9-tetrahydrocannabinol). This slowly eliminated metabolite can be present in urine for many days (or weeks) following the cessation of heavy marijuana use, and is the most famous example of slow elimination of a metabolite.

Methamphetamine is not extensively metabolized. It is detectable in blood or urine. Generally smaller concentrations of the active metabolite amphetamine are detectable alongside larger concentrations of the parent drug. Amphetamine is also a drug (prescription or illicit) in its own right. Its presence, unaccompanied by any methamphetamine, would indicate that amphetamine was used.

The metabolism of the **opiates (heroin, morphine, codeine)** is important and provides perhaps the best illustration of the role of the toxicologist in interpreting the toxicology findings. **Heroin (diacetylmorphine)** is rapidly and completely metabolized to morphine. But when morphine is found in urine, there are several very different possible explanations for its presence:

- Codeine is also metabolized to morphine. Following codeine use, the urine will show both codeine and smaller amounts of morphine.

- Morphine is a drug in its own right, the use of which will result in morphine in the urine.

- The ingestion of unwashed poppy seeds has been identified as a possible source of morphine in the body fluids. (The poppy plant is the natural source of morphine). This source of morphine would not cause impairment.

The above explanations for the presence of morphine in urine include such disparate sources as an illegal drug (heroin), a prescription drug, and a food component. The interpretation of the results by a toxicologist or qualified medical person can often aid in understanding the case. Consider:

- There exists an intermediate metabolite of heroin, **monoacetylmorphine,** which is chemically midway between heroin and morphine. Its presence serves as a "marker" for heroin use.

- A high ratio of codeine to morphine concentration is typical of codeine use. The opposite would be found following opium use because opium contains more morphine than codeine.

- In a specimen, the presence of both codeine and certain other drugs would strongly suggest the use of a popular prescription medication containing that very combination of drugs. (For example, Fiorinal® contains codeine and butalbital; Soma Compound with Codeine® contains carisoprodol and codeine.)

- The DRE evaluation, when considered in addition to the toxicology analysis, can provide important information which establishes the form of the

THE TOXICOLOGICAL ASPECTS OF DRUG RECOGNITION
EXPERT INVESTIGATIONS *(Continued)*

drug used, the mode of administration, and whether the user's intent was therapeutic or otherwise. This information may include injection sites, admissions, and impairment status.

It should be remembered that many drugs or their metabolites may be detected for days (or weeks in some cases) after the drug has cleared from the blood and the effects have worn off and are no longer observable.

Exercise: Try interpreting the following case. The suspect was very impaired and drowsy, and claims to have taken 2 "pain killer pills." The DRE concludes the signs and symptoms are inconsistent with the .02 breath alcohol test, and opines "CNS Depressants." The subsequent analysis of a urine specimen showed it to contain codeine, morphine, butalbital, and hydroxyalprazolam. (see Table 1). Answer the following questions. The answers can be found after Table 1.

- What was taken by the suspect?

- How many different drugs or medications were used?

- Was the DRE opinion supported?

- Was there "bad intent" (ie, drug abuse, irresponsibility) in this case?

- Do you know the phone number of a qualified toxicologist to assist you in reviewing the technical aspects of the case?

Table 1. Examples of Drug Metabolism (a, b)

Drug Taken	Analyte Detectable in Blood (c)	Analyte Detectable in Urine
Diacetylmorphine (heroin)	**Morphine**	**Morphine, monoacetylmorphine**
Codeine	Codeine, **morphine**	Codeine, **morphine**
Cocaine	Cocaine, **BE**	**BE, methylecgonine**
Methamphetamine	Methamphetamine, **amphetamine**	Methamphetamine, **amphetamine**
Amphetamine	Amphetamine	Amphetamine
Diazepam (Valium®)	Diazepam, **desmethydiazepam**	Diazepam, **desmethydiazepam, oxazepam**
Alprazolam (Xanax®)	Alprazolam	**Hydroxyalprazolam**
Triazolam (Halcyon®)	(Not detectable)	**Hydroxytriazolam**
Butalbital with codeine (Fiorinal®)	Codeine, **morphine,** butalbital	Codeine, **morphine,** butalbital
Phencyclidine (PCP)	Phencyclidine	Phencyclidine
Toluene (as inhalant)	Toluene	(Probably undetectable)

a. Metabolites are in bold type.

b. These examples are generalizations. Some are oversimplified.

c. The term "analyte" refers to the chemical substance sought in the analysis, whether a drug or metabolite.

Exercise answers: In all likelihood the suspect used "Fiorinal with codeine®" and Xanax®. The use (or abuse) of these two prescription medications would account perfectly for all the substances found in the urine. The DRE opinion was well supported by the presence of two depressant drugs other than the alcohol. (Although codeine is a narcotic analgesic, it will not necessarily produce all the signs and symptoms of stronger narcotics, and in this case the depressants predominated.) The use of these two medications and alcohol suggests a deliberate attempt to produce central nervous system effects (ie, a "rewarding subjective experience") rather than suggesting the responsible, sanctioned use of therapeutic drugs.

ANALYTICAL METHODS: SCREENING AND CONFIRMATORY TESTS

Note: A complete analysis requires a minimum of two independent tests, a screening test and a confirmatory test. A screening test alone does not provide the degree of specificity and certainty required and expected in a legal proceeding. Some jurisdictions report out the results of screening tests; such results should be clearly indicated as "preliminary" or "unconfirmed" results.

Screening Tests

A screening test is a rapid, relatively inexpensive, presumptive test which can tentatively identify common substances of interest. It is often applied to an entire batch of specimens from various donors. It yields either a negative or a presumptive positive result.

Negative screening results are reported out immediately. Positive results are analyzed further by appropriate confirmatory tests.

Various screening test technologies, or analytical techniques, are available, including **EMIT** (enzyme multiplied immunoassay technique), **RIA** (radioimmunoassay), **TLC** (thin layer chromatography), and **GC** (gas chromatography). Whatever the analytical technique chosen, screening tests are applied individually for important analytes such as cannabinoids, cocaine metabolite, methamphetamine, opiates, barbiturates, benzodiazepines, phencyclidine, and LSD.

Screening tests do not identify the specific substance present. Screening tests are based on chemical class similarities, not DRE drug categories.

Screening Test Cutoffs

Screening tests yield only a "reading" (ie, a number), not a detailed fingerprint. When the test reading is above an established cutoff (a predetermined number), the test result is positive; below the **cutoff** the test is negative. A "negative" screening test result does not mean that no analyte is present; it means that **the substances sought were not present at concentrations above the cutoff.**

Sometimes the question is asked: "Why can't cutoffs be lowered so that all positives are detected?" The choice of cutoff is constrained by several factors, one of which is sensitivity. This can easily be explained on an intuitive level by an analogy. Screening tests function like smoke or burglar alarms. If a smoke alarm sniffs enough smoke, it goes off; too little smoke and nothing happens. Imagine living in a world where all the car and burglar alarms are continually going off and where medical screening tests for HIV and cancer are always false-positive because their "cutoffs" are set too sensitively. Imagine car alarms triggered by the slightest breeze; dogs continually barking at imaginary intruders and the wind itself, creating an intolerable state of abject happiness. And, (key of F Major), imagine all the people... running around reacting constantly to perceived threats. The toxicology laboratory, like the rest of the world, needs good smoke alarms that discriminate between abnormal conditions (drug positives) and normal conditions. That is why the cutoffs must be sensitive, but not too sensitive.

Like smoke alarms, screening tests are subject to occasional false-positives and false-negatives. Given the need for conservative evidence in the administration of criminal justice, a low percentage of false negative screening results is acceptable.

THE TOXICOLOGICAL ASPECTS OF DRUG RECOGNITION EXPERT INVESTIGATIONS *(Continued)*

What is not acceptable are final laboratory reports representing complete analyses which misidentify drugs or report drugs which are not there. The requirement for a minimum of two independent tests, screening and confirmatory, prevents this.

Confirmatory Tests (GC-MS)

A single confirmatory technique is the most widely used: **gas chromatography-mass spectrometry**, or **GC-MS**. It is considered a sort of "gold standard" of confirmatory tests. This technique produces a great amount of information about drugs and metabolites in a specimen. For most chemical substances, GC-MS analysis provides a truly unique fingerprint. It is a sensitive, specific technique which can handle the "dirty" extracts from biological specimens.

If the confirmatory test supports (corroborates) the screening test result, the presence and identity of the analyte(s) is established with certainty, and the analysis is complete with respect to the identified substance(s).

> How a GC-MS works: The gas chromatograph (GC) separates the components of the sample, and introduces them into the mass spectrometer (MS). The MS uses a high energy electron beam in a high vacuum to break up molecules into smaller electrically charged particles, which are sorted, detected, and graphed out as highly detailed "spectra" or fragmentation pattern (fingerprint).

The prosecutor should be aware that the GC-MS analysis might be performed by the same analyst who did the screening test, or perhaps by another analyst.

THE LABORATORY'S APPROACH

Numerous substances qualify as drugs of abuse, but few are actually common in DUID cases in given geographical areas. Three illegal drugs predominate in some areas: marijuana, cocaine, and methamphetamine. Knowledge about the specific drugs likely to be found most frequently in specimens obtained from DUID suspects, accumulates over the life of a DRE program. That knowledge aids in the appropriate utilization of laboratory resources.

There are miscellaneous substances which are not detectable by a routine battery of screening tests. These **"blind spots"** generally include certain miscellaneous depressants and narcotics, for example: carisoprodol, propoxyphene, methadone, and various antidepressants. These drugs can be detected by supplemental screening procedures. Some laboratories do not offer such supplemental screening tests. Omitting the additional screening will result in fewer detections of these miscellaneous drugs, and a lower corroboration rate for DRE opinions concerning narcotic analgesics and depressants, but the merits of the supplemental screening must be weighed against the cost to laboratory resources.

Two Related Issues: Specimen Choice, and Qualitative vs Quantitative Analysis

Specimen choice is the subject of regular, sometimes acrimonious discussion among toxicologists. In DUID cases, the choice may be constrained by legal, logistical, and budgetary issues, as well as by toxicological considerations. Neither blood nor urine is perfect for analysis. Each has advantages and disadvantages (see Table 2).

Table 2. Summary of Advantages and Disadvantages of Blood and Urine

Blood Advantages:

- Provides evidence of drug use.

- Because the circulating blood transports the drug to the sites where the effects are caused, the presence of drugs in blood is more closely related to impairment.

Blood Disadvantages:

- Blood may be more difficult to obtain. It requires specially trained personnel.

- Some drugs are more difficult to detect in blood than in urine.

- Blood is generally more difficult and expensive to analyze.

Urine Advantages:

- Provides evidence of drug use.

- Urine is easy to obtain.

- Drugs and metabolites are concentrated in the urine, resulting in greater ease of detection.

- Drugs remain in the urine for a longer period of time than in blood. (This can also be a disadvantage when interpreting the results.)

- Urine can be comprehensively analyzed at reasonable cost.

Urine Disadvantages:

- The presence of drugs in urine has limited relationship to impairment

- A greater potential exists for dilution, substitution, or manipulation of the specimen by the suspect.

- There may be increased interpretation problems due to metabolism.

- Certain drugs may be present for weeks after the psychoactive effects have disappeared.

- Some drugs are more readily detected in blood than in urine.

Because alcohol concentrations are interpretable with respect to the existence of impairment and the degree (although this is not so simple), and because drug concentrations in fatal drug overdoses are often so high that their interpretation is straightforward, there exists a misconception that proving drug impairment in traffic cases is merely a simple matter of determining a number-- quantifying a drug concentration in blood. The **"alcohol model"** is not satisfactory for other drugs, because the relationship of blood drug concentrations and impaired driving skills has not been established for many potentially impairing substances. The difficulty of correlating drug concentrations to impairment is partly due to the inherently complex pharmacology, therefore, it should not be assumed that this nut will be cracked as soon as a few more studies are done.

The misapplication of the alcohol model was an early obstacle which had to be overcome by toxicologists who broke ground for the earliest DRE programs. They were repeatedly asked: "What is the official or "per-se" impairing concentration of Drug X?" There is no simple answer. Do not allow the burden of proving impairment to fall upon the toxicological analysis; it does not belong there alone. The DRE evaluation is usually the backbone evidence of impairment, and often only qualitative corroboration is required. The burden rests upon the **totality of all the evidence** in the case.

THE TOXICOLOGICAL ASPECTS OF DRUG RECOGNITION EXPERT INVESTIGATIONS *(Continued)*

At present, most crime laboratories which are successfully supporting DRE programs do not require quantitation "on principle," but approach this decision in terms of costs/benefits. In serious crashes, particularly if a suspect's injuries limit the opportunity to directly observe drug signs and symptoms, the collection and analysis of both blood and urine is beneficial. Routine analysis of both, however, is typically not an option, and a choice must be made between the two fluids.

Other specimen types are occasionally useful also. Vomitus containing undigested pills is a relevant biological specimen. Marijuana particles from the mouth, cocaine powder smears from the nasal passages, or rags with wet paint, are obviously relevant.

QUALITY ASSURANCE

Quality laboratory work is a necessary foundation of any DUID program. Quality assurance includes quality control, proficiency testing, and "all steps taken to ensure a quality work product." It is axiomatic that the laboratory must at all costs avoid misidentifying drugs.

Strong quality assurance and reliable performance are prerequisites for providing accurate toxicological data for both the support and the evaluation of a DRE program. External evaluation of laboratory performance is desirable. Find out if your laboratory participates in a proficiency testing program.

Professional organizations and agencies offer programs for laboratory assessment. The American Society of Crime Laboratory Directors has developed a laboratory accreditation program, and the College of American Pathologists offers several proficiency testing surveys to fit the needs of various laboratories. Participation in such programs is voluntary for certain types of laboratories, but nevertheless desirable.

THE ROLES OF TOXICOLOGISTS IN THE DRE PROGRAM

The toxicologist will often consult with attorneys prior to trial, to review the lab results, the case, and to provide an interpretation (opinion) which is generally not provided in the laboratory report. This initial phone call or meeting is the time for the prosecutor to obtain additional information from a potential key expert witness which can be crucial to preparing and conducting the case. However, the prosecutor may not know what to ask. As a general starting point, the following questions or checks may facilitate this interfacing of science and law:

1. Does the prosecutor have a copy of the laboratory report or reports?

2. Does the prosecutor have documentation of the chain of custody of any physical specimens?

3. Was the specimen refrigerated or frozen after analysis? Where is it now? Could it be reanalyzed if desired by the defense? (Note: Many labs no longer routinely bring biological specimens to court, due to the biological hazard.)

4. Does the laboratory report represent confirmed results, or preliminary (screening test) results?

5. Which tests were performed and by whom? Which drugs were or weren't tested for?

6. Who will testify and what are they qualified to testify about?

7. Is a resume available?

8. Was quantitative analysis performed? If yes, what does this indicate?

9. Overall, what do the laboratory results mean?

10. Is the toxicologist aware of any problems or limitations which the prosecutor should know about?

11. How familiar is the toxicologist with the DRE program? Do the lab results fully support, partially support, or not support, the DRE opinion? Should the toxicologist review the DRE evaluation report? If so, what additional opinions, if any, can the toxicologist reach?

12. Does the laboratory participate in a quality assurance program or proficiency testing program?

13. How do you pronounce the names of the substances found? (No kidding. The prosecutor and officer should know this. These chemical substances are key evidence.)

14. Has the local laboratory gathered any data which demonstrates how the local DRE program is generally working?

Court testimony is obviously an important role of the toxicologist. In addition, other roles are possible. Toxicologists provide scientific guidance to DRE programs by participating in training events, educational conferences or local meetings, and defining local guidelines pertaining to sample selection and submission, sample amounts, etc. As advisors to government, scientists are largely responsible for balancing costs and for program effectiveness, ie, determining how a DRE program can get the most bang for the buck.

It is desirable that local toxicologists should evaluate the correspondence of toxicology results to DRE opinions. This assessment of program performance constitutes program evaluation and validation on a local level.

Table 3. The Roles of Toxicologists in the DRE Program

Corroboration	Analysis of Drugs and Metabolism
Quality Assurance	Accurate, Legally Defensible Analysis
Expertise	Court Testimony
	Consultation
	Guidelines for Using Laboratory Services
	Training
Scientific Direction	Program Effectiveness, Costs, and Benefits
	Assessment of DRE Program Validity

THE DRE OPINION AND THE TOXICOLOGY FINDINGS: THE TOTALITY OF THE EVIDENCE

A DRE attributes impairment to one of seven drug categories, which are based upon shared patterns of signs and symptoms. The laboratory, however, identifies the specific drugs or metabolites. There are three possible outcomes when the DRE and lab reports are put side by side. The lab may fully support, partially support, or provide no support for, the DRE opinion. Table 4 provides examples of each scenario:

THE TOXICOLOGICAL ASPECTS OF DRUG RECOGNITION EXPERT INVESTIGATIONS (Continued)

Table 4. The DRE Opinion and the Toxicology Results

DRE Opinion	Lab Results	Outcome
Stimulants and Narcotics	Cocaine and Morphine	Fully supported
Stimulants and Narcotics	Morphine	Partially supported
Stimulants and Narcotics	No common drugs detected	Not supported
Narcotics	Morphine and marijuana metabolism	Fully supported

In the table, the second example could be considered a "disappointment" by the DRE, because one of the two drug categories recognized by the DRE (Narcotics) was not supported by the lab. The fourth example could be considered a "surprise" in that a drug category unrecognized by the DRE was nevertheless found by the lab. Many DRE opinions are only partially supported, and this is not a problem *per se*. To understand this better, consider the following comprehensive list of reasons why there is often not a perfect one to one correspondence between the DRE and Lab findings. Note that many of these are "good" reasons, representing underlying scientific principles in action, not problems.

The lab provides no support of a DRE opinion that a particular drug category is causing impairment (a disappointment) whenever:

- the DRE identifies signs and symptoms of a drug, but the limitations of the laboratory analysis result in a failure to detect it in the specimen; or,

- the DRE misinterprets impairment signs and symptoms.

The DRE does not attribute impairment to a drug category corresponding to a substance the lab found anyway (a surprise), whenever:

- a suspect exhibits the signs and symptoms of a drug, but the DRE does not recognize them;

- the DRE associates a drug's signs and symptoms with another drug which is also present;

- the signs and symptoms of one drug counteract or mask the signs and symptoms of another drug; or

- the suspect was not impaired at the time of the evaluation and exhibited no signs and symptoms of impairment, but the drug or metabolite was detected in the urine specimen. (In this case, the DRE evaluation insures that the motorist will not be charged erroneously with being under the influence of a drug.)

It is not possible to establish the reasons for misses retrospectively, but misses of cocaine and marijuana are not unexpected. Unless a large amount of stimulant has been ingested, the signs and symptoms typically are less obvious than the symptoms of other categories and can be very difficult to recognize. Cocaine is a fast-acting substance, and observable signs of use may be apparent at roadside but diminish significantly by the time of evaluation. The half-life of cocaine is approximately 90 minutes, but its metabolite, BE, can be detected in urine for 24-48 (possibly 72) hours, depending on amount ingested. Thus, it is possible for the laboratory to detect BE from cocaine, which was ingested at some time in the recent past, even though the suspect was not impaired at the time of the evaluation.

Similarly, the marijuana metabolite appears and can be detected in urine for days-to-weeks, depending on amount and chronicity of use. Because a specimen may test positive at a time when the suspect is not under the influence of marijuana, a DRE evaluation is crucial. Importantly, unless a marijuana positive from the laboratory is corroborated with evidence of impairment at the time of the evaluation, it does not speak to the question of drug influence.

In summary, a "surprise" may occur if a DRE fails to correctly observe, record, and interpret the signs and symptoms displayed by a suspect. It will also occur if the parent drug has been eliminated from the body, but a metabolite, which is not itself psychoactive, remains in the urine. It can occur if one substance produces severe symptoms, as PCP does, which entirely mask the symptoms of other drugs. Also, although two or more drugs may have been used, differences in amounts used and each drug's time course may be such that not all substances yield signs and symptoms at the time of the evaluation. A "disappointment" may occur if the DRE misinterprets signs and symptoms, or due to the limitations of the laboratory.

Conclusions: The DRE methodology mandates both a standardized evaluation and the analysis of a specimen. Together, the evaluation and the toxicological analysis create a balance, which is designed to identify impaired suspects, and equally important, to recognize unimpaired suspects.

DRE VALIDATION STUDIES

The questions asked and answered in the DRE validation studies include these: Does the DRE evaluation method do what it is intended to do? Does a particular DRE program realize the potential of the DRE methodology?

There have been three key validation studies. The first was a **laboratory evaluation** involving volunteer subjects who were dosed with known drugs and evaluated by DREs. The second was a **field evaluation study** of the LAPD drug detection procedure. The third was a **field evaluation study** of the Phoenix, Arizona DRE program. All three studies are described in more detail below.

The "John Hopkins" Study[2]

Method:

- This study was a laboratory evaluation of the drug recognition evaluation procedures, sponsored jointly by NHTSA and the National Institute of Drug Abuse (NIDA) during 1984.

- The experimental procedure involved the administration of specific drug doses to volunteer subjects who were then evaluated independently by each of four LAPD drug recognition experts.

- The drugs administered were:
    - marijuana (2 dose levels)
    - depressants:
        diazepam (Valium®) (2 dose levels)
        secobarbital (1 dose level)
    - stimulants:
        d-amphetamine (2 dose levels)

Results of the study:

- The subjects rated intoxicated had almost always received a drug. Raters were quite accurate in specifying which drug had been given to the subjects they rated as intoxicated.

THE TOXICOLOGICAL ASPECTS OF DRUG RECOGNITION EXPERT INVESTIGATIONS *(Continued)*

The "173 Case Study" (Field Evaluation of the Los Angeles Police Department Drug Detection Procedure)[3]

Method:

- Under NHTSA's sponsorship, independent analysis of blood specimens was performed for 173 individuals arrested by LAPD and examined by DREs. The study ran for three months during the summer of 1985.

Results of the study:

- In terms of accuracy of the DREs judgements, the important findings were:

  - When the DREs claimed drugs other than alcohol were present, they were almost always detected in the blood (94% of the time). It was rare for DREs to claim a suspect had used drugs and for no drugs to be found in the suspect's blood.

  - The DREs were able to correctly identify at least one drug other than alcohol in 87% of the suspects evaluated in this study.

  - When the DREs identified a suspect as impaired by a specific drug (category), the drug was present in the suspect's blood 79% of the time.

  - Only 6 of the suspects (3.7%) who had used drugs had alcohol concentrations equal to or greater than .10% w/v. It is likely that most (if not all) of the remainder of the suspects would have been released if the drug symptoms had not been recognized by the DREs.

- Conclusion: The results of the two studies sponsored by NHTSA showed that the LAPD drug recognition procedure enables the experienced police officer to accurately recognize the symptoms of drug use by drivers.

The "Arizona DRE Validation Study"[4,5]

Method:

Under sponsorship of the Arizona Governor's Office of Highway Safety and NHTSA, a retrospective field evaluation study of the entire work product of a DRE program was undertaken in Arizona. Study data were the DRE and toxicology records for 500 suspects who were evaluated over a 53-month period. This study examined: (1) the accuracy of the DREs decisions about drug impairment and drug categories; (2) the relationship of particular signs and symptoms to the DRE drug categories; and; (3) the characteristics and drug choices of the arrestees.

Results of the Study:

The major conclusion of the study were:

- The DRE program is a valid method for identifying and classifying drug-impaired drivers.

- Certified DREs recognize drug-impairment and identify the drug(s), by category, which cause the impairment.

- Observable signs and symptoms are associated with specific drugs.

- Observable signs and symptoms are associated with specific drugs.

- The DRE program requires scientifically sound support by the laboratory.

Acknowledgment

Many thanks are due to Dr. Marcelline Burns for invaluable discussion and guidance, and for permission to use several portions of text from the Arizona DRE Validation Study.[4,5]

References

1. Goodman J and Gilman A, *The Pharmacological Basis of Therapeutics*, 7th ed, 1985, MacMillan Publishing.
2. Bigelow GE, Bickel WE, Roache JD, et al, "Identifying Types of Drug Intoxication: Laboratory Evaluation of a Subject-examination Procedure," Report No. DOT-HS-806-753, NHTSA, U.S. Dept of Transportation and National Institute on Drug Abuse, 1985.
3. Compton RP, "Field Evaluation of the Los Angeles Police Department Drug Detection Program," Report No. DOT-HS-807-012, NHTSA, U.S. Dept of Transportation, 1986.
4. Adler E and Burns M, "Drug Recognition Expert (DRE) Program Validation Study," Final Report, Arizona GOHS, 1994.
5. Burns M and Adler E, "Study of a Drug Recognition Program," Proceedings of the 13th International Conference on Alcohol, Drugs, and Traffic Safety, Adelaide, Australia, 1995.

HORIZONTAL GAZE NYSTAGMUS STATE CASE LAW SUMMARY

ALABAMA

I. Evidentiary Admissibility

HGN is a scientific test that must satisfy the *Frye* standard of admissibility. Court held that HGN is generally accepted in the relevant scientific community and thus is admissible.

Malone v. City of Silverhill, 575 So.2d 101, 103-04 (Ala. Crim. App. 1990).

II. Police Officer Testimony Needed to Admit HGN Test Result

Testimony of one police officer, whose training consisted of one eight-hour course on HGN testing, was inadequate foundation for admission of HGN test results. "[A]t most, [the police officer] qualified as an expert in giving the test. The state offered no other evidence [at trial] to demonstrate the reliability of either the HGN test or the scientific principle upon which the HGN test is based..."

Malone, 575 So.2d at 104.

III. Purpose and Limits of HGN

Not addressed by court.

ALASKA

I. Evidentiary Admissibility

"The question of whether HGN evidence is admissible at criminal trials in [Alaska] is still open."

Williams v. State, 884 P.2d 167, 172 (Alaska Ct. App. 1994).

II. Police Officer Testimony Needed to Admit HGN Test Result

Not addressed by court.

III. Purpose and Limits of HGN

HGN is "sufficiently reliable" enough to be used in a probable cause determination hearing.

State v. Grier, 791 P.2d 627, 631 (Alaska Ct. App. 1990).

ARIZONA

Evidentiary Admissibility

HGN is a scientific test that needs to satisfy the *Frye* standard of admissibility. State has shown that HGN satisfies the *Frye* standard.

State v. Superior Court (Blake), 718 P.2d 171, 181 (Ariz. 1986) (seminal case on the admissibility of HGN).

II. Police Officer Testimony Needed to Admit HGN Test Result

"The proper foundation for [admitting HGN test results]... includes a description of the officer's training, education, and experience in administering the test and showing that proper procedures were followed."

State ex. rel. Hamilton v. City Court of the City of Mesa, 799 P.2d 855, 860 (Ariz. 1990).

See also *State ex. Rel. McDougall v. Ricke*, 778 P.2d 1358, 1361 (Ariz. App. 1989).

III. Purpose and Limits of HGN

HGN test results are admissible to establish probable cause to arrest in a criminal hearing.
State v. Superior Court (Blake), 718 P.2d at 182.

"Where a chemical analysis has been conducted, the parties may introduce HGN test results in the form of estimates of BAC over .10% to challenge or corroborate that chemical analysis."
Ricke, 778 P.2d at 1361.

When no chemical analysis is conducted, the use of HGN test results "is to be limited to showing a symptom or clue of impairment."
Hamilton, 799 P.2d at 858.

ARKANSAS

I. Evidentiary Admissibility

Novel scientific evidence must meet the *Prater* (relevancy) standard for admissibility. Because law enforcement has used HGN for over thirty-five years, a *Prater* inquiry is not necessary as the test is not "novel" scientific evidence.
Whitson v. State, 863 S.W.2d 794, 798 (Ark. 1993).

II. Police Officer Testimony Needed to Admit HGN Test Result

Not addressed by court.

III. Purpose and Limits of HGN

HGN may be admitted as evidence of impairment, but not admissible to prove a specific BAC.
Whitson, 863 S.W.2d at 798.

CALIFORNIA

I. Evidentiary Admissibility

HGN is a scientific test and the *Kelly/Frye* "general acceptance" standard must be applied.
People v. Leahy, 882 P.2d 321 (Cal. 1994), 34 Cal Rptr. 2d 663 (1994).
People v. Joehnk, 35 Cal. App. 4th 1488, 1493, 42 Cal. Rptr. 2d 6, 8 (1995).

"...[A] consensus drawn from a typical cross-section of the relevant, qualified scientific community accepts the HGN testing procedures..."
Joehnk, 35 Cal. App. 4th at 1507, 42 Cal. Rptr. 2d at 17.

II. Police Officer Testimony Needed to Admit HGN Test Result

Police officer testimony is insufficient to establish "general acceptance in the relevant scientific community."
Leahy, 882 P2d. at 609, 34 Cal Rptr. 2d at ___.

Police officer can give opinion, based on HGN and other test results, that defendant was intoxicated. Furthermore, police officer must testify as to the administration and result of the test.
Joehnk, 35 Cal. App. 4th at 1508, 42 Cal. Rptr. 2d at 18.

III. Purpose and Limits of HGN

HGN may be used, along with other scientific tests, as some evidence that defendant was impaired.
Joehnk, 35 Cal. App. 4th at 1508, 42 Cal. Rptr. 2d at 17.

HORIZONTAL GAZE NYSTAGMUS STATE CASE LAW
SUMMARY *(Continued)*

HGN test results may not be used to quantify the BAC level of the defendant.
People v. Loomis, 156 Cal. App. 3d Supp. 1, 5-6, 203 Cal. Rptr. 767, 769-70
(1984).

CONNECTICUT

I. Evidentiary Admissibility

HGN must meet the Frye test of admissibility. In this case, the state presented no
evidence to meet its burden under the *Frye* test.
State v. Merritt, 647 A.2d 1021, 1028 (Conn. App. Ct. 1994).

II. Police Officer Testimony Needed to Admit HGN Test Result

Not addressed by court.

III. Purpose and Limits of HGN

HGN test results can be used to establish probable cause to arrest in a criminal
hearing.
State v. Royce, 616 A.2d 284, 287 (Conn. App. Ct. 1992).

HGN test results can be used to establish probable cause to arrest in a civil
hearing.
Ward v. Commissioner of Motor Vehicles, ___ A.2d ___, ___, 1994 Conn.
Super. LEXIS 2324 (Conn. Super. Ct. Sept. 15, 1994).

DELAWARE

Evidentiary Admissibility

HGN evidence is scientific and must satisfy the Delaware Rules of Evidence
standard.
State v. Ruthardt, 680 A.2d 349, 356 (Del. Super. Ct. 1996).

HGN evidence is acceptable scientific testimony under the Delaware Rules of
Evidence.
Ruthardt, 680 A.2d at 362.

II. Police Officer Testimony Needed to Admit HGN Test Result

Police officer may be qualified as an expert to testify about the underlying scientific
principles that correlate HGN and alcohol. Delaware police receiving three day
(twenty-four hour) instruction on HGN test administration are not qualified to do
this.
Ruthardt, 680 A.2d at 361-62.

Police officer testimony about training and experience alone, without expert testimony, is not enough foundation to admit HGN test results.
Zimmerman v. State, 693 A.2d 311, ___ (Del. 1997).

III. Purpose and Limits of HGN

HGN test results admissible to show probable cause in a criminal hearing.
Ruthardt, 680 A.2d at 355.

HGN test results admissible to show probable cause in a civil hearing.
Cantrell v. Division of Motor Vehicles, 1996 Del. Super. LEXIS 265 (Jan 5,
1996).

HGN test results cannot be used to quantify the defendant's BAC. However, they can be used as substantive evidence that the defendant was "under the influence of intoxicating liquor."
Ruthardt, 680 A.2d at 361-62.

FLORIDA

I. Evidentiary Admissibility

HGN is a scientific test. However, because it is not novel, the *Frye* standard is not applicable. However, "[e]ven if not involving a new scientific technique, evidence of scientific tests is admissible only after demonstration of the traditional predicates for scientific evidence including the test's general reliability, the qualifications of test administrators and technicians, and the meaning of the results." Without this predicate, "the danger of unfair prejudice, confusion of issues or misleading the jury from admitting HGN test results outweighs any probative value." The state did not establish the appropriate foundation for the admissibility of HGN test results..
State v. Meador, 674 So. 2d 826, 835 (Fla. Dist. Ct. App. 1996).

II. Police Officer Testimony Needed to Admit HGN Test Result

No evidence presented as to the police officer's qualifications nor administration of the HGN test in this case.
Meador, 674 So. 2d at 835.

III. Purpose and Limits of HGN

Not addressed by court.

GEORGIA

I. Evidentiary Admissibility

The HGN test is admissible as a "scientifically reliable field sobriety evaluation" under the Harper "verifiable certainty" standard.
Manley v. State, 424 S.E.2d 818, 819-20 (Ga. Ct. App. 1992).

HGN testing is judicially noticed as a scientifically reliable test and, therefore, expert testimony is no longer required before the test results can be admitted.
Hawkins v. State, 476 S.E.2d 803, 808-09 (Ga. Ct. App. 1996).

II. Police Officer Testimony Needed to Admit HGN Test Result

Police officer, who received specialized training in DUI detection and worked with a DUI task force for two years, was permitted to testify that, in his opinion, defendant was under the influence.
Sieveking v. State, 469 S.E.2d 235, 219-20 (Ga. Ct. App. 1996).

III. Purpose and Limits of HGN

HGN test can be admitted to show that the defendant "was under the influence of alcohol to the extent that it was less safe for him to drive."
Sieveking, 469 S.E.2d at 219.

IDAHO

I. Evidentiary Admissibility

HGN test results admitted under the Idaho Rules of Evidence. Rule 702 is correct test in determining the admissibility of HGN.
State v. Gleason, 844 P.2d 691, 694 (Idaho 1992).

HORIZONTAL GAZE NYSTAGMUS STATE CASE LAW SUMMARY *(Continued)*

II. Police Officer Testimony Needed to Admit HGN Test Result

Officer may testify as to administration of HGN test, but not correlation of HGN and BAC.
State v. Garrett, 811 P.2d 488, 493 (Idaho 1991).

III. Purpose and Limits of HGN

"HGN test results may not be used at trial to establish the defendant's blood alcohol level... Although we note that in conjunction with other field sobriety tests, a positive HGN test result does supply probable cause for arrest, standing alone that result does not provide proof positive of DUI..."
Garrett, 811 P.2d at 493.

HGN may be "admitted for the same purpose as other field sobriety test evidence -- a physical act on the part of [defendant] observed by the officer contributing to the cumulative portrait of [defendant] intimating intoxication in the officer's opinion."
Gleason, 844 P.2d at 695.

ILLINOIS

I. Evidentiary Admissibility

HGN meets *Frye* standard of admissibility.
People v. Buening, 592 N.E.2d 1222, 1227 (Ill. App. Ct. 1992).

Despite the ruling of the *Buening* appellate court, the Fourth District Court of Appeals declined to recognize HGN's general acceptance without a *Frye* hearing. The court criticized the Buening court for taking judicial notice of HGN's reliability based on the decisions of other jurisdictions.
People v. Kirk, 681 N.E.2d 1073, 1077 (Ill. App. Ct. 1997).

II. Police Officer Testimony Needed to Admit HGN Test Result

"A proper foundation should consist of describing the officer's education and experience in administering the test and showing that the procedure was properly administered."
Buening, 592 N.E.2d at 1227.

III. Purpose and Limits of HGN

HGN test results may be used to establish probable cause in a criminal hearing.
People v. Furness, 526 N.E.2d 947, 949 (Ill. App. Ct. 1988).

HGN test results admissible to show probable cause in a civil hearing.
People v. Hood, 638 N.E.2d 264, 274 (Ill. App. Ct. 1994).

HGN test results may be used "to prove that the defendant is under the influence of alcohol."
Buening, 592 N.E.2d at 1228.

IOWA

I. Evidentiary Admissibility

HGN admissible as a field test under the Iowa Rules of Evidence. "[T]estimony by a properly trained police officer with respect to the administration and results of the horizontal gaze nystagmus test are admissible without need for further scientific evidence."
State v. Murphy, 451 N.W.2d 154, 158 (Iowa 1990).

II. Police Officer Testimony Needed to Admit HGN Test Result

Police officer may testify about HGN test results under Rule 702 if the officer is properly trained to administer the test and objectively records the results.
Murphy, 451 N.W.2d at 158.

III. Purpose and Limits of HGN

HGN test results may be used as an indicator of intoxication.
Murphy, 451 N.W.2d at 158.

KANSAS

I. Evidentiary Admissibility

HGN must meet *Frye* standard of admissibility and a *Frye* hearing is required at the trial level. There was no *Frye* hearing conducted and the appellate court refused to make a determination based on the record it had.
State v. Witte, 836 P.2d 1110, 1121 (Kan. 1992).

II. Police Officer Testimony Needed to Admit HGN Test Result

Not addressed by court.

III. Purpose and Limits of HGN

Not addressed by court.

KENTUCKY

I. Evidentiary Admissibility

HGN test results admitted due to defendant's failure to object.
Commonwealth v. Rhodes, 949 S.W.2d 621, ___ (Ky. Ct. App. 1996).

II. Police Officer Testimony Needed to Admit HGN Test Result

Not addressed by court.

III. Purpose and Limits of HGN

Not addressed by court.

LOUISIANA

I. Evidentiary Admissibility

HGN meets *Frye* standard of admissibility.
State v. Armstrong, 561 So. 2d 883, 887 (La. Ct. App. 1990).
State v. Regan, 601 So. 2d 5, 8 (La. Ct. App. 1992).
State v. Breitung, 623 So. 2d 23, 25-6 (La. Ct. App. 1993).

The standard of admissibility for scientific evidence is currently the Louisiana Rules of Evidence.
State v. Foret, 628 So. 2d 1116 (La. 1993).

II. Police Officer Testimony Needed to Admit HGN Test Result

Police officer may testify as to training in HGN procedure, certification in the administration of HGN test and that the HGN test was properly administered.
Armstrong, 561 So. 2d at 887.

III. Purpose and Limits of HGN

The HGN test may be used by the officer "to determine whether or not he [needs] to 'go any further' and proceed with other field tests."
Breitung, 623 So. 2d at 25.

HORIZONTAL GAZE NYSTAGMUS STATE CASE LAW SUMMARY *(Continued)*

HGN test results may be admitted as evidence of intoxication.
Armstrong, 561 So. 2d at 887.

MAINE

I. Evidentiary Admissibility

Because the HGN test relies on greater scientific principles than other field sobriety test, the reliability of the test must first be established.
State v. Taylor, 694 A.2d 907, 912 (Me. 1997).

The Maine Supreme Court took judicial notice of the reliability of the HGN test to detect impaired drivers.
Taylor, 694 A.2d at ___.

II. Police Officer Testimony Needed to Admit HGN Test Result

"A proper foundation shall consist of evidence that the officer or administrator of the HGN test is trained in the procedure and the [HGN] test was properly administered."
Taylor, 694 A.2d at 912.

III. Purpose and Limits of HGN

HGN test results may only be used as "evidence of probable cause to arrest without a warrant or as circumstantial evidence of intoxication. The HGN test may not be used by an officer to quantify a particular blood alcohol level in an individual case."
Taylor, 694 A.2d at 912.

MARYLAND

I. Evidentiary Admissibility

HGN is scientific and must satisfy the *Frye/Reed* standard of admissibility. The Court of Appeals took judicial notice of HGN's reliability and its acceptance in the relevant scientific communities.
Schultz v. State, 664 A.2d 60, 74 (Md. Ct. Spec. App. 1995).

II. Police Officer Testimony Needed to Admit HGN Test Result

Police officer must be properly trained or certified to administer the HGN test. [NOTE: In *Schultz*, the police officer failed to articulate the training he received in HGN testing and the evidence was excluded.]
Schultz, 664 A.2d at 77.

III. Purpose and Limits of HGN

Not addressed by court.

MASSACHUSETTS

I. Evidentiary Admissibility

HGN is scientific and is admissible on a showing of either general acceptance in the scientific community or reliability of the scientific theory.
See *Commonwealth v. Lanigan*, 641 N.E.2d 1342 (Mass. 1994).

HGN test results are inadmissible until the Commonwealth introduces expert testimony to establish that the HGN test satisfies one of these two standards.
Commonwealth v. Sands, 675 N.E.2d 370, 373 (Mass. 1997).

II. Police Officer Testimony Needed to Admit HGN Test Result

"[T]here must be a determination as to the qualification of the individual administering the HGN test and the appropriate procedure to be followed." In this case there was no testimony as to these facts, thus denying the defendant the opportunity to challenge the officer's qualifications and administration of the test.
Sands, 675 N.E.2d at ___.

III. Purpose and Limits of HGN

Not addressed by court.

MICHIGAN

I. Evidentiary Admissibility

Court found that HGN test is scientific evidence and is admissible under the *Frye* standard of admissibility.
State v. Berger, 551 N.W.2d 421, 424 (Mich. Ct. App. 1996).

II. Police Officer Testimony Needed to Admit HGN Test Result

Only foundation necessary for the introduction of HGN test results is evidence that the police officer properly performed the test and that the officer administering the test was qualified to perform it.
Berger, 551 N.W.2d at ___.

III. Purpose and Limits of HGN

HGN test results are admissible to indicate the presence of alcohol.
Berger, 551 N.W.2d at ___ n.1.

MINNESOTA

I. Evidentiary Admissibility

Court found that HGN meets the *Frye* standard of admissibility.
State v. Klawitter, 518 N.W.2d 577, 585 (Minn. 1994).

II. Police Officer Testimony Needed to Admit HGN Test Result

Police officers must testify about their training in and experience with the HGN test.
See generally *Klawitter*, 518 N.W.2d at 585-86.

III. Purpose and Limits of HGN

HGN admissible as evidence of impairment as part of a Drug Evaluation Examination in the prosecution of a person charged with driving while under the influence of drugs.
See generally *Klawitter*, 518 N.W.2d at 585.

MISSISSIPPI

I. Evidentiary Admissibility

HGN is a scientific test. However, it is not generally accepted within the relevant scientific community and is inadmissible at trial in the State of Mississippi.
Young v. City of Brookhaven, 693 So.2d 1355, 1360-61 (Miss. 1997).

II. Police Officer Testimony Needed to Admit HGN Test Result

Police officers cannot testify about the correlation between the HGN test and precise blood alcohol content.
Young, 693 So.2d at 1361.

HORIZONTAL GAZE NYSTAGMUS STATE CASE LAW
SUMMARY *(Continued)*

III. Purpose and Limits of HGN

HGN test results are admissible only to prove probable cause to arrest.
Young, 693 So.2d at 1361.

HGN test results cannot be used as scientific evidence to prove intoxication or as a mere showing of impairment.
Young, 693 So.2d at 1361.

MISSOURI

I. Evidentiary Admissibility

Court found that HGN test meets the *Frye* standard of admissibility.
State v. Hill, 865 S.W.2d 702, 704 (Mo. Ct. App. 1993), rev'd on other grounds,
State v. Carson, 941 S.W.2d 518, 520 (Mo. 1997).

II. Police Officer Testimony Needed to Admit HGN Test Result

Police officer must be adequately trained and able to properly administer the test.
Hill, 865 S.W.2d at 704.

III. Purpose and Limits of HGN

HGN can be admitted as evidence of intoxication.
Hill, 865 S.W.2d at 704.

MONTANA

I. Evidentiary Admissibility

Court found HGN test meets the Montana Rules of Evidence approach of admissibility.
State v. Clark, 762 P.2d 853, 857 (Mont. 1988).

II. Police Officer Testimony Needed to Admit HGN Test Result

Police officer testified to training and certification to administer the test, and that the HGN test was properly administered.
Clark, 762 P.2d at 857.

III. Purpose and Limits of HGN

HGN test results admissible as evidence of impairment.
Clark, 762 P.2d at 856.

NEBRASKA

I. Evidentiary Admissibility

Inadequate foundation laid by the state to determine if HGN is a scientifically valid test. One police officer testifying as to HGN testing is inadequate to show scientific validity of HGN.
State v. Borchardt, 395 N.W.2d 551, 557 (Neb. 1986).

II. Police Officer Testimony Needed to Admit HGN Test Result

Police officer testified as to training in HGN testing, which consisted of attending a seminar taught by another patrol officer, and performing HGN tests on both sober and intoxicated volunteers. Although the court ruled that this was inadequate testimony to determine whether the HGN test was admissible under the Nebraska

Rules of Evidence, it did not comment on whether this foundation would have been sufficient to allow the officer to testify about the HGN test results.
Borchardt, 395 N.W.2d at 557.

III. Purpose and Limits of HGN

Not addressed by court.

NEW YORK

I. Evidentiary Admissibility

Quinn held that HGN test results are admissible under Frye standard of "general acceptance." However, the case no longer has precedential value as it was later reversed on other grounds.
People v. Quinn, 580 N.Y.S.2d 818, 826 (Dist. Ct. 1991), rev'd on other grounds, 607 N.Y.S.2d 534 (App. Div. 1993).

II. Police Officer Testimony Needed to Admit HGN Test Result

Not addressed by court.

III. Purpose and Limits of HGN

Not addressed by court.

NORTH CAROLINA

I. Evidentiary Admissibility

North Carolina law allows a trial court to determine the reliability of scientific evidence by either judicial notice, testimony by experts or a combination of the two. HGN is scientific evidence, but there was no testimony on the scientific reliability of HGN in the trial court by experts nor did the trial court take judicial notice of that fact. The appellate court declined to take appellate judicial notice of HGN's reliability based on the record. Therefore, the trial court erred in admitting the testimony.
State v. Helms, 490 S.E.2d 565, ____ (N.C. App. 1997).

II. Police Officer Testimony Needed to Admit HGN Test Result

Not addressed by court.

III. Purpose and Limits of HGN

Not addressed by court.

NORTH DAKOTA

I. Evidentiary Admissibility

Court found that HGN test is admissible as a standard field sobriety test.
City of Fargo v. McLaughin, 512 N.W.2d 700, 706 (N.D. 1994).

II. Police Officer Testimony Needed to Admit HGN Test Result

Police officer must testify as to training and experience and that the test was properly administered.
City of Fargo, 512 N.W.2d at 708.

III. Purpose and Limits of HGN

"... HGN test results admissible only as circumstantial evidence of intoxication, and the officer may not attempt to quantify a specific BAC based upon the HGN test."
City of Fargo, 512 N.W.2d at 708.

HORIZONTAL GAZE NYSTAGMUS STATE CASE LAW SUMMARY *(Continued)*

OHIO

I. Evidentiary Admissibility

HGN test is objective in nature and does not require an expert interpretation.
State v. Nagel, 506 N.E.2d 285, 286 (Ohio Ct. App. 1986).

Court determined that HGN was a reliable indicator of intoxication without specifically ruling on whether HGN meets *Frye* or some other standard of admissibility.
State v. Bresson, 554 N.E.2d 1330, 1334 (Ohio 1990).

II. Police Officer Testimony Needed to Admit HGN Test Result

Police officer need only testify to training in HGN procedure, knowledge of the test and ability to interpret results.
Bresson, 554 N.E.2d at 1336.

III. Purpose and Limits of HGN

HGN can be used to establish probable cause to arrest and as substantive evidence of a defendant's guilt or innocence in a trial for DUI, but not to determine defendant's BAC.
Bresson, 554 N.E.2d at 1336.

OKLAHOMA

I. Evidentiary Admissibility

HGN test results excluded because state failed to lay adequate foundation regarding HGN's scientific admissibility under the *Frye* standard of admissibility. Police officer's testimony alone was insufficient.
Yell v. State, 856 P.2d 996, 996-97 (Okla. Crim. App. 1993).

The *Daubert* rationale replaces the *Frye* standard as the admissibility standard for scientific evidence.
Taylor v. State, 889 P.2d 319, 328-29 (Okla. Crim. App. 1995).

II. Police Officer Testimony Needed to Admit HGN Test Result

Police officer testified to training on how to administer HGN test and how the test was administered in this case. Officer also testified as to his training in analyzing HGN test results.
Yell, 856 P.2d at 997.

III. Purpose and Limits of HGN

If HGN testing was found to satisfy the *Frye* standard of admissibility, HGN test results would be considered in the same manner as other field sobriety test results. HGN test results are inadmissible as scientific evidence creating a presumption of intoxication.
Yell, 856 P.2d at 997.

OREGON

I. Evidentiary Admissibility

HGN test results are admissible under the Oregon Rules of Evidence. HGN test results are scientific in nature, are relevant in a DUII trial, and not unfairly prejudicial to the defendant.
State v. O'Key, 889 P.2d 663, 687 (Or. 1995).

II. Police Officer Testimony Needed to Admit HGN Test Result

"Admissibility is subject to a foundational showing that the officer who administered the test was properly qualified, that the test was administered properly, and that the test results were recorded accurately."
O'Key, 889 P.2d at 670.

III. Purpose and Limits of HGN

"...HGN test results are admissible to establish that a person was under the influence of intoxicating liquor, but is not admissible... to establish a person's BAC..."
O'Key, 889 P.2d at 689-90.

Officer may not testify that, based on HGN test results, the defendant's BAC was over .10.
State v. Fisken, 909 P.2d 206, 207 (Or. Ct. App. 1996).

PENNSYLVANIA

I. Evidentiary Admissibility

The state laid an inadequate foundation for the admissibility of HGN under the *Frye/Topa* standard.
Commonwealth v. Moore, 635 A.2d 625, 629 (Pa. Super. Ct. 1993).
Commonwealth v. Apollo, 603 A.2d 1023, 1028 (Pa. Super. Ct. 1992).
Commonwealth v. Miller, 532 A.2d 1186, 1189-90 (Pa. Super. Ct. 1987).

Testimony of police officer is insufficient to establish scientific reliability of HGN test.
Moore, 635 A.2d at 692.
Miller, 532 A.2d at 1189-90.

Testimony of behavioral optometrist did not establish general acceptance of HGN test.
Apollo, 603 A.2d at 1027-28.

II. Police Officer Testimony Needed to Admit HGN Test Result

County detective certified as HGN instructor. Court did not comment on whether this would be enough foundation to allow the detective to testify about HGN test results.
Moore, 635 A.2d 629.

Police officer had one day course on HGN. Court did not comment on whether this would be enough foundation to allow the officer to testify about HGN test results.
Miller, 603 A.2d at 1189.

III. Purpose and Limits of HGN

Not addressed by court.

SOUTH CAROLINA

I. Evidentiary Admissibility

HGN admissible in conjunction with other field sobriety tests. By implication, HGN is not regarded as a scientific test.
State v. Sullivan, 426 S.E.2d 766, 769 (S.C. 1993).

II. Police Officer Testimony Needed to Admit HGN Test Result

Police officer given twenty hours of HGN training.
Sullivan, 426 S.E.2d at 769.

HORIZONTAL GAZE NYSTAGMUS STATE CASE LAW
SUMMARY *(Continued)*

III. Purpose and Limits of HGN

HGN test results admissible "to elicit objective manifestations of soberness or insobriety.... [E]vidence from HGN tests is not conclusive proof of DUI. A positive HGN test result is to be regarded as merely circumstantial evidence of DUI. Furthermore, HGN test shall not constitute evidence to establish a specific degree of blood alcohol content."
Sullivan, 426 S.E.2d at 769.

TENNESSEE

I. Evidentiary Admissibility

HGN is a scientific test. State provided an inadequate amount of evidence to allow the court to conclude that HGN evidence meets the Frye standard.
State v. Murphy, 953 S.W.2d 200 (Tenn. 1997).

II. Police Officer Testimony Needed to Admit HGN Test Result

Not addressed by court.

III. Purpose and Limits of HGN

Not addressed by court.

TEXAS

I. Evidentiary Admissibility

HGN admissible under the Texas Rules of Evidence.
Emerson v. State, 880 S.W.2d 759, 769 (Tex. Crim. App. 1994).

II. Police Officer Testimony Needed to Admit HGN Test Result

A police officer must qualify as an expert on the HGN test, specifically concerning its administration and technique, before testifying about a defendant's performance on the test. Proof that the police officer is certified in the administration of the HGN test by the Texas Commission on Law Enforcement Officer Standards and Education satisfies this requirement.
Emerson, 880 S.W.2d at 769.

III. Purpose and Limits of HGN

HGN admissible to prove intoxication.
Emerson, 880 S.W.2d at 769.

UTAH

I. Evidentiary Admissibility

HGN test admissible as other field sobriety test. Court reserved judgment as to the scientific reliability of HGN.
Salt Lake City v. Garcia, 912 P.2d 997, 1001 (Utah Ct. App. 1996).

II. Police Officer Testimony Needed to Admit HGN Test Result

Police officer need only testify as to training, experience and observations when HGN admitted as a field test.
Garcia, 912 P.2d at 1001.

III. Purpose and Limits of HGN

Admissible as any other field sobriety test.
Garcia, 912 P.2d at 1000-01.

VERMONT

I. Evidentiary Admissibility

HGN test is scientific in nature and meets the Daubert standard of admissibility.
State v. Dufour, No. 586-4-96 Wmcr, Judge Robert Grussing, III ___ (Windham Dist. Ct. Jan. 24, 1997).

II. Police Officer Testimony Needed to Admit HGN Test Result

Officer must testify as to special training and experience in the administration of the test and that it was conducted in accordance with that training. Furthermore, expert testimony must be used in each case the State seeks to admit HGN evidence relating nystagmus in general and the observations of the officer as a cause of impairment as a result of consuming alcoholic beverages.
Dufour, No. 586-4-96 at ___.

III. Purpose and Limits of HGN

HGN test results can be used to indicate impairment. "The State may not offer evidence that the defendant 'failed' the test or relat[e] the results, either alone or in combination with other field sobriety tests, to a specific alcohol concentration or of an alcohol concentration at or above a specific level."
Dufour, No. 586-4-96 at ___.

WASHINGTON

I. Evidentiary Admissibility

"[T]he Frye standard applies to the admission of evidence based on HGN testing, unless... the State is able to prove that it rests on scientific principles and uses techniques which are not 'novel' and are readily understandable by ordinary persons." The state failed to present any evidence to this fact and the court declined to take judicial notice of HGN.
State v. Cissne, 865 P.2d 564, 569 (Wash. Ct. App. 1994).

II. Police Officer Testimony Needed to Admit HGN Test Result

Not addressed by court.

III. Purpose and Limits of HGN

Not addressed by court.

WEST VIRGINIA

I. Evidentiary Admissibility

"Because the State did not introduce evidence of the scientific reliability of the test... we do not reach the question of whether the HGN test is sufficiently reliable to be admissible." One police officer testifying about HGN is insufficient to establish HGN's reliability. If found to be admissible, HGN evidence would receive the same evidentiary weight as a field sobriety test.
State v. Barker, 366 S.E.2d 642, 646 (W. Va. 1988).

II. Police Officer Testimony Needed to Admit HGN Test Result

Police officer's training consisted of a one-day, eight-hour training session conducted by the state police. Officer testified to giving the HGN test about 100

HORIZONTAL GAZE NYSTAGMUS STATE CASE LAW
SUMMARY *(Continued)*

times. Court did not reach question of whether this would be enough to allow the officer to testify about the HGN test results.
Barker, 366 S.E.2d at 644.

III. Purpose and Limits of HGN

HGN test results admissible to show probable cause in a civil hearing.
Muscatell v. Cline, 474 S.E.2d 518, 525 (W. Va. 1996).
Boley v. Cline, 456 S.E.2d 38, 41 (W. Va. 1995).

"[I]f the reliability of the HGN test is demonstrated, an expert's testimony as to a driver's performance on the test is admissible only as evidence that the driver was under the influence," the same as other field sobriety tests.
Barker, 366 S.E.2d at 646.

WISCONSIN

I. Evidentiary Admissibility

HGN test is merely behavioral observations and admissible as a field sobriety test. Court rejected defendant's argument that HGN involves scientific principles.
State v. Peters, 419 N.W.2d 575, 578 (Wis. Ct. App. 1987).

II. Police Officer Testimony Needed to Admit HGN Test Result

Police officer has special competence as a "lay expert" based on training and experience.
Peters, 419 N.W.2d at ___.

III. Purpose and Limits of HGN

HGN test results given the same weight as other field sobriety test results.
Peters, 419 N.W.2d at ___.

UNITED STATES

I. Evidentiary Admissibility

HGN test was admitted as part of series of field tests. Its admission was not challenged on appeal.
U.S. v. Van Griffin, 874 F.2d 634 (9th Cir. 1989).

II. Police Officer Testimony Needed to Admit HGN Test Result

Not addressed by court.

III. Purpose and Limits of HGN

Not addressed by court.

Last update 2/5/98.

For future updates, please contact the National Traffic Law Center, 99 Canal Center Plaza, Suite 510, Alexandria, Virginia, 22314; Phone:(703) 549-4253, Fax: 703-836-3195

HORIZONTAL GAZE NYSTAGMUS STATE CHART SUMMARY

	AL	AK	AZ	AR	CA	CO	CT	DE	DC	FL	GA
I. Evidentiary admissibility											
A. Not a novel scientific test. Admissible as a field test.				X						X	
B. Scientific test. State requires:	X	X	X		X		X	X			X
1. Frye (general acceptance)	X	X	X		X	X	X		X	X	
2. Rules of Evid. (reliability)						X	X		X	X	
3. Other								X			
C. HGN meets scientific standard	X		X		X						X
D. Inadequate basis to conclude that HGN meets scientific standard								X			X
E. HGN does not meet scientific standard							X				
II. Police officer may testify about:											
A. HGN's scientific reliability at admissibility hearing											
B. Correlation between HGN and alcohol at trial	NO										
C. HGN test results based on training and experience in administration of test.											
III. Purpose and limits of HGN test results			YES		YES			YES			YES
A. Probable cause determination in criminal hearing		X	X				X	X			
B. Probable cause determination in civil hearing							X	X			
C. Evidence of impairment			X		X			X			
D. Quantity BAC			X		X						X
E. Same evidentiary weight as other field tests				X							

Horizontal Gaze Nystagmus State Chart Summary *(continued)*

	HI	ID	IL	IN	IA	KS	KY	LA	ME	MD	MA
I. Evidentiary admissibility											
A. Not a novel scientific test. Admissible as a field test.					X						
B. Scientific test. State requires:											
1. *Frye* (general acceptance)		X	X	X		X		X	X	X	X
2. Rules of Evid. (reliability)			X			X	X			X	
3. Other	X										
C. HGN meets scientific standard		X	X					X	X	X	
D. Inadequate basis to conclude that HGN meets scientific standard						X					X
E. HGN does not meet scientific standard											
II. Police officer may testify about:											
A. HGN's scientific reliability at admissibility hearing		NO									
B. Correlation between HGN and alcohol at trial											
C. HGN test results based on training and experience in administration of test.		YES	YES		YES			YES	YES	YES	YES
III. Purpose and limits of HGN test results											
A. Probable cause determination in criminal hearing		X	X					X	X		
B. Probable cause determination in civil hearing			X								
C. Evidence of impairment		X	X		X			X	X		
D. Quantity BAC		X									
E. Same evidentiary weight as other field tests					X						

Horizontal Gaze Nystagmus State Chart Summary *(continued)*

	MI	MN	MS	MO	MT	NB	NV	NH	NJ	NM	NY
I. Evidentiary admissibility											
A. Not a novel scientific test. Admissible as a field test.											
B. Scientific test. State requires:											
1. *Frye* (general acceptance)	X	X	X	X	X	X					X
2. Rules of Evid. (reliability)	X	X	X	X		X			X		X
3. Other					X		X			X	
C. HGN meets scientific standard	X	X		X	X						
D. Inadequate basis to conclude that HGN meets scientific standard						X					X
E. HGN does not meet scientific standard			X								
II. Police officer may testify about:											
A. HGN's scientific reliability at admissibility hearing						NO					
B. Correlation between HGN and alcohol at trial			NO								
C. HGN test results based on training and experience in administration of test.	YES	YES		YES	YES						
III. Purpose and limits of HGN test results											
A. Probable cause determination in criminal hearing											
B. Probable cause determination in civil hearing			X								
C. Evidence of impairment		X		X							
D. Quantity BAC	X	X									
E. Same evidentiary weight as other field tests											

683

Horizontal Gaze Nystagmus State Chart Summary *(continued)*

	NC	ND	OH	OK	OR	PA	RI	SC	SD	TN	TX
I. Evidentiary admissibility											
A. Not a novel scientific test. Admissible as a field test.		X	X								
B. Scientific test. State requires:	X			X	X	X		X		X	X
1. *Frye* (general acceptance)				X	X	X	X			X	X
2. Rules of Evid. (reliability)	X								X		
3. Other					X						X
C. HGN meets scientific standard											
D. Inadequate basis to conclude that HGN meets scientific standard	X			X		X				X	
E. HGN does not meet scientific standard											
II. Police officer may testify about:											
A. HGN's scientific reliability at admissibility hearing						NO					
B. Correlation between HGN and alcohol at trial					YES						
C. HGN test results based on training and experience in administration of test.		YES	YES	YES	YES			YES			YES
III. Purpose and limits of HGN test results											
A. Probable cause determination in criminal hearing			X								
B. Probable cause determination in civil hearing											
C. Evidence of impairment		X	X		X			X			X
D. Quantity BAC				X							
E. Same evidentiary weight as other field tests		X	X	X				X			

Horizontal Gaze Nystagmus State Chart Summary *(continued)*

	UT	VT	VA	WA	WV	WI	WY	US	TOTALS
I. Evidentiary admissibility									
A. Not a novel scientific test. Admissible as a field test.	X								8
B. Scientific test. State requires:									29
1. *Frye* (general acceptance)		X			X	X			23
2. Rules of Evid. (reliability)				X					19
3. Other		X	X		X		X		
C. HGN meets scientific standard		X	X						2
D. Inadequate basis to conclude that HGN meets scientific standard									18
E. HGN does not meet scientific standard				X	X				10
II. Police officer may testify about:									1
A. HGN's scientific reliability at admissibility hearing					NO				
B. Correlation between HGN and alcohol at trial						YES			
C. HGN test results based on training and experience in administration of test.	YES	YES				YES			
III. Purpose and limits of HGN test results									10
A. Probable cause determination in criminal hearing									
B. Probable cause determination in civil hearing									4
C. Evidence of impairment					X	X			21
D. Quantity BAC									0
E. Same evidentiary weight as other field tests	X				X	X			10

Those states in bold are directly addressing the admissibility of HGN evidence. Under Section II, a blank box means that a court has not ruled on the issues.

For future updates, please contact the National Traffic Law Center, 99 Canal Center Plaza, Suite 510, Alexandria, Virginia 22314; Phone (703) 549-4253, Fax: (703) 836-3195

Last update 1/15/98

STANDARDIZED FIELD SOBRIETY TESTS (SFSTs):

A Brief History

by Marcelline Burns, PhD

When motorized vehicles were introduced at the beginning of the 20th century, profound economic and social changes were set into motion. Although many of the changes could not have been fully and widely evident for some period of time, there was almost immediate recognition of the risks of driving while under the influence of alcohol. A journal article warning about such risks actually was published as early as 1904.

Since early vehicles and roadways were relatively primitive in comparison to 1990's cars and superhighways, the alcohol-related driving errors of that era surely would have been less catastrophic and, therefore, less apparent than those of the present day. That the relationship was recognized so soon, therefore, is initially somewhat puzzling, but it probably was due in some measure to the broad anti-alcohol sentiment which had begun to develop following the Civil War. Both the population and alcohol use began to increase after the war and by the late 1800s there was one saloon for every 400 men, women, and children. In a kind of backlash to the excesses, an aggressive Anti-Saloon movement arose. Over time, 23 states enacted laws limiting the manufacture and sale of intoxicating beverages, and in 1919 the 18th Amendment was ratified. With passage of the National Prohibition Act, also known as the Volstead Act (to provide for enforcement of the amendment), Federal Prohibition began in 1920.

Fiscal appropriations for enforcement were limited, however, and prohibition was an idea that fell short in reality. A colorful, if contentious, history of the era portrays an era of flourishing crime, speakeasies, and illegal production of alcohol. Many citizens disobeyed the law. Nonetheless, prohibition was not without an impact. The number of saloons declined, as did alcohol-related street crimes, and annual alcohol consumption fell from 2.6 gallons per person prior to the state and federal laws to a low of 0.97 gallon in 1934. Although many people continued to favor restrictions on alcohol production and sales, prohibition in the United States, as in other countries, was destined to be short-lived.

By the late 1920s, the concerns of many citizens had shifted from saloons and crime to the protection of individual freedom. A repeal movement was born. When the economic pressures of a looming depression focused attention on the lost jobs and revenues of the alcohol industry, prohibition was in fact doomed. It was repealed in 1933 by the 21st Amendment. Liquor control reverted to the states, and alcohol consumption began to increase. As a consequence, the traffic-safety issues of alcohol-impaired driving continued to grow in importance.

The offense of driving-under-the-influence was first defined in terms of a blood alcohol concentration (BAC) when the State of Indiana in 1939 set the limit for drivers at 0.15%. During ensuing years other states also established BAC limits. In retrospect, the legislative activity suggests that the seriousness of the problem was recognized and dealt with appropriately. There was, however, a widely-held assumption about alcohol-and-driving that shaped and limited the effectiveness of both legislation and law enforcement for many years.

The assumption was that the threat to roadway safety came primarily, if not solely, from drunk drivers. Setting BAC limits at 0.15% was tantamount to telling law enforcement to "Remove drunks from the roadway." Since a police officer could be expected to readily recognize a drunk or obviously-intoxicated individual, there was no compelling reason to provide special alcohol enforcement training to traffic officers. During the next several decades, however, data about alcohol effects on driving accumulated from laboratory experiments, accident investigations, and roadside surveys. Over time it became evident that alcohol-related traffic problems would not be solved by focusing only on the arrest of obviously-intoxicated drivers. With awareness that alcohol begins to affect performance at low BACs came the recognition that risks for driving do not arise only with drunk drivers. Accordingly, statutory limits were lowered, first to 0.10%, then to 0.08%.

As the statutes changed, the alcohol-related duties of traffic officers changed. Since an individual at 0.10% or 0.08% may or may not be obviously intoxicated (depending on his or her drinking practices and experience), it would no longer suffice for officers to arrest only the individuals they recognized as being drunk. Indeed, the mandate for alcohol enforcement had become the detection and arrest of alcohol-impaired drivers, and the traffic officer's task had become much more difficult. Just how difficult was reflected in the average BAC of arrested drivers. Despite the lower limits, it remained high (0.17% nationwide). Clearly, traffic officers were in need of specialized training.

To address the problem, during the 1970s the National Highway Traffic Safety Administration (NHTSA) funded a number of research projects, the objectives of which were to provide law enforcement with information and procedures for detecting and arresting alcohol-impaired drivers. Two of those studies, which were conducted by the Southern California Research Institute (SCRI), were designed to identify, develop, and standardize a battery of tests for roadside use (Burns & Moskowitz, 1977; Tharp, Burns, & Moskowitz, 1981).

Roadside conditions severely constrain the kind of tests which can be used to reliably indicate alcohol impairment, and it was necessary for SCRI investigators to consult with police and to search the scientific literature for tests which would be valid and reliable indices of the presence of alcohol. In pilot experiments, those which appeared to meet the criteria for roadside use were examined. In a laboratory experiment, six tests identified as candidates were administered by police officers to hundreds of drinking subjects. The data obtained during that experiment identified Horizontal Gaze Nystagmus (HGN), Walk and Turn (WAT), and One-Leg Stand (OLS) as the best tests. A second laboratory study with drinking subjects and police officers further examined, standardized, and field tested that set of three tests. A final report to NHTSA identified tests of walking (WAT) and balance (OLS), together with an examination of the eyes (HGN) as the optimal battery. Studies conducted in Finland, also during the 1970s, reported essentially identical findings (Penttila, Tenhu, & Kataja,1971; Penttila, Tenhu, & Kataja, 1974.)

The NHTSA staff...

- performed additional statistical analysis of the data obtained in the laboratory experiments,
- developed scoring methods and interpretation guidelines for the three tests,
- developed training standards and materials for students and instructors, and
- initiated training for law enforcement in the administrations of Standardized Field Sobriety Tests (SFSTs).

The SFSTs were developed during the 1970s for enforcement of the 0.10% BAC statute, which prevailed at that time. As states enacted a 0.08% statute, officers continued to rely on the 3-test battery. Although the 0.02% change appeared not to seriously affect their interpretation of suspects' test performance, it was important to re-validate the battery. A validation of the tests for 0.08% was provided by McKnight, Langston, Lange, & McKnight (1995). Officers in fifty states, who have been trained under NHTSA guidelines, now routinely use the SFSTs to examine

STANDARDIZED FIELD SOBRIETY TESTS (SFSTs):
(Continued)

drivers at roadside. In the years immediately after introduction of the test battery, courtroom challenges were relatively rare, but that changed over time. For more than a decade now, DUI defense attorneys have attempted to keep officers' testimony about the tests out of evidence. Although in some states the entire battery has been challenged, the most frequent target has been and continues to be HGN.

Courtroom challenges often focus on data obtained by SCRI, and the scientific rigor of the design, execution, and analysis of the experiments that identified the test battery certainly is relevant. A separate and important question is less frequently addressed: namely, "When police officers use the SFSTs in the field, what proportion of their decisions to arrest (or release) are correct?" Recently, DUI arrest records have been examined in three separate, highly-controlled field studies (Burns & Anderson, 1995; Burns & DioQuino, 1997; Stuster & Burns, 1998). The data obtained from three geographically separate and different locales strongly support the validity of the SFSTs for roadside use. In all data sets, arrest decisions were supported by measured BACs in more than 90% of the cases. The finding concerning release decisions is less directly relevant to court issues but also bodes less well for traffic safety. Officers err more frequently by releasing drivers whose BACs would have supported arrests.

The SFSTs are valid and reliable tests for roadside use in the examination of DUI suspects. Used in the context of all available information (ie, observations of driving, the driver's appearance and attitude, odors, speech, etc.), the tests aid officers to meet their duty of removing impaired drivers from the roadway. Importantly, the tests also protect the innocent in that they reduce the likelihood that an unimpaired driver will be detained.

References
Burns M and Anderson E, "A Colorado Validation Study of the Standardized Field Sobriety Test (SFST) Battery," Final Report to Colorado Department of Transportation, 1995.
Burns M and Dioquino T, "A Florida Validation Study of the Standardize Field Sobriety Test (SFST) Battery," Final Report to State Safety Office, Department of Transportation, State of Florida, 1997.
Burns M and Moskowitz H, "Psychophysical Tests for DWI Arrest. Final Report," DOT-HS-802 424, NHTSA, U.S. Department Of Transportation, 1977.
McKnight AJ, Langston EA, Lange JE, et al, "Development of Standardized Field Sobriety Test for Lower BAC Limits," Final Report to NHTSA, U.S. Department of Transportation, 1995.
Penttila A, Tenhu M, and Kataja M, "Clinical Examination for Intoxication in Cases of Suspected Drunken Driving," Statistical and Research Bureau of TALJA, Iso Roobertinkatu 20, Helsinki 13, Finland, 1971.
Penttila A, Tenhu M, and Kataja M, "Examination of Alcohol Intoxication in Cases of Suspected Drunken Drivers II," Liikenneturva, Iso Roobertinkatu 20, 00120 Helsinki 12, Finland, 1974.
Stuster J and Burns M, "Validation of the Standardized Field Sobriety Test Battery at BACs below 0.10 Percent," Final Report to NHTSA, U.S., Department of Transportation, 1998.
Tharp V, Burns M, and Moskowitz H, "Development and Field Test of Psychophysical Tests for DWI Arrests. Final Report," DOT-HS-805-864, NHTSA, U.S. Department of Transportation, 1981.

VISUAL DETECTION OF DWI MOTORISTS

Adapted from the National Highway Traffic Safety Administration
(DOT HS 808 677)

INTRODUCTION

More than a million people have died in traffic crashes in the United States since 1966, the year of the National Traffic and Motor Vehicle Safety Act, which led to the creation of the National Highway Traffic Safety Administration, or NHTSA.

During the late 1960s and early 1970s, more than 50,000 people lost their lives each year on our nation's streets, roads, and highways. Traffic safety has improved considerably since that time; the annual death toll has declined substantially, even though the numbers of drivers, vehicles, and miles driven all have increased. When miles traveled are considered, the likelihood of being killed in traffic during the 1960s was 3-4 times what it is today.

The proportion of all crashes in which alcohol is involved has declined. The declines in crash risk and the numbers of alcohol-involved crashes are attributable to several factors, including the effectiveness of public information and education programs, traffic safety legislation, a general aging of the population, and law enforcement effort.

NHTSA research contributed to the improved condition, in part, by providing patrol officers with useful and scientifically valid information concerning the behaviors that are most predictive of impairment. Continued enforcement of DWI laws will be a key to saving lives in the future. For this reason, NHTSA sponsored research leading to the development of a new DWI detection guide and training materials, including a new training video. Many things have changed since 1979, but like the original training materials, the new detection guide describes a set of behaviors that can be used by officers to detect motorists who are likely to be driving while impaired.

Building upon the previous NHTSA study, the researchers interviewed officers from across the United States and developed a list of more than 100 driving cues that have been found to predict blood alcohol concentrations, or BACs, of 0.08% or greater. The list was reduced to 24 cues during three field studies involving hundreds of officers and more than 12,000 enforcement stops. The driving behaviors identified by the officers are presented in the following four categories:

1. Problems in maintaining proper lane position
2. Speed and braking problems
3. Vigilance problems, and
4. Judgment problems

The cues presented in these categories predict that a driver is DWI at least 35% of the time. For example, if you observe a driver to be weaving or weaving across lane lines, the probability of DWI is more than .50 or 50%. However, if you observe either of the weaving cues and any other cue listed in this chapter, the probability of DWI jumps to at least .65 or 65%. Observing any two cues other than weaving indicated a probability of DWI of at least 50%, although some cues, such as swerving, accelerating for no reason, and driving on other than the designated roadway, have single-cue probabilities greater than 70%. Generally, the probability of DWI increases substantially when a driver exhibits more than one of the cues.

This chapter contains:

1. The DWI Detection Guide
2. A summary of the research that led to this information
3. Explanations of the 24 driving cues
4. A description of post-stop cues that are predictive of DWI

The research suggests that these training materials will be helpful to officers in:

1. Detecting impaired motorists
2. Articulating observed behaviors on arrest reports
3. Supporting officers' expert testimony

VISUAL DETECTION OF DWI MOTORISTS (Continued)

DWI DETECTION GUIDE

Weaving plus any other cue: p = at least .65
Any two cues: p = at least .50

Problems Maintaining Proper Lane Position   p = .50 - .75
- Weaving • Weaving across lane lines
- Straddling a lane line • Swerving
- Turning with a wide radius • Drifting
- Almost striking a vehicle or other object

Speed and Braking Problems   p = .45 - .70
- Stopping problems (too far, too short, or too jerky)
- Accelerating or decelerating for no apparent reason
- Varying speed • Slow speed (10+ mph under limit)

Vigilance Problems   p = .55 - .85
- Driving in opposing lanes or wrong way on one-way
- Slow response to traffic signals
- Slow or failure to respond to officer's signals
- Stopping in lane for no apparent reason
- Driving without headlights at night
- Failure to signal or signal inconsistent with action

Judgment Problems   p = .35 - .90
- Following too closely
- Improper or unsafe lane change
- Illegal or improper turn (too fast, jerky, sharp, etc)
- Driving on other than the designated roadway
- Stopping inappropriately in response to officer
- Inappropriate or unusual behavior (throwing, arguing, etc)
- Appearing to be impaired

POST-STOP CUES   p = ≥.85
- Difficulty with motor vehicle controls
- Difficulty exiting the vehicle
- Fumbling with driver's license or registration
- Repeating questions or comments
- Swaying, unsteady, or balance problems
- Leaning on the vehicle or other object
- Slurred speech
- Slow to respond to officer/officer must repeat
- Provides incorrect information. changes answers
- Odor of alcoholic beverage from the driver

- p ≥.50 when combined with any other cue:
- Driving without headlights at night
- Failure to signal or signal inconsistent with action

The probability of detecting DWI by random traffic enforcement stops at night has been found to be about 3% (.03).

PROBLEMS IN MAINTAINING PROPER LANE POSITION

Maintaining proper lane position can be a difficult task for an impaired driver. For example, we have all seen vehicles weaving before. **Weaving** is when the vehicle alternately moves toward one side of the lane and then the other. The pattern of lateral movements can be fairly regular, as one steering correction is closely followed by another. In extreme cases, the vehicle's wheels even cross the lines before a correction is made. You might even observe a vehicle straddling a center or lane line. That is, the vehicle is moving straight ahead with either the right or left tires on the wrong side of the lane line or markers.

Drifting is when a vehicle is moving in a generally straight line, but at a slight angle to the lane. The driver might correct his or her course as the vehicle approaches a lane line or other boundary, or fail to correct until after a boundary has been crossed. In extreme cases, the driver fails to correct in time to avoid a collision.

Course corrections can be gradual or abrupt. For example, you might observe a vehicle to **swerve**, making an abrupt turn away from a generally straight course, when a driver realizes that he or she has drifted out of proper lane position, or to avoid a previously-unnoticed hazard.

A related DWI cue is almost striking a vehicle or other object. You might observe a vehicle, either at slow speeds or moving with traffic, to pass unusually close to a sign, barrier, building, or other object. This cue also includes almost striking another vehicle, either moving or parked, and causing another vehicle to maneuver to avoid a collision.

Turning with a wide radius, or drifting during a curve, is the final cue in this category of driver behaviors. A vehicle appears to drift to the outside of the lane, or into another lane, through the curve or while turning a corner. Watch for this cue and stop the driver when you see it. Many alcohol-involved crashes are caused by an expanding turn radius, or drifting out of lane position during a curve.

SPEED AND BRAKING PROBLEMS

The research showed that braking properly can be a difficult task for an impaired driver. For example, there is a good chance the driver is DWI if you observe any type of stopping problem. Stopping problems include:

* Stopping too far from a curb or at an inappropriate angle
* Stopping too short or beyond a limit line
* Jerky or abrupt stops

Impaired drivers also can experience difficulty maintaining an appropriate speed. There is a good change the driver is DWI if you observe a vehicle to:

* Accelerate or decelerate rapidly for no apparent reason
* Vary its speed, alternating between speeding up and slowing down
* Drive at a speed that is 10 miles per hour or more under the limit

VIGILANCE PROBLEMS

Vigilance concerns a persons's ability to pay attention to a task or notice changes in surroundings. A driver whose vigilance has been impaired by alcohol might forget to turn his or her headlights on when required. Similarly, impaired drivers often forget to signal a turn or lane change, or their signal is inconsistent with their maneuver, for example, signaling left, but turning right.

Alcohol-impaired vigilance also results in motorists driving into opposing or crossing traffic, and turning in front of oncoming vehicles with insufficient headway.

Driving is a complex task that requires accurate information about surrounding traffic conditions. Failing to yield the right-of-way and driving the wrong way on a one-way street are dangerous examples of vigilance problems.

A driver whose vigilance has been impaired by alcohol also might respond more slowly than normal to a change in a traffic signal. For example, the vehicle might remain stopped for an unusually long period of time after the signal has turned green. Similarly, an

VISUAL DETECTION OF DWI MOTORISTS *(Continued)*

impaired driver might be unusually slow to respond to an officer's lights, siren, or hand signals.

The most extreme DWI cue in the category of vigilance problems is to find a vehicle stopped in a lane for no apparent reason. Sometimes when you observe this behavior, the driver will be just lost or confused, but more than half of the time the driver will be DWI - maybe even asleep at the wheel.

JUDGMENT PROBLEMS

Operating a motor vehicle requires continuous decision-making by the driver. Unfortunately, judgment abilities can be affected by even small amounts of alcohol. For example, alcohol-impaired judgment can cause a driver to follow another vehicle too closely, providing an unsafe stopping distance.

Alcohol-impaired judgment also can result in a driver taking risks or endangering others. If you observe a vehicle to make improper or unsafe lane changes, either frequently or abruptly, or with apparent disregard for other vehicles, there is a good chance the driver's judgment has been impaired by alcohol.

Similarly, impaired judgment can cause a driver to turn improperly. For example, misjudgments about speed and the roadway can cause a driver to take a turn too fast, or to make sudden corrections during the maneuver. These corrections can appear to the observer as jerky or sharp vehicle movements during the turn.

Alcohol-impaired judgment can affect the full range of driver behaviors. For example, the research found that impaired drivers are less inhibited about making illegal turns than unimpaired drivers.

Driving on other than the designated roadway is another cue exhibited by alcohol-impaired drivers. Examples include driving at the edge of the roadway, on the shoulder, off the roadway entirely, and straight through turn-only lanes.

In some cases, impaired drivers stop inappropriately in response to an officer, either abruptly as if they had been startled, or in an illegal or dangerous manner.

In fact, the research has shown that there is a good chance a driver is DWI if you observe the person to exhibit any inappropriate or unusual behavior. Unusual behavior includes throwing something from the vehicle, drinking in the vehicle, urinating at the roadside, arguing with another motorist, or otherwise being disorderly. If you observe inappropriate or unusual behavior, there is a good probability that the driver is DWI.

The final cue is actually one or more of a set of indicators related to the personal behavior or appearance of a driver. These indicators include gripping the steering wheel tightly, driving with one's face close to the windshield, slouching in the seat, and staring straight ahead with eyes fixed. Some officers routinely scrutinize the faces of drivers in oncoming traffic, looking for the indicators of impairment. If you observe a driver who appears to be impaired, the research showed that there is an excellent probability that you are correct in your judgment.

SUMMARY

To summarize, the DWI cues related to problems in maintaining proper lane position include:

- Weaving
- Weaving across lane lines
- Straddling a lane line
- Drifting
- Swerving
- Almost striking a vehicle or other object
- Turning with a wide radius, or drifting during a curve

The DWI cues related to speed and braking problems include:

- Stopping problems (too far, too short, too jerky)

- Accelerating for no reason
- Varying speed
- Slow speed

The DWI cues related to vigilance problems include:

- Driving without headlights at night
- Failure to signal a turn or lane change, or signaling inconsistently with actions
- Driving in opposing lanes or the wrong way on a one-way street
- Slow response to traffic signals
- Slow or failure to respond to officer's signals
- Stopping in the lane for no apparent reason

The DWI cues related to judgment problems include:

- Following too closely
- Improper or unsafe lane change
- Illegal or improper turn (too fast, jerky, sharp, etc)
- Driving on other than the designated roadway
- Stopping inappropriately in response to an officer
- Inappropriate or unusual behavior
- Appearing to be impaired

POST-STOP CUES

In addition to the driving cues, the following post-stop cues have been found to be excellent predictors of DWI:

- Difficulty with motor vehicle controls
- Difficulty exiting the vehicle
- Fumbling with driver's license or registration
- Repeating questions or comments
- Swaying, unsteady, or balance problems
- Leaning on the vehicle or other object
- Slurred speech
- Slow to respond to officer/officer must repeat questions
- Provides incorrect information or changes answers
- Odor of alcoholic beverage from the driver

DETECTION OF DWI MOTORCYCLISTS

Adapted from the National Highway Traffic
Safety Administration (DOT HS 807 856)

DRIFTING DURING TURN OR CURVE

Earlier studies have shown that the most common cause of single-vehicle, fatal
motorcycle crashes is for the road to curve and the motorcycle and rider to continue
in a straight line until they strike a stationary object; this type of crash is usually
caused by alcohol-impaired balance and coordination abilities. In less extreme
cases, the motorcycle's turn radius expands during the maneuver. The motorcycle
appears to drift to the outside of the lane, or into another lane, through the curve or
while turning a corner. If you see a motorcycle drifting during a turn or curve, do the
rider a favor and pull him over - our study showed there is an *excellent* chance that
he is DWI.

TROUBLE WITH DISMOUNT

Parking and dismounting a motorcycle can be a helpful field sobriety test. The
motorcyclist must turn off the engineer, and locate and deploy the kickstand. He
must then balance his weight on one foot while swinging the other foot over the
seat to dismount. But first, the operator must decide upon a safe place to stop his
bike. Problems with any step in this sequence can be evidence of alcohol impairment.

Not every motorcyclist that you see having some form of trouble with a dismount is
under the influence, but study results indicated that more than 50% of them are. In
other words, trouble with dismount is an excellent cue.

TROUBLE WITH BALANCE AT STOP

The typical practice at a stop is for the motorcyclist to place one foot on the ground
to keep the bike upright, while leaving the other foot on the peg nearest the gear
shift lever. Some riders favor placing both feet on the ground for stability. Riders
whose balance has been impaired by alcohol often have difficulty with this task.
They might be observed to shift their weight from side-to-side, that is from one foot
to another to maintain balance at a stop. From a block away, an officer might notice
a single tail light moving from side to side in a gentle rocking motion. If you observe
a motorcyclist to be having trouble with balance at a stop, there is an *excellent*
chance that he or she is DWI.

TURNING PROBLEMS

The research identified four turning problems that are indicative of rider impairment. Each of the problems is described separately in the following paragraphs.

UNSTEADY DURING TURN OR CURVE

The gyroscopic effects of a motorcycle's wheels tend to keep a motorcycle "on
track" as long as speed is maintained. As a motorcycle's speed decreases, the
demands placed on the operator's balance capabilities increase. As a result, an
officer might observe a motorcycle's front wheels or handlebars to wobble as an
impaired operator attempts to maintain balance at slow speeds or during a turn.

LATE BRAKING DURING TURN

The next turning problem is "late braking during a turn or on a curve." A motorcyclist always normally brakes prior to entering a turn or curve, so the motorcycle

can accelerate through the maneuver for maximum control. An impaired motor-cyclist might misjudge his speed or distance to the corner or curve, requiring him to apply the brakes during a maneuver.

IMPROPER LEAN ANGLE DURING TURN

Third, a motorcyclist normally negotiates a turn or curve by leaning into the turn. However, when balance or speed judgment are impaired, the operator frequently attempts to sit upright through the maneuver. An "improper lean angle" can be detected by the trained observer.

ERRATIC MOVEMENTS DURING TURN

The fourth turning problem is "erratic movements." An erratic movement or sudden correction of a motorcycle during a turn or curve can also indicate impaired oper-ator ability.

If you observe a motorcyclist to be unsteady during a turn or curve, brake late, assume an improper lean angle, or make erratic movements during a turn or curve, there is an *excellent* chance that the motorcyclist is DWI.

INATTENTIVE TO SURROUNDINGS

Vigilance concerns a person's ability to pay attention to a task or notice changes in surroundings. A motorcyclist whose vigilance has been impaired by alcohol might fail to notice that the light that he has been waiting for has changed to green.

A vigilance problem is also evident when a motorcyclist is inattentive to his surroundings or seemingly unconcerned with detection. For example, there is cause for suspicion of DWI when a motorcyclist fails to periodically scan the area around his bike when in traffic, a wise defensive riding procedure to guard against potential encroachment by other vehicles. There is further evidence of impairment if a motorcyclist fails to respond to an officer's emergency lights or hand signals.

If you observe a motorcyclist to be inattentive to his or her surroundings, there is an *excellent* chance that the motorcyclist is DWI.

INAPPROPRIATE OR UNUSUAL BEHAVIOR

There is a category or cues that we call "inappropriate or unusual behavior." This category of cues includes behaviors such as operating a motorcycle while holding an object with one hand or under an arm, carrying an open container of alcohol, dropping an item from a motorcycle, urinating at the roadside, arguing with another motorist or otherwise being disorderly. If you observe inappropriate or unusual behavior by a motorcyclist, there is an *excellent* probability that the motorcyclist is DWI.

WEAVING

You are probably familiar with weaving as a predictor of DWI. If you see an automobile weaving there is a good chance that the driver has exceeded the legal limits on alcohol, but if you observe a motorcycle to be weaving, the probability of DWI is even greater - weaving is an *excellent* cue. Weaving includes weaving within a lane and weaving across lane lines, but does not include the movements necessary to avoid road hazards.

ERRATIC MOVEMENTS WHILE GOING STRAIGHT

If you observe a motorcyclist making erratic movements or sudden corrections while attempting to ride in a straight line, study results indicated there is a *good* probability that the rider is DWI. In other words, during the study between 30% and 49% of the time erratic movements while going straight were observed in associa-tion with impaired operation.

DETECTION OF DWI MOTORCYCLISTS *(Continued)*

OPERATING WITHOUT LIGHTS AT NIGHT

Operating a motorcycle without lights at night is very dangerous and can indicate operator-impairment. Study results showed that if you detect a motorcyclist riding at night without lights, there is a *good* chance that the operator is DWI.

RECKLESSNESS

Motorcyclists tend to ride faster than autos, so speeding is not necessarily a good predictor of DWI for motorcyclists. However, recklessness, or riding too fast for the conditions, was found to be a *good* indicator of operator impairment.

FOLLOWING TOO CLOSELY

Following too closely, an unsafe following distance, is an indication of impaired operator judgment. This cue was found during the study to be a *good* predictor of motorcycle DWI.

RUNNING STOP LIGHT OR SIGN

Failure to stop at a red light or stop sign can indicate either impaired vigilance capabilities (ie, did not see the stop light or sign -or officer), or impaired judgment (ie, decided not to stop). Whatever the form of impairment, if you observe a motorcyclist to run a stop light or sign, there is a *good* chance that he or she is DWI.

EVASION

Evasion or fleeing an officer, is a relatively frequent occurrence. If a motorcyclist attempts to evade an officer's enforcement stop, study results indicate that there's a *good* chance he's DWI.

WRONG WAY

Obviously, riding into opposing traffic is extremely dangerous. Study results showed that when you find a motorcycle going the wrong way in traffic there is a good change that the operator is under the influence. This includes going the wrong way on a one-way street, and crossing a center divider line to ride into opposing traffic.

Motorcycle DWI Detection Guide

Excellent Cues (50% or Greater Probability)
• Drifting during turn or curve
• Trouble with dismount
• Trouble with balance at a stop
• Turning problems (eg, unsteady, sudden corrections, late braking, improper lean angle)
• Inattentive to surroundings
• Inappropriate or unusual behavior (eg, carrying or dropping object, urinating at roadside, disorderly conduct, etc)
• Weaving
Good Cues (30% to 50% Probability)
• Erratic movements while going straight
• Operating without lights at night
• Recklessness
• Following too closely
• Running stop light or sign
• Evasion
• Wrong way

AMERICA'S DRUG ABUSE PROFILE

(Reproduced from "America's Drug Abuse Profile,"*The National Drug Control Strategy*, Washington, DC The White House, February, 1997, 9-26.)

FEWER AMERICANS ARE USING ILLEGAL DRUGS

An estimated 12.8 million Americans, about 6% of the household population aged 12 and older, use illegal drugs on a current basis (within the past 30 days). This number of "past-month" drug users has declined by almost 50% from the 1979 high of 25 million – a decrease that represents an extraordinary change in behavior. Despite the dramatic drop, more than a third of all Americans 12 and older have tried an illicit drug. Ninety percent of those who have used illegal drugs used marijuana or hashish. Approximately a third used cocaine or took a prescription type drug for nonmedical reasons. About a fifth used LSD. Fortunately, nearly 60 million Americans who used illicit drugs during youth, as adults reject these substances.[1]

Figure 1. Past-Month Users of Any Illicit Drugs, Cocaine, and Marijuana

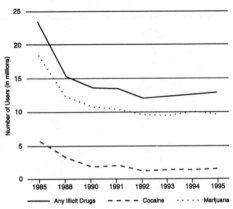

From *National Household Survey on Drug Abuse, National Institute on Drug Abuse (1985-91)*, Substance Abuse and Mental Health Services Administration, (1992-95).

DRUG USE IS A SHARED PROBLEM

Many Americans believe that drug abuse is not their problem. They have misconceptions that drug users belong to a segment of society different from their own or that drug abuse is remote from their environment. They are wrong. Almost three quarters of drug users are employed. A majority of Americans believe that drug use and drug-related crime are among our nation's most pressing social problems.[2] Approximately 45% of Americans know someone with a substance abuse problem.

While drug use and its consequences threaten Americans of every socioeconomic background, geographic region, educational level, and ethnic and racial identity, the effects of drug use are often felt disproportionately. Neighborhoods where illegal drug markets flourish are plagued by attendant crime and violence. Americans who lack comprehensive health plans and have smaller incomes may be less able to afford treatment programs to overcome drug dependence. What all Americans must understand is that no one is immune from the consequences of drug use. Every family is vulnerable. We must make a commitment to reducing drug abuse and not mistakenly assume that illegal drugs are someone else's concern.

Cocaine

The number of cocaine users in the United States has declined dramatically since the high point in 1985. In 1995, 1.5 million Americans were current cocaine users, a 74% decline from 5.7 million a decade earlier. In addition, fewer people are trying cocaine. The estimated 533,000 first-time users in 1994 represented a 60% decline from approximately 1.3 million cocaine initiates per year between 1980 and 1984. While these figures indicate significant progress, the number of frequent users in 1995, estimated at 582,000 (255,000 of whom use crack), has not changed markedly since 1985.[1] The Rand Corporation estimates that chronic users account for two-thirds of the U.S. demand for cocaine.[3] Thus, while the number of cocaine *users* has dropped, the *amount* of cocaine consumed in America has not declined commensurably.

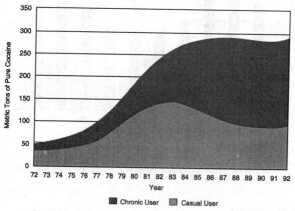

Figure 2. Annual U.S. Consumption of Cocaine by Type of User, 1972-1992

From *Modeling the Demand for Cocaine*, RAND Corporation, 1994.

Heroin

Some 600,000 people in the United States are addicted to heroin, an increase over the estimated number of addicts during the 1970s and 1980s.[4] While injection remains the most practical and efficient means of administering low-purity heroin,

699

AMERICA'S DRUG ABUSE PROFILE *(Continued)*

the availability of high-purity heroin makes snorting or smoking viable options. As more chronic users turn to snorting heroin, consumption has increased dramatically compared to consumption a decade ago when injection was the only option available.[5] The April 1996 *Pulse Check*, a survey conducted by the Office of National Drug Control Policy, found that while most heroin users are older, long-term drug abusers, growing numbers of teenagers and young adults are using the drug.[6]

Marijuana

In 1995, an estimated 9.8 million Americans (77% of all current illicit drug users) were smokers of marijuana, making it the most-commonly-used illicit drug. Approximately 57% of current illicit drug users limit consumption exclusively to marijuana. In 1995, 5 million U.S. citizens used marijuana frequently (defined as at least 51 days a year), which was a significantly lower figure than the estimated 8.4 million frequent marijuana users in 1985. However, the annual number of marijuana initiates rose since 1991, reaching 2.3 million in 1994.[1]

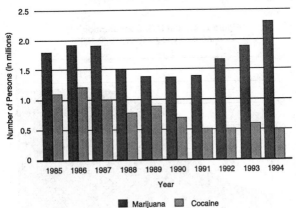

**Figure 3. Cocaine and Marijuana
First-Time Users, 1985-94**

From National Household Survey on Drug Abuse, Substance Abuse and Mental Health Services Administration, 1996.

Methamphetamine

Methamphetamine use is increasing. An estimated 4.7 million Americans have tried this drug.[1] Findings by the National Institute of Justice's Drug Use Forecasting program, which regularly tests arrestees for drug use in 23 cities, suggest that methamphetamine is present in many communities across the country and that its prevalence is greatest in the West, Southwest, and Midwest.[7] In 1995, approximately 6% of adult and juvenile arrestees, from all site, tested positive for methamphetamine. Eight locations (San Diego, Phoenix, San Jose, Portland, Omaha, Los Angeles, Denver, and Dallas) reported significant rates of methamphetamine use.

Figure 4. Drug Use Forecasting Sites Where Methamphetamine Use Was Highest in 1995

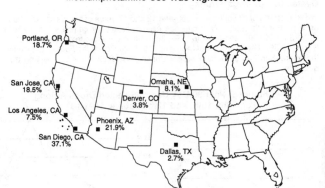

From *Drug Use Forecasting Program*, National Institute of Justice, 1996.

Other Illicit Drugs

In 1995, the prevalence of current use of other illicit drugs, including hallucinogens, inhalants, and psychotherapeutics, was <1%. Only hallucinogen use showed any significant change between 1994 and 1995, rising from 0.4% to 0.7%. Despite last years's ban on importation, Rohypnol, a powerful sedative, is still found in the Southeast and Mid-Atlantic regions. Ethnographers note that this substance was formerly one of several "club drugs" young people used, which now may be reaching a wider audience.[6]Other "club drugs", including ketamine, quaaludes, Xanax®, MDMA, and LSD, continue to gain popularity among young adults.

TRENDS IN YOUTH DRUG USE

The most alarming trend is the increasing use of illegal drugs, tobacco, and alcohol among youth. Children who use these substances increase the chance of acquiring life-long dependency problems. They also incur greater health risks. Every day, 3000 children begin smoking cigarettes regularly; as a result, a third of these youngsters will have their lives shortened.[1] According to a study conducted by Columbia University's Center on Addiction and Substance Abuse, children who smoke marijuana are 85 times more likely to use cocaine than peers who never tried marijuana.[8] The use of illicit drugs among eighth graders is up 150% over the past 5 years.[9] While alarmingly high, the prevalence of drug use among today's young people has not returned to near-epidemic levels of the late 1970s. The most important challenge for drug policy is to reverse these dangerous trends.

Early drug use often leads to other forms of unhealthy, unproductive behavior. Illegal drugs are associated with premature sexual activity (with attendant risks of unwanted pregnancy and exposure to sexually-transmitted diseases like HIV/AIDS), delinquency, and involvement in the criminal justice system.

AMERICA'S DRUG ABUSE PROFILE *(Continued)*

Overall Use of Illegal Drugs

In 1995, 10.9% of all youngsters between 12 and 17 years of age used illicit drugs on a past-month basis.[1] This rate has risen substantially compared to 8.2% in 1994, 5.7% in 1993, and 5.3% in 1992, the historic low in the trend since the 1979 high of 16.3%. The University of Michigan's 1996 *Monitoring the Future* study found that more than half of all high school students use illicit drugs by the time they graduate.

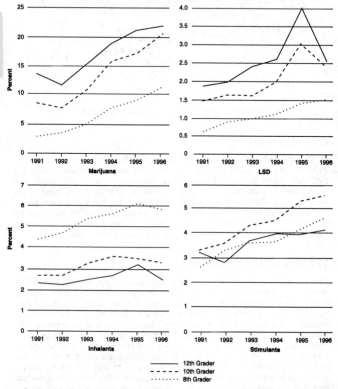

Figure 5. Past 30-Day Use of Selected Drugs Among 8th, 10th, and 12th Graders, 1991-96

From *Monitoring the Future Study*, University of Michigan, 1996.

702

Cocaine Use Among Youth

Cocaine use is not prevalent among young people. In 1996, approximately 2% of twelfth graders were current cocaine users. While this figure was up from a low of 1.4% in 1992, it was still 70% lower than the 6.7% high in 1985. Among twelfth graders in 1996, 7.1% had ever tried cocaine, up from the 1992 low of 6.1% but much lower than the 1985 high of 17.3%. However, during the past 5 years, lifetime use of cocaine has nearly doubled among eighth graders, reaching 4.5% in 1996.[9] A similar trend is identified in the 1995 National Household Survey on Drug Abuse, which showed a drop in the mean age for first use of cocaine from 23.3 years in 1990 to 19 in 1994.[1]

Heroin Use Among Youth

Heroin use is also not prevalent among young people. The 1996 *Monitoring The Future* study found that 1% of twelfth graders had used heroin in the past year, and half of 1% had done so within the last 30 days. Encouragingly, both figures were lower than the 1995 findings. However, the 1996 survey showed that the number of youths who ever used heroin doubled between 1991 and 1996 among eighth and twelfth graders, reaching 2.4% and 1.8% respectively.[9]

Marijuana Use Among Youth

Marijuana use continues to be a major problem among the nation's young people. Almost 1 in 4 high school seniors used marijuana on a "past-month" basis in 1996 while <10% used any other illicit drug with the same frequency. Within the past year, nearly twice as many seniors used marijuana as any other illicit drug.[9] Marijuana also accounts for most of the increase in illicit drug use among youths aged 12-17. Between 1994 and 1995, the rate of marijuana use among this age-group increased from 6% to 8.2% (a 37% increase). Furthermore, adolescents are beginning to smoke marijuana at a younger age. The mean age of first use dropped from 17.8 years in 1987 to 16.3 years in 1994.[1]

Alcohol Use Among Youth

Alcohol is the drug most often used by young people. Approximately 1 in 4 tenth grade students and one third of twelfth graders report having had 5 or more drinks on at least one occasion within 2 weeks of the survey.[9] The average age of first drinking has declined to 15.9 years, down from the 1987 average of 17.4 years.[1]

Tobacco Use Among Youth

Despite a decline in adult smoking, American youth continue to use tobacco products at rising rates. In 1996, more than a third of high school seniors smoked cigarettes, and more than 1 in 5 did so daily. These percentages are greater than at any time since the 1970s.[9]

Other Illicit Drug Use Among Youth

After marijuana, stimulants (a category that includes methamphetamine) are the second-most-commonly used illicit drug among young people. About 5% of high school students use stimulants on a monthly basis, and 10% have done so within the past year. Encouragingly, the use of inhalants, the third-most-common illicit substance, declined among eighth, tenth, and twelfth graders in 1996. LSD however, was used by 8.8% of twelfth graders during the past year.[9]

CONSEQUENCES OF ILLICIT DRUG USE

The social and health costs to society of illicit drug use are staggering. Drug-related illness, death, and crime cost the nation approximately $66.9 billion. Every man, woman, and child in America pays nearly $1,000 annually to cover the expense of unnecessary health care, extra law enforcement, auto accidents, crime, and lost productivity resulting from substance abuse.[10] Illicit drug use hurts families,

AMERICA'S DRUG ABUSE PROFILE *(Continued)*

business, and neighborhoods; impedes education; and chokes criminal justice, health, and social service systems.

HEALTH CONSEQUENCES

Drug-Related Medical Emergencies Are at a Historic High

The Drug Abuse Warning Network (DAWN), which studies drug-related hospital emergency room episodes, provides a useful snapshot of the health consequences of America's drug problem. In 1995, DAWN estimated that 531,800 drug-related episodes occurred, slightly more than the 518,500 incidents in 1994. The 1995 figure marks the first time in the past 5 years that drug-related emergency department episodes did not rise significantly.[11]

Figure 6. Trends in Drug-Related Emergency Room Mentions of Cocaine, Heroin, and Marijuana, 1988-95

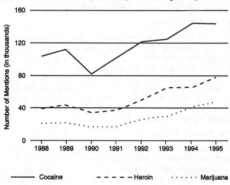

From Drug Abuse Warning Network, National Institute on Drug Abuse (1988-91) and Substance Abuse and Mental Health Services Administration (1992-95).

DAWN also found that cocaine-related episodes remain at a historic high. Heroin-related emergencies increased between 1990 and 1995 by 124%. While no meaningful change occurred in the number of methamphetamine-related episodes between 1994 and 1995, a marked increase did occur between 1991 and 1994 when the figure rose from 5000 to nearly 18,000.

Nearly 40% of deaths connected with illegal drugs strikes people between age 30 and 39, a group with elevated rates of chronic problems due to drug abuse.[12] Overall rates are higher for men than for women, and for blacks than for whites.[13] AIDS is the fastest-growing cause of all illegal drug-related deaths. More than 33% of new AIDS cases affect injecting drug users and their sexual partners.[14]

The Consequences of Heroin Addiction Are Becoming More Evident

Heroin-related deaths in some cities increased dramatically between 1993 and 1994 (the most recent year for which these statistics are available). In Phoenix, heroin fatalities were up 34%, 29% in Denver, and 25% in New Orleans.[15] The annual number of heroin-related emergency room mentions increased from 34,000 in 1990 to 76,023 in 1995.[11]

Maternal Drug Abuse Contributes to Birth Defects and Infant Mortality

A survey conducted between 1992 and 1993 estimated that 5.5%, or about 221,000 women, used an illicit drug at least once during their pregnancy.[16] Marijuana was used by about 2.9%, or 119,000; cocaine was used by about 1.1%, or 45,000.[16] Infants born to mothers who abuse drugs may go through withdrawal or have other medical problems at birth. Recent research also suggests that drug-exposed infants may develop poorly because of stress caused by the mother's drug use. These children experience double jeopardy; they often suffer from biological vulnerability due to prenatal drug exposure, which can be exacerbated by poor caretaking and multiple separations resulting from the drug user's lifestyle.

Maternal substance abuse is associated with increased risk of infant mortality or death of the child during the first year of life. An in-depth study of infant mortality conducted on women receiving Medicaid, in the state of Washington from 1988 through 1990, showed an infant mortality rate of 14.9 per 1000 births among substance-abusing women as compared to 10.7 per 1000 for women on Medicaid who were not substance abusers.[17] In addition, this research indicated that infants born to drug-abusing women are 2.5 times more likely to die from sudden infant death syndrome (SIDS).

Chronic Drug Use Is Related to Other Health Problems

The use of illegal drugs is associated with a range of other disease, including tuberculosis and hepatitis. Chronic users are particularly susceptible to sexually-transmittable diseases and represent "core transmitters" of these infections. High risk sexual behavior associated with crack and injection drug use has been shown to enhance the transmission and acquisition of both HIV and other STDs.

Underage Use of Alcohol and Tobacco Can Lead to Premature Death

Eighty-two percent of all people who try cigarettes do so by age 18.[18] Approximately 4.5 million American children younger than 18 now smoke, and every day another 3000 adolescents become regular smokers.[1] Seventy percent of adolescent smokers say they would not have started if they could choose again.[19] In excess of 400,000 people die every year from smoking-related diseases, more than from alcohol, crack, heroin, murder, suicide, car accidents, and AIDS combined.[20]

Alcohol has a devastating impact on young people. Eight young people a day die in alcohol-related car crashes.[21] According to the National Highway Traffic Safety Administration, 7738 intoxicated drivers between the ages of 16 and 20 were fatally injured in 1996.[22] The younger an individual starts drinking and the greater the intensity and frequency of alcohol consumption, the greater the risk of using other drugs.[21] Two and a half million teenagers reported they did not know that a person can die from alcohol overdose.[8]

Drug Abuse Burdens the Workplace

Seventy-one percent of all illicit drug users aged 18 and older (7.4 million adults) are employed, including 5.4 million full-time workers and 1.9 million part-time workers.[1] Drug users decrease workplace productivity. An ongoing, nationwide study conducted by the U.S. Postal Service has compared the job performance of drug users versus nonusers. Among drug users, absenteeism is 66% higher, health benefit utilization is 84% greater in dollar terms, disciplinary actions are 90% higher, and there is significantly higher employee turnover.[23]

The workplace can function as a conduit for information on substance-abuse prevention and identification both to adults, many of whom, as parents, are not being reached through more traditional means, and to youth who are employed while attending school. The threat of job loss remains one of the most effective ways to motivate substance abusers to get help. The workplace provides many

AMERICA'S DRUG ABUSE PROFILE *(Continued)*

employees (and families) who seek help for a substance-abuse problem with access to treatment. Since evidence shows that substance-abuse treatment can reduce job-related problems and result in abstinence, many employers sponsor employee-assistance programs (EAPs), conduct drug testing, or have procedures for detecting substance-abuse and promoting early treatment.

THE COST OF DRUG-RELATED CRIME

Drug abuse takes a toll on society that can only be partially measured. While we are able to estimate the number of drug-related crimes that occur each year, we can never determine fully the extent to which the quality of life in America's neighborhoods has been diminished by drug-related criminal behavior. With the exception of drug-related homicides, which have declined in recent years, drug-related crime is continuing at a strong and steady pace.

Numerous Drug-Related Arrests Occur Each Year

In 1994, state and local law enforcement agencies made an estimated 1.14 million arrests for drug law violations. The largest percentage of these arrests were for drug possession (75.1%).[24]

Figure 7. Drug-Related Arrests, 1988-95

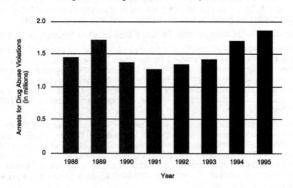

From *Uniform Crime Reports*, Federal Bureau of Investigation, 1996.

Arrestees Frequently Test Positive for Recent Drug Use

The National Institute of Justice Drug Use Forecasting (DUF) program calculates the percentage of arrested individuals whose urine indicates drug use. In 1995, DUF data collected from male arrestees in 23 cities showed that the percentage testing positive for any drug ranged from 51% to 83%. Female arrestees ranged from 41% to 84%. Among males, arrestees charged with drug possession or sale were most likely to test positive for drug use. Among females, arrestees charged with prostitution, drug possession, or sale were most likely to test positive for drug use. Both males and females arrested for robbery, burglary, and stealing vehicles had high positive rates.[7]

Drug Offenders Crowd the Nation's Prisons and Jails

At midyear 1996, there were 93,167 inmates in federal prisons, 1,019,281 in state prisons, and 518,492 in jails.[25] In 1994, 59.5% of federal prisoners were drug offenders[26] as were 22.3% of the inmates in state prisons.[27] The increase in drug offenders accounts for nearly three quarters of the total growth in federal prison inmates since 1980. Most drug offenders are imprisoned for possessing more drugs than possible could be consumed by one individual distributing drugs or committing serious crimes related to drug sales. In 1995, for example, only 4040 people were sentenced in federal courts for marijuana-related charges; 89.1% of those offenders were facing trafficking charges.[28]

Figure 8. Number of Persons in Federal and State Prisons and Local Jails, 1985-96

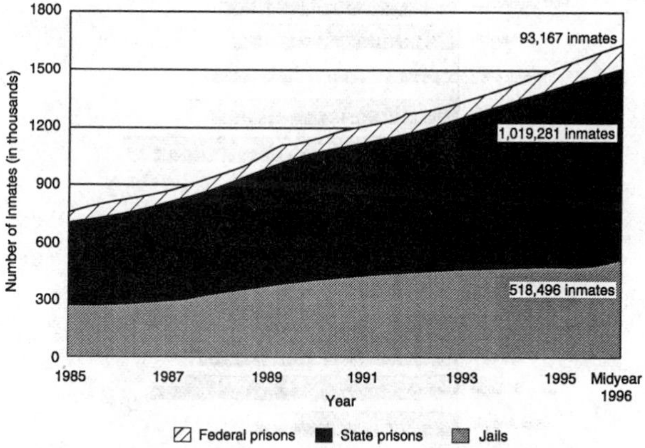

From Bureau of Justice Statistics, 1997.

Inmates in Federal and State Prisons Were Often Under the Influence of Drugs When They Committed Offenses

A 1991 survey of federal and state prisons, found that drug offenders, burglars, and robbers in state prisons were the most likely to report being under the influence of drugs while committing crimes. Inmates in state prisons who had been convicted of homicide, assault, and public order offenses were least likely to report being under the influence of drugs. With the exception of burglars, federal prison inmates were less likely than state inmates to have committed offenses under the influence of drugs.[29]

Offenders Often Commit Offenses to Support Drug Habits

According to a 1991 joint survey of federal and state prison inmates, an estimated 10% of federal prisoners and 17% of state prisoners reported committing offenses in order to pay for drugs.[29]

AMERICA'S DRUG ABUSE PROFILE *(Continued)*

Figure 9. Drug Use* Among Booked Arrestees, 1995

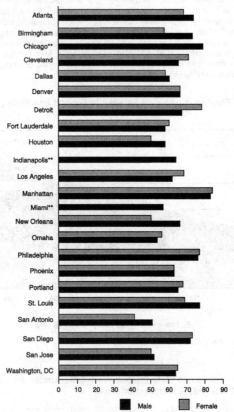

* Tested positive on urinalysis
** Data are not collected on female arrestees

From Drug use Forecasting Program, National Institute of Justice, 1996.

Drug Trafficking Generates Violent Crime

Trafficking in illicit drugs is often associated with violent crime. Reasons for this relationship include competition for drug markets and customers, disputes among individuals involved with legal drugs, and the location of drug markets in disadvantaged areas where legal and social controls against violence tend to be ineffective.

The proliferation of lethal weapons in recent years has also made drug violence more deadly.

Drug-Related Homicides Have Declined

There was a steady decline in drug-related homicide between 1989 and 1995. The Uniform Crime Reports (UCR) indicated that of 21,597 homicides committed in 1995 in which the circumstances of the crime were known, 1010 (or 4.7%) involved drugs. This figure was significantly lower than 7.4% in 1989.[24]

Figure 10. Drug-Related Murders, 1988-95

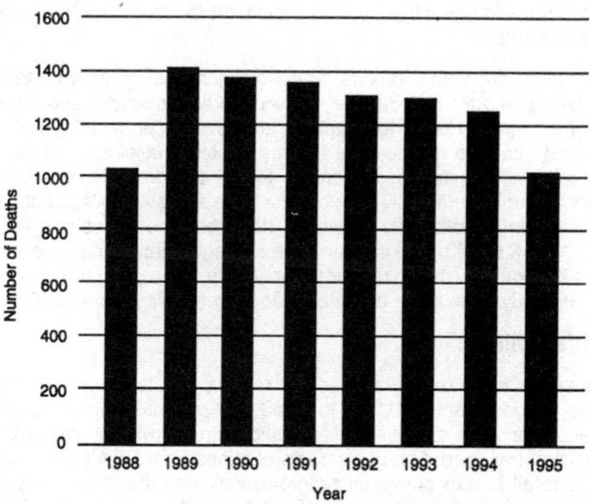

From *Uniform Crime Reports*, Federal Bureau of Investigation, 1996.

Money Laundering Harms Financial Institutions

Money laundering involves disguising financial assets so they can be used without the illegal activity that produced them being detected. Money laundering provides financial fuel not only for drug dealers but for terrorists, arms dealers, and other criminals who operate and expand criminal enterprises. Drug trafficking generates tens of billions of dollars a year; the total amount of money involved cannot be calculated precisely. In September 1996, the Internal Revenue Service (IRS) estimated that 60% of the money laundering cases it investigated during the fiscal year were drug-related.[30]

ILLEGAL DRUGS REMAIN AVAILABLE

Illegal drugs continue to be readily available almost anywhere in the United States. If measured solely in terms of price and purity, cocaine, heroin, and marijuana prove to be more available than they were a decade ago when the number of cocaine and marijuana users was much higher.

AMERICA'S DRUG ABUSE PROFILE *(Continued)*

Cocaine Availability

Colombian drug cartels continue to manage most aspects of the cocaine trade from acquisition of cocaine base, to cocaine production in South America and transportation, to wholesale distribution in the United States. Polydrug trafficking gangs in Mexico, which used to serve primarily as transporters for the Colombian groups, are increasingly assuming a more prominent role in the transportation and distribution of cocaine. Wholesale cocaine distribution and money laundering networks are typically organized into multiple cells functioning in major metropolitan areas. Domestically, retail level sales are conducted by a wide variety of criminal groups. These sellers are often organized along regional, cultural, and ethnic lines that facilitate internal security while serving a demand for drugs that permeates every part of our society.

Gangs, including the Crips, Bloods, and Dominican gangs as well as Jamaican "posses", are primarily responsible for widespread cocaine and crack-related violence. The migration of gang members and "posses" to smaller U.S. cities and rural areas has caused an increase in drug-related homicides, armed robberies, and assaults in those areas. According to the National Narcotics Intelligence Consumers Committee (NNICC) Report, the price and availability of cocaine in the United States remain relatively stable. In 1995, cocaine prices ranged nationally from $10,500 to $36,000 per kilogram. The average purity of cocaine at the gram, ounce, and kilogram level also remains high. Purity of the gram (retail level) in 1995 was approximately 61% while purity per kilogram (wholesale) was 83%.[5]

Heroin Availability

Heroin continues to be readily available in many cities. Nationally, in 1995 wholesale prices ranged from $50,000 to $260,000 per kilogram. This wide range reflected such variables as buyer-seller relationship, quantity purchased, frequency of delivery, and transportation costs. Data obtained from DEA's Domestic Monitor Program, a retail heroin purchase program, indicates that high-purity Southeast Asian heroin dominates the U.S. market. However, the availability of South American heroin has increased steadily, reflecting the fact that Colombian traffickers have gained a foothold in the U.S. heroin market.[5]

The NNICC Report also reveals that heroin purity levels have risen considerably. In 1995, the average purity for retail heroin from all sources was 39.7% nationwide, which was much higher than the average of 7% reported a decade ago. The retail purity of South American heroin was the highest of any source, averaging 56.4% nationwide and 76% in New York City, a major importation and distribution center. Heroin purity was generally highest in the Northeast where a large percentage of the nation's users live.

Marijuana Availability

Marijuana is the most readily available illicit drug in the United States. While no comprehensive survey of domestic cannabis cultivation has been conducted, the DEA estimates that much of the marijuana consumed in the United States is grown domestically. Cannabis is frequently cultivated in remote locations and on public lands. Major outdoor cultivation areas are found in Tennessee, Kentucky, Hawaii, California, and New York. Significant quantities of marijuana are also grown indoors. The controlled environments of indoor operations enable growers to use sophisticated agronomic techniques to enhance the drug's potency. The majority of the marijuana in the United States comes from Mexico, much of it being smuggled across the southwest border. However, marijuana shipments from Colombia and Jamaica are increasing.

Marijuana production and distribution in the United States are highly decentralized. Trafficking organizations range from complex operations that import the drug, grow it domestically, and trade within the U.S., to individuals cultivating and selling at the retail level. High quality marijuana is widely available in all parts of the United States. Prices vary with quality and range from $40 to $900 per ounce.[5] Over the past decade, marijuana prices have dropped even as the drug's potency has increased.

Methamphetamine Availability

Domestic methamphetamine production and trafficking are concentrated in the Western and Southwestern regions of the United States. Clandestine methamphetamine laboratories operating within Mexico and California are primary sources of supply for all areas of the United States. Mexican polydrug trafficking groups dominate wholesale methamphetamine distribution in the United States, saturating the western U.S. market with high-purity methamphetamine. These groups have also become a source of supply for Hawaii, threatening to displace traditional Asian suppliers.

LSD Availability

LSD in retail quantity can be found in virtually every state, and availability has increased in some states. LSD production facilities are thought to be located on the West Coast in the northern California and Pacific Northwest areas. A proliferation of mail-order sales has created a marketplace in which distributors have no personal contact with buyers.

Availability of Other Drugs

PCP production is centered in the greater Los Angeles metropolitan area. Los Angeles-based street gangs, primarily the Crips, continue to distribute PCP to a number of U.S. cities through cocaine trafficking operations. MDMA, a drug related to methamphetamine and known by such street names as Ecstasy, XTC, Clarity, Essence, and Doctor, is produced in west Texas and on the West Coast. It is distributed across the country by independent traffickers through the mail or commercial delivery services. MDMA is often sold in tablet form with dosage units of 55-150 mg. Retail prices range from $60 to $30.[5]

In 1995, an influx of flunitrazepam (Rohypnol) tablets reached the Gulf Coast and other areas of the United States. Manufactured legally by Hoffman-LaRoche in Colombia, Mexico, and Switzerland, Rohypnol has been reported to be combined with alcohol and cocaine, and is becoming known as the "date rape" drug. Illegal in the United States, it sells wholesale for a dollar a tablet and retail from $1.25 to $3 a tablet.[31]

WHILE PROGRESS HAS BEEN MADE, MORE REMAINS TO BE DONE

We have made progress in our efforts to reduce drug use and its consequences in America. While America's illegal drug problem is serious, it does not approach the emergency situation of the late 1970s or the cocaine epidemic in the 1980s. Just 6% of our household population age 12 and older were using drugs in 1995, down from 14.1% in 1979. Fewer than 1% were using cocaine, inhalants, or hallucinogens. The most-commonly-used illegal drug was marijuana, taken by 77% of drug users.[1]

As drug use became less prevalent through the 1980s, national attention to the drug problem decreased. The Partnership for a Drug-Free America suggests that an indicator or that decreased attention was the reduced frequency of antidrug public service announcements (PSAs) on TV, radio, and in print media. Our children also dropped their guard as drugs became less prevalent and first-hand

AMERICA'S DRUG ABUSE PROFILE *(Continued)*

knowledge of dangerous substances became scarce. Consequently, disapproval of drugs and the perception of risk on the part of young people has declined throughout this decade. As a result, since 1992 more youth have been using alcohol, tobacco, and illegal drugs.

A disturbing study prepared by CASA suggests that adults have become resigned to teen drug use. In fact, nearly half the parents from the "baby-boomer" generation expect their teenagers to try illegal drugs.[32] Forty percent believe they have little influence over teenagers' decisions about whether to smoke, drink, or use illegal drugs. Both of these assumptions are incorrect. Parents have enormous influence over the decisions young people make.

Figure 11. Marijuana: Disapproval and Perceived Harmfulness of Regular Use Compared With Past 30-Day Use Among 12th Graders, 1996

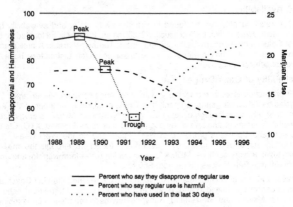

Percent who say they disapprove of regular use

Percent who say regular use is harmful

Percent who have used in the last 30 days

From *Monitoring the Future Study*, University of Michigan, 1996.

WE MUST ACT NOW TO PREVENT A FUTURE DRUG EPIDEMIC

The United States has failed to forestall resurgent drug use among children in the 90s. This problem did not develop recently. The 1993 *Interim National Drug Control Strategy* highlighted the problem of rising drug use among American youth, quoting the 1992 *Monitoring The Future* study which found that eighth graders and college students were "... reporting higher rates of drug use in 1992 than they did in 1991. Further, fewer eighth graders in 1992 perceived great risk with using cocaine or crack than did eighth graders in 1991." The continuation of these trends has been substantiated by every significant survey of drug use since 1993.

Our challenge is to reverse these negative trends. America cannot allow the relapse we have experienced to signal a return to catastrophic illegal drug use levels of the past. The government has committed itself to that end; so have nongovernmental organizations such as Community Anti-Drug Coalitions of America (CACDA), the Partnership for a Drug-Free America (PDFA), Columbia

University's Center on Addiction and Substance Abuse (CASA), the National Center for the Advancement of Prevention (NCAP), the Parent's Resource Institute for Drug Education (PRIDE), and many others. Working together, we can succeed.

Footnotes

1. Substance Abuse and Mental Health Services Administration, *Preliminary Estimates From the 1995 National Household Survey on Drug Abuse*, Rockville, MD: U.S. Department of Health and Human Services, 1996.
2. The Gallup Organization, *Consult With America: A Look at How Americans View the Country's Drug Problem, Summary Report*, Rockville, MD, March, 1996.
3. Rand Corporation, *Modeling the Demand for Cocaine*, Santa Monica, CA: Rand Corporation, 1994.
4. Rhodes W, Scheiman P, and Carlson K, *What America's Users Spend on Illegal Drugs, 1988-1991*, Washington, D.C.: Abt Associates, Inc, under contract to the Office of National Drug Control Policy, 1993.
5. National Narcotics Intelligence Consumers Committee, *The NNICC Report 1995: The Supply of Illicit Drugs to the United States*, Washington, D.C.: Drug Enforcement Administration, August, 1996.
6. Office of National Drug Control Policy, *Pulse Check, National Trends in Drug Abuse*, Washington, D.C.: Executive Office of the President, Spring, 1996.
7. National Institute of Justice, *1995 Drug Use Forecasting, Annual Report on Adult and Juvenile Arrestees*, Washington, D.C.: U.S. Department of Justice, 1996.
8. Merrill JC, Fox K, Lewis SR, et al, *Cigarettes, Alcohol, Marijuana: Gateways to Illicit Drug Use*, New York, NY: Center on Addiction and Substance Abuse at Columbia University, 1994.
9. Johnston L, *Monitoring the Future Study – 1996*, Ann Arbor, MI: University of Michigan, December, 1996, press release.
10. Rice DP, Kelman S, Miller LS, et al, *The Economic Costs of Alcohol and Drug Abuse and Mental Illness: 1985*, Report submitted to the Office of Financing and Coverage Policy of the Alcohol, Drug Abuse, and Mental Health Administration, San Francisco, CA: Institute for Health & Aging, University of California, U.S. Department of Health and Human Services, 1990.
11. Substance Abuse and Mental Health Services Administration, *Preliminary Estimates From the Drug Abuse Warning Network, 1995 Preliminary Estimates of Drug-Related Emergency Department Episodes*, Advance Report Number 17, Rockville, MD: U.S. Department of Health and Human Services, August, 1996.
12. U.S. National Center for Health Statistics, *Alcohol and Drugs: Advance Report of Final Mortality Statistics, 1989, Monthly Vital Statistics Report*, 40(8):Suppl 2, Hyattsville, MD: U.S. Department of Health and Human Services, 1992.
13. Centers for Disease Control and Prevention, *Monthly Vital Statistics Report, Advance Report of Final Mortality Statistics, 1994*, 45(3):Supplement, Hyattsville, MD: U.S. Department of Health and Human Services, September 30, 1996.
14. Centers for Disease Control and Prevention, *HIV and AIDS Trends, Progress in Prevention*, Hyattsville, MD: National Center for Health Statistics, 1996.
15. *Drug Abuse Warning Network, Statistical Series, Series 1, No. 14-B, Annual Medical Examiner Data*, 1994.
16. National Institute on Drug Abuse, *1992-93 National Pregnancy & Health Survey: Drug Use Among Women Delivering Livebirths*, Rockville, MD: U.S. Department of Health and Human Services, 1996.
17. Schrager L, Joyce J, and Cawthon L, *Substance Abuse, Treatment, and Birth Outcomes for Pregnant and Postpartum Women in Washington State*, Olympia, WA: Washington State Department of Social and Health Services, 1995.
18. Office on Smoking and Health, *Preventing Tobacco Use Among Young People, A Report of the Surgeon General*, Rockville, MD: Center for Disease Control and Prevention, U.S. Department of Health and Human Services, July, 1994.
19. American Cancer Society, *Facts About Children and Tobacco Use*, Atlanta, GA: American Cancer Society, 1997.
20. McGinnis JM and Foege WH, "Actual Causes of Death in the United States," *JAMA*, 1993, 270(18): 2207-12.
21. Center for Substance Abuse Prevention (CSAP), *Teen Drinking Prevention Program*, Rockville, MD: U.S. Department of Health and Human Services, 1996.
22. National Highway Traffic Safety Administration, *Fatal Accident Reporting System*, Washington, D.C.: U.S. Department of Transportation, July, 1996.
23. National Institute on Drug Abuse, *Research on Drugs and the Workplace: NIDA Capsule 24*, Rockville, MD: U.S. Department of Health and Human Services, 1990.
24. Federal Bureau of Investigation, *Crime in the United States: 1995: Uniform Crime Reports*, Washington, D.C.: U.S. Department of Justice, 1996.

AMERICA'S DRUG ABUSE PROFILE *(Continued)*

25. Bureau of Justice Statistics, *Prison and Jail Inmates at Midyear 1996*, Washington, D.C.: U.S. Department of Justice, January, 1997.
26. Bureau of Prisons, Washington, D.C.: U.S. Department of Justice, unpublished data.
27. Bureau of Justice Statistics, *Correctional Populations in the United States, 1994*, Washington, D.C.: U.S. Department of Justice, June, 1996.
28. Maguire K and Pastore AL, *Sourcebook of Criminal Justice Statistics 1995*, Washington, D.C.: Bureau of Justice Statistics, U.S. Department of Justice, 1996.
29. Bureau of Justice Statistics, *Comparing Federal and State Prison Inmates, 1991*, Washington, D.C.: U.S. Department of Justice, September, 1994.
30. Internal Revenue Service, unpublished data.
31. Office of National Drug Control Policy, *Fact Sheet: Rohypnol*, Rockville, MD: Drugs and Crime Clearinghouse, September, 1996.
32. Luntz Research Companies, *National Survey of American Attitudes on Substance Abuse II, Teens and Their Parents*, New York, NY: Center on Addition and Substance Abuse, September, 1996

1996 YEAR-END PRELIMINARY ESTIMATES FROM THE DRUG ABUSE WARNING NETWORK

(From Substance Abuse and Mental Health Services Administration, "Preliminary Estimates From the Drug Abuse Warning Network," Rockville, MD: U.S. Department of Health and Human Services, November 1997.)

HIGHLIGHTS

This report presents the results from the 1996 Drug Abuse Warning Network (DAWN). It shows trends since 1989 of the estimated number of hospital emergency department episodes that were directly related to the use of an illegal drug or the nonmedical use of a legal drug.

- In 1996, there were 487,600 drug-related hospital emergency department episodes. This was down significantly from 1994 (518,500 episodes) and 1995 (517,800 episodes).

- There was no statistically significant change in the total number of cocaine-related episodes between 1995 (138,000) and 1996 (144,200).

- Between 1995 and 1996, there were no changes in cocaine-related episodes by age, gender, or race/ethnicity; however, between 1994 and 1996 there was a 21% increase among those age 35 and older (from 54,200 to 65,500).

- Although heroin-related episodes had been increasing steadily since the early 1980s, there was no change in the number of heroin-related episodes reported from 1995 (72,200) to 1996 (70,500). However, between 1990 and 1996, there has been a 108% increase (from 33,900 to 70,500).

- Between 1995 and 1996, there were no changes in heroin-related episodes by age, gender, or race/ethnicity. However, between 1994 and 1996, there was a 20% increase among those age 35 and older (from 33,400 to 40,000).

- Marijuana/hashish-related episodes rose from 40,200 in 1994 to 50,000 in 1996, a 25% increase. Since 1990, marijuana/hashish-related episodes have increased 219%.

- Between 1995 and 1996, there were no changes in marijuana/hashish-related episodes by age, gender, or race/ethnicity. However, between 1994 and 1996, marijuana-related episodes have increased by 33% among those age 12-17, 27% among those age 26-34, and 41% among those age 35 and older.

- There was a statistically significant decrease in methamphetamine-related episodes reported between 1995 (16,200) and 1996 (10,800). However, there was a significant increase of 71% between the first half of 1996 and the second half of 1996 (from 4,000 to 6,800). Reports by local area epidemiologists indicate there was a shortage of methamphetamine in many cities in the Western United States in the last half of 1995 and first quarter of 1996.

- "Suicide attempt or gesture" (181,600) was the most commonly reported motive for taking a substance and comprised 37% of all drug-related episodes in 1996. The most frequently recorded reason for a drug-related emergency department visit was "overdose" (239,100).

1996 YEAR-END PRELIMINARY ESTIMATES FROM THE DRUG ABUSE WARNING NETWORK *(Continued)*

ANNUAL TRENDS IN PRESCRIPTION AND OVER-THE-COUNTER DRUG-RELATED EPISODES

DAWN also reports on cases involving the nonmedical use of legal drugs.

- Accidental overdoses of over-the-counter or prescription drugs taken as directed are not reportable unless they were used in combination with an illicit drug. Generally, most drug-related episodes involving over-the-counter drugs reported "suicide attempt or gesture" as the motive for use.

- Acetaminophen-related episodes comprised 7.5% of all drug-related emergency department episodes in 1996. From 1990 through 1996, a 44% increase was observed (from 25,400 to 36,500).

- From 1990 through 1995, trazodone-related emergency department episodes increased 215% (from 3000 to 9500). Trazodone is an antidepressant used in the treatment of aggressive behavior and cocaine withdrawal.

- From 1990 though 1995, clonazepam-related emergency department episodes increased 195% (from 4300 to 12,800). There was no change between 1995 and 1996 (12,800 in 1996). Clonazepam is an anticonvulsant.

- Diazepam (Valium®) is a benzodiazepine used in the treatment of anxiety disorders, seizures, and muscle spasms. There was no change in the number of diazepam-related episodes between 1994 and 1996.

- Alprazolam (Xanax®), a benzodiazepine used in the treatment of anxiety disorders, was first reported to DAWN in 1982. Alprazolam-related emergency department episodes increased from 1200 in 1982 to 16,200 in 1988. Alprazolam-related episodes have been fairly constant since 1988.

- Lorazepam (Ativan®) is a benzodiazepine used in the treatment of anxiety disorders. Lorazepam-related emergency department episodes increased from 1600 in 1978 to 12,200 in 1994. Between 1994 and 1995, lorazepam-related estimates decreased by 22% (from 12,200 to 9500).

KEY FINDINGS FROM THE 1996 PRELIMINARY DAWN ESTIMATES

Total Drug-Related Emergency Department (ED) Episodes:	487,600 - down significantly from the 1994 and 1995 estimates (518,500 and 517,800 respectively)
Cocaine-Related Episodes:	Did not change significantly between 1995 (138,000) and 1996 (144,200)
	No changes by age, gender, or race/ethnicity between 1995 and 1996; but, between 1994 and 1996, increased 21% among those age 35 and older (from 54, 200 to 65, 500
Heroin-Related Episodes:	After increasing steadily since the early 1980s, did not change significantly between 1995 (72,200) and 1996 (70,500)
	Increased 108% between 1990 and 1996 (from 33,900 to 70,500)
	No changes by age, gender, or race/ethnicity between 1995 and 1996; but, between 1994 and 1996, increased 20% among those age 35 and older (from 33,400 to 40,000)
Marijuana/Hashish Episodes:	Increased 25% between 1994 (40,200) and 1996 (50,000)
	Increased 219% since 1990
	No changes by age, gender, or race/ethnicity between 1995 and 1996; but, between 1994 and 1996, increased by 33% among those age 12 to 17, 27% among those age 26-34, and 41% among those age 35 and older
Methamphetamine-Related Episodes:	Declined significantly between 1995 (16,200) and 1996 (10,800), but increased significantly (71%) between the first and second halves of 1996 (from 4000 to 6800)
	Shortage of methamphetamine in many Western U.S. cities in the last half of 1995 and the first quarter of 1996 (according to local epidemiologists)
Motive/Reason:	"Suicide attempt or gesture" (181,600) the most commonly reported motive for taking a substance - 37% of all drug-related episodes in 1996
	"Overdose" (239,100) the most frequently recorded reason for a drug-related ED visit

KEY FINDINGS FROM THE 1996 PRELIMINARY DAWN ESTIMATES *(Continued)*

CHANGES IN METROPOLITAN AREAS

Between 1994 and 1996...	Increased in....	Declined in....
Drug-related ED Episodes:	New Orleans, Newark	Boston, Denver, New York, San Francisco, Washington DC
Cocaine-related ED Episodes:	Miami, New Orleans, Phoenix	Baltimore, Boston, Denver, San Francisco, Washington DC
Heroin-related ED Episodes:	Detroit, Newark, Philadelphia, Phoenix, Washington DC (Also in Dallas, Miami, and New Orleans - but the number of episodes is relatively small)	Denver

Adapted from *DAWN Briefings*, March 1998, 4.

ETHANOL AND BLOOD ALCOHOL DETERMINATION: WHAT DOES IT REALLY MEAN?

By Jerrold B. Leikin, MD

The association of alcohol (ethanol) use and traumatic events is so well established that alcohol use is considered a major risk factor in the etiology of accidents. It has been estimated that at least 52% of victims of head injury, 55% of drivers, and 77% of car passengers involved in fatal car accidents will have measurable blood alcohol levels in their bodies. As a result, emergency department physicians will now routinely obtain a blood alcohol level in a multiple traumatized patient.

However, when one attempts to extrapolate these specific blood alcohol levels to certain times or events, confusion can occur. It is in these circumstances that medical/scientific knowledge and legal interpretation can often diverge to two different conclusions.

One area of confusion is centered on the term "blood alcohol level." Simply put, a blood alcohol level may not be an alcohol level originating from blood. Essentially, alcohol can be measured from several sites in the body: blood, serum, eye (vitreous), bile, urine, kidney, saliva, bone marrow, or breath. Each of these sites has specific applications with respect to alcohol determination. For example, a urinary alcohol level is usually performed in conjunction with a blood alcohol level. When the urinary alcohol to blood alcohol ratio is >1.3, this indicates that the alcohol has been absorbed into the bloodstream and is dissipating (postabsorptive state).

A second example is that of determination of a blood alcohol level in the postmortem state. The alcohol level derived from blood can be falsely elevated when extensive decomposition or putrefaction has taken place. The eye (vitreous) can serve as a reliable site for postmortem alcohol determinations in that it is stable for prolonged intervals after death and that it may be closely related to the brain alcohol levels at time of death. For ethanol analysis from vitreous humor specimens, the blood alcohol concentration would be approximately 90% of the vitreous humor alcohol concentration.

While breath alcohol testing has been utilized since 1938, the interpretation of results derived by these instruments is constantly being challenged. It has been alleged that radio frequency interference, burping, severe emphysema or diabetes mellitus, gasoline or acetone vapors, aerosolized mouth sprays, paint thinner fumes, or mouthwash can interfere with its results. While most of these scenarios will (at most) only mildly affect the instrument, certain procedures should be followed by the operator of the unit to alleviate these concerns. Calibration of the instrument along with obtaining two separate breath sample (3-5 minutes apart) from a cooperative subject taking a deep breath is essential to proper interpretation of the method. It should be remembered that the value obtained from these instruments is then converted to a blood alcohol concentration (using a blood:breath ratio of 2100:1). If any discrepancy results, sampling from other sites should occur.

Saliva alcohol testing is a relatively new and simple technique which essentially entails the use of a cotton swab to sample saliva from a subject's mouth. While it correlates closely with blood alcohol levels, it should be performed at least 10 minutes after alcohol ingestion. Collection of specimens from patients with dry mouth may be particularly difficult.

While it may be obvious from medical or autopsy records where the origin of the specimen is, it is the difference between serum or plasma and whole blood alcohol levels that causes confusion. Some clinical laboratories may measure alcohol

ETHANOL AND BLOOD ALCOHOL DETERMINATION: WHAT DOES IT REALLY MEAN? *(Continued)*

levels from blood utilizing serum or plasma. Since alcohol distributes easily into a water medium and since there is a higher percentage of water in serum or plasma, the concentration of alcohol is about 12% to 20% higher in plasma or serum than in whole blood. Thus, one would need to divide the serum ethanol level (often described in units/dL or mmol/L) by 1.12-1.2 in order to obtain a blood alcohol concentration (often described as a percentage). It is in this way that an alcohol level derived from blood is not the same as "blood alcohol level". However, this discrepancy is rarely of any clinical importance and its relevance is questionable (see reference by Orsay E and Doan-Wiggins L).

The quantitative analysis of a blood alcohol concentration (BAC) can also lead to misinterpretation. In my opinion, most of the disputes regarding specific BAC center on the magic number of 0.1%. Since the first "per se" law was enacted by Nebraska in 1963, 37 states have established the "per se" BAC at 0.10%. Thus, chemical test evidence for alcohol intoxication has often centered on a specific level rather than merely it's presence (unlike cocaine or marijuana abuse).

Legal Adult Intoxication Driving Limits by Blood Alcohol Concentration (As of July 1997)

None	≥0.08%	≥0.10%
Massachusetts†	Alabama	All other states
South Carolina*	California	
	Florida	
	Hawaii	
	Idaho	
	Illinois	
	Kansas	
	Maine	
	New Hampshire	
	New Mexico	
	North Carolina	
	Oregon	
	Utah	
	Vermont	
	Virginia	

†BAC of 0.08% is evidence of alcohol impairment but is not illegal per se.
*BAC of 0.10% is evidence of alcohol impairment but is not illegal per se.
From Pearson R, "Committee Unbottles Bill to Trim DUI Level," *Chicago Tribune*, Feb 28, 1997, 24.

Clearly we are entering an age of "zero tolerance" to the adverse effects of toxins. For example, the Centers of Disease Control (CDC) has been a leader in reducing lead exposure to virtually zero; the Federal Government has initiated random and pre-employment urine drug testing to eliminate substance abuse from its employees; new campaigns are initiated by the Environmental Protection Agency against not only cigarette smoking but also the effects of inhaling passive smoke.

This zero tolerance attitude is making its way to the field of driving-under-the-influence (DUI) enforcement. The National Safety Council, American Medical

Association, Surgeon General, the Association for the Advancement of Automotive Medicine, and the American College of Emergency Physicians all have supported a lowering of "per se" BAC limits.

Certainly, the scientific data is plentiful in support of this attitude. It is clear that the crash risk increases as the level of the BAC of the driver increases. Deleterious effects of alcohol at a BAC at the range of 0.05% to 0.06% include impairment of curve-negotiating "driving" tasks, deterioration of information processing, and impairment in driving through narrow spaces. It has been estimated that 15% to 38% of drivers in injury-causing accidents had BAC of 0.05% or greater (see Figure 1 and Figure 2). Another way of quantitating the impairment cuase by a BAC of 0.05 is that this BAC is equivalent (in terms of decreased performance) to staying awake for 17 hours.

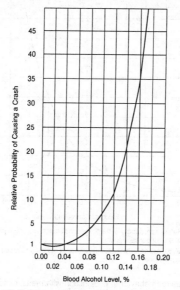

Figure 1. Relative probability of causing a crash rises with rising blood alcohol levels.

Reprinted from the Council on Scientific Affairs, "Alcohol and Driver," *JAMA*, 1992, 255:523, with permission.

Sweden gives us a good model of the effects of this "zero tolerance" attitude. In 1941, the Swedish Parliament enacted a BAC limit of 0.08%; by 1957, it was lowered to 0.05%. Public pressure following Parliamentary hearings resulted in a lowering of the BAC to 0.02% in July, 1990. Essentially, it is believed that Sweden has been successful in keeping the social drinker off the highway but is still having problems keeping the problem drinker from operating a motor vehicle.

Recent Department of Transportation and Nuclear Regulatory Commission guidelines define the alcohol-impaired worker at a BAC of 0.02%. Clearly, reliance

ETHANOL AND BLOOD ALCOHOL DETERMINATION: WHAT DOES IT REALLY MEAN? *(Continued)*

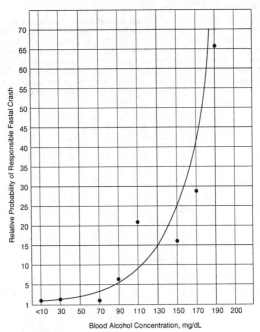

Figure 2. Relative probability of being responsible for fatal crash rises with rising blood alcohol concentrations.

Reprinted from the Council on Scientific Affairs, "Alcohol and Driver," *JAMA*, 1986, 255:523, with permission.

of documented impaired behavior in conjunction with measurable BAC will define the alcohol-impaired individual.

One guiding principle in medicine is that a physician utilizes a laboratory test to confirm a clinical diagnosis. In the case of an impaired driver, we have used the laboratory test exclusively to define and diagnose. This has often led to other very imprecise BAC calculations – such as in the area of "back dating" the BAC to a specific time. When one considers the metabolism of alcohol to be somewhat variable (anywhere from 10-30 mg/dL/hour), it is apparent that this practice is fraught with hazards. Furthermore, the issue of disinfectant (isopropyl alcohol) use affecting BAC is truly extraneous with virtually no scientific basis. Additionally, food coingestion is a variable which has questionable measurable clinical impact. Multiple traumatic injury with resultant paralytic ileus may also result in a delay of ethanol absorption. Misinterpretation of BAC will be minimized if one is cognizant of the intent of obtaining the specimen, site from which the level is obtained along with the circumstances and nature of the impairment.

References

American College of Emergency Physicians, "Blood Alcohol Concentration and Driving," *Ann Emerg Med*, 1988, 17(11):1252.

Angell M and Kassirer JP, "Alcohol and Other Drugs - Toward a More Rational and Consistent Policy," *N Engl J Med*, 1994, 331:537-8.

Brewer RD, Morris PD, Cole TB, et al, "The Risk of Dying in Alcohol-Related Automobile Crashes Among Habitual Drunk Drivers," *N Engl J Med*, 1994, 331:513-7.

Chang J and Kollman SE, "The Effect of Temperature on the Formation of Ethanol by *Candida albicans* in Blood," *J Forensic Sci*, 1989, 34(1):105-9.

Coe JI and Sherman RE, "Comparative Study of Postmortem Vitreous Humor and Blood Alcohol," *J Forensic Sciences*, 1970, 15(2):185-90.

Council on Scientific Affairs, "Alcohol and the Driver,"*JAMA*, 1986, 255(4):522-7.

Hedlund JH, "If They Didn't Drink, Would They Crash Anyway? The Role of Alcohol in Traffic Crashes," *Alcohol, Drugs and Driving*, 1994, 10(2):115-25.

Holloway FA, "Low-Dose Alcohol Effects on Human Behavior and Performance," *Alcohol, Drugs and Driving*, 1995, 1(1):39-56.

Laurell H, "The Swedish Experience: Changes in BAC Legislation,"*Alcohol, Drugs and Driving*, 1991, 7:261-5.

Lundberg GD, "Lets Stop Driving After Drinking and Using Other Psychoactive Drugs," *JAMA*, 1986, 255(4):529-30.

Orsay E and Doan-Wiggins L, "Serum Alcohol is Not the Same as Blood Alcohol Concentration," *Ann Emerg Med*, 1995, 25:430-1.

Tagliaro F, Lubli G, and Ghielmi S, "Chromatographic Methods for Blood Alcohol Determination," *J Chromatogr*, 1992, 580(1-2):161-90.

Voas RB, "Enforcement of DUI Laws," *Alcohol, Drugs and Driving*, 1991, 7:173-96.

Watson WA and Garriott JC, "Alcohol and Motorcycle Riders: A Comparison of Motorcycle and Car/Truck DWIs," *Vet Hum Toxicol*, 1992, 34(3):213-5.

DRUG TESTING IN HAIR

by Carl M. Selavka, PhD

Director of Forensic Services,
Division of Criminal Justice Services (DCJS), Albany, NY

For many years, hair has provided a useful matrix for tests designed to determine the routine/chronic exposure of individuals to heavy metals and other elemental agents. The simple theories of incorporation of such elements into the hair of exposed individuals suggested that each acute exposure led to the incorporation of a small amount of the element(s) into newly formed hair cells in the dermal papilla. The incorporation was based on the fact that these newly formed hair cells draw their cellular content from the serum available in this highly perfused region of tissue. Thus, if the blood contains an element due to the person's exposure to the element, the hair cells growing that day will contain traces related to serum level of the element.[1] It was also postulated that the element, once incorporated, would maintain its relative "position" in the hair cells (would not "migrate" from cell to cell), so that the pattern of exposure would be reflected in the pattern of incorporated element(s) in the hair.

Following these simple theories, it was not expected that a single exposure would lead to measurable levels of the element(s) in hair collected some time after the exposure, even with the most sensitive methods of analysis. However, if the individual experienced repetitive, chronic exposure, more routine uptake of the element(s) into hair would occur. The additive nature of these repetitive uptakes would ultimately allow for the analysis of hair to demonstrate that such chronic exposure to the element(s) had occurred. In essence, the sum of the exposures becomes more and more detectable, as the number of acute exposures in the finite time period increases. Also, since hair growth rates are generally understood (although not generally consistent across the population), a time period could be estimated from a given length of hair collected on a certain date from a particular part of the body.

While the simplicity of the theories regarding this hair uptake failed to account for all possible sources of the incorporated element(s) detected, they nonetheless provided insight into possible unique studies of chronic exposure available through the analysis of hair. The analysis of hair for drugs is a much younger field, with rapid progress being reported only within the last 15 years. It is interesting to note that the roots of hair drug testing lead back to the detection of an "unusual" drug in 1954, when Goldblum, Goldbaum, and Piper first reported on the spectrophotometric detection of phenobarbital in guinea pig hair.[2] It is somewhat humorous that this research endeavor was born in the laboratories of the U.S. Army's Medical Service Graduate School Department of Dermatology and Syphilology. However, this unique department of first report underscores the variety of disciplines in which hair drug testing can play a useful role.

THE UTILITY OF TESTS FOR DRUGS IN HAIR

Applications of hair drug testing can be categorized into three broad classes: civil/medical investigation, criminal investigation, and pharmacotoxicologic studies of drug incorporation into hair. A description of some applications within the first two classes illuminates the diversity of this analytical field.

Civil/Medical Investigations may include:

1. Workplace testing - pre-employment and random, routine or for-cause tests related to the identification of drug users during the hiring process, as part of on-going employee evaluations, or as a part of the investigation of accidents or other "incidents".

2. Divorce proceedings - verification of the truthfulness of the parties when allegations of drug use, with the related impact on the dissolution of a marriage, are made.

3. Child custody - verification of the drug use history of a party in a dispute over custody of children, often ordered by family judges or requested through these judges by one party in the dispute.

4. Neonatal testing - testing of newborn infants' hair, often to corroborate clinical indications (apparent in either the infant or mother) of drug use by the mother during pregnancy. This may be supplemented by, or a supplement to, segmented testing of the mother's hair.

5. Insurance cases - underwriters may require such testing before accepting an applicant for life, disability, or performance (such as with professional athletes) coverage.

6. Health surveys - when used in support of medical evaluations, results of hair tests offer guidance in the choice of treatment alternatives.

7. "Exposure" assay - through the use of segmented analyses, an approximate calendar of "exposures" (whether purposeful or fortuitous) can be constructed.

Criminal and Law Enforcement Investigations may include:

1. Postmortem tests - determination of drug use history may significantly impact on the medical examiner's findings for the cause and manner of death, as well as circumstances surrounding the death-producing events.

2. Personnel integrity - investigations of law enforcement personnel (especially those involved in drug trafficking work and crime laboratories) for indications of diversion and use of drugs, or of medical and pharmacy personnel who have access to drug supplies and unique abuse liabilities.

3. Criminal defendants - retrospective hair testing may be employed to assess the impact of chronic drug use on a defendant's ability to form intent, or on the state of mind of the defendant, during the broad time period surrounding the offense.

4. Victims of crime - testing of victims is often used to assess the drug use history of the victim, in attempts to impeach their credibility or to argue mitigation based on drug-mediated aggression by a victim, provoking self-defense.

As of the writing of this edition, there are six laboratories in the United States routinely offering hair drug testing in one or more of these categories of application. In addition, there are laboratories in Canada, Japan, Germany, France, Spain, Italy, and several other countries performing routine hair drug testing. Such testing is routinely used in Europe in qualifying or investigating applicants for drivers' licenses and those involved in traffic accidents, in post-mortem investigations, and many medical applications.

DRUG TESTING IN HAIR *(Continued)*

It should be noted that significant research effort has focused on understanding the mechanisms of incorporation ("uptake") of drugs and their metabolites into hair. The reason for this focus is the importance many authors have placed on the role that such mechanistic understanding can play on the interpretation of test results. For example, such understanding may contribute to the answers provided for the following questions:

- Can contamination of the outside of the hair by drug vapors, solutions (including sweat from another person), or particulate resides - but without any related ingestion by the hair donor - lead to positive hair drug test findings?

- Is the extent of incorporation of drug and their metabolites different for men and women, among the races, among those with different hair color, or among individuals of different ages?

- What effects could hair treatments have on the findings from hair drug tests?

- How many doses are required - and of what magnitude must the doses be - before it can be expected that a hair drug test will have positive results at or above a certain "threshold" level?

- Is it reasonable to expect a dose-response relationship for drugs and related hair drug test results?

- Should we expect to find all drugs in hair, or only select classes?

It is likely that there will never be sufficiently complete answers to these questions in order to satisfy everyone, and some researchers have called for a moratorium to be placed on any application of hair drug testing until sufficient "consensus" has been reached. This appears to be an unreasonable expectation, especially when considering the dearth of information available to assist in the interpretation of findings from tests on many other biological matrices. It is more likely that specific legal, medical, and social science forums will make their own decisions about the weight to be given to hair drug test findings when used in their context.

Much of the reported work in hair drug testing has focused on the application of conventional toxicological methods of analysis (such as the immunoassay and GC/MS methods used in the analysis of urine, blood, and other biological matrices) for the detection and estimation of cocaine and its metabolites,[3] opiates such as heroin, morphine and codeine,[4,5] and phenylethylamine derivatives such as methamphetamine and other stimulants[6]. In the past few years, however, a much broader range of xenobiotics have been detected in hair. The diversity of the drugs which have now been identified in hair suggested that the full range of applications for hair tests is only beginning to come into focus. Significant progress has been made in opening up the range of tests for opioids, sedative/hypnotics, and antidepressants. There have also been experimental findings of several more unusual therapeutic drugs classes, such as cardiac regulators, antimicrobials, and cancer chemotherapeutic agents, in hair.[7]

PREDICTING SUCCESS IN DETECTING DRUGS IN HAIR

For those interested in a potential application of hair drug testing in a case, the question often arises "Can you detect this drug in hair?" If the drug is one for which no previous successful determinations in hair have been reported, this does not mean that the task is impossible. To the contrary, recent reports suggest that the full range of drugs for which hair tests are likely to be successful is only now beginning to be explored. When facing the question, however, it is important to make four presumptions about the drug, its incorporation, and its recovery from hair:

1. Drug is incorporated into hair with some relationship to circulating levels of drug. Although the general experiences of researchers in the field have demonstrated this relationship for many drugs, some controversy (as noted above) still exists on this point.

2. Once incorporated, the drug can be liberated from the hair through the use of chemical or physical means. The presumption is also made that this liberation can be accomplished in a reproducible manner, which is important to the development of tests which deliver adequate precision.

3. If the drug is incorporated into, and can be liberated from, the hair, the level recovered will be within the analytical capability of the method and instrumentation available. From a practical point of view, the limits of detection for most drugs in hair are ≥0.1 ng/mg.

4. Drug from the environment which was not ingested can be distinguished from drug which was ingested. Although this is normally attempted using rinsing and other methodological manipulation of the hair specimen, it should be emphasized that when interpreting drug findings in urine and blood, the burden is placed on the individual to describe realistic exposure conditions which might have led to an apparent "environmental false-positive" finding. Just as in these "urine and blood" cases, brief investigation into the work and life experiences of the tested subject often rules out the possibility of environmental contributions to a hair drug positive result.

These presumptions can be used to guide the collection of hair, and develop the expectations for uncovering information which will be useful in the medical or legal forum involved. If engaged in a discussion with a laboratory in such a case, it is important to understand the sensitivity of the analytical methods that will be employed, so that it can be determined before any testing is even performed whether or not the assay will provide adequate sensitivity, and whether or not there will be any way to confirm a positive finding from the first test attempted. Also, the case facts will help interpret the role that environmental factors might play, especially the nature of the suspected use, the normal dosage forms available, and the manner in which the drugs are used. Finally, conservative interpretations should be made, in deference to the relative youth of this field, and in light of the lack of full understanding of the exact mechanisms by which drugs are incorporated into, and liberated from, the hair.

REALISTIC EXPECTATIONS ON THE DETECTABILITY OF DRUGS IN HAIR

If structural comparison is made of all of the compounds that have been conclusively identified (eg, GC/MS) in hair, several trends become apparent:

1. If the compound is a nitrogenous base, bearing either a primary, secondary, or tertiary amine functionality, it is reasonable to expect that the drug can be detected in hair.

2. The presence of any of the following chemical functionalities in the structure of the nitrogenous base does not appear to alter the likelihood of detecting the compound in hair:

phenyl	pyridinyl
ester	carbamoyl
halogen	piperidinyl
carbonyl	pyrrolidinyl
amide	hydroxyl
morpholine	methoxy
phenolic	ether
nitro	alkene

727

DRUG TESTING IN HAIR *(Continued)*

3. The presence of a strongly acidic moiety (eg, carboxylic acid) in the structure of the nitrogenous base does not appear to significantly alter the detectability of the drug. Some examples of such compounds include ofloxacin and temafloxcin, and benzoylecgonine. This might be affected by protein binding ("passivation") at the acidic functional group prior to incorporation into the hair.

4. There have been very few reports of the identification in hair of non-nitrogenous compounds which contain strongly acidic functional groups, and no reports of sulfur-containing compounds.

One interpretation of these observations is that the incorporation of drug into hair may well follow a cation exchange mechanism. This would suggest that drugs and their metabolites in the blood - at neutral pH - sense the acidic environment of the hair and through an active mechanism, cross into the hair and become bound there as cations to anionic or highly polar sites. However, this interpretation is but one possibility, and is based as much on empirical study of the functional groups of drug classes discovered in hair as it is on more basic research data available. Studies on the role of melanin, specific morphological features and many other factors are on-going. The future will, no doubt, continue to bring expanded insight to the application of drug testing in this unique toxicological matrix.

Recently, the state of Florida included the option of hair testing under its drug testing in the workplace guidelines, regardless of the controversial nature of this specimen. Hair testing laboratories wishing to participate must successfully identify drugs in three proficiency sets provided by the State of Florida, and one independent proficiency set, as well as pass a laboratory on-site inspection.

Footnotes

1. Razagui IB and Haswell SJ, "The Determination of Mercury and Selenium in Maternal and Neonatal Scalp Hair by Inductively Coupled Plasma-Mass Spectrometry," *J Anal Toxicol*, 1997, 21:149-53.
2. Goldblum RW, Goldbaum LR, and Piper WN, "Barbiturate Concentrations in the Skin and Hair of Guinea Pigs," *J Invest Dermatology*, 1954, 22:121-8.
3. Selavka CM and Rieders F, "The Determination of Cocaine in Hair: A Review," *Forensic Sci Int*, 1995, 70:155-64.
4. Cone EJ, Darwin WD, and Wang W-L, "The Occurrence of Cocaine, Heroin, and Metabolites in Hair of Drug Abusers," *Forensic Sci Int*, 1993, 63:55-68.
5. Wilkins DG, Haughey HM, Krueger GG, et al, "Disposition of Codeine in Female Human Hair After Multiple-Dose Administration," *J Anal Tox*, 1995, 19:492-8.
6. Nakahara Y, Takahashi K, Shimamine M, et al, "Hair Analysis for Drug Abuse: I. Determination of Methamphetamine and Amphetamine in Hair by Stable Isotope Dilution Gas Chromatography/ Mass Spectrometry Method," *J Forensic Sci*, 1991, 36(1):70-8.
7. Tracqui A, "Unusual Drugs in Hair," *Drug Testing in Hair*, Kintz P, ed, Boca Raton, FL: CRC Press, 1996, 191-210.

Selected Reference

Kikura R and Nakahara Y, "Hair Analysis for Drugs of Abuse: XVI. Disposition of Fenethylline and Its Metabolites Into Hair and Discrimination Between Fenethylline Use and Amphetamine Use by Hair Analysis," *J Anal Tox*, 1997, 27:291-6.

CHEMICAL SUBMISSIVE AGENTS

by Cheryl A. Kapustka, PharmD

Specialist in Poison Information,
Illinois Poison Center

INTRODUCTION

A chemical submissive agent, which also may be called a "Mickey Finn", a knockout drop, or a date rape drug, is a drug unknowingly given to a victim to facilitate rape or robbery. These agents generally produce drowsiness and amnesia soon after ingestion so many incidents are not reported because the victim cannot remember what happened. Thus, the prevalence of the problem is unknown. Today, the agents mentioned most often in the United States are flunitrazepam and gamma-hydroxybutyric acid, but there are other drugs with similar characteristics, such as scopolamine and chloral hydrate, that have been or could be used.

FLUNITRAZEPAM

Flunitrazepam (Rohypnol®) is a potent sedative that is marketed by Hoffmann-LaRoche, Inc in eighty countries to treat insomnia and to induce and maintain anesthesia. It belongs to the class of drugs called benzodiazepines, which also includes diazepam (Valium®). Although emphasis has been placed on the use of flunitrazepam in acquaintance rape, other benzodiazepines, especially those that have a fast onset and are potent such as triazolam (Halcion®), also can be used as chemical submissive agents. On the street, flunitrazepam usually costs $3-$5 per pill[1] and may be called "circles", the "forget me pill", "Mexican Valium", "R-2", "rib", "roaches", "la rocha", "roofenol", "roofies", "roofings", "rope", or other similar names. Flunitrazepam has never been legally available in the United States,[2] and it has been illegal to bring it into the country since March 1996[3]. Flunitrazepam usually enters the United States through Texas from Mexico or through Florida from Colombia.[4]

Flunitrazepam is available as a tablet and a solution for injection, but the injectable form is unlikely to be used illicitly because it is harder to obtain. There are three different strength tablets: 0.5 mg, 1 mg, and 2 mg. The 2 mg tablet has been taken off the market in all countries except Japan where it is used only in hospitals.[5]Hoffmann-LaRoche, Inc also recently changed the 1 mg tablet to a sage green, oval, scored tablet that has the imprint 526. This tablet has a coating, which slows dissolution in drinks, and contains a bright blue dye inside, which turns beer green if the tablet is broken.[5] Hoffmann-LaRoche, Inc has applied for regulatory approval for this new formulation in all of its markets but has received approval only in Argentina, Norway, Sweden, and the United Kingdom as of March 1998.[5] The other tablets are white, round, and scored, and the 1 mg and 2 mg tablets may have the imprints Roche 1 and Roche 2, respectively. These tablets quickly dissolve in alcohol without imparting a color or an odor,[4] but they are insoluble in water.[6]

Flunitrazepam causes drowsiness, dizziness, incoordination, and amnesia. The drowsiness begins about 20 minutes after ingestion, peaks in 1-2 hours,[6] and lasts 6-8 hours.[5]Because of these effects, flunitrazepam reportedly has been used to incapacitate victims before raping or robbing them. Flunitrazepam also has been used illicitly to enhance the effects of other central nervous system depressants such as alcohol or heroin, to relieve the symptoms of heroin withdrawal, and to moderate the effects of cocaine or crack.[3] In an overdose, flunitrazepam can cause a coma, inhibit breathing, and lower blood pressure. There is an antidote for flunitrazepam overdoses, flumazenil (Romazicon®), but it may result in seizures in

CHEMICAL SUBMISSIVE AGENTS *(Continued)*

certain patients. For this reason and because patients respond well to supportive care alone, flumazenil is usually unnecessary.

Routine drug screens for benzodiazepines usually will not detect flunitrazepam, but a laboratory test called gas chromatography with mass spectrometry can detect a 1 mg dose in a urine sample obtained 60-72 hours after ingestion.[5] Hoffmann-LaRoche, Inc is offering free urine testing for flunitrazepam and other drugs of abuse in cases of sexual assault through an independent laboratory which follows chain-of-custody procedures. Physicians, law enforcement personnel, and rape crisis center personnel can obtain more information about testing by calling 1-800-608-6540.

GAMMA-HYDROXYBUTYRIC ACID

Like flunitrazepam, gamma-hydroxybutyric acid (GHB) is a central nervous system depressant. It has a limited role in some countries as an anesthetic and has been studied as a treatment for narcolepsy and chemical dependence.[7] The Food and Drug Administration (FDA) has not approved it for marketing as a drug, but it may be used in approved research.[8] On the street, GHB may be called "cherry meth", "easy lay", "G", "G-riffick", "Georgia home boy", "grievous bodily harm" (GBH), "liquid E", "liquid ecstasy", "liquid G", "liquid X", "nature's Quaalude", "organic Quaalude", "salty water", "scoop", "soap", or "zonked". It has been ingested for its euphoric effects and its alleged stimulation of muscle growth, and there have been reports of its use to incapacitate women prior to sexual assault.[8]

Although GHB cannot be marketed as a drug in the United States, it was marketed as a dietary supplement under such names as Gamma-OH®, Somatomax PM®, and Somsanit® until 1990. At that time, the FDA declared that it is unsafe and banned its manufacture and sale.[8] Possession is not illegal under federal law,[9] but eleven states have classified GHB in their controlled substances acts as of February 1998. GHB is in schedule I in Georgia, Hawaii, Illinois, Louisiana, Nevada, and Rhode Island; schedule II in California and Florida; and schedule IV in Alaska, North Carolina, and Tennessee. In Texas, GHB has been classified in Penalty Group I.[8]

Since GHB became unavailable in health food stores, it has been made in illicit laboratories from gamma butyrol lactone, an industrial solvent that is available from scientific supply houses, and sodium hydroxide.[8,9] Gamma butyrol lactone has effects similar to GHB; thus, it also has the potential for abuse.[8] The relatively simple synthesis produces a liquid that is colorless and odorless with a slightly salty taste.[10] These characteristics make GHB difficult to detect if it is unknowingly added to a potential victim's drink.

Although GHB has been described as natural because it is a metabolite of the neurotransmitter gamma aminobutyric acid, its effects are dangerous. In addition to drowsiness, dizziness, weakness, and amnesia which have led to its use as a date rape drug, GHB can cause vomiting, tremors, seizures, and a coma, inhibit breathing, and slow the heart rate. The effects begin 15-30 minutes after ingestion[6] and usually last several hours[11] during which intensive care including mechanical ventilation may be necessary. GHB made in illicit laboratories is especially dangerous because its concentration and purity are unknown and because it may cause a severe chemical burn upon ingestion if it was made improperly.[9]

GHB can be detected in urine. However, most routine drug screens cannot detect it, and it is undetectable in samples obtained 12 or more hours after ingestion.[10] GHB can be detected by the drug screen offered by Hoffmann-LaRoche, Inc, which was described in the section on flunitrazepam.[5] The Drug Enforcement Administration (DEA) laboratories can analyze substances to determine whether they contain GHB.[6]

The DEA is trying to determine the magnitude of this problem. To assist the agency in this task, report abuse and overdose cases as well as information on illicit laboratories and trafficking to Christine Sannerud, PhD at 202-307-7192.

SCOPOLAMINE AND ATROPINE

Scopolamine belongs to the anticholinergic class of drugs and has many uses. In the United States, it is available as a patch to prevent motion sickness or treat vertigo, eye drops to treat certain conditions or dilate the pupils for examination, and a solution for injection to produce amnesia, decrease salivation, and decrease secretions in the respiratory tract before surgery. Scopolamine also is found in burundanga. Burundanga is the extract of *Datura arborea*, a small tree found in South America that is commonly called borrachero or borrachio. The amnesia and drowsiness produced by scopolamine have led to the reported administration of burundanga in thousands of rapes and robberies in Colombia over the past two decades.[12] Jimson weed, which is ingested to produce delirium, belongs to the same genus[6] and also could be used for involuntary intoxication.

In addition to amnesia and drowsiness, scopolamine can cause blurry vision; dry mouth; constipation; difficulty urinating; red, warm, dry skin; an increased heart rate; arrhythmias; delirium; seizures; or a coma. The symptoms usually begin 30-60 minutes after ingestion and last 4-6 hours.[13] There is an antidote, physostigmine (Antilirium®), but it is recommended only for severe signs such as arrhythmias, seizures, or a deep coma because there are risks associated with its use.

Atropine belongs to the same class of drugs as scopolamine and has similar effects. Atropine, however, causes less drowsiness and amnesia than scopolamine at therapeutic doses.[13] Atropine primarily is used to treat certain eye conditions or dilate the pupils for examination, to decrease salivation and secretions in the respiratory tract before surgery, and to treat arrhythmias in which the heart is beating too slowly. Unlike scopolamine, atropine is available as a tablet in the United States.

CHLORAL HYDRATE

Chloral hydrate, which is classified in schedule IV of the Federal Controlled Substances Act, is a sedative that was used routinely in the past but, generally, has been replaced by other drugs. Now it is used only occasionally for sedation prior to dental or diagnostic procedures and for short-term treatment of insomnia or anxiety. Although chloral hydrate is rarely mentioned today as a knockout drop, there are many reports of its use in the past.[14] Its sedative effect begins within 30 minutes of ingestion and lasts 4-8 hours.[13] In therapeutic doses, chloral hydrate often causes nausea and vomiting. In overdoses, it can cause a coma, low blood pressure, and heart arrhythmias and also inhibit breathing. Chloral hydrate poisoning has two distinguishing signs: the previously mentioned arrhythmias and a fruity odor on the breath.[6] There is not an antidote for chloral hydrate so signs and symptoms are treated as they occur.

Footnotes

1. Cloud J, "Is Your Kid on K?" *Time*, 20 Oct, 1997, 90-1.
2. Anglin D, Spears KL, and Hutson HR, "Flunitrazepam and Its Involvement in Date or Acquaintance Rape," *Acad Emerg Med*, 1997, 4:323-6.
3. Saum CA and Inciardi JA, "Rohypnol Misuse in the United States," *Subst Use Misuse*, 1997, 32:723-31.
4. Dillmann J, "Rohypnol - the Date Rape Drug," *EMS Professionals*, 1997, 15-6.
5. Safian G, Public Affairs, Hoffmann-LaRoche, Inc, Telephone Interview, 3 Mar, 1998.

CHEMICAL SUBMISSIVE AGENTS *(Continued)*

6.   Leikin JB and Paloucek FP, *Poisoning and Toxicology Compendium*, Hudson, OH: Lexi-Comp, Inc, 1998.
7.   Tunnicliff G, "Sites of Action of Gamma-Hydroxybutyrate (GHB) - A Neuroactive Drug With Abuse Potential," *J Toxicol Clin Toxicol*, 1997, 35:581-90.
8.   Sannerud C, Office of Diversion Control, Drug Enforcement Administration, Telephone Interview, 26 Mar, 1998.
9.   "Gamma-Hydroxybutyrate Use - New York and Texas, 1995-96," *MMWR Morb Mortal Wkly*, 1997, 46:281-3.
10. Dillmann J, "GHB - A Drug You Should Know," *Nursing 97*, Sept, 1997, 15-6.
11. "Gamma-Hydroxybutyrate: An Emerging Drug of Abuse," *DAWN Briefings*, Mar 1997, 1, 6.
12. Hollinger MA, "Beyond Rohypnol: Use of Gamma-Hydroxybutyrate and Burundanga in Rape," *Forensic Examiner*, Mar-Apr 1998, 25-7.
13. Lacy C, Armstrong LL, Ingrim NB, and Lance LL, *Drug Information Handbook*, 5th ed, Hudson, OH: Lexi-Comp, Inc, 1997.
14. DiPalma JR, ed, *Drill's Pharmacology in Medicine*, 4th ed, New York, NY: McGraw-Hill, 1971.

APPENDIX TABLE OF CONTENTS

ABBREVIATIONS & SYMBOLS COMMONLY USED IN MEDICAL ORDERS

Abbreviation	From	Meaning
μg		microgram
μmol		micromole
°C		degrees Celsius (Centigrade)
<		less than
>		greater than
≤		less than or equal to
≥		greater than or equal to
aa, aa	ana	of each
ABG		arterial blood gas
ac	ante cibum	before meals or food
ACE		angiotensin-converting enzyme
ACLS		adult cardiac life support
ad	ad	to, up to
a.d.	aurio dextra	right ear
ADH		antidiuretic hormone
ad lib	ad libitum	at pleasure
AED		antiepileptic drug
a.l.	aurio laeva	left ear
ALL		acute lymphoblastic leukemia
ALT		alanine aminotransferase (was SGPT)
AM	ante meridiem	morning
AML		acute myeloblastic leukemia
amp		ampul
amt		amount
ANA		antinuclear antibodies
ANC		absolute neutrophil count
ANL		acute nonlymphoblastic leukemia
aq	aqua	water
aq. dest.	aqua destillata	distilled water
APTT		activated partial thromboplastin time
a.s.	aurio sinister	left ear
ASA (class I-IV)		classification of surgical patients according to their baseline health (eg, healthy ASA I and II or increased severity of illness ASA III or IV)
ASAP		as soon as possible
AST		aspartate aminotransferase (was SGOT)
a.u.	aures utrae	each ear
A-V		atrial-ventricular
bid	bis in die	twice daily
bm		bowel movement
BMT		bone marrow transplant

Abbreviation	From	Meaning
bp		blood pressure
BSA		body surface area
BUN		blood urea nitrogen
$\underline{c}$	cong	a gallon
$\bar{c}$	cum	with
cal		calorie
cAMP		cyclic adenosine monophosphate
cap	capsula	capsule
CBC		complete blood count
cc		cubic centimeter
CHF		congestive heart failure
CI		cardiac index
CI_{cr}		creatinine clearance
cm		centimeter
CNS		central nervous system
comp	compositus	compound
cont		continue
COPD		chronic obstructive pulmonary disease
CSF		cerebral spinal fluid
CT		computed tomography
CVA		cerebral vascular accident
CVP		central venous pressure
d	dies	day
D_5W		dextrose 5% in water
$D_{5/0.45}$ NaCl		dextrose 5% in sodium chloride 0.45%
$D_{10}W$		dextrose 10% in water
d/c		discontinue
DIC		disseminated intravascular coagulation
dil	dilue	dilute
disp	dispensa	dispense
div	divide	divide
DNA		deoxyribonucleic acid
dtd	dentur tales doses	give of such a dose
DVT		deep vein thrombosis
EEG		electroencephalogram
EKG		electrocardiogram
elix, el	elixir	elixir
emp		as directed
ESR		erythrocyte sedimentation rate
E.T.		endotracheal
et	et	and
ex aq		in water
f, ft	fac, fiat, fiant	make, let be made
FDA		Food and Drug Administration
FEV_1		forced expiratory volume
FVC		forced vital capacity

ABBREVIATIONS & SYMBOLS COMMONLY USED IN MEDICAL ORDERS *(Continued)*

Abbreviation	From	Meaning
g	gramma	gram
G-6-PD		glucose-6-phosphate dehydrogenase
GA		gestational age
GABA		gamma-aminobutyric acid
GE		gastroesophageal
GI		gastrointestinal
gr	granum	grain
gtt	gutta	a drop
GU		genitourinary
h	hora	hour
HIV		human immunodeficiency virus
HPLC		high performance liquid chromatography
hs	hora somni	at bedtime
IBW		ideal body weight
ICP		intracranial pressure
IgG		immune globulin G
I.M.		intramuscular
INR		international normalized ratio
I.O.		intraosseous
I & O		input and output
IOP		intraocular pressure
I.T.		intrathecal
I.V.		intravenous
IVH		intraventricular hemorrhage
IVP		intravenous push
JRA		juvenile rheumatoid arthritis
kcal		kilocalorie
kg		kilogram
L		liter
LDH		lactate dehydrogenase
LE		lupus erythematosus
liq	liquor	a liquor, solution
LP		lumbar puncture
M.	misce	mix
MAO		monoamine oxidase
MAP		mean arterial pressure
mcg		microgram
m. dict	more dictor	as directed
mEq		milliequivalent
mg		milligram
MI		myocardial infarction
min		minute
mixt	mixtura	a mixture
mL		milliliter
mm		millimeter

Abbreviation	From	Meaning
mo.		month
mOsm		milliosmols
MRI		magnetic resonance image
ND		nasoduodenal
NF		National Formulary
ng		nanogram
NG		nasogastric
NMDA		n-methyl-d-aspartate
nmol		nanomole
no.	numerus	number
noc	nocturnal	in the night
non rep	non repetatur	do not repeat, no refills
NPO		nothing by mouth
NSAID		nonsteroidal anti-inflammatory drug
O, Oct	octarius	a pint
o.d.	oculus dexter	right eye
o.l.	oculus laevus	left eye
O.R.		operating room
o.s.	oculus sinister	left eye
OTC		over-the-counter (nonprescription)
o.u.	oculo uterque	each eye
PALS		pediatric advanced life support
pc, post cib	post cibos	after meals
PCA		postconceptional age
PCP		*Pneumocystis carinii* pneumonia
PCWP		pulmonary capillary wedge pressure
PDA		patent ductus arteriosus
per		through or by
PM	post meridiem	afternoon or evening
PNA		postnatal age
P.O.	per os	by mouth
P.R.	per rectum	rectally
prn	pro re nata	as needed
PSVT		paroxysmal supraventricular tachycardia
PT		prothrombin time
PTT		partial thromboplastin time
PUD		peptic ulcer disease
pulv	pulvis	a powder
PVC		premature ventricular contraction
q		every
qad	quoque alternis die	every other day
qd		every day
qh	quiaque hora	every hour
qid	quater in die	four times a day
qod		every other day
qs	quantum sufficiat	a sufficient quantity
qs ad		a sufficient quantity to make
qty		quantity

ABBREVIATIONS & SYMBOLS COMMONLY USED IN MEDICAL ORDERS (Continued)

Abbreviation	From	Meaning
qv	quam volueris	as much as you wish
Rx	recipe	take, a recipe
RAP		right atrial pressure
rep	repetatur	let it be repeated
$\bar{s}$	sine	without
S-A		sino-atrial
sa	secundum artem	according to art
sat	sataratus	saturated
S.C.		subcutaneous
S_{cr}		serum creatinine
SIADH		syndrome of inappropriate antidiuretic hormone
sig	signa	label, or let it be printed
S.L.		sublingual
SLE		systemic lupus erythematosus
sol	solutio	solution
solv		dissolve
$\overline{ss}$, ss	semis	one-half
sos	si opus sit	if there is need
stat	statim	at once, immediately
supp	suppositorium	suppository
SVR		systemic vascular resistance
SVT		supraventricular tachycardia
SWI		sterile water for injection
syr	syrupus	syrup
tab	tabella	tablet
tal		such
tid	ter in die	three times a day
tr, tinct	tincture	tincture
trit		triturate
tsp		teaspoonful
TT		thrombin time
u.d., ut dict	ut dictum	as directed
ung	unguentum	ointment
USAN		United States Adopted Names
USP		United States Pharmacopeia
UTI		urinary tract infection
V_d		volume of distribution
V_{dss}		volume of distribution at steady-state
v.o.		verbal order
w.a.		while awake
x3		3 times
x4		4 times
y		year

CBR* AGENTS, EFFECTS, AND TREATMENT SUMMARY

Type of Agent	Physical Characteristics	Symptoms in Man	Effects on Man	Rate of Action	Personnel Decontamination	Treatment
Biological Agents	Microscopic live organisms	Variable, depending on agent and resistance of victim	Lethal or incapacitating depending on agent	Delayed for days or longer	Wash with soap and water	Variable, specific if agent is known / Supportive
Blood Agents Hydrocyanic acid (AC) Cyanogen chloride (CK)	Colorless gas; Faint bitter almond odor (AC) Irritating odor (CK)	Increased respiration followed by dyspnea, nausea, vertigo, headache, convulsions, and coma	Inhibits cytochrome oxidase Incapacitates; lethal if high concentrations are inhaled	Rapid	None needed	Amyl nitrate ampuls/ Artificial respiration/ Sodium thiosulfate/ Sodium nitrite I.V.
Choking Agents Phosgene (CG)	Colorless gas; odor of corn, grass, or new mown hay	Coughing, choking, tightness in chest, nausea, and headache	Lethal Floods lungs, pulmonary edema	Immediate to 3 hours	None needed	Rest, oxygen, antibiotics
Incapacitating Agents BZ	Odorless Colorless Tasteless	Unpredictable, irrational behavior; may be accompanied by coughing, nausea, vomiting, and headache. Dilation of pupils	Temporarily incapacitates, mentally and physically Anticholinergic Psychotropic	Delayed	Wash with soap and water	Observation and physical restraint if indicated Physostigmine salicylate 2-3 mg I.M. q1-2h for duration of symptoms
Irritants Riot control agents CS, CN, CR, CA	Colorless to white vapor Pepperlike odor	Immediate lacrimation Coughing Skin irritation	Incapacitating Local irritant	Instantaneous	None needed	Removal to fresh air
Nerve Agents Tabun (GA) Sarin (GB) Soman (GD) VX	Colorless to light brown liquid Odorless to faint sweetish or fruity vapor Tasteless	Miosis, rhinorrhea, dimmed vision, salivation, nausea, abdominal cramping, increased bronchial secretions, dyspnea, pulmonary edema, headache, vertigo	Incapacitates; kills if high concentrations are inhaled or if contaminated skin is not decontaminated in time	Very rapid with inhalation Slow through the skin	None for aerosols or vapors Flush eyes with water Wash skin with soap and water or use skin pad from M-13 kit; M-5 kit for VX	Atropine I.M. or I.V. Artificial ventilation Oximes (2-PAM) as adjunct to atropine Benzodiazepines for seizure control

CBR* AGENTS, EFFECTS, AND TREATMENT SUMMARY
(Continued)

(continued)

Type of Agent	Physical Characteristics	Symptoms in Man	Effects on Man	Rate of Action	Personnel De- contamination	Treatment
Nuclear Burst	Bright intense flash of light Heat, wind, shock wave, Earth tremors	Temporary blindness Thermal burns Radiation burns Physical injuries	Blast destruction Radiation sickness	Immediate for blast Delayed for radiation	Wash with soap and water Shower Monitor	Immediate decontamination Treatment of physical injuries Antibiotics for radiation exposure
Vesicants Mustard (HD) Nitrogen Mustard (HN) Lewisite (L) Phosgene Oxime (CX)	Odor of garlic or horseradish (HD) None to slightly fishy odor (HN) Fruity or odor of geranium (L) Disagreeable (CX) Colorless to dark brown liquid Vapors are not usually visible	Lacrimation, eye pain, photophobia, cough, respiratory irritation, abdominal pain, nausea, vomiting, diarrhea; skin erythema and itching, headache	Generally, nonlethal Blisters skin, is destructive to upper respiratory tract; can cause temporary blindness. Some agents sting and form welts on skin, and others sear eyes.	Mustards have a delayed effect Arsenicals and phosgene oxime are rapid and intense	Remove contaminated clothing, wash skin with soap and water or use M-5 ointment or M-13 kit	Analgesics, sterile dressings, antibiotics, and treat for shock. For arsenicals, BAL in oil I.M. Fox CX, sodium bicarbonate dressings
Vomiting Agents Adamsite (DM)	Yellow or white to nonvisible gas Odor of burning fireworks	Pepperlike irritation of upper respiratory tract and eyes with lacrimation Uncontrolled sneezing and coughing and excessive salivation	Incapacitates Local irritant	Immediate	None needed	Supportive Chloroform inhalation for symptomatic relief Physical exercise shortens duration and speeds recovery Recovery spontaneous

*Chemical, bacteriologic, and radiologic

CONTROLLED SUBSTANCES – USES AND EFFECTS

Drugs	CSA Schedules	Trade or Other Names	Medical Uses
Narcotics			
Heroin	I	Diacetylmorphine, Horse, Smack	None in U.S; analgesic, antitussive
Morphine	II	Duramorph, MS-Contin, Roxanol, Oramorph SR	Analgesic
Codeine	II, III, V	Tylenol w/ codeine, Empirin w/ codeine, Robitussin A-C, Fiorinal w/ codeine, APAP w/ codeine	Analgesic, antitussive
Hydrocodone	II, III	Tussionex, Vicodin, Hycodan, Lortab, Lorcet	Analgesic, antitussive
Hydromorphone	II	Dilaudid	Analgesic
Oxycodone	II	Percodan, Percocet, Tylox, Roxicet, Roxicodone	Analgesic
Methadone and Levomethadyl Acetate Hydrochloride	I, II	Dolophine, Methadose, Levo-alpha-acetylmethadol, LAAM	Analgesic, treatment of dependence
Fentanyl and analogs	I, II	Innovar, Sublimaze, Alfenta, Sufenta, Duragesic	Analgesic, adjunct to anesthesia, anesthetic
Other narcotics	II, III, IV, V	Percodan, Percocet, Tylox, Opium, Darvon, Talwin[2], Buprenorphine, Meperidine (Pethidine), Demerol	Analgesic, antidiarrheal
Depressants			
Chloral hydrate	IV	Noctec	Hypnotic
Barbiturates	II, III, IV	Amytal, Fiorinal, Nembutal, Seconal, Tuinal, Phenobarbital, Pentobarbital	Anesthetic, anticonvulsant, sedative, hypnotic, veterinary euthanasia agent
Benzodiazepines	IV	Ativan, Dalmane, Diazepam, Librium, Xanax, Serax, Valium, Tranxene, Verstran, Versed, Halcion, Paxipam, Restoril	Antianxiety, sedative, anticonvulsant, hypnotic
Glutethimide	II	Doriden	Sedative, hypnotic
Other depressants	I, II, III, IV	Equanil, Miltown, Noludar, Placidyl, Valmid, Methaqualone	Antianxiety, sedative, hypnotic
Stimulants			
Cocaine[1]	II	Coke, Flake, Snow, Crack	Local anesthetic
Amphetamine/ methamphetamine	II	Biphetamine, Desoxyn, Dexedrine, Obetrol, Ice	Attention deficit disorder, narcolepsy, weight control
Methylphenidate	II	Ritalin	Attention deficit disorder, narcolepsy
Other stimulants	I, II, III, IV	Adipex, Didrex, Ionamin, Melfiat, Nistenal, Plegine, Captagon, Sanorex, Tenuate, Tepanil, Prelu-2, Preludin	Weight control

CONTROLLED SUBSTANCES – USES AND EFFECTS
(Continued)

Drugs	CSA Schedules	Trade or Other Names	Medical Uses
Cannabis			
Marijuana	I	Pot, Acapulco gold, Grass, Reefer, Sinsemilla, Thai sticks	None
Tetrahydrocannabinol	I, II	THC, Marinol	Antinauseant
Hashish and hashish oil	I	Hash, Hash oil	None
Hallucinogens			
LSD	I	Acid, Microdot	None
Mescaline and peyote	I	Mescal, Buttons, Cactus	None
Amphetamine variants	I	2,5-DMA, STP, MDA, MDMA, Ecstasy, DOM, DOB	None
Phencyclidine and analogs	I, II	PCE, PCPy, TCP, PCP, Hog, Loveboat, Angel dust	None
Other hallucinogens	I	Bufotenine, Ibogaine, DMT, DET, Psilocybin, Psilocyn	None
Anabolic Steroids			
Testosterone (Cypionate, Enanthate)	III	Depo-testosterone, Delatestryl	Hypogonadism
Nandrolone (Decanoate, Phenpropionate)	III	Nortestosterone, Durabolin, Deca-durabolin, Deca	Anemia, breast cancer
Oxymetholone	III	Anadrol-50	Anemia

From U.S. Department of Justice Drug Enforcement Administration, *Drugs of Abuse*, 1996 Edition, with permission.

[1] Designated a narcotic under the CSA.

[2] Not designated a narcotic under the CSA.

FEDERAL TRAFFICKING PENALTIES*

CSA	2nd Offense	1st Offense	Quantity	Drug	Quantity	1st Offense	2nd Offense
I and II	Not less than 10 years, not more than life. If death or serious injury, not less than 20 years or more than life. Fine of not more than $4 million individual, $10 million other than individual	Not less than 5 years, not more than 40 years. If death or serious injury, not less than 20 or more than life. Fine of not more than $2 million individual, $5 million other than individual	10-99 g pure of 100-999 g mixture	Methamphetamine	100 g or more pure or 1 kg or more mixture	Not less than 10 years, not more than life. If death or serious injury, not less than 20 or more than life. Fine of not more than $4 million individual, $10 million other than individual	Not less than 20 years, not more than life. If death or serious injury, not less than life. Fine of not more than $8 million individual, $20 million other than individual
			100-999 g mixture	Heroin	1 kg or more mixture		
			500-4999 g mixture	Cocaine	5 kg or more mixture		
			5-49 g mixture	Cocaine Base	50 g or more mixture		
			10-99 g pure or 100-999 g mixture	PCP	100 g or more pure or 1 kg or more mixture		
			1-9 g mixture	LSD	10 g or more mixture		
			40-399 g mixture	Fentanyl	400 g or more mixture		
			10-99 g mixture	Fentanyl Analogue	100 g or more mixture		

CSA	Drug	Quantity	1st Offense	2nd Offense
I and II	Others (law does not include marijuana, hashish, or hash oil)	Any	• Not more than 20 years • If death or serious injury, not less than 20 years, not more than life • Fine $1 million individual, $5 million not individual	• Not more than 30 years • If death or serious injury, life • Fine $2 million individual, $10 million not individual
III	All (includes anabolic steroids as of 2-27-91)	Any	• Not more than 5 years • Fine not more than $250,000 individual, $1 million not individual	• Not more than 10 years • Fine not more than $500,000 individual, $2 million not individual
IV	All	Any	• Not more than 3 years • Fine not more than $250,000 individual, $1 million not individual	• Not more than 6 years • Fine not more than $500,000 individual, $2 million not individual
V	All	Any	• Not more than 1 year • Fine not more than $100,000 individual, $250,000 not individual	• Not more than 2 years • Fine not more than $200,000 individual, $500,000 not individual

*Does not include marijuana, hashish, or hash oil

743

MEDICAL EXAMINER DATA

Number of Drug Abuse Deaths by Metropolitan Area: 1990-1993

Metropolitan Area	1990	1991	1992	1993	Percent Change in Numbers, 1992-1993
Atlanta, GA	110	113	120	145	20.8
Baltimore, MD	97	269	295	406	37.6
Buffalo, NY	23	20	32	10	-68.6
Chicago, IL	321	350	390	587	45.4
Cleveland, OH	60	56	84	95	13.1
Dallas, TX	100	143	194	360	85.6
Denver, CO	35	45	48	51	6.3
Detroit, MI	239	247	313	292	-6.7
Indianapolis, IN	13	23	11	29	163.6
Kansas City, KS/MO	40	60	27	35	29.6
Los Angeles, CA	985	924	1094	1083	-1.0
Miami, FL	86	151	141	178	26.2
Minneapolis, MN/WI	26	55	39	47	20.5
New Orleans, LA	63	63	61	62	1.6
New York, NY	1540	1439	1397	1465	4.9
Newark, NJ	117	194	178	187	5.1
Norfolk, VA	15	20	46	37	-19.6
Oklahoma City, OK	120	120	105	139	32.4
Philadelphia, NJ/PA	445	590	667	759	13.8
Phoenix, AZ	114	143	198	242	22.2
St Louis, IL/MO	163	195	210	236	12.4
San Antonio, TX	59	63	95	69	-27.4
San Diego, CA	245	211	270	251	-7.0
San Francisco, CA	273	268	398	340	-14.6
Seattle, WA	127	118	143	152	6.3
Washington, DC/MD/VA	223	232	212	248	17.0
Total DAWN system	5628	6099	6768	7485	10.6

Note: Excludes deaths in which AIDS was reported and deaths in which "drug unknown" was the only substance mentioned.

Adapted from Office of Applied Studies, SAMHSA, "Drug Abuse Warning Network," *Annual Medical Examiner Data 1993*, 1995, 57, with permission.

Drugs Mentioned Most Frequently by Emergency Departments and Medical Examiners According to Gender of Patient and Decedent

Emergency Department Data, 1994*

Rank	Drug Name	Number of Mentions	Percent of Total Episodes†
	Male Patients		
1	Alcohol-in-combination	97,327	36.96
2	Cocaine	96,125	36.50
3	Heroin/morphine‡	44,000	16.71
4	Marijuana/hashish	28,053	10.65
5	Methamphetamine/speed	11,394	4.33
6	Acetaminophen	9,956	3.78
7	Diazepam	6,007	2.28
8	Aspirin	5,726	2.17
9	Amphetamine	5,653	2.15
10	Alprazolam	5,394	2.05
11	Ibuprofen	5,188	1.97
12	Uspec benzodiazepine	4,817	1.83
13	PCP/PCP combinations	4,560	1.73
14	Lorazepam	4,291	1.63
15	Amitriptyline	4,143	1.57
	Female Patients		
1	Alcohol-in-combination	61,869	24.71
2	Cocaine	45,663	18.24
3	Acetaminophen	28,536	11.40
4	Heroin/morphine‡	19,515	7.80
5	Ibuprofen	13,786	5.51
6	Aspirin	13,434	5.37
7	Marijuana/hashish	11,762	4.70
8	Alprazolam	11,600	4.63
9	Clonazepam	8,442	3.37
10	Lorazepam	7,807	3.12
11	Diazepam	7,448	2.98
12	Amitriptyline	7,060	2.82
13	Methamphetamine/speed	6,210	2.48
14	Fluoxetine	6,165	2.46
15	Diphenhydramine	5,680	2.27

*Only the 15 most-mentioned drugs are listed.

†Percentages are based on weighted emergency department episode estimates of 263,334 male patients and 250,333 female patients.

‡Includes opiates not specified as to type.

MEDICAL EXAMINER DATA *(Continued)*

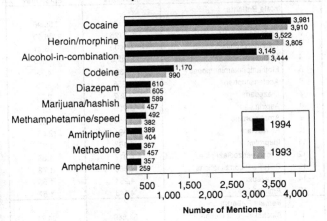

**Drugs Reported Most Frequently
By Medical Examiners Nationwide, 1993-94**

Drug	1994	1993
Cocaine	3,981	3,910
Heroin/morphine	3,522	3,805
Alcohol-in-combination	3,145	3,444
Codeine	1,170	990
Diazepam	610	605
Marijuana/hashish	589	457
Methamphetamine/speed	492	382
Amitriptyline	389	404
Methadone	367	457
Amphetamine	357	259

Number of Mentions

From "1994 DAWN ME Data Released," *DAWN Briefings*, June 1996, 2.

POISON INFORMATION CENTERS

Updated from "Poisoning Hotlines," *Emergency Medicine*, 1994, 26:96-102; and American Association of Poison Control Centers, *Vet Hum Toxicol*, 1994, 36:484-6.

*Denotes certified Regional Poison Control Centers by the American Association of Poison Control Centers (April, 1997)

Centers in each state are listed alphabetically by city.

ALABAMA

Regional Poison Control Center*
The Children's Hospital of Alabama
1600 7th Ave, S
Birmingham, AL 35233
(800) 292-6678 (Alabama only)
(205) 933-4050
(205) 939-9201
(205) 939-9202

The Alabama Poison Center*
408-A Paul Bryant Dr
Tuscaloosa, AL 35401
(800) 462-0800 (Alabama only)
(205) 345-0600

ALASKA

Anchorage Poison Control Center
Providence Hospital Pharmacy
3600 Providence Dr
PO Box 196604
Anchorage, AK 99516
(800) 478-3193 (Alaska only)
(907) 271-3193 (Anchorage only)
(907) 261-3633

ARIZONA

Samaritan Regional Poison Center*
Good Samaritan Regional Medical Center
1111 E McDowell Rd
Phoenix, AZ 85006
(602) 253-3334
(800) 362-0101 (Arizona only)

Arizona Poison and Drug Information Center*
University of Arizona
Arizona Health Sciences Center
1501 N Campbell Ave, Rm 1156
Tucson, AZ 85724
(800) 362-0101 (Arizona only)
(602) 626-6016

ARKANSAS

Arkansas Poison and Drug Information Center
University of Arkansas for Medical Sciences
College of Pharmacy
Slot 522 (internal mailing)
4301 W Markham St
Little Rock, AR 72205
(800) 376-4766 (MDs and hospitals; Arkansas only)

POISON INFORMATION CENTERS (Continued)

(501) 661-6161
(501) 666-5532 (MDs and hospitals)

CALIFORNIA

California Poison Control System – Fresno Division*
Valley Children's Hospital
3151 N Milbrook
Fresno, CA 93703
(209) 445-1222
(800) 876-4766 (Central California only)

Los Angeles County Regional Drug and Poison Information Center
1200 N State St, Rm 1107A and B
Los Angeles, CA 90033
(800) 777-6476 (Los Angeles, Santa Barbara, and Ventura counties only)
(213) 222-3212
(213) 222-8086 (MDs and hospitals)

Chevron Emergency Information Center
100 Chevron Way
Richmond, CA 94802
(800)231-0623
(510)231-0149

California Poison Control System – Sacramento Division*
2315 Stockton Blvd, Room 1024, house staff facility
Sacramento, CA 95817
(800) 876-4766 (Northern California only)
(916) 734-3692

California Poison Control System – San Diego Division*
UCSD Medical Center
200 West Arbor Dr
San Diego, CA 92103
(800) 876-4766
(619) 543-6000

California Poison Control System – San Francisco Division
San Francisco General Hospital
1001 Potrero Ave, Building 80, Rm 230
San Francisco, CA 94110
(800) 876-4766

Santa Clara Valley Regional Poison Center
Valley Health Center
750 S Bascom Ave, Suite 310
San Jose, CA 95128
(800) 662-9886 (CA only)
(408) 885-6000

COLORADO

Rocky Mountain Poison and Drug Center*
8802 E 9th Ave
Denver, CO 80220
(303) 629-1123
(800) 332-3073 (Colorado only)
(800) 446-6179 (Las Vegas, Idaho only)
(800) 525-5042 (Montana only)

CONNECTICUT

Connecticut Poison Control Center*
University of Connecticut Health Center
263 Farmington Ave
Farmington, CT 06030
(800) 343-2722 (Connecticut only)
(203) 679-3473 (Administration)
(203) 679-4346 (TDD)

DELAWARE

Interstate Centers
The Poison Control Center*
3600 Science Center, Suite 220
Philadelphia, PA
(800) 722-7112
(215) 386-2100

DISTRICT OF COLUMBIA

National Capital Poison Center*
George Washington University Medical Center
3201 New Mexico Ave, NW, Suite 310
Washington, DC 20016
(202) 625-3333
(202) 362-8563 (TTY)

FLORIDA

Florida Poison Information Center – Jacksonville*
University Medical Center
University of Florida Health Science Center-Jacksonville
655 W 8th St
Jacksonville, FL 32209
(800) 282-3171 (Florida only)
(305) 585-5253

Florida Poison Information Center – Miami*
University of Miami School of Medicine
Department of Pediatrics
PO Box 016960 (R-131)
Miami, FL 33101
(800) 282-3171
(305) 585-5250
(305) 585-5253

Tallahassee Memorial Regional Medical Center
1300 Miccosukee Road
Tallahassee, FL 32308
(904)681-5411

Florida Poison Information Center – Tampa*
Tampa General Hospital
PO Box 1289
Tampa, FL 33601
(800) 282-3171 (Florida only)
(813) 253-4444 (Tampa)

GEORGIA

Georgia Poison Center*
Grady Memorial Hospital
80 Butler St, SE

POISON INFORMATION CENTERS *(Continued)*

Box 26066
Atlanta, GA 30335
(800) 282-5846 (Georgia only)
(404) 616-9000

HAWAII

Hawaii Poison Center
Kapiolani Women's and Children's Medical Center
1319 Punahou St
Honolulu, HI 96826
(800) 362-3585 (outer islands of Hawaii only)
(800) 362-3586
(808) 941-4411

IDAHO

Idaho Poison Center
1055 North Curtis Road
Boise, ID 83706
(800) 860-0620 (Idaho only)

ILLINOIS

Illinois Poison Center
222 Riverside Plaza, Suite 1900
Chicago, IL 60606
(800) 942-5969 (Illinois only)
(312) 942-5969
(312) 942-7064

INDIANA

Indiana Poison Center*
Methodist Hospital of Indiana
I-65 and 21st Street
PO Box 1367
Indianapolis, IN 46206
(800) 382-9097 (Indiana only)
(317) 929-2323

Interstate Centers
Kentucky Regional Poison Center of Kosair Children's Hospital*
Louisville, KY
(502) 589-8222 (Southern Indiana only)

IOWA

Variety Club Poison and Drug Information Center
Iowa Methodist Medical Center
1200 Pleasant St
Des Moines, IA 50309
(800) 362-2327 (Iowa only)
(515) 241-6254

St Luke's Poison Center
St Luke's Regional Medical Center
2720 Stone Park Blvd
Sioux City, IA 51104
(800) 352-2222 (Western Iowa, Northeastern Nebraska, and Southern South Dakota only)
(712) 277-2222

Interstate Centers
McKennan Hospital Poison Center
PO Box 5045
Sioux Falls, SD
(800) 952-0123
(605) 322-3894

KANSAS

Mid-America Poison Control Center*
University of Kansas Medical Center
3901 Rainbow, Rm B-400
Kansas City, KS 66160
(800) 332-6633 (Kansas only)
(913) 588-6633

Stormont-Vail Regional Medical Center Emergency Department
1500 West 10th St
Topeka, KS 66604
(913) 354-6106

HCA Wesley Poison Control Center Medical Center
550 N Hillside Ave
Wichita, KS 67214
(316) 688-2277

KENTUCKY

Kentucky Regional Poison Center of Kosair Children's Hospital*
Medical Towers South, Ste 572
PO Box 35070
Louisville, KY 40232
(800) 722-5725 (Kentucky only)
(502) 629-7275
(502) 589-8222

LOUISIANA

Louisiana Drug and Poison Information Center*
Northeast Louisiana University School of Pharmacy
Sugar Hall
Monroe, LA 71209
(800) 256-9822 (Louisiana only)
(318) 362-5393

MAINE

Maine Poison Control Center
Maine Medical Center
22 Bramhall St
Portland, ME 04102
(800) 442-6305 (Maine only)
(207) 871-2950

MARYLAND

Maryland Poison Center*
University of Maryland School of Pharmacy
20 N Pine St
Baltimore, MD 21201
(800) 492-2414 (Maryland only)
(410) 706-7701

Interstate Centers
National Capital Poison Center*

POISON INFORMATION CENTERS *(Continued)*

3201 New Mexico Ave, NW, Suite 310
Washington, DC 20016
(202) 625-3333 (DC suburbs only)
(202) 362-8563 (TTY)

MASSACHUSETTS

Massachusetts Poison Control System*
300 Longwood Ave
Boston, MA 02115
(800) 682-9211 (Massachusetts only)
(617) 355-6609 (Administration)
(617) 232-2120 (Boston)

MICHIGAN

Children's Hospital of Michigan Poison Control Center*
4160 John R, Ste 425
Detroit, MI 48201
(313) 745-5711
(800) 764-7661 (Michigan only)

Blodgett Regional Poison Center*
Blodgett Memorial Medical Center
1840 Wealthy St, SE
Grand Rapids, MI 49506
(800) 764-7661 (Michigan only)
(800) 356-3232 (TTY)
(616) 774-7851 (Administration)

MINNESOTA

Hennepin Regional Poison Center*
Hennepin County Medical Center
701 Park Ave
Minneapolis, MN 55415
(612) 347-3141
(612) 337-7474 (TDD)
(612) 337-7387 (Petline)

Minnesota Regional Poison Center*
St Paul-Ramsey Medical Center
8100 34th Ave, S
Minneapolis, MN 55440-1309
(800) 222-1222 (Minnesota only)
(612) 221-2113

MISSISSIPPI

Mississippi Regional Poison Control Center
University Medical Center
2500 N State St
Jackson, MS 39216
(601) 354-7660

MISSOURI

Children's Mercy Hospital
2401 Gillham Rd
Kansas City, MO 64108
(816) 234-3430

Cardinal Glennon Children's Hospital Regional Poison Center*
1465 S Grand Blvd
St Louis, MO 63104
(800) 366-8888
(314) 772-5200

MONTANA

Interstate Centers
Rocky Mountain Poison and Drug Center*
8802 E 9th Ave
Denver, CO 80204
(303) 629-1123

NEBRASKA

The Poison Center*
Childrens Memorial Hospital
8301 Dodge St
Omaha, NE 68114
(800) 955-9119 (Nebraska and Wyoming only)
(402) 354-5555

NEVADA

Interstate Centers
Rocky Mountain Poison and Drug Center*
645 Bannock St
Denver, CO 80204
(800) 446-6179 (Las Vegas only)
(303) 629-1123

Poison Center
Humana Hospital Sunrise
3186 Maryland Pkwy
Las Vegas, NV 89109
(800) 446-6179 (Clark and Nye County only)

Poison Center
Washoe Medical Center
77 Pringle Way
Reno, NV 89520
(702) 328-4144
(702) 328-4100
(702) 328-4129

NEW HAMPSHIRE

New Hampshire Poison Information Center
Dartmouth Hitchcock Memorial Hospital
1 Medical Center Dr
Lebanon, NH 03756
(800) 562-8236 (New Hampshire only)
(603) 650-5000 (New Hampshire and bordering towns in Maine, Massachusetts, and Vermont only)

NEW JERSEY

New Jersey Poison Information and Education System*
Newark Beth Israel Medical Center
201 Lyons Ave
Newark, NJ 07112
(800) 764-7661
(201) 926-8008 (TTY)

POISON INFORMATION CENTERS *(Continued)*

Warren Hospital Poison Control Center
185 Roseberry St
Phillipsburg, NJ 08865
(800) 962-1253
(908) 859-6767

NEW MEXICO

New Mexico Poison and Drug Information Center*
University of New Mexico
Health Sciences Library, Rm 125
Albuquerque, NM 87131
(800) 432-6866 (New Mexico only)
(505) 272-2222

NEW YORK

Western New York Regional Poison Control Center
Children's Hospital of Buffalo
219 Bryant St
Buffalo, NY 14222
(716) 878-7654
(716) 878-7655

Long Island Regional Poison Control Center*
Winthrop-University Hospital
259 First St
Mineola, NY 11501
(516) 542-2323
(516) 542-6315
(516) 542-6316
(516) 542-6317

New York City Poison Control Center*
New York City Department of Health
455 First Ave, Rm 123
New York, NY 10016
(212) 340-4494
(212) POISONS (764-7667)
(212) 689-9014 (TDD)

Hudson Valley Regional Poison Center*
Phelps Memorial Hospital Center
701 N Broadway
Sleepy Hollow, NY 10591
(800) 336-6997 (New York only)
(914) 366-3030

Finger Lakes Poison Center*
University of Rochester Medical Center
Box 321
601 Elmwood Ave
Rochester, NY 14642
(800) 333-0542
(716) 275-3232
(716) 275-2700 (TTY)

Central New York Regional Poison Control Center*
SUNY Health Science Center at University Hospital
750 E Adams St

Syracuse, NY 13210
(800) 252-5655 (New York only)
(315) 476-4766

NORTH CAROLINA

Western NC Poison Control Center
St Joseph's Hospital
428 Biltmore Ave, Box 60
Asheville, NC 28801
(800) 542-4225 (North Carolina only)
(704) 255-4490

Carolinas Poison Center*
1012 S Kings Drive, Ste 206
PO Box 32861
Charlotte, NC 28232
(800) 84-TOXIN (848-6946)
(704) 355-4000

Triad Poison Center at Moses H Cone Memorial Hospital
1200 N Elm St
Greensboro, NC 27401
(800) 953-4001 (Alamance, Forsyth, Guilford, Rockingham, and Randolph counties only)
(910) 574-8105

NORTH DAKOTA

North Dakota Poison Information Center*
MeritCare Medical Center
720 Fourth St, N
Fargo, ND 58122
(800) 732-2200 (North Dakota, Minnesota only)
(701) 234-5575 (local)

OHIO

Akron Regional Poison Center
1 Perkins Square
Akron, OH 44308
(800) 362-9922 (Ohio only)
(330) 379-8562
(330) 379-8446 (TTY)

Cincinnati Drug & Poison Information Center and Regional Poison Control System*
PO Box 670144
Cincinnati, OH 45267-0144
(800) 872-5111 (Ohio only)
(513) 558-5111

Greater Cleveland Poison Control Center
11100 Euclid Ave
Cleveland, OH 44106
(216) 231-4455
(888) 234-4455

Central Ohio Poison Center*
700 Children's Dr
Columbus, OH 43205-2696
(800) 682-7625 (Ohio only)
(614) 461-2012

POISON INFORMATION CENTERS *(Continued)*

(614) 228-1323
(614) 228-2272 (TTY)

Firelands Community Hospital Poison Information Center
1101 Decatur St
Sandusky, OH 44870
(419) 626-7423

Poison and Drug Information Center of Northwest Ohio
Medical College of Ohio
3000 Arlington Ave
Toledo, OH 43614
(800) 589-3897 (Ohio only)
(419) 381-3897

Bethesda Poison Control Center
2951 Maple Ave
Zanesville, OH 43701
(614) 454-4000
(800) 682-7625

OKLAHOMA

Oklahoma Poison Control Center
Children's Hospital of Oklahoma
940 NE 13 St
Oklahoma City, OK 73104
(800) 764-7661 (Oklahoma only)
(405) 271-5454

OREGON

Oregon Poison Center*
Oregon Health Sciences University
3181 SW Sam Jackson Park Rd, CB550
Portland, OR 97201
(800) 452-7165 (Oregon only)
(503) 494-8968

PENNSYLVANIA

Regional Poison Prevention Education Center
Mercy Regional Health System
2500 7th Ave
Altoona, PA 16602
(814) 949-4197

Central Pennsylvania Poison Center*
Milton S Hershey Medical Center
University Dr, PO Box 850
Hershey, PA 17033
(800) 521-6110
(717) 531-6111

St Joseph Hospital and Health Care Center
250 College Ave
PO Box 3509
Lancaster, PA 17604
(717) 299-4546
(717) 291-8314
(717) 291-8425

The Poison Control Center*
3600 Sciences Center, Ste 220
Philadelphia, PA 19104-2641
(800) 722-7112
(215) 386-2100

Pittsburgh Poison Center*
Children's Hospital of Pittsburgh
1 Children's Pl
3705 Fifth Ave
Pittsburgh, PA 15213
(412) 681-6669

RHODE ISLAND

Rhode Island Poison Center
Rhode Island Hospital
593 Eddy St
Providence, RI 02903
(401) 444-5727

SOUTH CAROLINA

Palmetto Poison Center
University of South Carolina
College of Pharmacy
Columbia, SC 29208
(800) 922-1117 (South Carolina only)
(803) 777-1117 (Columbia area only)

SOUTH DAKOTA

McKennan Poison Control Center
McKennan Hospital
800 E 21 St
PO Box 5045
Sioux Falls, SD 57117
(800) 952-0123 (South Dakota only)
(800) 843-0505 (Iowa, Minnesota, North Dakota, and Nebraska only)
(605) 336-3894

TENNESSEE

Southern Poison Center, Inc
847 Monroe Ave, Suite 230
Memphis, TN 38163
(901) 528-6048 (East Arkansas)
(901) 448-6800
(800) 288-9999 (Tennessee)

Middle Tennessee Regional Poison Center*
The Center for Clinical Toxicology
1161 21st Ave S
501 Oxford House
Nashville, TN 37232-4632
(800) 288-9999
(615) 936-2034

TEXAS

Texas Panhandle Poison Center
PO Box 1110
15012 Coulter

757

POISON INFORMATION CENTERS *(Continued)*

Amarillo, TX 79175
(800) 764-7661 (Texas only)

North Texas Poison Center*
Parkland Hospital
5201 Harry Hines Blvd
PO Box 35926
Dallas, TX 75235
(800) 764-7661 (Northern Texas only)
(214) 590-5000

West Texas Poison Control Center
RE Thomason General Hospital
4815 Alameda Ave
El Paso, TX 79905
(800) 764-7661
(915) 521-7661

Southeast Texas Poison Center*
University of Texas Medical Branch
301 University Ave
Galveston, TX 77550-2780
(800) 764-7661
(409) 765-1420 (Galveston only)
(713) 654-1701 (Houston)

South Texas Poison Center
University of Texas Health Science Center at San Antonio
Forensic Science Building, Room 146
7703 Floyd Curl Drive
San Antonio, TX 78284
(800) 764-7661
(210) 764-7661

Central Texas Poison Center at Scott and White
2401 S 31st St
Temple, TX 76508
(800) 764-7661
(817) 724-7401

UTAH

Utah Poison Control Center*
410 Chipeta Way, Ste 230
Salt Lake City, UT 84108
(800) 456-7707 (Utah only)
(801) 581-2151

VERMONT

Vermont Poison Center
Medical Center Hospital of Vermont
111 Colchester Ave
Burlington, VT 05401
(802) 658-3456

VIRGINIA

Blue Ridge Poison Center*
University of Virginia Health Sciences Center
Blue Ridge Hospital
Box 67

Charlottesville, VA 22901
(800) 451-1428
(804) 924-5543

Virginia Poison Center
Virginia Commonwealth University
MCV Station, Box 980522
401 N 12th St
Richmond, VA 23298
(800) 552-6337 (Virginia only)
(804) 828-4780

Interstate Centers
National Capital Poison Center* (Northern VA only)
3201 New Mexico Ave, NW, Ste 310
Washington, DC 20016
(202) 625-3333
(202) 362-8563 (TTY)

WASHINGTON

Washington Poison Center*
155 NE 100th St, Ste 400
Seattle, WA 98125
(800) 732-6985
(800) 572-0638 (TDD)
(206) 526-2121
(206) 517-2394 (TDD)

WEST VIRGINIA

West Virginia Poison Center*
West Virginia University
Robert C. Byrd Health Sciences Center/Charleston Division
3110 MacCorkle Ave, SE
Charleston, WV 25304
(800) 642-3625 (West Virginia only)
(304) 348-4211

WISCONSIN

Regional Poison Control Center
University of Wisconsin Hospital and Clinics
600 Highland Ave
Madison, WI 53792
(800) 815-8855
(608) 262-3702 (also TDD)

Milwaukee Poison Center
Children's Hospital of Wisconsin
9000 W Wisconsin Ave
PO Box 1997
Milwaukee, WI 53201
(800) 815-8855
(414) 266-2222

WYOMING

Interstate Centers
The Poison Center*
8301 Dodge St
Omaha, NE 68114
(800) 955-9119 (Wyoming only)
(402) 390-5555 (Omaha)

POISON INFORMATION CENTERS (Continued)

FOREIGN

†Denotes American Association of Poison Control Centers:
Canadian Poison Center members.

CANADA

Alberta

PADIS (Poison and Drug Information Service)†
Foothills Provincial General Hospital
1403 29th St, NW
Calgary, Alberta T2N 2T9
(403) 670-1414

British Columbia

BC Drug and Poison Information Centre†
St Paul's Hospital
1081 Burrard St
Vancouver, BC V6Z 1Y6
(604) 682-5050

Manitoba

Poison Control Centre†
Children's Hospital
685 Bannatyne Ave
Winnipeg, Manitoba R3E OW1
(204) 787-2444

Nova Scotia

Izaak Walton Killan Children's Hospital
PO Box 3070
Halifax, Nova Scotia B3J 3G9
(800) 565-8161 (Prince Edward Island)
(902) 428-8161 (Nova Scotia)

Ontario

Provincial Regional Poison Control Centre
Children's Hospital
Eastern Ontario
401 Smyth Rd
Ottawa, Ontario K1H 8L1
(800) 267-1373
(613) 737-1100

Ontario Regional Poison Centre†
Hospital for Sick Children
555 University Ave
Toronto, Ontario M5G 1X8
(800) 268-9017
(416) 813-5900

Quebec

Quebec Poison Control Center†
Centre Hospitalier de l'Universite Laval
2705 Boulevard Laurier; J-782
Sainte-Foy Quebec
Canada GIV 4G2

(418) 656-8090
(418) 654-2731

COSTA RICA

Centro Nacional de Control de Intoxicaciones
Hospital Nacional de Ninos
"Dr Carlos Saenz Herrera"
Apartado 1654
San Jose, Costa Rica
(506) 23-10-28

MEXICO

Centro Panamerico de Ecologia Humana y
Salud — Toxicologia
Rancho Guadalupe
Metepec, Edo de Mexico
Apartado 37-473
06696 Mexico, DF
52-(91-721)
6-44-04
6-43-44

PUERTO RICO

University of Puerto Rico
College of Pharmacy
GPO Box 5067
San Juan, Puerto Rico
(809) 758-2525 ext 1516
(809) 763-0196

SLANG/STREET NAMES GLOSSARY

Slang	Meaning
1 on 1	Glutethimide and codeine
1-Way	LSD
10-dollar ready rock	Cocaine
10's	Amphetamine
100x	Amphetamine-like hallucinogen
1980 supergrass	Ketamine
2 on 2	Glutethimide and codeine
20th anniversary	LSD
21	LSD
3 on 3	Glutethimide and codeine
3's & 8's	Glutethimide and codeine
357 magnum	Caffeine
4's and doors	Glutethimide and codeine
45-minute psychosis	DMT
5-dollar ready rock	Cocaine
51	Cocaine and marijuana
68	Oil of peppermint
69-69	Cocaine; heroin
712	Methaqualone
714	Methaqualone
750	Ethchlorvynol
8-ball	Cocaine
930 Porsche turbo	Heroin
A boot	Under the influence of drugs
AB	Abscess at injection site
Abe	$5 worth of drugs
A Bean	Methamphetamine
Abe's cabe	$5 bill
Abolic	Veterinary steroid
A-bomb	Marijuana and heroin
Aborts	Absolut vodka and port mixed together
Acapulco gold	Marijuana
Acapulco red	Marijuana
Ace	Marijuana; PCP
Aceite	Heroin
Acid	LSD
Acid head	LSD user
AD	PCP
Adam	Methamphetamine
Afgano	Marijuana
African black	Marijuana
African bush	Marijuana
African tea	Cathinone
African woodbine	Marijuana cigarette

Slang	Meaning
Afterburner	Amphetamines
Agonies	Withdrawal symptoms
Ah-pen-yen	Abscess at injection site
Aimies	Amphetamine; amyl nitrate
AIP	Heroin from Afghanistan, Iran, & Pakistan
Air blast	Inhalants
Airhead	Marijuana user
Airplane	Marijuana
A.J.	Heroin
AK-47	Heroin
Alamout black hash	Hash, belladona (small amount)
Alice	LSD or mushrooms
Alice B. Toklas brownies	Recipe using LSD and marijuana
Alien sex fiend	Powdered PCP with heroin
All-American drug	Cocaine
Alley juice	Methanol
All lit up	Under the influence
All star	multiple drug user
Alpha-ET	Alpha-ethyltyptamine
Amarillas	Pentobarbital
Ames	Amyl nitrate
Amidone	Methadone
Ammo	Amobarbital
Amoeba	PCP
Amp	Marijuana soaked in formaldehyde; amphetamine
Amped & Queer	High on coke or crystal
Amped out	Fatigue after amphetamine use
Amping	Accelerated heartbeat
Amp joint	Marijuana cigarette laced with a narcotic
Amps	Glass ampuls of amphetamine
A.M.T.	Dimethyltryptamine
Amys	Amyl nitrate
Anadrol	Oral steroid
Anatrofin	Injectable steroid
Anavar	Oral steroid
Anfeta	Amphetamine
Angel	PCP
Angel dust	PCP
Angel hair	PCP
Angel mist	PCP
Angel poke	PCP
Angels in the sky	LSD
Angel tears	Liquid LSD
Angie	Cocaine
Angola	Marijuana
Animal	LSD

SLANG/STREET NAMES GLOSSARY (Continued)

Slang	Meaning
Animal trank	PCP
Animal tranquilizer	PCP
Antifreeze	Heroin
Antilog	Peyote
Anything going on?	Do you have drugs for sell?
Apache	Heroin; fentanyl
Apple jacks	Crack
Apples	Marijuana
Arabian tea	Cathinone
Aries	Heroin
Aroma of men	Isobutyl nitrite
Artillery	Equipment for injecting drugs
A's	Amphetamine
Ashes	Marijuana
Asthmador	*Datura stramonium*
Ate up	Someone that's always wasted
Atom bomb	Marijuana and heroin
Atshitshi	Marijuana
Aunt Hazel	Heroin
Aunt Mary	Marijuana
Aunt Nora	Cocaine
Aunti	Opium
Aunti Em, Aunti Emma	Opium
Aurora borealis	PCP
Azucar	LSD
B	PCP
B-40	Cigar laced with marijuana dipped in malt liquor
Babe	Detoxification drug
Baby	Marijuana
Baby bhang	Marijuana
Baby habit	Occasional use of drugs
Babysit	Guide someone through their first drug experience
Baby slits	Methamphetamine
Baby T	Crack
Bacha	Marijuana
Bachica	Marijuana
Backbreakers	LSD and strychnine
Back door	Residue left in a pipe
Backjack	Injecting opium
Back to back	Smoking crack after injecting heroin or heroin used after smoking crack
Backtrack	allow blood to flow back into a needle during injection
Backup	Prepare vein for injection
Backwards	Depressant

Slang	Meaning
Bad	Crack
Bad bundle	Inferior quality heroin
Bad go	Bad reaction to a drug
Bad seed	Heroin; marijuana; peyote
Bad trip	Bad acid trip
Bag	Container for drugs
Bag boy	Someone who sells dope for someone else
Bag bride	Crack-addicted prostitute
Bagging	Using inhalant
Bag man	Person who transports drug money
Bale	Marijuana
Ball	Crack
Baller	Person who sells a variety of drugs
Balling	Vaginally implanted cocaine
Balloon	Heroin supplier
Ballot	Heroin
Bam	Depressant, amphetamine
Bamate	Meprobamate
Bambalacha	Marijuana
Bambita	Methamphetamine
Bambs	Depressant
Bam D	Preludin® and Dilaudid®
Bammer	Term given to weak marijuana
Bammies	Marijuana
Bammo	Meprobamate
Bams	Pure amphetamine
Banana with cheese	Marijuana and cocaine free-base cigarette
Bananas	Talwin NX® and Pyribenzamine®
Ban-apple gas	N-butyl nitrite
Bang	Isobutyl nitrite; marijuana
Bank bandit pills	Barbiturate
Bar	Marijuana
Barb	Depressant
Barbara Jean	Marijuana
Barbies	Depressants
Barbs	Barbiturate; phenobarbital; cocaine
Barrels	LSD
Bart Simpsons	LSD
Base	Freebase cocaine; crack
Baseball	Freebase cocaine
Base crazies	Searching on hands and knees for crack
Base head	Person who bases
Basehouse	Place for smoking freebase cocaine or crack
Base pipe	Pipe for smoking freebase cocaine or crack
Bash	Marijuana
Basuco	Cocaine

SLANG/STREET NAMES GLOSSARY *(Continued)*

Slang	Meaning
Bat	Marijuana pipe disguised as a cigarette
Bathtub crank	Homemade speed; propylhexedrine
Bathtub crystal	Propylhexedrine
Bathtub speed	Methcathinone; propylhexedrine
Batt	I.V. needle
Battery acid	LSD
Batu	Smokable methamphetamine
Bazooka	Cocaine; crack; marijuana
Bazooka paste	Marijuana and procaine
Bazulco	Cocaine
B-bombs	Benzedrine® inhalers
BC Budd	High grade marijuana from British Columbia
Beamer	Crack user
Beam-me-up	Freebase cocaine
Beam me up, Scottie	Crack dipped in PCP
Bean	Benzedrine® inhalers; Doriden® and Valium® with codeine cough syrup
Beaners	Drugys
Beans	Amphetamines; mescaline
Beast	LSD
Beat artist	Person selling bogus drugs
Beat vials	Vials containing sham crack to cheat buyers
Beauties	Amphetamines
Beautiful boulders	Crack
Bebe	Crack
Bedbugs	Fellow addicts
Beemer	Crack
Bees	Marijuana
Behind the scale	To weigh and sell cocaine
Beiging	To alter cocaine with chemicals to make it appear purer
Belladonna	PCP
Belt	Effect of a drug
Belushi	Cocaine and heroin
Belyando spruce	Marijuana
Bender	Drug party
Bennie	Amphetamine
Benz	Benzedrine®
Berkley blood	LSD
Berkley boo	Marijuana
Bernice	Cocaine
Bernies	Cocaine
Bernie's flakes	Cocaine
Bernie's gold dust	Cocaine
Bhang	Marijuana

Slang	Meaning
Big 8	1/8 kilogram of crack
Big Bag	Heroin
Big bloke	Cocaine
Big C	Cocaine
Big chief	Peyote
Big D	LSD
Big flake	Cocaine
Big H	Heroin
Big Harry	Heroin
Big man	Drug supplier
Big O	Opium
Big rush	Cocaine
Big T	Talwin® and Pyribenzamine®
Bill Blass	Cocaine
Billie hoke	Cocaine
Bindle	Heroin
Bing	Amount or enough of a drug for one injection
Binger	Bong hit
Bingers	Crack addicts
Bingo	To inject a drug
Bings	Crack
Binky	Marijuana cigarette
Bioski	Gamma hydroxybutyrate
Birdie powder	Heroin; cocaine
Birds	Marijuana
Biscuit	50 rocks of crack
Bite one's lips	To smoke marijuana
Bitter	Paregoric
Biz	Bag or portion of drugs
BJs	Crack
Black	Opium; marijuana
Black acid	LSD; LSD and PCP
Black afghan	Hashish
Black and green capsules	Amitriptyline and salicylamide
Black and red capsules	Caffeine
Black and white	Amphetamine
Black bart	Marijuana
Black beauties	Amphetamines
Black birds	Amphetamines
Black bombers	Amphetamines
Black button	Dried button of peyote
Black capsules	Amphetamines
Black dex	Dextroamphetamine
Black doves	LSD
Black dust	PCP
Black ganga	Marijuana resin

SLANG/STREET NAMES GLOSSARY *(Continued)*

Slang	Meaning
Black glass	Heroin
Black gold	High potency marijuana
Black gum	Heroin
Black gungi	Marijuana from India
Black gunion	Marijuana
Black hash	Marijuana and opium
Black heroin	Heroin and molasses
Black horses	Heroin
Black Jack	Paregoric
Black Maria	High potency marijuana
Black mo/black moat	Highly potent marijuana
Black mollies	Amphetamines
Black mote	Marijuana
Black pearl	Diazepam
Black pills	Opium
Black powder	Black hash ground into powder
Black rock	Crack
Black Russian	Marijuana with opium
Blacks	Amphetamine
Black star	LSD
Black stone	Bufotenin
Black stuff	Opium
Black sunshine	LSD
Black tabs	LSD
Black tar	Heroin
Black whack	PCP
Black widow	Biphetamine®
Blake	Cocaine
Blanco	Heroin
Blank	Low grade heroin
Blanket	Marijuana cigarette
Blanks	Low quality drugs
Blast	To smoke marijuana or crack
Blast a joint	To smoke marijuana
Blast a roach	To smoke marijuana
Blast a stick	To smoke marijuana
Blasted	Under the influence
Blind squid	Ketamine, belladonna, LSD
Blinky	Cocaine
Blitzed	Under the influence
Blizzard	White cloud formed from smoking cocaine in a pipe
Block	Marijuana
Block busters	Barbiturate
Blonde	Marijuana
Blotter	LSD; cocaine

Slang	Meaning
Blotter acid	LSD
Blotter cube	LSD
Blow	Heroin; cocaine
Blow a fix	Wasted injection caused by missing a vein
Blow a shot	Wasted injection caused by missing a vein
Blow a stick	To smoke marijuana
Blow blue	To inhale cocaine
Blowcaine	Crack diluted with cocaine
Blow coke	To inhale cocaine
Blowing smoke	Marijuana
Blow one's roof	To smoke marijuana
Blowout	Crack
Blow smoke	To inhale cocaine
Blow the vein	Missing the vein when injecting a drug
Blue	Depressant; crack
Blue acid	LSD
Blue angels	Amobarbital
Blue bands	Carbital®
Blue barrels	LSD
Blue Berkley	LSD
Bluebird	Heroin and cocaine; depressant
Blue bombers	Diazepam
Blue boys	Diazepam; amphetamines
Blue bullets	Amobarbital
Blue caps	Mescaline
Blue chairs	LSD
Blue cheer	LSD
Blue clouds	Amobarbital
Blue cross	Pyrilamine maleate
Blue de hue	Marijuana from Vietnam
Blue devils	Amobarbital; depressants
Blue diamonds	Heroin
Blue dolls	Amobarbital
Blue dots	LSD
Blue dragon	LSD
Blue egg	Caffeine
Blue fly	LSD
Blue heaven	Isopropyl alcohol; LSD
Blue heavens	Depressant
Blue madman	PCP
Blue Magoo's	Diazepam
Blue microdots	LSD
Blue mist	LSD
Blue moon	LSD
Blue morphine	Numorphan®
Blue octopus	LSD

SLANG/STREET NAMES GLOSSARY (Continued)

Slang	Meaning
Blues	Amobarbital; diazepam
Blue sage	Marijuana
Blue sky blonde	High potency marijuana from Columbia
Blue speckled meth	Obetrol®
Blue star	LSD
Blue tips	Depressants
Blue velvet	Paregoric and tripelennamine or pyribenzamine
Blunted out	Smoked many "blunts" of marijuana
Blunts	Marijuana in cigar casings
Blue vials	LSD
Blunt	Marijuana and cocaine in a cigar
Boat	PCP
Bob	Marijuana cigarette
Bo-bo	Marijuana; crack
Bobo bush	Marijuana
Body packer	Someone who ingests crack or cocaine to transport it
Body stuffer	Someone who ingests crack vials to avoid prosecution
Bogart a joint	To salivate on a marijuana cigarette; refuse to share
Bohd	Marijuana; PCP
Bolasterone	Injectable steroid
Bolivian marching powder	Cocaine
Bolivian rock	Cocaine
Bolo	Crack
Bolt	Isobutyl nitrite
Bomb	Heroin; crack
Bomber	Marijuana cigarette
Bombido	Injectable amphetamine; heroin; depressant
Bombita	Amphetamine; heroin
Bombs away	Heroin
Bomb squad	Group selling crack
Bone	Marijuana
Bonecrusher	Crack
Bones	Crack
Bong	Pipe used to smoke marijuana
Bonita	Heroin
Boo	Marijuana
Booger	Cocaine
Boogered up	High on cocaine (in the Florida Keys)
Boom	Marijuana
Boomers	Psilocybin/psilocin
Boost	To inject a drug; to steal
Boost and shoot	Steal to support a habit

Slang	Meaning
Booster	To inhale cocaine
Boot	To inject a drug
Booted	Under the influence of drugs
Boot the gong	To smoke marijuana
Booty juice	MDMA dissolved in liquid
Boppers	Amyl nitrite
Botray	Crack
Bottles	Crack vials; amphetamine
Boubou	Crack
Boulder	crack; $20 worth of crack
Boulya	Crack
Bouncing powder	Cocaine
Bowl	Between 1/32 and 1/16 ounce of marijuana
Boxed	In jail
Boy	Heroin
Bozo	Heroin
Brain ticklers	Amphetamines
Breakdowns	$40 crack rock sold for $20
Breakfast of Champions	Crack
Break night	Staying up all night until daybreak
Brewery	Place where drugs are made
Brick	1 kilogram of marijuana; crack
Brick gum	Heroin
Bridge up, bring up	Prepare a vein for injection
Britton	Peyote
Broccoli	Marijuana
Broker	Go-between in a drug deal
Brome; bromage	Dextromethorphan hydrobromide
Brown	Heroin; marijuana
Brown bombers	LSD
Brown crystal	Heroin
Brown dots	LSD
Brownies	Amphetamine
Brown rhine	Heroin
Brown sugar	Heroin
Browns	Amphetamine
Bubble gum	Cocaine; crack
Bud	Marijuana
Buda	Marijuana joint filled with crack
Budda	Marijuana
Buffer	Crack smoker; woman who exchanges oral sex for crack
Buger sugar	Powdered cocaine
Bugged	Covered with sores/abscesses from repeated use of unsterile needles
Bull	Narcotics agent or police officer
Bullet	Isobutyl nitrite

SLANG/STREET NAMES GLOSSARY (Continued)

Slang	Meaning
Bullet bolt	Inhalant
Bullia capital	Crack
Bullion	Crack
Bullyon	Marijuana
Bumblebees	Amphetamine
Bummer trip	Unsettling and threatening experience from PCP intoxication
Bump	Crack; fake crack; boost a high; small dose of crystal meth
Bundle	Heroin
Bunk	Fake cocaine
Bunk weed	Poor quality marijuana
Burese	Cocaine
Burnie	Marijuana
Burning logs	Smoking marijuana cigarettes
Burn one	To smoke marijuana
Burn the main line	To inject a drug
Burned	Purchased fake drugs
Burned out	Collapse of veins from repeated injections; permanent impairment from drug abuse
Burn out	Heavy abuser of drugs
Burnt	Smoked too much marijuana
Bush	Cocaine; marijuana
Businessman's LSD	Dimethyltryptamine
Businessman's trip	Dimethyltryptamine
Businessman's special	Dimethyltryptamine
Busted	Arrested
Busters	Depressants
Busy bee	PCP
Butt naked	PCP
Butter	Marijuana; crack
Butter flower	Marijuana
Buttons	Peyote; Mescaline
Butu	Heroin
Buzz	To feel the effects or to be under the influence of drugs or alcohol
Buzz bomb	Nitrous oxide
C	Cocaine
C & H	Cocaine and heroin
C & M	Cocaine and morphine
Caballo	Heroin
Cabello	Cocaine
Cabo	Marijuana
Caca	Heroin
Cacti joint	A joint of dried and ground-up peyote
Cactus	Peyote; Mescaline

Slang	Meaning
Cactus buttons	Mescaline
Cactus head	Mescaline
Cad/cadillac	1 ounce
Cadillac	PCP
Cadillac express	Methcathinone
Cadillac of drugs	Cocaine
Cafe	Marijuana
Cakes	Round discs of crack
Caine	Cocaine; crack
Cakes and syrup	Glutethimide and codeine
California cornflakes	Cocaine
California glass	Methamphetamine
California sunshine	LSD
California white cross	Methamphetamine
Cambodian red; Cam red	Marijuana from Cambodia
Came	Cocaine
Cam trip	To smoke high potency Cambodian marijuana
Can	PCP; marijuana
Canadian black	Marijuana
Canamo	Marijuana
Canappa	Marijuana
Canary	Phenobarbital
Cancelled stick	Marijuana
Candy	Tuinal® and Seconal™
Candy C	Cocaine
Candy flip	1 hit XTC per 3 hit(s) LSD
Cane	Cocaine
Cannabinol	PCP
Cannabis indica	Very strong marijuana that causes hallucinations
Cannabis tea	Marijuana
Canned sativa	Marijuana
Canned stuff	Opium
Cannon	Large marijuana cigarette
Canoe	Marijuana cigarette that resembles a canoe or gets a hole in the side
Cap	Crack; LSD
Capital H	Heroin
Capricorn tabs	Caffeine
Caps	Crack; heroin; psilocybin/psilocin
Cap up	To make capsules out of bulk form drugs
Carburetor	Crack stem attachment
Carga	Heroin
Carmabis	Marijuana
Carne	Heroin
Carnie	Cocaine
Carpet patrol	Crack smokers searching the floor for crack
Carrie	Cocaine

SLANG/STREET NAMES GLOSSARY *(Continued)*

Slang	Meaning
Carrie Nation	Cocaine
Cartucho	Package of marijuana cigarettes
Cartwheels	Amphetamine
Cashed	Bowl is empty/finished
Casper the Ghost	Crack
Cat	Methcathinone
Catnip	Marijuana cigarette
Cat valium	Ketamine
Caviar	Crack
Cavite all star	Marijuana
CB	Glutethimide
CC-duct	Cocaine
CD	Glutethimide
C-dust	Cocaine
Cecil	Cocaine
Centurion	Benzodiazepine
Cereal	Marijuana smoked in a bowl
Cess	Marijuana
C-game	Cocaine
Cha cha	Cocaine
Chafa	Marijuana
Chalk	Methamphetamine; amphetamine
Chalked up	Under the influence of cocaine
Chalking	To chemically alter the color of cocaine to make it look white
Chamber	Marijuana pipe
Champagne of drugs	Cocaine
Chandoo/chandu	Opium
Channel	Vein into which a drug is injected
Channel swimmer	Someone who injects heroin
Charas	Marijuana
Charge	Marijuana
Charged up	Under the influence
Charley	Heroin
Charlie	Cocaine
Chase	To smoke cocaine or marijuana
Chaser	Compulsive crack user
Chasing the dragon	Heroin and crack
Chasing the tiger	To smoke heroin
Chaze	To christen a new bowl or pipe
Cheap basing	Crack
Check	Personal supply of drugs
Checkboard	LSD
Checkmate	Heroin
Cheeba-cheeba	Marijuana soaked in formaldehyde

Slang	Meaning
Cheeo	Marijuana
Chemical	Crack
Cherry meth	Gamma hydroxybutyric acid
Chestbonz	The one who takes the biggest bong hit
Cheva	Heroin
Chewies	Crack; blunt filled with powdered cocaine
Chiba-chiba	Marijuana
Chicago black	Marijuana
Chicago green	Marijuana and opium
Chicarra	Marijuana and tobacco
Chicken powder	Amphetamines
Chicken scratch	Searching on hands and knees for crack
Chicle	Cocaine; heroin
Chiclosa	Heroin
Chief	LSD; mescaline
Chieva	Heroin
Chillie willies	Snorting vodka or gin out of a bottle cap
Chillun	Pipe used to smoke hashish
China	Opium
China cat	Heroin
China girl	Fentanyl
China town	Fentanyl
China white	Fentanyl; heroin
Chinese blowing	Heroin
Chinese dragons	LSD
Chinese eyed	Temporary slanting of the eyes from the influence of marijuana
Chinese molasses	Opium
Chinese red	Heroin
Chinese tobacco	Opium
Chinesing	Heroin
Chip; chippy	Heroin
Chipper	Hispanic occasional user
Chippie	Marijuana
Chipping	Occasional drug use
Chippy	Cocaine
Chira	Marijuana
Chiva	Heroin
Chocolate	Heroin; opium
Chocolate chips	LSD
Chocolate ecstasy	Crack made brown by adding chocolate milk powder during processing
Chocolate rock	Heroin and cocaine
Chocolate rocket	Crack made brown by adding chocolate milk powder during processing
Chocolate thi	Marijuana
Choker	Powerful hit of crack cocaine

SLANG/STREET NAMES GLOSSARY *(Continued)*

Slang	Meaning
Chokers	Heroin and tobacco
Cholly	Cocaine
Chorals	Depressants
Chris	Methamphetamine
Christina	Amphetamine
Christine	Crystal methamphetamine
Christmas rolls	Depressants
Christmas tree	Amphetamines
Chronic	Marijuana; marijuana mixed with crack
Church	LSD paper with a cross on it
Chucks	Hunger following withdrawal from heroin
Churro	Marijuana
Churus	Marijuana
Cibas	Glutethimide
Cibas and codeine	Glutethimide and codeine
Cid	LSD
Cigarette paper	Packet of heroin
Cigarrode cristal	PCP
Citexal	Methaqualone
Citrol	High potency marijuana from Nepal
CJ	PCP
C joint	Place where cocaine is sold
Clarity	MDMA
Clear and blues	Caffeine, ephedrine, and phenylpropanolamine
Clear and green	Methapyrilene
Clear and pink	Diphenhydramine
Clear and yellow	Caffeine and phenylpropanolamine
Clear lights	LSD
Clear up	TO stop using drugs
Clicker	Crack and PCP
Clickers	Marijuana, PCP, and formaldehyde
Clicks	Marijuana, PCP, and formaldehyde
Clickums	Marijuana and PCP
Cliffhanger	PCP
Climax	Isobutyl nitrite; crack; heroin
Climb	Marijuana cigarette
Clips	Rows of vials heat-sealed together
Clocking paper	Profits from selling drugs
Closet baser	Person who uses crack but does not want it to be known
Cloud	Large hit from an ice pipe
Cloud 9	Ephedra
Cloud nine	Crack
Cluck	Crack smoker
Coast	Methylphenidate hydrochloride

Slang	Meaning
Coasting	Under the influence
Coast to coast	Amphetamines
Cobra	Heroin
Coca	Cocaine
Coca Cola®	Cocaine
Cocaine blues	Depression after extended cocaine use
Cochornis	Marijuana
Cocktail	Marijuana
Cocoa	Heroin
Cocoa leaf	Procaine and caffeine
Cocoa puff	To smoke cocaine and marijuana
Cocoa snow	Benzocaine, procaine, and caffeine
Coconuts	Cocaine
Coco rocks	Dark brown crack made by adding chocolate pudding during production
Coco snow	Benzocaine used as cutting agent for crack
Cod cock	Cocaine mixed with other medications
Coffee	LSD
Coffin	Tobacco
Coffin nails	Tobacco
Cohete	Heroin
Cohobe	DMT in powdered seeds
Coke	Cocaine
Coke bar	Bar where cocaine is openly used
Cokomo	Cocaine
Cola	Glue; cocaine
Cold turkey	Sudden withdrawal from drugs
Coli	Marijuana
Coliflor tostao	Marijuana
Colombian	Marijuana
Colombian sinsemilla	Marijuana
Colonial spirit	Methanol
Colorado	Cocaine
Colorado cocktail	Marijuana
Colombian	Marijuana
Colombian spirit	Methanol
Columbo	PCP
Columbus	Marijuana
Columbus black	Marijuana
Comeback	Cocaine
Come home	End a "trip" from LSD
Conductor	LSD
Coney only	Heroin and cocaine
Connect	Purchase drugs; supplier of illegal drugs
Contact lens	LSD
Cook	Mix heroin with water; heating heroin to prepare it for injection

SLANG/STREET NAMES GLOSSARY (Continued)

Slang	Meaning
Cook down	The liquefying process of heroin in order to inhale it
Cooker	To inject a drug
Cookies	Crack
Cool	Someone who uses drugs
Cooler	Cigarette laced with a drug
Coolie	Cigarette laced with cocaine
Cop	To obtain drugs
Copilot	Amphetamine
Copping zones	Area to procure drugs
Coral	Chloral hydrate
Corga	Heroin
Corgy	Heroin
Coriander seeds	Cash
Cork the air	To inhale cocaine
Corn stalker	Marijuana cigarette rolled in the shuck of a corn cob sealed with honey
Corrine, corrinne	Cocaine
Cosa	Marijuana
Costo	Marijuana
Cotics	Heroin
Cotton	Currency
Cotton brothers	Cocaine, heroin, and morphine
Courage pills	Barbiturates
Course note	Bill larger than $2
Cow growth hormone	Gamma hydroxybutyrate
Cozmos	PCP
Crack	Cocaine
Crack attack	Cocaine
Crack back	Crack and marijuana
Crack cooler	Crack soaked in wine cooler
Cracker jacks	Crack smokers
Crackers	LSD
Crack gallery	Place where crack is bought and sold
Crack Head	Someone who uses crack cocaine
Crack meth	Methamphetamine
Crack spot	Area where people can purchase crack
Crak star	Someone who does crack cocaine
Crack weed	Marijuana laced with crack
Crank	Methamphetamine
Crankster	Someone using crank
Cranking up	To inject a drug
Crap, crop	Low quality heroin
Crash	To sleep off effect of drugs
Crazy coke	PCP
Crazy dust	PCP

Slang	Meaning
Crazy Eddie	Cocaine in formaldehyde
Crazy K	PCP
Crazy weed	Marijuana
Credit card	Crack stem
Crib	Crack
Crill	Marijuana cigarette laced with cocaine
Crimmie	Cigarette laced with crack
Crink	Methamphetamine
Crip	Meth
Cripple	Marijuana cigarette
Cris	Methamphetamine
Crisco	Crystal methamphetamine
Criss-cross, crisscross	Amphetamine
Crissy	Crystal methamphetamine
Cristina	Methamphetamine
Cristy	Crack and methamphetamine
Croak, croke	Methamphetamine and cocaine
Cross	Methamphetamine
Crossroads	Amphetamine
Cross-tops	Amphetamine
Crown crap	Heroin
Crumbs	Tiny pieces of crack
Crumbsnatcher	A junkie who steals tiny pieces of crack
Crunch & Munch	Crack
Crusty treats	Cocaine
Cruz	Opium from Veracruz, Mexico
Crying weed	Marijuana
Crypt	Isobutyl nitrite
Crypto	Methamphetamine
Crystal	Methamphetamine; PCP; amphetamine; cocaine
Crystal caine	Caffeine and phenylpropanolamine
Crystal joint	PCP
Crystal meth	Methamphetamine
Crystal pop	Cocaine and PCP
Crystal T	PCP
Crystal tea	LSD
Crystal THC	PCP
Cuartel	Marijuana
Cube	LSD
Cube juice	Morphine
Cubes	Marijuana tablets
Cucaracha	Marijuana
Cujo	Heroin and cocaine
Culican	High potency marijuana from Mexico
Culley	Marijuana
Cupcakes	LSD

SLANG/STREET NAMES GLOSSARY *(Continued)*

Slang	Meaning
Cura	Heroin
Cushion	Vein into which a drug is injected
Cut	Adulterate drugs
Cut-deck	Heroin mixed with powdered milk
Cycline	PCP
Cyclone	PCP
D	LSD
Dabble	Use drugs occasionally
Daddy	Marijuana cigarette
Dagga	Marijuana
Dama blanca	Cocaine
Dance fever	Fentanyl
Dank	Marijuana
Date rape pill	Rohypnol
Datura	Belladonna and jimson weed
Dava	Heroin
Dawamesk	Marijuana and spices in green cake
Deadly	Heroin
Dead on arrival	PCP; heroin
Dealer	One who sells drugs
Deca-duabolin	Injectable steroid
Decadence	Methamphetamine
Deck	Narcotics
Deeda	LSD
Deep fry	Marijuana
Delatestryl	Injectable steroid
Demo	Crack stem; a sample-size quantity of crak
Demolish	Crack
Dental floss	LSD
Dep-testosterone	Injectable steroid
Descontin	LSD
Det	Diethyltryptamine
Detroit pink	PCP
Deuce	Heroin
Devil's dandruff	Crack
Devil's dick	Crack pipe
Devil's dust	PCP
Devilsmoke	Crack
Dew	Marijuana
Dews	$10 worth of drugs
Dexies	Dexedrine®; Amphetamine
Dex	Dexedrine®
Diablitos	Marijuana and crack
Diablo	LSD paper with a devil on it
Diambista	Marijuana

Slang	Meaning
Dianabol	Veterinary steroid
Diane	Demerol®
Dice	Methamphetamine
Dicoroma	Isobutyl nitrite
Diesel	Heroin
Diet pills	Amphetamines
Digie	Refers to scales used to weigh drugs
Diggity	Good herb
Dihydrolone	Injectable steroid
Dillies	Dilaudid®; hydromorphone
Dimba	Marijuana
Dime	$10 worth of crack; 1/16 ounce of marijuana
Dime back	$10 worth of drugs
Dime bag	$10 worth of drugs
Dime's worth	Amount of heroin to cause death
Ding	Marijuana
Dinky dows	Marijuana
Dinosaurs	LSD
Dip	Crack
Dip jimming	Marijuana dipped in PCP and formaldehyde
Dipper	PCP
Dipping out	Crack runners taking a portion of crack from vials
Dips	Marijuana dipped in PCP
Dirge	PCP
Dirt	Heroin
Dirt grass	Inferior quality marijuana
Dirty basing	Crack
Disco biscuits	Methaqualone
Disco hits	LSD
Disease	Drug of choice
Dish rag	Heroin
Ditch	Marijuana
Ditch weed	Marijuana inferior quality, Mexican
Divider	Sharing a joint with someone else
Dizz	Marijuana
Djamba	Marijuana
Djoma	Marijuana
DL spot	Safe place to buy and use drugs
DMA	Dimethoxyamphetamine
DMDA	Synthetic amphetamine
DMT	Dimethyltryptamine
DMZ	Benactyzine
DOA	PCP; crack
Do a joint	Smoke marijuana
Do a line	Inhale cocaine
Doctor	MDMA

SLANG/STREET NAMES GLOSSARY *(Continued)*

Slang	Meaning
Doe	Methamphetamine
Dog	Good friend
Dog food	Heroin
Dogie	Heroin
Do it Jack	PCP
Doja	Strong marijuana
Dollar	$100 worth of drugs
Dolls	Depressants
Dolly	Methadone
DOM	Dimethoxyamphetamine
Domes	LSD
Domestic	Locally grown marijuana
Domex	PCP and MDMA
Dominos	Amphetamines
Don jem	Marijuana
Dona Juana	Marijuana
Dona Juanita	Marijuana
Doobie/dubie/duby	Marijuana
Doogie/doojee/dugie	Heroin
Dooley	Heroin
Dopar	Levodopa
Dope	Marijuana; heroin
Dope fiend	Crack or marijuana addict
Doper	Levodopa
Dope smoke	To smoke marijuana
Dopium	Opium
Doradilla	Marijuana
Doriden® load	Glutethimide, codeine, and aspirin
Dors and fours	Doriden® and Empirin® #4
Dose	Cocaine
Doses	LSD
Dot	LSD; mescaline
Doub	$20 rock of crack
Double bubble	Cocaine
Double cross	Amphetamines
Double dome	LSD
Double rock	Crack diluted with procaine
Double trouble	Amobarbital and secobarbital
Double ups	$20 rock that can be broken into two $20 rocks
Double yoke	Crack
Dove	$35 piece of crack
Dover's powder	Opium
Downers	Depressants or sedatives; chlordiazepoxide; phenobarbital
Down head	Heroin

Slang	Meaning
Downie	Depressants or sedatives
Downs	Depressants or sedatives
Downtown	Heroin
Do-wop	Heroin
Down head	Heroin
Doxy	Desoxyn® (amphetamine)
DPT	Dipropyltryptamine
Draf weed	Marijuana
Drag weed	Marijuana
Draw up	To inject a drug
Dream	Cocaine
Dream dust	PCP
Dreamer	Morphine
Dream gum	Opium
Dreams	Opium
Dream stick	Opium
Dreck	Heroin
Drink	PCP
Drivers	Amphetamine
Dropper	To inject a drug
Drowsy high	Depressant
Drug deal	The exchange of money for drugs
Dry high	Marijuana
Dry whiskey	Peyote
Ds	Hydromorphone
D's & B's	Dilaudid® and Pyribenzamine®
D's & T's	Doriden® and codeine
DT	Heroin
Dubie	Marijuana
Dub sack	$20 worth of drugs
Duby	Marijuana
Duct	Cocaine
Due	Residue of oils trapped in a pipe after smoking base
Dugie	Heroin
Dugout	Marijuana pipe
Duji, dujie	Heroin
Dummy dust	PCP
Durabolin	Injectable steroid
Durog	Marijuana
Duros	Marijuana
Dust	Cocaine; heroin; heroin and cocaine; morphine; PCP
Dusted	High on PCP
Dusted parsley	PCP
Dusting	Adding PCP, heroin, or another drug to marijuana
Dust joint	PCP

SLANG/STREET NAMES GLOSSARY *(Continued)*

Slang	Meaning
Dust of angels	PCP
Dymethzine	Injectable steroid
Dynamite	Marijuana and cocaine; marijuana and heroin
Dynamites	Amphetamines
Dyno	Heroin
Dyno-pure	Heroin
E	Methamphetamine
Earth	Marijuana cigarette
Easing powder	Opium
Eastside player	Crack
Easy score	Obtaining drugs easily
Eat	To take acid or mushrooms
Eater	Someone who eats marijuana
Eating	Taking a drug orally
Ebenieghber	Hash
Ecstasy	Methamphetamine
Eden	Methamphetamine
Egg	Crack
Eight ball	Cocaine; crack and heroin; one-eighth ounce of drugs
Eightball	Crack and heroin
Eighth	Heroin or marijuana
Elaine	Ecstasy
El Cid	LSD
El Diablito	Marijuana, cocaine, heroin and PCP
El Diablo	Marijuana, cocaine, and heroin
Electric Kool-Aid®	LSD
Elephant	Marijuana
Elephant tranquilizer	PCP
El Gato Diablo	Crystal methamphetamine
Elle momo	Marijuana plus PCP
Ellis Day	LSD
Embalming fluid	PCP
Emergency gun	Instrument used to inject other than a syringe
Emsel	Morphine
Endo	Marijuana
Endurets®	Preludin®
Energizer	PCP
Enoltestovis	Injectable steroid
Ephedrone	Methcathinone
E's & V's	Elavil® and Valium®
Erth	PCP
Esra	Marijuana
Essence	Methamphetamine
Estasy	Methamphetamine

Slang	Meaning
Estofa	Heroin
Estuffa	Heroin
ET	Alpha-ethyltryptamine
Euphoria	Methamphetamine, mescaline, and crystal methamphetamine
Eve	MDA
Exotic	Sinsemilla
Exotic mushroom	Psilocybin
Explorer's Club	Group of LSD users
Extasy	MDMA
Eye of horus	LSD
Eye opener	Crack; amphetamine
F-40's	Secobarbital
F-66's	Tuinal®
Face Drano®	Cocaine
Fachiva	Heroin
Factitious air	Nitrous oxide
Factory	Place where drugs are packaged, diluted, or manufactured
Fag	Tobacco
Fake STP	PCP
Fall	Arrested
Fallbrook redhair	Marijuana
Famous dimes	Crack
Fantasia	Dimethyltryptamine
Fat bags	Crack
Fat Pappy	Fat joint or blunt
Fatty	Marijuana cigarette
Feed bag	Container for marijuana
Fentanyl	Synthetic heroin
Ferry dust	Heroin
Fi-do-nie	Opium
Fields	LSD
Fiend	Someone who smokes marijuana alone
Fifteen cents	$15 worth of drugs
Fifty-one	Crack
Finajet/finaject	Veterinary steroid
Fine stuff	Marijuana
Fingers	Marijuana cigarettes
Fir	Marijuana
Fire	Heroin; crack and methamphetamine
Fire it up	To smoke marijuana
First line	Morphine
Fish scales	Crack
Five cent bag	$5 worth of drugs
Five C note	$500 bill
Five dollar bag	$50 worth of drugs

SLANG/STREET NAMES GLOSSARY (Continued)

Slang	Meaning
Fives	Amphetamine
Fix	To inject a drug
Fizzies	Methadone
Flag	Appearance of blood in the vein
Flake	Cocaine
Flakes	PCP
Flame cooking	Smoking cocaine base by putting the pipe over a stove flame
Flamethrower	Heroin, cocaine, and tobacco
Flash	LSD
Flashers	LSD that is very hallucinogenic
Flat blues	LSD
Flat chunks	Crack cut with benzocaine
Flats	LSD
Flea powder	Heroin
Flesh of the gods	Peyote
Florida	Lidocaine
Florida snow	Cocaine
Flower	Marijuana
Flower tops	Marijuana
Fly	Cocaine
Flying	Under the influence
Flying saucers	Morning glory seeds; PCP
Fly Mexican Airlines	Smoke marijuana
Foil	Cocaine and baking soda
Following that cloud	Searching for drugs
Foo-foo stuff	Heroin; cocaine
Foo-foo dust	Cocaine
Foolish powder	Heroin
Footballs	Amphetamine; Elavil® and ethanol; Talwin NX® and Pyribenzamine®
Forget me pill	Flunitrazepam
Forget pill	Rohypnol
Forty-five minute psychosis	DMT
Forwards	Amphetamine
Four doors	Doriden®, codeine and ASA/acetaminophen
Fours	Acetaminophen and codeine (Tylenol® #4); aspirin and codeine (Empirin® #4)
Four-way	LSD
Fraho, frajo	Marijuana
Freebase	Smoking cocaine; crack
Freedy	Ephedrine
Freeze	Cocaine; renege on a drug deal
French blue	Amphetamine and barbiturate
French fries	Cocaine

Slang	Meaning
Fresh	PCP
Friend	Fentanyl
Fries	Crack
Frios	Marijuana laced with PCP
Frisco special	Cocaine, heroin, and LSD
Frisco speedball	Heroin, cocaine, and PCP
Frisky powder	Cocaine
Fry	Crack
Fry daddy	Crack and marijuana; cigarette laced with crack
Fu	Marijuana
Fuel	Marijuana mixed with insecticides; amphetamine
Fuete	Hypodermic needle
F.U.K.	STP
Full moon	Peyote
Fuma D'Angola	Marijuana Portugese term
Fun-foon-fong	Opium
Future	Crystal
"G"	Gamma-hydroxybutyric acid
G	$1000 or 1 gram of drugs
Gaffel	Fake cocaine
Gaffus	Hypodermic needle
Gage	Marijuana
Gagers	Methcathinone
Gaggers	Methcathinone
Gak	Line of methamphetamine or coke
Galloping horse	Heroin
Gama hydrate	Gamma hydroxybutyrate
Gamma-Oh	Gamma hydroxybutyrate
Gammon	LSD
Gamot	Heroin
Gange	Marijuana
Gangster	Marijuana
Gangster pills	Depressant
Ganja	Marijuana
Gank	Fake crack
Gar	Marijuana rolled in cigar paper
Garbage	Inferior quality drugs
Garbage heads	Users who buy crack from street dealers instead of cooking it themselves
Garbage rock	Crack
Gash	Marijuana
Gasper	Marijuana cigarette
Gasper stick	Marijuana cigarette
Gato	Heroin
Gauge	Marijuana
Gauge butt	Marijuana
G.B.'s	Barbiturate; Doriden®; heroin

SLANG/STREET NAMES GLOSSARY (Continued)

Slang	Meaning
Gee	Opium
Geek	Crack and marijuana
Geeker	Crack user
Geeze	To inhale cocaine
Geezer	To inject a drug
Geezin a bit of dee gee	Injecting a drug
Gekoote coke	Cocaine
Genga	Marijuana
George smack	Heroin
Georgia Home Boy	Gamma hydroxybutyrate
Geronimo	Barbiturate and ethanol
Get a gauge up	To smoke marijuana
Get a gift	Obtain drugs
Get down	To inject a drug
Get high	To smoke marijuana
Get lifted	Under the influence
Get off	To be under the influence; to inject a drug
Get the wind	To smoke marijuana
Get through	Obtain drugs
Ghana	Marijuana
GHB	Gamma hydroxy butyrate
Ghost	LSD
Ghostbuster	Cocaine and PCP
Ghost busting	Smoking cocaine; searching for white particles in the belief that they are crack
Gick monster	Crack smoker
Gift-of-the-sun-god	Cocaine
Giggle smoke	Marijuana
GI gin	Terpin hydrate with codeine elixir
Gimmick	Equipment for drug injection
Gimmie	Crack and marijuana
Gin	Cocaine
Girl	Cocaine
Girl and boy	Heroin and cocaine
Girlfriend	Cocaine
Give wings	Inject someone or teach someone to inject heroin
Glacines	Heroin
Flash	LSD
Glad stuff	Cocaine
Glading	Using an inhalant
Glass	Methamphetamine
Glass gun	Hypodermic needle
Glo	Crack
Globe	Heroin
Glory seeds	Morning glory seeds

Slang	Meaning
Gluey	Person who sniffs glue
Go	Methamphetamine
Goblet of jam	Marijuana
Godfather	Marijuana and cocaine; cigar filled with marijuana or other drug
God's drug	Morphine
God's flesh	Psilocybin
God's medicine	Morphine; opium
Go-fast	Methcathinone
Going 90 miles an hour	The peak of a drug effect
Going to the dentist	Nitrous oxide
Go into a sewer	To inject a drug
Gold	Marijuana
Gold dolphin	LSD
Gold dust	Cocaine
Golden dragon	LSD
Golden girl	Heroin
Golden leaf	Marijuana
Gold hornet	LSD
Gold star	Marijuana
Golf ball	Crack; depressant; LSD
Golf balls	Depressant or LSD
Go loco	To smoke marijuana
Golpe	Heroin
Goma	Heroin; opium
Gomero	Heroin
Gondola	Opium
Gong	Marijuana; opium
Gong ringer	A fat joint
Goob	Methcathinone
Good	PCP
Good and Plenty	Heroin
Good butt	Marijuana cigarette
Goodfellas	Fentanyl
Good giggles	Marijuana
Good go	Proper amount of drugs for the money paid
Good H	Heroin
Good lick	Good drugs
Goofballs	Amphetamines; barbiturates; barbiturates and ethanol; phenobarbital
Goof butt	Marijuana
Goofers	Barbiturates
Goof juice	Novahistine® DH
Goofys	LSD
Goon	PCP
Goon dust	PCP
Go on a sleigh ride	To inhale cocaine

SLANG/STREET NAMES GLOSSARY (Continued)

Slang	Meaning
Gopher	Person paid to pickup drugs
Goric	Opium
Gorilla biscuits	PCP
Gorilla pills	Tuinal®
Gorilla tab	PCP
Got it going on	Quick sale of drugs
Graduate	Completely stop using drugs; progress to stronger drugs
Gram	Hashish
Grape parfait	LSD
Grapes	Morphine; wine
Grasa	Marijuana
Grash	Marijuana
Grass	Marijuana
Grass brownies	Marijuana
Grass spaghetti sauce	Marijuana
Grata	Marijuana
Grateful Dead	LSD
Gravel	Cocaine
Gravy	To inject a drug; heroin
Grease	Amphetamine
Great bear	Fentanyl
Great tobacco	Opium
Green	Dexamyl®; ketamine; marijuana; PCP on parsley or mint leaves
Green and black	Librium®; cocaine
Green apples	Librium®
Green button	Fresh button of peyote
Green cigarette	Marijuana
Green domes	LSD
Green double domes	LSD
Green dragon	LSD; barbiturate; depressant
Green frog	Chloral hydrate; phenylpropanolamine, ephedrine, and caffeine
Green goddess	Marijuana
Green gold	Cocaine
Green goods	Paper currency
Green hearts	Dextroamphetamine and amobarbital
Greenies	Dextroamphetamine and amobarbital
Green leaves	PCP
Green octopus	LSD
Greens/green stuff	Paper currency
Green single domes	LSD
Green-speckled pups	Phendimetrazine
Green tea	PCP

Slang	Meaning
Green wedge	LSD
Green weenie	Ethchlorvynol
Greeter	Marijuana
Greta	Marijuana
Grey shields	LSD
Griefo	Marijuana
Grievous bodily harm	Gamma hydroxybutyrate
Grifa, griff, griffa, griffo	Marijuana
Grit	Crack
Groceries	Crack
G-rock	1 gram of rock cocaine
Grogged	Really stoned or burnt out on marijuana
Ground control	Guide or caretaker during a hallucinogenic experience
G-shot	Small dose of drugs used to hold off withdrawal symptoms until full dose can be taken
G-Spot Tornado	Equal parts of Nyquil and rum
Guarumo	Marijuana
Guato	Marijuana
Gum	Heroin; opium
Guma	Opium
Gumball	Heroin
Gummy	Heroin
Gun	To inject a drug; needle
Gunga	Marijuana
Gungeon	Marijuana
Gungi	Marijuana
Gungun	Marijuana
Gunther	Neighborhood marijuana dealer
Gutter	Vein into which a drug is injected
Gutter junkie	Addict who relies on others to obtain drugs
Gyve	Marijuana cigarette
H	Heroin
H & C	Heroin and Crack
Hache	Heroin
Hail	Crack
Hairy	Heroin
Half	A half-ounce
Half-a-C	$50
Half-a-football field	50 rocks of crack
Half G	$500
Half load	15 bags (decks) of heroin
Half moon	Peyote
Half piece	1/2 ounce of heroin or cocaine
Half track	Crack
Hamburger helper	Crack
Hand-to-hand	Direct delivery and payment

791

SLANG/STREET NAMES GLOSSARY *(Continued)*

Slang	Meaning
Hand-to-hand man	Transient dealers who carry small amounts of crack
Hanhich	Marijuana
Hanyak	Smokable speed
Happy cigarette	Marijuana
Happy dust	Cocaine
Happy powder	Cocaine
Happy sticks	Marijuana with PCP
Happy trails	Cocaine
Hard candy	Heroin; cocaine
Hardcore	Heavy drug user
Hard line	Crack
Hard rock	Crack
Hard stuff	Heroin; morphine
Hardware	Isobutyl nitrite
Harm reducer	Marijuana
Harry	Heroin
Harry Jones	Heroin
Hash	Hashish; marijuana
Hats	LSD
Have a dust	Cocaine
Haven dust	Cocaine
Hawaiian sinsemian	Marijuana
Hawaiian sunshine	LSD
Hawaiin	Very high potency marijuana
Hawaiis finest	Ice
Hawk	LSD
Hay	Marijuana
Hay butt	Marijuana cigarette
Haze	LSD
Hazel	Heroin
H-caps	Heroin
H.C.P.	PCP
Head drugs	Amphetamine
Headlights	LSD
Heart on	Isobutyl nitrite
Hearts	Amphetamine and dextroamphetamine
Heeled	Having plenty of money
Heaven and Hell	PCP
Heaven dust	Cocaine
Heavenly blue	LSD; morning glory seeds
Heavenly sunshine	LSD
Helen	Heroin
Hell dust	Heroin
He-man	Fentanyl
Hemp	Marijuana

Slang	Meaning
Henpicking	Searching on hands and knees for crack
Henry	Heroin
Henry VIII	Cocaine
Her	Cocaine
Herb	Marijuana
Herba	Marijuana
Herb and Al	Marijuana and alcohol
Herb Cooler	Crack soaked in wine cooler
Herms	PCP
Hero	Heroin
Hero of the Underworld	Heroin
Heroina	Heroin
Hessle	Heroin
Hi ball	Isobutyl nitrite
Hierba	Marijuana
Hierbabuena	Marijuana
High	The effect felt when using drugs
Highbeams	Wide eyes of a person on crack
Hikori	Peyote
Hikuli	Peyote
Hilo high	Marijuana
Him	Heroin
Hinkley	PCP
Hippie crack	Inhalant
Hiropong	Methamphetamine
Hiroppon	Methamphetamine
Hit	Crack; marijuana cigarette; to smoke marijuana
Hits	Glutethimide and codeine
Hit the hay	To smoke marijuana
Hit the main line	To inject a drug
Hit the needle	To inject a drug
Hit the pit	To inject a drug
Hitch up the reindeer	To inhale cocaine
Hitter	Little pipe designed for only one hit
Hitting up	Injecting drugs
H-O	Half ounce of marijuana
Hocus	Morphine
Hog	Benactyline; choral hydrate; PCP
Holli	A marijuana cigarette stuck in a pipe and then smoked
Holding	Possessing drugs
Hombre	Heroin
Hombrecitos	Psilocybin
Home brew	Ethanol
Homegrown	Marijuana
Home-made crank	Propylhexedrine Hydrochloride

SLANG/STREET NAMES GLOSSARY (Continued)

Slang	Meaning
Homicide	Combination of cocaine, heroine, dextromethorphan, thiamine, and scopolamine
Honey	Currency
Honey blunts	Marijuana cigars sealed with honey
Honey oil	Ketamine; inhalant
Honeymoon	Early stages of drug use before addiction or dependency develops
Hong Kong rock heroin	Strychnine, morphine, heroin, and caffeine
Hong-yen	Heroin in pill form
Hooch	Marijuana cigarette
Hoochie-mama	A two-paper joint
Hooked	Addicted
Hootch	Ethanol
Hooter	Marijuana; cocaine
Hop	Opium
Hopped up	Under the influence
Horn	To inhale cocaine; crack pipe
Horning	Heroin; to inhale cocaine
Horse	Heroin
Horse heads	Amphetamines
Horse hearts	Amphetamine; Benzedrine®; Dexedrine®
Horse tracks	PCP
Horse trank	PCP
Horse tranquilizer	PCP
Horseweed	PCP
Hot box	To fill up a closed area with second-hand marijuana smoke
Hotcakes	Crack
Hot dope	Heroin
Hot heroin	Poisoned to give to a police informant
Hot ice	Smokable methamphetamine
Hot load/hot shot	Lethal injection of an opiate
Hot pot fudge	LSD or marijuana
Hot shot	Heroin, strychnine, and potassium cyanide
Hot sticks	Marijuana
House fee	Money paid to enter a crackhouse
House piece	Crack given to the owner of a crackhouse or apartment where crack users congregate
How do you like me now?	Crack
Hows	Morphine
HRN	Heroin
Huarache	Marijuana; barbiturate
Huatari	Peyote
Hubba	Cocaine
Hubba, I am back	Crack

Slang	Meaning
Hubba pigeon	Crack user looking for rocks on a floor after a police raid
Huff	Inhalant
Huffer	Inhalant abuser (gas, glue, pam, etc)
Hulling	Using others to get drugs
Human powder	Heroin
Hunter	Cocaine
Hustle	Attempt to obtain drug customers
Hyatari	Peyote
Hydro	Marijuana
Hydrophonic	Hydrophonically grown marijuana
Hyke	Hycodan®
Hype	Addict; heroin addict
Hype stick	Hypodermic needle
I am back	Crack
Ice	Methamphetamine; cocaine
Ice cream habit	Occasional use of drugs
Ice cube	Crack
Icing	Cocaine
Idiot pills	Barbiturates
I Love New York	Heroin
In	Connected with drug suppliers
In-betweens	Barbiturate and amphetamine
Inca messages	Cocaine
Incense	Opium
Incentive	Cocaine
Indian boy	Marijuana
Indian hat	Marijuana
Indian hay	Marijuana
Indica	Marijuana
Indo	Marijuana, term from Northern California
Indonesian bud	Marijuana; opium
Infinity	LSD that lasts for a long period of time
Instant Zen	LSD
Interplanetary mission	Travel from one crackhouse to another in search of crack
Isda	Heroin
Isobutyl nitrite	Inhalant drug
Issues	Crack
IT 290	Alpha-methyl tryptamine
IZM	Marijuana
J	Marijuana cigarette
J's	Joints
Jab, job	To inject a drug
Jac aroma	Isobutyl nitrite
Jack	Heroin
Jackpot	Fentanyl

SLANG/STREET NAMES GLOSSARY *(Continued)*

Slang	Meaning
Jack up	Amobarbital
Jag	To keep a high going
Jam	Cocaine; amphetamine
Jamaican	Marijuana
Jamaican red	Potent marijuana from Jamaica
Jam cecil	Amphetamine
Jammy whammy	Marijuana
Jane	Marijuana
Jay	Marijuana
Jay joint	Marijuana
Jay smoke	Marijuana
JB 318	Methyl piperidyl benzilate
JB 336	Methyl piperidyl benzilate
Jee gee	Heroin
Jeff	Methcathinone
Jefferson airplane	To use a match cut in half to hold a partially smoked marijuana cigarette
Jellies	Chloral hydrate
Jelly	Cocaine
Jelly babies	Temazepam; amphetamine
Jelly bean	Amphetamines; depressants
Jelly beans	Crack
Jerry Lewis's kids	Fentanyl analog
Jesus Christ acid	Highly potent LSD
Jet	Ketamine
Jet fuel	PCP
Jim Jones	Marijuana laced with cocaine and PCP
Jive	Marijuana; heroin
Jive doojee	Heroin
Jive stick	Marijuana
Jock aroma	Amyl or butyl nitrite
John Hinckley	PCP
Johnny go-fast	Amphetamine
Johnson	Crack
Joint	Marijuana cigarette
Jojee	Heroin
Jolly babies	Amphetamines
Jolly beans	Amphetamines
Jolly greens	Ethchlorvynol (Placidyl®); marijuana
Jolly pop	Casual use of heroin
Jolt	To inject a drug; strong reaction to a drug
Jones	Heroin
Jonesing	Need for drugs
Joy flakes	Heroin
Joy juice	Chloral hydrate

Slang	Meaning
Joy plant	Opium
Joy pop	To inject a drug
Joy popping	Occasional use of drugs
Joy powder	Cocaine; heroin
Joy ride	Going out and getting high
Joy smoke	Marijuana
Joy sticks	Marijuana and PCP
Juana	Marijuana
Juanita	Marijuana
Juan Valdez	Marijuana
Judas	Heroin
Juggle	Sell drugs to another addict to maintain a habit
Juggler	Teen-aged street dealer
Jugs	Amphetamine
Jugs and beans	Codeine; Darvon®; Doriden®; flurazepam
Juice	Ethanol; Novahistine® DH; PCP; hydromorphone
Juice joint	Marijuana cigarette sprinkled with crack
Ju-ju	Marijuana cigarette
Jum	Sealed plastic bag containing crack
Jumbos	Large vials of crack sold on the streets
Jungle love tablets	Red pepper
Junk	Heroin; narcotics
Junkie	Addict
K	PCP
K2	LSD
Kabayo	Heroin
Kabuki	Heroin
Kaksonjae	Methamphetamine
Kali	Marijuana
Kaleidoscope	Type of LSD
K-amine	Ketamine
Kangaroo	Crack
Kansas grass	Marijuana
Kaps	PCP
Karachi	Heroin with phenobarbital
Kat	Methcathinone; cathinone
Kate bush	Kind bud
Kay	Ketamine
Kaya	Marijuana
Kay jay	PCP
KB	Potent marijuana
K-blast	PCP
Keef	Marijuana
Keesh	A fat bag
Keller	Ketamine
Kelly's day	Ketamine

SLANG/STREET NAMES GLOSSARY *(Continued)*

Slang	Meaning
Kentucky blue	Marijuana
Kerochi	Heroin
Keyed	High on drugs
KGB (killer green bud)	Marijuana
Khat	Amphetamine-like stimulant; marijuana; cathinone
Khib	Marijuana
K-hole	Periods of ketamine-induced confusion
Kibbles and Bits	Talwin® and Ritalin®
Kick	Getting off a drug habit; inhalant
Kicked	To pass out or about to pass out
Kick stick	Marijuana cigarette
Kiddie dope	Ritalin®
Kif, kiff	Marijuana
Killer	Marijuana; PCP
Killer bee	Heroin
Killer weed	Marijuana and PCP; PCP
Kilo	2.2 pounds
Kilter	Marijuana
Kind, kind bud	Marijuana
King ivory	Fentanyl
King-Kong pills	Barbiturates; glutethimide
King's habit	Cocaine
King Tut	LSD
Kit	Equipment used to inject drugs
KJ	PCP
Kleenex	Methamphetamine
Klingons	Crack addicts
Knock-out drops	Chloral hydrate
Knuckle samich	Phat joint
Kokomo	Crack
Koller joints	PCP
Kona gold	Marijuana
Kool-Aid®	LSD
Kools	PCP
K-pot	Marijuana
Kram	To pack the bowl tight
Kreteks	Clove cigarette
Krippies	Moist marijuana only to be smoked out of a bowl or bong
Kristal	PCP
Kristal joint	PCP
Kryptonite	Cocaine
Krystal	PCP
Krystal joint	PCP
Kumba	Marijuana

Slang	Meaning
Kushempeng	Marijuana
Kutchie	Marijuana
KW	Marijuana and PCP
L	LSD
L.A.	Long-acting amphetamine
Lace	Marijuana and cocaine
La cura	Heroin
Lady	Cocaine
Lady caine	Cocaine
Lady Jane	Heroin
Lady snow	Cocaine
L.A. glass	Smokable methamphetamine
L.A. ice	Smokable methamphetamine
Lakbay diva	Marijuana
Lambjam	Marijuana
Lamborghini	Crack pipe made from plastic rum bottle and a rubber sparkplug cover
Lamb's breath	Marijuana
La rocha	Flunitrazepam
Las mujercitas	Psilocybin
Lason sa daga	LSD
L.A. turnabouts or turnarounds	Amphetamines
Laugh and scratch	To inject a drug
Laughing dust	PCP
Laughing gas	Nitrous oxide
Laughing grass	Marijuana
Laughing tobacco	Marijuana
Laughing weed	Marijuana
Lay back	Barbiturates
Lay-out	Equipment for taking drugs
LBJ	LSD; PCP; heroin
LBJ-336	Methyl piperidyl benzilate
Leaf	Cocaine; marijuana
Leaky bolla	PCP
Leaky leak	PCP
Leapers	Amphetamines
Leaping	Under the influence of drugs
Leary's	LSD
Leather jackets	Phentermine
Lebanese	Marijuana
Lebanese blond	Hashish
Legal speed	Over-the-counter asthma drug (Mini-thin®)
Lemmons	Methaqualone
Lemon 714	PCP
Lemonade	Heroin
Lenllo	Joint
Leno	Marijuana

SLANG/STREET NAMES GLOSSARY *(Continued)*

Slang	Meaning
Lens	LSD
Le power	Heroin
Lethal weapon	PCP
Lettuce	Money
Lhesca	Marijuana
Lib (librium)	Depressant
Liberty	Heroin
Lick'em, lickum	MDMA powder in Jello®
Licorice	Codeine; paregoric
Licorice drops	Morning glory seeds
Lid	1 ounce of marijuana
Lid poppers	Amphetamines
Life in death	Heroin
Life saver	Heroin
Lightning	Amphetamines
Light stuff	Marijuana
Lilly	Seconal™
Lima	Marijuana
Lime acid	LSD
Line	Cocaine
Linga	Crack
Lipton tea	Narcotics
Liquid ecstasy	Gamma hydroxybutyrate
Liquid lady	Cocaine and ethanol
Liquid G	Gamma hydroxybutyrate
Liquid X	Gamma hydroxybutyrate; flunitrazepam
Lit up	Under the influence
Little bomb	Amphetamine, heroin, and barbiturate
Little bowl of buddha	10-gram bowl of marijuana buds or hash
Little green friends	Marijuana
Little ones	PCP
Little smoke	Marijuana; psilocybin/psilocin
Live ones	PCP
LL	Marijuana
Llesca	Marijuana
Load	25 bags of heroin
Loaded	Under the influence, high
Loads	Doriden® and ASA/acetaminophen with codeine
Loaf	Marijuana
Lobo	Marijuana
Locker room	Isobutyl nitrite
Locoweed	Marijuana
Log	Marijuana
Logor	LSD
Lords	Dilaudid®

Slang	Meaning
Los ninos	Psilocybin
Loused	Covered by sores/abscesses from repeated use of unsterile needles
Love	PCP
Love affair	Cocaine
Love boat	Marijuana dipped in formaldehyde
Love doctor	Methamphetamine
Love drug	Methaqualone; PCP; Ecstasy
Love lace	PCP
Lovelies	Marijuana laced with PCP
Love nuggets	Marijuana
Love pearls	Alpha-ethyltryptamine
Love pills	Alpha-ethyltyptamine
Love potion #9	Methamphetamine
Love stone	Bufotenin
Love trip	MDMA and mescaline
Love weed	Marijuana
Lovely	PCP
LSD	Lysergic acid diethylamide
Lucy in the sky with diamonds	LSD
Lubage	Marijuana
Luch head	Alcoholic
Lucky Charms	Ecstasy
Ludes	Methaqualone
Luding out	Methaqualone
Luds	Methaqualone
Lumber	Marijuana
Lunchbox	Kids that do drugs
Lunch hour trip	DMT
M	Marijuana; morphine
M & C	Morphine and cocaine
M & M's	MDMA
Mac	Marijuana and cocaine
Mace	Nutmeg
Machaca	Marijuana
Machine	Devices used to inject drugs
Machinery	Marijuana
Macizo	Marijuana
Mackers	Marijuana and cocaine
Macon	Marijuana
Mad Dog 20-20	Wine
Madman	PCP
Madness	MDA/MDMA
Mad scientist	Someone who makes crank
Magic	PCP
Magic dust	PCP
Magic five	DMT

SLANG/STREET NAMES GLOSSARY *(Continued)*

Slang	Meaning
Magic mist	PCP
Magic mushroom	Psilocybin/psilocin
Magic pumpkin	Mescaline
Magic pumpkin seeds	STP
Magic smoke	Marijuana
Magnum 357	Caffeine
Magoo's blue	Mescaline
Mainline	Heroin
Mainliner	Someone who injects into the vein
Make up	Need to find more drugs
Mama coca	Cocaine
Mama poppers	Isobutyl nitrite
Mandies	Methaqualone
Manhattan silver	Marijuana
Manhattan spirit	Methanol
Maniac	Heroin and cocaine
Man-o-man	Cocaine; heroin
Manteca	Marijuana
Marathons	Amphetamines
Marax	Methaqualone and diphenhydramine
Mari	Marijuana cigarette
Marimba	Marijuana
Marro	Marijuana
Marsh mallow reds	Barbiturates
Mary	Marijuana
Mary and Johnny	Marijuana
Mary Ann	Marijuana
Mary Jane	Marijuana
Mary Jonas	Marijuana
Mary Warner	Marijuana
Mary Weaver	Marijuana
Masa	Cocaine
Maserati	Crack pipe made from a plastic rum bottle and a rubber sparkplug cover
Mash allah	Opium
Matchbox	1/4 ounce of marijuana or 6 marijuana cigarettes
Masterblaster	Cocaine and PCP; marijuana and PCP
Mata	Marijuana
Matchbook acid	LSD
Material	Heroin
Material Negro	Opium
Matsakow	Heroin
Maui wowie	Hawaiian marijuana
Mauve	Ketamine
Max	GHB and amphetamines

Slang	Meaning
Maxibolin	Oral steroid
Mayo	Cocaine; heroin
Maze	Fentanyl derivative
McCoy	Narcotics
MDA	LSD, heroin, and cocaine; methylene-dioxy amphetamine
MDM	N-methyl-3,4-methylene-dioxy amphetamine
MDMA	3,4-methylene-dioxy methamphetamin; Ecstasy
Mean green	PCP
Meg, megg, meggie	Marijuana cigarette
Mellow drug of America	MDA
Mellow T	PCP
Mellow yellow	Dried banana skins with LSD
Melter	Morphine
Memish	Nembutal®
Mercancia	Heroin
Mercedes Benz	Heroin
Merchandise	Drugs
Merk	Cocaine
Mervalon	Methaqualone
Mesc	Mescaline
Mescal	Peyote; Mescaline
Mescal beans	Peyote; Mescaline
Mescal buttons	Peyote; Mescaline
Mescalito	Peyote; Mescaline
Mescap	Capsule of mescaline
Mescy	Peyote
Mese	Mescaline
Messerole	Marijuana
Met	Methamphetamine
Meth	Methadone; methamphetamine
Meth head	Regular user of methamphetamine
Meth monster	Person who has a violent reaction to methamphetamine
Method	Marijuana
Methyltestosterone	Oral steroid
Metro	Heroin
Mexican brown	Heroin; marijuana; fentanyl
Mexican green	Marijuana
Mexican horse	Heroin
Mexican landmines	Methaqualone
Mexican locoweed	Marijuana
Mexican mud	Heroin
Mexican mushroom	Psilocybin
Mexican red	Marijuana; depressant
Mexican tar	Heroin
Mexican valium	Flunitrazepam

SLANG/STREET NAMES GLOSSARY (Continued)

Slang	Meaning
Mexican yellow	Pentobarbital
Mezc	Mescaline
Mezy	Marijuana
Mezz	Marijuana
MG	Marijuana
Mickey Finn	Chloral hydrate
Mickey Mouse	LSD
Mickey's	Depressant
Microdot	LSD
Midnight hour	LSD
Midnight oil	Opium
Midnight toker	Someone who smokes marijuana before bed
Mighty Joe Young	Depressant
Mighty mezz	Marijuana cigarette
Mighty Mite	Type of marijuana plant with big buds
Mighty Quinn	LSD
Milky trails	Lidocaine and ephedrine
Milwaukee road	Marijuana
Mind detergent	LSD
Minglewood	Hash and marijuana-filled blunt
Minibennies	Amphetamine
Mini-whites	Amphetamine
Minstrel	Durophet
Mint leaf	PCP
Mint leaves	Marijuana with formaldehyde
Mintweed	PCP
Mira	Cathinone
Miss Emma	Morphine
Missile	Cocaine and PCP
Missile basing	Crack liquid and PCP
Mission	Trip out of the crackhouse to obtain crack
Mist	PCP; crack smoke
Mister blue	Synthetic morphine
Mister jive	Heroin
Mister natural	LSD
Mister sinse	Marijuana
Mixto	Coca paste and tobacco
MJ	Marijuana
M & M	Depressant
MMDA	Synthetic amphetamine
MO	Marijuana
Modams	Marijuana
Mohasky	Marijuana
Mojaun	Marijuana
Mojo	Marijuana; morphine

Slang	Meaning
Molly	Biphetamine®
Monkey	Morphine
Monkey dust	PCP
Monkey tranquilizer	PCP
Monos	Cigarette made from cocaine paste and tobacco
Monster	Methedrine
Monte	Marijuana from South America
Mooca, moocah, moocha	Marijuana
Moon 1	Marijuana; mescaline; peyote
Moon rock	Cocaine and heroin
Moonshine	Ethanol
Mooster	Marijuana
Moota, mutah	Marijuana
Mooters	Marijuana cigarettes
Mootie	Marijuana
Mootos	Marijuana
Mor-a-grifa	Marijuana
More	PCP
Morf	Morphine
Morning wake-up	First hit of crack from the pipe
Moroccan	Marijuana
Morotgara	Heroin
Morph	Morphine
Morphie, morphy	Morphine
Morpho	Morphine
Mortal combat	High potency heroin
Mosquitoes	Cocaine
Mostaza	Marijuana
Mota, moto	Marijuana
Moth	Methamphetamine
Mother	Marijuana
Mother Goose	LSD
Mother of God	LSD paper with naked woman on it
Mother of pearl	Cocaine
Mother's little helper	Depressant; Valium®
Mountain Dew	Ethanol
Mouth worker	Someone who takes drugs orally
Movie star drug	Cocaine
Mow the grass, mow the lawn	Smoke marijuana
MPPP	Meperidine analog
Mr Clean	LSD
Mr Natural	LSD
Mrs White	Heroin
MS	Morphine
MU	Marijuana
Mud	Heroin; opium; marijuana

SLANG/STREET NAMES GLOSSARY *(Continued)*

Slang	Meaning
Muerte	Overdosing
Muggie	Marijuana
Mujer	Marijuana
Mule	Drug carrier
Munchies	Hunger after taking/smoking drugs
Murder one	Heroin and cocaine
Murder 8	Fentanyl
Mushrooms	Psilocybin/psilocin
Musk	Psilocybin/psilocin
Muta, mutah, mutha	Marijuana
Muzzle	Heroin
Nail	Marijuana cigarette
Nailed	Got arrested
Nanoo	Heroin
Narc	Narcotic agent
Narco	Narcotic agent
Narcoland	Environment of the drug user
Narghile	Turkish water pipe
NASA	Heroin
Natch trips	Highs produced by natural substances
Nats	Barbiturate
Nazi vitamins	Crystal methamphetamine
Neat	Uncut drugs
Nebbies	Phenobarbital
Needle freak	User who enjoys the sensation of using a needle
Needle happy	Frequent user
Nembies	Pentobarbital; phenobarbital
Nemish	Phenobarbital
Nemmies	Phenobarbital
Nepal charas	Marijuana
Nepalese	Marijuana
Nepalese fingers	Hashish
New acid	PCP
New boy	Heroin
New heroin	Meperidine derivative
New jack swing	Heroin and morphine
New magic	PCP
Newspapers	LSD
New York loads	Glutethimide and codeine
Nexus	2C-B
Nice and easy	Heroin
Nick, nickel	1/2 gram of marijuana
Nickel bag	$5 worth of drugs
Nickel deck	Heroin
Nickel note	$5

Slang	Meaning
Nickelonians	Crack addicts
Niebla	PCP
Nieve	Cocaine
Nigerian white	Heroin
Night shift	Heroin
Night train	PCP
Nimbies	Nembutal®; barbiturate
Nimby	Nembutal®
Nitro	Speed or nitrous
Nitroglycerin tabs	Heroin
Nitrous oxide	nitrous
Nix	Stranger among the group
NO	Nitric oxide
No. 1	Heroin and cocaine
No. 2s	Hydromorphone
No. 4s	Hydromorphone
No. 714	Methaqualone
Nod	Effects of heroin
Noise	Heroin
Nols	Nembutal®
Nontoucher	Crack user who doesn't want affection during or after smoking crack
Noodlars	Noludar®
Northern lights	Extremely high grade of marijuana
Nose	Cocaine
Nose candy	Cocaine
Nose drops	Liquefied heroin
Nose powder	Cocaine
Nose stuff	Cocaine
Nova	Novahistine® DH
Nubs	Peyote
Nugget	Amphetamine
Nuggets	Crack
Number	Marijuana
Number 3	Cocaine; heroin
Number 4	Heroin
Number 8	Heroin
Number 9	Ecstasy
Nut	Heroin and cocaine
NY 89	Heroin
O	Opium
O2	Isobutyl nitrite
Oboy	Marijuana
Ocean	Ethylene glycol
Octane	PCP laced with gasoline
Ogoy	Heroin
Oil	Heroin; PCP

SLANG/STREET NAMES GLOSSARY *(Continued)*

Slang	Meaning
OJ	Marijuana
Old Steve	Heroin
On a mission	Looking for crack
On a trip	Under the influence of drugs
One-box tissue	One ounce of crack
One-fifty-one	Crack
One hitter-quitter	Marijuana that takes one hit to obtain a high
One on one	Doriden®, codeine, and aspirin
One-way	LSD
On ice	In jail
On the bricks	Walking the streets
On the nod	Under the influence of narcotics of depressants
O.P., ope	Opium
O.P.P.	PCP
Optical illusions	LSD
Orange and blue	Methapyrilene
Orange barrels	LSD
Orange bulb acid	LSD
Orange caps	Methapyrilene
Orange crystal	PCP
Orange cubes	LSD
Orange haze	LSD
Orange hearts	Amphetamines
Orange micro	LSD
Orange mushrooms	LSD
Orange sunshine	LSD
Orange tabs	Caffeine, ephedrine, and phenylpropanolamine
Orange Tang® mesc	LSD
Orange wedges	LSD
Oranges	Dexedrine®
Oregano	Hash
Organic mescaline	Morning glory seeds
Outerlimits	Crack and LSD
Outfit	Heroin
Owl	LSD
Owsley	LSD
Owsley's acid	LSD
Oz	Inhalant
Ozone	PCP
Ozzie	Ounce of marijuana
P	Peyote; PCP
Pack	Heroin
Pack of rocks	Marijuana cigarettes
Packs	Glutethimide and codeine
Paid	Heroin and cocaine

Slang	Meaning
Pajao rojo	Barbiturates
Pakalolo	Marijuana
Pakistani black	Marijuana
Pall Mall	Cigarette soaked in paregoric
Panama cut	Marijuana
Panama gold	Marijuana
Panama red	Marijuana
Panama reed	Marijuana
Panatella	Marijuana
Pancakes and syrup	Glutethimide and codeine cough syrup
Pane	LSD
Pangonadalot	Heroin
Panic	Drugs not available
Paper	Heroin; LSD; methamphetamine
Paper acid	LSD
Paper bag	Container for drugs
Paper blunts	Marijuana within a paper casing rather than a tobacco leaf casing
Paper boy	Heroin peddler
Paps	Rolling papers
Parabolin	Veterinary steroid
Parachute	Crack and PCP smoked; heroin
Paradise	Cocaine
Paradise white	Cocaine
Paris 400	Methaqualone
Parlay	Crack
Parsley	Marijuana; PCP
Pasta de coca	Coca paste
Paste lavada paste	Coca paste
Paste	Crack
Pat	Marijuana
Pata	Marijuana
Patico	Crack
Pattillo	Tobacco and coca paste cigarette
Paz	PCP
PCC	PCP analog
PCE	PCP analog
PCPA	PCP
PCPY	PCP analog
P-Dope	Heroin
Peace	LSD; PCP
Peace pills	PCP
Peace tablets	LSD
Peace weed	PCP
Peaches	Amphetamines
Peanut butter	Heroin; PCP mixed with peanut butter
Peanut butter crank	Methamphetamine

SLANG/STREET NAMES GLOSSARY *(Continued)*

Slang	Meaning
Peanut butter meth	Propylhexedrine
Peanuts	Barbiturates
Pearl	Cocaine
Pearls	Amyl nitrate
Pearly gates	Morning glory seeds; LSD
Pea shooter	Caffeine
Pebbles	Crack
Pedazo	Heroin
Peddlar	Drug supplier
Pee	Heroin
Peep	PCP
Pee Wee	Crack; $5 worth of crack
Peg	Heroin
Pellets	LSD
Pennies	Phenobarbital
Pen-Yan	Opium
Pepaop	Meperidine analog
Pep pills	Amphetamines; methamphetamine
Pepsi habit	Occasional use of drugs
Percs	Percodan®
Perfect high	Heroin
Perico	Cocaine
Permafried	Always high
Perp	Crack look-alike
Persian	Heroin
Persian brown	Heroin
Persian white	Fentanyl
Peruvian	Cocaine
Peruvian flake	Cocaine
Peruvian lady	Cocaine
Peruvian marching powder	Cocaine
Peter	Chloral hydrate
Peter Pan	PCP
Peth	Depressant
Peyote	Mescaline
Pez	LSD on Pez® candies
P-Funk	Heroin; crack and PCP
P.G.	Paregoric
Phantos	Phenobarbital and amphetamine
Phennies	Depressant
Phenos	Phenobarbital
Philly blunt	Marijuana
Phoenix	LSD
Pianoing	Using the fingers to find lost crack
Pickles	Placidyl®

Slang	Meaning
Pid	Possession with intent to distribute
Piece	1 ounce; cocaine; crack
Piedras	Crack
Pig killer	PCP
Piki	Smoker of opium
Piles	Crack
Pillows	Methaqualone
Pimp	Cocaine
Pimp your pipe	Lending or renting your crack pipe
Pin, pine	Marijuana
Pineapple	Heroin and Ritalin®
Ping-in-wing	To inject a drug
Pin gon	Opium
Pink bam	Preludin®
Pink blotters	LSD
Pink caps	Diphenhydramine; ephedrine; methapyrilene
Pink football	Caffeine, ephedrine, and phenylpropanolamine
Pink hearts	Amphetamines
Pink ladies	Barbiturates
Pink lemons	Dexedrine®
Pink panther	LSD
Pink passion	LSD
Pink robots	LSD
Pinks	Seconal™
Pink spoon	Percodan®
Pink tablet	Caffeine
Pink wedge	DOM; LSD
Pink witches	LSD
Pinner	Small joint of marijuana
Pin yen	Opium
Pipe	Crack pipe; marijuana pipe; vein into which a drug is injected; mix drugs with other substances
Piperidine	PCP
Pipero	Crack user
Pistola	Tobacco and cocaine
Pit	PCP
Pito	Marijuana
Pits	PCP
Pixies	Amphetamine
Piznacle	Marijuana pipe
Pizza	Marijuana
Pizza toppings	Psilocybin/psilocin mushrooms
Placids	Placidyl®
Plants	Mescaline
P.O.	Paregoric
Pocket rocket	Marijuana
Pod	Marijuana

SLANG/STREET NAMES GLOSSARY *(Continued)*

Slang	Meaning
Point on point	Heroin and scopolamine
Poison	Heroin; fentanyl
Poke	Marijuana
Polo	Heroin and scopolamine
Polvo	Heroin; marijuana
Polvo blanco	Cocaine
Polvo de angel	PCP
Polvo de estrellas	PCP
Polvoron	Marijuana
Pony	Crack
Poof	Smoking ice
Poor man's pot	Inhalant
Pop	Codeine
Poppers	Amyl nitrite; isobutyl nitrite; nitrous oxide
Poppy	Heroin
Porker	PCP
Porsche	Heroin
Pot	Marijuana
Potato	LSD
Potato alcohol	Ethanol
Potato chips	Crack cut with benzocaine
Pothead	Frequent marijuana smoker
Potten bush	Marijuana
Powder	Amphetamines; heroin
Powder 95	Heroin
Powder 2000	Heroin
Powder diamonds	Cocaine
Powder stew	Codeine and Ritalin®
Power puller	Rubber piece attached to crack stem
Pox	Opium
P.R. (panama red)	Marijuana
Pregnant	When a joint has a lump in the middle
Premo	Marijuana and cocaine
Prescription	Marijuana cigarette
President	Heroin
Press	Cocaine; crack
Pretendica	Marijuana
Pretendo	Marijuana
Primo	Heroin; crack; marijuana mixed with crack
Primobolan	Injectable and oral steroid
Primos	Cigarettes laced with cocaine and heroin
Procrystal	Benzocaine
Product	Heroin
Product IV	LSD and PCP
Prope-dope	Methamphetamine

Slang	Meaning
Proviron	Oral steroid
Prudential	Crack user
Pseudocaine	Ephedrine combination
Puff	To smoke marijuana
Puff the Dragon	To smoke marijuana
Puffer	Crack smoker
Puffy	PCP
Puke weed	Indian tobacco
Pulborn	Heroin
Pull a will	Vomiting from too much drug use
Pullers	Crack users who pull at parts of their bodies excessively
Pumping	Selling crack
Pumpkin seeds	Propoxyphene napsylate
Puna buds	Marijuana
Pure	Heroin; narcotics
Pure love	LSD
Purple	Ketamine
Purple barrels	LSD
Purple dragon	LSD
Purple flats	LSD
Purple haze	LSD
Purple hearts	LSD; amphetamine
Purple Jesus	Amphetamine on a microdot; LSD; PCP; PCP and LSD
Purple owsleys	LSD
Purple ozoline	LSD
Purple ozolone	LSD
Purple rain	PCP
Purple splash	LSD
Purple star	PCP
Purple wedges	LSD
Push	Sell drugs
Push shorts	To cheat or sell short amounts
Pusher	One who sells drugs; metal hanger or umbrella rod used to scrape residue in crack stems
Pyramids	LSD
Q	Methaqualone
Q.P.	1/4 pound of marijuana
Quaaludes	Methaqualone
Quaas	Methaqualone
Quacks	Methaqualone
Quads	Methaqualone
Quarter	1/4 ounce or $25 worth of drugs
Quarter bag	$25 worth of drugs
Quarter moon	Hashish
Quarter piece	1/4 ounce

SLANG/STREET NAMES GLOSSARY *(Continued)*

Slang	Meaning
Quartz	Methamphetamine
Quas	Depressant
Quat	Cathinone
Quay	Methaqualone
Queen Anne's Lace	Marijuana
Queeted	When you get way too high off half a bowl
Quick silver, quicksilver	Isobutyl nitrite
Quill	Methamphetamine; heroin; cocaine
Quinolone	Injectable steroid
R-2	Flunitrazepam
RB	Resin bud (marijuana)
R-ball	Ritalin®
R & R	Ripple® wine and Seconal™
Racehorse Charlie	Cocaine; heroin
Raggedy Andy	LSD
Raggedy Ann	LSD
Ragweed	Inferior quality marijuana; heroin
Rail	Large dose of crystal meth
Railroad weed	Marijuana
Rainbows	Tuinal®, amobarbital, and secobarbital
Rainy day woman	Marijuana
Rambo	Heroin
Rane	Cocaine; heroin
Rangood	Marijuana grown wild
Rap	Criminally charged; to talk with someone
Raspberry	Female who trades sex for crack or money to buy crack
Rasta weed	Marijuana
Rat	Informant
Rave	Party designed to enhance a hallucinogenic experience through music and behavior
Raw	Crack
Raw fusion	Heroin
Razed	Under the influence
Readyrock, ready rock	Cocaine; crack; heroin
Reaganomics	Cocaine; heroin
Recompress	Change the shape of cocaine flakes to resemble "rock"
Recycle	LSD
Red	Under the influence of drugs
Red and black	Caffeine
Red and blues	Barbiturates; Tuinal®
Red and greys	Propoxyphene
Red birds	Seconal™
Red bullets	Depressants

Slang	Meaning
Red caps	Crack
Red chicken	Heroin
Red cross	Marijuana
Red crow beads	Amitriptyline
Red devils	Seconal™; depressant; PCP
Red dirt	Marijuana
Red eagle	Heroin
Red lilies	Seconal™
Redneck cocaine	Methamphetamine
Red phosphorus	Smokable speed
Red pop	Novahistine® DH
Red rum	Heroin
Reds	Barbiturates; chloral hydrate; Seconal™
Reefer	Marijuana
Register	To allow blood to flow back into needle just prior to injecting heroin
Regular P	Crack
Reina	Flunitrazepam
Reindeer dust	Heroin
Repro crystals	Procaine and caffeine
Rerock	Heroin
Rev Ike	PCP
Rhapsody	MDMA
Rhine	Heroin
Rhythm	Amphetamine
Rib	Flunitrazepam
Ribbets	Librax®
Rich man's	Cocaine
Riding the train	Using cocaine
Riding the wave	Under the influence of drugs
Rig	Equipment used to inject drugs
Righteous bush	Marijuana
Ringer	Good hit of crack
Ripped	Under the influence
Rippers	Amphetamines
Ripple	Ripple® wine
Ripple and reds	Ripple® wine and Seconal™
Rising high	Heroin
Ritz and T	Ritalin® and Talwin®
R.J.'s	Biphetamine®
RO5-4200	Flunitrazepam
Roach	Marijuana
Roach-2	Flunitrazepam
Roach clip	Utensil used to hold marijuana cigarette (usually too small to hold in fingers)
Roaches	Flunitrazepam
Road dope	Amphetamines

SLANG/STREET NAMES GLOSSARY *(Continued)*

Slang	Meaning
Roar	Methaqualone
Robe	Robitussin® A-C
Robin eggs	Methamphetamine
Roboing, robo-ing	Drinking Robitussin® with codeine
Roca	Crack (spanish)
Roche	Flunitrazepam
Roches	Benzodiazepines, flunitrazepam
Rock	Cocaine
Rock attack	Crack
Rock crystal	Procaine and benzocaine
Rocket caps	Dome-shaped caps on crack vials
Rocket fuel	PCP
Rockets	Marijuana
Rockette	Female who used crack
Rock hard	Bufotenin
Rockhouse	Place where crack is sold and smoked
Rocks of hell	Crack
Rock star	Female who trades sex for crack or money to buy crack
Rocky III	Crack
Roid rage	Aggressive behavior from too much steroid use
Roll	Methamphetamine
Roller	To inject a drug
Rollers	Police
Rolling	MDMA
Roofenol	Flunitrazepam
Roofer	Marijuana
Roofies	Flunitrazepam
Roofings	Flunitrazepam
Rook	Person who can't handle their drugs
Rooms	Psilocybin
Rooster	Crack
Root	Marijuana
Rope	Marijuana; flunitrazepam
Rophies	Flunitrazepam
Ropies	Flunitrazepam
Roples	Rophynol; (see 'roofies')
Rosa	Amphetamine
Rose Maria	Marijuana
Roses	Amphetamines
Rot	Flunitrazepam
Rox	Crack
Roxanne	Cocaine; crack
Royal blue	LSD
Royal Temple Ball	Resin mixed with LSD then rolled into a ball

Slang	Meaning
Roz	Crack
Rubber band	Cocaine
Ruby reds	Placidyl®
Ruderalisw	Cannabis species found in Russia
Ruffies, Rufies	Flunitrazepam
Rufus	Heroin
Runners	People who sell drugs for others
Rupture	PCP
Rush	Heroin; isobutyl nitrite
Rush 5	Haldol® 5 mg
Rush snappers	Isobutyl nitrite
Russian sickles	LSD
R-Z	Flunitrazepam
Sack	Heroin
Sacraments	LSD
Sacre mushroom	Psilocybin
Sak	Bag of marijuana
Salmon River skunk	Marijuana
Salt	Heroin
Salt and pepper	Heroin in milk sugar
Sam	Federal narcotics agent
Sancocho	To steal (spanish)
Sandoz	LSD
Sandwich	Two layers of cocaine with a layer of heroin in the middle
San Pedro	Mescaline
Santa Marta	Marijuana
Sasfras	Marijuana
Satan's scent	Butyl nitrite
Satan's secret	Inhalant
Satch	Papers, letters, cards, clothing, etc saturated with drug solution (used to smuggle drugs into prisons or hospitals)
Satch cotton	Fabric used to filter a solution of narcotics before injection
Sativa	Marijuana
Saturn	LSD
Sauce	Ethanol
Savage	Heroin
Scaffle	PCP
Scag	Heroin
Scarface	Heroin
Scat	Heroin
Scate	Heroin
Schmack	Cocaine
Schmeck	Heroin
Schoolboy	Codeine

SLANG/STREET NAMES GLOSSARY *(Continued)*

Slang	Meaning
Schoolboy scotch	Codeine
Schoolcraft	Crack
Schrooms	Psilocybin
Scissors	Marijuana
Scoop	Gamma hydroxybutyrate
Score	Purchase drugs
Scorpion	Cocaine
Scott	Heroin
Scottie	Cocaine
Scotty	Cocaine; crack; the high from crack
Scramble	Heroin
Scratch	PCP
Scruples	Crack
Scuffle	PCP
Seals	Amphetamines
Seccy	Secobarbital
Second-to-none	Heroin
Seeds	Marijuana; morning glory seeds
Seeds and stems	Marijuana; morning glory seeds
Seeds and twigs	Marijuana
Seggy	Depressant
Semi	Peyote
Sen	Marijuana
Seni	Peyote
Senylan	PCP
Serenity	DOM
Serenity, tranquility, and peace	Dimethoxyamphetamine (DOM)
Sernyl	PCP
Serpico 21	Cocaine
Server	Crack dealer
Sess	Marijuana
Set	Place where drugs are sold
Sets	Glutethimide and codeine; Talwin® and Pyribenzamine®
Seven-fourteen	Methaqualone
Seven-fifty special	Placidyl®
Seventy-two hour bummer	STP
Seven-Up	Cocaine
Sewer	Vein into which a drug is injected
Sezz	Marijuana
Shabu, shabu-shabu	Methamphetamine
Shake	Marijuana
Shaker/baker/water	Materials needed to freebase cocaine (shaker bottle, baking soda, water)
Sharps	Needles

Slang	Meaning
Shaman	Peyote
She	Cocaine
Sheetrock	Crack and LSD
Sheets	PCP
Sherm	PCP
Shermans	PCP or PCP-laced cigarette
Sherms	PCP; crack
Shill	Heroin
Shmagma	Marijuana
Shmeck, schmeek	Heroin
Shoot, shoot up	To inject a drug
Shoot the breeze	Nitrous oxide
Shooting gallery	Place where drugs are used
Shot	To inject a drug
Shot down	Under the influence of drugs
Shot gun	The act of putting a joint in mouth backwards and blowing smoke into someone else's mouth
Shrimp	Marijuana
Shrooms	Psilocybin/psilocin
Shwag	Low grade marijuana
Siddi	Marijuana
Sightball	Crack
Silent partner	Heroin
Silly	Psilocybin
Silly putty	Psilocybin
Simple Simon	Psilocybin
Sinse	Marijuana
Sinsemilla	Marijuana
Sixteenths	1/16 ounce
Sixty-two	2-1/2 ounces of crack
Skag	Heroin
Skee	Opium
Skeegers, skeezers	Crack-smoking prostitute
Sketch	Bad reaction to LSD or marijuana
Sketching	Coming down from a speed-induced high
Skid	Heroin
Skied	Under the influence of drugs
Skies	Refers to scales used to weigh drugs
Skin popping	Injecting drugs under the skin
Skot	Heroin
Skuffle	PCP
Skunk, Skunk weed	Marijuana
Slab	Cocaine
Slack	Bag of drugs that doesn't weight out
Slam, slamming	Intravenous injection of street drug
Slanging	Selling drugs
Slang nut	Strychnine

SLANG/STREET NAMES GLOSSARY *(Continued)*

Slang	Meaning
Sled	One ounce of heroin
Sleepers	Barbiturates; heroin; depressants
Sleet	Crack
Sleigh ride	Under the influence of drugs
Slick superspeed	Methcathinone
Slime	Heroin
Slinging	Selling/dealing drugs
Slits	Methamphetamine
Smack	Cocaine; heroin
Smash	Marijuana
Smears	LSD
Smeck	Heroin
Smoke	Crack and heroin
Smoke Canada	Marijuana
Smoke-out	Under the influence of drugs
Smoke you out	Sharing a marijuana cigarette
Smoking	PCP
Smoking gun	Heroin and cocaine
Smoochywoochypoochy	Marijuana
Snap	Amphetamine
Snappers	Isobutyl nitrite
Sniff	To inhale cocaine; inhalant; methcathinone
Snite	Lighter used to smoke drugs
Snop	Marijuana
Snort	To inhale cocaine; use inhalant
Snorts	PCP
Snot	Residue produced from smoking amphetamines
Snot balls	Rubber cement rolled into balls and burned
Snow	Amphetamine; heroin; cocaine
Snowball	Cocaine and heroin
Snow bird	Cocaine
Snow cones, snowcones	Cocaine
Snowdust	Cocaine
Snowflake	Cocaine
Snow pellets, snow pallets	Amphetamine
Snow seal	PCP
Snow seals	Amphetamine and cocaine
Snow soke	Crack
Snow white	Cocaine
Snow toke	Codeine and PCP
Soapers	Methaqualone
Society high	Cocaine
Soda	Injectable cocaine used in hispanic communities
Soft stuff	Marijuana
Softballs	Barbiturates

Slang	Meaning
Sole	Marijuana
Solid	Heroin; marijuana
Solid gold	Heroin
Soma	PCP
Somatomax	Gamma hydroxybutyrate
Sopes	Methaqualone
Sopors	Methaqualone
Sorcerer's apprentice	LSD
Sound	Benactyzine
Soup	Talwin® and Benadryl®
Soup and beans	Glutethimide and codeine cough syrup
Space base	Crack dipped in PCP; hollowed out cigar filled with PCP and crack
Space cadet	Crack dipped in PCP
Spaced out	High on drugs
Space dust	Crack dipped in PCP
Space ship	Glass pipe used to smoke crack
Spaghetti sauce	Robitussin® A-C
Spare time	Possessing marijuana
Spark an owl	Light a huge "'joint'"
Spark it up	Smoke marijuana
Sparkle plenties	Amphetamines
Sparklers	Amphetamine
Spearmint	PCP
Special K	Ketamine
Special LA coke	Ketamine
Speckled birds	Amphetamine
Speed	Methamphetamine; amphetamine; methedrine
Speedball	Cocaine and heroin; cocaine and marijuana
Speedboat	PCP and heroin
Speed for lovers	MDA
Speedfreak	Habitual user of methamphetamine
Spider blue	Heroin
Spiderman	Heroin
Spike	To inject a drug; needle
Splaff	Marijuana cigarette laced with acid
Splash	Amphetamines
Spliff	Marijuana
Spliffy	Joint of marijuana
Splim	Marijuana
Splint	Marijuana
Splits	Tranquilizers
Spliven, splivin	Amphetamines
Spoc	Police officers (cops spelled backwards)
Spoon	1/16 ounce of heroin; paraphernalia used to prepare heroin for injection
Spores	PCP

SLANG/STREET NAMES GLOSSARY *(Continued)*

Slang	Meaning
Sporting	To inhale cocaine
Spray	Inhalant
Sprung	Person just starting to use drugs
Square	Cigarette
Square dancing tickets	LSD
Square mackerel	Marijuana
Square time bob	Crack
Squirrel	LSD; Marijuana and PCP
Stack	Marijuana
Stacking	Taking steroids with a prescription
Stackola	Stacking money
Stamp	LSD
Stanley's stuff	LSD
Star	LSD; methcathinone
Star dust	Cocaine; cocaine and PCP; heroin and cocaine; PCP
Star-spangled powder	Cocaine
Stash	Place to hide drugs
Stash areas	Drug storage and distribution areas
Stat	Methcathinone
Steamroller	Pipe used to smoke marijuana
Steerer	Person who directs customers to spots for buying crack
Stem	Cylinder used to smoke crack
Stems	Marijuana
Step on	Dilute drugs
Stick	Marijuana
Stimey	Dime bag
Sting	Heroin and scopolamine
Stinkweed	Marijuana
Stinky	Marijuana
Stofa	Heroin
Stone	Bufotenin
Stoned	Under the influence
Stoner	Someone who stays high on marijuana
Stones	Crack
Stoppers	Barbiturates
STP	Amphetamines; DOM; PCP
Straw	Marijuana
Strawberries	Depressant
Strawberry	Female who trades sex for crack or money to buy crack
Strawberry fields	LSD
Strawberry flats	LSD
Strawberry shortcakes	Methamphetamine and pentobarbital

Slang	Meaning
Strawberry tablets	Mescaline
Street acid	LSD
Street speed	Ephedrine
Strung out	Under the influence of drugs
Stuff	Heroin
Stumble cookies	Methaqualone
Stumblers	Barbiturates
Suey	Opium
Sugar	cocaine; LSD; heroin
Sugar block	Crack
Sugar cubes	LSD
Sugar lump	LSD
Sugar weeds	Marijuana and sugar
Suma caine	Phenylpropanolamine
Summer skies	Morning glory seeds
Sunny	Heroin
Sunshine	Heroin; LSD; PCP
Super	PCP
Super acid	Ketamine
Super Buick	Combination of cocaine, heroin, dextromethorphan, thiamine, and scopolamine
Super C	Ketamine
Super grass	PCP
Super ice	Smokable methamphetamine
Super jaded	Unable to think clearly from the influence of drugs
Super joint	Marijuana and PCP
Super K	Ketamine
Super Kools	Marijuana and PCP
Super P	Heroin
Super pot	Marijuana soaked in alcohol
Super tobacco	Tobacco and PCP
Super weed	PCP
Supergrass	Marijuana; PCP
Supra	Heroin
Surfer	PCP
Surprise	Cocaine; heroin
Survival	Cocaine; heroin
Swag	Methadone
Sweet Jesus	Heroin
Sweet Lucy	Marijuana; wine
Sweet lunch	Marijuana
Sweet stuff	Heroin; cocaine
Sweet tart	DOM
Sweeties	Phenmetrazine
Sweets	Amphetamines
Swilly	Kind of drunk
Swisher	Cigar emptied and filled with marijuana

SLANG/STREET NAMES GLOSSARY *(Continued)*

Slang	Meaning
Syndicate acid	2,5-Dimethoxy-4-methylamphetamine
Synth coke	Pseudoephedrine
Synthetic cocaine	PCP
Synthetic dope	Heroin
Synthetic marijuana	PCP
Synthetic THT	PCP
T	Marijuana; PCP
T2P	Cocaine sprayed with chlopyrifos; marijuana sprayed with chlopyrifos
Tabs	LSD
TAC	PCP; THC
Tail lights	LSD
Taima	Marijuana
Taking a cruise	PCP
Takkouri	Marijuana
Talco	Cocaine
Tampon	Fat marijuana cigarette
Tango and Cash	Fentanyl
Tanks	PCP
Tar	Heroin; opium
Tar baby	Heroin
Tar balls	Heroin
Tar dust	Cocaine
Taste	Heroin; small sample of drugs
Tatto	LSD
Taxing	Price paid to enter a crackhouse; charging more per vial based on race or regularity
T-buzz	PCP
Tchai	Cathinone
T-Birds	Secobarbital and amobarbital
TCH	THC
Tea	Marijuana; PCP
Teacher	LSD
Tea party	To smoke marijuana
Teardrops	Crack packaged in dose units in the cut-off corners of plastic bags
Tecata, tecate	Heroin
Tecatos	Heroin addicts; hispanic heroin addicts
Teddies and Betties	Talwin® and pyribenzamine
Teddy bears	LSD
Teenage	1/16 gram of methamphetamine
Teenage short	Coricidin® and beer
Teener	1/16 crack rock
Teeth	Cocaine; crack
Tens	Amphetamine 10 mg tablet

Slang	Meaning
Tension	Crack
Terps	Terpin hydrate with codeine elixir
Terron	LSD
Tessies and Betties	Talwin® and pyribenzamine
Texas pot	Marijuana
Texas reefer	Marijuana
Texas tea	Marijuana
Tex-Mex	Marijuana
Thai sticks	Bundles of marijuana soaked in hashish oil; marijuana buds bound on short sections of bamboo
Thai weed	Marijuana
THC	Tetrahydrocannabinol
The beast	Heroin
The bomb No. 1	Heroin
The C	Methcathinone
The devil	Crack
The Great White Hope	Crack
The kind	Marijuana
The pits	PCP
Therobolin	Injectable steroid
The smart drug	Ritalin®
The white lady	Heroin
The witch	Heroin
The wizard	LSD
The yuppie drug	MDMA
Thing	Cocaine; heroin; main drug interest at the moment
Thirst monsters	Heavy crack smokers
Thirteen	Marijuana
Thoroughbred	Drug dealer who sells pure narcotics
Three on three	Codeine with aspirin or acetaminophen; glutethimide
Threes and eights	Glutethimide and codeine
Thriller	Cocaine; heroin
Thrust	Isobutyl nitrite
Thrusters	Amphetamines
Thumb	Marijuana
Thunder	Heroin
Thunderbird	Wine
Tias	Barbiturates
Tic	PCP
Tic tac	PCP
Tick	THC
Ticket	LSD
Tickle	Titanium
Tie	To inject a drug
Tiger	Tiger rose wine
Time bomb	Heroin
Tin	Marijuana; opium

SLANG/STREET NAMES GLOSSARY *(Continued)*

Slang	Meaning
Tish	PCP
Tissue	Crack
Titch	PCP
TMA	Trimethoxyphenyl-aminopropane
TMM	Trimethoxyphenyl-aminopropane
TNT	Heroin
Toilet water	Isobutyl nitrite
Toke	To inhale cocaine; to smoke marijuana
Toke up	To smoke marijuana
Tolley	Toluene
Toms and Bettys	Talwin® and pyribenzamine
Toncho	Octaine booster which is inhaled
Tooies	Amobarbital and secobarbital
Tooles	Depressant
Tools	Equipment used for injecting drugs
Toot	Benzocaine and caffeine; cocaine
Tootie	Meth
Tooties	Barbiturates
Tootonium	Cocaine
Tootsie Roll	Heroin
Top gun	Crack
Top rank	Heroin
Tope	Marijuana
Topi	Peyote
Tops	Marijuana; peyote
Tops and bottoms	Talwin® and pyribenzamine
Torch	Marijuana
Torch cooking	Smoking cocaine base by using a propane or butane torch as a source of flame
Torch up	To smoke marijuana
Torpedo	Drink with chloral hydrate
Tortilla discs	Marijuana
Toss up	Female who trades sex for crack or money to buy crack
Totally spent	Methamphetamine hangover
Toucher	User of crack who wants affection before, during, or after smoking crack
Tout	Person who introduces buyers to sellers
Toxy	Opium
Toys	Opium
TR 6's	Amphetamine
TR 8's	Amphetamine
Tracers	Visual effects of hallucinogenics
Track	To inject a drug
Tracks	Row of needle marks on a person

Slang	Meaning
Tragic magic	Crack dipped in PCP
Trails	LSD-induced perception that moving objects leave multiple images or trails behind them
Trank	PCP; chlordiazepoxide
Trap	Hiding place for drugs
Tranq	PCP
Tranquility	DOM
Trash	Heroin
Trashed	Under the influence
Travel agent	LSD supplier
Trays	Bunches of vials
Trees	Amytal®; Tuinal®
Triad trip	Strychnine, LSD, and methedrine
Tricycles and bicycles	Talwin® and pyribenzamine
Trip	LSD
Troop	Crack
Trophobolene	Injectable steroid
Truck drivers	Amphetamines
True-1984	Heroin and cocaine
Trunks	PCP
T's	Talwin®
TS	Talwin® and pyribenzamine
T's & B's	Talwin® and pyribenzamine
T's & Blue's, T's and blues	Talwin® and pyribenzamine; pentazocine and tripelennamine
T's and purples	Talwin® and pyribenzamine
T's and R's	Talwin® and Ritalin®
T shirts and blue jeans	Talwin® and pyribenzamine
TT's	Talwin® and pyribenzamine
TT1	PCP
TT2	PCP
TT3	PCP
Tubes	Water pipes or bongs
Tui's	Tuinal®
Tuie's	Tuinal®
Turbo	Crack and marijuana
Turf	Neighborhood; place where drugs are sold
Turkey	Cocaine; amphetamine; hash
Turn abouts	Amphetamines
Turned on	Introduced to drugs; under the influence
Turps	Terpin hydrate
Tutti-frutti	Flavored cocaine developed by a Brazillian
Tweaking	Drug-induced paranoia; peaking on speed
Tweak mission	On a mission to find crack
Tweeds	Marijuana
Tweek	Methamphetamine-like substance
Tweeker	Methcathinone

SLANG/STREET NAMES GLOSSARY *(Continued)*

Slang	Meaning
Twenty	$20 rock of crack
Twenty-five	LSD
Twist, twistum	Marijuana
Two for nine	Two $5 vials or bags of crack for $9
Two on two	Codeine and glutethimide
Ultima xphoria	Herbal Ecstasy
Ultimate	Crack
Ultra caine	Ephedrine
Uncle	Federal agents
Uncle Fester	Glass pipe
Uncle Milty	Meprobamate
Unicorn acid	LSD
Unkie	Morphine
Up against the stem	Addicted to smoking marijuana
Up-head	LSD
Uppers	Amphetamine; methamphetamine
Uppies	Amphetamine
Up-Quaalude®	Cocaine
Ups and downs	Depressants
Uptown	Cocaine
USDA	Heroin
Utopiates	Hallucinogens
Uzi	Crack; crack pipe
V	Valium®
Valley dolls	LSD
Valleys	Valium®
Venom	Heroin
Venus	MDMA
Vaporizer	Vaporizes marijuana and leaves you with just the THC
Victory	Heroin
Viper's weed	Marijuana
Vitamin A	LSD
Vitamin Q	Methaqualone
Vitamin R	Ritalin®
Vodka acid	LSD
Volcano 5	Red LSD paper
Vomit wort	Indian tobacco
WAC	Marijuana laced with insecticides
Wack	PCP and heroin
Wacky tobaccy	Marijuana
Wacky weed	Marijuana
Wafer	LSD
Waffles	Hits of LSD
Waimea wipeout	Marijuana

Slang	Meaning
Wake-ups	Amphetamines
Water	Methamphetamine; methedrine; PCP solution
Watergate	Heroin
Wave	Crack
Weasel dust	MDMA
Wedding bells	LSD; morning glory seeds
Wedge, wedges	LSD
Weed	Marijuana
Weed out	Weed for sale
Weed tea	Marijuana
Weightless	High on crack
Weisels taub	MDMA
Weltschmerz	Heroin withdrawal
Wen-Shee	Opium
West coast	Amphetamines; methylphenidate hydrochloride
Wet	PCP
Whack	PCP and heroin
Wheat	Marijuana
When-Shee	Opium
Whippet	Nitrous oxide
White	Cocaine
White acid	LSD
White ball	Crack
White blotter	LSD
White boy	Heroin
White cloud	Crack smoke
White cross	Methamphetamine; phenylpropanolamine and ephedrine
White dexies	Amphetamines
White double	LSD
White dust	LSD
White fluff	LSD
White ghost	Crack
White girl	Cocaine; heroin
White gold	Cocaine
White haired lady	Marijuana
White horizon	PCP
White horses	Cocaine
White junk	Heroin
White lady	Cocaine; heroin; morphine
White light	Mescaline
White lightning	LSD
White merchandise	Morphine
White mosquito	Cocaine
White nurse	Heroin
Whiteout	Isobutyl nitrite
White owsley's	LSD

SLANG/STREET NAMES GLOSSARY *(Continued)*

Slang	Meaning
White paste	Coca paste
White powder	Cocaine
Whites	Amphetamines; phenobarbital
White single domes	LSD
White stuff	Heroin; morphine
White sugar	Crack
White tornado	Cocaine
White water	LSD
White wedge	DOM
Whiz bang	Cocaine and heroin; morphine and cocaine
Wickistick	PCP
Wiggin	In need of drugs
Wiki stick	PCP
Wild cat	Methcathinone and cocaine
Wild Geronimo	Barbiturate and ethanol
Window glass	LSD
Window pane	LSD; MDMA
Wings	Heroin; cocaine
Winstrol	Oral steroid
Winstrol V	Veterinary steroid
Witch	Heroin; cocaine
Witch hazel	Heroin
Wizzard, wizzard of oz	Ounce of marijuana
Wobble	PCP
Wokouri	Peyote
Wokowi	Peyote
Wolf	PCP
Wollie	Rocks of crack rolled into a marijuana joint
Wonder star	Methcathinone
Wooer	Marijuana cigarette
Woolah	Hollowed out cigar filled with marijuana and crack
Woolass	Cigarette laced with cocaine; marijuana cigarette sprinkled with crack
Woolies	Marijuana and crack or PCP
Wooly	Cocaine and marijuana cigarette
Wooly blunts	Marijuana plus PCP
Wooz	Marijuana
Working	Selling crack
Working half	Crack rock weighing a half gram or more
Works	Equipment for injecting drugs
World series	Cocaine
Worm	PCP
Wrecking crew	Crack
Wuwoo	Marijuana and cocaine
X	MDMA

Slang	Meaning
X-ing	Methamphetamine
X's	Amphetamine
XTC	MDMA
Yaamaa	Methamphetamine
Yaegermeister	Opium
Yahoo, yeaho	Crack
Yale	Crack
Yeh	Marijuana
Yellow	LSD; depressant
Yellow bam	Methamphetamine
Yellow bullets	Pentobarbital
Yellow dimples	LSD
Yellow dolls	Pentobarbital
Yellow eggs	Temazepam
Yellow fever	PCP
Yellow jackets	Pentobarbital; phentermine
Yellow kimples	LSD
Yellow Mollies	Phentermine
Yellow pyramid	LSD
Yellow speed	Ionamin®
Yellow submarine	Marijuana
Yellow sunshine	LSD
Yellow T	PCP
Yellow tablet	Caffeine and phenylpropanolamine; ephedrine
Yellow wedge	DOM
Yellows	LSD; pentobarbital; phentermine; diazepam
Yen pop	Marijuana
Yen shee suey	Opium wine
Yen sleep	Restless, drowsy state after LSD use
Yerba	Marijuana
Yerba mala	PCP and marijuana
Yesca, yesco	Marijuana
Yeyo	Cocaine, spanish term
Yimyom	Crack
Ying	Marijuana
Ying gee	Marijuana
Yo-Yo	Yohimbine hydrochloride
Yocaine	Cocaine
Yuppie drug	MDMA
Yuppie flu	Ongoing effects of a cocaine-snorting habit
Z	1 ounce of heroin
Zacatecas purple	Marijuana
Zambi	Marijuana
Zen	LSD
Zero	Opium
Zig-zag man	LSD; marijuana

SLANG/STREET NAMES GLOSSARY *(Continued)*

Slang	Meaning
Zip	Cocaine
Zips	An ounce of any type drug
Zoinked	Intoxicated on drugs to the point of uselessness
Zol	Marijuana cigarette
Zombie	PCP
Zombie weed	PCP
Zooie	Holder for a butt of a marijuana cigarette
Zoom	PCP; marijuana laced with PCP
Zoomers	Individuals who sell fake crack and then flee

Medical Terms
Glossary/Dictionary

ab- From, away from, off.

abasia (a-ba′ze-a) Inability to walk.

abdomen (ab-dō′men, ab′dō-men) The part of the trunk that lies between the thorax and the pelvis. The abdomen is considered by some anatomists to include the pelvis (abdominopelvic cavity). It includes the greater part of the abdominal cavity (cavum abdominis [NA]), and is divided by arbitrary planes into nine regions.

abiotic (a-b-i-ot′ik) Incompatible with life.

abrasion (a-bra′zhun) An excoriation, or circumscribed removal of the superficial layers of skin or mucous membrane.

abscess (ab′ses) A circumscribed collection of purulent exudate appearing in an acute or chronic localized infection, caused by tissue destruction and frequently associated with swelling and other signs of inflammation.

abulia (a-bu′le-a) Loss or impairment of the ability to perform voluntary actions or to make decisions.

abuse (a-byus′) Misuse, wrong use, especially excessive use, of anything.

drug abuse habitual use of drugs not needed for therapeutic purposes, such as solely to alter one's mood, affect, or state of consciousness, or to affect a body function unnecessarily (as in laxative abuse); non-medical use of drugs.

acanthesthesia (a-kan-thes-the′ze-a) Paresthesia in which there is the sensation of a pinprick.

accident (ak′si-dent) An unanticipated but often predictable event leadi ng to injury, *e.g.,* in traffic, industry, or a domestic setting, or such an event developing in the course of a disease.

accommodation (a-kom′o-da′shun) The act or state of adjustment or adaptation; especially change in the shape of the ocular lens for various focal distances.

accuracy (ak′kyu-ra-se) The degree to which a measurement represents the true value of the attribute that is being measured. In the laboratory accuracy of a test is determined when possible by comparing results from the test in question with results generated from an established reference method.

acetone (as′e-tōn) a colorless, volatile, inflammable liquid; small amounts are found in normal urine, but larger quantities occur in urine and blood of diabetic persons, sometimes imparting an ethereal odor to the urine and breath. Used as a solvent in some pharmaceutical and commercial preparations.

acetyl (as′e-til) the radical; an acetic acid molecule from which the hydroxyl group has been removed.

acetylation (a-set-i-la′shun) Formation of an acetyl derivative.

acetylcholine (as-e-til-kō′len) the neurotransmitter substance at cholinergic synapses, which causes cardiac inhibition, vasodilation, gastrointestinal peristalsis, and other parasympathetic effects.

ACH Acetylcholine

ache (ak) A dull, poorly localized pain, usually one of less than severe intensity.

acid (as′id) A compound yielding a hydrogen ion in a polar solvent (*e.g.,* in water); acid's form salts by replacing all or part of the ionizable hydrogen with an electropositive element or radical.

acidophilic (as′i-dō-fil′ik, a-sid′ō-fil-ik) Having an affinity for acid dyes; denoting a cell or tissue element that stains with an acid dye, such as eosin.

acidosis (as-i-dō′sis) Actual or relative decrease of alkali in body fluids; depending on the degree of compensation for the acidosis, the pH of body fluids may be normal or decreased; an accumulation of acid metabolites often is present.

aciduria (as-i-du′re-a) Excretion of an acid urine.

acne (ak′ne) An inflammatory follicular, papular, and pustular eruption involving the pilosebaceous apparatus.

acne vulgaris an eruption, predominantly of the face, upper back, and chest, composed of comedones, cysts, papules, and pustules on an inflammatory base; the condition occurs in a majority of cases during puberty and adolescence, due to androgenic stimulation of sebum secretion, with plugging of follicles by keratinization, associated with proliferation of *Propionibacterium acnes.*

-acousis Suffix referring to hearing and the ability to hear.

acro- Extremity, tip, end, peak, topmost.

acroanesthesia (ak′rō-an-es-the′ze-a) Anesthesia of one or more of the extremities.

acromyotonia (ak′rō-mi-ō-tō′ne-a) Myotonia affecting the extremities only, resulting in spastic deformity of the hand or foot.

acroparesthesia (ak′rō-par-es-thes′e-a) Paresthesia of one or more of the extremities.

acrophobia (ak-rō-fō′be-a) Morbid fear of heights.

acrotic (a-krot′ik) Marked by weakness or absence of the pulse; pulseless.

acute (a-kyut′) Referring to a health effect, brief, not chronic; sometimes loosely used to mean severe.

adaptation (ad-ap-ta′shun) Preferential survival of members of a species because of a phenotype that gives them an enhanced capacity to withstand the environment.

> **dark adaptation** the visual adjustment occurring under reduced illumination in which the retinal sensitivity to light is increased.

> **light adaptation** the visual adjustment occurring under increased illumination in which the retinal sensitivity to light is reduced.

> **photopic adaptation** syn light adaptation

> **retinal adaptation** adjustment to degree of illumination.

> **scotopic adaptation** syn dark adaptation

addict (ad′ikt) A person who is habituated to a substance or practice, especially one considered harmful or illegal.

addiction (a-dik′shun) Habitual psychological and physiological dependence on a substance or practice that is beyond voluntary control.

adduction (a-duk′shun) Movement of a body part toward the median plane (of the body, in the case of limbs; of the hand or foot, in the case of digits).

adenitis (ad-e-ni′tis) Inflammation of a lymph node or of a gland.

adenoid (ad′e-noyd) Glandlike; of glandular appearance.

adipose (ad′i-pōs) Denoting fat.

adjuvant (ad′ju-vant) A substance added to a drug product formulation which affects the action of the active ingredient in a predictable way.

ad lib. L. *ad libitum*, freely, as desired.

adrenal (a-dre′nal) Near or upon the kidney; denoting the suprarenal (adrenal) gland.

adrenergic (ad-re-ner′jik) Relating to nerve cells or fibers of the autonomic nervous system that employ norepinephrine as their neurotransmitter.

adreno- Relating to the adrenal gland.

adrenomimetic (a-dre′nō-mi-met′ik) Having an action similar to that of the compounds epinephrine and norepinephrine; a term proposed to replace the less specific term, sympathomimetic.

adulterant (a-dul′ter-ant) An impurity; an additive that is considered to have an undesirable effect or to dilute the active material so as to reduce its therapeutic or monetary value.

advanced life support Definitive emergency medical care that includes defibrillation, airway management, and use of drugs and medications.

aerate (ar′ate) To supply (blood) with oxygen.

aerobic (ar-ō′bik) Living in air.

aerosol (ar′ō-sol) Liquid or particulate matter dispersed in air in the form of a fine mist for therapeutic, insecticidal, or other purposes.

afebrile (a-feb′ril) syn apyretic

affect (af′fekt) The emotional feeling, tone, and mood attached to a thought, including its external manifestations.

> **blunted affect** a disturbance in mood seen in schizophrenic patients manifested by shallowness and a severe reduction in the expression of feeling.

affective (af-fek′tiv) Pertaining to mood, emotion, feeling, sensibility, or a mental state.

afferent (af′er-ent) Inflowing; conducting toward a center, denoting certain arteries, veins, lymphatics, and nerves. Opposite of efferent.

afterbirth (af′ter-berth) The placenta and membranes that are extruded from the uterus after birth.

afterimage (af′ter-im′ij) Persistence of a visual response after cessation of the stimulus.

afterperception (af′ter-per-sep′shun) Subjective persistence of a stimulus after its cessation.

age (aj) The period that has elapsed since birth.

> **chronologic age** age expressed in years and months; used as a measurement against which to evaluate a child's mental age in computing the Stanford-Binet intelligence quotient.

> **mental age** a measure, expressed in years and months, of a child's intelligence relative to age norms as determined by testing with the Stanford-Binet intelligence scale.

agent (a′jent) An active force or substance capable of producing an effect. For agents not listed here, see the specific name.

> **adrenergic blocking agent** a compound that selectively blocks or inhibits responses to sympathetic adrenergic nerve activity (sympatholytic

agent) and to epinephrine, norepinephrine, and other adrenergic amines (adrenolytic agent); two distinct classes exist, alpha- and beta-adrenergic receptor blocking agent's.

α-adrenergic blocking agent an agent that competitively blocks α-adrenergic receptors; used in the treatment of hypertension.

β-adrenergic blocking agent a class of drugs that compete with β-adrenergic agonists for available receptor sites; some compete for both β_1 and β_2 receptors (e.g., propranolol) while others are primarily either β_1 (e.g., metoprolol) or β_2 blockers; used in the treatment of a variety of cardiovascular diseases where β-adrenergic blockade is desirable.

adrenergic neuronal blocking agent a drug that prevents the release of norepinephrine from sympathetic nerve terminals.

antianxiety agent a functional category of drugs useful in the treatment of anxiety and able to reduce anxiety at doses which do not cause excessive sedation (e.g., diazepam).

antipsychotic agent a functional category of neuroleptic drugs that are helpful in the treatment of psychosis and have a capacity to ameliorate thought disorders (e.g., chlorpromazine, haloperidol).

blocking agent a class of drugs that inhibit (block) a biologic activity or process; frequently called "blockers."

calcium channel-blocking agent a class of drugs that have the ability to inhibit movement of calcium ions across the cell membrane; of value in the treatment of cardiovascular disorders.

ageusia (a-gu'se-a) Loss of the sense of taste.

aggression (a-gresh'un) A domineering, forceful, or assaultive verbal or physical action toward another person as the motor component of anger, hostility, or rage.

agnosia (ag-nō'ze-a) Impairment of ability to recognize, or comprehend the meaning of, various sensory stimuli, not attributable to disorders of the primary receptors or general intellect; agnosia are receptive defects caused by lesions in various portions of the cerebrum.

agonist (ag'on-ist) Denoting a muscle in a state of contraction, with reference to its opposing muscle, or antagonist.

agoraphobia (ag'ŏr-a-fō'be-a) A mental disorder characterized by an irrational fear of leaving the familiar setting of home, or venturing into the open; often associated with panic attacks.

AIDS (adz) A syndrome of the immune system characterized by opportunistic diseases, including candidiasis, Pneumocystis carinii pneumonia, oral hairy leukoplakia, herpes zoster, Kaposi's sarcoma, toxoplasmosis, isosporiasis, cryptococcosis, non-Hodgkin's lymphoma, and tuberculosis. The syndrome is caused by the human immunodeficiency virus (HIV-1, HIV-2), which is transmitted in body fluids (notably blood and semen) through sexual contact, sharing of contaminated needles (by IV drug abusers), accidental needle sticks, contact with contaminated blood, or transfusion of contaminated blood or blood products. Hallmark of the immunodeficiency is depletion of T4+ helper/inducer lymphocytes, primarily the result of selective tropism of the virus for the lymphocytes.

air (ar) A mixture of odorless gases found in the atmosphere in the following approximate percentages: oxygen, 20.95; nitrogen, 78.08; argon 0.93; carbon dioxide, 0.03; other gases, 0.01.

alveolar air syn alveolar gas

airway (ar'wa) Any part of the respiratory tract through which air passes during breathing.

akathisia (ak-a-thiz'e-a) A syndrome characterized by an inability to remain in a sitting posture, with motor restlessness and a feeling of muscular quivering; may appear as a side effect of antipsychotic and neuroleptic medication.

akinesia (a-ki-ne'se-a, a-ki-) Absence or loss of the power of voluntary movement, due to an extrapyramidal disorder.

akinesthesia (a-kin'es-the'ze-a) Inability to perceive movement or position.

alalia (a-la'le-a) Mutism; inability to speak.

albinism (al'bi-nizm) A group of inherited (usually autosomal recessive) disorders with deficiency or absence of pigment in the skin, hair, and eyes, or eyes only, due to an abnormality in production of melanin.

albumin (al-byu'min) A type of simple protein, varieties of which are widely distributed throughout the tissues and fluids of plants and animals; albumin's are soluble in pure water, precipitable from solution by strong acids, and coagulable by heat in acid or neutral solution.

albuminuria (al-byu-mi-nu're-a) Presence of protein in urine, chiefly albumin but also globulin; usually indicative of disease, but sometimes resulting from a temporary or transient dysfunction.

alcohol (al'kō-hol) One of a series of organic chemical compounds in which a hydrogen (H) attached to carbon is replaced by a hydroxyl (OH); alcohol's react with acids to form esters and with alkali metals to form alcoholates. For individual alcohol's not listed here, see specific name.

alcohol dehydrogenase (al'ko-hol de-hi-droj'en-az) An oxidoreductase that reversibly converts an alcohol to an aldehyde (or ketone) with NAD⁺ as the H acceptor. For example, ethanol + NAD⁺ ⇌ acetaldehyde + NADH. Plays an important role in alcoholism.

alcoholism (al'kō-hol-izm) Chronic alcohol abuse, dependence, or addiction; chronic excessive drinking of alcoholic beverages resulting in impairment of health and/or social or occupational functioning, and increasing adaptation to the effects of alcohol requiring increasing doses to achieve and sustain a desired effect.

aldehyde (al'de-hid) A compound containing the radical —CHO, reducible to an alcohol (—CH₂OH), oxidizable to a carboxylic acid (—COOH); e.g., acetaldehyde.

aleukocytosis (a-lu-kō-si-tō'sis) Absence or great reduction of white blood cells in the circulating blood, or the lack of leukocytes in an anatomical lesion.

alexia (a-lek'se-a) An inability to comprehend the meaning of written or printed words and sentences, caused by a cerebral lesion. Also called OPTICAL ALEXIA, SENSORY ALEXIA, or VISUAL ALEXIA, in distinction to MOTOR ALEXIA (anarthria), in which there is loss of the power to read aloud although the significance of what is written or printed is understood.

algesic (al-jez-ik) Painful; related to or causing pain.

algolagnia (al-gō-lag'ne-a) Form of sexual perversion in which the infliction or the experiencing of pain increases the pleasure of the sexual act or causes sexual pleasure independent of the act; includes both sadism (active algolagnia) and masochism (passive algolagnia).

alimentary (al-i-men'ter-e) Relating to food or nutrition.

alkali (al'ka-li) A strongly basic substance yielding hydroxide ions (OH⁻) in solution; e.g., sodium hydroxide, potassium hydroxide.

alkaline (al'ka-lin) Relating to or having the reaction of an alkali.

alkalinuria (al'ka-li-nu're-a) The passage of alkaline urine.

alkaloid (al'ka-loyd) Originally, any one of hundreds of plant products distinguished by alkaline (basic) reactions, but now restricted to heterocyclic nitrogen-containing and often complex structures possessing pharmacological activity; their trivial names usually end in -ine (e.g., morphine, atropine, colchicine). Alkaloids are synthesized by plants and are found in the leaf, bark, seed, or other parts, usually constituting the active principle of the crude drug; they are a loosely defined group, but may be classified according to the chemical structure of their main nucleus. For medicinal purposes, due to improved water solubility, the salts of alkaloids are usually used. see also individual alkaloid or alkaloid class.

allergen (al'er-jen) Term for an incitant of altered reactivity (allergy), an antigenic substance.

allergic (a-ler'jik) Relating to any response stimulated by an allergen.

allergy (al'er-je) Hypersensitivity caused by exposure to a particular antigen (allergen) resulting in a marked increase in reactivity to that antigen upon subsequent exposure sometimes resulting in harmful consequences.

allolalia (al-ō-la'le-a) Any speech defect, especially one caused by a cerebral disorder.

alternans (awl-ter'nanz) Alternating; used as a noun in the sense of pulsus alternans.

> **auscultatory alternans** alternation in the intensity of heart sounds or murmurs in the presence of a regular cardiac rhythm.

alveolar (al-ve'ō-lar) Relating to an alveolus.

alveolus (al-ve'ō-lus) syn pulmonary alveolus

> **pulmonary alveolus** one of the thin-walled saclike terminal dilations of the respiratory bronchioles, alveolar ducts, and alveolar sacs across which gas exchange occurs between alveolar air and the pulmonary capillaries.

Amanita (am-a-ni'ta) A genus of fungi, many members of which are highly poisonous.

ambient (am'be-ent) Surrounding, encompassing; pertaining to the environment in which an organism or apparatus functions.

ambilateral (am-bi-lat'er-al) Relating to both sides.

amblyopia (am-ble-ō'pe-a) Poor vision in one eye, without detectable cause, that cannot be corrected with a lens; almost synonymous with suppression amblyopia.

amine (a-men', am'in) A substance formally derived from ammonia by the replacement of one or more of the hydrogen atoms by hydrocarbon or other radicals. The substitution of one hydrogen atom constitutes a PRIMARY AMINE, *e.g.*, NH_2CH_3; that of two atoms, a SECONDARY AMINE, *e.g.*, $NH(CH_3)_2$; that of three atoms, a TERTIARY AMINE, *e.g.*, $N(CH_3)_3$; and that of four atoms, a QUATERNARY AMMONIUM ION, *e.g.*, $^+N(CH_3)_4$, a positively charged ion isolated only in association with a negative ion. The amine's form salts with acids.

> **sympathomimetic amine** an agent that evokes responses similar to those produced by adrenergic nerve activity (*e.g.*, epinephrine, ephedrine, isoproterenol).

amino acid (a-me'nō) An organic acid in which one of the hydrogen atoms on a carbon atom has been replaced by NH_2. Usually refers to an aminocarboxylic acid. However, taurine is also an amino acid.

aminuria (am-i-nu're-a) Excretion of amines in the urine.

amnesia (am-ne'ze-a) A disturbance in the memory of information stored in long-term memory, in contrast to short-term memory, manifested by total or partial inability to recall past experiences.

> **anterograde amnesia** amnesia in reference to events occurring after the trauma or disease that caused the condition.

> **retrograde amnesia** amnesia in reference to events that occurred before the trauma or disease (*e.g.*, cerebral concussion) that caused the condition.

> **traumatic amnesia** the loss or disturbance of memory following an insult or injury to the brain of the type that accompanies a head injury, or excessive use of alcohol, or following the cessation of alcohol ingestion or other psychoactive drugs; or loss or disturbance of memory of the type seen in

hysteria and other forms of dissociative disorders.

amorphous (a-mōr'fus) Without definite shape or visible differentiation in structure.

amphi- On both sides, surrounding, double; corresponds to L. *ambi-*.

amphophil (am'fō-fil) Having an affinity for both acid and basic dyes.

amyelination (a-mi'e-li-na'shun) Failure of formation of myelin sheath of a nerve.

amygdala (a-mig'da-la) Denoting the cerebellar tonsil, as well as the lymphatic tonsils (pharyngeal, palatine, lingual, laryngeal, and tubal).

amylasuria (am-i-la-su're-a) The excretion of amylase (sometimes termed diastase) in the urine, especially increased amounts in acute pancreatitis.

amyoesthesia (a-mi'ō-es-the'ze-a) Absence of muscle sensation.

amyosthenia (a-mi'os-the'ne-a) Muscular weakness.

amyotonia (a-mi-ō-tō'ne-a) Generalized absence of muscle tone, usually associated with flabby musculature and an increased range of passive movement at joints.

amyotrophy (a-mi-ot'rō-fe) Muscular wasting or atrophy.

amyxorrhea (a-mik-sō-re'a) Absence of the normal secretion of mucus.

anabolic (an-a-bol'ik) Relating to or promoting anabolism.

anabolism (a-nab'ō-lizm) The building up in the body of complex chemical compounds from simpler compounds (*e.g.*, proteins from amino acids), usually with the use of energy.

anadrenalism (an-a-dre'nal-izm) Complete lack of adrenal function.

anaerobic (an-ar-ō'bik) Relating to an anaerobe; living without oxygen.

analeptic (an-a-lep'tik) Strengthening, stimulating, or invigorating.

analgesia (an-al-je'ze-a) A neurologic or pharmacologic state in which painful stimuli are so moderated that, though still perceived, they are no longer painful.

analgesic (an-al-je'zik) A compound capable of producing analgesia, *i.e.*, one that relieves pain by altering perception of nociceptive stimuli without producing anesthesia or loss of consciousness.

analog (an'a-log) One of two organs or parts in different species of animals or plants which differ in structure or development but are similar in function.

analysis (a-nal′i-sis) The breaking up of a chemical compound or mixture into simpler elements; a process by which the composition of a substance is determined.

qualitative analysis determination of the nature, as opposed to the quantity, of each of the elements composing a substance.

quantitative analysis determination of the amount, as well as the nature, of each of the elements composing a substance.

analyte (an′a-lit) A material or substance whose presence or concentration in a specimen is determined by analysis.

anaphylactic (an′a-fi-lak′tik) Relating to anaphylaxis; manifesting extremely great sensitivity to foreign protein or other material.

anaphylaxis (an′a-fi-lak′sis) The immediate, transient kind of immunologic (allergic) reaction characterized by contraction of smooth muscle and dilation of capillaries due to release of pharmacologically active substances (histamine, bradykinin, serotonin, and slow-reacting substance), classically initiated by the combination of antigen (allergen) with mast cell-fixed, cytophilic antibody (chiefly IgE); the reaction can be initiated, also, by relatively large quantities of serum aggregates (antigen-antibody complexes, and others) that seemingly activate complement leading to production of anaphylatoxin, a reaction sometimes termed "aggregate anaphylaxis."

anatomy (a-nat′o-me) The morphologic structure of an organism.

andro- Masculine.

androgen (an′drō-jen) Generic term for an agent, usually a hormone (*e.g.*, androsterone, testosterone), that stimulates activity of the accessory male sex organs, promotes development of male sex characteristics, or prevents changes in the latter that follow castration; natural androgen's are steroids, derivatives of androstane.

anemia (a-ne′me-a) Any condition in which the number of red blood cells per cu mm, the amount of hemoglobin in 100 ml of blood, and the volume of packed red blood cells per 100 ml of blood are less than normal; clinically, generally pertaining to the concentration of oxygen-transporting material in a designated volume of blood, in contrast to total quantities as in oligocythemia, oligochromemia, and oligemia. Anemia is frequently manifested by pallor of the skin and mucous membranes, shortness of breath, palpitations of the heart, soft systolic murmurs, lethargy, and fatigability.

anesthekinesia (an-es′the-ki-ne′ze-a) Combined sensory and motor paralysis.

anesthesia (an′es-the′ze-a) Loss of sensation resulting from pharmacologic depression of nerve function or from neurological dysfunction.

general anesthesia loss of ability to perceive pain associated with loss of consciousness produced by intravenous or inhalation anesthetic agents.

topical anesthesia superficial loss of sensation in conjunctiva, mucous membranes or skin, produced by direct application of local anesthetic solutions, ointments, or jellies.

anesthetic (an-es-thet′ik) A compound that reversibly depresses neuronal function, producing loss of ability to perceive pain and/or other sensations.

aneurysm (an′yu-rizm) Circumscribed dilation of an artery or a cardiac chamber, usually due to an acquired or congenital weakness of the wall of the artery or chamber.

angiectasia (an-je-ek-ta′ze-a) Dilation of a lymphatic or blood vessel.

angina (an′ji-na, an-ji′na) A severe, often constricting pain; usually refers to angina pectoris.

angina pectoris severe constricting pain in the chest, often radiating from the precordium to a shoulder (usually left) and down the arm, due to ischemia of the heart muscle usually caused by coronary disease.

angio- Blood or lymph vessels; a covering, an enclosure; corresponds to L. vas-,vaso-, vasculo-.

anhedonia (an-he-dō′ne-a) Absence of pleasure from the performance of acts that would ordinarily be pleasurable.

animus (an′i-mus) An animating or energizing spirit.

aniseikonia (an′i-si-kō′ne-a) An ocular condition in which the image of an object in one eye differs in size or shape from the image of the same object in the fellow eye.

aniso- Unequal, dissimilar, unlike.

anomaly (a-nom′a-le) Deviation from the average or norm; anything that is structurally unusual or irregular or contrary to a general rule. Congenital defects are an example of the definition of anomaly.

anorectic (an-ō-rek'tic) Relating to, characteristic of, or suffering from anorexia, especially anorexia nervosa.

anorexia (an-ō-rek'se-a) Diminished appetite; aversion to food.

anorexiant (an-ō-rek'se-ant) A drug ("diet pills"), process, or event that leads to anorexia.

anoxia (an-ok'se-a) Absence or almost complete absence of oxygen from inspired gases, arterial blood, or tissues; to be differentiated from hypoxia.

antagonist (an-tag'o-nist) Something opposing or resisting the action of another; certain structures, agents, diseases, or physiologic processes that tend to neutralize or impede the action or effect of others.

    opioid antagonists agents such as naloxone and naltrexone which have high affinity for opiate receptors but do not activate these receptors. These drugs block the effects of exogenously administered opioids such as morphine, heroin, meperidine, and methadone, or of endogenously released endorphins and enkephalins.

ante- Before, in front of (in time or place or order).

antegrade (an'te-grad) In the direction of normal movement, as in blood flow or peristalsis.

antemortem (an'te-mōr-tem) Before death.

anterior (an-ter'e-ōr) human anatomy Denoting the front surface of the body; often used to indicate the position of one structure relative to another, i.e., situated nearer the front part of the body.

anterograde (an'ter-ō-grad) Moving forward.

antesystole (an-te-sis'tō-le) Premature activation of the ventricle, responsible for the pre-excitation syndrome of the Wolff-Parkinson-White or Lown-Ganong-Levine types.

anthropometry (an-thrō-pom'e-tre) The branch of anthropology concerned with comparative measurements of the human body.

antiadrenergic (an'te-ad-re-ner'jik) Antagonistic to the action of sympathetic or other adrenergic nerve fibers.

antibody (an'te-bod-i) An immunoglobulin molecule with a specific amino acid sequence evoked in man or other animals by an antigen, and characterized by reacting specifically with the antigen in some demonstrable way, antibody and antigen each being defined in terms of the other. It is believed that antibodies may also exist naturally, without being present as a result of the stimulus provided by the introduction of an antigen: 1) in the broad sense any body or substance, soluble or cellular, which is evoked by the stimulus provided by the introduction of antigen and which reacts specifically with antigen in some demonstrable way; 2) one of the classes of globulins (immunoglobulins) present in the blood serum or body fluids of an animal as a result of antigenic stimulus or occurring "naturally." Different genetically inherited determinants, Gm (found on IgG H chains), Am (found on IgA H chains), and Km (found on K-type L chains and formerly called InV), control the antigenicity of the antibody molecule; subclasses are denoted either alphabetically or numerically (e.g., G3mb1 or G3m5). The various classes differ widely in their ability to react in different kinds of serologic tests.

anticholinergic (an'te-kol-i-ner'jik) Antagonistic to the action of parasympathetic or other cholinergic nerve fibers (e.g., atropine).

anticholinesterase (an'te-kō-lin-es'ter-as) One of the drugs that inhibit or inactivate acetylcholinesterase, either reversibly (e.g., physostigmine) or irreversibly (e.g., tetraethyl pyrophosphate).

anticonvulsant (an'te-kon-vul'sant) Preventing or arresting seizures.

antidepressant (an'te-de-pres'ant) Counteracting depression.

antidiuresis (an'te-di-yu-re'sis) Reduction of urinary volume.

antidote (an'te-dōt) An agent that neutralizes a poison or counteracts its effects.

antiemetic (an'te-e-met'ik) Preventing or arresting vomiting.

antigen (an'ti-jen) Any substance that, as a result of coming in contact with appropriate cells, induces a state of sensitivity and/or immune responsiveness after a latent period (days to weeks) and which reacts in a demonstrable way with antibodies and/or immune cells of the sensitized subject in vivo or in vitro. Modern usage tends to retain the broad meaning of antigen, employing the terms "antigenic determinant" or "determinant group" for the particular chemical group of a molecule that confers antigenic properties.

antihistamines (an-te-his'ta-menz) Drugs having an action antagonistic to that of histamine; used in the treatment of allergy symptoms.

antihypertensive (an'te-hi-per-ten'siv) Indicating a drug or mode of treatment that reduces the blood pressure of hypertensive individuals.

anti-inflammatory (an'te-in-flam'a-tō-re) Reducing inflammation by acting on body mechanisms, without directly antagonizing the causative agent; denoting agents such as glucocorticoids and aspirin.

antipruritic (an'te-pru-rit'ik) Preventing or relieving itching.

antipsychotic (an'te-si-kot'ik) syn antipsychotic agent

antipyretic (an'te-pi-ret'ik) Reducing fever.

antisepsis (an-te-sep'sis) Prevention of infection by inhibiting the growth of infectious agents.

antitussive (an-te-tus'iv) Relieving cough.

anuria (an-yu're-a) Absence of urine formation.

anxiety (ang-zi'e-te) Apprehension of danger and dread accompanied by restlessness, tension, tachycardia, and dyspnea unattached to a clearly identifiable stimulus.

anxiolytic (ang'ze-ō-lit'ik) syn antianxiety agent

aorta (a-ōr'ta) A large artery which is the main trunk of the systemic arterial system, arising from the left ventricle and ending at the lumbar vertebra by dividing to form the right and left common iliac arteries. The aorta is formed from: ascending aorta; aortic arch; and descending aorta, which is divided into the thoracic aorta and the abdominal aorta.

apathetic (ap-a-thet'ik) Exhibiting apathy; indifferent.

aperture (ap'er-chur) An inlet or entrance to a cavity or channel; in anatomy, an open gap or hole.

aphagia (a-fa'je-a) Inability to eat.

aphasia (a-fa'ze-a) Impaired or absent comprehension or production of, or communication by, speech, writing, or signs, due to an acquired lesion of the dominant cerebral hemisphere.

apnea (ap'ne-a) Absence of breathing.

apperception (ap-er-sep'shun) The final stage of attentive perception in which something is clearly apprehended and thus is relatively prominent in awareness; the full apprehension of any psychic content.

apraxia (a-prak'se-a) A disorder of voluntary movement, consisting of impairment in the performance of skilled or purposeful movements, notwithstanding the preservation of comprehension, muscular power, sensibility, and coordination in general; due to acquired cerebral disease.

apyretic (a-pi-ret'ik) Without fever, denoting apyrexia; having a normal body temperature.

aqueous (ak'we-us, a'kwe-us) Watery; of, like, or containing water.

arachnephobia (a-rak-ne-fō'be-a) Morbid fear of spiders.

arrest (a-rest') To stop, check, or restrain.

   cardiac arrest complete cessation of cardiac activity either electric, mechanical, or both; may be purposely induced for therapeutic reasons.

arrhythmia (a-rith'me-a) Loss of rhythm; denoting especially an irregularity of the heartbeat.

arsenic (ar'se-nik) A metallic element, atomic no. 33, atomic wt. 74.92159; forms a number of poisonous compounds, some of which are used in medicine.

arterial (ar-te're-al) Relating to one or more arteries or to the entire system of arteries.

arteriosclerosis (ar-ter'e-ō-skler-ō'sis) Hardening of the arteries; types generally recognized are: atherosclerosis, Mönckeberg's arteriosclerosis, and arteriolosclerosis.

arteriospasm (ar-ter'e-ō-spazm) Spasm of an artery or arteries.

artery (ar'ter-e) A relatively thick-walled, muscular, pulsating blood vessel conveying blood in a direction away from the heart. With the exception of the pulmonary and umbilical arteries, the arteries convey red or aerated blood. At the major arteries, the arterial branches are listed separately following the designation *branches*.

   ascending artery the branch of the inferior branch of the ileocolic artery that passes superiorly up the ascending colon to communicate with a branch of the right colic artery and supplying the ascending colon.

   atrial arteries branches of the right and left coronary arteries distributed to the muscle of the atria.

   brachial artery *origin*, is a continuation of the axillary beginning at the inferior border of the teres major muscle; *branches*, deep brachial, superior ulnar collateral, inferior ulnar collateral, muscular, and nutrient; terminates in the cubital fossa by bifurcating into radial and ulnar arteries.

coronary artery right coronary artery: *origin*, right aortic sinus; *distribution*, it passes around the right side of the heart in the coronary sulcus, giving branches to the right atrium and ventricle, including the atrioventricular branches and the posterior interventricular branch.

ventricular arteries branches of the right and left coronary arteries distributed to the muscle of the ventricles.

arthralgia (ar-thral′je-a) Pain in a joint, especially one not inflammatory in character.

arthritis (ar-thri′tis) Inflammation of a joint or a state characterized by inflammation of joints.

arthrosclerosis (ar′thrō-skler-ō′sis) Stiffness of the joints, especially in the aged.

articulated (ar-tik′yu-la-ted) Jointed.

artifact (ar′ti-fakt) Anything, especially in a histologic specimen or a graphic record, that is caused by the technique used or is not a natural occurrence, but is merely incidental.

ascorbic acid (as-kŏr′bik) used in preventing scurvy, as a strong reducing agent, and as an antioxidant in foodstuffs.

-ase A termination denoting an enzyme, suffixed to the name of the substance (substrate) upon which the enzyme acts; *e.g.*, phosphatase, lipase, proteinase. May also indicate the reaction catalyzed *e.g.*, decarboxylase, oxidase.

asepsis (a-sep′sis, a-) A condition in which living pathogenic organisms are absent; a state of sterility (2).

asphyxia (as-fik′se-a) Impairment of ventilatory exchange of oxygen and carbon dioxide; combined hypercapnia and hypoxia or anoxia.

aspiration (as-pi-ra′shun) Removal, by suction, of a gas or fluid from a body cavity, from unusual accumulations, or from a container.

assay (as′sa, a-sa′) Test of purity; trial.

astasia (a-sta′ze-a) Inability, through muscular incoordination, to stand.

asthenia (as-the′ne-a) Weakness or debility.

asthma (az′ma) Originally, a term used to mean "difficult breathing"; now used to denote bronchial asthma.

astigmatism (a-stig′ma-tizm) A lens or optical system having different refractivity in different meridians.

asymptomatic (a′simp-tō-mat′ik) Without symptoms, or producing no symptoms.

asystole (a-sis′tō-le) Absence of contractions of the heart.

ataxia (a-tak′se-a) An inability to coordinate muscle activity, causing jerkiness, incoordination, and inefficiency of voluntary movement. Most often due to disorders of the cerebellum or the posterior columns of the spinal cord; may involve limbs, head, or trunk.

atherosclerosis (ath′er-ō-skler-ō′sis) Arteriosclerosis characterized by irregularly distributed lipid deposits in the intima of large and medium-sized arteries; such deposits provoke fibrosis and calcification. Atherosclerosis is set in motion when cells lining the arteries are damaged as a result of high blood pressure, smoking, toxic substances in the environment, and other agents. Plaques develop when high density lipoproteins accumulate at the site of arterial damage and platelets act to form a fibrous cap over this fatty core. Deposits impede or eventually shut off blood flow. See free radicals, low-fat diets.

athetosis (ath-e-tō′sis) Slow, writhing, involuntary movements of flexion, extension, pronation, and supination of the fingers and hands, and sometimes of the toes and feet. Usually caused by an extrapyramidal lesion.

atrioventricular (a′tre-ō-ven-trik′yu-lar) Relating to both the atria and the ventricles of the heart, especially to the ordinary, orthograde transmission of conduction or blood flow.

atrium (a′tre-um) A chamber or cavity to which are connected several chambers or passageways.

atrophy (at′rō-fe) A wasting of tissues, organs, or the entire body, as from death and reabsorption of cells, diminished cellular proliferation, decreased cellular volume, pressure, ischemia, malnutrition, lessened function, or hormonal changes.

auri- Combining form denoting the ear.

auricle (aw′ri-kl) The projecting shell-like structure on the side of the head, constituting, with the external acoustic meatus, the external ear.

auricular (aw-rik′yu-lar) Relating to the ear, or to an auricle in any sense.

auscultation (aws-kul-ta′shun) Listening to the sounds made by various body structures and functions as a diagnostic method, usually with a stethoscope.

autism (aw′tizm) A tendency to morbid self-absorption at the expense of regulation by outward reality.

autoecholalia (aw'tō-ek-ō-la'le-a) A morbid repetition of another person's or one's own words.

autoerotism (aw-tō-ar'ō-tizm) Sexual arousal or gratification using one's own body, as in masturbation.

autoimmune (aw-tō-i-myun') Arising from and directed against the individual's own tissues, as in autoimmune disease.

autointoxication (aw'tō-in-toks-i-ka'shun) A disorder resulting from absorption of the waste products of metabolism, decomposed matter from the intestine, or the products of dead and infected tissue as in gangrene.

autonomic (aw-tō-nom'ik) Relating to the autonomic nervous system.

axodendritic (ak'sō-den-drit'ik) Pertaining to the synaptic relationship of an axon with a dendrite of another neuron.

axon (ak'son) The single process of a nerve cell that under normal conditions conducts nervous impulses away from the cell body and its remaining processes (dendrites). Axons 0.5 μm thick or over are generally enveloped by a segmented myelin sheath provided by oligodendroglia cells (in brain and spinal cord) or Schwann cells (in peripheral nerves). Nerve cells synaptically transmit impulses to other nerve cells or to effector cells (muscle cells, gland cells) exclusively by way of the synaptic terminals of their axon.

AZT Azidothymidine; a thymidine analogue that is an inhibitor of replication of HIV virus *in vitro* and is used in the management of AIDS.

bacterium (bak-ter'e-um) A unicellular prokaryotic microorganism that usually multiplies by cell division and has a cell wall that provides a constancy of form; may be aerobic or anaerobic, motile or nonmotile, and free-living, saprophytic, parasitic, or pathogenic.

ballismus (bal-iz'mus) A type of involuntary movement affecting the proximal limb musculature, manifested as jerking, flinging movements of the extremity; caused by a lesion of or near the contralateral subthalamic nucleus. Usually only one side of the body is involved, resulting in hemiballismus.

barrier (bar'e-er) An obstacle or impediment.

blood-air barrier the material intervening between alveolar air and the blood; it consists of a nonstructural film or surfactant, alveolar epithelium, basement lamina, and endothelium.

blood-brain barrier a selective mechanism opposing the passage of most ions and large-molecular weight compounds from the blood to brain tissue.

basic life support Emergency cardiopulmonary resuscitation, control of bleeding, treatment of shock, acidosis, and poisoning, stabilization of injuries and wounds, and basic first aid.

basophil (ba'sō-fil) A cell with granules that stain specifically with basic dyes.

battery (bat'e-re) A group or series of tests administered for analytic or diagnostic purposes.

beat (bet) To strike; to throb or pulsate.

ectopic beat a cardiac beat originating elsewhere than at the sinoatrial node.

heart beat a complete cardiac cycle, including spread of the electrical impulse and the consequent mechanical contraction.

behavior (be-hav'yer) Any response emitted by or elicited from an organism.

benign (be-nin') Denoting the mild character of an illness or the nonmalignant character of a neoplasm.

beta-blocker (ba'ta-blok'er) syn β-adrenergic blocking agent

bile (bil) The yellowish brown or green fluid secreted by the liver and discharged into the duodenum, where it aids in the emulsification of fats, increases peristalsis, and retards putrefaction; contains sodium glycocholate and sodium taurocholate, cholesterol, biliverdin and bilirubin, mucus, fat, lecithin, cells, and cellular debris.

bilirubin (bil-i-ru'bin) A yellow bile pigment found as sodium bilirubinate (soluble), or as an insoluble calcium salt in gallstones, formed from hemoglobin during normal and abnormal destruction of erythrocytes by the reticuloendothelial system. Excess bilirubin is associated with jaundice.

biluria (bil-e-yu're-a) The presence of various bile salts, or bile, in the urine.

binaural (bin-aw'ral) Relating to both ears.

binocular (bin-ok'yu-lar) Adapted to the use of both eyes; said of an optical instrument.

bioassay (bi-ō-as'a) Determination of the potency or concentration of a compound by its effect upon animals, isolated tissues, or microorganisms, as contrasted with analysis of its chemical or physical properties.

bioavailability (bi'ō-a-val'a-bil'i-te) The physiological availability of a given amount of a drug, as distinct from its chemical potency; proportion of the administered dose which is absorbed into the bloodstream.

biochemistry (bi-ō-kem'is-tre) The chemistry of living organisms and of the chemical, molecular, and physical changes occurring therein.

biodegradable (bi'ō-de-grad'a-bl) Denoting a substance that can be chemically degraded or decomposed by natural effectors (e.g., weather, soil bacteria, plants, animals).

biopsy (bi'op-se) Process of removing tissue from living patients for diagnostic examination.

biotransformation (bi'ō-trans-fōr-ma'shun) The conversion of molecules from one form to another within an organism, often associated with change in pharmacologic activity; refers especially to drugs and other xenobiotics.

bipolar (bi-pō'ler) Having two poles, ends, or extremes.

blepharedema (blef'ar-e-de'ma) Edema of the eyelids, causing swelling and often a baggy appearance.

blepharitis (blef'a-ri'tis) Inflammation of the eyelids.

blepharochalasis (blef'a-rō-kal'a-sis) Redundancy of the skin of the upper eyelids so that a fold of skin hangs down, often concealing the tarsal margin when the eye is open.

blepharoconjunctivitis (blef'a-rō-kon-junk-ti-vi'tis) Inflammation of the palpebral conjunctiva.

blepharoptosis (blef'a-rop'tō-sis) Drooping of the upper eyelid.

blindness (blind'nes) Loss of the sense of sight; absolute blindness denotes total absence of perception.

  color blindness misleading term for anomalous or deficient color vision; complete color blindness is the absence of one of the primary cone pigments of the retina.

  legal blindness generally, visual acuity of less than 6/60 or 20/200 using Snellen test types, or visual field restriction to 20° or less in the better eye; the criteria used to define legal blindness vary.

block To obstruct; to arrest passage through.

  atrioventricular block partial or complete block of electric impulses originating in the atrium or sinus node preventing them from reaching the atrioventricular node and ventricles. In first degree A-V block, there is prolongation of A-V conduction time (P-R interval); in SECOND DEGREE A-V BLOCK, some but not all atrial impulses fail to reach the ventricles, thus some ventricular beats are dropped; in COMPLETE A-V BLOCK, complete atrioventricular dissociation (2) occurs; no impulses can reach the ventricles despite even a slow ventricular rate (under 45 per minute); atria and ventricles beat independently.

  bundle-branch block intraventricular block due to interruption of conduction in one of the two main branches of the bundle of His and manifested in the electrocardiogram by marked prolongation of the QRS complex.

  nerve block interruption of conduction of impulses in peripheral nerves or nerve trunks by injection of anesthetic.

  spinal block an obstruction to the flow of cerebrospinal fluid in the spinal subarachnoid space; used inaccurately to refer to spinal anesthesia.

blockade (blok'ad) Intravenous injection of colloidal dyes or other substances whereby the reaction of the reticuloendothelial cells to other influences (e.g., by phagocytosis) is temporarily prevented.

  adrenergic blockade selective inhibition by a drug of the responses of effector cells to adrenergic sympathetic nerve impulses (sympatholytic) and to epinephrine and related amines (adrenolytic).

  cholinergic blockade inhibition by a drug of nerve impulse transmission at autonomic ganglionic synapses (ganglionic blockade), at postganglionic parasympathetic effector cells (e.g., by atropine), and at myoneural junctions (myoneural blockade);

  narcotic blockade the use of drugs to inhibit the effects of narcotic substances, as with naloxone.

blocker (blok'er) An instrument used to obstruct a passage.

  calcium channel blocker a class of drugs with the capacity to prevent calcium ions from passing through biologic membranes. These agents are used to treat hypertension, angina pectoris, and cardiac arrhythmias; examples include nifedipine, diltiazem, and verapamil.

blood (blud) The fluid and its suspended formed elements that are circulated through the heart, arteries, capillaries, and veins; blood is the means by which 1) oxygen and nutritive materials are transported to the tissues, and 2) carbon dioxide and various metabolic products are removed for excretion. The blood consists of a pale yellow or gray-yellow fluid, plasma, in which are suspended red blood cells (erythrocytes), white blood cells (leukocytes), and platelets.

arterial blood blood that is oxygenated in the lungs, found in the left chambers of the heart and in the arteries, and relatively bright red.

venous blood blood which has passed through the capillaries of various tissues, except the lungs, and is found in the veins, the right chambers of the heart, and the pulmonary arteries; it is usually dark red as a result of a lower content of oxygen.

whole blood blood drawn from a selected donor under rigid aseptic precautions; contains citrate ion or heparin as an anticoagulant; used as a blood replenisher.

blood vessel A tube (artery, capillary, vein, or sinus) conveying blood.

bolus (bō'lus) A single, relatively large quantity of a substance, usually one intended for therapeutic use, such as a bolus dose of a drug.

bone (bōn) A hard connective tissue consisting of cells embedded in a matrix of mineralized ground substance and collagen fibers. The fibers are impregnated with a form of calcium phosphate similar to hydroxyapatite as well as with substantial quantities of carbonate, citrate sodium, and magnesium; by weight, bone is composed of 75% inorganic material and 25% organic material; a portion of osseous tissue of definite shape and size, forming a part of the animal skeleton; in man there are 200 distinct ossa in the skeleton, not including the ossicula auditus of the tympanic cavity or the ossa sesamoidea other than the two patellae. Bone consists of a dense outer layer of compact substance or cortical substance covered by the periosteum, and an inner loose, spongy substance; the central portion of a long bone is filled with marrow.

bouton (bu-ton') A button, pustule, or knob-like swelling.

terminal boutons syn axon terminals

brachial (bra'ke-al) Relating to the arm.

bradyarrhythmia (brad'e-a-rith'me-a) Any disturbance of the heart's rhythm

resulting in a rate under 60 beats per minute.

bradycardia (brad-e-kar'de-a) Slowness of the heartbeat, usually a rate under 60 beats per minute.

bradypnea (brad-ip-ne'a) Abnormal slowness of respiration, specifically a low respiratory frequency.

bradysphygmia (brad-e-sfig'me-a) Slowness of the pulse; can occur without bradycardia, as in ventricular bigeminy when every other beat may fail to produce a peripheral pulse.

brain (bran) That part of the central nervous system contained within the cranium.

bromide (brō'mid) The anion Br⁻; salt of hydrogen bromide (HBr); several salts formerly used as sedatives, hypnotics, and anticonvulsants.

bronchitis (brong-ki'tis) Inflammation of the mucous membrane of the bronchial tubes.

bronchodilatation (brong'kō-dil-a-ta'shun) Increase in caliber of the bronchi and bronchioles in response to pharmacologically active substances or autonomic nervous activity.

bronchodilator (brong-kō-di-la'ter, -tōr) Causing an increase in caliber of a bronchus or bronchial tube.

bronchus (brong'kus) One of the two subdivisions of the trachea serving to convey air to and from the lungs. The trachea divides into right and left main bronchi, which in turn form lobar, segmental, and subsegmental bronchi. In structure, the intrapulmonary bronchi have a lining of pseudostratified ciliated columnar epithelium, and a lamina propria with abundant longitudinal networks of elastic fibers; there are spirally arranged bundles of smooth muscle, abundant mucoserous glands, and, in the outer part of the wall, irregular plates of hyaline cartilage.

bruxism (bruk'sizm) A clenching of the teeth, associated with forceful lateral or protrusive jaw movements, resulting in rubbing, gritting, or grinding together of the teeth, usually during sleep; sometimes a pathologic condition.

buccal (buk'al) Pertaining to, adjacent to, or in the direction of the cheek.

buccolingual (buk-ō-ling'wal) Pertaining to the cheek and the tongue.

bulimia (bu-lim'e-a) syn bulimia nervosa

bulimia nervosa a chronic morbid disorder involving repeated and secretive episodic bouts of eating characterized by uncontrolled rapid ingestion of large quantities of food over a short period of time (binge eating), followed by self-induced vomiting, use of laxatives or diuretics, fasting, or vigorous exercise in order to prevent weight gain; often accompanied by feelings of guilt, depression, or self-disgust.

butane (byu'tan) A gaseous hydrocarbon present in natural gas.

calcitonin (kal-si-tō'nin) A peptide hormone, of which eight forms are known; produced by the parathyroid, thyroid, and thymus glands; its action is opposite to that of parathyroid hormone in that calcitonin increases deposition of calcium and phosphate in bone and lowers the level of calcium in the blood.

calcium (kal'se-um) A metallic bivalent element; atomic no. 20, atomic wt. 40.078, density 1.55, melting point 842°C. Many calcium salts have crucial uses in metabolism and in medicine. Calcium salts are responsible for the radiopacity of bone, calcified cartilage, and arteriosclerotic plaques in arteries.

caliber (kal'i-ber) The diameter of a hollow tubular structure.

calorie (kal'ō-re) A unit of heat content or energy. The amount of heat necessary to raise 1 g of water from 14.5°C to 15.5°C (small calorie). Calorie is being replaced by joule, the SI unit equal to 0.239 calorie.

canal (ka-nal') A duct or channel; a tubular structure.

bony semicircular canals the three bony tubes in the labyrinth of the ear within which the membranous semicircular ducts are located; they lie in planes at right angles to each other and are known as anterior semicircular canal, posterior semicircular canal, and lateral semicircular canal.

cochlear canal the winding tube of the bony labyrinth which makes two and a half turns about the modiolus of the cochlea; it is divided incompletely into two compartments by a winding shelf of bone, the bony spiral lamina.

pyloric canal the segment of the stomach that succeeds the antrum and ends at the gastroduodenal junction.

Candida (kan'did-a) A genus of yeastlike fungi found in nature; a few species are isolated from the skin, feces, and vaginal and pharyngeal tissue, but the gastrointestinal tract is the source of the single most important species, *Candida albicans*.

cannabinoids (ka-nab'i-noydz) Organic substances present in *Cannabis sativa*, having a variety of pharmacologic properties.

cannabis (kan'a-bis) The dried flowering tops of the pistillate plants of *Cannabis sativa* (family Moraceae) containing isomeric tetrahydrocannabinols, cannabinol, and cannabidiol. Preparations of cannabis are smoked or ingested by members of various cultures and subcultures to induce psychotomimetic effects such as euphoria, hallucinations, drowsiness, and other mental changes. Cannabis was formerly used as a sedative and analgesic; now available for restricted use in management of iatrogenic anorexia, especially that associated with oncologic chemotherapy and radiation therapy. Known by many colloquial or slang terms such as marijuana; marihuana; pot; grass; bhang; charas; ganja; hashish.

carbamate (kar'ba-mat) A salt or ester of carbamic acid forming the basis of urethane hypnotics.

carbohydrates (kar-bō-hī'drats) Class name for the aldehydic or ketonic derivatives of polyhydric alcohols. Most such compounds have formulas that may be written $C_n(H_2O)_n$, although they are not true hydrates. The group includes simple sugars (monosaccharides, disaccharides, etc.), as well as macromolecular (polymeric) substances such as starch, glycogen, and cellulose polysaccharides.

carbon (kar'bon) A nonmetallic tetravalent element, atomic no. 6, atomic wt. 12.011; the major bioelement. It has two natural isotopes, ^{12}C and ^{13}C (the former, set at 12.00000, being the standard for all molecular weights), and two artificial, radioactive isotopes of interest, ^{11}C and ^{14}C. The element occurs in diamond, graphite, charcoal, coke, and soot, and in the atmosphere as CO_2. Its compounds are found in all living tissues, and the study of its vast number of compounds constitutes most of organic chemistry.

carboxy- Combining form indicating addition of CO or CO_2.

carcinogen (kar-sin'ō-jen, kar'si-nō-jen) Any cancer-producing substance or organism, such as polycyclic aromatic hydrocarbons, or agents such as certain types of irradiation.

carcinoma (kar-si-nō'ma) Any of the various types of malignant neoplasm derived from epithelial tissue, occurring more frequently in the skin and large intestine in both sexes, the lung and prostate gland in men, and the lung and breast in women. Carcinomas are identified histologically on the basis of invasiveness and the changes that indicate anaplasia, *i.e.*, loss of polarity of nuclei, loss of orderly maturation of cells (especially in squamous cell type), variation in the size and shape of cells, hyperchromatism of nuclei (with clumping of chromatin), and increase in the nuclear-cytoplasmic ratio. Carcinomas may be undifferentiated, or the neoplastic tissue may resemble (to varying degree) one of the types of normal epithelium.

cardiovascular (kar'de-ō-vas'kyu-lar) Relating to the heart and the blood vessels or the circulation.

cartilage (kar'ti-lij) A connective tissue characterized by its nonvascularity and firm consistency; consists of cells (chondrocytes), an interstitial matrix of fibers (collagen), and a ground substance (proteoglycans). There are three kinds of cartilage: hyaline cartilage, elastic cartilage, and fibrocartilage. Nonvascular, resilient, flexible connective tissue found primarily in joints, the walls of the thorax, and tubular structures such as the larynx, air passages, and ears; comprises most of the skeleton in early fetal life, but is slowly replaced by bone.

catabolism (ka-tab'ō-lizm) The breaking down in the body of complex chemical compounds into simpler ones, often accompanied by the liberation of energy.

catalepsy (kat'a-lep-se) A morbid condition characterized by waxy rigidity of the limbs, lack of response to stimuli, mutism and inactivity; occurs with some psychoses, especially catatonic schizophrenia.

catalyst (kat'a-list) A substance that accelerates a chemical reaction but is not consumed or changed permanently thereby.

cataplexy (kat'a-plek-se) A transient attack of extreme generalized muscular weakness, often precipitated by an emotional state such as laughing, surprise, fear, or anger.

cataract (kat'a-rakt) Loss of transparency of the lens of the eye, or of its capsule.

catarrh (ka-tahr') Inflammation of a mucous membrane with increased flow of mucus or exudate.

catatonia (kat-a-tō'ne-a) A syndrome of psychomotor disturbances characterized by periods of physical rigidity, negativism, or stupor; may occur in schizophrenia, mood disorders, or organic mental disorders.

catecholamines (kat-e-kol'a-menz) Pyrocatechols with an alkylamine side chain; examples of biochemical interest are epinephrine, norepinephrine, and l-dopa. Catecholamines are major elements in responses to stress.

catharsis (ka-thar'sis) syn purgation

catheter (kath'e-ter) A tubular instrument to allow passage of fluid from or into a body cavity.

cathexis (ka-thek'sis) A conscious or unconscious attachment of psychic energy to an idea, object, or person.

cell (sel) The smallest unit of living structure capable of independent existence, composed of a membrane-enclosed mass of protoplasm and containing a nucleus or nucleoid. Cells are highly variable and specialized in both structure and function, though all must at some stage replicate proteins and nucleic acids, utilize energy, and reproduce themselves.

　ganglion cell a neuron the cell body of which is located outside the limits of the brain and spinal cord, hence forming part of the peripheral nervous system; ganglion cell's are either 1) the pseudounipolar cell's of the sensory spinal and cranial nerves (sensory ganglia), or 2) the peripheral multipolar motor neurons innervating the viscera (visceral or autonomic ganglia).

　photoreceptor cells rod and cone cell's of the retina.

　red blood cell syn erythrocyte

　visual receptor cells the rod and cone cell's of the retina.

　white blood cell syn leukocyte

centi- Prefix used in the SI and metric systems to signify one hundredth (10^{-2}).

centigrade (sen'ti-grad) Basis of the former temperature scale in which 100 degrees separated the melting and boiling points of water.

centigram (sen'ti-gram) One hundredth of a gram.

centile (sen'til) One-hundredth.

centiliter (sen'ti-le-ter) 10 milliliters; one hundredth of a liter; 162.3073 minims (U.S.).

centimeter (sen'ti-me-ter) One hundredth of a meter; 0.3937008 inch.

　cubic centimeter one thousandth of a liter; 1 milliliter.

centrifugal (sen-trif'yu-gal) Denoting the direction of the force pulling an object outward (away) from an axis of rotation.

centrifuge (sen'tri-fuj) An apparatus by means of which particles in suspension in a fluid are separated by spinning the fluid, the centrifugal force throwing the particles to the periphery of the rotated vessel.

cephalo- The head.

cerebellum (ser-e-bel'um) The large posterior brain mass lying dorsal to the pons and medulla and ventral to the posterior portion of the cerebrum; it consists of two lateral hemispheres united by a narrow middle portion, the vermis.

cerebrospinal (ser'e-brō-spi-nal, se-re'brō-) Relating to the brain and the spinal cord.

cerebrovascular (ser'e-brō-vas'kyu-lar) Relating to the blood supply to the brain, particularly with reference to pathologic changes.

cerebrum (ser'e-brum, se-re'brum) Originally referred to the largest portion of the brain; it now usually refers only to the parts derived from the telencephalon and includes mainly the cerebral hemispheres (cerebral cortex and basal ganglia).

cervical (ser'vi-kal) Relating to a neck, or cervix, in any sense.

chemoreceptor (kem'ō-re-sep'tor, ke'mō-) Any cell that is activated by a change in its chemical milieu and results in a nerve impulse. Such cells can be either 1) "transducer" cells innervated by sensory nerve fibers (*e.g.*, the gustatory cells of the taste buds); or 2) nerve cells proper, such as the olfactory receptor cells of the olfactory mucosa.

chemotherapy (kem'ō-thar-a-pe, ke'mō-) Treatment of disease by means of chemical substances or drugs; usually used in reference to neoplastic disease.

chiro- The hand.

chlorate (klōr'at) A salt of chloric acid.

chloride (klōr'id) A compound containing chlorine, at a valence of -1, as in the salts of hydrochloric acid.

chlorophyll (klōr'ō-fil) A complex of light-absorbing green pigments that, in living plants, convert light energy into oxidizing and reducing power, thus fixing CO_2 and evolving O_2; the naturally occurring forms are chlorophyll *a*, *b*, *c*, and *d*.

chole- Bile.

cholecystitis (kō'le-sis-ti'tis) Inflammation of the gallbladder.

cholera (kol'er-a) An acute epidemic infectious disease caused by the bacterium *Vibrio cholerae*, occurring primarily in Asia. A toxin elaborated by the bacterium activates the adenylate cyclase of the mucosa, causing active secretion of an isotonic fluid resulting in watery diarrhea, loss of fluid and electrolytes, and dehydration and collapse, but no gross morphologic change in the intestinal mucosa.

cholesteremia (kō-les-ter-e'me-a) The presence of excessive cholesterol in the blood.

cholesterol (kō-les'ter-ol) 5-Cholesten-3β-ol; the most abundant steroid in animal tissues; circulates in the plasma complexed to proteins of various densities and plays an important role in the pathogenesis of atheroma formation in arteries.

cholinergic (kol-in-er'jik) Relating to nerve cells or fibers that employ acetylcholine as their neurotransmitter.

cholinesterase (kō-lin-es'ter-as) One of a family of enzymes capable of catalyzing the hydrolysis of acylcholines and a few other compounds. Found in cobra venom.

cholinolytic (kō'lin-ō-lit'ik) Preventing the action of acetylcholine.

cholinomimetic (kol'i-nō-mi-met'ik) Having an action similar to that of acetylcholine; term proposed to replace the less accurate term, parasympathomimetic.

chorea (kor-e'a) Irregular, spasmodic, involuntary movements of the limbs or facial muscles, often accompanied by hypotonia.

    Huntington's chorea a hereditary progressive disorder usually beginning by middle age, consisting of choreoathetosis and dementia.

choroid (ko'royd) The middle vascular tunic of the eye lying between the retina and the sclera.

chromatography (krō-ma-tog'ra-fe) The separation of chemical substances and particles by differential movement through a two-phase system.

    gas chromatography a chromatographic procedure in which the mobile phase is a mixture of gases or vapors, which are separated by their differential adsorption on a stationary phase.

    thin-layer chromatography chromatography through a thin layer of cellulose or similar inert material supported on a glass or plastic plate.

chromaturia (krō-ma-tu're-a) Abnormal coloration of the urine.

chromosome (krō'mō-sōm) One of the bodies (normally 46 in humans) in the cell nucleus that is the bearer of genes, has the form of a delicate chromatin filament during interphase, contracts to form a compact cylinder segmented into two arms by the centromere during metaphase and anaphase stages of cell divison, and is capable of reproducing its physical and chemical structure through successive cell divisons.

chronic (kron´ik) Referring to a health-related state, lasting a long time.

ciliary (sil´e-ar-e) Relating to any cilia or hairlike processes, specifically, the eyelashes.

circadian (ser-ka´de-an) Relating to biologic variations or rhythms with a cycle of about 24 hours.

circulation (ser-kyu-la´shun) Movements in a circle, or through a circular course, or through a course which leads back to the same point; usually referring to blood circulation unless otherwise specified.

   pulmonary circulation the passage of blood from the right ventricle through the pulmonary artery to the lungs and back through the pulmonary veins to the left atrium.

   systemic circulation the circulation of blood through the arteries, capillaries, and veins of the general system, from the left ventricle to the right atrium.

cirrhosis (sir-rō´sis) Progressive disease of the liver characterized by diffuse damage to hepatic parenchymal cells, with nodular regeneration, fibrosis, and disturbance of normal architecture; associated with failure in the function of hepatic cells and interference with blood flow in the liver, frequently resulting in jaundice, portal hypertension, ascites, and ultimately hepatic failure.

   alcoholic cirrhosis cirrhosis that frequently develops in chronic alcoholism, characterized in an early stage by enlargement of the liver due to fatty change with mild fibrosis, and later by Laënnec's cirrhosis with contraction of the liver.

   fatty cirrhosis early nutritional cirrhosis, especially in alcoholics, in which the liver is enlarged by fatty change, with mild fibrosis.

citrate (sit´rat, si´trat) A salt or ester of citric acid; used as anticoagulants because they bind calcium ions.

citric acid (sit´rik) The acid of citrus fruits, widely distributed in nature and a key intermediate in intermediary metabolism.

clairvoyance (klar-voy´ans) Perception of objective events (past, present, or future) not ordinarily discernible by the senses; a type of extrasensory perception.

classification (klas´i-fi-ka´shun) A systematic arrangement into classes or groups based on perceived common characteristics; a means of giving order to a group of disconnected facts.

claudication (klaw-di-ka´shun) Limping, usually referring to intermittent claudication.

claustrophobia (klaw-strō-fō´be-a) A morbid fear of being in a confined place.

clavicle (klav´i-kl) A doubly curved long bone that forms part of the shoulder girdle. Its medial end articulates with the manubrium sterni at the sternoclavicular joint, its lateral end with the acromion of the scapula at the acromioclavicular joint.

clearance (kler´ans) (*C* with a subscript indicating the substance removed). Removal of a substance from the blood, *e.g.*, by renal excretion, expressed in terms of the volume flow of arterial blood or plasma that would contain the amount of substance removed per unit time; measured in ml/min.

   creatinine clearance a mathematical calculation of the total amount of creatinine excreted in the urine over a period of time. It tests renal function. The calculation is: creatinine clearance (ml/min) = urine creatinine concentration (ml/dl) × volume of urine (ml/24 hour) ÷ plasma creatinine concentration (mg/dl) x 1440 min/24 hour.

   inulin clearance an accurate measure of the rate of filtration through the renal glomeruli, because inulin filters freely with water and is neither excreted nor reabsorbed through tubule walls. Inulin is not a normal constituent of plasma and must be infused continously to maintain a steady plasma concentration and a steady rate of urinary excretion during the measurement.

   urea clearance the volume of plasma (or blood) that would be completely cleared of urea by one minute's excretion of urine.

cleft (kleft) A fissure.

cm centimeter; cm^2 for square centimeter; cm^3 for cubic centimeter.

CNS central nervous system

coagulant (kō-ag´yu-lant) An agent that causes, stimulates, or accelerates coagulation, especially with reference to blood.

coagulation (kō-ag-yu-la´shun) Clotting; the process of changing from a liquid to a solid, said especially of blood.

cocaine (kō-kan´) an alkaloid obtained from the leaves of *Erythroxylon coca*, or by synthesis from ecgonine or its derivatives; it has moderate vasoconstrictor activity and pronounced psychotropic effects; its salts are used as a topical anesthetic.

crack cocaine a derivative of cocaine, usually smoked, producing brief, intense euphoria. Crack cocaine is relatively inexpensive and extremely addictive; dependency can develop in less than 2 weeks. Like snorted or injected cocaine, it has both acute and chronic adverse effects, including heart and nasopharyngeal damage, seizures, sudden death, and psychosis.

coccyx (kok'siks) The small bone at the end of the vertebral column in man, formed by the fusion of four rudimentary vertebrae; it articulates above with the sacrum.

cochlea (kok'le-a) A cone-shaped cavity in the petrous portion of the temporal bone, forming one of the divisions of the labyrinth or internal ear. It consists of a spiral canal making two and a half turns around a central core of spongy bone, the modiolus; this spiral canal of the cochlea contains the membranous cochlea, or cochlear duct, in which is the spiral organ (Corti).

cocktail (kok'tal) A mixture that includes several ingredients or drugs.

Brompton cocktail a cocktail of morphine and cocaine usually used for analgesia in terminal cancer patients; the formulations vary, but typically it contains 15 mg of morphine hydrochoride and 10 mg of cocaine hydrochloride per 10 ml of the cocktail.

coefficient (kō-e-fish'ent) The expression of the amount or degree of any quality possessed by a substance, or of the degree of physical or chemical change normally occurring in that substance under stated conditions.

cognition (kog-ni'shun) The mental activities associated with thinking, learning, and memory.

colic (kol'ik) Relating to the colon.

colitis (kō-li'tis) Inflammation of the colon.

collagen (kol'la-jen) The major protein of the white fibers of connective tissue, cartilage, and bone; insoluble in water but can be altered to easily digestible, soluble gelatins by boiling in water, dilute acids, or alkalies.

colorectal (kol'ō-rek'tal) Relating to the colon and rectum, or to the entire large bowel.

colostomy (kō-los'tō-me) Establishment of an artificial cutaneous opening into the colon.

coma (kō'ma) A state of profound unconsciousness from which one cannot be roused.

diabetic coma coma that develops in severe and inadequately treated diabetes mellitus and is commonly fatal, unless appropriate therapy is instituted promptly; results from reduced oxidative metabolism of the central nervous system that, in turn, stems from severe ketoacidosis and possibly also from the histotoxic action of the ketone bodies and disturbances in water and electrolyte balance.

hypoglycemic coma a metabolic encephalopathy caused by hypoglycemia; usually seen in diabetics, and due to exogenous insulin excess.

metabolic coma coma resulting from diffuse failure of neuronal metabolism, caused by such abnormalities as intrinsic disorders of neuron or glial cell metabolism, or extracerebral disorders that produce intoxication or electrolyte imbalances.

uremic coma a metabolic encephalopathy caused by renal failure.

communicable (ko-myun'i-ka-bl) Capable of being communicated or transmitted; said especially of disease.

comorbidity (kō-mōr-bid'i-te) A concomitant but unrelated pathologic or disease process; usually used in epidemiology to indicate the coexistence of two or more disease processes.

complaint (kom-plant') A disorder, disease, or symptom, or the description of it.

chief complaint the primary symptom that a patient states as the reason for seeking medical care.

compos mentis (kom'pos men'tis) Of sound mind; usually used in its opposite form, non compos mentis.

compound (kom'pownd) chemistry a substance formed by the covalent or electrostatic union of two or more elements, generally differing entirely in physical characteristics from any of its components.

concussion (kon-kush'un) A violent shaking or jarring.

brain concussion a clinical syndrome due to mechanical, usually traumatic, forces; characterized by immediate and transient impairment of neural function, such as alteration of consciousness, disturbance of vision and equilibrium, etc.

spinal cord concussion injury to the spinal cord due to a blow to the vertebral column with transient or prolonged dysfunction below the level of the lesion.

conduction (kon-duk'shun) The act of transmitting or conveying certain forms of energy, such as heat, sound, or electricity, from one point to another, without evident movement in the conducting body.

synaptic conduction the conduction of a nerve impulse across a synapse.

confabulation (kon'fab-yu-la'shun) The making of bizarre and incorrect responses, and a readiness to give a fluent but tangential answer, with no regard whatever to facts, to any question put; seen in amnesia, presbyophrenia, and Wernicke-Korsakoff syndrome.

congenital (kon-jen'i-tal) Existing at birth, referring to mental or physical traits, anomalies, malformations, or diseases, which may be either hereditary or due to an influence occurring during gestation up to the moment of birth.

congestion (kon-jes'chun) Presence of an abnormal amount of fluid in the vessels or passages of a part or organ; especially, of blood due either to increased influx or to an obstruction to the return flow.

conjugate (kon'ju-gat) Joined or paired.

conjunctiva (kon-junk-ti'va) The mucous membrane investing the anterior surface of the eyeball and the posterior surface of the lids.

conjunctivitis (kon-junk-ti-vi'tis) Inflammation of the conjunctiva.

conscious (con'shus) Aware; having present knowledge or perception of oneself, one's acts and surroundings.

consciousness (con'shus-nes) The state of being aware, or perceiving physical facts or mental concepts; a state of general wakefulness and responsiveness to environment; a functioning sensorium.

contagious (kon-ta'jus) Relating to contagion; communicable or transmissible by contact with the sick or their fresh secretions or excretions.

contamination (kon-tam-i-na'shun) The presence of an infectious agent on a body surface; also on or in clothes, bedding, toys, surgical instruments or dressings, or other inanimate articles or substances including water, milk and food or that infectious agent itself.

contraction (kon-trak'shun) A shortening or increase in tension;

denoting the normal function of muscular tissue.

tonic contraction sustained contraction of a muscle, as employed in the maintenance of posture.

contraindication (kon-tra-in-di-ka'shun) Any special symptom or circumstance that renders the use of a remedy or the carrying out of a procedure inadvisable, usually because of risk.

contralateral (kon-tra-lat'er-al) Relating to the opposite side, as when pain is felt or paralysis occurs on the side opposite to that of the lesion.

contusion (kon-tu'shun) Any mechanical injury (usually caused by a blow) resulting in hemorrhage beneath unbroken skin.

convulsion (kon-vul'shun) A violent spasm or series of jerkings of the face, trunk, or extremities.

coordination (kō-ōr'di-na'shun) The harmonious working together, especially of several muscles or muscle groups in the execution of complicated movements.

bilateral coordination the ability to coordinate the two sides of the body.

cornea (kōr'ne-a) The transparent tissue constituting the anterior sixth of the outer wall of the eye, with a 7.7 mm radius of curvature as contrasted with the 13.5 mm of the sclera; it consists of stratified squamous epithelium continuous with that of the conjunctiva, a substantia propria, regularly arranged collagen imbedded in mucopolysaccharide, and an inner layer of endothelium. It is the chief refractory structure of the eye.

coroner (kōr'on-er) An official whose duty it is to investigate sudden, suspicious, or violent death to determine the cause; in some communities, the office has been replaced by that of medical examiner.

corporeal (kōr-pō're-al) Pertaining to the body, or to a corpus.

corpse (kōrps) syn cadaver

corpulence (kōr'pyu-lens) syn obesity

corpus (kōr'pus) syn body

corpus callosum the great commissural plate of nerve fibers interconnecting the cortical hemispheres (with the exception of most of the temporal lobes which are interconnected by the anterior commissure). Lying at the floor of the longitudinal fissure, and covered on each side by the cingulate gyrus, it is arched from behind forward and is thick at each extremity (splenium and genu) but thinner in its long central portion (truncus); it curves back underneath itself at the genu to form the rostrum of the corpus callosum.

corpuscle (kŏr'pus-l) A small mass or body.

cortex (kŏr'teks) The outer portion of an organ, such as the kidney, as distinguished from the inner, or medullary, portion.

cerebellar cortex the thin gray surface layer of the cerebellum, consisting of an outer molecular layer or stratum moleculare, a single layer of Purkinje cells (the ganglionic layer), and an inner granular layer or stratum granulosum.

cerebral cortex the gray cellular mantle (1 to 4 mm thick) covering the entire surface of the cerebral hemisphere of mammals; characterized by a laminar organization of cellular and fibrous components such that its nerve cells are stacked in defined layers varying in number from one, as in the archicortex of the hippocampus, to five or six in the larger neocortex; the outermost (molecular or plexiform) layer contains very few cell bodies and is composed largely of the distal ramifications of the long apical dendrites issued perpendicularly to the surface by pyramidal and fusiform cells in deeper layers. From the surface inward, the layers as classified in K. Brodmann's parcellation are: 1) molecular or plexiform layer; 2) outer granular layer; 3) pyramidal cell layer; 4) inner granular layer; 5) inner pyramidal layer (ganglionic layer); and 6) multiform cell layer, many of which are fusiform. This multilaminate organization is typical of the neocortex (homotypic cortex; isocortex in O. Vogt's terminology), which in humans covers the largest part by far of the cerebral hemisphere. The more primordial heterotypic cortex or allocortex (Vogt) has fewer cell layers. A form of cortex intermediate between isocortex and allocortex, called juxtallocortex (Vogt) covers the ventral part of the cingulate gyrus and the entorhinal area of the parahippocampal gyrus. On the basis of local differences in the arrangement of nerve cells (cytoarchitecture), Brodmann outlined 47 areas in the cerebral cortex which, in functional terms, can be classified into three categories: motor cortex (areas 4 and 6), characterized by a poorly developed inner granular layer (agranular cortex) and prominent pyramidal cell layers; sensory cortex, characterized by a prominent inner granular layer (granular cortex or koniocortex) and comprising the somatic sensory cortex (areas 1 to 3), the auditory cortex (areas 41 and 42), and the visual cortex (areas 17 to 19); and association cortex, the vast remaining expanses of the cerebral cortex.

motor cortex the region of the cerebral cortex most immediately influencing movements of the face, neck, trunk, arms, and leg; its effects upon the motor neurons innervating the skeletal musculature are mediated by the pyramidal tract.

sensory cortex formerly denoting specifically the somatic sensory cortex, but now used to refer collectively to the somatic sensory, auditory, visual, and olfactory regions of the cerebral cortex.

somatic sensory cortex the region of the cerebral cortex receiving the somatic sensory radiation from the ventrobasal nucleus of the thalamus; it represents the primary cortical processing mechanism for sensory information originating at the body surfaces (touch) and in deeper tissues such as muscle, tendons, and joint capsules (position sense).

visual cortex the region of the cerebral cortex occupying the entire surface of the occipital lobe, and composed of Brodmann's areas 17 to 19. Area 17 (which is also called striate cortex or area because the line of Gennari is grossly visible on its surface) is the primary visual cortex, receiving the visual radiation from the lateral geniculate body of the thalamus. The surrounding areas 18 (parastriate cortex or area) and 19 (peristriate cortex or area) are probably involved in subsequent steps of visual information processing; area 18 is referred to as the secondary visual cortex.

cortisone (kŏr'ti-sōn) A glucocorticoid not normally secreted in significant quantities by the human adrenal cortex. It exhibits no biological activity until converted to hydrocortisone (cortisol); it acts upon carbohydrate metabolism and influences the nutrition and growth of connective (collagenous) tissues.

cranium (kra'ne-um) syn skull

creatinine (kre-at'i-nen, -nin) A component of urine and the final product of creatine catabolism; formed by the nonenzymatic dephosphorylative cyclization of phosphocreatine to form the internal anhydride of creatine.

crystal (kris'tal) A solid of regular shape and, for a given compound, characteristic angles, formed when an element or compound solidifies slowly enough, as a result either of freezing from the liquid form or of precipitating out of solution, to allow the individual molecules to take up regular positions with respect to one another.

crystallin (kris'ta-lin) A type of protein found in the lens of the eye.

crystalline (kris'ta-len) Clear; transparent.

cubital (kyu'bi-tal) Relating to the elbow or to the ulna.

cuff (kuf) Any structure shaped like a cuff.

   rotator cuff of shoulder the upper half of the capsule of the shoulder joint reinforced by the tendons of insertion of the supraspinatus, infraspinatus, teres minor, and subscapularis muscles.

culture (kul'chur) The propagation of microorganisms on or in media of various kinds.

   cell culture the maintenance or growth of dispersed cells after removal from the body, commonly on a glass surface immersed in nutrient fluid.

   smear culture a culture obtained by spreading material presumed to be infected on the surface of a solidified medium.

   tissue culture the maintenance of live tissue after removal from the body, by placing in a vessel with a sterile nutritive medium.

curettage (kyu-re-tahzh', ku-) A scraping, usually of the interior of a cavity or tract, for the removal of new growths or other abnormal tissues, or to obtain material for tissue diagnosis.

cutaneous (kyu-ta'ne-us) Relating to the skin.

CVA cerebrovascular accident

cyano- blue.

cyanosis (si-a-nō'sis) A dark bluish or purplish coloration of the skin and mucous membrane due to deficient oxygenation of the blood, evident when reduced hemoglobin in the blood exceeds 5 g per 100 ml.

cycle (si'kl) A recurrent series of events.

   cardiac cycle the complete round of cardiac systole and diastole with the intervals between, commencing with any event in the heart's action and ending when same event is repeated.

cycles per second The number of successive compressions and rarefactions per second of a sound wave. The

preferred designation for this unit of frequency is hertz.

cystinuria (sis-ti-nu're-a) Excessive urinary excretion of cystine, along with lysine, arginine, and ornithine, arising from defective transport systems for these acids in the kidney and intestine; renal function is sometimes compromised by cystine crystalluria and nephrolithiasis; occurs in certain heritable diseases, such as Fanconi's syndrome (cystinosis) and hepatolenticular degeneration.

cystitis (sis-ti'tis) Inflammation of the urinary bladder.

cytogenesis (si-tō-jen'e-sis) The origin and development of cells.

cytokine (si'tō-kin) Hormone-like proteins, secreted by many cell types, which regulate the intensity and duration of immune responses and are involved in cell-to-cell communication.

cytology (si-tol'ō-je) The study of the anatomy, physiology, pathology, and chemistry of the cell.

cytoplasm (si'tō-plazm) The substance of a cell, exclusive of the nucleus, which contains various organelles and inclusions within a colloidal protoplasm.

cytosome (si'tō-sōm) The cell body exclusive of the nucleus.

cytotoxic (si-tō-tok'sik) Detrimental or destructive to cells; pertaining to the effect of noncytophilic antibody on specific antigen, frequently, but not always, mediating the action of complement.

cyturia (si-tu're-a) The passage of cells in unusual numbers in the urine.

Δ delta.

dactylo- The fingers, and (less often) toes.

deafness (def'nes) General term for loss of the ability to hear, without designation of the degree or cause of the loss.

   psychogenic deafness hearing loss without evidence of organic cause or malingering; often follows severe psychic shock.

   sensorineural deafness hearing impairment due to disorders of the cochlear division of the 9th cranial nerve (auditory nerve), the cochlea, or the retrocochlear nerve tracts, as opposed to conductive deafness.

death (deth) The cessation of life. In higher organisms, a cessation of integrated tissue and organ functions; in humans, manifested by the loss of heartbeat, the absence of spontaneous breathing, and cerebral death.

deca- Prefix used in the SI and metric systems to signify 10. Also spelled deka-.

decarboxylation (de'kar-boks-e-la'shun) A reaction involving the removal of a molecule of carbon dioxide from a carboxylic acid.

decay (de-ka') Destruction of an organic substance by slow combustion or gradual oxidation.

deci- Prefix used in the SI and metric system to signify one-tenth (10^-).

deduction (de-duk'shun) The logical derivation of a conclusion from certain premises. The conclusion will be true if the premises are true and the deductive argument is valid.

defect (de'fekt) An imperfection, malformation, dysfunction, or absence; an attribute of quality, in contrast with deficiency, which is an attribute of quantity.

defibrillation (de-fib-ri-la'shun) The arrest of fibrillation of the cardiac muscle (atrial or ventricular) with restoration of the normal rhythm.

defibrillator (de-fib'ri-la-ter) Any agent or measure, *e.g.*, an electric shock, that arrests fibrillation of the ventricular muscle and restores the normal beat.

deformity (de-fôr'mi-te) A permanent structural deviation from the normal shape or size, resulting in disfigurement; may be congenital or acquired.

degenerate To pass to a lower level of mental, physical, or moral state; to fall below the normal or acceptable type or state.

dehydration (de-hi-dra'shun) Deprivation of water.

dehydrogenase (de-hi'drō-jen-as) Class name for those enzymes that oxidize substrates by catalyzing removal of hydrogen from metabolites (hydrogen donors) and transferring it to other substances (hydrogen acceptors).

delirium (de-lir'e-um) An altered state of consciousness, consisting of confusion, distractibility, disorientation, disordered thinking and memory, defective perception (illusions and hallucinations), prominent hyperactivity, agitation and autonomic nervous system overactivity; caused by a number of toxic structural and metabolic disorders.

    delirium tremens a severe, sometimes fatal, form of delirium due to alcoholic withdrawal following a period of sustained intoxication.

delusion (de-lu'zhun) A false belief or wrong judgment held with conviction despite incontrovertible evidence to the contrary.

dementia (de-men'she-a) The loss, usually progressive, of cognitive and intellectual functions, without impairment of perception or consciousness; caused by a variety of disorders, most commonly structural brain disease. Characterized by disorientation, impaired memory, judgment, and intellect, and a shallow labile affect.

demi- Half, lesser.

demography (de-mog'ra-fe) The study of populations, especially with reference to size, density, fertility, mortality, growth rate, age distribution, migration, and vital statistics.

demyelination (de-mi'e-li-na'shun) Loss of myelin with preservation of the axons or fiber tracts. Central demyelination occurs within the central nervous system (*e.g.,* the demyelination seen with multiple sclerosis); peripheral demyelination affects the peripheral nervous system (*e.g.,* the demyelination seen with Guillain-Barré syndrome).

denatured (de-na'tyurd) Made unnatural or changed from the normal; often applied to proteins or nucleic acids heated or otherwise treated to the point where tertiary structural characteristics are altered.

dendrite (den'drit) One of the two types of branching protoplasmic processes of the nerve cell (the other being the axon).

denervation (de-ner-va'shun) Loss of nerve supply.

density (den'si-te) The compactness of a substance; the ratio of mass to unit volume, usually expressed as g/cm^3 (kg/m^3 in the SI system).

dentition (den-tish'un) The natural teeth, as considered collectively, in the dental arch; may be deciduous, permanent, or mixed.

deoxyribonucleic acid (de-oks'e-ri'bō-nu-kle'ik) The type of nucleic acid containing deoxyribose as the sugar component, found principally in the nuclei (chromatin, chromosomes) and mitochondria of animal and vegetable cells, usually loosely bound to protein (hence the term deoxyribonucleoprotein); the autoreproducing component of chromosomes and of many viruses, and the repository of hereditary characteristics. Chromosomes are composed of double-stranded DNA; mitochondrial DNA is circular.

dependence (de-pen'dens) The quality or condition of relying upon, being influenced by, or being subservient to a person or object reflecting a particular need.

substance dependence a pattern of behavioral, physiologic, and cognitive symptoms due to substance use or abuse; usually indicated by tolerance to the effects of the substance and withdrawal symptoms when use of the substance is terminated.

depersonalization (de-per'son-al-i-za'shun) A state in which a person loses the feeling of his own identity in relation to others in his family or peer group, or loses the feeling of his own reality.

depressant (de-pres'ant) Diminishing functional tone or activity.

derm- The skin; corresponds to the L. *cut-*.

dermal (der'mal) Relating to the skin.

dermatitis (der-ma-ti'tis) Inflammation of the skin.

dermis (der'mis) A layer of skin composed of a superficial thin layer that interdigitates with the epidermis, the stratum papillare, and the stratum reticulare; it contains blood and lymphatic vessels, nerves and nerve endings, glands, and, except for glabrous skin, hair follicles.

desensitization (de-sen'si-ti-za'shun) The reduction or abolition of allergic sensitivity or reactions to the specific antigen (allergen).

desflurane (dés'flur'an) An inhalation anesthetic with physical characteristics that provide rapid induction of and recovery from anesthesia.

desiccant (des'i-kant) Drying; causing or promoting dryness.

desmitis (dez-mi'tis) Inflammation of a ligament.

desmopressin (des-mō-pres'in) An analog of vasopressin (antidiuretic hormone, ADH) possessing powerful antidiuretic activity.

detoxication (de-tok-si-ka'shun) Recovery from the toxic effects of a drug.

detoxification (de-tok'si-fi-ka'shun) syn detoxication

dextro- Right, toward, or on the right side.

dextroamphetamine sulfate (deks'trō-am-fet'a-men sul'fat) similar in action to racemic amphetamine sulfate, but more stimulating to the central nervous system; sympathomimetic and appetite depressant.

diabetes (di-a-be'tez) Either diabetes insipidus or diabetes mellitus, diseases having in common the symptom polyuria; when used without qualification, refers to DIABETES MELLITUS.

diabetes mellitus a metabolic disease in which carbohydrate utilization is reduced and that of lipid and protein enhanced; it is caused by an absolute or relative deficiency of insulin and is characterized, in more severe cases, by chronic hyperglycemia, glycosuria, water and electrolyte loss, ketoacidosis, and coma; long-term complications include development of neuropathy, retinopathy, nephropathy, generalized degenerative changes in large and small blood vessels, and increased susceptibility to infection.

type I diabetes syn insulin-dependent diabetes mellitus

type II diabetes non-insulin-dependent diabetes mellitus.

diagnosis (di-ag-nō'sis) The determination of the nature of a disease.

clinical diagnosis a diagnosis made from a study of the signs and symptoms of a disease.

differential diagnosis the determination of which of two or more diseases with similar symptoms is the one from which the patient is suffering, by a systematic comparison and contrasting of the clinical findings.

Diagnostic and Statistical Manual An American Psychiatric Association publication that classifies mental illnesses. Currently in its fourth edition (DSM-IV), the manual provides health practitioners with a comprehensive system for diagnosing mental illnesses based on specific ideational and behavioral symptoms.

dialysis (di-al'i-sis) A form of filtration to separate crystalloid from colloid substances (or smaller molecules from larger ones) in a solution by interposing a semipermeable membrane between the solution and water; the crystalloid (smaller) substances pass through the membrane into the water on the other side, the colloids do not.

diaphoretic (di-a-fō-ret'ik) Relating to, or causing, perspiration.

dicrotism (di'krō-tizm) That form of the pulse in which a double beat can be appreciated at any arterial pulse for each beat of the heart; due to accentuation of the dicrotic wave.

diffusion (di-fyu'zhun) The random movement of molecules or ions or small particles in solution or suspension toward a uniform distribution throughout the available volume.

dilation (di-la'shun) Physiologic or artificial enlargement of a hollow structure or opening.

diluent Ingredient in a medicinal preparation which lacks pharmacological activity but is pharmaceutically necessary or desirable. May be a liquid for the dissolution of drugs to be injected, ingested, or inhaled.

dilute (di-lut') To reduce the concentration, strength, quality, or purity of a solution or mixture.

diplopia (di-plŏ'pe-a) The condition in which a single object is perceived as two objects.

disability (dis-a-bil'i-te) Any restriction or lack of ability to perform an activity in a manner or within the range considered normal for a human being.

disaggregation (dis'ag-gre-ga'shun) A breaking up into component parts.

discrete (dis-kret') Separate; distinct; not joined to or incorporated with another; denoting especially certain lesions of the skin.

disease (di-zez') An interruption, cessation, or disorder of body functions, systems, or organs.

    endemic disease continued prevalence of a disease in a specific population or area.

    epidemic disease marked increase in prevalence of a disease in a specific population or area, usually with an environmental cause, such as an infectious or toxic agent.

    Ménière's disease an affection characterized clinically by vertigo, nausea, vomiting, tinnitus, and progressive deafness due to swelling of the endolymphatic duct.

    primary disease a disease that arises spontaneously and is not associated with or caused by a previous disease, injury, or event, but which may lead to a secondary disease.

    secondary disease a disease that follows and results from an earlier disease, injury, or event;

disorder (dis-ŏr'der) A disturbance of function, structure, or both, resulting from a genetic or embryologic failure in development or from exogenous factors such as poison, trauma, or disease.

    affective disorders a class of mental disorder's characterized by a disturbance in mood.

    anxiety disorders a category of interrelated mental illnesses involving anxiety reactions in response to stress. The types include: 1) generalized anxiety, by far the most prevalent condition, which strikes slightly more females than males, mostly in the 20–35 age group; 2) panic disorder, in which a person suffers repeated panic attacks. Some 2–5 percent of Americans are subject to this ailment, about twice as many women as men; 3) obsessive-compulsive disorder, afflicting 2–3 percent of the U.S. population. About two-thirds of these patients go on to experience a major depressive episode; 4) posttraumatic stress disorder, most frequent among combat veterans or survivors of major physical trauma; and 5) the phobias (*e.g.*, fear of snakes, crowds, confinement, heights, etc.), which on a minor scale affect about one in eight people in the U.S. Drugs that have proven effective against anxiety disorders are beta-blockers, which act on adrenaline receptors; anxiolytics; antidepressants; and serotonergic drugs. Regular exercise has also proved beneficial.

    attention deficit disorder a disorder of attention and impulse control with specific DSM criteria, appearing in childhood and sometimes persisting to adulthood. Hyperactivity may be a feature, but is not necessary for the diagnosis.

    bipolar disorder an affective disorder characterized by the occurrence of alternating periods of euphoria (mania) and depression.

    cyclothymic disorder an affective disorder characterized by mood swings including periods of hypomania and depression; a form of depressive disorder.

    dysthymic disorder a chronic disturbance of mood characterized by mild depression or loss of interest in usual activities.

    substance abuse disorders a class of mental disorders in which behavioral and biological changes are associated with regular use of alcohol, drugs, and related substances that affect the central nervous system and personal and social functioning.

diuresis (di-yu-re'sis) Excretion of urine; commonly denotes production of unusually large volumes of urine.

diuretic (di-yu-ret'ik) Promoting the excretion of urine.

diurnal (di-er'nal) Pertaining to the daylight hours; opposite of nocturnal.

diverticulitis (di'ver-tik-yu-li'tis) Inflammation of a diverticulum, especially of the small pockets in the wall of the colon which fill with stagnant fecal material and become inflamed; rarely, they may cause obstruction, perforation, or bleeding.

dopa (dō'pa) An intermediate in the catabolism of l-phenylalanine and l-tyrosine, and in the biosynthesis of norepinephrine, epinephrine, and melanin; the l form, levodopa, is biologically active.

dopamine (dō'pa-men) an intermediate in tyrosine metabolism and precursor of norepinephrine and epinephrine.

dope (dōp) Any drug, either stimulating or depressing, administered for its temporary effect, or taken habitually or addictively.

doping (dōp'ing) The administration of foreign substances to an individual; often used in reference to athletes who try to stimulate physical and psychological strength.

    blood doping infusion of red blood cells, usually freeze-preserved autologous blood, to increase hematocrit and hemoglobin levels; used by endurance athletes to increase blood's oxygen-carrying capacity and thus enhance endurance performance.

dorsalgia (dōr-sal'je-a) Pain in the upper back.

dose (dōs) The quantity of a drug or other remedy to be taken or applied all at one time or in fractional amounts within a given period.

    curative dose the quantity of any substance required to effect the cure of a disease or that will correct the manifestations of a deficiency of a particular factor in the diet;

    effective dose the dose that produces the desired effect; when followed by a subscript (generally "ED_{50}"), it denotes the dose having such an effect on a certain percentage (e.g., 50%) of the test animals; ED_{50} is the median effective dose;

    lethal dose the dose of a chemical or biologic preparation (e.g., a bacterial exotoxin or a suspension of bacteria) that is likely to cause death; it varies in relation to the type of animal and the route of administration; when followed by a subscript (generally "LD_{50}" or median lethal dose), it denotes the dose likely to cause death in a certain percentage (e.g., 50%) of the test animals; median lethal dose is LD_{50}, absolute lethal dose is LD_{100}, and minimal lethal dose is LD_{05}.

dram A unit of weight: $1/8$ oz.; 60 gr., apothecaries' weight; $1/16$ oz., avoirdupois weight.

drug (drug) Therapeutic agent; any substance, other than food, used in the prevention, diagnosis, alleviation, treatment, or cure of disease. For types or classifications of drug's, see the specific name.

    nonsteroidal anti-inflammatory drugs drugs exerting anti-inflammatory (and also usually analgesic and antipyretic) actions; examples include aspirin, diclofenac, ibuprofen, and naproxen. A contrast is made with steroidal compounds (such as hydrocortisone or prednisone) exerting anti-inflammatory activity.

    street drug a controlled substance taken for non-medical purposes. Street drugs comprise various amphetamines, anesthetics, barbiturates, opiates, and psychoactive drugs, and many are derived from natural sources (e.g., the plants *Papaver somniferum, Cannibis sativa, Amanita pantherina, Lophophora williamsii*). Slang names include acid (lysergic acid diethylamide), angel dust (phencyclidine), coke (cocaine), downers (barbiturates), grass (marijuana), hash (concentrated tetrahydrocannibinol), magic mushrooms (psilocybin), and speed (amphetamines). During the 1980s, a new class of "designer drugs" arose, mostly analogs of psychoactive substances intended to escape regulation under the Controlled Substances Act. Also, crack cocaine, a potent, smokable form of cocaine, emerged as a major public health problem. In the U.S., illicit use of drugs such as cocaine, marijuana, and heroin historically has occurred in cycles.

    therapeutic drug prescription or over-the-counter medication used to treat an injury or illness.

drug interactions The pharmacological result, either desirable or undesirable, of drugs interacting with other drugs, with endogenous physiologic chemical agents (e.g., MAOI with epinephrine), with components of the diet, and with chemicals used in diagnostic tests or the results of such tests.

DT delirium tremens; duration tetany.

duodenum (du-ō-de'num, du-od'e-num) The first division of the small intestine, about 25 cm in length, extending from the pylorus to the junction with the jejunum at the level of the first or second lumbar vertebra on the left side. It is divided into the superior part, the first part of which is the duodenal cap, the descending part, into which the bile and pancreatic ducts open, the horizontal (inferior) part and the ascending part, terminating at the duodenojejunal junction.

dura mater (du'ra ma'ter) Pachymeninx (as distinguished from leptomeninx, the combined pia mater and arachnoid); a tough, fibrous membrane forming the outer covering of the central nervous system.

dyad (di'ad) A pair.

dys- Bad, difficult, un-, mis-; opposite of eu-.

dysarthria (dis-ar'thre-a) A disturbance of speech and language due to emotional stress, to brain injury, or to paralysis, incoordination, or spasticity of the muscles used for speaking.

dyscoria (dis-kō're-a) Abnormality in the shape of the pupil.

dyslexia (dis-lek'se-a) Impaired reading ability with a competence level below that expected on the basis of the individual's level of intelligence, and in the presence of normal vision and letter recognition and normal recognition of the meaning of pictures and objects.

dyspepsia (dis-pep'se-a) Impaired gastric function or "upset stomach" due to some disorder of the stomach; characterized by epigastric pain, sometimes burning, nausea, and gaseous eructation.

dysphagia (dis-fa'je-a) Difficulty in swallowing.

dysphoria (dis-fōr'e-a) A mood of general dissatisfaction, restlessness, depression, and anxiety; a feeling of unpleasantness or discomfort.

dyspnea (disp-ne'a) Shortness of breath, a subjective difficulty or distress in breathing, usually associated with disease of the heart or lungs; occurs normally during intense physical exertion or at high altitude.

dysthymia (dis-thi'me-a) A chronic mood disorder manifested as depression for most of the day, more days than not, accompanied by some of the following symptoms: poor appetite or overeating, insomnia or hypersomnia, low energy or fatigue, low self-esteem, poor concentration, difficulty making decisions, and feelings of hopelessness.

dystonia (dis-tō'ne-a) A state of abnormal (either hypo- or hyper-) tonicity in any of the tissues.

dystrophy (dis'trō-fe) Progressive changes that may result from defective nutrition of a tissue or organ.

muscular dystrophy a general term for a number of hereditary, progressive degenerative disorders affecting skeletal muscles, and often other organ systems as well.

dysuria (dis-yu're-a) Difficulty or pain in urination.

ear (er) The organ of hearing: composed of the EXTERNAL EAR, which includes the auricle and the external acoustic, or auditory, meatus; the MIDDLE EAR, or the tympanic cavity with its ossicles; and the INTERNAL EAR or INNER EAR, or labyrinth, which includes the semicircular canals, vestibule, and cochlea.

echolalia (ek-ō-la'le-a) Involuntary parrot-like repetition of a word or sentence just spoken by another person. Usually seen with schizophrenia.

eclampsia (ek-lamp'se-a) Occurrence of one or more convulsions, not attributable to other cerebral conditions such as epilepsy or cerebral hemorrhage, in a patient with preeclampsia.

ecology (e-kol'ō-je) The branch of biology concerned with interrelationships among living organisms, encompassing the relations of organisms to each other, to the environment, and to energy balance within a given ecosystem.

ecosystem (e'kō-sis-tem) The fundamental unit in ecology, comprising the living organisms and the nonliving elements that interact in a defined region.

edema (e-de'ma) An accumulation of an excessive amount of watery fluid in cells, tissues, or serous cavities.

EEG electroencephalogram; electroencephalography.

EENT eye, ear, nose, and throat.

effector (e-fek'tor, -tōr) A peripheral tissue that receives nerve impulses and reacts by contraction (muscle), secretion (gland), or a discharge of electricity (electric organ of certain bony fishes).

efferent (ef'er-ent) Conducting (fluid or a nerve impulse) outward from a given organ or part thereof; *e.g.*, the efferent connections of a group of nerve cells, efferent blood vessels, or the excretory duct of an organ.

effusion (e-fu'zhun) The escape of fluid from the blood vessels or lymphatics into the tissues or a cavity.

ego (e'gō) psychoanalysis One of the three components of the psychic apparatus in the freudian structural framework, the other two being the id and superego. The ego occupies a position between the primal instincts (pleasure principle) and the demands of the outer world (reality principle), and therefore mediates between the person and external reality by performing the important functions of perceiving the needs of the self, both physical and psychological, and the qualities and attitudes of the environment. It is also responsible for certain defensive functions to protect the person against the demands of the id and superego.

egomania (e-gō-ma′ne-a) Extreme self-centeredness, self-appreciation, or self-content.

ejaculate (e-jak′yu-lat) To expel suddenly, as of semen.

EKG electrocardiogram.

electrocardiogram (e-lek-trō-kar′de-ō-gram) Graphic record of the heart's integrated action currents obtained with the electrocardiograph.

electroencephalograph (e-lek′trō-en-sef′a-lō-graf) A system for recording the electric potentials of the brain derived from electrodes attached to the scalp.

electrolysis (e-lek-trol′i-sis) Decomposition of a salt or other chemical compound by means of an electric current.

electrolyte (e-lek′trō-lit) Any compound that, in solution, conducts electricity and is decomposed (electrolyzed) by it; an ionizable substance in solution.

electron (e-lek′tron) One of the negatively charged subatomic particles that are distributed about the positive nucleus and with it constitute the atom; in mass they are estimated to be 1/1836.15 of a proton; when emitted from inside the nucleus of a radioactive substance, electron's are called beta particles.

electronystagmography (e-lek′trō-nis′tag-mog′ra-fe) A method of nystagmography based on electro-oculography; skin electrodes are placed at outer canthi to register horizontal nystagmus or above and below each eye for vertical nystagmus.

element (el′e-ment) A substance composed of atoms of only one kind, i.e., of identical atomic (proton) number, that therefore cannot be decomposed into two or more elements, and that can lose its chemical properties only by union with some other element or by a nuclear reaction changing the proton number.

ELISA enzyme-linked immunosorbent assay.

embolism (em′bō-lizm) Obstruction or occlusion of a vessel by an embolus.

embolus (em′bō-lus) A plug, composed of a detached thrombus or vegetation, mass of bacteria, or other foreign body, occluding a vessel.

emesis (em′e-sis) syn vomiting

emetic (e-met′ik) Relating to or causing vomiting.

EMG electromyogram.

EMIT enzyme-multiplied immunoassay technique.

emotion (e-mō′shun) A strong feeling, aroused mental state, or intense state of drive or unrest directed toward a definite object and evidenced in both behavior and in psychologic changes, with accompanying autonomic nervous system manifestations.

empathy (em′pa-the) The ability to intellectually and emotionally sense the emotions, feelings, and reactions that another person is experiencing and to effectively communicate that understanding to the individual.

emphysema (em-fi-se′ma) Presence of air in the interstices of the connective tissue of a part.

empirical (em-pir′i-kal) Founded on practical experience, rather than on reasoning alone, but not proved scientifically, in contrast to RATIONAL.

encephalitis (en-sef-a-li′tis) Inflammation of the brain.

endemic (en-dem′ik) Present in a community or among a group of people; said of a disease prevailing continually in a region.

endo- Prefixes indicating within, inner, absorbing, or containing.

endocrine (en′dō-krin) Secreting internally, most commonly into the systemic circulation; of or pertaining to such secretion.

endocrinology (en′dō-kri-nol′ō-je) The science and medical specialty concerned with the internal or hormonal secretions and their physiologic and pathologic relations.

endogenous (en-doj′e-nus) Originating or produced within the organism or one of its parts.

endointoxication (en′dō-in-tok-si-ka′shun) Poisoning by an endogenous toxin.

endolymph (en′dō-limf) The fluid contained within the membranous labyrinth of the inner ear.

endometriosis (en′dō-me-tre-ō′sis) Ectopic occurrence of endometrial tissue, frequently forming cysts containing altered blood.

endometrium (en'dō-me'tre-um) The mucous membrane comprising the inner layer of the uterine wall; it consists of a simple columnar epithelium and a lamina propria that contains simple tubular uterine glands. The structure, thickness, and state of the endometrium undergo marked change with the menstrual cycle.

endoplasm (en'dō-plazm) The inner or medullary part of the cytoplasm, as opposed to the ectoplasm, containing the cell organelles.

end organ the special structure containing the terminal of a nerve fiber in peripheral tissue such as muscle, tissue, skin, mucous membrane, or glands.

endoskeleton (en-dō-skel'e-ton) The internal bony framework of the body; the skeleton in its usual context as distinguished from exoskeleton.

energy (en'er-je) The exertion of power; the capacity to do work, taking the forms of kinetic energy, potential energy, chemical energy, electrical energy, etc.

chemical energy energy liberated or absorbed by a chemical reaction, *e.g.,* oxidation of carbon, or absorbed in the formation of a chemical compound.

kinetic energy the energy of motion.

potential energy the energy, existing in a body by virtue of its position or state of existence, which is not being exerted at the time.

enervation (en-er-va'shun) Failure of nerve force; weakening.

ENG electronystagmography.

ENT ears, nose, and throat.

enteric (en-ter'ik) Relating to the intestine.

ento- Inner, or within.

entopic (ent-op'ik) Placed within; occurring or situated in the normal place; opposed to ectopic.

enuresis (en-yu-re'sis) Urinary incontinence; may be intentional or involuntary but not due to a physical disorder.

enzyme (en'zim) A protein that acts as a catalyst to induce chemical changes in other substances, itself remaining apparently unchanged by the process. Enzymes, with the exception of those discovered long ago (*e.g.,* pepsin, emulsin), are generally named by adding -ase to the name of the substrate on which the enzyme acts (*e.g.,* glucosidase), the substance activated (*e.g.,* hydrogenase), and/or the type of reaction (*e.g.,* oxidoreductase, transferase, hydrolase, lyase,

isomerase, ligase or synthetase. For individual enzymes not listed below, see the specific name.

angiotensin-converting enzyme a hydrolase responsible for the conversion of angiotensin I to the vasoactive angiotensin II by removal of a dipeptide (histidylleucine) from angiotensin I. Drugs that inhibit ACE are used to treat hypertension and congestive heart failure.

epidemiology (ep-i-de-me-ol'ō-je) The study of the distribution and determinants of health-related states or events in specified populations, and the application of this study to control of health problems.

epidermis (ep-i-derm'is) The superficial epithelial portion of the skin (cutis). The epidermis of the palms and soles has the following strata: stratum corneum (horny layer), stratum lucidum (clear layer), stratum granulosum (granular layer), stratum spinosum (prickle cell layer), and stratum basale (basal cell layer); in other parts of the body, the stratum lucidum may be absent.

epidural (ep-i-du'ral) Upon (or outside) the dura mater.

epiglottis (ep-i-glot'is) A leaf-shaped plate of elastic cartilage, covered with mucous membrane, at the root of the tongue, which serves as a diverter valve over the superior aperture of the larynx during the act of swallowing; it stands erect when liquids are being swallowed, but is passively bent over the aperture by solid foods being swallowed.

epilepsy (ep'i-lep'se) A chronic disorder characterized by paroxysmal brain dysfunction due to excessive neuronal discharge, and usually associated with some alteration of consciousness. The clinical manifestations of the attack may vary from complex abnormalities of behavior including generalized or focal convulsions to momentary spells of impaired consciousness. These clinical states have been subjected to a variety of classifications, none universally accepted to date and, accordingly, the terminologies used to describe the different types of attacks remain purely descriptive and nonstandardized; they are variously based on 1) the clinical manifestations of the seizure (motor, sensory, reflex, psychic or vegetative), 2) the pathological substrate (hereditary, inflammatory, degenerative, neoplastic, traumatic, or cryptogenic), 3) the location of the epileptogenic lesion (rolandic, temporal, diencephalic regions), and 4) the time of life at which the attacks occur (nocturnal, diurnal, menstrual, etc.).

epinephrine (ep'i-nef'rin) A catecholamine that is the chief neurohormone of the adrenal medulla. The l-isomer is the most potent stimulant (sympathomimetic) of adrenergic α- and β-receptors, resulting in increased heart rate and force of contraction, vasoconstriction or vasodilation, relaxation of bronchiolar and intestinal smooth muscle, glycogenolysis, lipolysis, and other metabolic effects; used in the treatment of bronchial asthma, acute allergic disorders, open-angle glaucoma, and heart block, and as a topical and local vasoconstrictor.

episode (ep'i-sōd) An important event or series of events taking place in the course of continuous events, *e.g.*, an episode of depression.

> **manic episode** manifestation of a major mood disorder in which there is a distinct period during which the predominant mood of the individual is either elevated, expansive, or irritable, and there are associated symptoms of the excited or manic phase of the bipolar disorder.

epistaxis (ep'i-stak'sis) Profuse bleeding from the nose.

equation (e-kwa'zhun) A statement expressing the equality of two things, usually with the use of mathematical or chemical symbols.

equilibrium (e-kwi-lib're-um) The condition of being evenly balanced; a state of repose between two or more antagonistic forces that exactly counteract each other.

equitoxic (e-kwi-tok'sik) Of equivalent toxicity.

ergotism (er'got-izm) Poisoning by a toxic substance contained in the sclerotia of the fungus, *Claviceps purpura*, growing on rye grass; characterized by necrosis of the extremities (gangrene) due to contraction of the peripheral vascular bed.

eruption (e-rup'shun) A breaking out, especially the appearance of lesions on the skin.

> **drug eruption** any eruption caused by the ingestion, injection, or inhalation of a drug, most often the result of allergic sensitization; reactions to drugs applied to the cutaneous surface are not generally designated as drug eruption, but as contact-type dermatitis.

> **fixed drug eruption** a type of drug eruption that recurs at a fixed site (or sites) following the administration of a particular drug.

erythema (er-i-the'ma) Redness of the skin due to capillary dilatation.

erythro- Combining form denoting red or red blood cell; corresponds to L. *rub-*.

erythrocyte (e-rith'rō-sit) A mature red blood cell.

erythropenia (e-rith-rō-pe'ne-a) Deficiency in the number of red blood cells.

erythruria (er-i-thru're-a) The passage of red urine.

Escherichia (esh-e-rik'e-a) A genus of aerobic, facultatively anaerobic bacteria containing short, motile or nonmotile, Gram-negative rods. Motile cells are peritrichous. Glucose and lactose are fermented with the production of acid and gas. These organisms are found in feces; some are pathogenic to man, causing enteritis, peritonitis, cystitis, etc. It is the type genus of the family Enterobacteriaceae. The type species is *Escherichia coli*.

> *Escherichia coli* a species that occurs normally in the intestines of man and other vertebrates, is widely distributed in nature, and is a frequent cause of infections of the urogenital tract and of diarrhea in infants; enteropathogenic strains (serovars) of *Escherichia coli* cause diarrhea due to enterotoxin, the production of which seems to be associated with a transferable episome; the type species of the genus.

esophagus (e-sof'a-gus, -gi) The portion of the digestive canal between the pharynx and stomach. It is about 25 cm long and consists of three parts: the cervical part, from the cricoid cartilage to the thoracic inlet; the thoracic part, from the thoracic inlet to the diaphragm; and the abdominal part, below the diaphragm to the cardiac opening of the stomach.

esophoria (es-ō-fō're-a) A tendency for the eyes to turn inward, prevented by binocular vision.

esterase (es'ter-as) A generic term for enzymes that catalyze the hydrolysis of esters.

estrogen (es'trō-jen) Generic term for any substance, natural or synthetic, that exerts biological effects characteristic of estrogenic hormones. Estrogens are formed by the ovary, placenta, testes, and possibly the adrenal cortex, as well as by certain plants; stimulate secondary sexual characteristics, and exert systemic effects, such as growth and maturation of long bones; given after menopause or oophorectomy to lower the risk of heart attack and prevent osteoporosis; also used to prevent or stop lactation,

ether (e'ther) Any organic compound in which two carbon atoms are independently linked to a common oxygen atom, thus containing the group –C–O–C–.

ethopharmacology (eth'ō-far-ma-kol'ō-je) The study of drug effects on behavior, relying on observation and description of species-specific elements (acts and postures during social encounters).

ethyl (eth'il) The hydrocarbon radical, CH_3CH_2–.

etiology (e-te-ol'ō-je) The science and study of the causes of disease and their mode of operation.

euphoria (yu-fōr'e-a) A feeling of well-being, commonly exaggerated and not necessarily well founded.

euphoriant (yu-fōr'e-ant) Having the capability to produce a sense of well-being.

eupnea (yup-ne'a) Easy, free respiration; the type observed in a normal individual under resting conditions.

euthanasia (yu-tha-na'ze-a) The intentional putting to death of a person with an incurable or painful disease, intended as an act of mercy.

exacerbation (eg-zas-er-ba'shun, -ek-sas-) An increase in the severity of a disease or any of its signs or symptoms.

examination (eg-zam-i-na'shun) Any investigation or inspection made for the purpose of diagnosis; usually qualified by the method used.

excoriate (eks-kō're-at) To scratch or otherwise denude the skin by physical means.

exocrine (ek'sō-krin) Denoting glandular secretion delivered to an apical or luminal surface.

exogenous (eks-oj'e-nus) Originating or produced outside of the organism.

exophoria (ek'so-fō're-a) Tendency of the eyes to deviate outward when fusion is suspended.

exoskeleton (ek-sō-skel'e-ton) All hard parts, such as hair, teeth, nails, feathers, dermal plates, scales, etc., developed from the ectoderm or somatic mesoderm in vertebrates.

experiment (eks-per'i-ment) A study in which the investigator intentionally alters one or more factors under controlled conditions in order to study the effects of doing so.

double blind experiment an experiment conducted with neither experimenter nor subjects knowing which experiment is the control; prevents bias in recording results.

exteroceptive (eks'ter-ō-sep'tiv) Relating to the exteroceptors; denoting the surface of the body containing the end organs adapted to receive impressions or stimuli from without.

extract A concentrated preparation of a drug obtained by removing the active constituents with suitable solvents, evaporating all or nearly all of the solvent, and adjusting the residual mass or powder to the prescribed standard.

extrinsic (eks-trin'sik) Originating outside of the part where found or upon which it acts; denoting especially a muscle, such as extrinsic muscles of hand.

eye (i) The organ of vision that consists of the eyeball and the optic nerve.

eyeball (i'bawl) The eye proper without the appendages.

fascia (fash'e-a) A sheet of fibrous tissue that envelops the body beneath the skin; it also encloses muscles and groups of muscles, and separates their several layers or groups.

fatigue (fa-teg') That state, following a period of mental or bodily activity, characterized by a lessened capacity for work and reduced efficiency of accomplishment, usually accompanied by a feeling of weariness, sleepiness, or irritability; may also supervene when, from any cause, energy expenditure outstrips restorative processes and may be confined to a single organ.

fatty acid Any acid derived from fats by hydrolysis (*e.g.*, oleic, palmitic, or stearic acids); any long-chain monobasic organic acid; they accumulate in disorders associated with the peroxisomes.

febrile (feb'ril, fe'bril) Denoting or relating to fever.

femoral (fem'o-ral) Relating to the femur or thigh.

femur (fe'mur) The thigh.

fermentation (fer-men-ta'shun) A chemical change induced in a complex organic compound by the action of an enzyme, whereby the substance is split into simpler compounds.

ferrous (far'us) Relating to iron, especially denoting a salt containing iron in its lowest valence state, Fe^{2+}.

fetid (fet'id, fe'tid) Foul-smelling.

fever (fe′ver) A complex physiologic response to disease mediated by pyrogenic cytokines and characterized by a rise in core temperature, generation of acute phase reactants and activation of immunologic systems.

fiber (fi′ber) Extracellular filamentous structures such as collagenic or elastic connective tissue fiber's.

adrenergic fibers nerve fiber's that transmit nervous impulses to other nerve cells (or smooth muscle or gland cells) by the medium of the adrenaline-like transmitter substance norepinephrine (noradrenaline).

afferent fibers those that convey impulses to a ganglion or to a nerve center in the brain or spinal cord.

cholinergic fibers nerve fiber's that transmit impulses to other nerve cells, muscle fibers, or gland cells by the medium of the transmitter substance acetylcholine.

exogenous fibers nerve fiber's by which a given region of the central nervous system is connected with other regions; the term applies to both afferent and efferent fiber connections.

inhibitory fibers nerve fiber's that inhibit the activity of the nerve cells with which they have synaptic connections, or of the effector tissue (smooth muscle, heart muscle, glands) in which they terminate.

motor fibers nerve fiber's that transmit impulses that activate effector cells, *e.g.*, in muscle or gland tissue.

pressor fibers sensory nerve fiber's whose stimulation causes vasoconstriction and rise of blood pressure.

projection fibers nerve fiber's connecting the cerebral cortex with other centers in the brain or spinal cord; fibers arising from cells in the central nervous system that pass to distant loci.

fibula (fib′yu-la) The lateral and smaller of the two bones of the leg; it is not-weight bearing and articulates with the tibia above and the tibia and talus below.

fingerprint (fing′ger-print′) An impression of the inked bulb of the distal phalanx of a finger, showing the configuration of the surface ridges, used as a means of identification.

DNA fingerprinting a technique used to compare individuals by molecular genotyping. DNA is isolated from a specific individual, digested, and fractionated according to size. A Southern hybridization with a radiolabeled repetitive DNA probe provides an autoradiographic pattern unique to the individual.

DNA fingerprinting offers a statistical basis for evaluating the probability that samples of blood, hair, semen, or tissue have originated from a given individual.

flaccid (flak′sid, flas′id) Relaxed, flabby, or without tone.

flashback An involuntary recurrence of some aspect of a hallucinatory experience or perceptual distortion occurring some time after ingestion of the hallucinogen that produced the original effect and without subsequent ingestion of the substance.

flatulence (flat′yu-lens) Presence of an excessive amount of gas in the stomach and intestines.

fluidextract (flu-id-eks′trakt) Pharmacopeial liquid preparation of vegetable drugs, made by percolation, containing alcohol as a solvent or as a preservative, or both, and so made that each milliliter contains the therapeutic constituents of 1 g of the standard drug that it represents.

fluidounce (flu′id-owns′) A measure of capacity: 8 fluidrams. The imperial fluidounce is a measure containing 1 avoirdupois ounce, 437.5 grains, of distilled water at 15.6°C, and equals 28.4 ml; the U.S. fluidounce is $1/128$ gallon, contains 454.6 grains of distilled water at 25°C, and equals 29.57 ml.

fluidrachm (flu′i-dram′) A measure of capacity: $1/8$ of a fluidounce; a teaspoonful. The imperial fluidrachm contains 54.8 grains of distilled water, and equals 3.55 ml; the U.S. fluidrachm contains 57.1 grains of distilled water and equals 3.70 ml.

fluorescence (flur-es′ens) Emission of a longer wavelength radiation by a substance as a consequence of absorption of energy from a shorter wavelength radiation, continuing only as long as the stimulus is present; distinguished from phosphorescence in that, in the latter, emission persists for a perceptible period of time after the stimulus has been removed.

fluoride (flur′id) A compound of fluorine with a metal, a nonmetal, or an organic radical; the anion of fluorine; inhibits enolase; found in bone and tooth apatite; fluoride has a cariostatic effect; high levels are toxic.

fluoroimmunoassay (flur-o-im-yu-no-as-a) An immunoassay that has antigen or antibody labeled with a fluorophore.

flutter (flut′er) Agitation; tremulousness.

atrial flutter rapid regular atrial contractions occurring usually at rates between 250 and 350 per minute and often producing "saw-tooth" waves in the electrocardiogram, particularly leads II, III, and aVF.

ventricular flutter a form of rapid ventricular tachycardia in which the electrocardiographic complexes assume a regular undulating pattern without distinct QRS and T waves.

folic acid (fō′lik) Collective term for pteroylglutamic acids and their oligoglutamic acid conjugates.

follicle (fol′i-kl) A more or less spherical mass of cells usually containing a cavity.

footcandle (fut′kan-dl) Illumination or brightness equivalent to 1 lumen per square foot; replaced in the SI system by the candela.

foot-drop (fut′drop) Paralysis or weakness of the dorsiflexor muscles of the foot, as a consequence of which the foot falls, the toes dragging on the ground in walking; many causes, both central and peripheral.

forensic (fō-ren′sik) Pertaining or applicable to personal injury, murder, and other legal proceedings.

formation (fōr-ma′shun) A formation; a structure of definite shape or cellular arrangement.

  reticular formation a massive but vaguely delimited neural apparatus composed of gray and white matter extending throughout the central core of the brainstem into the diencephalon; the term refers to the large neuronal population of the brainstem that does not compose motoneuronal cell groups or cell groups forming part of specific sensory conduction systems; its neurons generally have long dendrites and heterogeneous afferent connections; the reticular formation has complex, largely polysynaptic ascending and descending connections that play a role in the central control of autonomic (respiration, blood pressure, THERMOREGULATION, etc.) and endocrine functions, as well as in bodily posture, skeletomuscular reflex activity, and general behavioral states such as alertness and sleep.

formic acid the smallest carboxylic acid; a strong caustic, used as an astringent and counterirritant.

formication (fōr-mi-ka′shun) A form of paresthesia or tactile hallucination; a sensation as if small insects were creeping under the skin.

formulary (fōr′myu-la-re) A collection of formulas for the compounding of medicinal preparations.

fovea (fō′ve-a) A relatively small cup-shaped depression or pit.

  central retinal fovea a depression in the center of the macula retinae containing only cones and lacking blood vessels.

fracture (frak′chur) To break.

  closed fracture a fracture in which skin is intact at site of fracture.

  compound fracture syn open fracture

  direct fracture a fracture, especially of the skull, occurring at the point of injury.

  dislocation fracture a fracture of a bone near an articulation with its concomitant dislocation from that joint.

  displaced fracture a fracture in which the fragments are separated and are not in alignment.

  hairline fracture a fracture without separation of the fragments, the line of break being hairlike, as seen sometimes in the skull.

  impacted fracture a fracture in which one of the fragments is driven into the cancellous tissue of the other fragment.

  indirect fracture a fracture, especially of the skull, that occurs at a point not at the site of impact.

  multiple fracture fracture at two or more places in a bone;

  open fracture fracture in which the skin is perforated and there is an open wound down to the fracture.

  simple fracture syn closed fracture

  stress fracture a fatigue fracture caused by repetitive, relatively low-magnitude local stress on a bone, as in marching or running, rather than by a single violent injury.

  torsion fracture a fracture resulting from twisting of the limb.

friable (fri′a-bl) Easily reduced to powder.

frostbite (frost′bit) Local tissue destruction resulting from exposure to extreme cold; in mild cases, it results in superficial, reversible freezing followed by erythema and slight pain; in severe cases, it can be painless or paresthetic and result in blistering, persistent edema, and gangrene.

fructo- Chemical prefix denoting the fructose configuration.

fructose (fruk′tōs, fruk-) the d-isomer (also referred to as fruit sugar, levoglucose, levulose, and d-*arabino*-2-

hexulose, is a 2-ketohexose that in d form is physiologically the most important of the ketohexoses and one of the two products of sucrose hydrolysis, and is metabolized or converted to glycogen in the absence of insulin.

Fungi (fun'ji) A division of eukaryotic organisms that grow in irregular masses, without roots, stems, or leaves, and are devoid of chlorophyll or other pigments capable of photosynthesis. Each organism (thallus) is unicellular to filamentous, and possesses branched somatic structures (hyphae) surrounded by cell walls containing cellulose or chitin or both, and containing true nuclei. They reproduce sexually or asexually (spore formation), and may obtain nutrition from other living organisms as parasites or from dead organic matter as saprobes (saprophytes).

fungus (fung'gus) A general term used to encompass the diverse morphological forms of yeasts and molds. Originally classified as primitive plants without chlorophyll, the fungi are placed in the kingdom Fungi and some in the kingdom Protista, along with algae, protozoa, and slime molds. Fungi share with bacteria the ability to break down complex organic substances and are essential to the recycling of carbon and other elements. Fungi are important as foods and to the fermentation process in the development of substances of industrial and medical importance, including alcohol, the antibiotics, other drugs, and antitoxins. Relatively few fungi are pathogenic for humans, whereas most plant diseases are caused by fungi.

gait (gat) Manner of walking.

  ataxic gait syn cerebellar gait

gallon (gal'un) A measure of U.S. liquid capacity containing 4 quarts, 231 cubic inches, or 8.3293 pounds of distilled water at 20° C; it is the equivalent of 3.785412 liters. The British imperial gallon contains 277.4194 cubic inches.

gallstone (gal'stōn) A concretion in the gallbladder or a bile duct, composed chiefly of a mixture of cholesterol, calcium bilirubinate, and calcium carbonate, occasionally as a pure stone composed of just one of these substances.

ganglion (gang'gle-on) Originally, any group of nerve cell bodies in the central or peripheral nervous system; currently, an aggregation of nerve cell bodies located in the peripheral nervous system.

  parasympathetic ganglia those ganglia of the autonomic nervous system composed of cholinergic neurons receiving afferent fibers from preganglionic visceral motor neurons in either the brainstem or the middle sacral spinal segments (S2 to S4); on the basis of their location with respect to the organs they innervate, most parasympathetic ganglia, at least outside the head, can be categorized as juxtamural or intramural ganglia.

  sensory ganglion a cluster of primary sensory neurons forming a usually visible swelling in the course of a peripheral nerve or its dorsal root; such nerve cells establish the sole afferent neural connection between the sensory periphery (skin, mucous membranes of the oral and nasal cavities, muscle tissue, tendons, joint capsules, special sense organs, blood vessel walls, tissues of the internal organs) and the central nervous system; they are the cells of origin of all sensory fibers of the peripheral nervous system.

  sympathetic ganglia those ganglia of the autonomic nervous system that receive efferent fibers originating from preganglionic visceral motor neurons in the intermediolateral cell column of thoracic and upper lumbar spinal segments (T1–L2). On the basis of their location, the sympathetic ganglia can be classified as paravertebral ganglia (ganglia trunci sympathici) and prevertebral ganglia (ganglia celiaca).

gangrene (gang'gren) Necrosis due to obstruction, loss, or diminution of blood supply; it may be localized to a small area or involve an entire extremity or organ (such as the bowel), and may be wet or dry.

gastroenterology (gas'trō-en-ter-ol'ō-je) The medical specialty concerned with the function and disorders of the gastrointestinal tract, including stomach, intestines, and associated organs.

gastrointestinal (gas'trō-in-tes'tin-al) Relating to the stomach and intestines.

gene (jen) A functional unit of heredity which occupies a specific place (locus) on a chromosome, is capable of reproducing itself exactly at each cell division, and directs the formation of an enzyme or other protein. The gene as a functional unit consists of a discrete segment of a giant DNA molecule containing purine and pyrimidine bases in the correct sequence to code the sequence of amino acids of a specific peptide. Protein synthesis is mediated by molecules of messenger-RNA formed on the chromosome with the gene acting as template. Genes normally occur in pairs in all cells except gametes.

generic (je-nar′ik) Relating to or denoting a genus.

generic name chemistry A noun that indicates the class or type of a single compound; *e.g.*, salt, saccharide (sugar), hexose, alcohol, aldehyde, lactone, acid, amine, alkane, steroid, vitamin. "Class" is more appropriate and more often used than is "generic."

genital (jen′i-tal) Relating to reproduction or generation.

genitourinary (jen′i-tō-yu′ri-nar-e) Relating to the organs of reproduction and urination.

genome (je′nōm, -nom) A complete set of chromosomes derived from one parent, the haploid number of a gamete.

genotype (jen′ō-tip) The genetic constitution of an individual.

genus (je′nus) In natural history classification, the taxonomic level of division between the family, or tribe, and the species; a group of species alike in the broad features of their organization but different in detail, and incapable of fertile mating.

geriatric (jar-e-at′rik) Relating to old age or to geriatrics.

germ (jerm) A microbe; a microorganism.

gerontology (jar-on-tol′ō-je) The scientific study of the process and problems of aging.

gestalt (ge-stahlt) A perceived entity so integrated as to constitute a functional unit with properties not derivable from its parts.

giga- Prefix used in the SI and metric systems to signify one billion (10^9).

gingiva (jin′ji-va) The dense fibrous tissue, covered by mucous membrane, that envelops the alveolar processes of the upper and lower jaws and surrounds the necks of the teeth.

gingivitis (jin-ji-vi′tis) Inflammation of the gingiva as a response to bacterial plaque on adjacent teeth; characterized by erythema, edema, and fibrous enlargement of the gingiva without resorption of the underlying alveolar bone.

gland An organized aggregation of cells functioning as a secretory or excretory organ.

glaucoma (glaw-kō′ma) A disease of the eye characterized by increased intraocular pressure and excavation and atrophy of the optic nerve; produces defects in the visual field and may result in blindness.

GLC gas-liquid chromatography.

glucocorticoid (glu-kō-kōr′ti-koyd) Any steroid-like compound capable of promoting hepatic glycogen deposition and of exerting a clinically useful anti-inflammatory effect. Cortisol is the most potent of the naturally occurring glucocorticoid's; most semisynthetic glucocorticoid's are cortisol derivatives.

glucose (glu′kōs) A dextrorotatory monosaccharide found in the free form in fruits and other parts of plants, and in combination in glucosides, glycogen, disaccharides, and polysaccharides (starch cellulose); the chief source of energy in human metabolism, the final product of carbohydrate digestion, and the principal sugar of the blood; insulin is required for the use of glucose by cells; in diabetes mellitus the level of glucose in the blood is excessive, and it also appears in the urine.

glue-sniffing (glu′snif-ing) Inhalation of fumes from plastic cements; the solvents, which include toluene, xylene, and benzene, induce central nervous system stimulation followed by depression.

glyco- Combining form denoting relationship to sugars (*e.g.*, glycogen), or to glycine (*e.g.*, glycocholate).

glycopenia (gli-kō-pe′ne-a) A deficiency of any or all sugars in an organ or tissue.

gnosia (nō′se-a) The perceptive faculty enabling one to recognize the form and the nature of persons and things; the faculty of perceiving and recognizing.

GnRH gonadotropin-releasing hormone.

gonad (gō′nad) An organ that produces sex cells; a testis or an ovary.

gonadotropin (gō′nad-ō-trō′pin, gon′a-dō-) A hormone capable of promoting gonadal growth and function; such effects, as exerted by a single hormone, usually are limited to discrete functions or histological components of a gonad, such as stimulation of follicular growth or of androgen formation; most gonadotropin's exert their effects in both sexes, although the effect of a given gonadotropin will differ in males and females.

gout (gowt) A disorder of purine metabolism, occurring especially in men, characterized by a raised but variable blood uric acid level and severe recurrent acute arthritis of sudden onset resulting from deposition of crystals of sodium urate in connective tissues and articular cartilage; most cases are inherited, resulting from a variety of abnormalities of purine metabolism.

gram A unit of weight in the metric or centesimal system, the equivalent of 15.432358 grains or 0.03527 avoirdupois ounce.

granuloma (gran-yu-lō'ma) Indefinite term applied to nodular inflammatory lesions, usually small or granular, firm, persistent, and containing compactly grouped mononuclear phagocytes.

gravity (grav'i-te) The attraction toward the earth that makes any mass exert downward force or have weight.

specific gravity the weight of any body compared with that of another body of equal volume regarded as the unit; usually the weight of a liquid compared with that of distilled water.

GSR galvanic skin response.

habit An act, behavioral response, practice, or custom established in one's repertoire by frequent repetition of the same act.

habituation (ha-bit-chu-a'shun) The process of forming a habit, referring generally to psychological dependence on the continued use of a drug to maintain a sense of well-being, which can result in drug addiction.

half-life (haf'lif) The period in which the radioactivity or number of atoms of a radioactive substance decreases by half; similarly applied to any substance whose quantity decreases exponentially with time. Time required for the serum concentration of a drug to decline by 50%.

halitosis (hal-i-tō'sis) A foul odor of the breath.

hallucination (ha-lu'si-na'shun) The subjective perception of an object or event when no such stimulus or situation is present; may be visual, auditory, olfactory, gustatory, or tactile.

hallucinogen (ha-lu'si-nō-jen) A mind-altering chemical, drug, or agent, specifically a chemical whose most prominent pharmacologic action is on the central nervous system; in normal subjects, it elicits optical or auditory hallucinations, depersonalization, perceptual disturbances, and disturbances of thought processes.

hamstring One of the tendons bounding the popliteal space on either side; the MEDIAL HAMSTRING comprises the tendons of the semimembranosus and semitendinosus, gracilis, and sartorius muscles; the LATERAL HAMSTRING is the tendon of the biceps femoris muscle. Hamstring muscles (a) have origin from the ischial tuberosity, (b) act across (at) both the hip and knee joints (producing extension and flexion, respectively), and (c) are innervated by the tibial portion of the sciatic nerve. The medial hamstring contributes to medial rotation of the leg at the flexed knee joint, while the lateral hamstring contributes to lateral rotation.

haptics (hap'tiks) The science concerned with the tactile sense.

hashish (hash'ish) A form of cannabis that consists largely of resin from the flowering tops and sprouts of cultivated female hemp plants of the species *Cannabis sativa*; contains the highest concentration of cannabinols among the preparations derived from cannabis.

hearing (her'ing) The ability to perceive sound; the sensation of sound as opposed to vibration.

heart (hart) A hollow muscular organ which receives the blood from the veins and propels it into the arteries. It is divided by a musculomembranous septum into two halves—right or venous and left or arterial—each of which consists of a receiving chamber (atrium) and an ejecting chamber (ventricle).

heartbeat (hart'bet) A single complete cycle of contraction and dilation of heart muscle.

heartburn (hart'bern) syn pyrosis

heatstroke (het'strōk) A severe and often fatal illness produced by exposure to excessively high temperatures, especially when accompanied by marked exertion; characterized by headache, vertigo, confusion, hot dry skin, and a slight rise in body temperature; in severe cases, very high fever, vascular collapse, and coma develop.

hemat- Blood.

hematocrit (he'ma-tō-krit, hem'a-) Percentage of the volume of a blood sample occupied by cells.

hematoma (he-ma-tō'ma, hem-a-) A localized mass of extravasated blood that is relatively or completely confined within an organ or tissue, a space, or a potential space; the blood is usually clotted, and, depending on how long it has been there, may manifest various degrees of organization and decolorization.

hematuria (he-ma-tu'-re-a, hem-a-) Any condition in which the urine contains blood or red blood cells.

hemi- One-half.

hemiparesis (hem-e-pa-re′sis, -par′e-sis) Weakness affecting one side of the body.

hemocyte (he′mō-sit) Any cell or formed element of the blood.

hemodynamic (he′mō-di-nam′ik) Relating to the physical aspects of the blood circulation.

hemoglobin (he-mō-glō′bin) The red respiratory protein of erythrocytes, consisting of approximately 3.8% heme and 96.2% globin, with a molecular weight of 64,450, which as oxyhemoglobin (HbO_2) transports oxygen from the lungs to the tissues where the oxygen is readily released and HbO_2 becomes Hb. When Hb is exposed to certain chemicals, its normal respiratory function is blocked; *e.g.,* the oxygen in HbO_2 is easily displaced by carbon monoxide, thereby resulting in the formation of fairly stable carboxyhemoglobin (HbCO), as in asphyxiation resulting from inhalation of exhaust fumes from gasoline engines. When the iron in Hb is oxidized from the ferrous to ferric state, as in poisoning with nitrates and certain other chemicals, a nonrespiratory compound, methemoglobin (MetHb), is formed. In humans there are five kinds of normal Hb: two embryonic Hb's (Hb Gower-1, Hb Gower-2), fetal (Hb F), and two adult types (Hb A, Hb A_2). There are two α globin chains containing 141 amino acid residues, and two of another kind (β, γ, δ, ε, or ζ), each containing 146 amino acid residues in four of the Hb's. Hb Gower-1 has two ζ chains and two ε chains. The production of each kind of globin chain is controlled by a structural gene of similar Greek letter designation; normal individuals are homozygous for the normal allele at each locus. Substitution of one amino acid for another in the polypeptide chain can occur at any codon in any of the five loci and have resulted in the production of many hundreds of abnormal Hb types, most of no known clinical significance. In addition, deletions of one or more amino acid residues are known, as well as gene rearrangements due to unequal crossing over between homologous chromosomes. The Hb types below are the main abnormal types known to be of clinical significance. Newly discovered abnormal Hb types are first assigned a name, usually the location where discovered, and a molecular formula is added when determined. The formula consists of Greek letters to designate the basic chains, with subscript 2 if there are two identical chains; a superscript letter (^{A} if normal for adult Hb, etc.) is added, or the superscript may designate the site of amino acid substitution (numbering amino acid residues from the N terminus of the polypeptide) and specifying the change, using standard abbreviations for the amino acids. There is an exhaustive listing of variant hemoglobin's in MIM where a composite numbering system is used.

hemorrhage (hem′o-rij) An escape of blood through ruptured or unruptured vessel walls.

hemostasis (he′mō-sta-sis, he-mos′ta-sis) The arrest of bleeding.

hemostat (he′mō-stat) Any agent that arrests, chemically or mechanically, the flow of blood from an open vessel.

hepar (he′par) syn liver, liver

heparin (hep′a-rin) An anticoagulant that is a component of various tissues (especially liver and lung) and mast cells. Its principal active constituent is a glycosaminoglycan composed of d-glucuronic acid and d-glucosamine. In conjunction with a serum protein cofactor (the so-called heparin cofactor), heparin acts as an antithrombin and an antiprothrombin by preventing platelet agglutination and consequent thrombus formation.

hepat- The liver.

hepatitis (hep-a-ti′tis) Inflammation of the liver; usually from a viral infection, but sometimes from toxic agents.

   hepatitis A syn viral hepatitis type A

   hepatitis B syn viral hepatitis type B

   hepatitis C a viral hepatitis, usually mild but often progressing to a chronic stage; the most prevalent type of post-transfusion hepatitis.

hepatomegaly (hep′a-tō-meg′a-le) Enlargement of the liver.

heroin (her′ō-in) An alkaloid prepared from morphine by acetylation; formerly used for the relief of cough. Except for research, its use in the United States is prohibited by federal law because of its potential for abuse.

herpes (her′pez) An inflammatory skin disease caused by herpesvirus; an eruption of groups of deep-seated vesicles on erythematous bases.

   genital herpes herpetic lesions on the penis of the male or on the cervix, perineum, vagina, or vulva of the female, caused by herpesvirus (herpes simplex virus) type 2.

hetero- The other, different; opposite of homo.

heterogeneous (het'er-ō-je'ne-us) Comprising elements with various and dissimilar properties.

hexane (hek'san) A saturated hydrocarbon, C_6H_{14}, of the paraffin series.

hippocampus (hip-ō-kam'pus) The complex, internally convoluted structure that forms the medial margin of the cerebral hemisphere, bordering the choroid fissure of the lateral ventricle, and composed of two gyri (Ammon's horn and the dentate gyrus), together with their white matter, the alveus and fimbria hippocampi. In humans the hippocampus is confined to the temporal lobe by the massive development of the corpus callosum. The hippocampus forms part of the limbic system. Its major afferent connections are with the entorhinal area of the parahippocampal gyrus, and transparent septum; by way of the fornix it projects to the septum, anterior nucleus of the thalamus, and mamillary body.

hippus (hip'us) Intermittent pupillary dilation and constriction, independent of illumination, convergence, or psychic stimuli.

histamine (his'ta-men) A depressor amine derived from histidine and present in ergot and in animal tissues. It is a powerful stimulant of gastric secretion, a constrictor of bronchial smooth muscle and a vasodilator (capillaries and arterioles) that causes a fall in blood pressure. Histamine is liberated in the skin as a result of injury. When pricked into the skin in high dilution, it causes the triple response.

histo- Tissue.

histology (his-tol'ō-je) The science concerned with the minute structure of cells, tissues, and organs in relation to their function.

HIV human immunodeficiency virus.

holo- Whole, entire, complete.

homeo- The same, alike.

homeopathy (hō-me-op'a-the) A system of therapy developed by Samuel Hahnemann based on the "law of infinitesimal doses" in *similia similibus curantur* (likes are cured by likes), which holds that a medicinal substance that can evoke certain symptoms in healthy individuals may be effective in the treatment of illnesses having symptoms closely resembling those produced by the substance.

homeostasis (hō'me-ō-sta'sis, -os'ta-sis) The state of equilibrium (balance between opposing pressures) in the body with respect to various functions and to the chemical compositions of the fluids and tissues.

homo- Combining form meaning the same, alike; opposite of hetero.

hormone (hōr'mōn) A chemical substance, formed in one organ or part of the body and carried in the blood to another organ or part; depending on the specificity of their effects, hormone's can alter the functional activity, and sometimes the structure, of just one organ or of various numbers of them. A number of hormone's are formed by ductless glands, but secretin and pancreozymin, formed in the gastrointestinal tract, by definition are also hormone's. For hormone's not listed below, see specific names.

HPLC high-pressure liquid chromatography; high-performance liquid chromatography.

humerus (hyu'mer-us) The bone of the arm, articulating with the scapula above and the radius and ulna below.

humor (hyu'mer) Any clear fluid or semifluid hyaline anatomical substance.

    aqueous humor the watery fluid that fills the anterior and posterior chambers of the eye. It is secreted by the ciliary processes within the posterior chambers and passes through the the pupil into the anterior chamber where it filters through the trabecular meshwork and is reabsorbed into the venous system at the iridocorneal angle by way of the sinus venosus of the sclera;

hydrate (hi'drat) An aqueous solvate (in older terminology, a hydroxide); a compound crystallizing with one or more molecules of water.

hydration (hi-dra'shun) Chemically, the addition of water; differentiated from hydrolysis, where the union with water is accompanied by a splitting of the original molecule and the water molecule.

hydro- Water, watery.

hydrochloric acid (hi-drō-klōr'ik) the acid of gastric juice. The gas and the concentrated solution are strong irritants.

hydrochloride (hi-drō-klōr'id) A compound formed by the addition of a hydrochloric acid molecule to an amine or related substance.

hydrocortisone (hi-drō-kōr'ti-sōn) A steroid hormone secreted by the adrenal cortex and the most potent of the naturally occurring glucocorticoids in humans.

hydroxy- Prefix indicating addition or substitution of the –OH group to or in the compound whose name follows.

hyp- Variation of the prefix hypo-, often used before a vowel.

hyper- Excessive, above normal; opposite of hypo.

hyperacusis (hi'per-a-ku'sis) Abnormal acuteness of hearing due to increased irritability of the auditory apparatus.

hyperaphia (hi'per-a'fe-a) Extreme sensitivity to touch.

hyperphoria (hi-per-fō're-a) A tendency of the visual axis of one eye to deviate upward, prevented by binocular vision.

hyperpnea (hi-per-ne'a, hi-perp'ne-a) Breathing that is deeper and more rapid than is normal at rest.

hyperpyrexia (hi'per-pi-rek'se-a) Extremely high fever.

hypertension (hi'per-ten'shun) High blood pressure. Despite many discrete and inherited but rare forms that have been identified, the evidence is that for the most part blood pressure is a multifactorial, perhaps galtonian trait. Its strong cybernetic properties may also be largely inherited but would not be reflected in measurements of heritability. The definition of what is "high" or "low" blood pressure is then entirely arbitrary, but extreme cases are undoubtedly dysgenic.

hyperthermia (hi-per-ther'me-a) Therapeutically induced hyperpyrexia.

    malignant hyperthermia rapid onset of extremely high fever with muscle rigidity, precipitated by exogenous agents in genetically susceptible persons, especially by halothane or succinylcholine.

hypertonia (hi-per-tō'ne-a) Extreme tension of the muscles or arteries.

hypervascular (hi'per-vas'kyu-ler) Abnormally vascular; containing an excessive number of blood vessels.

hyperventilation (hi'per-ven-ti-la'shun) Increased alveolar ventilation relative to metabolic carbon dioxide production, so that alveolar carbon dioxide pressure decreases to below normal.

hypnagogue (hip'na-gog) An agent that induces sleep.

hypnosis (hip-nō'sis) An artificially induced trancelike state, resembling somnambulism, in which the subject is highly susceptible to suggestion and responds readily to the commands of the hypnotist.

hypo- Deficient, below normal.

hypoglossal (hi-pō-glos'al) Below the tongue.

hypoglottis (hi'pō-glot'is) The undersurface of the tongue.

hypopnea (hi-pop'ne-a) Breathing that is shallower, and/or slower, than normal.

hyporeflexia (hi'pō-re-flek'se-a) A condition in which the deep tendon reflexes are weakened.

hyposalivation (hi'pō-sal'i-va'shun) Reduced salivation.

hypotension (hi'pō-ten'shun) Subnormal arterial blood pressure.

    orthostatic hypotension a form of low blood pressure that occurs in a standing posture.

hypothalamus (hi'pō-thal'a-mus) The ventral and medial region of the diencephalon forming the walls of the ventral half of the third ventricle; it is delineated from the thalamus by the hypothalamic sulcus, lying medial to the internal capsule and subthalamus, continuous with the precommissural septum anteriorly and with the mesencephalic tegmentum and central gray substance posteriorly. Its ventral surface is marked by, from before backward, the optic chiasma, the unpaired infundibulum that extends by way of the infundibular stalk into the posterior lobe of the hypophysis, and the paired mamillary bodies. The nerve cells of the hypothalamus are grouped into the supraoptic paraventricular, lateral preoptic, lateral hypothalamic, tuberal, anterior hypothalamic, ventromedial, dorsomedial, arcuate, posterior hypothalamic, and premamillary nuclei and the mamillary body. It has afferent fiber connections with the mesencephalon, limbic system, cerebellum, and efferent fiber connections with the same structures and with the posterior lobe of the hypophysis; its functional connection with the anterior lobe of the hypophysis is established by the hypothalamohypophysial portal system. The hypothalamus is prominently involved in the functions of the autonomic nervous system and, through its vascular link with the anterior lobe of the hypophysis, in endocrine mechanisms; it also appears to play a role in neural mechanisms underlying moods and motivational states.

hypothermia (hi'pō-ther'me-a) A body temperature significantly below 98.6°F (37°C).

hysteresis (his-ter-e'sis) Failure of either one of two related phenomena to keep pace with the other; or any situation in which the value of one depends upon whether the other has been increasing or decreasing.

hysteria (his-ter'e-a, his-ter') A somatoform disorder in which there is an alteration or loss of physical functioning that suggests a physical disorder such as paralysis of an arm or disturbance of vision, but that is instead apparently an expression of a psychological conflict or need.

idiopathic (id'e-ō-path'ik) Denoting a disease of unknown cause.

illusion (i-lu'zhun) A false perception; the mistaking of something for what it is not.

-imine Suffix denoting the group NH.

immunoassay (im'yu-nō-as'a) Detection and assay of substances by serological (immunological) methods.

impairment (im-par'ment) Any loss or abnormality of psychological, physiological or anatomical structure or function.

incidence (in'si-dens) The number of specified new events, *e.g.*, persons falling ill with a specified disease, during a specified period in a specified population.

incoordination (in-kō-ōr-di-na'shun) syn ataxia

indication (in-di-ka'shun) The basis or rationale for using a particular treatment or diagnostic test; may be furnished by a knowledge of the cause (CAUSAL INDICATION), by the symptoms present (SYMPTOMATIC INDICATION), or by the nature of the disease (SPECIFIC INDICATION).

indole (in'dōl) basis of many biologically active substances (*e.g.*, serotonin, tryptophan); formed in degradation of tryptophan.

inebriant (in-e'bre-ant) Making drunk; intoxicating.

inebriation (in-e-bre-a'shun) Intoxication, especially by alcohol.

infarction (in-fark'shun) Sudden insufficiency of arterial or venous blood supply due to emboli, thrombi, vascular torsion, or pressure that produces a macroscopic area of necrosis; the heart, brain, spleen, kidney, intestine, lung, and testes are likely to be affected, as are tumors, especially of the ovary or uterus.

infectious (in-fek'shus) Capable of being transmitted by infection, with or without actual contact.

ingestion (in-jes'chun) Introduction of food and drink into the stomach.

inhalant (in-ha'lant) That which is inhaled; a remedy given by inhalation.

inhibition (in-hi-bish'un) Depression or arrest of a function.

inject (in-jekt') To introduce into the body; denoting a fluid forced beneath the skin or into a blood vessel.

inquest (in'kwest) A legal inquiry into the cause of sudden, violent, or mysterious death.

inscription (in-skrip'shun) The main part of a prescription; that which indicates the drugs and the quantity of each to be used in the mixture.

insufflate (in-suf'lat) To blow air, gas, or fine powder into a cavity.

insulin (in'su-lin) A polypeptide hormone, secreted by beta cells in the islets of Langerhans, that promotes glucose utilization, protein synthesis, and the formation and storage of neutral lipids; obtained from various animals and available in a variety of preparations, insulin is used parenterally in the treatment of diabetes mellitus.

integument (in-teg'yu-ment) The enveloping membrane of the body; includes, in addition to the epidermis and dermis, all of the derivatives of the epidermis, *e.g.*, hairs, nails, sudoriferous and sebaceous glands, and mammary glands.

interferon (in-ter-fer'on) A class of small glycoproteins that exert antiviral activity at least in homologous cells through cellular metabolic processes involving synthesis of double-stranded RNA.

intoxicant (in-tok'si-kant) Having the power to intoxicate.

intoxication (in-tok-si-ka'shun) syn poisoning

intumesce (in-tu-mes') To swell up; to enlarge.

involuntary (in-vol'un-tar-e) Independent of the will; not volitional.

ipsilateral (ip-si-lat'er-al) On the same side, with reference to a given point, *e.g.*, a dilated pupil on the same side as an extradural hematoma with contralateral limbs being paretic.

irides (ir'i-dez) Plural of iris.

iridodilator (ir'i-dō-di-la'ter) Causing dilation of the pupil; applied to the musculus dilator pupillae.

ischuria (is-ku're-a) Retention or suppression of urine.

iso- Prefix meaning equal, like.

isocoria (i-sō-kō're-a) Equality in the size of the two pupils.

jejunum (je-ju'num) The portion of small intestine, about 8 feet in length, between the duodenum and the ileum. The jejunum is distinct from the ileum in being more proximal, of larger diameter with a thicker wall, having larger, more highly developed plicae circulares, being more vascular (redder in appearance), with the jejunal arteries forming fewer tiers of arterial arcades and longer vasa recta.

judgment Ability to evaluate the positive and negative aspects of a behavior or situation and act or react appropriately.

keloid (ke'loyd) A nodular, firm, often linear mass of hyperplastic scar tissue, consisting of irregularly distributed bands of collagen; occurs in the dermis, usually after trauma, surgery, a burn, or severe cutaneous disease.

keratitis (ker-a-ti'tis) Inflammation of the cornea.

kg kilogram.

kidney (kid'ne) One of the two organs that excrete the urine. The kidney's are bean-shaped organs (about 11 cm long, 5 cm wide, and 3 cm thick) lying on either side of the vertebral column, posterior to the peritoneum, about opposite the twelfth thoracic and first three lumbar vertebrae.

kilo- Prefix used in the SI and metric systems to signify one thousand (10^3).

kilogram (kil'ō-gram) The SI unit of mass, 1000 g; equivalent to 15,432.358 gr, 2.2046226 lb. avoirdupois, or 2.6792289 lb. troy.

kinematics (kin-e-mat'iks) physiology The science concerned with movements of the parts of the body.

kinesiology (ki-ne-se-ol'ō-je) The science or the study of movement, and the active and passive structures involved.

labile (la'bil, -bil) An adaptability to alteration or modification, i.e., relatively easily changed or rearranged.

labyrinth (lab'i-rinth) The internal or inner ear, composed of the semicircular ducts, vestibule, and cochlea.

> **bony labyrinth** a series of cavities (cochlea, vestibule, and semicircular canals) contained within the otic capsule of the petrous portion of the temporal bone; the bony labyrinth is filled with perilymph, in which the delicate, endolymph-filled membranous labyrinth is suspended.

lacerated (las'er-a-ted) Torn; rent; having a ragged edge.

lacrimal (lak'ri-mal) Relating to the tears, their secretion, the secretory glands, and the drainage apparatus.

lacrimation (lak'ri-ma'shun) The secretion of tears, especially in excess.

larynx (lar'ingks) The organ of voice production; the part of the respiratory tract between the pharynx and the trachea; it consists of a framework of cartilages and elastic membranes housing the vocal

folds and the muscles which control the position and tension of these elements.

lateral (lat'er-al) On the side.

lavage (la-vahzh') The washing out of a hollow cavity or organ by copious injections and rejections of fluid.

learning (lern'ing) Generic term for the relatively permanent change in behavior that occurs as a result of practice.

> **state-dependent learning** learning during a specific state of sleep or wakefulness, or during a chemically altered state, where retrieval of learned information cannot be demonstrated unless the subject is restored to the state that originally existed during learning.

lens (lenz) A transparent material with one or both surfaces having a concave or convex curve; acts upon electromagnetic energy to cause convergence or divergence of light rays.

leuc- White; white blood cell.

leukoplakia (lu-kō-pla'ke-a) A white patch of oral mucous membrane which cannot be wiped off and cannot be diagnosed clinically; biopsy may show malignant or premalignant changes.

levo- Left, toward or on the left side.

libido (li-be'dō, -bi'dō) Conscious or unconscious sexual desire.

limb (lim) An extremity; a member; an arm or leg.

lipemia (lip-e'me-a) The presence of an abnormally high concentration of lipids in the circulating blood.

lipid (lip'id) An operational term describing a solubility characteristic, not a chemical substance, i.e., denoting substances extracted from animal or vegetable cells by nonpolar or "fat" solvents; included are fatty acids, glycerides and glyceryl ethers, phospholipids, sphingolipids, alcohols and waxes, terpenes, steroids, and "fat-soluble" vitamins A, D, and E.

lipophilic (lip-ō-fil'ik) Capable of dissolving, of being dissolved in, or of absorbing lipids.

liter (le'ter) A measure of capacity of 1000 cubic centimeters or 1 cubic decimeter; equivalent to 1.056688 quarts (U.S., liquid).

lithium (lith'e-um) An element of the alkali metal group, atomic no. 3, atomic wt. 6.941. Many salts have clinical applications.

liver (liv'er) The largest gland of the body, lying beneath the diaphragm in the right hypochondrium and upper part of the epigastrium; it is of irregular shape and weighs from 1 to 2 kg, or about ¹/₄₀ the weight of the body. It secretes the bile and is also of great importance in both carbohydrate and protein metabolism.

locomotor (lō-kō-mō'ter) Relating to locomotion, or movement from one place to another.

-logia The study of the subject noted in the body of the word, or a treatise on the same; the Eng. equivalent is -logy, or, with a connecting vowel, -ology.

logo- Speech, words.

lung (lung) One of a pair of viscera occupying the pulmonary cavities of the thorax, the organs of respiration in which aeration of the blood takes place. As a rule, the right lung is slightly larger than the left and is divided into three lobes (an upper, a middle, and a lower or basal), while the left has but two lobes (an upper and a lower or basal). Each lung is irregularly conical in shape, presenting a blunt upper extremity (the apex), a concave base following the curve of the diaphragm, an outer convex surface (costal surface), an inner or mediastinal surface (mediastinal surface), a thin and sharp anterior border, and a thick and rounded posterior border.

lymph (limf) A clear, transparent, sometimes faintly yellow and slightly opalescent fluid that is collected from the tissues throughout the body, flows in the lymphatic vessels (through the lymph nodes), and is eventually added to the venous blood circulation. Lymph consists of a clear liquid portion, varying numbers of white blood cells (chiefly lymphocytes), and a few red blood cells.

lymph node One of numerous round, oval, or bean-shaped bodies located along the course of lymphatic vessels, varying greatly in size (1 to 25 mm in diameter) and usually presenting a depressed area, the hilum, on one side through which blood vessels enter and efferent lymphatic vessels emerge. The structure consists of a fibrous capsule and internal trabeculae supporting lymphoid tissue and lymph sinuses; lymphoid tissue is arranged in nodules in the cortex and cords in the medulla of a node, with afferent vessels entering at many points of the periphery.

μ mu.

μg microgram.

μl microliter.

macro- Large, long.

mal (mahl) A disease or disorder.

malaise (ma-laz') a feeling of general discomfort or uneasiness, an out-of-sorts feeling, often the first indication of an infection or other disease.

malignant (ma-lig'nant) occurring in severe form, and frequently fatal; tending to become worse.

mania (ma'ne-a) An emotional disorder characterized by euphoria or irritability, increased psychomotor activity, rapid speech, flight of ideas, decreased need for sleep, distractibility, grandiosity, and poor judgment; usually occurs in bipolar disorder.

manic-depressive Pertaining to a manic-depressive psychosis (BIPOLAR DISORDER).

manifestation (man'i-fes-ta'shun) The display or disclosure of characteristic signs or symptoms of an illness.

manometer (ma-nom'e-ter) An instrument for measuring the pressure of gases or liquids.

marihuana (mar-i-wah'na) Popular name for the dried flowering leaves of *Cannabis sativa*, which are smoked as cigarettes, "joints," or "reefers." In the U.S. marihuana includes any part of, or any extracts from, the female plant. Alternative spellings are mariguana, marijuana.

MAST military antishock trousers.

mastication (mas-ti-ka'shun) The process of chewing food in preparation for deglutition and digestion; the act of grinding or comminuting with the teeth.

maxillary (mak'si-lar-e) Relating to the maxilla, or upper jaw.

medicine (med'i-sin) A drug.

   forensic medicine the relation and application of medical facts to legal matters;

medicolegal (med'i-kō-le'gal) Relating to both medicine and the law.

mega- Large, oversize; opposite of micro.

melatonin (mel-a-tōn'in) A substance formed by the pineal gland that appears to depress gonadal function; a precursor is serotonin, melatonin is rapidly metabolized and is taken up by all tissues; it is involved in circadian rhythms.

memory (mem'o-re) General term for the recollection of that which was once experienced or learned.

   long-term memory that phase of the memory process considered the permanent storehouse of information which has been registered, encoded, passed into the short-term memory, coded, rehearsed, and finally transferred and stored for future retrieval; material and information retained in LTM underlies cognitive abilities.

873

short-term memory that phase of the memory process in which stimuli that have been recognized and registered are stored briefly; decay occurs rapidly, typically within seconds, but may be held indefinitely by using rehearsal as a holding process by which to recycle material over and over through STM.

meningitis (men-in-ji'tis, -jit'i-dez) Inflammation of the membranes of the brain or spinal cord.

mesencephalon (mez-en-sef'a-lon) That part of the brainstem developing from the middle of the three primary cerebral vesicles of the embryo. In the adult, the mesencephalon is characterized by the unique conformation of its roof plate, the lamina of the mesencephalic tectum, composed of the bilaterally paired superior and inferior colliculi, and by the massive paired prominence of the crus cerebri at its ventral surface. Prominent cell groups of the mesencephalon include the motor nuclei of the trochlear and oculomotor nerves, the red nucleus, and the substantia nigra.

meso- Middle, mean, intermediate.

meta- After, subsequent to, behind, or hindmost.

metabolism (me-tab'ō-lizm) The sum of the chemical and physical changes occurring in tissue, consisting of anabolism, those reactions that convert small molecules into large, and catabolism, those reactions that convert large molecules into small, including both endogenous large molecules as well as biodegradation of xenobiotics.

metabolite (me-tab'ō-lit) Any product (foodstuff, intermediate, waste product) of metabolism, especially of catabolism.

meter (me'ter) The fundamental unit of length in the SI and metric systems, equivalent to 39.37007874 inches. Defined to be the length of path traveled by light in a vacuum in $1/299792458$ sec.

meth- Chemical prefixes usually denoting a methyl, methoxy group.

methane (meth'an) an odorless gas produced by the decomposition of organic matter; explosive when mixed with 7 or 8 volumes of air, constituting then the firedamp in coal mines.

methanol (meth'a-nol) syn methyl alcohol

methyl (meth'il) The radical, $-CH_3$.

methyl alcohol a flammable, toxic, mobile liquid, used as an industrial solvent, antifreeze, and in chemical manufacture; ingestion may result in severe acidosis, visual impairment, and other effects on the central nervous system.

mg milligram.

MI myocardial infarction.

micro- Prefixes denoting smallness.

microcoria (mi-krō-kō're-a) A congenitally small pupil with an inability to dilate.

microgram (mi'krō-gram) One-millionth of a gram.

microliter (mi'krō-le-ter) One-millionth of a liter.

milieu (me-lyu') Surroundings; environment.

milli- Prefix used in the SI and metric systems to signify one-thousandth (10^{-3}).

miosis (mi-ō'sis) Contraction of the pupil.

mL milliliter.

mm millimeter.

mmol millimole.

molecule (mol'e-kyul) The smallest possible quantity of a di-, tri-, or poly-atomic substance that retains the chemical properties of the substance.

monaural (mon-aw'ral) Pertaining to one ear.

monocular (mon-ok'yu-lar) Relating to, affecting, or visible by one eye only.

mood (mud) The pervasive feeling, tone, and internal emotional state which, when impaired, can markedly influence virtually all aspects of a person's behavior or perception of external events.

mood swing Oscillation of a person's emotional feeling tone between euphoria and depression.

morbid (mōr'bid) Diseased or pathologic.

morbidity (mōr-bid'i-te) A diseased state.

morphine (mōr'fen, mōr-fen') The major phenanthrene alkaloid of opium, which contains 9–14% of anhydrous morphine. It produces a combination of depression and excitation in the central nervous system and some peripheral tissues; predominance of either central stimulation or depression depends upon the species and dose; repeated administration leads to the development of tolerance, physical dependence, and (if abused) psychic dependence. Used as an analgesic, sedative, and anxiolytic.

morphine sulfate morphine used for formulation of tablets as well as solutions for parenteral, epidural, or intrathecal injection to relieve pain.

motor (mō'ter) anatomy, physiology Denoting those neural structures which by the impulses generated and transmitted by them cause muscle fibers or pigment cells to contract, or glands to secrete.

muco- Mucous, mucous (mucous membrane).

mucosa (myu-kō'sa) A mucous tissue lining various tubular structures, consisting of epithelium, lamina propria, and, in the digestive tract, a layer of smooth muscle.

mucous (myu'kus) Relating to mucus or a mucous membrane.

mucus (myu'kus) The clear viscid secretion of the mucous membranes, consisting of mucin, epithelial cells, leukocytes, and various inorganic salts suspended in water.

murmur (mer'mer) An abnormal, usually periodic sound heard on auscultation of the heart or blood vessels.

muscle (mus'el) A primary tissue, consisting predominantly of highly specialized contractile cells, which may be classified as skeletal muscle, cardiac muscle, or smooth muscle; microscopically, the latter is lacking in transverse striations characteristic of the other two types.

    cardiac muscle the muscle comprising the myocardium, consisting of anastomosing transversely striated muscle fibers formed of cells united at intercalated disks.

    extraocular muscles the muscles within the orbit including the four rectus muscles (superior, inferior, medial and lateral); two oblique muscles (superior and inferior), and the levator of the superior eyelid (levator palpebrae superioris).

    involuntary muscles muscle's not ordinarily under control of the will; except in the case of the heart, they are smooth (nonstriated) muscle's, innervated by the autonomic nervous system.

    skeletal muscle grossly, a collection of striated muscle fibers connected at either or both extremities with the bony framework of the body; it may be an appendicular or an axial muscle; histologically, a muscle consisting of elongated, multinucleated, transversely striated skeletal muscle fibers together with connective tissues, blood vessels, and nerves; individual muscle fibers are surrounded by fine reticular and collagen fibers (endomysium); bundles (fascicles) of muscle fibers are surrounded by irregular connective tissue (perimysium); the entire muscle is surrounded, except at the muscle tendon junction, by a dense connective tissue (epimysium).

    smooth muscle one of the muscle fibers of the internal organs, blood vessels, hair follicles, etc.; contractile elements are elongated, usually spindle-shaped cells with centrally located nuclei and a length from 20 to 200 μm, or even longer in the pregnant uterus; although transverse striations are lacking, both thick and thin myofibrils occur; smooth muscle fibers are bound together into sheets or bundles by reticular fibers, and frequently elastic fiber nets are also abundant.

    striated muscle skeletal or voluntary muscle in which cross striations occur in the fibers as a result of regular overlapping of thick and thin myofilaments; contrast with smooth muscle. Although cardiac muscle is also striated in appearance, the term "striated muscle" is commonly used as a synonym for voluntary, skeletal muscle.

musculoskeletal (mus'kyu-lō-skel'e-tal) Relating to muscles and to the skeleton, as, for example, the musculoskeletal system.

mutation (myu-ta'shun) A change in the chemistry of a gene that is perpetuated in subsequent divisions of the cell in which it occurs; a change in the sequence of base pairs in the chromosomal molecule.

myasthenia (mi-as-the'ne-a) Muscular weakness.

    myasthenia gravis disorder of neuromuscular transmission, marked by fluctuating weakness, especially of the oculofacial muscles and the proximal limb muscles; the weakness characteristically increases with activity; due to an immunological disorder.

myco- Fungus.

mydriasis (mi-dri'a-sis) Dilation of the pupil.

myoneural (mi-ō-nu'ral) Relating to both muscle and nerve; denoting specifically the synapse of the motor neuron with striated muscle fibers: myoneural junction or motor endplate.

myopathy (mi-op'a-the) Any abnormal condition or disease of the muscular tissues; commonly designates a disorder involving skeletal muscle.

myopia (mi-ō'pe-a) That optical condition in which only rays from a finite distance from the eye focus on the retina.

myotonus (mi-ot'o-nus) A tonic spasm or temporary rigidity of a muscle or group of muscles.

nail (nal) One of the thin, horny, translucent plates covering the dorsal surface of the distal end of each terminal phalanx of fingers and toes. A nail consists of corpus or body, the visible part, and radix or root at the proximal end concealed under a fold of skin. The under part of the nail is formed from the stratum germinativum of the epidermis, the free surface from the stratum lucidum, the thin cuticular fold overlapping the lunula representing the stratum corneum.

nanogram (nan'ō-gram) One-billionth of a gram (10^{-9} g).

narco- Stupor, narcosis.

narcolepsy (nar'kō-lep-se) A sleep disorder that usually appears in young adulthood, consisting of recurring episodes of sleep during the day, and often disrupted nocturnal sleep; frequently accompanied by cataplexy, sleep paralysis, and hypnagogic hallucinations; a genetically determined disease.

narcosis (nar-kō'sis) General and nonspecific reversible depression of neuronal excitability, produced by a number of physical and chemical agents, usually resulting in stupor rather than in anesthesia (with which narcosis was once synonymous).

narcotic (nar-kot'ik) Any drug derived from opium or opium-like compounds with potent analgesic effects associated with both significant alteration of mood and behavior and potential for dependence and tolerance.

naso- The nose.

nauseant (naw'ze-ant) Nauseating; causing nausea.

necro- Death, necrosis.

necrosis (ne-krō'sis) Pathologic death of one or more cells, or of a portion of tissue or organ, resulting in irreversible damage.

nephro- The kidney.

nerve (nerv) A whitish cordlike structure composed of one or more bundles (fascicles) of myelinated or unmyelinated nerve fibers, or more often mixtures of both, coursing outside of the central nervous system, together with connective tissue within the fascicle and around the neurolemma of individual nerve fibers (endoneurium), around each fascicle (perineurium), and around the entire nerve and its nourishing blood vessels (epineurium), by which stimuli are transmitted from the central nervous system to a part of the body or the reverse. Nerve branches are given in the definition of the major nerve; many are also listed and defined under branch.

afferent nerve a nerve conveying impulses from the periphery to the central nervous system.

cranial nerves those nerves that emerge from, or enter, the cranium or skull, in contrast to the spinal nerves, which emerge from the spine or vertebral column. The twelve paired cranial nerves are the olfactory, optic, oculomotor, trochlear, trigeminal, abducent, facial, vestibulocochlear, glossopharyngeal, vagal, accessory, and hypoglossal nerves.

efferent nerve a nerve conveying impulses from the central nervous system to the periphery.

motor nerve an efferent nerve conveying an impulse that excites muscular contraction; motor nerves in the autonomic nervous system also elicit secretions from glandular epithelia.

oculomotor nerve the third cranial nerve; it supplies all the extrinsic muscles of the ey

neural (nur'al) Relating to any structure composed of nerve cells or their processes, or that on further development will evolve into nerve cells.

neurogenic (nur-ō-jen'ik) Originating in, starting from, or caused by, the nervous system or nerve impulses.

neurohormone (nur-ō-hōr'mōn) A hormone formed by neurosecretory cells and liberated by nerve impulses (e.g., norepinephrine).

neuroleptic (nur-ō-lep'tik) Any of a class of psychotropic drugs used to treast psychosis, particularly schizophrenia; includes the phenothiazine, thioxanthene, and butyrophenone derivatives and the dihydroindolones.

neurologist (nu-rol'ō-jist) A specialist in the diagnosis and treatment of disorders of the neuromuscular system: the central, peripheral, and autonomic nervous systems, the neuromuscular junction, and muscle.

neuromuscular (nur-ō-mus'kyu-lar) Referring to the relationship between nerve and muscle, in particular to the motor innervation of skeletal muscles and its pathology (e.g., neuromuscular disorders).

neuron (nur'on) The morphological and functional unit of the nervous system, consisting of the nerve cell body with its the dendrites and axon.

motor neuron a nerve cell in the spinal cord, rhombencephalon, or mesencephalon characterized by an axon that leaves the central nervous system to establish a functional connection with an effector (muscle or glandular) tissue; SOMATIC MOTOR NEURONS directly synapse with striated muscle fibers by motor endplates; VISCERAL MOTOR NEURONS or AUTONOMIC MOTOR NEURONS (preganglionic m. neuron's), by contrast, innervate smooth muscle fibers or glands only by the intermediary of a second, peripheral, neuron (postganglionic or ganglionic m. neuron) located in an autonomic ganglion.

neuro-ophthalmology (nur'ō-of-thal-mol'ō-je) That branch of medicine concerned with the neurological aspects of the visual apparatus.

neurosciences (nur-ō-si'en-sez) The scientific disciplines concerned with the development, structure, function, chemistry, pharmacology, clinical assessments, and pathology of the nervous system.

neurotransmitter (nur'ō-trans-mit'er) Any specific chemical agent released by a presynaptic cell, upon excitation, that crosses the synapse to stimulate or inhibit the postsynaptic cell.

ng nanogram.

niacin (ni'a-sin) syn nicotinic acid

nicotine (nik'ō-ten) A poisonous volatile alkaloid derived from tobacco (*Nicotiana* spp.) and responsible for many of the effects of tobacco; it first stimulates (small doses), then depresses (large doses) at autonomic ganglia and myoneural junctions. N. is an important tool in physiologic and pharmacologic investigation and is used as an insecticide and fumigant.

nil per os [L.] nothing by mouth.

nitric acid (ni'trik) a strong acid oxidant and corrosive.

nitric oxide A colorless, free-radical gas; it reacts rapidly with O_2 to form other nitrogen oxides (*e.g.*, NO_2, N_2O_3, and N_2O_4) and ultimately is converted to nitrite (NO_2^-) and nitrate (NO_3^-). Physiologically, it is a naturally occurring vasodilator formed in endothelial cells, macrophages, neutrophils, and platelets, and a mediator of cell-to-cell communication formed in bone, brain, endothelium, granulocytes, pancreatic β-cells and peripheral nerves.

nitrite (ni'trit) A salt of nitrous acid.

nitrous oxide a nonflammable, nonexplosive gas that will support combustion; widely used as a rapidly acting, rapidly reversible, nondepressant, and nontoxic inhalation analgesic to supplement other anesthetics and analgesics; its anesthetic potency is inadequate to provide surgical anesthesia.

nm nanometer

noci- Hurt, pain, injury.

noct- Nocturnal.

nocturia (nok-tu're-a) Excessive urination at night.

nonproprietary name (non-prō-pri'e-tar-e) A short name (often called a generic name) of a chemical, drug, or other substance that is not subject to trademark (proprietary) rights but is, in contrast to a trivial name, recognized or recommended by government agencies (*e.g.*, Federal Food and Drug Administration) and by quasi-official organizations (*e.g.*, U.S. Adopted Names Council) for general public use.

norepinephrine (nōr'ep-i-nef'rin) A catecholamine hormone, the postganglionic adrenergic mediator, acting on alpha and beta receptors; it is stored in chromaffin granules in the adrenal medulla and secreted in response to hypotension and physical stress; used pharmacologically as a vasopressor.

normo- Normal, usual.

NPO L. *non per os* or *nil per os*, nothing by mouth.

nucleus (nu'kle-us) In cytology, typically a rounded or oval mass of protoplasm within the cytoplasm of a plant or animal cell; it is surrounded by a nuclear envelope, which encloses euchromatin, heterochromatin, and one or more nucleoli, and undergoes mitosis during cell division.

nycto- Night, nocturnal.

nystagmus (nis-tag'mus) Rhythmical oscillation of the eyeballs, either pendular or jerky.

    caloric nystagmus jerky nystagmus induced by labyrinthine stimulation with hot or cold water in the ear.

    congenital nystagmus nystagmus present at birth or caused by lesions sustained *in utero* or at the time of birth;

    conjugate nystagmus a nystagmus in which the two eyes move simultaneously in the same direction.

    dissociated nystagmus a nystagmus in which the movements of the two eyes are dissimilar in direction, amplitude, and periodicity.

    jerky nystagmus nystagmus in which there is a slow drift of the eyes in one direction, followed by a rapid recovery movement, always described in the direction of the recovery movement; it usually arises from labyrinthine or neurologic lesions or stimuli.

optokinetic nystagmus nystagmus induced by looking at moving visual stimuli.

pendular nystagmus a nystagmus that has oscillations equal in speed and amplitude, usually arising from a visual disturbance.

positional nystagmus nystagmus occurring only when the head is in a particular position.

rotational nystagmus jerky nystagmus arising from stimulation of the labyrinth by rotation of the head around any axis and induced by change of motion.

rotatory nystagmus a movement of the eyes around the visual axis.

vertical nystagmus an up-and-down oscillation of the eyes.

vestibular nystagmus nystagmus resulting from physiological stimuli to the labyrinth that may be rotatory, caloric, compressive, or galvanic, or due to labyrinthial lesions.

OBS syn organic brain syndrome

occipital (ok-sip'i-tal) Relating to the occiput. referring to the occipital bone or to the back of the head.

ocular (ok'yu-lar) syn ophthalmic

oculomotor (ok'yu-lō-mō'tor) Pertaining to the oculomotor cranial nerve.

oculopupillary (ok'yu-lō-pu'pi-lar-e) Pertaining to the pupil of the eye.

OD overdose; optical density (see absorbance).

odyn- Pain.

-ol Suffix denoting that a substance is an alcohol or a phenol.

olfaction (ol-fak'shun) The sense of smell.

olfactory (ol-fak'to-re) Relating to the sense of smell.

oligo- A few, a little; too little, too few.

onco- A tumor.

ontogeny (on-toj'e-ne) Development of the individual, as distinguished from phylogeny, which is evolutionary development of the species.

onycho- A finger nail, a toenail.

ophthalmic (of-thal'mik) Relating to the eye.

ophthalmologist (of-thal-mol'ō-jist) A specialist in ophthalmology.

ophthalmology (of-thal-mol'ō-je) The medical specialty concerned with the eye, its diseases, and refractive errors.

opiate (ō'pe-at) Any preparation or derivative of opium.

opioid (ō'pe-oyd) A narcotic substance, either natural or synthetic.

optic (op'tik) Relating to the eye, vision, or optics.

optician (op-tish'an) One who practices opticianry.

opticianry (op-tish'an-re) The professional practice of filling prescriptions for ophthalmic lenses, dispensing spectacles, and making and fitting contact lenses.

optometry (op-tom'e-tre) The profession concerned with the examination of the eyes and related structures to determine the presence of vision problems and eye disorders, and with the prescription and adaptation of lenses and other optical aids or the use of visual training for maximum visual efficiency.

oro- The mouth.

orthostatic (ōr-thō-stat'ik) Relating to an erect posture or position.

oscillation (os-i-la'shun) A to-and-fro movement.

ossicle (os'i-kl) A small bone; specifically, one of the bones of the tympanic cavity or middle ear.

osteo- Bone.

osteoarthritis (os'te-ō-ar-thri'tis) Arthritis characterized by erosion of articular cartilage, which becomes soft, frayed, and thinned with eburnation of subchondral bone and outgrowths of marginal osteophytes; pain and loss of function result; mainly affects weight-bearing joints, is more common in overweight and older persons.

osteoporosis (os'te-ō-pō-rō'sis) Reduction in the quantity of bone or atrophy of skeletal tissue; occurs in postmenopausal women and elderly men, resulting in bone trabeculae that are scanty, thin, and without osteoclastic resorption.

otic (ō'tik) Relating to the ear.

otitis (ō-ti'tis) Inflammation of the ear.

oto- The ear.

oxide (ok'sid) A compound of oxygen with another element or a radical.

pachy- Thick.

pain (pan) An unpleasant sensation associated with actual or potential tissue damage, and mediated by specific nerve fibers to the brain where its conscious appreciation may be modified by various factors.

palate (pal'at) The bony and muscular partition between the oral and nasal cavities.

palikinesia (pal-i-ki-ne′ze-a) Involuntary repetition of movements.

palinopsia (pal-i-nop′se-a) Abnormal recurring visual hallucinations.

palpable (pal′pa-bl) Perceptible to touch; capable of being palpated.

pan- All, entire (properly affixed to words derived from G. roots).

pancreas (pan′kre-as) An elongated lobulated retroperitoneal gland extending from the duodenum to the spleen; it consists of a flattened head (caput) within the duodenal concavity, an elongated three-sided body extending transversely across the abdomen, and a tail in contact with the spleen. The gland secretes from its exocrine part pancreatic juice that is discharged into the intestine, and from its endocrine part the internal secretions, insulin and glucagon.

papilla (pa-pil′a) Any small, nipplelike process.

papule (pap′yul) A small, circumscribed, solid elevation on the skin.

paralysis (pa-ral′i-sis) Loss of power of voluntary movement in a muscle through injury to or disease of its nerve supply.

paranoia (par-a-noy′a) A disorder characterized by the presence of systematized delusions, often of a persecutory character involving being followed, poisoned, or harmed by other means, in an otherwise intact personality.

parasympathetic (par-a-sim-pa-thet′ik) Pertaining to a division of the autonomic nervous system.

parasympatholytic (par-a-sim′pa-thō-lit′ik) Relating to an agent that annuls or antagonizes the effects of the parasympathetic nervous system; *e.g.,* atropine.

parasympathomimetic (par-a-sim′pa-thō-mi-met′ik) Relating to drugs or chemicals having an action resembling that caused by stimulation of the parasympathetic nervous system.

parenteral (pa-ren′ter-al) By some other means than through the gastrointestinal tract; referring particularly to the introduction of substances into an organism by intravenous, subcutaneous, intramuscular, or intramedullary injection.

paresthesia (par-es-the′ze-a) An abnormal sensation, such as of burning, pricking, tickling, or tingling.

parkinsonism (par′kin-son-izm) A neurological syndrome usually resulting from deficiency of the neurotransmitter dopamine as the consequence of degenerative, vascular, or inflammatory changes in the basal ganglia; characterized by rhythmical muscular tremors, rigidity of movement, festination, droopy posture, and masklike facies.

paroxysm (par′ok-sizm) A sharp spasm or convulsion.

pathogen (path′ō-jen) Any virus, microorganism, or other substance causing disease.

pathologist (pa-thol′ō-jist) A specialist in pathology; a physician who practices, evaluates, or supervises diagnostic tests, using materials removed from living or dead patients, and functions as a laboratory consultant to clinicians, or who conducts experiments or other investigations to determine the causes or nature of disease changes.

pathology (pa-thol′ō-je) The medical science, and specialty practice, concerned with all aspects of disease, but with special reference to the essential nature, causes, and development of abnormal conditions, as well as the structural and functional changes that result from the disease processes.

pectoral (pek′to-ral) Relating to the chest.

pederasty (ped′er-as-te) Sexual relations between a man and a boy.

pedophilia (pe-dō-fil′e-a) An abnormal sexual attraction to children in an adult.

penta- five.

pentyl (pen′til) syn amyl

peptic (pep′tik) Relating to the stomach, to gastric digestion, or to pepsin A.

perception (per-sep′shun) The mental process of becoming aware of or recognizing an object or idea; primarily cognitive rather than affective or conative, although all three aspects are manifested.

percutaneous (per-kyu-ta′ne-us) Denoting the passage of substances through unbroken skin, as in absorption by inunction; also passage through the skin by needle puncture, including introduction of wires and catheters by Seldinger technique.

perfuse (per-fyus′) To force blood or other fluid to flow from the artery through the vascular bed of a tissue or to flow through the lumen of a hollow structure (*e.g.,* an isolated renal tubule).

pericardium (per-i-kar′de-um) The fibroserous membrane, consisting of mesothelium and submesothelial connective tissue, covering the heart and beginnings of the great vessels. It is a closed sac having two layers: the visceral layer (epicardium), immediately surrounding the heart, and the outer parietal layer, forming the sac, composed of strong fibrous tissue, the fibrous pericardium fibrosum, lined with serous membrane, serous pericardium.

periglottis (per-i-glot'is) The mucous membrane of the tongue.

periodicity (per'e-ō-dis'i-te) Tendency to recurrence at regular intervals.

per os By or through the mouth, denoting a method of medication.

perspiration (pers-pi-ra'shun) The excretion of fluid by the sweat glands of the skin.

pharmacist (far'ma-sist) One who is licensed to prepare and dispense drugs and compounds and is knowledgeable concerning their properties.

pharmacodynamic (far'ma-kō-di-nam'ik) Relating to drug action, particularly at the receptor level.

pharmacodynamics (far'ma-kō-di-nam'iks) The study of uptake, movement, binding, and interactions of pharmacologically active molecules at their tissue site(s) of action.

pharmacokinetic (far'ma-kō-ki-net'ik) Relating to the disposition of drugs in the body (*i.e.,* their absorption, distribution, metabolism, and elimination).

pharmacokinetics (far'ma-kō-ki-net'iks) Study of the movement of drugs within biological systems, as affected by absorption, distribution, metabolism, and secretion; particularly the rates of such movements.

pharmacologic (far'ma-kō-loj'ik) Relating to pharmacology or to the composition, properties, and actions of drugs.

pharmacology (far-ma-kol'ō-je) The science concerned with drugs, their sources, appearance, chemistry, actions, and uses.

Pharmacopeia (far'ma-kō-pe'a) A work containing monographs of therapeutic agents, standards for their strength and purity, and their formulations. The various national pharmacopeias are referred to by abbreviations, of which the most frequently encountered are *USP*, the Pharmacopeia of the United States of America (United States Pharmacopeia); and *BP*, British Pharmacopoeia.

pharynx (far'ingks) The upper expanded portion of the digestive tube, between the esophagus below and the mouth and nasal cavities above and in front.

-phil Affinity for, craving for.

phlegm (flem) Abnormal amounts of mucus, especially as expectorated from the mouth.

phobia (fō'be-a) Any objectively unfounded morbid dread or fear that arouses a state of panic. The word is used as a combining form in many terms expressing the object that inspires the fear.

phosphorus (fos'fōr-us) A nonmetallic chemical element, atomic no. 15, atomic wt. 30.973762, occurring extensively in nature, always in chemical combination; the elemental form is extremely poisonous, causing intense inflammation and fatty degeneration; repeated inhalation of phosphorus fumes may cause necrosis of the jaw (phosphonecrosis).

photic (fō'tik) Relating to light.

physician (fi-zish'un) A doctor; a person who has been educated, trained, and licensed to practice the art and science of medicine.

physio- Physical, physiological.

physiology (fiz-e-ol'ō-je) The science concerned with the normal vital processes of animal and vegetable organisms, especially as to how things normally function in the living organism rather than to their anatomical structure, their biochemical composition, or how they are affected by drugs or disease.

pico- Small.

picogram (pi'kō-gram, pe'kō-gram) One-trillionth of a gram.

pill A small globular mass of some coherent but soluble substance, containing a medicinal substance to be swallowed.

piloerection (pi'lō-e-rek'shun) Erection of hair due to action of arrectores pilorum muscles.

pinkeye (pink'i) syn acute contagious conjunctivitis

pint (pint) A measure of quantity (U.S. liquid), containing 16 fluid ounces, 28.875 cubic inches; 473.1765 cc. An imperial pint contains 20 British fluid ounces, 34.67743 cubic inches; 568.2615 cc.

placebo (pla-se'bō) A medicinally inactive substance given as a medicine for its suggestive effect.

plasmacrit (plaz'ma-krit) A measure of the percentage of the volume of blood occupied by plasma, in contrast to a hematocrit.

platelet (plat'let) An irregularly shaped disklike cytoplasmic fragment of a megakaryocyte that is shed in the marrow sinus and subsequently found in the peripheral blood where it functions in clotting. A platelet contains granules in the central part (granulomere) and, peripherally, clear protoplasm (hyalomere), but no definite nucleus; is about one-third to one-half the size of an erythrocyte.

pleura (plur'a) The serous membrane enveloping the lungs and lining the walls of the pleural cavity.

pluri- Several, more.

-pnea Breath, respiration.

pneo- Combining form denoting breath or respiration.

pneumonia (nu-mō'ne-a) Inflammation of the lung parenchyma characterized by consolidation of the affected part, the alveolar air spaces being filled with exudate, inflammatory cells, and fibrin. Most cases are due to infection by bacteria or viruses, a few to inhalation of chemicals or trauma to the chest wall, and a small minority to rickettsias, fungi, and yeasts. Distribution may be lobar, segmental, or lobular; when lobular, in association with bronchitis, it is termed bronchopneumonia.

pod- Foot, foot-shaped.

poison (poy'zun) Any substance, either taken internally or applied externally, that is injurious to health or dangerous to life.

poisoning (poy'zon-ing) The administering of poison.

    carbon monoxide poisoning a potentially fatal acute or chronic intoxication caused by inhalation of carbon monoxide gas which competes favorably with oxygen for binding with hemoglobin (carboxyhemoglobinemia) and thus interferes with the transportation of oxygen and carbon dioxide by the blood.

poly- Many; multiplicity.

polydipsia (pol-e-dip'se-a) Excessive thirst that is relatively prolonged.

polygraph (pol'e-graf) An instrument to obtain simultaneous tracings from several different sources; *e.g.,* radial and jugular pulse, apex beat of the heart, phonocardiogram, electrocardiogram. The ECG is nearly always included for timing.

polyp (pol'ip) A general descriptive term applied to any mass of tissue that bulges or projects outward or upward from the normal surface level, thereby being macroscopically visible as a hemispheroidal, spheroidal, or irregular moundlike structure growing from a relatively broad base or a slender stalk; polyp's may be neoplasms, foci of inflammation, degenerative lesions, or malformations.

polypharmacy (pol-e-far'ma-se) The administration of many drugs at the same time.

polyuria (pol-e-yu're-a) Excessive excretion of urine resulting in profuse micturition.

pons (ponz) neuroanatomy The pons varolii or pons cerebelli; that part of the brainstem between the medulla oblongata caudally and the mesencephalon rostrally, composed of the ventral part of pons and the tegmentum pontis. On the ventral surface of the brain the ventral part of pons, the white pontine protuberance, is demarcated from both the medulla oblongata and the mesencephalon by distinct transverse grooves.

pore (pōr) An opening, hole, perforation, or foramen. A pore, meatus, or foramen.

    sweat pore the surface opening of the duct of a sweat gland.

position (po-zish'un) An attitude, posture, or place occupied.

    anatomical position the erect position of the body with the face directed forward (skull aligned in orbitomeatal or Frankfort plane); the arms at the side and the palms of the hands directed forward; the terms posterior, anterior, lateral, medial, etc., are applied to the parts as they stand related to each other and to the axis of the body when in this position.

post- After, behind, posterior; opposite of anti-.

postictal (pōst-ik'tal) Following a seizure, *e.g.,* epileptic.

postmortem (pōst-mōr'tem) Pertaining to or occurring during the period after death.

potency (pō'ten-se) Power, force, or strength; the condition or quality of being potent.

potential (pō-ten'shal) Capable of doing or being, although not yet doing or being; possible, but not actual.

    action potential the change in membrane potential occurring in nerve, muscle, or other excitable tissue when excitation occurs.

potentiation (pō-ten'she-a'shun) Interaction between two or more drugs or agents resulting in a pharmacologic response greater than the sum of individual responses to each drug or agent.

pound (pownd) A unit of weight, containing 12 ounces, apothecaries' weight, or 16 ounces, avoirdupois; equivalent to 2.2046 kg.

pre- Anterior; before (in time or space).

preanesthetic (pre-an-es-thet'ik) Before anesthesia.

precursor (pre-ker'ser) That which precedes another or from which another is derived, applied especially to a physiologically inactive substance that is converted to an active enzyme, vitamin, hormone, etc., or to a chemical substance that is built into a larger structure in the course of synthesizing the latter.

preictal (pre-ik'tal) Occurring before a seizure or stroke.

presby- Old age.

presbyopia (prez-be-ō'pe-a) The physiologic loss of accommodation in the eyes in advancing age, said to begin when the near point has receded beyond 22 cm (9 inches).

prescribe (pre-skrib') To give directions, either orally or in writing, for. the preparation and administration of a remedy to be used in the treatment of any disease.

preservative (pre-zer'va-tiv) A substance added to food products or to an organic solution to prevent chemical change or bacterial action.

pressure (presh'ur) A stress or force acting in any direction against resistance.

  blood pressure the pressure or tension of the blood within the systemic arteries, maintained by the contraction of the left ventricle, the resistance of the arterioles and capillaries, the elasticity of the arterial walls, as well as the viscosity and volume of the blood; expressed as relative to the ambient atmospheric pressure.

  diastolic pressure the intracardiac pressure during or resulting from diastolic relaxation of a cardiac chamber; the lowest arterial blood pressure reached during any given ventricular cycle.

  intraocular pressure the pressure of the intraocular fluid (usually measured in millimeters of mercury) with a manometer.

  systolic pressure the intracardiac pressure during or resulting from systolic contraction of a cardiac chamber; the highest arterial blood pressure reached during any given ventricular cycle.

presynaptic (pre'si-nap'tik) Pertaining to the area on the proximal side of a synaptic cleft.

prevalence (prev'a-lens) The number of cases of a disease existing in a given population at a specific period of time (*period prevalence*) or at a particular moment in time (*point prevalence*).

pro- Before, forward.

procedure (prō-se'jur) Act or conduct of diagnosis, treatment, or operation.

prognosis (prog-nō'sis) A forecast of the probable course and/or outcome of a disease.

pronate (prō'nat) To assume, or to be placed in, a prone position.

prone (prōn) Denoting the position of the body when lying face downward.

propane (prō'pan) one of the alkane series of hydrocarbons.

prophylactic (prō-fi-lak'tik) Preventing disease; relating to prophylaxis.

proprietary name (prō-pri'e-tar-e) The protected brand name or trademark, registered with the U.S. Patent Office, under which a manufacturer markets a product. It is written with a capital initial letter and is often further distinguished by a superscript R in a circle (®).

pro rat. aet. Abbreviation for L. *pro ratione aetatis*, according to (patient's) age.

pro re nata (prō re na'ta) As the occasion arises; as necessary.

prosthesis (pros'the-sis, -sez) Fabricated substitute for a diseased or missing part of the body.

protocol (prō'tō-kol) A precise and detailed plan for the study of a biomedical problem or for a regimen of therapy, especially cancer chemotherapy.

protuberance (prō-tu'ber-ans) A swelling or knoblike outgrowth. A bulging, swelling, or protruding part.

proximal (prok'si-mal) Nearest the trunk or the point of origin, said of part of a limb, of an artery or a nerve, etc., so situated.

pseudo- False (often used about a deceptive resemblance).

psi pounds per square inch.

psyche (si'ke) Term for the subjective aspects of the mind, self, soul; the psychological or spiritual as distinct from the bodily nature of persons.

psychedelic (si-ke-del'ik) Pertaining to a category of drugs with mainly central nervous system action, said to be the expansion or heightening of consciousness, *e.g.*, LSD, hashish, mescaline.

psychiatry (si-ki'a-tre) The medical specialty concerned with the diagnosis and treatment of mental disorders.

forensic psychiatry the application of psychiatry in courts of law, *e.g.,* in determinations for commitment, competency, fitness to stand trial, responsibility for crime.

psycho- The mind; mental; psychological.

psychoactive (si-kō-ak'tiv) Possessing the ability to alter mood, anxiety, behavior, cognitive processes, or mental tension; usually applied to pharmacologic agents.

psychologist (si-kol'ō-jist) A specialist in psychology licensed to practice professional psychology (*e.g.,* clinical psychologist), or qualified to teach psychology as a scholarly discipline (academic psychologist), or whose scientific specialty is a subfield of psychology (research psychologist).

psychology (si-kol'ō-je) The profession (*e.g.,* clinical psychology), scholarly discipline (academic psychology), and science (research psychology) concerned with the behavior of humans and animals, and related mental and physiological processes.

psychomotor (si-kō-mō'ter) Relating to the psychological processes associated with muscular movement, and to the production of voluntary movements.

psychopharmacology (si'kō-far'ma-kol'ō-je) The use of drugs to treat mental and psychological disorders.

psychophysical (si-kō-fiz'i-kal) Relating to the mental perception of physical stimuli.

psychosis (si-kō'sis) A mental and behavioral disorder causing gross distortion or disorganization of a person's mental capacity, affective response, and capacity to recognize reality, communicate, and relate to others to the degree of interfering with the person's capacity to cope with the ordinary demands of everyday life.

Korsakoff's psychosis syn Korsakoff's syndrome

manic-depressive psychosis syn bipolar disorder

psychosomatic (si'kō-sō-mat'ik) Pertaining to the influence of the mind or higher functions of the brain (emotions, fears, desires, etc.) upon the functions of the body, especially in relation to bodily disorders or disease.

psychostimulant (si-kō-stim'yu-lant) An agent with antidepressant or mood-elevating properties.

psychotogenic (si-kot-ō-jen'ik) Capable of inducing psychosis; particularly referring to drugs of the LSD series and similar substances.

psychotomimetic (si-kot'ō-mi-met'ik) A drug or substance that produces psychological and behavioral changes resembling those of psychosis; *e.g.,* LSD.

psychotropic (si-kō-trop'ik) Capable of affecting the mind, emotions, and behavior; denoting drugs used in the treatment of mental illnesses.

ptosis (tō'sis) A sinking down or prolapse of an organ.

pulmo- The lungs.

pulmonary (pul'mō-nar-e) Relating to the lungs, to the pulmonary artery, or to the aperture leading from the right ventricle into the pulmonary artery.

pulsate (pul'sat) To throb or beat rhythmically; said of the heart or an artery.

pulse (puls) Palpable rhythmic expansion of an artery, produced by the increased volume of blood thrown into the vessel by the contraction of the heart. A pulse may also at times occur in a vein or a vascular organ, such as the liver.

puncture (punk'chur) To make a hole with a small pointed object, such as a needle.

pupil (pyu'pil) The circular orifice in the center of the iris, through which light rays enter the eye.

pupilla (pyu-pil'a) syn pupil

pupillometer (pyu'pil-lom'e-ter) An instrument for measuring and recording the diameter of the pupil.

purulence (pyur'u-lens, -len-se) The condition of containing or forming pus.

pus (pus) A fluid product of inflammation containing leukocytes and the debris of dead cells and tissue elements.

pylorus (pi-lōr'us) A muscular or myovascular device to open (musculus dilator) and to close (musculus sphincter) an orifice or the lumen of an organ.

pyreto- Fever.

pyrexia (pi-rek'se-a) syn fever

pyro- fire, heat, or fever.

QNS quantity not sufficient (amount of specimen submitted to laboratory is inadequate to perform test requested).

quotidian (kwō-tid'e-an) Daily; occurring every day.

Rx Symbol for *recipe* in a prescription.

radial (ra'de-al) Relating to the radius (bone of the forearm), to any structures named from it, or to the radial or lateral aspect of the upper limb as compared to the ulnar or medial aspect.

radioimmunoassay (ra'de-ō-im'u-nō-as'sa) An immunological (immunochemical) procedure that uses the competition between radioisotope-labeled antigen (hormone) or other substance and unlabeled antigen for antiserums, resulting in quantitation of the unlabeled antigen; any method for detecting or quantitating antigens or antibodies using radiolabeled reactants.

range (ranj) A statistical measure of the dispersion or variation of values determined by the endpoint values themselves or the difference between them; *e.g.,* in a group of children aged 6, 8, 9, 10, 13, and 16, the range would be from 6 to 16 or, alternately, 10 (16 minus 6).

  normal range syn reference range

rash Lay term for a cutaneous eruption.

rate (rat) A measurement of an event or process in terms of its relation to some fixed standard; measurement is expressed as the ratio of one quantity to another (*e.g.,* velocity, distance per unit time).

  heart rate rate of the heart's beat, recorded as the number of beats per minute.

  pulse rate rate of the pulse as observed in an artery; recorded as beats per minute.

  respiration rate frequency of breathing, recorded as the number of breaths per minute.

re- Prefix meaning again or backward.

reaction (re-ak'shun) The response of a muscle or other living tissue or organism to a stimulus.

  adverse drug reaction any noxious, unintended, and undesired effect of a drug after its administration for prophylaxis, diagnosis, or therapy.

  allergic reaction a local or general reaction of an organism following contact with a specific allergen to which it has been previously exposed and sensitized.

  anxiety reaction a psychological reaction or experience involving the apprehension of danger accompanied by a feeling of dread and such physical symptoms as an increase in the rate of breathing, sweating, and tachycardia, in the absence of a clearly identifiable fear stimulus; when chronic, it is called GENERALIZED ANXIETY DISORDER.

  false-negative reaction an erroneous or mistakenly negative response.

  false-positive reaction an erroneous or mistakenly positive response.

receptor (re-sep'tor, tōr) A structural protein molecule on the cell surface or within the cytoplasm that binds to a specific factor, such as a hormone, antigen, or neurotransmitter.

  opiate receptors regions of the brain which have the capacity to bind morphine; some, along the aqueduct of Sylvius and in the centromedian nucleus, are in areas related to pain, but others, as in the striatum, are not related.

recipe (res'i-pe) The superscription of a prescription, usually indicated by the sign Rx.

reflex (re'fleks) An involuntary reaction in response to a stimulus applied to the periphery and transmitted to the nervous centers in the brain or spinal cord. Most of the deep reflex's listed as subentries are stretch or myotatic reflex's, elicited by striking a tendon or bone, causing stretching, even slight, of the muscle which then contracts as a result of the stimulus applied to its proprioceptors.

  accommodation reflex increased convexity of the lens, due to contraction of the ciliary muscle and relaxation of the suspensory ligament, to maintain a distinct retinal image.

  light reflex syn pupillary reflex

  pupillary reflex change in diameter of the pupil as a reflex response to any type of stimulus; *e.g.,* constriction caused by light.

regurgitate (re-ger'ji-tat) To flow backward.

relaxant (re-lak'sant) Relaxing; causing relaxation; reducing tension, especially muscular tension.

  muscular relaxant an agent that relaxes striated muscle; includes drugs acting at the brain and/or spinal cord level or directly on muscle to decrease tone, as well as the neuromuscular relaxant's.

respiration (res-pi-ra'shun) A fundamental process of life, characteristic of both plants and animals, in which oxygen is used to oxidize organic fuel molecules, providing a source of energy as well as carbon dioxide and water. In green plants, photosynthesis is not considered respiration)

retch To make an involuntary effort to vomit.

retina (ret'i-na) The light-sensitive membrane forming the innermost layer of the eyeball. Grossly, the retina consists of three parts: optic part of retina, ciliary part of retina, and iridial part of retina. The optic part, the physiologic portion that receives the visual light rays, is further divided into two parts, pigmented part (pigment epithelium) and nervous part, which are arranged in the following layers: 1) pigment epithelium; 2) layer of rods and cones; 3) external limiting lamina, actually a row of junctional complexes; 4) external nuclear lamina; 5) external plexiform lamina; 6) internal nuclear lamina; 7) internal plexiform lamina; 8) ganglionic cell lamina; 9) lamina of nerve fibers; 10) internal limiting lamina. Layers 2 through 10 comprise the nervous part. At the posterior pole of the visual axis is the macula, in the center of which is the fovea, the area of acute vision. Here layers 6, 7, 8, and 9 and blood vessels are absent, and only elongated cones are present. About 3 mm medial to the fovea is the optic disk, where axons of the ganglionic cells converge to form the optic nerve. The ciliary and iridial parts of the retina are forward prolongations of the pigmented layer and a layer of supporting columnar or epithelial cells over the ciliary body and the posterior surface of the iris, respectively.

retrograde   (ret'rō-grad) Moving backward.

reversal   (re-ver'sal) A turning or changing to the opposite direction, as of a process, disease, symptom, or state.

  narcotic reversal the use of narcotic antagonists, such as naloxone, to terminate the action of narcotics.

rhinalgia   (ri-nal'je-a) Pain in the nose.

rhinedema   (ri'ne-de'ma) Swelling of the nasal mucous membrane.

rhinitis   (ri-ni'tis) Inflammation of the nasal mucous membrane.

rhinorrhea   (ri-nō-re'a) A discharge from the nasal mucous membrane.

rigidity   (ri-jid'i-te) Stiffness or inflexibility.

saccadic   (sa-kad'ik) Jerky.

saline   (sa'len, -lin) Relating to, of the nature of, or containing salt; salty.

saliva   (sa-li'va) A clear, tasteless, odorless, slightly acid (pH 6.8) viscid fluid, consisting of the secretion from the parotid, sublingual, and submandibular salivary glands and the mucous glands of the oral cavity; its function is to keep the mucous membrane of the mouth moist, to lubricate the food during mastication, and to convert starch into maltose.

salve   (sav) syn ointment

sample A selected subset of a population; a sample may be random or

nonrandom (haphazard); representative or nonrepresentative.

scab   (skab) A crust formed by coagulation of blood, pus, serum, or a combination of these, on the surface of an ulcer, erosion, or other type of wound.

scale   (skal) A standardized test for measuring psychological, personality, or behavioral characteristics.

  Celsius scale a temperature scale that is based upon the triple point of water (defined to be 273.16 K) and assigned the value of 0.01°C; this has replaced the centigrade scale because the triple point of water can be more accurately measured than the ice point; for most practical purposes, the two scales are equivalent.

  Fahrenheit scale a thermometer scale in which the freezing point of water is 32°F and the boiling point of water 212°F; 0°F indicates the lowest temperature Fahrenheit could obtain by a mixture of ice and salt in 1724; °C = (5/9)(°F - 32).

scar   (skar) The fibrous tissue replacing normal tissues destroyed by injury or disease.

schema   (ske'ma) A plan, outline, or arrangement.

schizophrenia   (skiz-ō-fre'ne-a, skits'ō-) A term, coined by Bleuler synonymous with and replacing dementia praecox; a common type of psychosis, characterized by a disorder in perception, content of thought, and thought processes (hallucinations and delusions), and extensive withdrawal of one's interest from other people and the outside world, and the investment of it in one's own; now considered a group or spectrum of schizophrenic disorders rather than as a single entity.

science   (si'ens) The branch of knowledge that produces theoretical explanations of natural phenomena based on experiments and observations.

sclera   (skler'a) A portion of the fibrous tunic forming the outer envelope of the eye, except for its anterior sixth, which is the cornea.

sclerose   (skle-rōz') To harden; to undergo sclerosis.

sclerosis   (skle-rō'sis)

  amyotrophic lateral sclerosis a disease of the motor tracts of the lateral columns and anterior horns of the spinal cord, causing progressive muscular atrophy, increased reflexes, fibrillary twitching, and spastic irritability of muscles; associated with a defect in superoxide dismutase.

multiple sclerosis common demyelinating disorder of the central nervous system, causing patches of sclerosis (plaques) in the brain and spinal cord; occurs primarily in young adults; clinical manifestations depend upon the location and size of the plaques; typical symptoms include visual loss, diplopia, nystagmus, dysarthria, weakness, paresthesias, bladder abnormalities, and mood alterations; characteristically, the symptoms show exacerbations and remissions.

scoliosis (skō-le-ō'sis) Abnormal lateral curvature of the vertebral column. Depending on the etiology, there may be one curve, or primary and secondary compensatory curves; scoliosis may be "fixed" as a result of muscle and/or bone deformity or "mobile" as a result of unequal muscle contraction.

score (skōr) An evaluation, usually expressed numerically, of status, achievement, or condition in a given set of circumstances.

sedate (se-dat') To bring under the influence of a sedative.

sedation (se-da'shun) The act of calming, especially by the administration of a sedative.

sedative (sed'a-tiv) Calming; quieting.

seizure (se'zher) An attack; the sudden onset of a disease or of certain symptoms.

sensation (sen-sa'shun) A feeling; the translation into consciousness of the effects of a stimulus exciting any of the organs of sense.

sense (sens) The faculty of perceiving any stimulus.

    special sense one of the five senses related respectively to the organs of sight, hearing, smell, taste, and touch.

sensorimotor (sen'sōr-i-mō'ter) Both sensory and motor; denoting a mixed nerve with afferent and efferent fibers.

septum (sep'tum) A thin wall dividing two cavities or masses of softer tissue.

serotonergic (ser-ō-tō-ner'jik, ser-) Related to the action of serotonin or its precursor l-tryptophan.

serotonin (ser-ō-tō'nin) A vasoconstrictor, liberated by platelets, that inhibits gastric secretion and stimulates smooth muscle; also acts as a neurotransmitter, present in the central nervous system, many peripheral tissues and cells, and carcinoid tumors.

shock (shok) A sudden physical or mental disturbance.

    anaphylactic shock a severe, often fatal form of shock characterized by smooth muscle contraction and capillary dilation initiated by cytotropic (IgE class) antibodies.

    insulin shock severe hypoglycemia produced by administration of insulin, manifested by sweating, tremor, anxiety, vertigo, and diplopia, followed by delirium, convulsions, and collapse.

side effect A result of drug or other therapy in addition to or in extension of the desired therapeutic effect; usually, but not necessarily, connoting an undesirable effect.

sign (sin) Any abnormality indicative of disease, discoverable on examination of the patient; an objective symptom of disease, in contrast to a symptom which is a subjective sign of disease.

    physical sign a sign that is evident on inspection or elicited by auscultation, percussion, or palpation.

    Romberg's sign with feet approximated, the patient stands with eyes open and then closed; if closing the eyes increases the unsteadiness, a loss of proprioceptive control is indicated, and the sign is positive.

    vital signs objective measurements of temperature, pulse, respirations, and blood pressure as a means of assessing general health and cardiorespiratory function.

signature (sig'na-chur, -tur) The part of a prescription containing the directions to the patient.

sinus (si'nus) A channel for the passage of blood or lymph, without the coats of an ordinary vessel; *e.g.*, blood passages in the gravid uterus or those in the cerebral meninges.

skeleton (skel'e-ton) The bony framework of the body in vertebrates (endoskeleton) or the hard outer envelope of insects (exoskeleton or dermoskeleton).

skin The membranous protective covering of the body, consisting of the epidermis and corium (dermis).

sleep (slep) A physiologic state of relative unconsciousness and inaction of the voluntary muscles, the need for which recurs periodically. The stages of sleep have been variously defined in terms of depth (light, deep), EEG characteristics (delta waves, synchronization), physiological characteristics (REM, NREM), and presumed anatomical level (pontine, mesencephalic, rhombencephalic, rolandic, etc.).

snuff (snuf) To inhale forcibly through the nose.

SOAP *s* ubjective, *o* bjective, *a* ssessment, and *p* lan; used in problem-oriented records for organizing follow-up data, evaluation, and planning.

sodium (sō′de-um) A metallic element, atomic no. 11, atomic weight 22.989768; an alkali metal oxidizing readily in air or water; its salts are extensively used in medicine and industry. For organic sodium salts not listed below, see under the name of the organic acid portion.

solvent A liquid that holds another substance in solution, *i.e.*, dissolves it.

somnolence (som′nō-lens) An inclination to sleep.

soporific (sō-pōr-if′ik, sop′ōr-) Causing sleep.

sound (sownd) The vibrations produced by a sounding body, transmitted by the air or other medium, and perceived by the internal ear.

Korotkoff sounds sounds heard during blood pressure determination. Sounds originating within the blood passing through the vessel or produced by a vibrating motion of the arterial wall.

spasticity (spas-tis′i-te) A state of increased muscular tone with exaggeration of the tendon reflexes.

specificity (spes-i-fis′i-te) The condition or state of being specific, of having a fixed relation to a single cause or to a definite result; manifested in the relation of a disease to its pathogenic microorganism, of a reaction to a certain chemical union, or of an antibody to its antigen or the reverse.

specimen (spes′i-men) A small part, or sample, of any substance or material obtained for testing.

sphincter (sfingk′ter) A muscle that encircles a duct, tube or orifice in such a way that its contraction constricts the lumen or orifice; it is the closing component of a pylorus (the outer component is the musculus dilator).

sphincter pupillae a ring of smooth muscle fibers surrounding the pupillary border of the iris.

pyloric sphincter a thickening of the circular layer of the gastric musculature encircling the gastroduodenal junction.

sphygmic (sfig′mik) Relating to the pulse.

sphygmo- Pulse.

sphygmoid (sfig′moyd) Pulselike; resembling the pulse.

sphygmomanometer (sfig′mō-ma-nom′e-ter) An instrument for measuring arterial blood pressure consisting of an inflatable cuff, inflating bulb, and a gauge showing the blood pressure.

spirit (spir′it) An alcoholic liquor stronger than wine, obtained by distillation.

spleen (splen) A large vascular lymphatic organ lying in the upper part of the abdominal cavity on the left side, between the stomach and diaphragm, composed of white and red pulp; the white consists of lymphatic nodules and diffuse lymphatic tissue; the red consists of venous sinusoids between which are splenic cords; the stroma of both red and white pulp is reticular fibers and cells. A framework of fibroelastic trabeculae extending from the capsule subdivides the structure into poorly defined lobules. It is a blood-forming organ in early life and later a storage organ for red corpuscles and platelets; because of the large number of macrophages, it also acts as a blood filter, both identifying and destroying effete erythrocytes.

sprain (spran) An injury to a ligament when the joint is carried through a range of motion greater than normal, but without dislocation or fracture.

SSRI selective serotonin reuptake inhibitor.

-stat An agent intended to keep something from changing or moving.

statistics (sta-tis′tiks) A collection of numerical values, items of information, or other facts which are numerically grouped into definite classes and subject to analysis, particularly analysis of the probability that the resulting empirical findings are due to chance.

steno- Narrowness, constriction; opposite of eury-.

steroid (ster′oyd, ster′oyd) Pertaining to the steroids.

anabolic steroid prescription drug abused by some athletes to increase muscle mass; functions in a manner similar to that of the chief male hormone, testosterone. Masculinizing effects are minimized by synthetically manipulating chemical structure to emphasize tissue-building, nitrogen-retaining processes.

stethoscope (steth′ō-skōp) An instrument originally devised by Laënnec for aid in hearing the respiratory and cardiac sounds in the chest, but now modified in various ways and used in auscultation of any of vascular or other sounds anywhere in the body.

stimulant (stim′yu-lant) Stimulating; exciting to action.

general stimulant a stimulant that affects the entire body.

stimulation (stim-yu-la′shun) Arousal of the body or any of its parts or organs to increased functional activity.

stimulus (stim′yu-lus) A stimulant.

stomach (stum′uk) A large, irregularly piriform sac between the esophagus and the small intestine, lying just beneath the diaphragm. Its wall has four coats or tunics: mucous, submucous, muscular, and peritoneal; the muscular coat is composed of three layers, the fibers running longitudinally in the outer, circularly in the middle, and obliquely in the inner layer.

strabismus (stra-biz′mus) A manifest lack of parallelism of the visual axes of the eyes.

stroke (strōk) Term denoting the sudden development of focal neurological deficits usually related to impaired cerebral blood flow; more appropriate terms indicate the nature of the disturbance; *e.g.,* thrombosis, hemorrhage, or embolism.

strychnine (strik′nin, -nen, -nin) An alkaloid from *Strychnos nux-vomica*; colorless crystals of intensely bitter taste, nearly insoluble in water. It stimulates all parts of the central nervous system, and was formerly used as a stomachic, an antidote for depressant poisons, and in the treatment of myocarditis. Strychnine blocks the inhibitory neurotransmitter, glycine, and thus can cause convulsions. It is a potent chemical capable of producing acute or chronic poisoning.

stylus (sti′lus) Any pencil-shaped structure.

sub- Prefix to words formed from L. roots, denoting beneath, less than the normal or typical, inferior.

subcutaneous (sub-kyu-ta′ne-us) Beneath the skin.

substance (sub′stans) Stuff; material.

controlled substance a substance subject to the Controlled Substances Act (1970), which regulates the prescribing and dispensing, as well as the manufacturing, storage, sale, or distribution of substance's assigned to five schedules according to their 1) potential for or evidence of abuse, 2) potential for psychic or physiologic dependence, 3) contributing a public health risk, 4) harmful pharmacologic effect, or 5) role as a precursor of other controlled substance's.

sunstroke (sun′strōk) A form of heatstroke resulting from undue exposure to the sun's rays, probably caused by the action of actinic rays combined with high temperature; symptoms are those of heatstroke, but often without fever.

super- (Properly prefixed to words of L. derivation) denoting in excess, above, superior, or in the upper part of; often the same usage as L. *supra-*.

superscription (su′per-skrip′shun) The beginning of a prescription, consisting of the injunction, *recipe*, take, usually denoted by the sign Rx.

supine (su-pin′) Denoting the body when lying face upward; opposite of prone.

suppository (su-poz′i-tōr-e) A small, solid body shaped for ready introduction into one of the orifices of the body other than the oral cavity (*e.g.,* rectum, urethra, vagina), made of a substance, usually medicated, which is solid at ordinary temperatures but melts at body temperature.

sympath- The sympathetic part of the autonomic nervous system.

sympatholytic (sim′pa-thō-lit′ik) Denoting antagonism to or inhibition of adrenergic nerve activity.

sympathomimetic (sim′pa-thō-mi-met′ik) Denoting mimicking of action of the sympathetic system.

symptom (simp′tom) Any morbid phenomenon or departure from the normal in structure, function, or sensation, experienced by the patient and indicative of disease.

cardinal symptom the primary or major symptom of diagnostic importance.

objective symptom a symptom that is evident to the observer.

subjective symptom a symptom apparent only to the patient.

withdrawal symptoms a group of morbid symptom's, predominantly erethistic, occurring in an addict who is deprived of the accustomed dose of the addicting agent.

symptomatology (simp′tō-ma-tol′ō-je) The science of the symptoms of disease, their production, and the indications they furnish.

syn- Together, with, joined; appears as sym- before b, p, ph, or m; corresponds to L. *con-*.

synapse (sin′aps, si-naps′) The functional membrane-to-membrane contact of the nerve cell with another nerve cell, an effector (muscle, gland) cell, or a sensory receptor cell. The synapse subserves the transmission of nerve impulses, commonly from a club-shaped axon terminal (the presynaptic element) to the circumscripta patch of the receiving cell's plasma membrane (the postsynaptic element) on which the synapse occurs. In most cases the impulse is transmitted by means of a chemical transmitter substance (such as acetylcholine, γ-aminobutyric acid, dopamine, norepinephrine) released into a synaptic cleft that separates the presynaptic from the postsynaptic membrane; the transmitter is stored in synaptic vesicles in the presynaptic element. In other synapse's transmission takes place by direct propagation of the bioelectrical potential from the presynaptic to the postsynaptic membrane.

syncope (sin′ko-pe) Loss of consciousness and postural tone caused by diminished cerebral blood flow.

syndrome (sin′drōm) The aggregate of signs and symptoms associated with any morbid process, and constituting together the picture of the disease.

Korsakoff's syndrome an alcohol amnestic syndrome characterized by confusion and severe impairment of memory, especially for recent events, for which the patient compensates by confabulation; typically encountered in chronic alcoholics; delirium tremens may precede the syndrome, and Wernicke's syndrome often coexists; the precise pathogenesis is uncertain, but direct toxic effects of alcohol are probably less important than severe nutritional deficiencies often associated with chronic alcoholism.

organic brain syndrome a constellation of behavioral or psychological signs and symptoms including problems with attention, concentration, memory, confusion, anxiety, and depression caused by transient or permanent dysfunction of the brain.

sudden infant death syndrome abrupt and inexplicable death of an apparently healthy infant; various theories have been advanced to explain such deaths (e.g., sleep-induced apnea, laryngospasm, overwhelming infectious disease) but none has been generally accepted or demonstrated at autopsy.

Tourette syndrome a tic disorder appearing in childhood, characterized by multiple motor tics and vocal tics present for more than one year. Obsessive-compulsive behavior, attention-deficit disorder, and other psychiatric disorders may be associated; coprolalia and echolalia rarely occur; autosomal dominant inheritance.

Wernicke's syndrome a condition frequently encountered in chronic alcoholics, largely due to thiamin deficiency and characterized by disturbances in ocular motility, pupillary alterations, nystagmus, and ataxia with tremors; an organic-toxic psychosis is often an associated finding, and Korsakoff's syndrome often coexists; characteristic cellular pathology found in several areas of the brain.

withdrawal syndrome a substance-specific syndrome that follows the cessation of, or reduction in, intake of a psychoactive substance previously used regularly. The syndrome that develops varies according to the psychoactive substance used. Common symptoms include anxiety, restlessness, irritability, insomnia, and impaired attention.

synergism (sin′er-jizm) Coordinated or correlated action of two or more structures, agents, or physiologic processes so that the combined action is greater than the sum of each acting separately.

synesthesia (sin-es-the′ze-a) A condition in which a stimulus, in addition to exciting the usual and normally located sensation, gives rise to a subjective sensation of different character or localization; e.g., color hearing, color taste.

syringe (si-rinj′, sir′inj) An instrument used for injecting or withdrawing fluids.

hypodermic syringe a small syringe with a barrel (which may be calibrated), perfectly matched plunger, and tip; used with a hollow needle for subcutaneous injections and for aspiration.

system (sis′tem) A consistent and complex whole made up of correlated and semi-independent parts. A complex of anatomical structures functionally related.

autonomic nervous system that part of the nervous system which represents the motor innervation of smooth muscle, cardiac muscle, and gland cells. It consists of two physiologically and anatomically distinct, mutually antagonistic components: the sympathetic and parasympathetic divisions. In both of these the pathway of innervation consists of a synaptic sequence of two motor neurons, one of which lies in the spinal cord or brainstem as the preganglionic neuron, the thin but myelinated axon of which emerges with an outgoing spinal or cranial nerve and synapses with one or more of the postganglionic neurons composing the autonomic ganglia; the unmyelinated postganglionic fibers in turn innervate the smooth muscle, cardiac muscle, or gland cells. The preganglionic neurons of the sympathetic part lie in the intermediolateral cell column of the thoracic and upper two lumbar segments of the spinal gray matter; those of the parasympathetic part compose the visceral motor (visceral efferent) nuclei of the brainstem as well as the lateral column of the second to fourth sacral segments of the spinal cord. The ganglia of the sympathetic division are the paravertebral ganglia of the sympathetic trunk and the prevertebral or collateral ganglia; those of the parasympathetic division lie either near the organ to be innervated or as intramural ganglia within the organ itself except in the head, where there are four discrete parasympathetic ganglia (ciliary, otic, pterygopalatine, and submandibular). Impulse transmission from preganglionic to postganglionic neuron is mediated by acetylcholine in both the sympathetic and parasympathetic parts; transmission from the postganglionic fiber to the visceral effector tissues is classically said to be by acetylcholine in the parasympathetic part and by noradrenalin in the sympathetic part; recent evidence suggests the existence of further noncholinergic, nonadrenergic classes of postganglionic fibers.

cardiovascular system the heart and blood vessels considered as a whole.

central nervous system the brain and the spinal cord.

circulatory system syn vascular system

digestive system the digestive tract from the mouth to the anus with all its associated glands and organs.

endocrine system collective designation for those tissues capable of secreting hormones.

genital system the complex system consisting of the male or female gonads, associated ducts, and external genitalia dedicated to the function of reproducing the species.

immune system an intricate complex of interrelated cellular, molecular, and genetic components which provides a defense (immune response) against foreign organisms or substances and aberrant native cells.

limbic system collective term denoting a heterogeneous array of brain structures at or near the edge (limbus) of the medial wall of the cerebral hemisphere, in particular the hippocampus, amygdala, and fornicate gyrus; the term is often used so as to include also the interconnections of these structures, as well as their connections with the septal area, the hypothalamus, and a medial zone of mesencephalic tegmentum. By way of the latter connections, the limbic system exerts an important influence upon the endocrine and autonomic motor system's; its functions also appear to affect motivational and mood states.

lymphatic system the bodily system concerned with the circulation of lymph and the production of lymphocytes; it consists of lymphatic vessels, nodes, and lymphoid tissue (spleen, tonsils, thymus, and other lymphoid structures); it empties into the veins at the level of the superior aperture of the thorax.

muscular system all the muscles of the body collectively.

nervous system the entire nerve apparatus, composed of a central part, the brain and spinal cord, and a peripheral part, the cranial and spinal nerves, autonomic ganglia, and plexuses.

parasympathetic nervous system see autonomic nervous system

peripheral nervous system the peripheral part of the nervous system external to the brain and spinal cord from their roots to their peripheral terminations. This includes the ganglia, both sensory and autonomic and any plexuses through which the nerve fibers run.

reproductive system syn genital system

respiratory system all the air passages from the nose to the pulmonary alveoli.

reticular activating system a physiological term denoting that part of the brainstem reticular formation that plays a central role in the organism's bodily and behavioral alertness; it extends as a diffusely organized neural apparatus through the central region of the brainstem into the subthalamus and the intralaminar nuclei of the thalamus; by its ascending connections it affects the function of the cerebral cortex in the sense of behavioral responsiveness; its descending (reticulospinal) connections transmit its activating influence upon bodily posture and reflex mechanisms (*e.g.*, muscle tonus), in part by way of the gamma motor neurons.

sympathetic nervous system originally, the entire autonomic nervous system;

urogenital system includes all the organs concerned in reproduction and in the formation and discharge of urine.

systemic (sis-tem'ik) Relating to a system; specifically somatic, relating to the entire organism as distinguished from any of its individual parts.

systole (sis'tō-le) Contraction of the heart, especially of the ventricles, by which the blood is driven through the aorta and pulmonary artery to traverse the systemic and pulmonary circulations, respectively; its occurrence is indicated physically by the first sound of the heart heard on auscultation, by the palpable apex beat, and by the arterial pulse.

tablet A solid dosage form containing medicinal substances with or without suitable diluents; it may vary in shape, size, and weight, and may be classed according to the method of manufacture, as molded tablet and compressed tablet.

tachy- Rapid.

tachyarrhythmia (tak'e-a-ridh'me-a) Any disturbance of the heart's rhythm, regular or irregular, resulting by convention in a rate over 100 beats per minute during physical examination.

tachycardia (tak'i-kar'de-a) Rapid beating of the heart, conventionally applied to rates over 100 per minute.

tachypnea (tak-ip-ne'a) Rapid breathing.

tactile (tak'til) Relating to touch or to the sense of touch.

technologist (tek-nol'o-jist) One trained in and using the techniques of a profession, art, or science.

temperature (tem'per-a-chur) The sensible intensity of heat of any substance; the manifestation of the average kinetic energy of the molecules making up a substance due to heat agitation.

core temperature the temperature of the interior of the body.

tendon (ten'don) A fibrous cord or band of variable length that connects a muscle with its bony attachment or other structure; it may unite with the muscle at its extremity or may run along the side or in the center of the muscle for a longer or shorter distance, receiving the muscular fibers along its lateral border. It consists of

fascicles of very densely arranged, almost parallel collagenous fibers, rows of elongated fibrocytes, and a minimum of ground substance.

test To prove; to try a substance; to determine the chemical nature of a substance by means of reagents.

finger-nose test a test of voluntary eye-motor coordination of the upper limb(s); the subject is asked to slowly touch the tip of the nose with the extended index finger; assesses cerebellar function.

screening test any testing procedure designed to separate people or objects according to a fixed characteristic or property.

testosterone (tes-tos'te-rōn) The most potent naturally occurring androgen, formed in greatest quantities by the interstitial cells of the testes, and possibly secreted also by the ovary and adrenal cortex; used in the treatment of hypogonadism, cryptorchism, certain carcinomas, and menorrhagia.

theorem (the'ō-rem) A proposition that can be proved, and so is established as a law or principle.

theory (the'ōr-e) A reasoned explanation of known facts or phenomena that serves as a basis of investigation by which to reach the truth.

therapeutic (thar-a-pyu'tik) Relating to therapeutics or to the treatment, remediating, or curing of a disorder or disease.

thermometer (ther-mom'e-ter) An instrument for indicating the temperature of any substance; usually a sealed vacuum tube containing mercury, which expands with heat and contracts with cold, its level accordingly rising or falling in the tube, with the exact degree of variation of level being indicated by a scale.

thiamin (thi'a-min) A heat-labile and water-soluble vitamin contained in milk, yeast, and in the germ and husk of grains; also artificially synthesized; essential for growth; a deficiency of thiamin is associated with beriberi and Wernicke-Korsakoff's syndrome.

thoraco- The chest (thorax).

thorax (thō'raks) The upper part of the trunk between the neck and the abdomen; it is formed by the 12 thoracic vertebrae, the 12 pairs of ribs, the sternum, and the muscles and fasciae attached to these; below, it is separated from the abdomen by the diaphragm; it contains the chief organs of the circulatory and respiratory systems.

throat (thrōt) The fauces and pharynx.

thrombo- Blood clot; coagulation; thrombin.

thrombus (throm'bus) A clot in the cardiovascular system formed during life from constituents of blood; it may be occlusive or attached to the vessel or heart wall without obstructing the lumen (mural thrombus).

TIA transient ischemic attack.

tic (tik) Habitual, repeated contraction of certain muscles, resulting in stereotyped individualized actions that can be voluntarily suppressed for only brief periods, *e.g.,* clearing the throat, sniffing, pursing the lips, excessive blinking; especially prominent when the person is under stress; there is no known pathologic substrate.

tincture (tingk'chur) An alcoholic or hydroalcoholic solution prepared from vegetable materials or from chemical substances.

tinnitus (ti-ni'tus) A sensation of noises (ringing, whistling, booming, etc.) in the ears.

tissue (tish'u) A collection of similar cells and the intercellular substances surrounding them. There are four basic tissues in the body: 1) epithelium; 2) the connective tissues, including blood, bone, and cartilage; 3) muscle tissue; and 4) nerve tissue.

tolerance (tol'er-ans) The ability to endure or be less responsive to a stimulus, especially over a period of continued exposure.

  cross tolerance the resistance to one or several effects of a compound as a result of tolerance developed to a pharmacologically similar compound.

tolerant (tol'er-ant) Having the property of tolerance.

tone (tōn) A musical sound.

  muscle tone the internal state of muscle-fiber tension within individual muscles and muscle groups.

tonic (ton'ik) In a state of continuous unremitting action; denoting especially a muscular contraction.

tonicity (tō-nis'i-te) A state of normal tension of the tissues by virtue of which the parts are kept in shape, alert, and ready to function in response to a suitable stimulus. In the case of muscle, it refers to a state of continuous activity or tension beyond that related to the physical properties; *i.e.,* it is active resistance to stretch; in skeletal muscle it is dependent upon the efferent innervation.

toxic (tok'sik) syn poisonous

toxicity (tok-sis'i-te) The state of being poisonous.

toxico- Poison, toxin.

toxicologist (tok-si-kol'o-jist) A specialist or expert in toxicology.

toxicology (tok-si-kol'o-je) The science of poisons, including their source, chemical composition, action, tests, and antidotes.

toxin (tok'sin) A noxious or poisonous substance that is formed or elaborated during the metabolism and growth of certain microorganisms and some higher plant and animal species.

trachea (tra'ke-a) The air tube extending from the larynx into the thorax (level of the fifth or sixth thoracic vertebra) where it bifurcates into the right and left main bronchi. The trachea is composed of from 16 to 20 rings of hyaline cartilage connected by a membrane (annular ligament); posteriorly, the rings are deficient for one-fifth to one-third of their circumference, the interval forming the membranous wall being closed by a fibrous membrane containing smooth muscular fibers. Internally, the mucosa is composed of a pseudostratified ciliated columnar epithelium with mucous goblet cells; numerous small mixed mucous and serous glands occur, the ducts of which open to the surface of the epithelium.

trauma (traw'ma) An injury, physical or mental.

tremor (trem'er, -ōr) Repetitive, often regular, oscillatory movements caused by alternate, or synchronous, but irregular contraction of opposing muscle groups; usually involuntary.

triage (tre'ahzh) Medical screening of patients to determine their relative priority for treatment; the separation of a large number of casualties, in military or civilian disaster medical care, into three groups: 1) those who cannot be expected to survive even with treatment; 2) those who will recover without treatment; 3) the highest priority group, those who will not survive without treatment.

tropia (trō'pe-a) Abnormal deviation of the eye.

tryptophan (trip'tō-fan) The l-isomer is a component of proteins; a nutritionally essential amino acid.

tumefaction (tu-me-fak'shun) A swelling.

tumescence (tu-mes'ens) The condition of being or becoming tumid.

tussive (tus'siv) Relating to a cough.

unilateral (yu-ni-lat'e-ral) Confined to one side only.

ureter (yu-re'ter, yu're-ter) The thick-walled tube that conducts the urine from the renal pelvis to the bladder; it consists of an abdominal part and a pelvic part, is lined with transitional epithelium surrounded by smooth muscle, both circular and longitudinal, and is covered externally by a tunica adventitia.

urethra (yu-re'thra) A canal leading from the bladder, discharging the urine externally.

uric (yur'ik) Relating to urine.

urinalysis (yu-ri-nal'i-sis) Analysis of the urine.

urine (yur'in) The fluid and dissolved substances excreted by the kidney.

urticaria (er'ti-kar'i-a) An eruption of itching wheals, usually of systemic origin; it may be due to a state of hypersensitivity to foods or drugs, foci of infection, physical agents (heat, cold, light, friction), or psychic stimuli.

variable (var'e-a-bl) That which is inconstant, which can or does change, as contrasted with a constant.

vascular (vas'kyu-lar) Relating to or containing blood vessels.

vasculo- A blood vessel.

vaso- Vas, blood vessel.

vasoconstriction (va'sō-kon-strik'shun, vas'ō-) Narrowing of the blood vessels.

vasoconstrictor (va'sō-kon-strik'ter, vas'ō-) An agent that causes narrowing of the blood vessels.

vasodepression (va'sō-de-presh'un, vas'ō) Reduction of tone in blood vessels with vasodilation and resulting lowered blood pressure.

vasodilation (va'sō-di-la'shun, vas-ō-) widening of the lumen of blood vessels.

vasodilative (va'sō-di-la'tiv, vas'ō-) Causing dilation of the blood vessels.

vasodilator (va'sō-di-la'ter, vas'ō-) An agent that causes dilation of the blood vessels.

vasopuncture (va-sō-punk'chur, vas-ō-) The act of puncturing a vessel with a needle.

vein (van) A blood vessel carrying blood toward the heart; all the veins except the pulmonary carry dark or oxygenated blood.

vena (ve'na) syn vein

venipuncture (ven'i-punk-chur, ve'ni-) The puncture of a vein, usually to withdraw blood or inject a solution.

venous (ve'nus) Relating to a vein or to the veins.

ventricle (ven'tri-kl) A normal cavity, as of the brain or heart.

left ventricle the lower chamber on the left side of the heart that receives the arterial blood from the left atrium and drives it by the contraction of its walls into the aorta.

right ventricle the lower chamber on the right side of the heart which receives the venous blood from the right atrium and drives it by the contraction of its walls into the pulmonary artery.

vertigo (ver'ti-gō, ver-ti'gō) A sensation of spinning or whirling motion. Vertigo implies a definite sensation of rotation of the subject or of objects about the subject in any plane.

vesicle (ves'i-kl) syn vesicula

synaptic vesicles the small (average diameter 30 nm), intracellular, membrane-bound vesicle's near the presynaptic membrane of a synaptic junction, containing the transmitter substance which, in chemical synapses, mediates the passage of nerve impulses across the junction.

vestibular (ves-tib'yu-lar) Relating to a vestibule, especially the vestibule of the ear.

vestibule (ves'ti-bul) A small cavity or a space at the entrance of a canal.

viscous (vis'kus) Sticky; marked by high viscosity.

vision (vizh'un) The act of seeing.

visuomotor (vizh'yu-ō-mō'ter) Denoting the ability to synchronize visual information with physical movement, *e.g.*, driving a car..

vital (vit-al) Relating to life.

vitamin (vit'a-min) One of a group of organic substances, present in minute amounts in natural foodstuffs, that are essential to normal metabolism; insufficient amounts in the diet may cause deficiency diseases.

void (voyd) To evacuate urine or feces.

volatile (vol'a-til) Tending to evaporate rapidly.

voluntary (vol'un-tar-e) Relating or acting in obedience to the will; not obligatory.

weight (wat) The product of the force of gravity, defined internationally as 9.80665 m/s^2, times the mass of the body.

apothecaries' weight a system of weights based upon the weight of a grain of wheat; now superseded by the metric system (based on grams). One grain is the equivalent of 64.8 milligrams. One scruple contains 20 grains; one dram contains 60 grains; one apothecary ounce contains 8 drams (480 grains); one apothecary pound contains 12 ounces (5760 grains).

avoirdupois weight a system of weights based on the grain; 7000 grains equal 256 drams, or 16 ounces, or 1 pound.

xeno- Strange; foreign material; parasite.

zero (ze'rō) The figure 0, indicating the absence of magnitude, or nothing.

THERAPEUTIC CATEGORY INDEX

ANALGESIC, NON-NARCOTIC

ANALGESIC, TOPICAL

ANDROGEN

ANGIOTENSIN-CONVERTING ENZYME (ACE) INHIBITORS

ANOREXIANT

ANTIANXIETY AGENT

ANTIARRHYTHMIC AGENT, CLASS I-B

ANTIARRHYTHMIC AGENT, CLASS II

ANTIARRHYTHMIC AGENT, CLASS III

ANTIARRHYTHMIC AGENT, CLASS IV

ANTIARRHYTHMIC AGENT, MISCELLANEOUS

ANTIBIOTIC, AMINOGLYCOSIDE

ANTIBIOTIC, OPHTHALMIC

ANTIBIOTIC, TOPICAL

ANTIBIOTIC, MISCELLANEOUS

ANTICHOLINERGIC AGENT

ANTICHOLINERGIC/ADRENERGIC AGONIST

ANTICONVULSANT

ANTIDEPRESSANT

ANTIDIABETIC AGENT (ORAL)

ANTIDIABETIC AGENT, PARENTERAL

ANTIDIARRHEAL

BARBITURATE

BENZODIAZEPINE

BETA-ADRENERGIC BLOCKER

BRONCHODILATOR

CALCIUM CHANNEL BLOCKER

CARDIAC GLYCOSIDE

CENTRAL NERVOUS SYSTEM STIMULANT, NONAMPHETAMINE

(Continued)

CANADIAN BRAND NAME INDEX

NOTES

NOTES